Glencoe Introduction to Physical Science

Contents in Brief

Teacher Wraparound Edition

Correlations and Standards

Program Resources

Support for All Learners

Classroom Activities and Materials

Student Edition

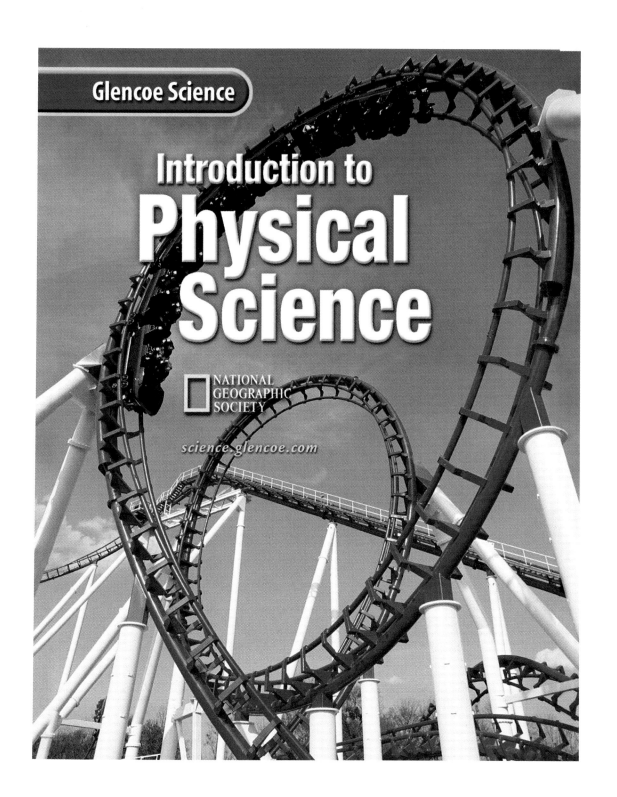

Glencoe Science

Introduction to Physical Science

NATIONAL GEOGRAPHIC SOCIETY

science.glencoe.com

New York, New York   Columbus, Ohio   Woodland Hills, California   Peoria, Illinois

GLENCOE INTRODUCTION TO PHYSICAL SCIENCE

Student Edition
Teacher Wraparound Edition
Interactive Teacher Edition CD-ROM
Interactive Lesson Planner CD-ROM
Lesson Plans
Content Outline for Teaching
  Directed Reading for Content Mastery
  Foldables: Reading and Study Skills
Assessment
  Chapter Review
  Chapter Tests
  ExamView Pro Test Bank Software
  Assessment Transparencies
  Performance Assessment in the Science Classroom
  The Princeton Review Test Practice Booklet
Spanish Directed Reading for Content Mastery
Spanish Resources
Reinforcement
Enrichment
Activity Worksheets
Section Focus Transparencies
Teaching Transparencies
Laboratory Activities
Science Inquiry Labs
Critical Thinking/Problem Solving
Reading and Writing Skill Activities
Mathematics Skill Activities
Cultural Diversity
Laboratory Management and Safety
Mindjogger Videoquizzes and Teacher Guide
Interactive Explorations and Quizzes CD-ROM with Presentation Builder
Vocabulary Puzzlemaker Software
Cooperative Learning
Environmental Issues in the Science Classroom
Home and Community Involvement
Using the Internet in the Science Classroom
Dinah Zike's Teaching Science with Foldables

"Test-Taking Tip," "Study Tip," and Test practice features in this book were written by The Princeton Review, the nation's leader in test preparation. Through its association with McGraw-Hill, The Princeton Review offers the best way to help students excel on standardized assessments.

The Princeton Review is not affiliated with Princeton University or Educational Testing Service.

Glencoe/McGraw-Hill

A Division of The ***McGraw-Hill*** *Companies*

The "Science and Society" and the "Science and History" features that appear in this book were designed and developed by TIME for Kids, a division of TIME Magazine.

Send all inquiries to:
Glencoe/McGraw-Hill
8787 Orion Place
Columbus, OH 43420

ISBN 0-07-826881-8

Printed in the United States of America
1 2 3 4 5 6 7 8 9 10 071/043 10 09 08 07 06 05 04 03 02 01

Authors, Reviewers, and Consultants

for the *Teacher Wraparound Edition*

Authors

Cathy Ezrailson
Science Department Head
Academy for Science and Health Professions
Conroe, Texas

Patricia Horton
Mathematics and Science Teacher
Summit Intermediate School
Etiwanda, California

Deborah Lillie
Math and Science Writer
Sudbury, Massachusetts

Thomas McCarthy, PhD
Physics/Astronomy Teacher
St. Paul's School
Concord, New Hampshire

Peter Rillero, PhD
Professor of Science Education
Arizona State University West
Phoenix, Arizona

Dinah Zike
Educational Consultant
Dinah-Might Activities, Inc.
San Antonio, Texas

Margaret K. Zorn
Science Writer
Yorktown, Virginia

Reviewers

Lee Meadows, PhD
Associate Professor of Science Education
University of Alabama
Birmingham, Alabama

Gilbert Naizer, PhD
Assistant Professor of Elementary Education
Texas A&M University
Commerce, Texas

Kimberly S. Roempler, PhD
Associate Director
Eisenhower National Clearinghouse
for Math and Science
The Ohio State University
Columbus, Ohio

Cultural Diversity Consultants

Nedaro Bellamy
Associate Director,
Rice Model Science Laboratory
Lanier Middle School, Houston ISD
Houston, Texas

Joyce Hilliard-Clark, PhD
Director, Imhotep Academy
North Carolina State University
Raleigh, North Carolina

Inclusion Strategies Consultant

Barry Barto
Special Education Teacher
John F. Kennedy Elementary School
Manistee, Michigan

National Science Education Standards

"The National Science Education Standards *are premised on a conviction that all students deserve and must have the opportunity to become scientifically literate. The* Standards *look toward a future in which all Americans, familiar with basic scientific ideas and processes, can have fuller and more productive lives."*

—National Science Education Standards

About the Standards

This book, published by the National Research Council, represents the contributions of thousands of educators and scientists, and offers a comprehensive vision of a scientifically literate society. The standards describe what all students should know at the end of grades 4, 8, and 12, and offer guidelines for science teaching and assessment.

How *Glencoe Introduction to Physical Science* Aligns with *The National Science Education Standards*

Content Standards

The correlations that follow show the close alignment between ***Glencoe Introduction to Physical Science*** and the grade-appropriate standards. ***Glencoe Introduction to Physical Science*** allows students to discover concepts within each of the content standards and gives students opportunities to make connections among the science disciplines. Hands-on activities and inquiry-based lessons reinforce the science processes emphasized in the standards.

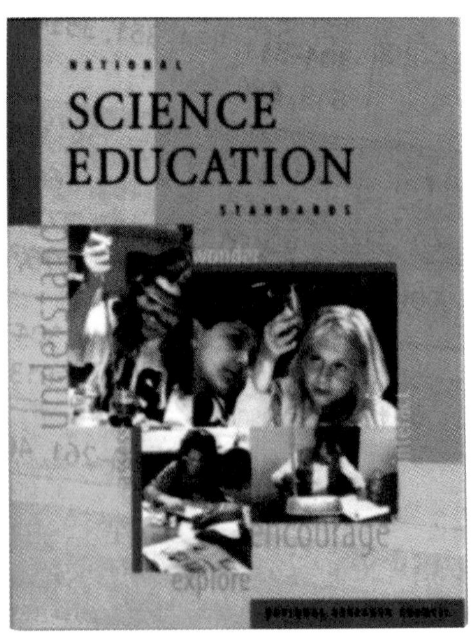

Teaching Standards

Glencoe Introduction to Physical Science provides activities and discussions that allow students to discover science concepts through inquiry and to apply the knowledge they've constructed to their own lives. The ***Teacher Wraparound Edition*** supports this endeavor with an abundance of effective strategies for guiding students of different ability levels and interests as they explore science.

Assessment Standards

Glencoe Introduction to Physical Science provides many opportunities in many different formats to assess students' understanding of important concepts. Ideas for portfolios, performance activities, and written assessments accompany every section. Glencoe's Professional Series booklet *Performance Assessment in the Science Classroom* contains rubrics and Performance Task Assessment Lists. This booklet also contains information about evaluating cooperative work. Learning outcomes improve for students of all ability levels in a cooperative learning environment.

Correlation to **National Science Education Standards**

The following chart illustrates how *Glencoe Introduction to Physical Science* addresses the National Science Education Standards.

Content Standard	Chapter and Section
(UCP) Unifying Concepts and Processes	
1. Systems, order, and organization	3-1, 4-1, 9-1, 9-2, 9-3, 10-3
2. Evidence, models, and explanation	1-1, 1-2, 1-3, 1-4, 3-2, 3-3, 5-1, 5-2, 5-3, 11-3, 12-1, 12-2, 13-1, 13-2, 13-3, 14-1, 14-2, 14-3, 14-4, 16-1, 16-2
3. Change, constancy, and measurement	2-1, 2-2, 2-3, 4-2, 4-3, 5-3, 6-1, 6-2, 6-3, 7-1, 7-2, 7-3, 8-1, 8-2, 9-1, 9-2, 9-3, 10-1, 10-2, 11-2, 15-1, 15-2, 15-3
4. Evolution and equilibrium	5-3, 9-1, 9-2, 9-3
5. Form and function	8-3, 11-1
(A) Science as Inquiry	
1. Abilities necessary to do scientific inquiry	1-1, 1-2, 1-3, 1-4, 2-1, 2-2, 2-3, 3-1, 3-2, 3-3, 4-2, 4-3, 5-1, 5-3, 6-1, 6-2, 6-3, 7-1, 7-3, 8-2, 8-3, 9-1, 9-3, 10-2, 10-3, 11-1, 11-2, 11-3, 12-1, 12-2, 13-1, 13-2, 13-3, 14-1, 14-2, 14-4, 15-2, 15-3, 16-1, 16-2
2. Understandings about scientific inquiry	1-1, 1-2, 1-3, 1-4, 3-1, 3-2, 3-3
(B) Physical Science	
1. Properties and changes of properties in matter	2-1, 2-2, 2-3, 3-1, 3-2, 3-3, 4-1, 4-2, 4-3, 5-1, 5-2, 5-3, 10-1, 10-2, 10-3, 11-1, 11-3, 16-1, 16-2
2. Motion and forces	6-1, 6-2, 6-3, 7-1, 7-2, 7-3, 9-1, 9-2, 9-3, 16-1, 16-2
3. Transfer of energy	4-2, 8-1, 8-2, 8-3, 9-1, 9-2, 9-3, 10-1, 10-2, 10-3, 11-1, 11-2, 11-3, 12-1, 12-2, 13-1, 13-2, 13-3, 14-1, 14-2, 14-3, 14-4, 15-1, 15-2, 15-3, 16-2
(C) Life Science	
1. Structure and function in living systems	9-3, 12-2, 15-1
(D) Earth and Space Science	
1. Structure of the Earth system	4-3, 11-3, 15-1
2. Earth's history	16-2
3. Earth in the solar system	12-1, 13-2
(E) Science and Technology	
1. Abilities of technological design	6-3, 7-1, 7-2, 7-3, 9-2, 9-3, 10-3, 14-2, 14-3, 14-4
2. Understandings about science and technology	5-3, 7-3, 9-2, 9-3, 10-2, 10-3, 14-4, 15-2, 15-3, 16-1
(F) Science in Personal and Social Perspectives	
1. Personal Health	9-3, 12-2, 14-3, 14-4, 15-3
2. Populations, resources, and environments	8-3
3. Natural hazards	15-1
4. Risks and benefits	6-3, 7-3, 8-3, 10-3
5. Science and technology in society	5-3, 7-3, 8-2, 10-3, 12-1, 12-2, 13-2, 13-3, 15-3, 16-2
(G) History and Nature of Science	
1. Science as a human endeavor	1-2, 3-3, 6-3, 14-4, 16-2
2. Nature of science	1-1, 1-4, 4-3, 6-3, 15-3
3. History of science	1-4, 3-3, 5-3, 6-3, 13-3, 14-4

National Council of Teachers of Mathematics
Principles and Standards for School Mathematics

Students often make personal, educational, and career choices on their own that can influence the rest of their lives. Throughout their school years, they acquire skills that help them make these decisions. The development of keen mathematical skills can ensure that students have a wide variety of life options.

Principles and Standards for School Mathematics of the National Council of Teachers of Mathematics describes the foundation of mathematical concepts and applications that can provide students with the necessary mathematical skills to help achieve their life goals.

The ten categories of mathematical concepts and applications, as shown in the table below, include a broad range of topics that build on previous knowledge. They also allow students to increase their abilities to visualize, describe, and analyze situations in mathematical terms.

In ***Glencoe Introduction to Physical Science***, each Math Skill Activity and Problem-Solving Activity provides students with the opportunity to practice and apply some of the mathematical concepts and applications described in the Standards. These activities serve to reinforce mathematical skills in real-life situations, thus, preparing students to meet their needs in an ever-changing world.

Correlation of *Glencoe Introduction to Physical Science* to NCTM Standards

Standard	Page
1. Number and Operations	48, 168, 174, 178, 203, 288, 391, 453
2. Algebra	17, 137, 168, 174, 178, 203, 260, 261, 265, 267, 288, 331, 391, 453, 473
3. Geometry	473
4. Measurement	48, 168, 174, 178, 203, 260, 261, 265, 267, 288
5. Data Analysis and Probability	17, 244, 331
6. Problem Solving	17, 91, 113, 123, 137, 168, 174, 178, 244, 288, 331, 350, 453, 473
7. Reasoning and Proof	244
8. Communication	17, 91, 113, 123, 168, 174, 178, 244, 260, 261, 265, 267, 331, 350, 391, 453
9. Connections	17, 91, 113, 123, 168, 174, 178, 203, 244, 260, 261, 265, 267, 288, 331, 350, 391, 453, 473
10. Representation	17, 244, 288, 331, 473

Benchmarks for Science Literacy

Benchmarks for Science Literacy is a publication by the American Association for the Advancement of Science that describes how students should progress toward science literacy. People who are science literate are "equipped with knowledge and skills they need to make sense of how the world works, to think critically and independently, and to lead interesting, responsible, and productive lives in a culture increasingly shaped by science and technology."

Benchmarks was the culmination of Project 2061, the work of scientists, mathematicians, engineers, and educators to develop benchmarks, or statements, of what *all* students should know or be able to do in science, mathematics, and technology by the end of grades 2, 5, 8, and 12.

Glencoe Introduction to Physical Science is aligned with ***Benchmarks*** in the following ways:

- Concepts are presented in ways that help students understand the how and why of science, not just requiring them to learn facts that they commit to short-term memory.
- Science concepts are related to students' daily experiences.
- Teachers are provided strategies for encouraging students in independent work and for addressing the needs of students of varied abilities.
- Specific strategies are provided for identifying and addressing student misconceptions.

IDENTIFYING Misconceptions

Educators are becoming increasingly aware of the importance of identifying and addressing misconceptions—prescientific or naïve ideas—that students may hold about science. Students often develop these from their experiences as a way to make sense of the world.

A one-page feature, Identifying Misconceptions, is found on the F interleaf pages preceding selected chapters in the ***Teacher Wraparound Edition.*** This feature provides specific teaching strategies to find out what students think about a particular concept, to help them understand the concept, and to assess the accuracy of their understanding after learning the concept. These strategies were developed by Peter Rillero, Ph.D., Professor of Science Education at Arizona State University West.

Correlation to Benchmarks

Glencoe Introduction to Physical Science **addresses many of the Benchmarks for Science Literacy.**

Benchmark	Chapter(s)
4 The Physical Setting	
4D. Structure of Matter	2, 3, 4, 5
4E. Energy Transformation	8, 9, 10, 11, 13, 15, 16
4F. Motion	4, 6, 7, 9, 11, 12, 16
4G. Forces of Nature	5, 6, 7, 11, 13, 15, 16
8 The Designed World	
8B. Materials and Manufacturing	5, 10, 14, 15, 16
8C. Energy Sources and Use	8, 9, 10, 11, 12, 13, 15, 16
8D. Communication	11, 12, 13, 14, 15, 16
9 The Mathematical World	
9A. Numbers	Chapter 2; All Math Skills and Problem-Solving Activities
9B. Symbolic Relationships	Chapter 2; All Math Skills and Problem-Solving Activities
9E. Reasoning	All Math Skills and Problem-Solving Activities
10 Historical Perspectives	
10B. Uniting the Heavens and Earth	4, 6, 7
10G. Harnessing Power	8, 9
12 Habits of Mind	
12A. Values and Attitudes	1, 2
12B. Computation and Estimation	All Chapters 1–16
12D. Communication Skills	All Activities and Skill Builders

Planning Your Course

Glencoe Introduction to Physical Science **is a flexible program that allows you to decide the pace at which you cover the content and which topics to present, based on the needs of your students and on district requirements. The** ***Glencoe Interactive Lesson Planner*** **integrates the** ***Teacher Classroom Resources*** **with an electronic lesson planner to make your job easier.**

Pacing Options

Two approaches to covering all content are provided in the Planning Guide.

- A **traditional, full-year** course comprises 180 periods of approximately 45 minutes each.
- A **block scheduling** approach involves covering the same information in fewer days but in longer class periods.

Chapter Organizers

A two-page organizer (A–B pages) precedes every chapter in the teacher edition. These organizers include:

- pacing information and objectives.
- correlations to standards.
- lists of activities and the materials needed.
- lists of reproducible resources, assessments, and technologies with page or booklet references.

Interactive Lesson Planner

This easy-to-use CD-ROM allows you to:

- plan daily, weekly, monthly, or yearlong lessons in a versatile calendar format.
- select or customize a built-in plan, or make a new plan.
- print lesson plans.
- access all print components of the *Teacher Classroom Resources* through a convenient pop-up menu.
- print student pages and answer keys from the resource list or from the lesson plan.

Unit	Chapter	Single-Class (180 days*)	Block (90 days*)
1	The Nature of Science		
	1 The Nature of Science	14	7
	2 Measurement	10	5
2	Matter		
	3 Atoms, Elements, and the Periodic Table	13	6.5
	4 States of Matter	11	5.5
	5 Properties and Changes of Matter	10	5
3	Motion and Forces		
	6 Motion and Momentum	14	7
	7 Forces and Newton's Law	10	5
4	Energy		
	8 Energy	10	5
	9 Work and Simple Machines	10	5
	10 Thermal Energy	10	7
5	Waves, Sound, and Light		
	11 Waves	13	6.5
	12 Sound	7	3.5
	13 Electromagnetic Waves	10	5
	14 Light, Mirrors, and Lenses	18	9
6	Electricity and Magnetism		
	15 Electricity	13	6.5
	16 Magnetism	7	3.5

**The suggested number of days are the recommended maximum number of days needed to thoroughly cover a chapter. Individual planning will vary.*

Student Edition Features

This table will help you choose from many options that will help you teach the chapter.

Feature	Location and Suggestions For Use
Design Your Own Experiment	• Find near end of chapter where concept is taught. • Promote inquiry learning through open-ended activities. • Reinforce understanding of scientific methods.
Use the Internet	• Find near end of chapter where concept is taught. • Strengthen skills in collecting, organizing, and sharing data. • Integrate the Internet into your class easily.
Model and Invent	• Find near end of chapter where concept is taught. • Reinforce the use of models to represent relationships or abstract ideas, and to predict outcomes. • Strengthen investigative skills.
Other Full-Length Activities	• Find near end of chapter where concept is taught. • Strengthen lab skills. • Reinforce understanding of science process.
Mini LAB TRY AT HOME Mini LAB	• Find in every chapter. • Do as a demonstration. • Involve parents in the student's learning. • Reinforce that science is not restricted to the classroom.
Explore Activity	• Find at beginning of each chapter. • Stimulate curiosity for the topic and focus students' attention.
Problem-Solving Skills Math Skills Activity	• Find one in every chapter at the point where the concept is taught. • Use after reading or other work to strengthen critical thinking and math skills.
SCIENCE Online	• Find in every chapter. • Focus students' Internet time with predetermined links.

Feature	Location and Suggestions For Use
Skill Builders	• Find at the end of every Section Assessment. • Assign as homework or class work.
FOLDABLES Reading & Study Skills	• Find on every Chapter Opener and Chapter Study Guide. • Provide a purpose for reading with these fun, simple, hands-on activities. • Encourage students to use as a study tool for review of chapter content.
Interdisciplinary Connections	• Find one of these five features in every chapter.
Oops! **Accidents in Science**	• Stimulate students' interest by studying science-related events that are out of the ordinary.
Science and Language Arts	• Advance reading and writing skills through literature connected to science.
Science Stats	• Show students the fun side of mathematics and how it is an integral part of science.
TIME **Science & History**	• Illustrate how scientific phenomena, discoveries, and inventions shape history.
TIME **Science & Society**	• Connect science to people's everyday lives.
NATIONAL GEOGRAPHIC **Visualizing**	• Find in every chapter. • Use the discussion and activities to teach science content.
Career Connection	• Find in every Science & Language Arts feature. • Point out that people of all ages, ethnicities, and training work in science.
Field GUIDE	• Find in the back of the student text. • Promote interest and independent study. • Teach students how to use a classification key.
Science, Technology, and Math Skill Handbooks	• Find at the back of the student and teacher editions. • Use to teach students scientific processes. • Use to teach students how to organize information. • Refer students to handbooks for assistance.

Teacher Wraparound Edition Features

This table will help you locate features of the *Teacher Wraparound Edition* that will help you develop your lesson plans.

Program Resources

Component	Where and How Many	What It Provides
Teacher to Teacher	Every Unit Opener	Teaching tip that relates to teaching unit content or activities.
Chapter Organizer	A and B pages preceding every chapter	• Objectives • Occurrence of activities and other features within each section • List of materials needed for each activity • List of materials from the *Teachers Classroom Resources* box • List of technology resources
Science Content Background	In every chapter on E page and F page where an Identifying Misconceptions feature does not appear	• Helps you prepare for the lesson by giving you more information about each section • Assists you with questions the students might ask
IDENTIFYING Misconceptions	F page of some chapters	Strategies to • determine misconceptions students may hold • promote understanding of concept • assess understanding
Key to Teaching Strategies	B page preceding every chapter	Coding to assist in planning for individual needs
Three-Step Teaching Cycle 1 Motivate 2 Teach 3 Assess	Every chapter	• Help for a first-year teacher • Help for experienced teacher in the first year in a new program
Resource Manager	C and D pages of every chapter Every two pages throughout each chapter	**C and D pages:** • List of transparencies • List of chapter teacher resources **Throughout chapter:** • List of reproducible resources • List of technology resources
Activity	Throughout all chapters in side wrap	Reinforces science concepts

Component	Where and How Many	What It Provides
Quick Demo	Throughout all chapters in side wrap	Idea to illustrate a concept; performed in a short amount of time, using available materials
LAB DEMONSTRATION	Throughout all chapters in bottom wrap	Teacher-performed activity, more complex than Quick Demo, often involving students
Extension	Throughout all chapters in side wrap	An activity idea for: • more advanced students • students who finish their work early • students who want to learn more about the topic
Teacher FYI	Throughout all chapters in side wrap	Additional information about a concept
Visual Learning	Throughout all chapters in side and bottom wrap	Idea for discussion or activity related to a graphic
Fun Fact	Throughout all chapters in side and bottom wrap	Interesting science content to share with students
Make a Model	Throughout all chapters in side wrap	Idea for model that students can make to clarify or illustrate abstract concepts
Use an Analogy	Throughout all chapters in side wrap	Way to make abstract concepts more concrete
Curriculum Connection	Throughout all chapters in bottom wrap	Way that science ties in with other curricular areas
Cultural Diversity	Throughout all chapters in bottom wrap	Current or historical background on a custom or belief associated with a science concept
Use Science Words	Throughout all chapters in side wrap	Strategies for students to learn word origins, meanings, and uses
Active Reading Strategies	Throughout all chapters in bottom wrap	Strategies to help students read and understand content
Science Journal	Throughout all chapters in bottom wrap	Writing exercises that promote writing and critical thinking skills
Assessment **Section Assessment** **Chapter Assessment** **Assessment Resources**	First page of every section Chapter Assessment page Chapter Assessment page	• Location of Portfolio, Performance, and Content Assessments in the section • Ideas for Portfolio and Performance Assessments • List of Reproducible Masters, CD-ROMs, and other technologies for assessment

Technology Resources

Online Science

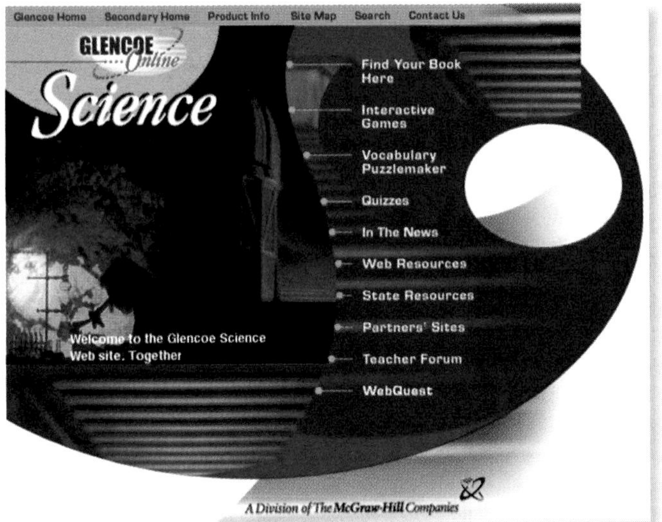

The Glencoe Science Web site is an invaluable resource for all teachers and students.

Teachers can:

- share ideas on Teacher Bulletin Board.
- access current scientific information on your textbooks updates.

Students can:

- access previewed web links.
- record information on printable Internet log worksheets.
- review chapter content with the Interactive Tutor.
- prepare for tests using Interactive Quizzes.
- share data with students worldwide using our exclusive Internet Activities.

Interactive Explorations, Quizzes, and Presentation CD-ROM Program

Provides students the opportunity to:

- develop hypotheses.
- manipulate variables.
- build presentations.
- review content.
- think critically.

ExamView Pro Computer
TestMaker Software

You can design and create your own test instruments in minutes, using Glencoe Introduction to Physical Science ExamView Pro TestMaker software. This versatile program allows you to create paper tests as well as tests that can be used on your school LAN system, or posted on your class Web site. Choose and edit questions from a question bank, or write your own.

Interactive Lesson Planner

Need help planning your lessons and organizing you resources? Glencoe's Interactive Lesson Planner is the perfect solution. All you need to do is to identify your length of course and number of class days and the program automatically places all the materials available for each day for each chapter into the calendar. Every page of your Teacher Classroom Resources are available to you at the click of a mouse.

Guided Reading Audio Program
English/Spanish

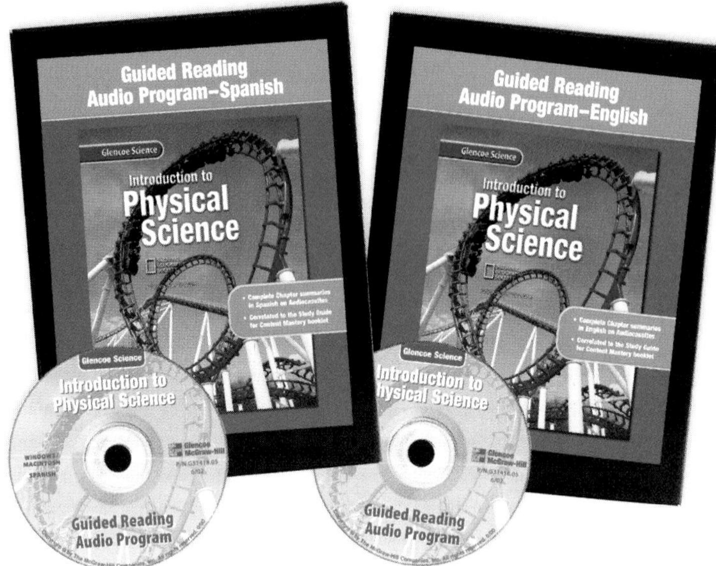

Complete chapter text read in English and Spanish provides another way for students who are auditory learners, or for ELL students, to access chapter content. Students can listen individually in class or at home. They can also choose to read along with their texts to improve reading skills. Tie to the Directed Reading for Content Mastery in the *Chapter Resources* booklets to give students a way to check their understanding of the material. The Guided Reading program is provided in CD format.

MindJogger Videoquizzes

The interactive quiz-show format of the Glencoe Introduction to Physical Science MindJogger Videoquizzes provides fun for your students while reviewing key concepts for every chapter. The three levels of increasing difficulty add to the drama and excitement of the game, and help you assess your students' understanding of the concepts.

Interactive Teacher Edition

Imagine having your entire Teacher Edition and all your Teacher Classroom Resources available to you on one CD-ROM. That is what the Interactive Teacher Edition provides for you. The program allows you to view all teacher material and the student text on your computer screen. You can export all worksheet masters to your own word processor for editing.

Vocabulary PuzzleMaker Software

This software program allows you to create crossword puzzles, jumble puzzles, or word searches in minutes to review chapter vocabulary. The puzzles can be printed or played on the computer screen.

Teacher Classroom Resources

Chapter Resources—An Easy Way to Stay Organized!

We've organized all of the materials you need for each chapter into convenient chapter-based booklets!

Program Resources
Chapter Resources
Chapter 13 Electromagnetic Waves
Electromagnetic Waves
FAST FILE
INCLUDES:
Reproducible Student Pages
ASSESSMENT
Chapter Tests
Chapter Review
HANDS-ON ACTIVITIES
Activity Worksheets for each Student Edition Activity
Two additional Laboratory Activities
Foldables–Reading and Study Skills activity sheet
MEETING INDIVIDUAL NEEDS
Extension and Intervention
Directed Reading for Content Mastery
Directed Reading for Content Mastery in Spanish
Reinforcement
Glencoe Science
Introduction to Physical Science
Note-taking Worksheet
Section 1
Directions: Answer the following questions on the lines provided.
10. Why are sound waves not electromagnetic waves?
11. What are two uses for electromagnetic waves?
Copyright © Glencoe/McGraw-Hill, a division of the McGraw-Hill Companies, Inc.

Each **Chapter Resources** booklet contains:

Reproducible Student Pages

Assessment
- Chapter Review
- Chapter Test

Hands-On Activities
- Activity Worksheets for each activity in the ***Student Edition***
- Two additional laboratory activities
- Foldables: Reading and Study Skills

Meeting Individual Needs
- Extension and Intervention
- Directed Reading for Content Mastery
- Directed Reading for Content Mastery *in Spanish*
- Reinforcement
- Enrichment
- Note-taking Worksheets

Transparency Activities
- Section Focus Activity
- Teaching Transparency Activity
- Assessment Transparency Activity

Teacher Support and Planning
- Content Outline for Teaching
- Spanish Resources
- Teacher Guide and Answers

Program Resources

Additional Resources

These resources are available as stand-alone booklets to give you the flexibility to decide when to use them.

Transparencies

Section Focus Transparencies

Teaching Transparencies

Assessment Transparencies

Content Outline for Teaching

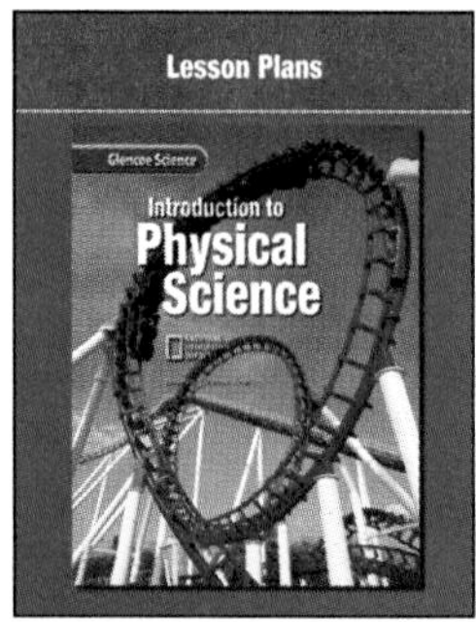

Lesson Plans

Laboratory Activities *SE*

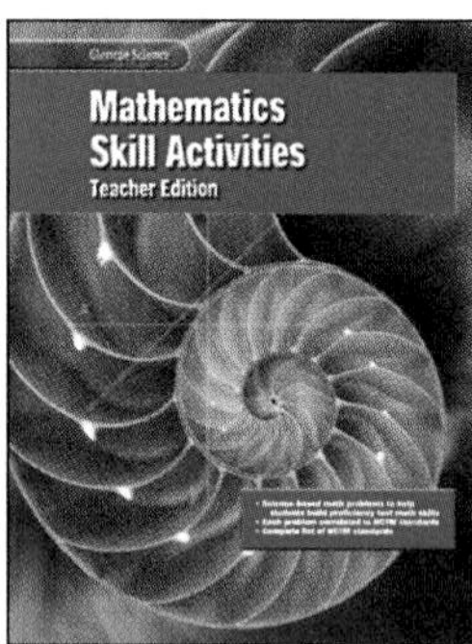

Math Skills Activities *(SE and TE)*

Reading and Writing Skills Activities *(SE and TE)*

Science Inquiry Labs *(SE and TE)*

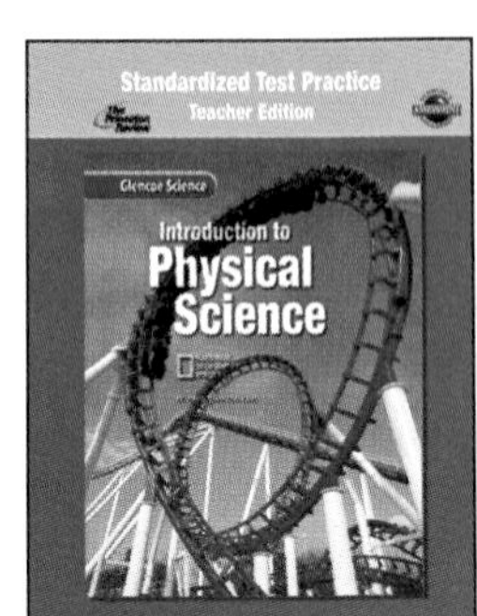

Standardized Test Practice *(SE and TE)*

Critical Thinking/ Problem Solving

Physical Science

Home and Community Involvement

Laboratory Management and Safety

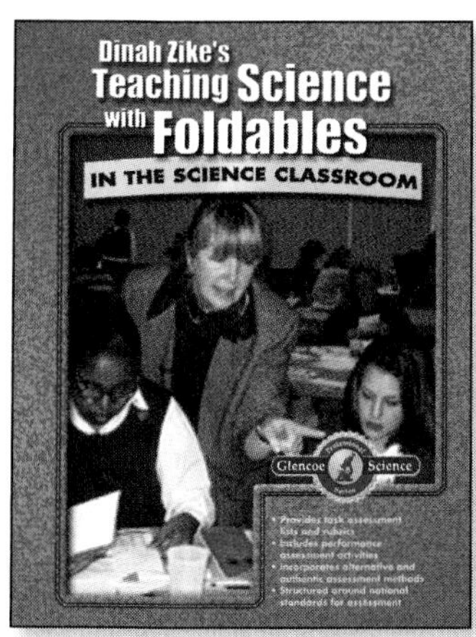

Dinah Zike's Teaching Science with Foldables

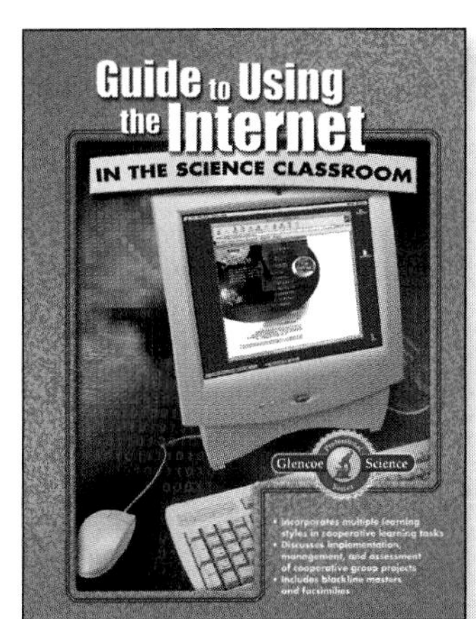

Guide to Using the Internet

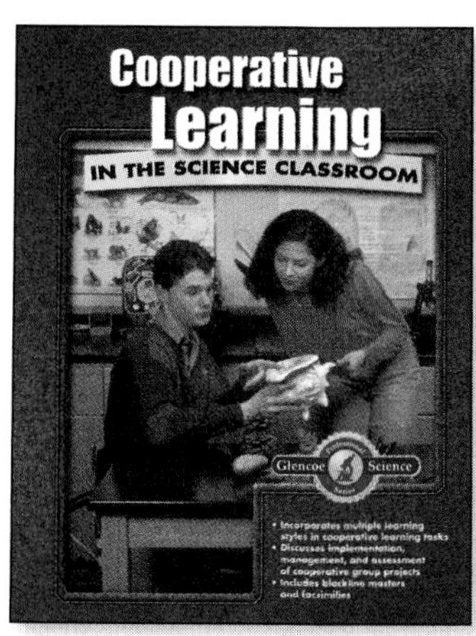

Cooperative Learning

Cultural Diversity

Performance Assessment

Meeting Individual Needs

Each student brings his or her unique set of abilities, perceptions, and needs into the classroom. *Glencoe Introduction to Physical Science Teacher Wraparound Edition* offers you a variety of strategies so that your students can learn science concepts through many different methods.

Strategy	Designation
Ability Levels Activities are provided that accommodate students of all ability levels.	L1 Basic activities that reinforce the concepts for lower-ability students L2 Application activities that give all students an opportunity for practical application of concepts L3 Challenging activities that allow students to expand their perspectives on the basic concepts
English-Language Learners These strategies focus on overcoming a language barrier. It is important not to confuse ability in speaking/reading English with academic ability or "intelligence."	ELL These activities reinforce content and aid in the development of science vocabulary.
Learning Styles A variety of instructional strategies help students to learn science concepts through their preferred learning styles. Students generally display more than one of these styles. You may want to assign activities to students that accommodate their strongest learning styles, but assign other activities that help to develop their weaker styles.	LS Look for these bold-faced designations wherever you see this logo: • **Kinesthetic** learners learn through touch, movement, and manipulating objects. • **Visual-Spatial** learners think in terms of images, illustrations, and models. • **Logical-Mathematical** learners understand numbers easily and have highly-developed reasoning skills. • **Linguistic** learners write clearly and easily understand the written word. • **Auditory-Musical** learners remember spoken words and can create rhythms and melodies. • **Interpersonal** learners understand and work well with other people. • **Intrapersonal** learners can analyze their own strengths and weaknesses and may prefer to work on their own.

Strategy	Designation
Inclusion Strategies Inclusion strategies provide you with additional support for helping students with special needs.	Look for these bold-faced designations and strategies wherever you see the **Inclusion** Strategies • **Learning Disabled**—ideas for additional concept review • **Behaviorally Disordered**—activities for helping to keep students on task • **Physically Challenged**—tips for adjusting activities to accommodate students who have less mobility or dexterity than others • **Visually Impaired** or **Hearing Impaired**—ideas for aiding these students in grasping concepts • **Gifted**—challenging activities and research projects that extend chapter concepts
Cooperative Learning In cooperative learning, students work together in small groups to learn content and interpersonal skills. Group members learn that each is responsible for accomplishing an assigned group task as well as for learning the material. Cooperative learning fosters academic, personal, and social success for all students.	COOP LEARN Strategies with this designation are suitable for group work that will help students to: • develop positive attitudes toward science and school; • build respect for others, regardless of race, ethnic origin, or gender; and • increase their sensitivity to and tolerance of diverse perspectives.
Cultural Diversity Classrooms in the United States reflect the rich and diverse cultural heritage of the American people. Students come from different ethnic backgrounds and different cultural experiences into a common classroom that must assist all of them in learning.	Cultural **Diversity** The Cultural Diversity features provide insights into unique ways in which different people have approached science or adapted to their environments. The intent of these features is to build awareness and appreciation for the global community in which we live.
Misconceptions Students have had many experiences outside the science classroom that have shaped their understandings of the natural world. Unfortunately, interpretations based on casual observation are not always accurate. For example, based on their observations, some students might think that the Sun moves around Earth. As a science teacher, you need strategies to help replace these naive conceptions with scientific facts.	 **Misconceptions** This one-page feature provides ideas about the types of misconceptions your students may have. It provides you with teaching strategies to uncover misconceptions and to help students understand concepts. You can find these preceding many chapters on the F interleaf pages of the Teacher Wraparound Edition. In addition, you will find several misconceptions stated, followed by the correct information, in the teacher wrap throughout each chapter.

Reading and Writing in the Content Area

***Glencoe Introduction to Physical Science* is designed to increase science literacy through improving reading comprehension and deepening students' understanding of ideas and concepts. The reading strategies are active, constructive, and engaging.**

In the Student Edition

Pre-Reading Activities on each Unit Opener prepare students to read by helping them focus on important content before reading and studying the chapter. Previewing the chapters' visuals, questions, vocabulary, and captions will set a purpose for reading the material for all students.

Pre-Reading Activity

Have students read the objectives for each section, and search for charts and pictures that relate to each objective.

Reading Checks throughout each chapter stimulate quick recall to keep students focused on main ideas and important details.

What type of chemical reaction is burning?

The Before You Read and After You Read Activities in every chapter set a purpose for reading and help students to construct a graphic organizer to use for learning content and as a study aide.

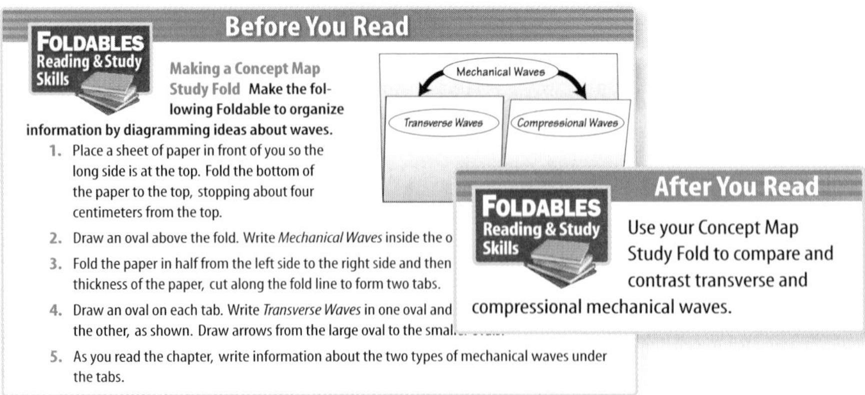
Before You Read

FOLDABLES Reading & Study Skills

Making a Concept Map Study Fold **Make the following Foldable to organize information by diagramming ideas about waves.**

1. Place a sheet of paper in front of you so the long side is at the top. Fold the bottom of the paper to the top, stopping about four centimeters from the top.
2. Draw an oval above the fold. Write *Mechanical Waves* inside the o
3. Fold the paper in half from the left side to the right side and then thickness of the paper, cut along the fold line to form two tabs.
4. Draw an oval on each tab. Write *Transverse Waves* in one oval and the other, as shown. Draw arrows from the large oval to the smal
5. As you read the chapter, write information about the two types of mechanical waves under the tabs.

After You Read

FOLDABLES Reading & Study Skills

Use your Concept Map Study Fold to compare and contrast transverse and compressional mechanical waves.

Skill Builder Activities in each Section Assessment often include questions that directly address reading and writing skills. Students are referred to the *Science Skill Handbook* for help.

Communicating Watch carefully as you travel home from school or walk down your street. What examples of wave reflection and refraction do you notice? Describe each of these in your Science Journal and explain your reasons. **For more help, refer to the Science Skill Handbook.**

Caption Questions throughout each chapter help students to comprehend what they have read through interpreting the visual. This is especially useful for less proficient readers.

Figure 6
After a golf ball is thrown, it follows a curved path toward the ground. *How does this curved path show that the ball is accelerating?*

Support for All Learners

Print and **Technology Resources** to Promote **Reading** and **Writing** in the Content Area

Ancillaries

Chapter Resources

- Directed Reading for Content Mastery pages *(in English and Spanish)*
- Foldables: Reading and Study Skills Worksheets
- Note-taking Worksheets

Dinah Zike's Teaching Science with Foldables

Reading and Writing Skill Activities

Technology

Guided Reading Audio Program *(English and Spanish)*

MindJogger VideoQuizzes

Interactive CD-ROM

Vocabulary PuzzleMaker

Glencoe Science Online

Glencoe Exclusive

Foldables: Improving Reading and Study Skills

Students love Foldables because they're fun. Teachers love them because they're effective.

What is a Foldable?

Foldables are three-dimensional, interactive graphic organizers. As students fold paper, cut tabs, write, and manipulate what they have made, they are kinesthetically involved in learning. These unique, hands-on tools for studying and reviewing were created exclusively for Glencoe Science by teaching specialist Dinah Zike.

FOLDABLES
Reading & Study Skills

Foldables are Useful!

Reading in the Content Area

Foldables help students develop ways of organizing information that are fun and creative. These useful activities help students practice basic writing skills, find and report main ideas, organize information, review key vocabulary terms, and much more!

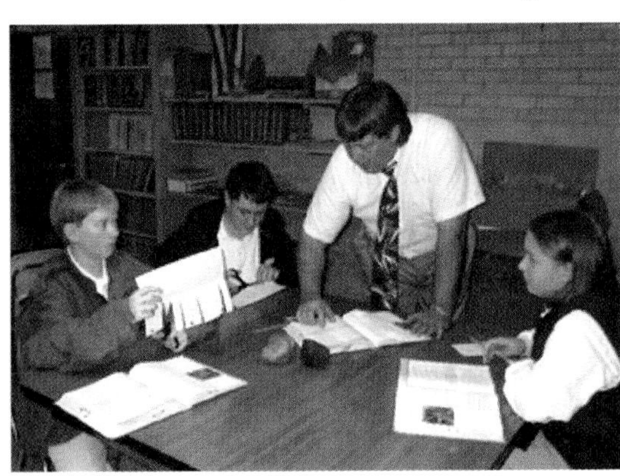

Every chapter begins with a Foldable activity. Students make the physical structure of a Foldable that incorporates one of many prereading strategies. Then, as students read through the chapter and do the activities, students record information as they learn it in the appropriate part of the foldable. In the Chapter Study Guide, the After You Read feature gives students a strategy for using the fold they made to help them review the chapter concepts.

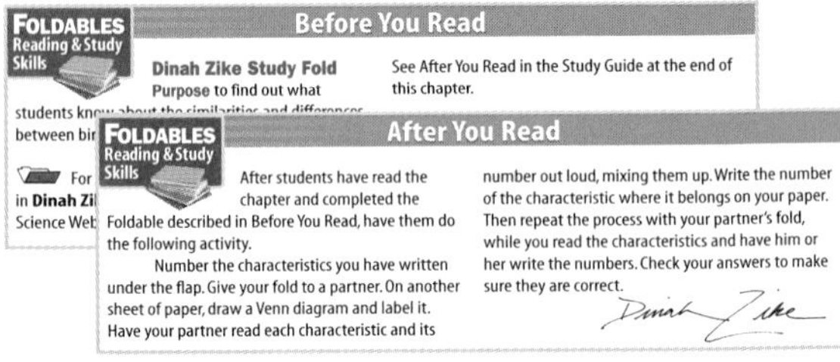

FOLDABLES Reading & Study Skills

Before You Read

Dinah Zike Study Fold
Purpose to find out what students kn[...]
between bi[...]

For [...] in **Dinah Zi**[...] Science Web[...]

See After You Read in the Study Guide at the end of this chapter.

FOLDABLES Reading & Study Skills

After You Read

After students have read the chapter and completed the Foldable described in Before You Read, have them do the following activity.

Number the characteristics you have written under the flap. Give your fold to a partner. On another sheet of paper, draw a Venn diagram and label it. Have your partner read each characteristic and its number out loud, mixing them up. Write the number of the characteristic where it belongs on your paper. Then repeat the process with your partner's fold, while you read the characteristics and have him or her write the numbers. Check your answers to make sure they are correct.

Dinah Zike

Review One advantage of Foldables is that they result in an organized study guide. The Foldables then can be used not only while preparing for the chapter test, but they can also be used for reviewing for unit tests, end of course exams, and even standardized tests.

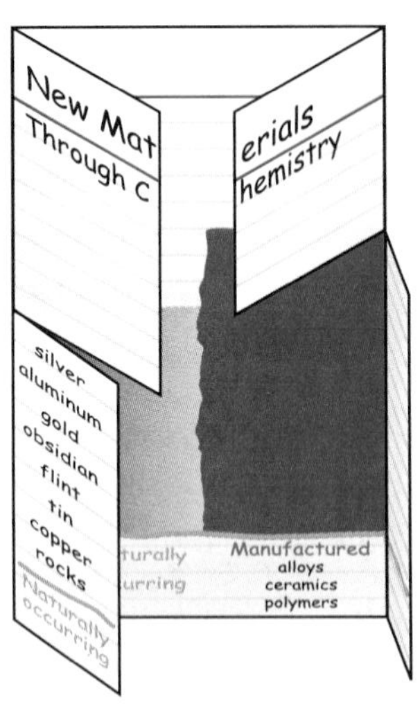

Assessment Foldables present an ideal opportunity for you to probe the depth of your students' knowledge. You'll get detailed feedback on exactly what they know and what misconceptions they may have.

Support for All Learners

Foldables are Easy!

Anyone who has paper, scissors, and maybe a stapler or some glue can implement Foldables in the classroom. Glencoe's Foldables have been tested with teachers and middle school students to make sure the directions are easy for both students and teachers. After doing a couple of them, your class will quickly become seasoned experts. Don't be surprised if you find them inventing their own for use in projects and reports in all of their classes!

A message from **the creator of Foldables,** Dinah Zike

You might not know my name or me, but I bet you have seen at least one of my graphic organizers or folds used in supplemental programs or teacher workshops. Today, my graphic organizers and manipulatives are used internationally. I present workshops and keynote presentations to over 50,000 teachers a year, sharing the manipulatives I began inventing, designing, and adapting over thirty years ago. Around the world, students of all ages are using them as daily work, note-taking activities, student-directed projects, forms of alternative assessment, science lab journals, quantitative and qualitative observation books, graphs, tables, and more. But through all my years of teaching, designing, and publishing, my materials had never been featured in a middle school textbook. When Glencoe/McGraw-Hill approached me to share some of my three-dimensional, manipulative graphic organizers with you in this new and innovative science series, I was thrilled.

Working with Glencoe, we all had the vision that Foldables should be an integral part of the curriculum, not simply tacked on. What we ended up with was a strategy that will help students read and learn science concepts. One of the advantages of using the same manipulative repeatedly is that students are immersed in what they are learning. It is not out of sight and out of mind. How long is your average student actively involved with a duplicated activity sheet? Ten minutes? Fifteen? Students will use the Foldable at the beginning of each chapter, before reading the chapter, during reading, and after reading. That's a lot of immersion!

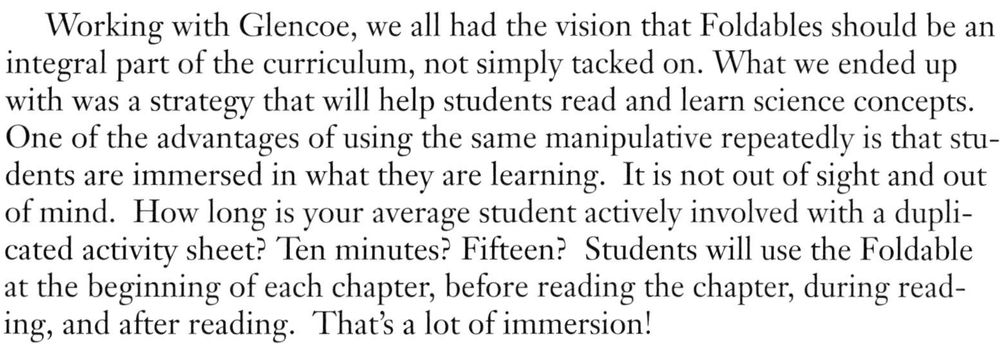

Dinah Zike

Reading and Writing in the Content Area

In the Teacher Edition

Science & Language Arts

Pre-Reading Activity helps students draw upon their personal experience and sets a purpose for reading.

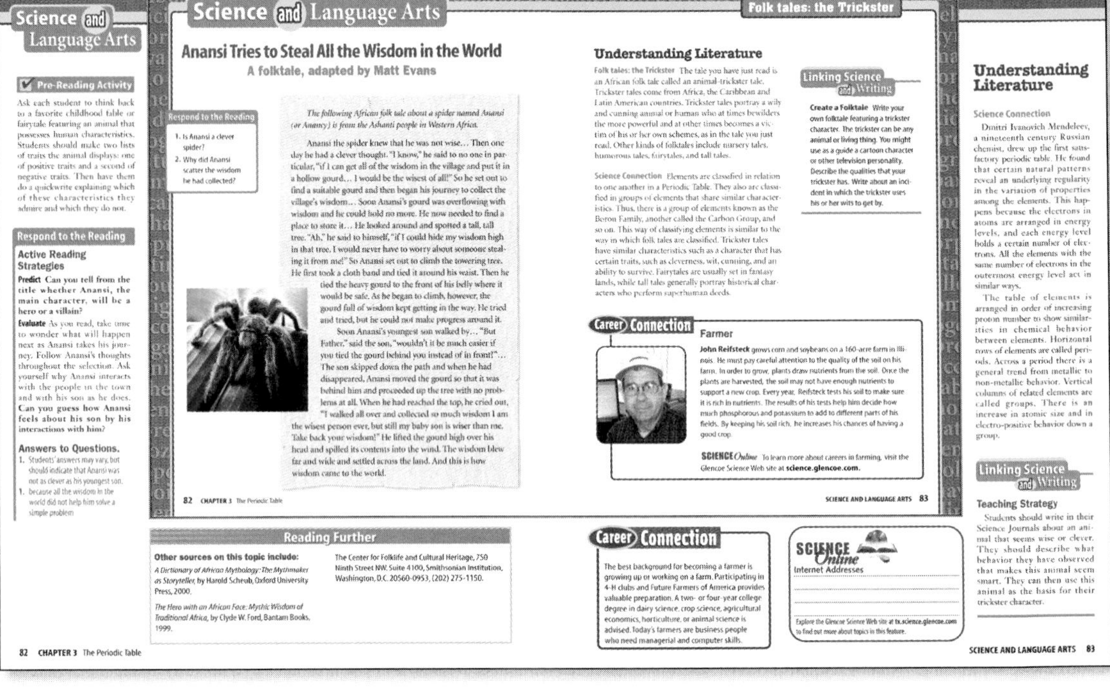

Respond to the Reading provides active reading strategies that provide a variety of ways for students to respond to the feature through listening, speaking, and writing activities. It also provides students with an opportunity to make connections to the theme.

Linking Science and Writing provides options that all students can use to respond in writing to the feature.

Use Science Words

Word Usage The distinction between distance and displacement can be confusing. Have students use each of these words correctly in a sentence. Possible response: When I go to school and then back home, my displacement is zero, even though the distance from home to school is 2 km. L2 LS Linguistic

Use Science Words appears throughout each chapter and provides three types of reading strategies. Students structurally analyze root words (Word Origin), develop vocabulary (Word Meaning), or apply their knowledge of science terms (Word Usage).

Science Journal

Cathode-Ray Tube Ask students to pretend that they are coworkers with Crookes at the time of his experiments with a cathode-ray tube. Have students write letters in their Science Journals to a fellow scientist telling about the exciting results they obtained and how they interpreted the results. L2 LS Linguistic

Science Journals throughout each chapter provide opportunities for students to write responses to questions that require critical thinking; to conduct research and write about it; or to practice creative writing skills.

Active Reading Strategies

A variety of active reading strategies are provided throughout the *Teacher Wraparound Edition*. These strategies utilize a variety of learning styles, and encourage cooperative learning and intrapersonal reflection on chapter content.

Active Reading

Think-Pair Share This strategy encourages students to think first before discussing their ideas or thoughts about a topic. Ask students to respond to a question by writing a response. After thinking for a few minutes, partners share responses to the question. Finally, ask the students to share responses with the class. Have students become involved in a Think-Pair Share about cathode rays.

Making Concept Maps and Charts

Bubble Map Students brainstorm and organize words in clusters to describe concepts.

Double-Bubble Map Students compare concepts using two bubble maps.

Flow Chart Students logically analyze and draw a sequence of events.

Cause and Effect Chart Students visually represent the causes and effects of an event or process.

Supporting Idea Chart Students make a concept map to analyze the relationship between a whole and its parts.

Using the Science Journal

Double Entry Journal Students read and record ideas, then reflect on the text and respond to the ideas.

Metacognition Students analyze what and how they have learned.

Learning Journal Students write and reflect on notes about content.

Problem-Solution Journal Students analyze problems and suggest workable solutions.

Speculation About Effects/ Prediction Journal Students examine events and speculate about their possible long-term effects.

Synthesis Journal Students reflect on a project, a paper, or a performance task and plan how to apply what they have learned to their own lives.

Reflective Journal Students identify what they learned in an activity and record responses.

Quickwrites Students use spontaneous writing to discover what they already know.

Collaborative Learning Strategies

Pair of Pairs Partners respond to a question and compare their response to that of other pairs and to the class.

Write-Draw-Discuss Students write about and draw a picture of a concept, then share it with the class.

Four-Corner Discussion The class works in four groups to debate a complex issue.

Jigsaw Students work in groups to become experts on a portion of text and share their expertise with their "home" group.

Buddy Interviews Students interview one another to find out what helps them to understand what they are reading.

Reciprocal Teaching Students take turns reading the text and retelling it in their own words, then asking one another questions.

News Summary Students are given several minutes to summarize, retell, or analyze an activity for a "TV" audience.

ReQuest The teacher reads aloud an article or story. Student pairs then construct discussion questions and review the content.

Concept Maps

Helping students understand concepts through visuals

Concept maps are visual representations or graphic organizers of relationships among particular concepts. Concept maps can be generated by individual students, small groups, or an entire class. Four types of concept maps that are most applicable to studying science are developed and reinforced in this program. Students can learn how to construct each of these types of concept maps by referring to the Skill Handbook in the ***Student Edition.***

Concept maps can be used to increase understanding of science concepts, to strengthen reading skills, to promote cooperative learning, and to assess learning. When evaluating concept maps, look for the conceptual strength of student responses, not absolute accuracy.

- **Science Concepts** Concept mapping helps students to understand science concepts through analyzing relationships among ideas and reinforcing those relationships by visualizing them.
- **Reading Skills** Concept maps can help students preview a chapter's content by visually relating the concepts to be learned and aiding students to read with purpose. Students learn key science terms by choosing the terms to use, supplying connecting words, or by placing terms and connecting words when provided by the teacher. To further develop concept mapping skills, the *Chapter Resources* booklet for each chapter contains concept maps in the reproducible student pages Directed Reading for Content Mastery.
- **Cooperative Learning** Construction of concept maps using cooperative learning strategies allows students to practice interpersonal skills as they work together to build the map.
- **Review and Assessment** As a review, constructing concept maps reinforces main ideas and clarifies their relationships. As an assessment tool, concept maps can be constructed by students or students can fill in the terms. Look for concept mapping assessment in the Chapter Assessment section of every chapter.

Network Tree

- Order information from general to specific.
- Show a hierarchy.
- Use branching procedures.
- Explain relationships with connecting terms.

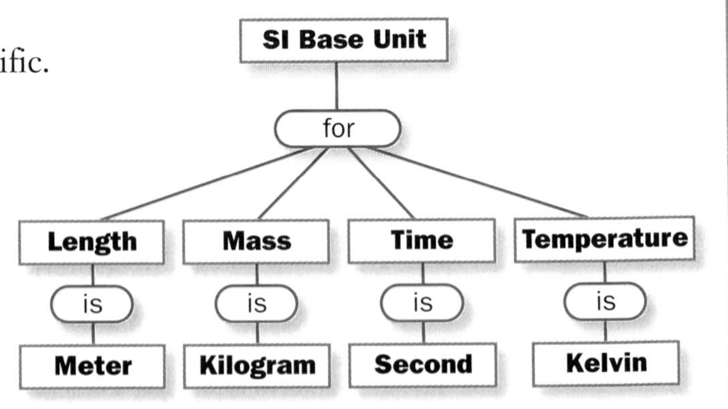

Events Chain

- Describe the stages of a process.
- Order the steps in a linear procedure.

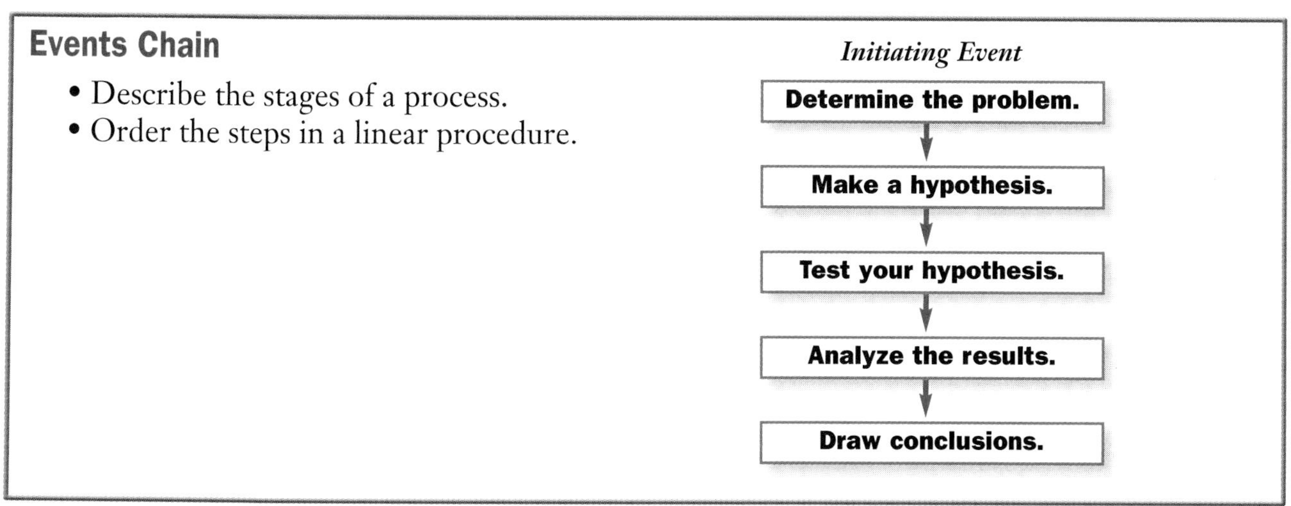

Cycle Concept Map

- Show how a series of events interact.
- Depict how the last event relates to the initiating event.

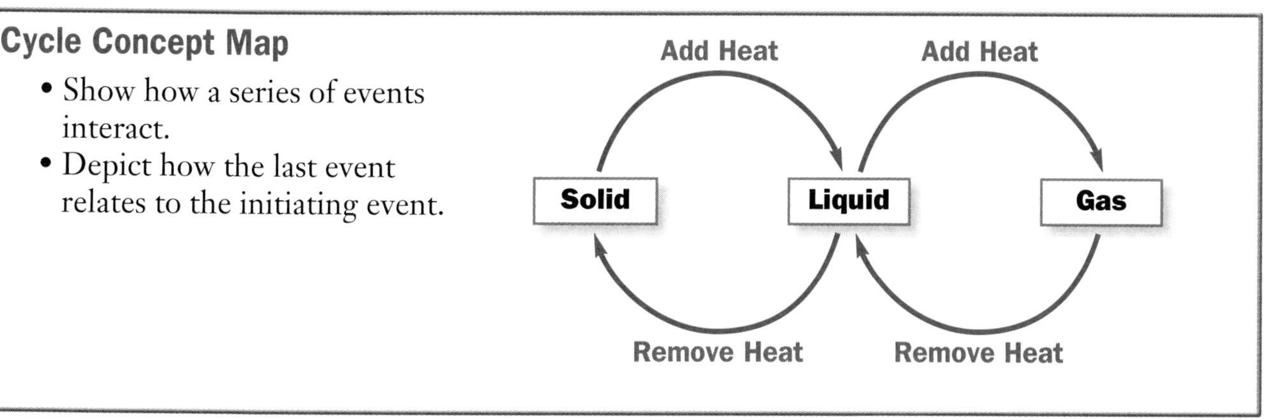

Spider Concept Map

- Use for brainstorming.
- Separate and group unrelated terms.
- Show relationship of nonrelated terms to a central idea.

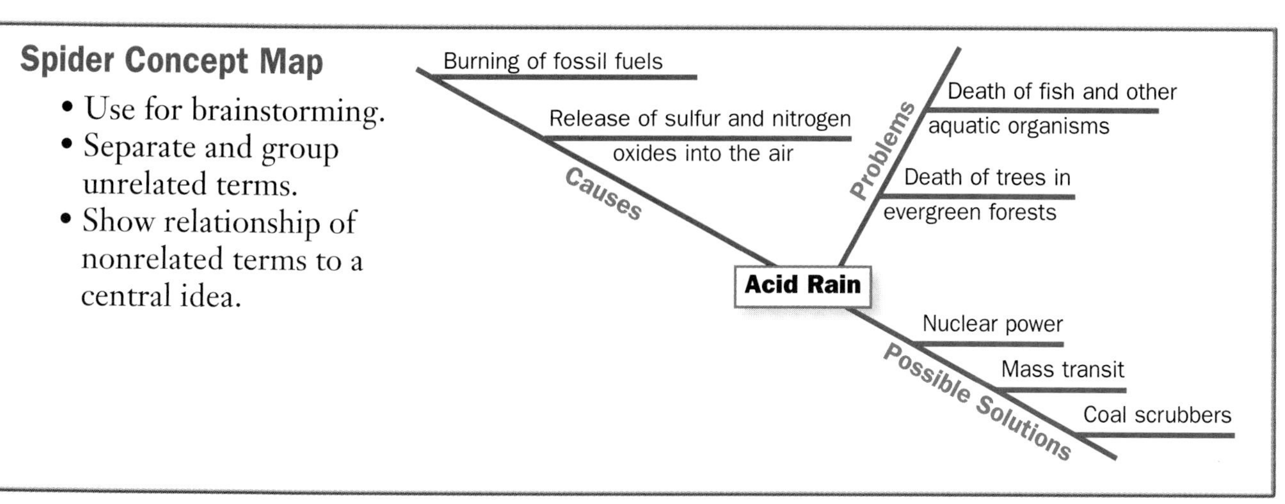

Support for All Learners

Assessment Support

Glencoe Introduction to Physical Science **offers the Glencoe Assessment Advantage, a system of assessment options designed to give you the flexibility and tools to conduct standardized test preparation, and content and performance assessment.**

Glencoe has partnered with *The Princeton Review*, a nationally renowned company that helps students prepare for state and national tests. This partnership has resulted in the Study Tips and Test Practice questions at the end of each Chapter Assessment in the ***Student Edition.*** Test practice booklets help prepare students for success on standardized tests.

Content Assessment

- **Section Assessment** questions and **Skill Builder Activities** appear in every chapter of the ***Student Edition.***
- A **Study Guide** at the end of each chapter in the ***Student Edition*** allows you to determine whether reteaching is needed.
- The **Chapter Assessment** questions in the ***Student Edition*** help you evaluate students' knowledge and ability to apply science concepts.

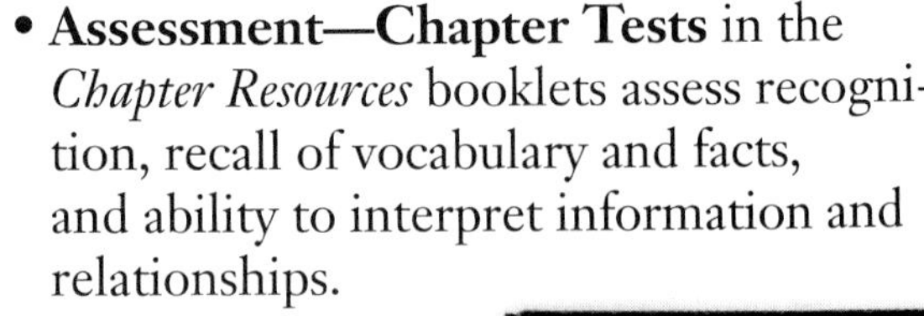

- **Assessment—Chapter Tests** in the *Chapter Resources* booklets assess recognition, recall of vocabulary and facts, and ability to interpret information and relationships.
- **MindJogger Videoquizzes** offer interactive videos that provide a fun way for your students to review chapter concepts.

- The **Interactive CD-ROM/DVD** provides quizzes that can be used as a whole-class presentation or as a review for individual students. These materials also are available on the Glencoe Science Web site.
- **ExamView Pro Test Bank Software (English/Spanish)** Software for Macintosh and Windows provides an easy way to make, edit, and print tests. You can add your own questions and graphics.

Performance Assessment

Performance Assessment refers to the strategies used to assess students' level of science literacy. Performance Assessment is based on judging the quality of a student's response to a performance task. A performance task is constructed to require the use of important concepts with supporting information, work habits important to science, and one or more of the elements of scientific literacy.

Performance Task Assessment Lists

Performance Assessments accompany **Activities** and **Chapter Assessments** in the ***Glencoe Introduction to Physical Science Student Edition***. Task Assessment Lists are provided in Glencoe's *Performance Assessment in the Science Classroom*. Both the teacher and the student assess the work and assign points based on the well-defined categories and possible points for each category. These task lists were developed for the summative performance tasks included in the booklet.

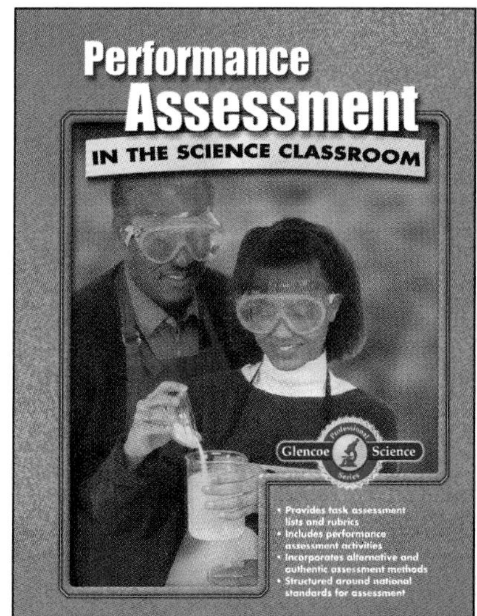

Assessing Student Work with Rubrics

A rubric is a set of descriptions of the quality of a process and a product. The set of descriptions includes a continuum of quality from excellent to poor. Rubrics for various types of assessment products are provided in the Glencoe Professional Development Series booklet *Performance Assessment in the Science Classroom*. In addition to sample rubrics, blank rubric forms allow teachers to customize assessment methods. The booklet also provides a step-by step model showing teachers how to use the materials most effectively.

Portfolios

Portfolio suggestions are featured throughout each chapter in the ***Glencoe Introduction to Physical Science Teacher Wraparound Edition***. The Portfolio should help the student see the big picture of how he or she is performing in gaining knowledge and skills and how effective his or her work habits are. The performance portfolio is not a complete collection of all worksheets and other assignments but rather a collection that reflects the student's growth in concept attainment and skill development. Writings and drawings from the student's **Science Journal**, featured in the ***Student Edition*** and the ***Teacher Wraparound Edition***, often are suggested to include in portfolios.

Group Assessment

All students benefit from a cooperative learning environment. Research has shown that student-learning outcomes improve for students of all ability levels. An example, along with information about evaluating cooperative work, is provided in the booklet *Performance Assessment in the Science Classroom*.

Lab Safety

The activities in *Glencoe Introduction to Physical Science* have been tested in the laboratory and have been reviewed by safety consultants. Even so, there are no guarantees against accidents. For additional help, refer to the *Laboratory Management and Safety* booklet, which contains safety guidelines and masters to test students' lab and safety skills.

General Guidelines

- Post safety guidelines, fire escape routes, and a list of emergency procedures in the classroom. Make sure students understand these procedures. Remind them at the beginning of *every* lab session.

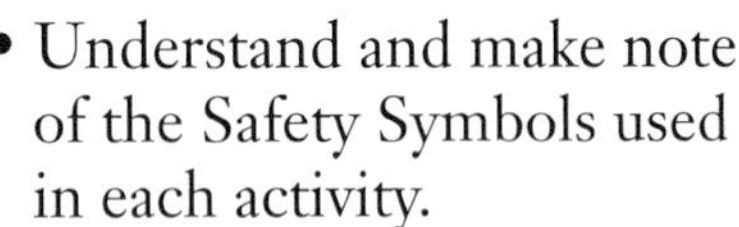

- Understand and make note of the Safety Symbols used in each activity.
- Have students fill out a safety contract. Students should pledge to follow the rules, to wear safety attire, and to conduct themselves in a responsible manner.
- Know where emergency equipment is stored and how to use it.
- Supervise students at all times. Check assembly of all setups.
- Perform all activities before you allow students to do so.
- Instruct students to follow directions carefully.
- Make sure that all students are wearing proper safety attire: goggles and aprons when using chemicals, a heat source, or a hammer. They should secure long hair and loose clothing. Do not permit wearing contact lenses, even with safety glasses; splashing chemicals could infuse under a lens and cause eye damage.

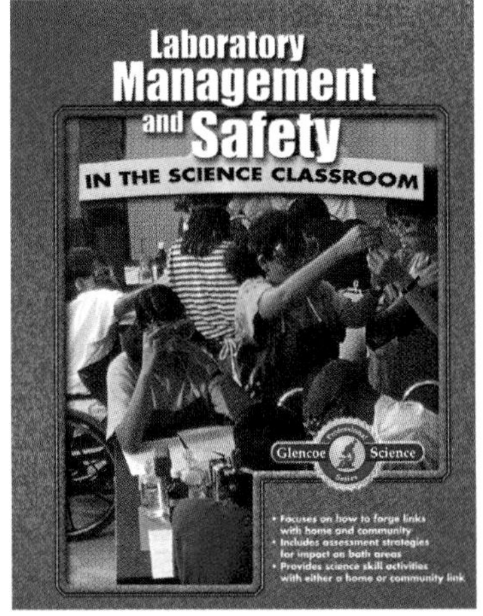

Handling Chemicals

- Handle chemicals carefully at all times. Always wear safety goggles, gloves, and an apron when handling chemicals. Treat all chemicals as potentially dangerous.
- Never ingest chemicals. Use proper techniques to smell solutions.
- Use a fume hood when handling chemicals that are poisonous or corrosive or that give off a vapor.
- *Always add acids to water, never the reverse.*
- Prepare solutions by adding the solid to a small amount of distilled water and then diluting with water to the volume listed. If you use a hydrate that is different from the one specified in a particular preparation, you will need to adjust the amount of hydrate to obtain the correct concentration.
- Consider purchasing premixed solutions from a scientific supply house to reduce the amount of chemicals on hand.
- Maintain appropriate MSDS (Materials Safety Data Sheets) in the laboratory.

Chemical Storage and Disposal

The following are some commonly used guidelines for chemical storage and disposal, but your school or local government may have additional requirements for handling chemicals. It is your responsibility to be informed of the rules governing chemical storage and disposal in your area.

- Use wood shelving rather than metal. All shelving should be firmly attached to the wall and have antiroll edges.
- Store only those chemicals you intend to use. Do not store chemicals above eye level.
- Store chemicals in labeled containers that indicate the contents, concentration, source, date purchased (or prepared), safety precautions for handling, and expiration date.
- Separate chemicals by reaction type. Store acids in one place and bases in another. Oxidants should be stored away from easily oxidized materials, for example.
- Dispose of outdated or waste chemicals properly.
- Follow regulations for storing hazardous chemicals.

Disposal of Chemicals

Local, state, and federal laws regulate the disposal of chemicals. Consult these laws before attempting to dispose of any chemicals. The following resource provides some general guidelines for handling and disposing of chemicals: *Prudent Practices in the Laboratory: Handling and Disposal of Chemicals.* Washington, DC: National Academy Press, 1995. Current laws in your area supersede the information in this book.

Disclaimer

Glencoe/McGraw-Hill makes no claims to the completeness of this discussion of laboratory safety and chemical storage. The material presented is not all-inclusive, nor does it address all of the hazards associated with handling, storage, and disposal of chemicals, or with laboratory management.

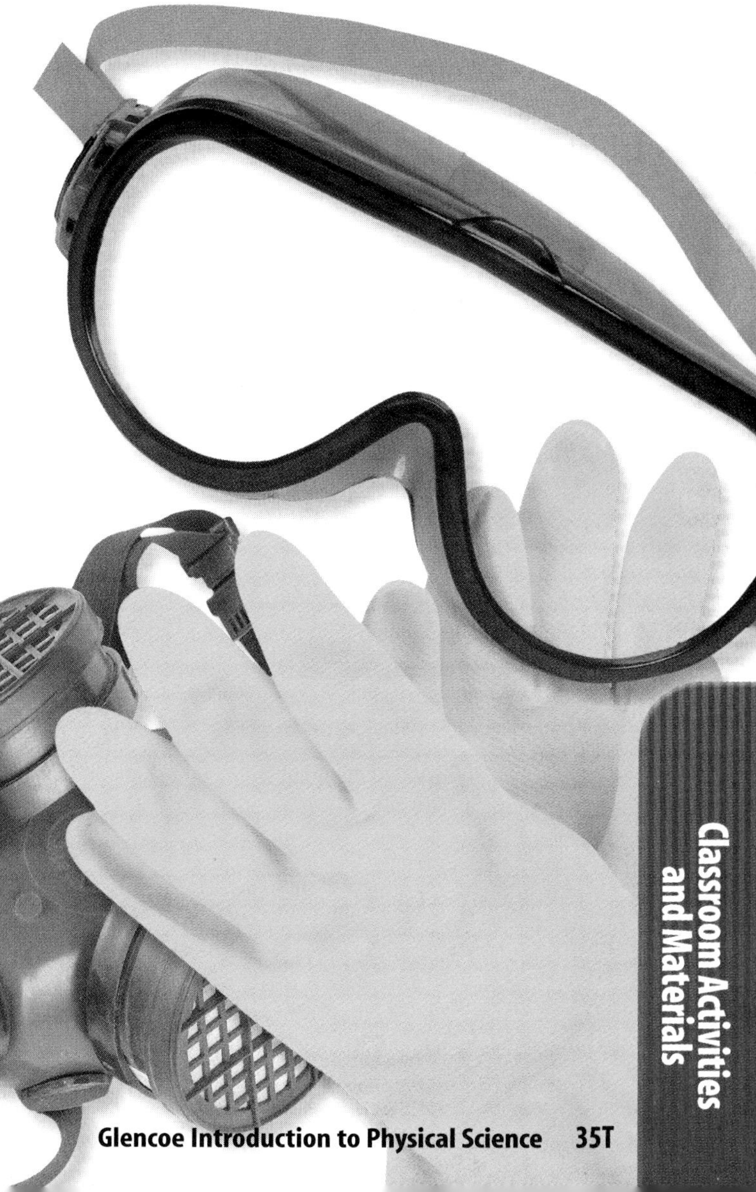

Activity Materials

Glencoe Introduction to Physical Science **makes it easy for you to plan and facilitate activities in your classroom.**

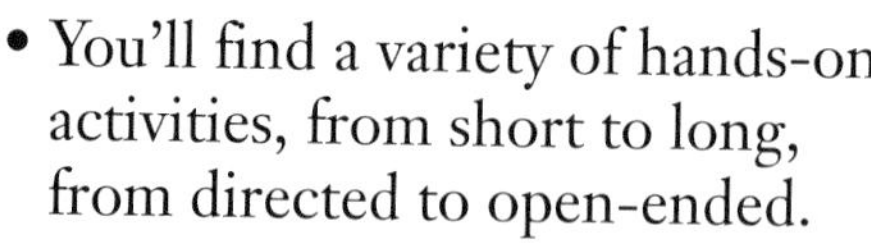

- You'll find a variety of hands-on activities, from short to long, from directed to open-ended.
- Many activities use common, inexpensive materials.
- Activities are easy to manage, with clearly numbered steps and illustrations.
- All MiniLABS have been teacher tested.

All laboratory activities have been thoroughly reviewed by a safety expert.

All full-length labs were bench tested by Science Kit to ensure quality and safety.

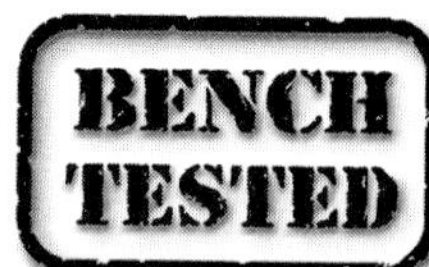

It's Quick and Easy to Order

Glencoe and Science Kit, Inc., have teamed up to make materials for ***Glencoe Introduction to Physical Science*** easier with an activity-materials folder. This folder contains two convenient ways to order materials and equipment for the program—the **Activity Plan Checklist** and the **Activity Materials List** master. Call Science Kit at 1-800-828-7777 to get your folder.

Materials Support Provided by

Science Kit® & Boreal®
Laboratories
Your Classroom Resource
777 East Park Drive
Tonawanda, NY 14151-5003
Phone: 800-828-7777
Fax 800-828-3299
www.sciencekit.com

List of Activity Materials

It is assumed that goggles, laboratory aprons, tap water, textbooks, paper, calculators, pencils, and pens are available for all activities.

Non-Consumables

Item	Explore Activity Page	MiniLAB Page	Activity Chapter/Section
Bag, large plastic		245	
Balance		138	4-2, 9-2
Ball(s)	135, 165	121, 235	7-2
Basin			4-2
Bathroom scale		262	
Battery(ies)		454, 478	15-1, 16-2
Battery holders (2)			15-1
Beaker(s)	285	293	3-2, 4-1, 10-1, 10-2, 15-2
Beverage containers with covers, various			10-2
Board, wooden			16-2
Bowl or pot	73, 135	245, 346	
Brick			9-2
Broomsticks (2)		274	
Clay		235	
Clock	373	292	
Clock or watch with second hand		44	2-2, 4-1
Coffee cups (s)		292	
Coffee maker			10-2
Comb, hard plastic		377, 448	
Cup(s), plastic	73, 285		4-2
Diffraction grating			13-2
Dropper	315	114, 293	
Dropper bottles			3-2
Electric heater		381	
Fast-food trays			6-2
Faucet		377	
Flashlight			13-1, 14-1, 14-2
Flashlight bulb		454	
Force spring scale			9-2
Funnel, plastic			15-2
Glass prism	373		
Glass, drinking		90, 292, 328	
Graduated cylinder	285	44	4-2, 5-1, 10-2
Hammer			16-2
Headphone jack			8-2
Hose clamp			15-2
Hot plate	285	293	3-2, 4-1, 10-1, 10-2
Iron filings		474	
Key(s)		198, 346	
Lens, convex			14-2
Light, clear incandescent with dimmer switch			13-2
Lightbulbs, 1.5 V (4)			15-1
Magnet(s)	469	474	16-1, 16-2
Marble(s)	193	235	4-2, 6-1
Measuring cup		44, 52	
Measuring tape			12-2
Microscope slide(s)			13-1
Minibulb sockets (4)			15-1
Mirror, concave		381	
Motor, small electrical			8-2
Musical instruments			12-2
Nail(s)		478	16-2
Needle			16-1, 16-2
Pennies	403	293	
Petri dish		474	16-1
pH paper			5-2

Non-Consumables *continued*

Item	Explore Activity Page	MiniLAB Page	Activity Chapter/Section
Pipe	227		
Pie pan, small			3-2
Plane mirror, 10 cm per side			14-1
Plastic eggs			6-2
Plastic lids			7-2
Plastic wrap		245	
Plate	315	448	
Protractor			12-1, 14-1
Pulley system, single and multiple			9-2
Radio or CD player			8-2
Reference-data table from fertilizer experiment			1-2
Reference-description of fertilizer experiment			1-2
Reference-Merck Index			3-1
Reference-pH color chart			5-2
Ring stand with ring			15-2
Scissors	373		1-1, 4-2, 14-1
Scoops, small (3)			3-2
Shirt, flannel		377	
Sink	73		4-2
Spoon		90, 346	16-1
Spring scale(s)		44, 211	7-2, 9-1
Spring toy, long, coiled			11-1, 11-2
Steel bar			9-2
Steel wool, fine		147	
Stirring rod			4-1, 10-1
Stopwatch		169, 262	2-2, 7-1, 7-2, 10-1, 10-2, 11-1, 11-2, 15-2
Straight pins			6-2
Sweater, wool		377	
Teaspoon(s)			5-1
Test tube(s)	103	422	3-2
Test-tube holder			3-2
Test-tube rack	103		
Test-tube stopper		422	
Thermal mitts			10-2
Thermometer(s)	103, 285, 373	245	4-1, 10-1, 10-2
Thumbtack(s)			3-1
Tongs		293	10-2
Towel		346	
Tub		346	
Tuning forks			12-2
Watch	373	292	
Watch with second hand, ticks audibly			12-1
Weights, variety			9-2
Wire		454	15-1, 16-2
Wire cutters			16-2
Wood, piece or block(s)	227	138	9-1, 16-2

Chemical Supplies

Item	Explore Activity Page	MiniLAB Page	Activity Chapter/Section
Calcium chloride			5-1
Iodine solution			3-2
Phenol red solution			5-1

Consumables

Item	Explore Activity Page	Mini LAB Page	Activity Chapter/Section
Aluminum foil	285		
Antacids			5-2
Balloons, different sizes and shapes	439		7-1
Card, 10 cm X 10cm		422	
Cardboard mailing tubes			1-1
Cardboard tubes, 20- to 30-cm long			12-1
Cardboard, white surface, 20 cm square			14-2
Clay			13-1
Cloth, wool, small piece	439	448	
Construction paper, black			14-1
Cork	315		
Cup, polystyrene	285		
Cups, paper (2)	403		
Detergent			5-2
Food coloring		23, 293	
Food-baking soda			3-2, 5-1
Food-can of diet soda, unopened		14	
Food-can of regular soda, unopened		14	
Food-coffee			10-2
Food-cornstarch			3-2
Food-fruit juices			5-2
Food-pepper		448	
Food-salad oil		90	
Food-salt		448	5-2
Food-soft drinks			5-2
Food-sugar		90	3-2, 5-2
Food-tea			10-2
Food-vegetable oil		23	
Food-vinegar			3-2, 5-2
Household cleaners			5-2
Ice cubes		292	4-1
Index card(s)			3-1
Insulated foam cups			6-2
Insulated foam meat trays			6-2
Matches			3-2
Modeling clay			14-1, 14-2
Paper plate		147	
Paper towel(s)	73		
Paper, black, large sheet	373		
Pencils, colored			13-2
Plastic bag, resealable			5-1
Plastic tubings, 1 m, different diameters			15-2
Rope		274	1-1, 9-2
Rubber band(s)		358	
Rubber tubings, 1 m, different diameters			15-2
Rubbing alcohol		90, 114	
Salt water		147	
Sandpaper			16-2
Shoebox		76, 358	
Soap			5-2
Spoon, plastic		121	
Straw(s)	315	328	6-2, 7-1
String		121, 346	7-1
Tape	5, 73, 373	175	6-1, 6-2, 7-1, 7-2, 9-1, 11-2, 13-1, 14-1, 14-2, 16-1, 16-2
Tissue	73		
Water	73, 135, 285, 315, 403	14, 23, 52, 90, 147, 245, 292, 293, 328, 346, 422	3-2, 5-1, 5-2, 10-1, 10-2, 11-1, 13-1, 16-1
Yarn, colored			11-1

Classroom Activities and Materials

Suppliers

Scientific Suppliers

Carolina Biological Supply Company
2700 York Road
Burlington, NC 27215
800-334-5551
www.carolina.com

Fisher Scientific Educational
485 South Frontage Road
Burr Ridge, IL 60521
800-955-1177
www.fisheredu.com

Fisher Scientific Company
4500 Turnberry Drive
Hanover Park, IL 60103
800-766-7000
www.fishersci.com

Flinn Scientific
P.O. Box 219
770 N. Raddant Road
Batavia, IL 60510
800-452-1261
www.flinnsci.com

Frey Scientific
100 Paragon Road
Mansfield, OH 44903
800-225-3739
www.freyscientific.com

Sargent-Welch/Cenco
P.O. Box 5229
911 Commerce Court
Buffalo Grove, IL 60089
800-727-4368
www.sargentwelch.com

Science Kit & Boreal Laboratories
777 East Park Drive
Tonawanda, NY 14150
800-828-7777
www.sciencekit.com

Ward's Natural Science Establishment, Inc.
P.O. Box 92912
5100 Henrietta Road
Rochester, NY 14692
800-962-2660
www.wardsci.com

Software Distributors

(AIT) Agency for Instructional Technology
Box A
Bloomington, IN 47402-0120
800-457-4509
www.ait.net

Educational Activities, Inc.
1937 Grand Avenue
Baldwin, NY 11510
800-645-3739
www.edact.com

IBM Educational Systems
Department PC
4111 Northside Parkway
Atlanta, GA 30327
800-426-4968
www.IBM.com

Microphys
12 Bridal Way
Sparta, NJ 07871
800-832-6591
www.microphys.com

Queue, Inc.
338 Commerce Drive
Fairfield, CT 06432
800-335-0906
www.queueinc.com

School Division of The Learning Company
6160 Summit Drive
Minneapolis, MN 55430
www.learningcompanyschool.com

Ventura Educational Systems
P.O. Box 425
Grover Beach, CA 93483
2782 Sevada
Arroyo, CA 93420
800-336-1022
www.venturaES.com

Audiovisual Distributors

Aims Multimedia
9710 Desoto Avenue
Chatsworth, CA 91311-4409
800-367-2467
www.amismultimedia.com

BFA Educational Media
2349 Chaffee Drive
St. Louis, MO 63146
800-221-1274
www.phoenixcoronet.com

CRM Films
2215 Faraday Avenue
Carlsbad, CA 92008
800-421-0833
www.crmfilms.com

Encyclopedia Britannica Educational Corp (EBEC)
310 S. Michigan Avenue
Chicago, IL 60604
800-554-9862 ext. 7007
www.ebec.com

Hawkill Associates, Inc.
125 E. Gilman Street
Madison, WI 53703
800-422-4295
www.hawkill.com

Lumivision
877 Federal Boulevard.
Denver, CO 80204
303-446-0400
www.lumivision.com

National Geographic School Publishing
P.O. Box 10579
De Moines, IA 50340
17th and "M" Streets, NW
Washington, DC 20009
800-368-2728
www.nationalgeographic.com\education

Time-Life Education
P.O. Box 8502
Richmond, VA 23285
800-449-2010
www.timelifeedu.com

Video Discovery
Suite 600
1700 Westlake Avenue, N
Seattle, WA 98109
800-548-3472
www.videodiscovery.com

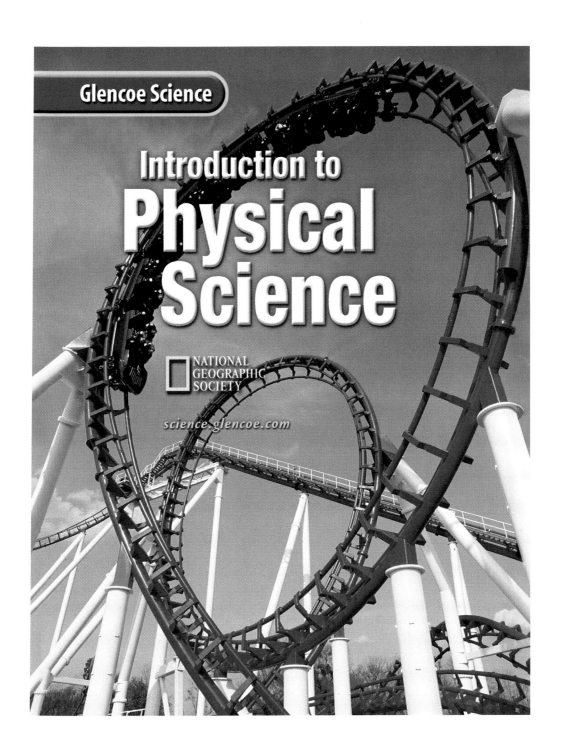

Glencoe Science

Introduction to Physical Science

NATIONAL GEOGRAPHIC SOCIETY

science.glencoe.com

New York, New York Columbus, Ohio Woodland Hills, California Peoria, Illinois

Glencoe Science

Introduction to Physical Science

Student Edition
Teacher Wraparound Edition
Interactive Teacher Edition CD-ROM
Interactive Lesson Planner CD-ROM
Lesson Plans
Content Outline for Teaching
Dinah Zike's Teaching Science with Foldables
Directed Reading for Content Mastery
Foldables: Reading and Study Skills
Assessment
- *Chapter Review*
- *Chapter Tests*
- *ExamView Pro Test Bank Software*
- *Assessment Transparencies*
- *Performance Assessment in the Science Classroom*
- *The Princeton Review Standardized Test Practice Booklet*

Directed Reading for Content Mastery in Spanish
Spanish Resources
English/Spanish Guided Reading Audio Program
Reinforcement
Enrichment
Activity Worksheets
Section Focus Transparencies
Teaching Transparencies
Laboratory Activities
Science Inquiry Labs
Critical Thinking/Problem Solving
Reading and Writing Skill Activities
Mathematics Skill Activities
Cultural Diversity
Laboratory Management and Safety in the Science Classroom
Mindjogger Videoquizzes and Teacher Guide
Interactive Explorations and Quizzes CD-ROM with Presentation Builder
Vocabulary Puzzlemaker Software
Cooperative Learning in the Science Classroom
Environmental Issues in the Science Classroom
Home and Community Involvement
Using the Internet in the Science Classroom

"Study Tip," "Test-Taking Tip," and the "Test Practice" features in this book were written by The Princeton Review, the nation's leader in test preparation. Through its association with McGraw-Hill, The Princeton Review offers the best way to help students excel on standardized assessments.

The Princeton Review is not affiliated with Princeton University or Educational Testing Service.

Glencoe/McGraw-Hill
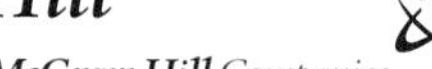
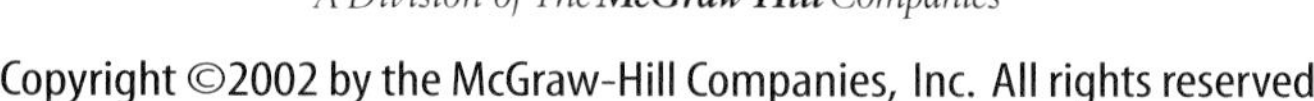
A Division of The McGraw-Hill Companies

The "Science and Society" and the "Science and History" features that appear in this book were designed and developed by TIME for Kids, a division of TIME Magazine.

Cover Images: Paul Rubin
A ride on this roller coaster lasts for about one minute and 20 seconds and reaches a speed of more than 80 km/h.

Send all inquires to:
Glencoe/McGraw-Hill
8787 Orion Place
Columbus, OH 43240

ISBN 0-07-826880-X
Printed in the United States of America.
1 2 3 4 5 6 7 8 9 10 071/043 06 05 04 03 02 01

Authors

Cathy Ezrailson
Science Department Head
Academy for Science and Health Professions
Conroe, Texas

Thomas McCarthy, PhD
Science Department Chair
St. Edward's School
Vero Beach, Florida

Patricia Horton
Mathematics and Science Teacher
Summit Intermediate School
Etiwanda, California

Dinah Zike
Educational Consultant
Dinah-Might Activities, Inc.
San Antonio, Texas

Deborah Lillie
Math and Science Writer
Sudbury, Massachusetts

Margaret K. Zorn
Science Writer
Yorktown, Virginia

Reading Consultants

Barry Barto
Special Education Teacher
John F. Kennedy Elementary
Manistee, Michigan

Rachel Swaters
Science Teacher
Rolla Middle School
Rolla, Missouri

Nancy Woodson, PhD
Professor of English
Otterbein College
Westerville, Ohio

Math Consultant

Michael Hopper, DEng
Manager of Aircraft Certification
Raytheon Company
Greenville, Texas

Content Consultants

Alan Bross, PhD
High-Energy Physicist
Fermilab
Batavia, Illinois

Lisa McGaw
Science Teacher
Hereford High School
Hereford, Texas

Jack Cooper
Adjunct Faculty Math and Science
Navarro College
Corsicana, Texas

Madelaine Meek
Physics Consultant
Editor
Lebanon, Ohio

Carl Zorn, PhD
Staff Scientist
Jefferson Laboratory
Newport News, Virginia

Safety Consultants

Malcolm Cheney, PhD
OSHA Chemical Safety Officer
Hall High School
West Hartford, Connecticut

Aileen Duc, PhD
Science II Teacher
Hendrick Middle School
Plano, Texas

Sandra West, PhD
Associate Professor of Biology
Southwest Texas State University
San Marcos, Texas

Activity Testers

José Luis Alvarez, PhD
Math and Science Mentor Teacher
Yseleta ISD
El Paso, Texas

Mary Helen Mariscal-Cholka
Science Teacher
William D. Slider Middle School
El Paso, Texas

Nerma Coats Henderson
Teacher
Pickerington Jr. High School
Pickerington, Ohio

José Alberto Marquez
TEKS for Leaders Trainer
Yseleta ISD
El Paso, Texas

Science Kit and Boreal Laboratories
Tonawanda, New York

Reviewers

Sharla Adams
McKinney High School North
McKinney, Texas

Desiree Bishop
Baker High School
Mobile, Alabama

Nora M. Prestinari Burchett
Saint Luke School
McLean, Virginia

Anthony DiSipio
Octorana Middle School
Atglen, Pennsylvania

George Gabb
Great Bridge Middle School
Chesapeake, Virginia

Barbara Jo Green
Wilkinson Middle School
Mesquite, Texas

Maria Kelly
St. Leo School
Fairfax, Virginia

Eddie K. Lindsay
Vansant Middle School
Buchanan County, Virginia

H. Keith Lucas
Stewart Middle School
Fort Defiance, Virginia

Thomas E. Lynch, Jr.
Northport High School
East Northport, New York

Linda Melcher
Woodmont Middle School
Piedmont, South Carolina

Amy Morgan
Berry Middle School
Hoover, Alabama

Annette Parrott
Lakeside High School
Atlanta, Georgia

Meredith Pickett
Memorial Middle School
Houston, Texas

Pam Starnes
North Richland Middle School
Fort Worth, Texas

Clabe Webb
Sterling City High School
Sterling City, Texas

Contents

Contents in Brief

UNIT 1 The Nature of Science—2

CHAPTER 1 The Nature of Science—4

CHAPTER 2 Measurement—40

CONTENTS

UNIT 2 Matter—70

CHAPTER 3

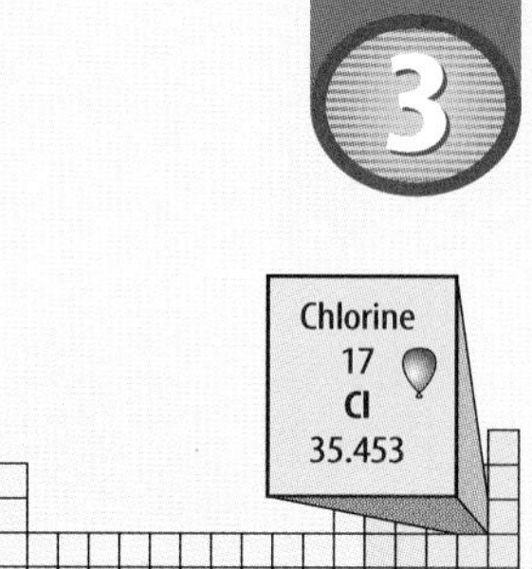

Atoms, Elements, and the Periodic Table—72

States of Matter—102

Properties and Changes—134

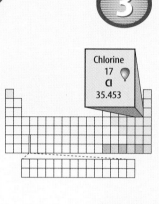

UNIT 3 Motion and Forces—162

CHAPTER 6 Motion and Momentum—164

CHAPTER 7 Force and Newton's Laws—192

CONTENTS

UNIT 4 Energy—224

Thermal Energy—284

UNIT 5 Waves, Sound, and Light—312

Waves—314

CONTENTS

Contents

UNIT 6 Electricity and Magnetism—436

CHAPTER 15 Electricity—438

CHAPTER 16 Magnetism—468

Interdisciplinary Connections

NATIONAL GEOGRAPHIC Unit Openers

NATIONAL GEOGRAPHIC VISUALIZING

Interdisciplinary Connections

TIME SCIENCE AND Society

TIME SCIENCE AND HISTORY

Science Stats

Activities

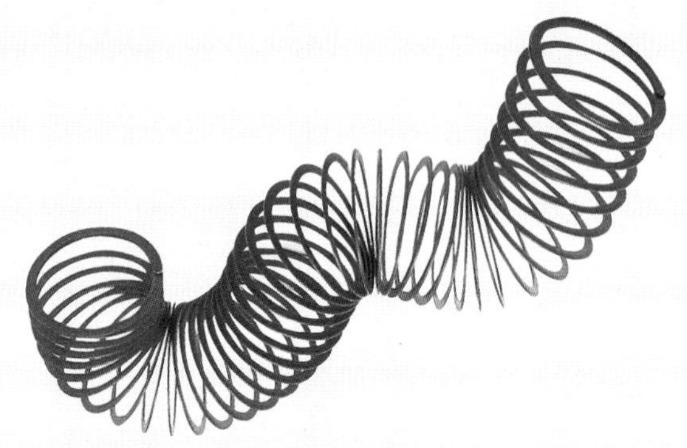

Feature Contents

Full Period Labs

Mini
LAB

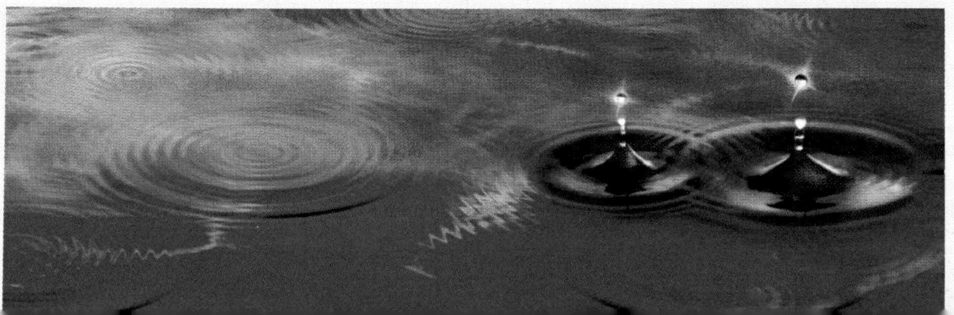

Activities

Explore Activity

Problem Solving Activities

Activities

Math Skills Activities

Skill Builder Activities

Science

Activities

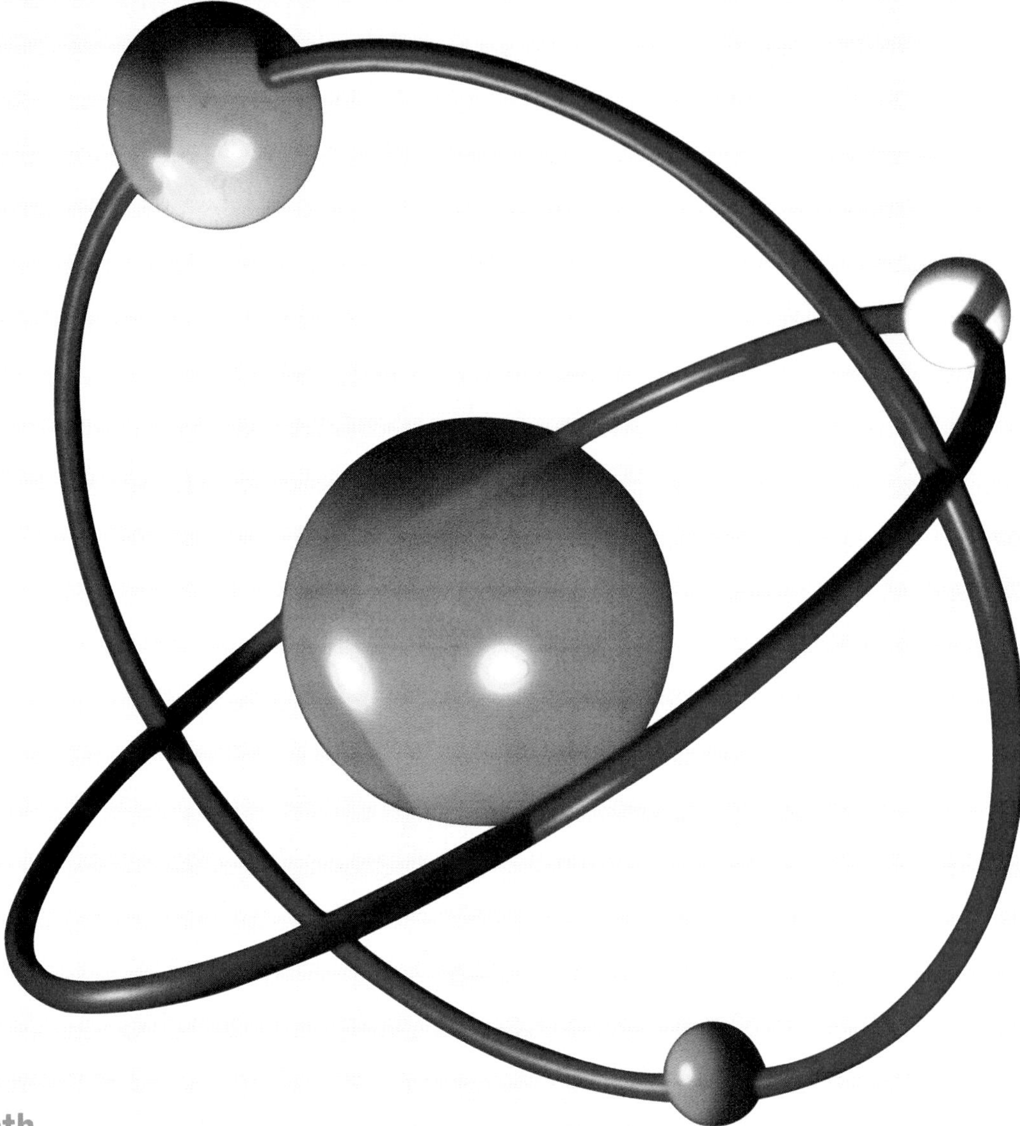

Science INTEGRATION

SCIENCE *Online*

THE PRINCETON REVIEW

UNIT 1

Unit Contents

Pre-Reading Activity

Have students look through these chapters and identify as many tools for measuring as they can. Have them indicate the ones they have used.

UNIT 1

The Nature of Science

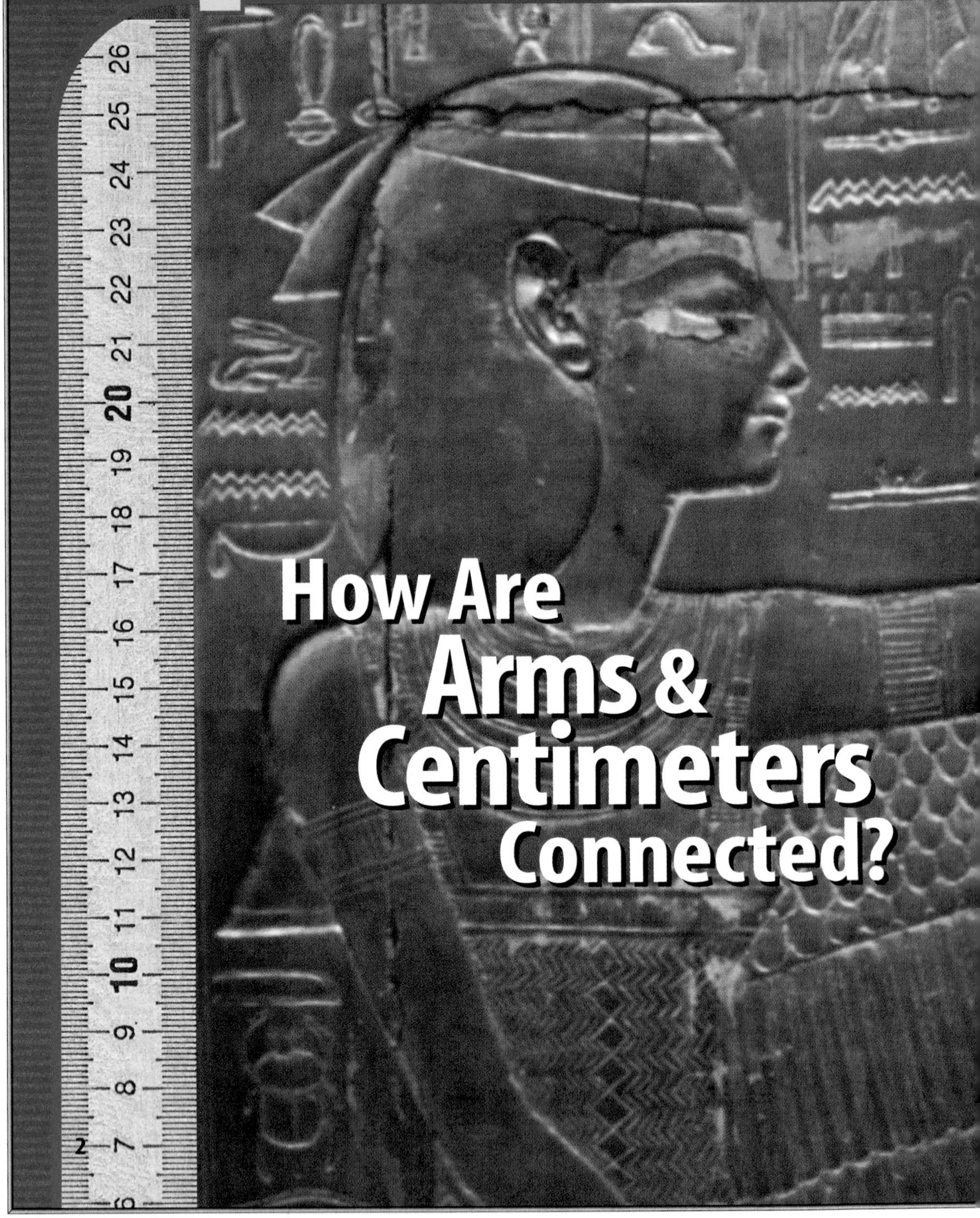

How Are Arms & Centimeters Connected?

Teacher to Teacher

"To help students visualize a variety of concepts, I have them use modeling clay. For example, to better understand the size of a cubic centimeter, a milliliter, and a gram, students can use the clay to make a 1-cm^3 box, a box that has a mass of 1 g, and a box that holds 1 mL of water."

Patrolia Moss, Teacher
North Heights Junior High
Texarkana, AR

About 3,000 years ago, the Egyptians developed one of the earliest recorded units of measurement—the cubit, which was based on the length of the arm from elbow to fingertip. The Egyptian measurement system probably influenced later systems, many of which also were based on body parts such as arms and feet. Such systems, however, could be problematic, since arms and feet vary in length from one person to another. Moreover, each country had its own system, which made it hard for people from different countries to share information. The need for a precise, universal measurement system eventually led to the adoption of the meter as the basic international unit of length. A meter is defined as the distance that light travels in a vacuum in a certain fraction of a second—a distance that never varies. Meters are divided into smaller units called centimeters, which are seen on the rulers here.

SCIENCE CONNECTION

MEASUREMENT SYSTEMS Ancient systems of measurement had their flaws, but they paved the way for the more exact and uniform systems used today. Devise your own measurement system based on parts of your body (for example, the length of your hand or the width of your shoulders) or common objects in your classroom or home. Give names to your units of measurement. Then calculate the width and height of a doorway using one or more of your units.

Introducing the Unit

How Are Arms & Centimeters Connected?

As ancient peoples travelled and trade began, a need for accuracy in measuring became necessary. Tell students that early weight units may have been derived from containers or calculations of what a person or animal could haul. Explain that early linear measurements were often based on body parts.

Because of its accuracy, the Egyptian cubit was the standard of linear measurement. The accuracy of the Egyptian cubit stick is attested by the dimensions of the Great Pyramid of Giza. Its sides vary only slightly even though thousands of people were employed to build it. This is because the cubit was standardized by a royal master cubit of black granite. All cubit sticks used in Egypt were measured against the master at regular intervals.

Today, the only SI or fundamental unit of measurement based on a physical object is the kilogram, which the Babylonians developed as the basic unit of mass. It is accurate down to one part per million. Other SI units are defined with physical descriptions based on stable properties in the universe. There are seven basic SI units, one of which is the meter. The centimeter is a subunit of the meter.

SCIENCE Online

Internet Addresses

Explore the Glencoe Science Web site at **science.glencoe.com** to find out more about topics in this unit.

SCIENCE CONNECTION

Activity

Have students develop their own systems of measurement, then divide the class into pairs. Each student should use his or her partner's system of measurement to see how measurements vary when two students use the same system. Explain that this is why a standard system of measurement is needed.

Section/Objectives	Standards		Activities/Features
	National	State/Local	
Chapter Opener	See p. 5T for a Key to Standards.		**Explore Activity:** Observe how gravity accelerates objects, p. 5 **Before You Read,** p. 5
Section 1 What is Science 3 sessions 1.5 blocks 1. **Define** science and identify questions that science cannot answer. 2. **Compare and contrast** theories and laws. 3. **Identify** a system and its components. 4. **Identify** the three branches of science.	National Content Standards: UCP2, A1, A2, G2		**MiniLAB:** Classify Parts of a System, p. 8 **Science Online** p. 9
Section 2 Science in Action 4 sessions 2 blocks 1. **Identify** some skills scientists use. 2. **Define** hypothesis. 3. **Recognize** the difference between observation and inference.	National Content Standards: UCP2, A1, A2, G1		**Life Science Integration,** p. 13 **MiniLAB:** Forming a Hypothesis, p. 14 **Problem Solving Activity,** p. 17 **Science Online,** p. 18
Section 3 Models in Science 3 sessions 1.5 blocks 1. **Describe** various types of models. 2. **Discuss** limitations of models.	National Content Standards: UCP2, A1, A2		**Earth Science Integration,** p. 22 **MiniLAB:** Thinking Like a Scientist, p. 23 **Visualizing the Modeling of King Tut,** p. 24
Section 4 Evaluating Scientific Explanation 4 sessions 2 blocks 1. **Evaluate** scientific explanations. 2. **Evaluate** promotional claims.	National Content Standards: UCP2, A1, A2, G2, G3		**Activity:** What is the right answer?, p. 31 **Activity:** Identifying Parts of an Investigation, pp. 32–33 **Science and History:** Women in Science, pp. 34–35

Activity Materials	Reproducible Resources	Section Assessment	Technology
Explore Activity: 3 identical unsharpened pencils, tape	**Chapter Resources Booklet** Foldables Worksheet, p. 19 Directed Reading Overview, p. 21 Note-taking Worksheets, pp. 37–39	GLENCOE'S ASSESSMENT ADVANTAGE	
MiniLAB: paper, pencil or pen *Need materials?* Contact Science Kit at 1-800-828-7777 or www.sciencekit.com on the Internet.	**Chapter Resources Booklet** Transparency Activity, p. 48 MiniLAB, p. 3 Enrichment, p. 33 Reinforcement, p. 29 Directed Reading, p. 22 **Life Science Critical Thinking/ Problem Solving,** p. 1	Portfolio Assessment, p. 8 Performance Skill Builder Activities, p. 11 Content Section Assessment, p. 11	Section Focus Transparency Interactive CD-ROM/DVD Guided Reading Audio Program
MiniLAB: large pot of water, unopened can of diet soda, unopened can of regular soda	**Chapter Resources Booklet** Transparency Activity, p. 49 MiniLAB, p. 4 Enrichment, p. 34 Reinforcement, p. 30 Directed Reading, p. 23 Lab Activity, pp. 11–14 Transparency Activity, pp. 53–54	Portfolio Active Reading, p. 16 Performance MiniLAB, p. 14 Skill Builder Activities, p. 20 Content Section Assessment, p. 20	Section Focus Transparency Teaching Transparency Interactive CD-ROM/DVD Guided Reading Audio Program
MiniLAB: 15 mL water, test tube, 5 mL vegetable oil, 2 drops food coloring	**Chapter Resources Booklet** Transparency Activity, p. 50 MiniLAB, p. 5 Enrichment, p. 35 Reinforcement, p. 31 Directed Reading, p. 23 Lab Activity, pp. 15–18 **Science Inquiry Labs,** p. 47	Portfolio Curriculum Connection, p. 22 Performance MiniLAB, p. 23 Skill Builder Activities, p. 26 Content Section Assessment, p. 26	Section Focus Transparency Interactive CD-ROM/DVD Guided Reading Audio Program
Activity: cardboard mailing tubes, length of rope, scissors **Activity:** description of fertilizer experiment, data table from the fertilizer experiment	**Chapter Resources Booklet** Transparency Activity, p. 51 Enrichment, p. 36 Reinforcement, p. 32 Directed Reading, pp. 23, 24 Activity Worksheet, pp. 7–8, 9–10 **Lab Management and Safety,** p. 71	Portfolio Assessment, p. 30 Performance Skill Builder Activities, p. 30 Content Section Assessment, p. 30	Section Focus Transparency Interactive CD-ROM/DVD Guided Reading Audio Program

End of Chapter Assessment

GLENCOE'S ASSESSMENT ADVANTAGE

Blackline Masters	Technology	Professional Series
Chapter Resources Booklet Chapter Review, pp. 41–42 Chapter Tests, pp. 43–46 **Standardized Test Practice by The Princeton Review,** pp. 7–10	MindJogger Videoquiz CD-ROM Explorations and Quizzes Vocabulary Puzzle Makers ExamView Pro Test Bank Interactive Lesson Planner Interactive Teacher's Edition	Performance Assessment in the Science Classroom (PASC)

Transparencies

Section Focus

Section 1 Section Focus Transparency **Dress for the occasion.**

Researching the area around an active volcano requires special precautions. High temperatures and gases like sulfur dioxide make this a hostile environment, but the safety suit enables the scientist to collect data.

1. What are some other hostile environments that scientists explore?
2. How does technology help this scientist gather and analyze information?
3. Compare and contrast work in a laboratory with work in the field.

L1

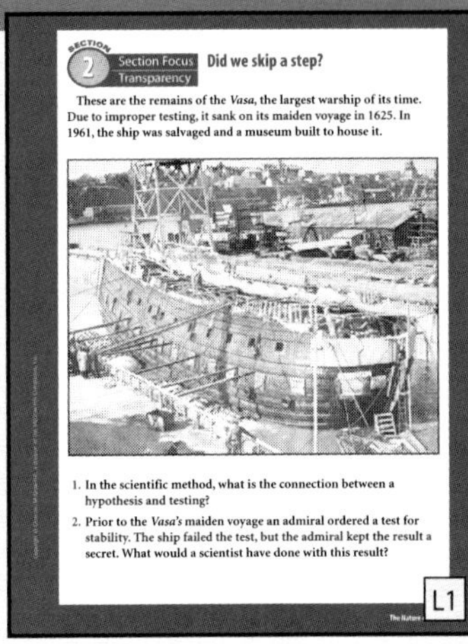

Section 2 Section Focus Transparency **Did we skip a step?**

These are the remains of the *Vasa*, the largest warship of its time. Due to improper testing, it sank on its maiden voyage in 1625. In 1961, the ship was salvaged and a museum built to house it.

1. In the scientific method, what is the connection between a hypothesis and testing?
2. Prior to the *Vasa's* maiden voyage an admiral ordered a test for stability. The ship failed the test, but the admiral kept the result a secret. What would a scientist have done with this result?

L1

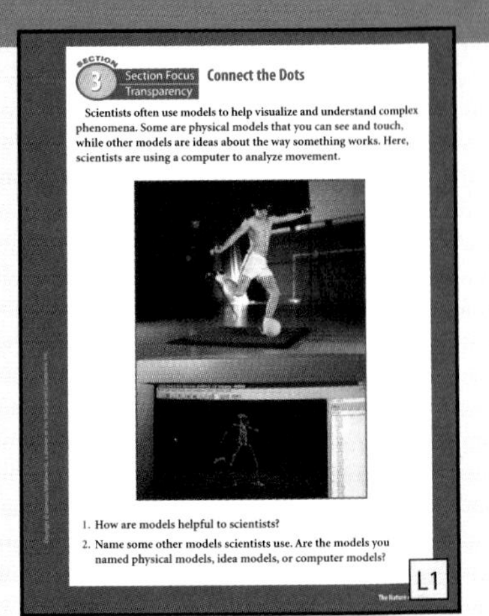

Section 3 Section Focus Transparency **Connect the Dots**

Scientists often use models to help visualize and understand complex phenomena. Some are physical models that you can see and touch, while other models are ideas about the way something works. Here, scientists are using a computer to analyze movement.

1. How are models helpful to scientists?
2. Name some other models scientists use. Are the models you named physical models, idea models, or computer models?

L1

This is a representation of key blackline masters available in the Teacher Classroom Resources. See Resource Manager boxes within the chapter for additional information.

Assessment

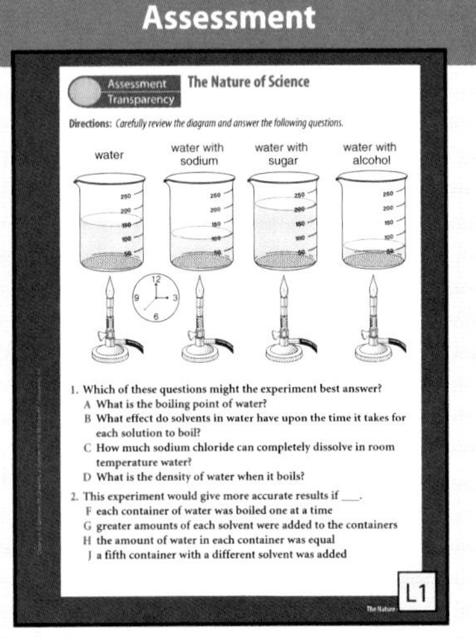

Assessment Transparency **The Nature of Science**

Directions: Carefully review the diagram and answer the following questions.

1. Which of these questions might the experiment best answer?
   A What is the boiling point of water?
   B What effect do solvents in water have upon the time it takes for each solution to boil?
   C How much sodium chloride can completely dissolve in room temperature water?
   D What is the density of water when it boils?
2. This experiment would give more accurate results if ___.
   F each container of water was boiled one at a time
   G greater amounts of each solvent were added to the containers
   H the amount of water in each container was equal
   J a fifth container with a different solvent was added

L1

Teaching

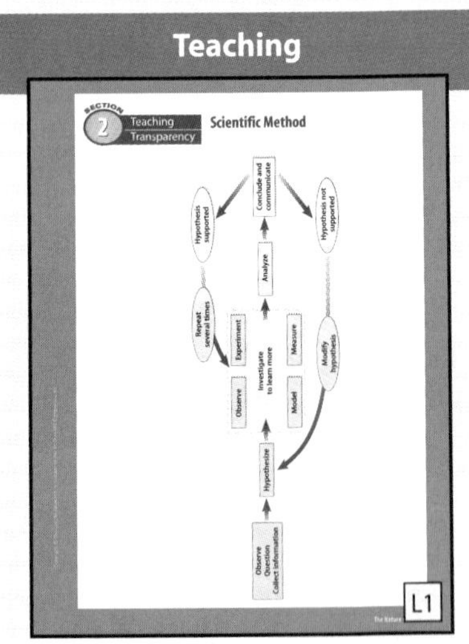

Section 2 Teaching Transparency **Scientific Method**

L1

Key to Teaching Strategies

The following designations will help you decide which activities are appropriate for your students.

- L1 Level 1 activities should be appropriate for students with learning difficulties.
- L2 Level 2 activities should be within the ability range of all students.
- L3 Level 3 activities are designed for above-average students.
- ELL ELL activities should be within the ability range of English Language Learners.
- COOP LEARN Cooperative Learning activities are designed for small group work.
- LS Multiple Learning Styles logos, as described on page 22T, are used throughout to indicate strategies that address different learning styles.
- P These strategies represent student products that can be placed into a best-work portfolio.

Hands-on Activities

Activity Worksheets

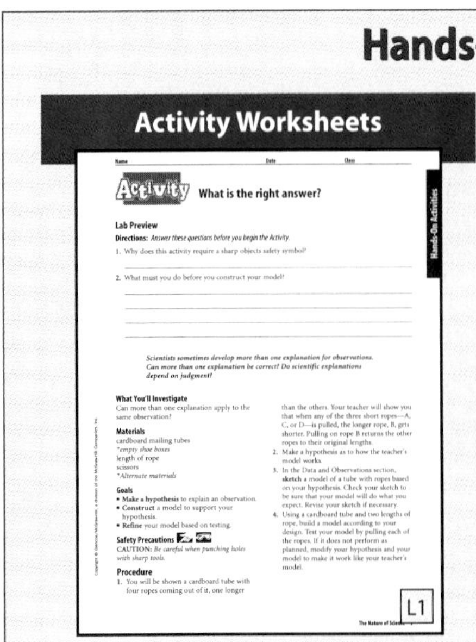

Activity **What is the right answer?**

Lab Preview

Directions: Answer these questions before you begin the Activity.

1. Why does this activity require a sharp objects safety symbol?
2. What must you do before you construct your model?

Scientists sometimes develop more than one explanation for observations. Can more than one explanation be correct? Do scientific explanations depend on judgment?

What You'll Investigate

Can more than one explanation apply to the same observation?

Materials

Goals

Safety Precautions

Procedure

L1

Laboratory Activities

Laboratory Activity 1 **Solving a Problem with a Scientific Method**

Strategy

Materials

Procedure

Part A. Observation

Data and Observations

Table 1

Similarities	Differences

L1

Meeting Different Ability Levels

Content Outline

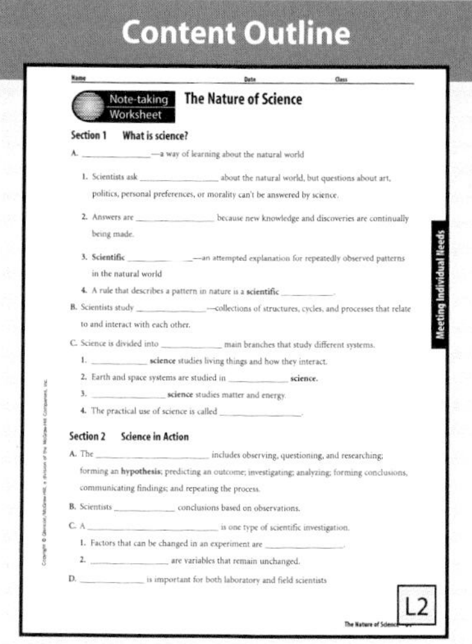
Note-taking Worksheet — The Nature of Science

L2

Reinforcement

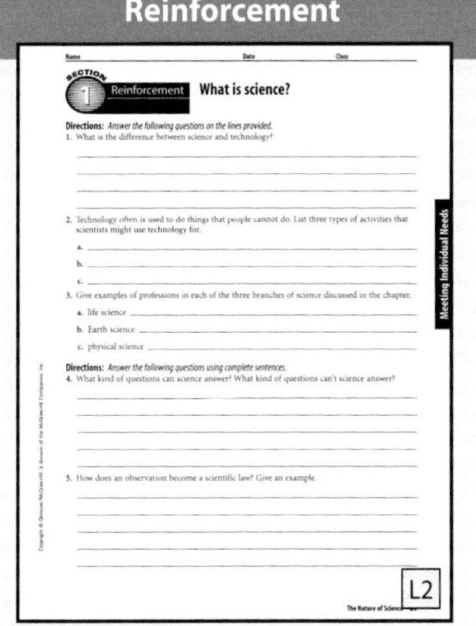
Section 1 Reinforcement — What is science?

L2

Directed Reading

Directed Reading for Content Mastery — Overview: The Nature of Science

L1

Enrichment

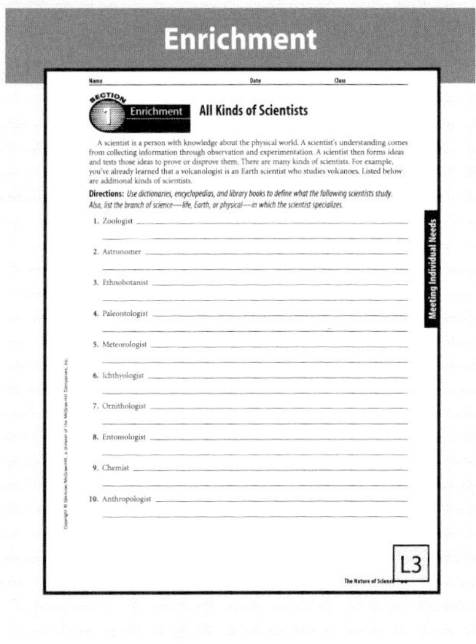
Section 1 Enrichment — All Kinds of Scientists

L3

Spanish Directed Reading

Lectura Dirigida para la Maestría del Contenido — Sinopsis: La Naturaleza de la Ciercia

L1

Assessment

Chapter Tests

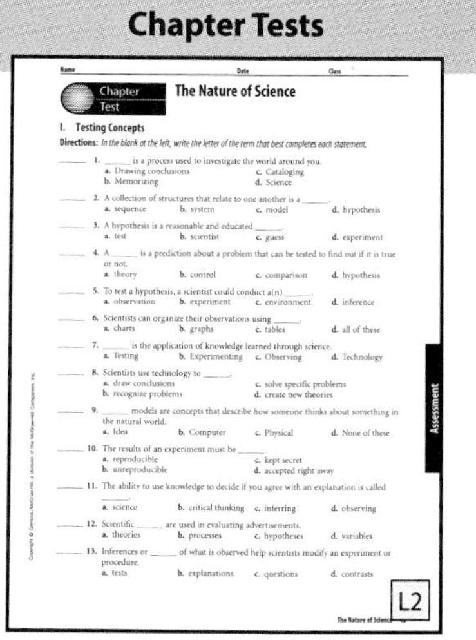
Chapter Test — The Nature of Science

L2

Test Practice Workbook

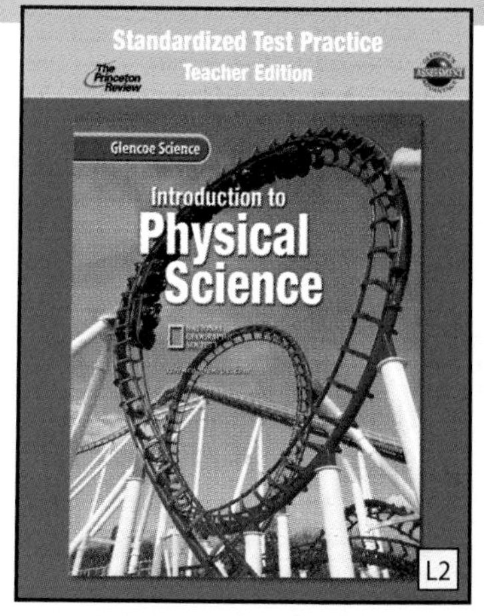

L2

Chapter Review

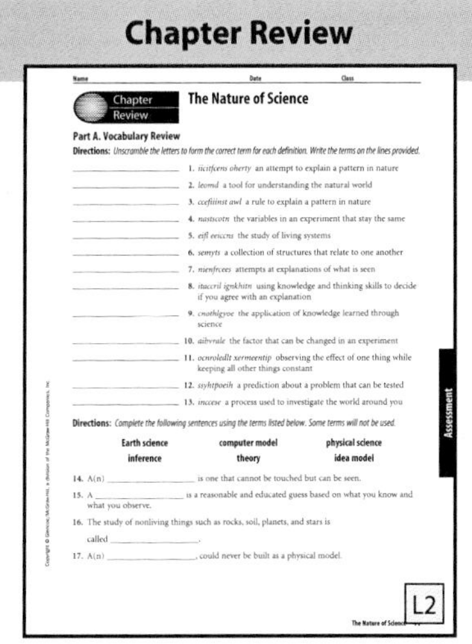
Chapter Review — The Nature of Science

L2

Science Content Background

SECTION 1

What is science?

Learning About the World

Science has a dual nature. On the one hand it can be thought of as an organized body of agreed upon descriptions and explanations about the natural world. On the other hand it can be thought of as the methods that lead to these development of the descriptions and explanations about the world.

One key aspect of science, whether it is at the Nobel prize level or the science fair level, is that success depends upon choosing a question that can be answered with the time and resources available to the investigators. People of science become famous for answering questions they posed. While all scientists pose questions they cannot answer, this is clearly not the path to fame or fortune. As Einstein wrote, "The formulation of the problem is often more essential than its solution."

Fun Fact

Ecotourists to Rwanda can visit the mountain gorillas that Dian Fossey worked so hard to study and save. Only small groups are led on a remote trek to a family of gorillas. The guides warn the visitors not to look the male silverback in the eyes and, if he attacks, not to run but rather to assume a submissive posture, such as bending over and eating grass.

Even scientific laws can be disproved. The Law of Conservation of Energy was accepted as truth until Einstein argued that mass could be turned into energy and energy into mass. Einstein had no physical proof of this, but his theories were later confirmed by investigations. So today we accept the Law of Conservation of Mass and Energy.

A good benchmark for knowing if you have a system is to see if components of it interact. Systems in science include solar systems, ecosystems, and weather systems. Systems can be narrowly defined such as the lymphatic system of broadly stated such as the Earth system.

The Branches of Science

Often the most fertile ground for investigation is at the periphery of two or more branches of science. Biochemistry originated at the borders of biology and chemistry and today is its own branch of science. In a similar way, biophysics is arising from biology and physics.

Science in Action

Science Skills

Science skills or science process skills are abilities that lead to the development of agreed upon descriptions of the natural world. Observations are the basis of science, in that any hypothesis, theory, or law must meet the standard that it is consistent with all observations. Other process skills include classifying, predicting, and communicating.

The term *The Scientific Method* is an inaccurate description of the work of scientists. For one, the *The* makes it seem as though all scientists use one method, which is certainly not the case. There are differences between methods of an astronomer and a medical researcher as there are between a theoretical physicist and a conservation biologist. Further, science does not proceed in a linear fashion. There are many false starts and dead ends, and back tracking and detours can occur often in the path. Thus the term *Science Methods* is preferred, as it is more inclusive of the diverse ways of science. It is, however, still useful to talk about components of methods of science, such as problems and hypotheses, because they shed light on aspects

Micheal Simpson/FPG International

of scientific endeavors and because scientific papers often use this format to report results.

The difference between observations and inferences is shown in the discovery of different solar systems. The observation of unusual movements in stars is used to infer the presence of a large planet near that star.

Experiments

Scientists usually apply the term *experiment* to situations in which they manipulate a variable to see the effect. Observing a star would not be an experiment because no variable was manipulated.

In past experiments, many sick people who believed they were receiving medicine, but in fact were given only sugar pills, actually got better. For this reason, in drug trials, the participants never know whether or not they are actually being given a drug. The treatment group is given the drug while the control group is given a placebo—something that resembles the drug but, like a sugar pill, has no effect.

Models in Science

Making Models

An important part of science is to construct models that approximate the real world. Models come in many forms such as physical, conceptual, or mathematical. In many cases, models are analogies: balls and springs, for example, can be presented as analogous to molecules and forces. Models may be similar to the real world, but they are never perfect matches. Perhaps for this reason it is common to have different models attempting to describe the same phenomenon.

For additional content background on this topic, go to the Glencoe Science Web site at science.glencoe.com.

Terry Vine/Stone

Evaluating Scientific Explanation

Believe it or not?

Many of the most common fallacies of logic also afflict scientific inquiry, and even the most experienced scientist must be aware of the various errors that can invalidate an investigation. The design of an experiment can be flawed from the beginning—for instance, a variable that will affect the result is not rigorously controlled or is completely overlooked. Even in a well-designed experiment, the scientist's observations might be biased, however subtly. If the data collected from a perfectly designed and properly executed experiment are based on too small a sample, conclusions drawn from the data may not be reliable for wider application. And it is even possible that an incorrect conclusion will be drawn from completely reliable data. A successful scientific investigation is the result of careful thought and painstaking procedure.

The Nature of Science

Chapter Vocabulary

science
scientific theory
scientific law
system
life science
Earth science
physical science
technology
hypothesis
infer
controlled experiment
variable
constant
model
critical thinking

What do you think?

Science Journal This photograph shows the circle of bubbles made by humpback whales working together to trap fish and krill for food.

CHAPTER 1

The Nature of Science

An important part of science is asking questions. Over time, scientists observed an unusual behavior among humpback whales and wondered why they did it. Through scientific investigations, they learned that the humpbacks work together to get food. They swim in circles and blow bubbles. This makes a bubble net that traps small fish and krill—tiny shrimplike animals. Then the whales can swoop up mouthfuls of food.

What do you think?

Science Journal Look at the picture below with a classmate. Discuss what you think this is. Here's a hint: *Dinner is served.* Write your answer or best guess in your Science Journal.

4

Theme Connection

Systems and Interactions Science is a systematic way of studying the world to find relationships and interactions among the processes, cycles, and structures that make up the systems of the world.

Gravity is a familiar natural force. It keeps you anchored on Earth, but how does it work? Scientists learn about gravity and other concepts by making observations. Noticing things is how scientists start any study of nature. Do the activity below to see how gravity affects objects.

Observe how gravity accelerates objects

1. Collect three identical, unsharpened pencils.
2. Tape two of the pencils together.
3. Hold all the pencils at the same height, as high as you can. Drop them together and observe what happens as they fall.

Observe

Did the single pencil fall faster or slower than the pair? Predict in your Science Journal what would happen if you taped 30 pencils together and dropped them at the same time as you dropped a single pencil.

Before You Read

Making a Know-Want-Learn Study Fold **Make the following Foldable to help you identify what you already know and what you want to know about science.**

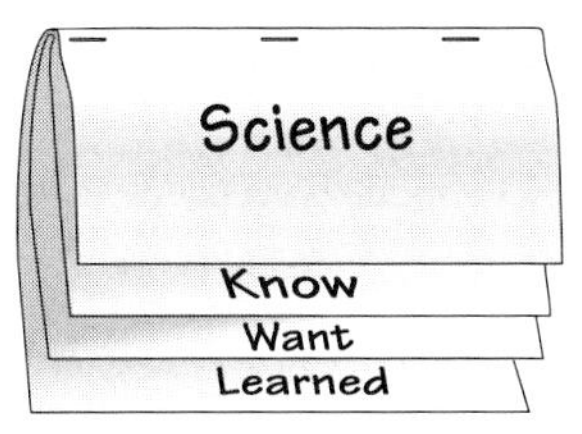

1. Stack two sheets of paper in front of you so the short side of both sheets is at the top.
2. Slide the top sheet up so that about 4 cm of the bottom sheet show.
3. Fold both sheets top to bottom to form four tabs and staple along the topfold, as shown.
4. Label the top flap *Science*. Then, label the other flaps *Know, Want,* and *Learned,* as shown. Before you read the chapter, write what you know about science on the *Know* tab and what you want to know on the *Want* tab.
5. As you read the chapter, list the things you learn about science on the *Learned* tab.

EXPLORE ACTIVITY

Purpose Students explore how gravity affects objects of different masses. L2 LS **Kinesthetic**

Materials 3 unsharpened pencils, tape

Teaching Strategies Make sure students drop the pencils from the greatest height possible.

Observe

The single pencil and the pair of pencils fall at the same rate. From this, we can infer that 30 pencils also should fall just as quickly as one pencil.

Process Have students design other experiments to test how quickly objects of different sizes and weights fall. Encourage them to compare objects of different shapes and sizes. Use **Performance Assessment in the Science Classroom,** p. 95.

Before You Read

FOLDABLES Reading & Study Skills

Dinah Zike Study Fold

Purpose Students make a KWL Foldable to help them determine before they read the chapter what they know about science and what they would like to know about science. As they read the chapter they add things they learn about science.

For additional help, see Foldables Worksheet, p. 19 in **Chapter Resources Booklet,** or go to the Glencoe Science Web site at **science.glencoe.com.** See After You Read in the Study Guide at the end of this chapter.

SECTION 1

What is science?

1 Motivate

Bellringer Transparency

Display the Section Focus Transparency for Section 1. Use the accompanying Transparency Activity Master. L2 ELL

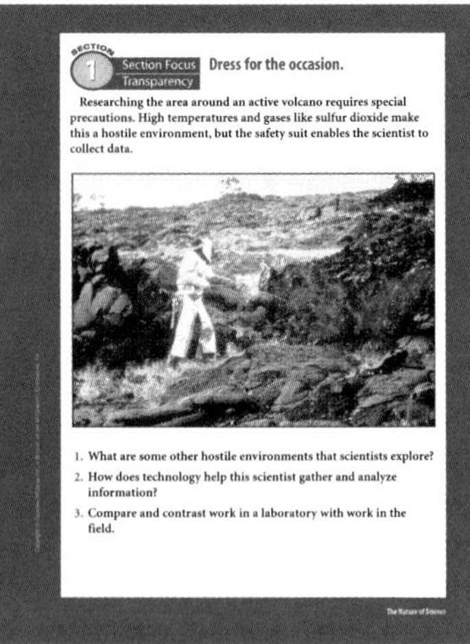

SECTION 1 Section Focus Transparency **Dress for the occasion.**

Researching the area around an active volcano requires special precautions. High temperatures and gases like sulfur dioxide make this a hostile environment, but the safety suit enables the scientist to collect data.

1. What are some other hostile environments that scientists explore?
2. How does technology help this scientist gather and analyze information?
3. Compare and contrast work in a laboratory with work in the field.

The Nature of Science

Tie to Prior Knowledge

Ask students to name events that occur every day, such as the Sun rising in the morning. Tell students that in this section they will learn how science uses regularities like these to make sense of the world.

SECTION 1

What is science?

As You Read

***What* You'll Learn**

- **Define** science and identify questions that science cannot answer.
- **Compare and contrast** theories and laws.
- **Identify** a system and its components.
- **Identify** the three branches of science.

Vocabulary

science, scientific theory, scientific law, system, life science, Earth science, physical science, technology

***Why* It's Important**

Science can be used to learn more about the world you live in.

Learning About the World

When you think of a scientist, do you imagine a person in a laboratory surrounded by charts, graphs, glass bottles, and bubbling test tubes? It might surprise you to learn that anyone who tries to learn something is a scientist. **Science** is a way of learning more about the natural world. Scientists want to know why, how, or when something occurred. This learning process usually begins by keeping your eyes open and asking questions about what you see.

Asking Questions Scientists ask many questions, too. How do things work? What do things look like? What are they made of? Why does something take place? Science can attempt to answer many questions about the natural world, but some questions cannot be answered by science. Look at the situations in **Figure 1.** Who should you vote for? What does this poem mean? Who is your best friend? Questions about art, politics, personal preference, or morality can't be answered by science. Science can't tell you what is right, wrong, good, or bad.

Figure 1
Some questions about topics such as politics, literature, and art cannot be answered by science.

Section Assessment Planner

PORTFOLIO
Assessment, p. 8

PERFORMANCE ASSESSMENT
Try At Home MiniLAB, p. 8
Skill Builder Activities, p. 11
See page 38 for more options.

CONTENT ASSESSMENT
Section, p. 11
Challenge, p. 11
Chapter, pp. 38–39

Figure 2
With new information, explanations can be modified or discarded and new explanations can be made.

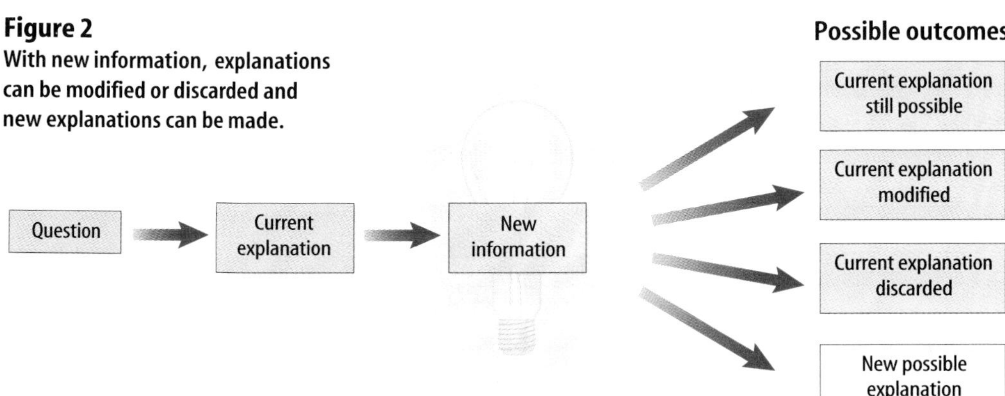

Possible Explanations If learning about your world begins with asking questions, can science provide answers to these questions? Science can answer a question only with the information available at the time. Any answer is uncertain because people will never know everything about the world around them. With new knowledge, they might realize that some of the old explanations no longer fit the new information. As shown in **Figure 2,** some observations might force scientists to look at old ideas and think of new explanations. Science can only provide possible explanations.

Reading Check *Why can't science answer questions with certainty?*

Scientific Theories An attempt to explain a pattern observed repeatedly in the natural world is called a **scientific theory.** Theories are not simply guesses or someone's opinions, nor are theories only vague ideas. Theories in science must be supported by observations and results from many investigations. They are the best explanations that have been found so far. However, theories can change. As new data become available, scientists evaluate how the new data fit the theory. If enough new data do not support the theory, the theory can be changed to fit the new observations better.

Scientific Laws A rule that describes a pattern in nature is a **scientific law.** For an observation to become a scientific law, it must be observed repeatedly. The law then stands until someone makes observations that do not follow the law. A law helps you predict that an apple dropped from arm's length will always fall to Earth. The law, however, does not explain why gravity exists or how it works. A law, unlike a theory, does not attempt to explain why something happens. It simply describes a pattern.

2 Teach

Learning About the World

Use Science Words

Word Origins The word *scientist* was first used in 1835, when William Whewell suggested this term for those who studied the natural world. He thought of it as a counterpart to the word *artist*. An artist is a person skilled in one of the arts. Have students look up the words *science* and *scientist* in the dictionary and suggest how the word *scientist* relates to the word *artist.* The word *science* comes from the Latin word *sciare,* which means "to know." A scientist is a person learned in science like an artist is a person skilled in art. L2
LS **Linguistic**

Reading Check

Answer People will never know everything about the world around them.

Discussion

Have students state things they know about the world and determine whether they are theories or laws. Possible statements: "The Sun rises in the east every morning" is a law because it describes an observation. "The Sun rises every day because gravity keeps Earth in orbit around the Sun" is a theory because it explains something.

Visual Learning

Figure 2 **How could you use this flow chart to answer the question proposed in the Explore Activity about how gravity affects objects?** Write the question and then propose possible explanations. After completing the experiment, see whether any of your observations make sense based upon the data. L2
LS **Logical-Mathematical**

Resource Manager

Chapter Resources Booklet
- Transparency Activity, p. 48
- Directed Reading for Content Mastery, pp. 21, 22
- Note-taking Worksheets, pp. 37–39

Systems in Science

Caption Answer

Figure 3 Possible answers: the desks and their arrangements, the pictures on the wall, the students, the teacher, the chalkboard, the lights

Purpose Students study a familiar system. L2

LS Logical-Mathematical

Teaching Strategy Have a cafeteria worker come to class to answer questions about his or her job and how the food is prepared.

Analysis

Structures in the cafeteria include the tables, serving plates, warmers, ovens, spoons, and forks. Processes include preparing and serving the food. Cycles include the different jobs a worker does during the course of a day, from cooking to serving to cleaning up afterward.

Process Have each student make a timeline showing the sequence of events during a typical day in the cafeteria. Use **Performance Assessment in the Science Classroom**, p. 163. P

Reading Check

Answer a collection of structures, cycles, and processes that relate to and interact with one another

Figure 3
Systems are a collection of structures, cycles, and processes.
What systems can you identify in this classroom?

Systems in Science

Scientists can study many different things in nature. Some might study how the human body works or how planets move around the Sun. Others might study the energy carried in a lightning bolt. What do all of these things have in common? All of them are systems. A **system** is a collection of structures, cycles, and processes that relate to and interact with each other. The structures, cycles, and processes are the parts of a system, just like your stomach is one of the structures of your digestive system.

Reading Check *What is a system?*

Systems are not found just in science. Your school is a system with structures such as the school building, the tables and chairs, you, your teacher, the school bell, your pencil, and many other things. **Figure 3** shows some of these structures. Your school day also has cycles. Your daily class schedule and the calendar of holidays are examples of cycles. Many processes are at work during the school day. When you take a test, your teacher has a process. You might be asked to put your books and papers away and get out a pencil before the test is distributed. When the time is over, you are told to put your pencil down and pass your test to the front of the room.

Parts of a System Interact In a system, structures, cycles, and processes interact. Your daily schedule influences where you go and what time you go. The clock shows the teacher when the test is complete, and you couldn't complete the test without a pencil.

TRY AT HOME Mini LAB

Classify Parts of a System

Procedure

Think about how your school's cafeteria is run. Consider the physical structure of the cafeteria. How many people run it? Where does the food come from? How is it prepared? Where does it go? What other parts of the cafeteria system are necessary?

Analysis

Classify the parts of your school cafeteria's system as structures, cycles, or processes.

Systems in Your Day Have students write in their Science Journals about the different systems that are important to their day. They can choose to concentrate on structures, processes, or cycles, or they can describe the parts of each system in chronological order. L2

LS Linguistic

Parts of a Whole All systems are made up of other systems. For example, you are part of your school. The human body is a system—within your body are other systems. Your school is part of a system—district, state, and national. You have your regional school district. Your district is part of a statewide school system. Scientists often break down problems by studying just one part of a system. A scientist might want to learn about how construction of buildings affects the ecosystem. Because an ecosystem has many parts, one scientist might study a particular animal, while another might study the effect of construction on plantlife.

The Branches of Science

Science often is divided into three main categories, or branches—life science, Earth science, and physical science. Each branch asks questions about different kinds of systems.

Life Science The study of living systems and the ways in which they interact is called **life science.** Life scientists attempt to answer questions like "How do whales navigate the ocean?" and "How do vaccines prevent disease?" Life scientists can study living organisms, where they live, and how they interact. Dian Fossey, shown in **Figure 4,** was a life scientist who studied gorillas, their habitat, and their behaviors.

People who work in the health field are life scientists. Physicians, nurses, physical therapists, dieticians, medical researchers, and others focus on the systems of the human body. Some other examples of careers that use life science include biologists, zookeepers, botanists, farmers, and beekeepers.

SCIENCE Online

Research Visit the Glencoe Science Web site at **science.glencoe.com** for information on Dian Fossey's studies. Write a summary of your research in your Science Journal.

Figure 4
Life scientist Dian Fossey spent more than 18 years observing mountain gorillas in Rwanda, Africa. She was able to play with them as she learned about their behavior.

The Branches of Science

SCIENCE Online

Internet Addresses

Explore the Glencoe Science Web site at **science.glencoe.com** to find out more about topics in this section.

Use Science Words

Word Meaning Have students look up the names of various branches of science. Have them determine how the name came to be applied to that branch of science. Possible examples: Zoology comes from the Greek word *zoe*, which means "life." Zoology is the study of living animals. Medicine derives from the Latin word *medicinas,* which means "remedy." L2 LS **Linguistic**

Discussion

Ask students to name their favorite activities and discuss the types of science that are important to these activities. Possible responses: Reading—chemistry is involved in the processes for making the ink and the paper; physics was applied in the designing of the printing press. Sports—athletes regularly consult physicians and trainers who use their knowledge of life science to help athletes stay in good condition. L2 LS **Logical-Mathematical**

Teacher FYI

Dian Fossey was an occupational therapist by training. She went to Africa to study and observe gorillas without any formal training. Her research led to a new view of these animals, once believed to be savage. She found the gorillas to be gentle vegetarians who developed family relationships. She also found that some would even sacrifice themselves in defense of the group.

Resource Manager 

Chapter Resources Booklet
MiniLAB, p. 3
Enrichment, p. 33

Life Science Critical Thinking/Problem Solving, p. 1

The Branches of Science, continued

✔ Reading Check

Answer nonliving things, such as rocks, soil, clouds, rivers, oceans, planets, stars, meteors, black holes, weather, and climate, on Earth and in space

IDENTIFYING Misconceptions

Students may think that each branch of science is isolated and that the branches never overlap. In fact, a scientist doing work in one of the branches of science often must rely on information obtained from the other branches. Have students think of investigations in which the different sciences would interact. Possible examples: To study how the Sun produces heat, an Earth scientist would need to know about physical science. To study an organism's interaction with its environment, a life scientist would have to know something about the rocks, soil, and water the organism comes into contact with. L3 LS **Logical-Mathematical**

Extension

Have each student research careers that are of interest to him or her and then make a table showing how each career relies on the different branches of science. L3 LS **Linguistic**

Activity

Ask professionals in Earth, life, and physical science to come to class and tell students about the things they do. L2 LS **Auditory-Mathematical**

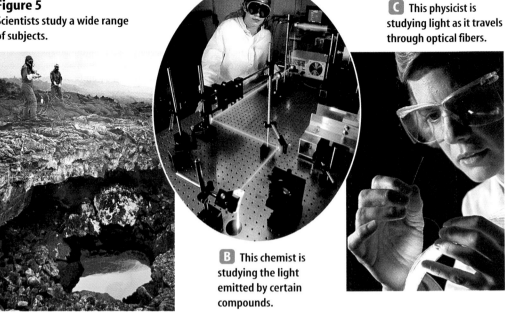

Figure 5
Scientists study a wide range of subjects.

A **These volcanologists are studying the temperature of the lava flowing from a volcano.**

B **This chemist is studying the light emitted by certain compounds.**

C **This physicist is studying light as it travels through optical fibers.**

Earth Science The study of Earth systems and the systems in space is **Earth science.** It includes the study of nonliving things such as rocks, soil, clouds, rivers, oceans, planets, stars, meteors, and black holes. Earth science also covers the weather and climate systems that affect Earth. Earth scientists ask questions like "How can an earthquake be detected?" or "Is water found on other planets?" They make maps and investigate how geologic features formed on land and in the oceans. They also use their knowledge to search for fuels and minerals. Meteorolgists study weather and climate. Geologists study rocks and geologic features. **Figure 5A** shows a volcanologist—a person who studies volcanoes—measuring the temperature of lava.

✔ **Reading Check** *What do Earth scientists study?*

Physical Science The study of matter and energy is **physical science.** Matter is anything that takes up space and has mass. The ability to cause change in matter is energy. Living and nonliving systems are made of matter. Examples include plants, animals, rocks, the atmosphere, and the water in oceans, lakes, and rivers. Physical science can be divided into two general fields—chemistry and physics. Chemistry is the study of matter and the interactions of matter. Physics is the study of energy and its ability to change matter. **Figures 5B** and **5C** show physical scientists at work.

Resource Manager

Chapter Resources Booklet
Reinforcement, p. 29

Earth Science Critical Thinking/Problem Solving, p. 14

Physical Science Critical Thinking/Problem Solving, p. 1

Inclusion Strategies

Learning Disabled Have each student make three flash cards, one saying life science, one saying Earth science, and one saying physical science. Name different structures or processes, and have students raise the card naming the branch of science that studies those structures or processes. Ask students to explain their responses.

Careers Chemists ask questions such as "How can I make plastic stronger?" or "What can I do to make aspirin more effective?" Physicists might ask other types of questions, such as "How does light travel through glass fibers?" or "How can humans harness the energy of sunlight for our energy needs?"

Many careers are based on the physical sciences. Physicists and chemists are some obvious careers. Engineers often apply physical science to construct things. Ultrasound and X-ray technicians working in the medical field study physical science because they study the energy in ultrasound or X rays and how it affects a living system.

Science and Technology Although learning the answers to scientific questions is important, these answers do not help people directly unless they can be applied in some way. **Technology** is the practical use of science, or applied science, as illustrated in **Figure 6.** Engineers apply science to develop technology. The study of how to use the energy of sunlight is science. Using this knowledge to create solar panels is technology. The study of the behavior of light as it travels through thin, glass, fiber optic wires is science. A scientist uses science to study how the skin of a shark repels water. The application of this knowledge to create a material that helps swimmers slip through the water faster is technology.

Figure 6
Solar-powered cars and the swimsuits worn in the Olympics are examples of technology—the application of science.

Section 1 Assessment

1. What is science?
2. Compare scientific theory and scientific law. Explain how a scientific theory can change.
3. What are the components of a system?
4. Name the three branches of science.
5. **Think Critically** List two questions that can be answered by science and one that can't be answered by science. Explain.

Skill Builder Activities

6. **Comparing and Contrasting** Compare and contrast life science and physical science. **For more help, refer to the Science Skill Handbook.**
7. **Communicating** In your Science Journal, describe how science and technology are related. **For more help, refer to the Science Skill Handbook.**

3 Assess

Reteach

Ask students to name the different systems in a baseball game and classify them as structures, processes, or cycles. The bat, ball, bases, and field are structures; the rules and different strategies of play are processes; and the batting lineup, the nine innings, and each team's turn at bat are cycles. L2 LS **Logical-Mathematical**

Challenge

Have students propose scientific laws. These do not have to be accepted laws but can be any general statement. Possible response: On the second Tuesday of each month, there is a science test. Next, have them provide theories to explain why the law holds. Possible response: There's a science test on the second Tuesday of each month, because the teacher plans it that way. Accept multiple explanations and have the class decide which makes the most sense. L3 LS **Logical-Mathematical**

Assessment

Performance Have students act out a play in which a group of scientists propose a scientific law. Be sure the play includes the scientists' making detailed observations to determine the exact nature of the regularity they are seeing. Use **Performance Assessment in the Science Classroom,** p. 147.

Answers to Section Assessment

1. Science is a way of learning about the natural world.
2. A scientific theory tries to explain why something happens. A scientific law describes a regularity in nature. A theory can change if new information becomes available.
3. structures, cycles, and processes that relate and interact with one another
4. life science, Earth science, and physical science
5. Answers will vary. For example, "Why does the Sun shine?" and "Why do bears hibernate in the winter?" are two questions that science can answer. "Why was that movie such a big hit?" is a question science cannot answer.
6. Life science is concerned with all living things in the universe. Physical science is the study of matter and energy.
7. Science answers scientific questions, and technology applies those answers to make products that help people.

SECTION

Science in Action

1 Motivate

Bellringer Transparency

Display the Section Focus Transparency for Section 2. Use the accompanying Transparency Activity Master. L2 ELL

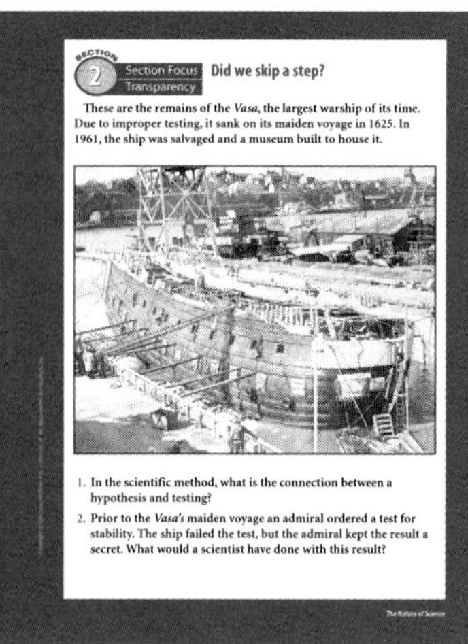

Section 2 Section Focus Transparency **Did we skip a step?**

These are the remains of the *Vasa*, the largest warship of its time. Due to improper testing, it sank on its maiden voyage in 1625. In 1961, the ship was salvaged and a museum built to house it.

1. In the scientific method, what is the connection between a hypothesis and testing?
2. Prior to the *Vasa's* maiden voyage an admiral ordered a test for stability. The ship failed the test, but the admiral kept the result a secret. What would a scientist have done with this result?

The Nature of Science

Tie to Prior Knowledge

Ask students whether they've ever tried to move a big piece of furniture through a doorway. Ask them to describe the process they used. They probably looked at the piece first, thought of a way to get it through the doorway, and then tried moving it. If this didn't work, they then might have put it down and rethought the problem. Explain that this is similar to the process scientists use when they try to solve a problem in science.

SECTION

Science in Action

As You Read

What You'll Learn

- **Identify** some skills scientists use.
- **Define** hypothesis.
- **Recognize** the difference between observation and inference.

Vocabulary

hypothesis
infer
controlled experiment
variable
constant

Why It's Important

Science can be used to learn more about the world you live in.

Science Skills

You know that science involves asking questions, but how does asking questions lead to learning? Because no single way to gain knowledge exists, a scientist doesn't start with step one, then go to step two, and so on. Instead, scientists have a huge collection of skills from which to choose. Some of these skills include thinking, observing, predicting, investigating, researching, modeling, measuring, analyzing, and inferring. Science also can advance with luck and creativity.

Science Methods Investigations often follow a general pattern. As illustrated in **Figure 7,** most investigations begin by seeing something and then asking a question about what was observed. Scientists often research by talking with other scientists. They read books and scientific magazines to learn as much as they can about what is already known about their question. Usually, scientists will state a possible explanation for their observation. To collect more information, scientists almost always make more observations. They might build a model of what they study or they might perform investigations. Often, they do both. How might you combine some of these skills in an investigation?

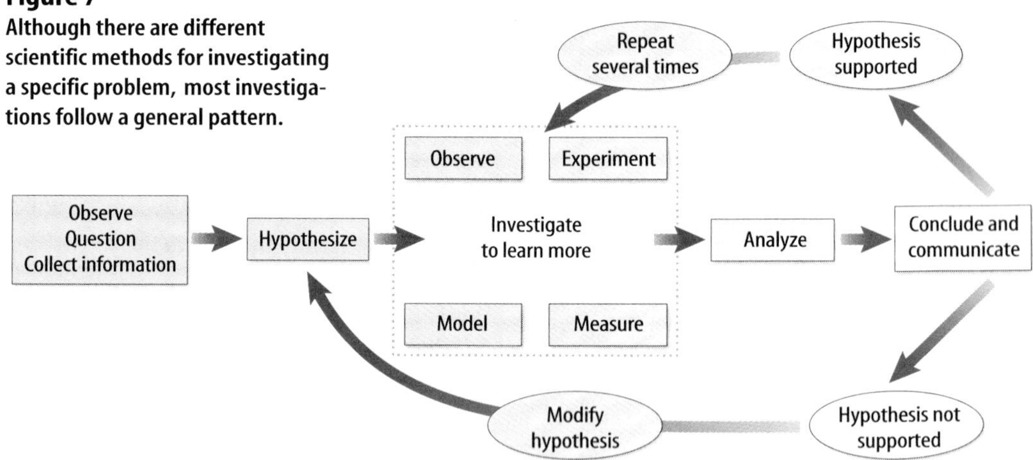

Figure 7
Although there are different scientific methods for investigating a specific problem, most investigations follow a general pattern.

Section Assessment Planner

PORTFOLIO
Active Reading, p. 16

PERFORMANCE ASSESSMENT
Try At Home MiniLAB, p.14
Skill Builder Activities, p. 20
See page 38 for more options.

CONTENT ASSESSMENT
Section, p. 20
Challenge, p. 20
Chapter, pp. 38–39

It's not
very heavy.
I think it's
a stapler.
What's that
metal-like
sound?

Figure 8
Investigations often begin by making observations and asking questions.

Questioning and Observing Ms. Clark placed a sealed shoe box on the table at the front of the laboratory. Everyone in the class noticed the box. Within seconds the questions flew. "What's in the box?" "Why is it there?"

Ms. Clark said she would like the class to see how they used some science skills without even realizing it.

"I think that she wants us to find out what's in it," Isabelle said to Marcus.

"Can we touch it?" asked Marcus.

"It's up to you," Ms. Clark said.

Marcus picked up the box and turned it over a few times.

"It's not heavy," Marcus observed. "Whatever is inside slides around." He handed the box to Isabelle.

Isabelle shook the box. The class heard the object strike the sides of the box. With every few shakes, the class heard a metallic sound. The box was passed around for each student to make observations and write them in his or her Science Journal. Some observations are shown in **Figure 8.**

Taking a Guess "I think it's a pair of scissors," said Marcus.

"Aren't scissors lighter than this?" asked Isabelle, while shaking the box. "I think it's a stapler."

"What makes you think so?" asked Ms. Clark.

"Well, staplers are small enough to fit inside a shoe box, and it seems to weigh about the same," said Isabelle.

"We can hear metal when we shake it," said Enrique.

"So, you are guessing that a stapler is in the box?"

"Yes," they agreed.

"You just stated your hypothesis," exclaimed Ms. Clark.

"A what?" asked Marcus.

Life Science INTEGRATION

Some naturalists study the living world, using mostly their observational skills. They observe animals and plants in their natural environment, taking care not to disturb the organisms they are studying. Make observations of organisms in a nearby park or backyard. Record your observations in your Science Journal.

2 Teach

Science Skills

Visual Learning

Figure 7 Although there is no one right way to carry out a scientific investigation, most follow the pattern outlined in this flow chart. **Think of a scientific investigation as trying to make a tasty pot of soup. How would the steps outlined in the figure help you do this?** Possible response: You select ingredients and decide which ones should go in the soup (hypothesize). You add them and sample the soup to see how it tastes (observe and analyze). You keep adding to and taking away from the recipe until it tastes the best (experiment). You write down the recipe so others can make it in exactly the same way (conclude and communicate).

Life Science INTEGRATION

Before they attempt the activity, have students identify which animals they might see (for example, squirrels, rabbits, turtles, frogs), and have them research some of the habits of these animals. Caution students not to get too close to any wild animal.

Inclusion Strategies

Visually Impaired Glue string to a sheet of construction paper to make a three-dimensional map of **Figure 7.** Place Braille labels on the different skills. Visually impaired students can use this for later reference.

Resource Manager

Chapter Resources Booklet
Transparency Activity, p. 49
Directed Reading for Content Mastery, p. 23

Life Science Critical Thinking/Problem Solving, p. 7

Science Skills, continued

Purpose Students form a hypothesis based on observations. L2 IS **Kinesthetic**

Materials large pot, water, can of regular soda, can of diet soda

Teaching Strategies Not all regular soda cans will sink. If regular soda cans float, have students suggest possible reasons this occurs.

Safety Precautions Caution students not to shake the cans or handle them roughly.

Analysis

1. The can of regular soda did not float, but the can of diet soda did.
2. Possible answer: It led me to think that the cans behaved differently because they contained different ingredients.
3. Answers may vary. The regular soda uses a lot of sugar for sweetening. The diet soda uses only a little artificial sweetener.

Assessment

Process Have students measure the mass and volume of the soda in each can and determine the density of the soda. Ask them to suggest how the soda's density affected the behavior of the can in the water. Use **PASC**, p. 97.

TRY AT HOME Mini LAB

Forming a Hypothesis

Procedure

1. Fill a large **pot** with **water.** Drop an unopened **can of diet soda** and an unopened **can of regular soda** into the pot of water and observe what each can does.
2. In your Science Journal, make a list of the possible explanations for your observation. Select the best explanation and write a hypothesis.
3. Read the nutritional facts on the back of each can and compare their ingredients.
4. Revise your hypothesis based on this new information.

Analysis

1. What did you observe when you placed the cans in the water?
2. How did the nutritional information on the cans change your hypothesis?
3. Infer why the two cans behaved differently in the water.

The Hypothesis "A **hypothesis** is a reasonable and educated guess based on what you know and what you observe."

"We know that a stapler is small, it can be heavy, and it is made of metal," said Isabelle.

"We observed that what is in the box is small, heavier than a pair of scissors, and made of metal," continued Marcus.

Analyzing Hypotheses "What other possible explanations fit with what you observed?" asked Ms. Clark.

"Well, it has to be a stapler," said Enrique.

"What if it isn't?" asked Ms. Clark. "Maybe you're overlooking explanations because your minds are made up. A good scientist keeps an open mind to every idea and explanation. What if you learn new information that doesn't fit with your original hypothesis? What new information could you gather to verify or disprove your hypothesis?"

"Do you mean a test or something?" asked Marcus.

"I know," said Enrique, "We could get an empty shoe box that is the same size as the mystery box and put a stapler in it. Then we could shake it and see whether it feels and sounds the same." Enrique's test is shown in **Figure 9.**

Making a Prediction "If your hypothesis is correct, what would you expect to happen?" asked Ms. Clark.

"Well, it would be about the same weight and it would slide around a little, just like the other box," said Enrique.

"It would have that same metallic sound when we shake it," said Marcus.

"So, you predict is that the test box will feel and sound the same as your mystery box. Go ahead and try it," said Ms. Clark.

Figure 9
Comparing the known information with the unknown information can be valuable even though you cannot see what is inside the closed box.

LAB DEMONSTRATION

Purpose to make predictions based on sounds

Materials 5 identical glasses, spoon, water

Preparation Put a different amount of water in each glass. Make sure students can't see what you are doing.

Procedure Tap on the glass containing the most water, and tell students this glass contains the most water. Do the same with the glass containing the least water. Then tap on two of the other glasses one after the other, and ask which has more water in it. Repeat this process until students have ranked the five glasses from the one containing the most water to the one with the least water.

State the relationship between the amount of water in a glass and the pitch produced when the glass is hit. The more water in the glass, the higher the pitch. **Is this a hypothesis, a theory, or a law? Why?** It is a law—it is based on observation.

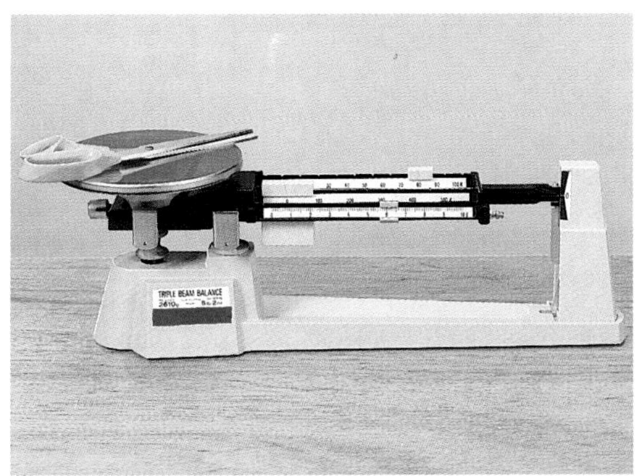

Figure 10
Laboratory balances are used to find the mass of objects.
What is the mass of the object being measured?

Testing the Hypothesis Ms. Clark gave the class an empty shoe box that appeared to be identical to the mystery box. Isabelle found a metal stapler. Enrique put the stapler in the box and taped the box closed. Marcus shook the box.

"The stapler does slide around but it feels just a little heavier than what's inside the mystery box," said Marcus. "What do you think?" he asked Isabelle as he handed her the box.

"It is heavier," said Isabelle "and as hard as I shake it, I can't get a metallic sound. What if we find the mass of both boxes? Then we'll know the exact mass difference between the two."

Using a balance, as shown in **Figure 10,** the class found that the test box had a mass of 410 g, and the mystery box had a mass of 270 g.

Organizing Your Findings "Okay. Now you have some new information," said Ms. Clark. "But before you draw any conclusions, let's organize what we know. Then we'll we have a summary of our observations and can refer back to them when we are drawing our conclusions."

"We could make a chart of our observations in our Science Journals," said Marcus.

"We could compare the observations of the mystery box with the observations of the test box," said Isabelle. The chart that the class made is shown in **Table 1.**

Table 1 Observation Chart

Questions	Mystery Box	Our Box
Does it roll or slide?	It slides and appears to be flat.	It slides and appears to be flat.
Does it make any sounds?	It makes a metallic sound when it strikes the sides of the box.	The stapler makes a thudding sound when it strikes the sides of the box.
Is the mass evenly distributed in the box?	No. The object doesn't completely fill the box.	No. The mass of the stapler is unevenly distributed.
What is the mass of the box?	270 g	410 g

Caption Answer

Figure 10 The triple-beam balance shows a mass of about 86.15 g.

Fun Fact

One of the first known stapling machines was built in the 1700s for King Louis XV of France. The staples it used were handmade and had the insignia of the Royal Court on them. Staplers only came into general use in the early 1900s.

IDENTIFYING Misconceptions

Students may think that a hypothesis, once made, is never changed. Explain that many of the great scientists of the past made hypotheses that later were abandoned. A good hypothesis does not have to be one that is proven correct. It only has to be a reasonable explanation that is based upon observations and allows you to make predictions.

Discussion

Why is it important to collect data accurately? Possible response: Recording data inaccurately can cause you to draw inaccurate conclusions. It would be like studying for a test using the wrong book. L2

LS **Logical-Mathematical**

Curriculum Connection

History A Scientific Revolution occurred in western Europe from about the late fifteenth century to the mid-seventeenth century. Have students use an encyclopedia to find out more about the Scientific Revolution. This Scientific Revolution was important because it introduced a new way of thinking about how to carry out scientific investigations. L2

LS **Linguistic**

Resource Manager 

Chapter Resources Booklet
Enrichment, p. 34
MiniLAB, p. 4

Reading and Writing Skill Activities, p. 7

Drawing Conclusions

Caption Answer

Figure 11 The pot was knocked to the floor. You might infer that the cat did it.

Teacher FYI

The students in the story are doing what is called inductive reasoning, in which a generalized conclusion is drawn from specific circumstances. They are making observations and eliminating possibilities until they arrive at a suitable answer to the question. Deductive reasoning, on the other hand, is the kind of reasoning in which a conclusion about particulars is drawn from general or universal premises. This is the type of reasoning that says that if you do the steps of a math problem correctly, the process must give you the correct answer.

Extension

Have students critique the investigation of the students in the story. Ask them to suggest ways in which the students in the story might have done things differently and to describe other things the students might do to get a better idea of what is inside the box. Possible responses: They could try to guess at the size of the object in the box by noticing how long it takes to slide. They also could find objects of the same weight as the object in the box and see how the objects sound when shaken inside a box. They could experiment with objects to find one that makes a metallic sound like the sound made by the object in the box. L3

LS **Logical-Mathematical**

Drawing Conclusions

"What have you learned from your investigation so far?" asked Ms. Clark.

"The first thing that we learned was that our hypothesis wasn't correct," answered Marcus.

"Would you say that your hypothesis was entirely wrong?" asked Ms. Clark.

"The boxes don't weigh the same, and the box with the stapler didn't make the same sound as the mystery box. But there could be a difference in the kind of stapler in the box. It could be a different size."

"So you infer that the object in the mystery box is not exactly the same type of stapler, right?" asked Ms. Clark.

"What does infer mean?" asked Isabelle.

"To **infer** something means to draw a conclusion based on what you observe," answered Ms. Clark.

Figure 11
Observations are important tools used by scientists. *Looking at both of these photos, what has taken place?*

"So we inferred that the things in the boxes had to be different because our observations of the two boxes are different," said Marcus.

"I guess we're back to where we started," said Enrique. "We still don't know what's in the mystery box."

"Do you know more than you did before you started?" asked Ms. Clark.

"We eliminated one possibility," Isabelle added.

"Yes. We inferred that it's not a stapler, at least not like the one in the mystery box." said Marcus.

"So even if your observations don't support your hypothesis, you know more than you did when you started," said Ms. Clark.

Continuing to Learn "So when do we get to open the box and see what it is?" asked Marcus.

"Let me ask you this," said Ms. Clark. "Do you think scientists always get a chance to look inside to see if they are right?"

"If they are studying something too big or too small to see, I guess they can't," replied Isabelle. "What do they do in those cases?"

"As you learned, your first hypothesis might not be supported by your investigation. Instead of giving up, you continue to gather information by making more observations, making new hypotheses, and by investigating further. Some scientists have spent lifetimes researching their questions. Science takes patience and persistence," said Ms. Clark.

Active Reading

Learning Journal This strategy encourages students to interact with the reading, allowing personal responses. Students should draw a vertical line down the center of each page of the Learning Journal. The left column entries can be research notes, lecture notes, or vocabulary terms. The right column entries are the students' responses to, interpretations of, questions about, or analysis of the left column entries. Have students write a Learning Journal that incorporates all the scientific methods described in this section. P

Communicating Your Findings A big part of science is communicating your findings. It is not unusual for one scientist to continue the work of another or to try to duplicate the work of another scientist. It is important for scientists to communicate to others not only the results of the investigation, but also how the methods by which the investigation was done. Scientists often publish reports in journals, books, and on the Internet to show other scientists the work that was completed. They also might attend meetings where they make speeches about their work. Scientists from around the world learn from each other, and it is important for them to exchange information freely.

Like the science-fair student in **Figure 12** demonstrates, an important part of doing science is the ability to communicate methods and results to others.

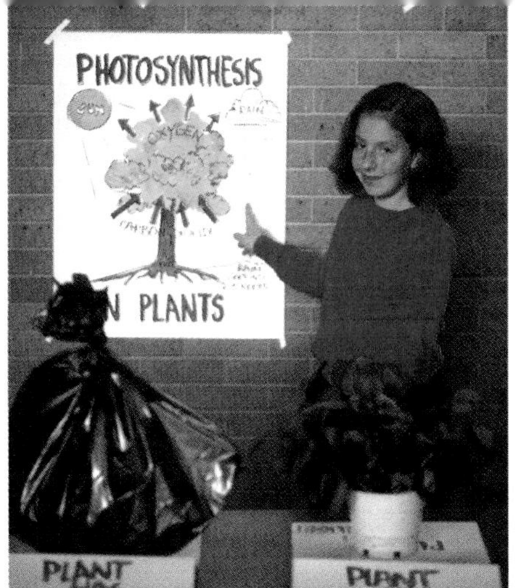

Figure 12
Books, presentations, and meetings are some of the many ways people in science communicate their findings.

Reading Check *Why do scientists share information?*

Problem-Solving Activity

How can you use a data table to analyze and present data?

Suppose you were given the average temperatures in a city for the four seasons in 1997, 1998, and 1999: spring 1997 was 11°C; summer 1997 was 25°C; fall 1997 was 5°C; winter 1997 was −5°C; spring 1998 was 9°C; summer 1998 was 36°C; fall 1998 was 10°C; winter 1998 was −3°C; spring 1999 was 10°C; summer 1999 was 30°C; fall 1999 was 9°C; and winter 1999 was −2°C. How can you tell in which of the years each season had its coldest average?

Seasonal Temperatures (°C)

	1997	1998	1999
Spring	11	9	10
Summer	25	36	30
Fall	5	10	9
Winter	−5	−3	−2

Identifying the Problem

The information that is given is not in a format that is easy to see at a glance. It would be more helpful to put it in a table that allows you to compare the data.

Solving the Problem

1. Create a table with rows for seasons and columns for the years. Now substitute the values you were given. You should be able to see that the four coldest seasons were spring 1998, summer 1997, fall 1997, and winter 1997.
2. Use your new table to find out which season has the greatest difference in temperatures over the three years from 1997 through 1999.
3. What other observations or comparisons can you make from the table on seasonal temperatures you've created?

Reading Check

Answer so other scientists can continue the work or try to duplicate it

Activity

Have students look in a major library for copies of scientific journals such as *Journal of the American Chemical Society*, *Nature*, and *Physical Review*. They also can look at journal Web sites on the Internet. Although students may not understand the articles, ask them to note features about them that make them appear scientific. Possible answers: The design of scientific journals is simple and not visually catchy. Many articles have complex tables, diagrams, graphs, and charts. The articles are written very dryly and use a lot of big words. L2 LS **Visual-Spatial**

Problem-Solving Activity

National Math Standards

Correlation to Mathematics Objectives

2, 5, 6, 8–10

Answers

1. See student page.
2. Summer; it had a range of 11°C.
3. Possible answers: You can say that spring temperatures changed the least and that fall and spring temperatures are the closest to each other.

Inclusion Strategies

Learning Disabled To help students organize the data given in the Problem-Solving Activity, suggest that before they construct their tables, they write the data as a list.

Spring 1997: 11°C
Summer 1997: 25°C
Fall 1997: 5°C
Winter 1997: –5°C
Spring 1998: 9°C, and so on.

Resource Manager

Chapter Resources Booklet
Lab Activity, pp. 11–14

Physical Science Critical Thinking/Problem Solving, p. 2

Mathematics Skill Activities, p. 29

Experiments

Explore the Glencoe Science Web site at **science.glencoe.com** to find out more about topics in this section.

Discussion

Suppose you wanted to know whether more salt or more sugar could dissolve in water. **What is the variable? What are the constants?** The variable is the substance to be dissolved in water. Constants include the amount of salt or sugar, the amount of water, the temperature of the water, the type of container used for the water, the amount of stirring, and so on. L2 LS **Logical-Mathematical**

Discussion

How can the things you are learning in this section help you do things other than science experiments? Possible answer: Making observations and forming hypotheses about technique and practice could help students play baseball or a musical instrument better. L2 LS **Linguistic**

Research Visit the Glencoe Science Web site at **science.glencoe.com** for information on variables, constants, and controls. Make a poster showing the differences between these three parts of a reliable investigation.

Experiments

Different types of questions call for different types of investigations. Ms. Clark's class made many observations about their mystery box and about their test box. They wanted to know what was inside. To answer their question, building a model—the test box—was an effective way to learn more about the mystery box. Some questions ask about the effects of one factor on another. One way to investigate these kinds of questions is by doing a controlled experiment. A **controlled experiment** involves changing one factor and observing its effect on another while keeping all other factors constant.

Variables and Constants **Variables** are factors that can be changed in an experiment. Reliable experiments, like the race shown in **Figure 13,** attempt to change one variable and observe the effect of this change on another variable. The variable that is changed in an experiment is called the independent variable. The dependent variable changes as a result of a change in the independent variable. It usually is the dependent variable that is observed in an experiment. Scientists attempt to keep all other variables constant—or unchanged.

The variables that are not changed in an experiment are called **constants.** Examples of constants in the running race include track material, wind speed, and distance. This way it is easier to determine exactly which variable is responsible for the runners' finish times. In this race, the runners' abilities were varied. The runners' finish times were observed.

Figure 13
The 400-m race is an example of a controlled experiment. The distance, track material, and wind speed are constants. The runners' abilities and their finish times varied.

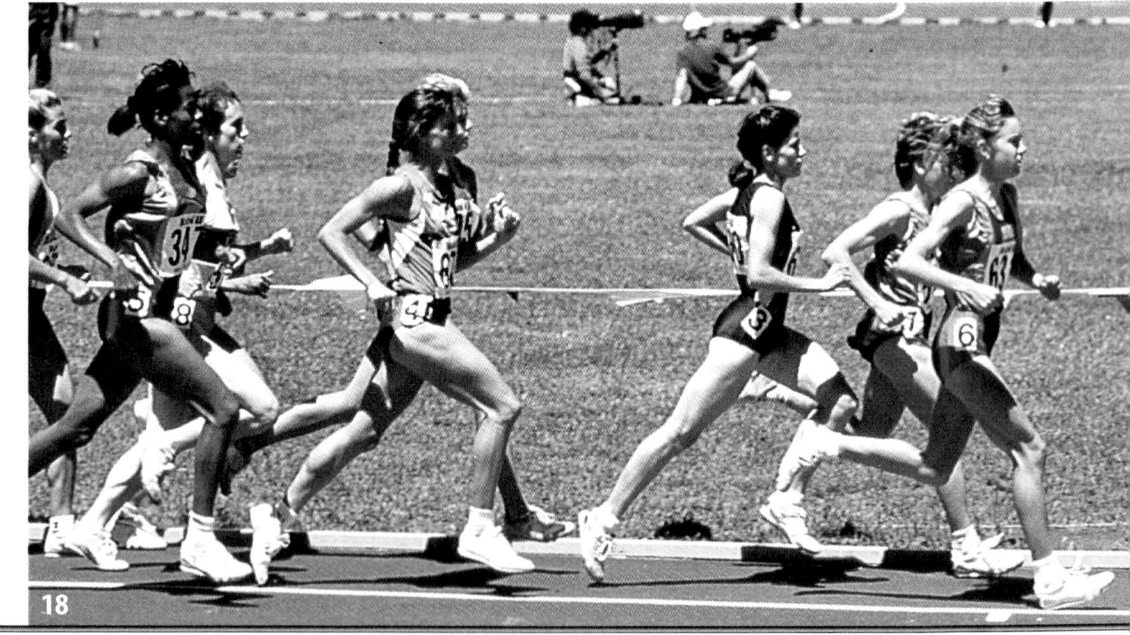

18

Cultural Diversity

Ancient Greek Science Ancient Greeks did not do experiments. They believed that everything that was important to know about the world could be learned through reasoning. One of the greatest contributions of the Scientific Revolution of the sixteenth and seventeenth centuries was the idea that experiments were an important part of science.

Figure 14
Safety is the most important aspect of any investigation.

Laboratory Safety

In your science class, you will perform many types of investigations. However, performing scientific investigations involves more than just following specific steps. You also must learn how to keep yourself and those around you safe by obeying the safety symbol warnings, shown in **Figure 15.**

In a Laboratory When scientists work in a laboratory, as shown in **Figure 14,** they take many safety precautions. Following proper laboratory procedures and using available safety equipment in your science lab results in a safe learning environment.

The most important safety advice in a science lab is to think before you act. Always check with your teacher several times in the planning stage of any investigation. Also make sure your actions and materials are safe when investigating in the lab. Know what types of safety equipment are present in the laboratory room and how to use this equipment, including the fire extinguisher, thermal mitts, and eye washes.

Some good safety habits include the following suggestions. Before conducting any investigation, find and follow all safety symbols listed in your investigation. You always should wear an apron and goggles to protect yourself from chemicals, flames, and all pointed or flying objects. Always slant test tubes away from yourself and others when heating them. Never eat or drink in the lab. Report all accidents and injuries to your teacher and always wash your hands after working with lab materials.

In the Field Investigations also take place outside the lab, in streams, farm fields, and other places. Scientists must follow safety regulations there, as well, such as wearing eye goggles and any other special safety equipment that is needed.

Eye Safety
 Clothing Protection
 Disposal
 Biological
 Extreme Temperature
 Sharp Object
 Fume
 Irritant
Toxic
 Animal Safety
 Open Flame

Figure 15
Safety symbols are present on nearly every investigation you will do this year. *What safety symbols would be on the lab the student is doing in* ***Figure 14?***

Laboratory Safety

Discussion

What are some of the advantages of using standardized safety symbols in addition to writing separate safety precautions for each activity? Safety symbols are easy to recognize. You can see quickly what safety precautions the activity requires. Even those who can't read very well can see what precautions need to be taken. The symbols also take up less space.

Visual Learning

Figure 14 Ask students to name each safety precaution this boy is taking as he works in the lab and describe a possible problem that could occur without each precaution. Possible answers: If he were not wearing goggles, he could get harmful chemicals in his eyes. If he were not wearing gloves, or an apron he could get harmful chemicals on his hands or his clothing. L2 LS **Visual-Spatial**

Activity

Taking steps to keep people safe is a concern in many parts of life. Have each student make a list of activities outside the science laboratory in which safety could be a problem, and the steps people take to make the activities safe. Possible answers include using pot holders in the kitchen, wearing safety gear when playing football or soccer, wearing a bicycle helmet when bicycling, and wearing ear protection when mowing the lawn. L2 LS **Naturalist**

Caption Answer

Figure 15 symbols for Eye Safety, Irritant, Clothing Protection

Curriculum Connection

Art Safety symbols are icons—images that convey information. Have students design icons to alert students to the laboratory safety hazards of long hair, clothing with loose sleeves, jewelry, or any other safety hazard they can think of. L2 LS **Visual-Spatial**

Resource Manager

Chapter Resources Booklet
Reinforcement, p. 30
Transparency Activity, pp. 53–54

Performance Assessment in the Science Classroom, p. 42

3 Assess

Reteach

Have students draw their own diagrams showing the steps in a scientific investigation. Encourage them to incorporate safety notes into their diagrams. L2

LS **Visual-Spatial**

Challenge

Ask students what might be some of the variables and constants in a study of local wildlife. Variables might include the amount of daylight at the time of year and the time an animal can spend looking for food. A constant might be the physical features of the land the animal lives on. L2

LS **Logical-Mathematical**

Content Have each student write an ending to the story in this section. Have groups of students act the story out as a play, incorporating the different endings written by the students in the group. Use **Performance Assessment in the Science Classroom,** p. 147.

Resource Manager

Chapter Resources Booklet

Transparency Activity, p. 50

Directed Reading for Content Mastery, p. 23

Reading and Writing Skill Activities, p. 41

Figure 16
Accidents are not planned. Safety precautions must be followed to prevent injury.

Why have safety rules? Doing science in the class laboratory or on a field trip can be much more interesting than reading about it. However, safety rules must be strictly followed, so that the possibility of an accident greatly decreases. However, you can't predict when something will go wrong.

Think of a person taking a trip in a car. Most of the time when someone drives somewhere in a vehicle, an accident, like the one shown in **Figure 16,** does not occur. But to be safe, drivers and passengers always should wear safety belts. Likewise, you always should wear and use appropriate safety gear in the lab—whether you are conducting an investigation or just observing. The most important aspect of any investigation is to conduct it safely.

Section  Assessment

1. What are four steps scientific investigations often follow?
2. Is a hypothesis as firm as a theory? Explain.
3. What is the difference between an inference and an observation?
4. Why is it important always to use the proper safety equipment?
5. **Think Critically** You are going to use bleach in an investigation. Bleach can irritate your skin, damage your eyes, and stain your clothes. What safety symbols should be listed with this investigation? Explain.

Skill Builder Activities

6. **Drawing Conclusions** While waiting outside your classroom door, the bell rings for school to start. According to your watch, you still have 3 min to get to your classroom. Based on these observations, what can you conclude about your watch? **For more help, refer to the Science Skill Handbook.**
7. **Using a Word Processor** Describe the different types of safety equipment you should use if you are working with a flammable liquid in the lab. **For more help, refer to the Technology Skill Handbook.**

Answers to Section Assessment

1. The main steps are observe, investigate, analyze, and conclude.
2. No; a theory has been tested more than a hypothesis.
3. An observation is something that comes from your senses. An inference is a conclusion your mind draws.
4. to avoid accidents in the lab and in the field
5. Symbols to follow: disposal alert, irritant alert, fume safety, clothing protection, eye safety, toxic alert, and chemical safety.
6. Possible answer: You can conclude that your watch and the bell are three minutes apart.
7. You should wear an apron, goggles, and gloves. You also should wear long, tight sleeves to protect your arms. You should make sure an eyewash and a fire extinguisher are nearby.

Models in Science

Why are models necessary?

Just as you can take many different paths in an investigation, you can test a hypothesis in many different ways. Ms. Clark's class tested their hypothesis by building a model of the mystery box. A model is one way to test a hypothesis. In science, a **model** is any representation of an object or an event used as a tool for understanding the natural world.

Models can help you visualize, or picture in your mind, something that is difficult to see or understand. Ms. Clark's class made a model because they couldn't see the item inside the box. Models can be of things that are too small or too big to see. They also can be of things that can't be seen because they don't exist anymore or they haven't been created yet. Models also can show events that occur too slowly or too quickly to see. **Figure 17** shows different kinds of models.

As You Read

What **You'll Learn**

- **Describe** various types of models.
- **Discuss** limitations of models.

Vocabulary
model

Why **It's Important**

Models can be used to help understand difficult concepts.

Figure 17
Models help scientists visualize and study complex things and things that can't be seen.

Solar system model

Prototype model

Cell model

Dinosaur model

Section Assessment Planner

PORTFOLIO
Curriculum Connection, p. 22

PERFORMANCE ASSESSMENT
MiniLAB, p. 23
Skill Builder Activities, p. 26
See page 38 for more options.

CONTENT ASSESSMENT
Section, p. 26
Challenge, p. 26
Chapter, pp. 38–39

SECTION

Models in Science

1 Motivate

Bellringer Transparency

Display the Section Focus Transparency for Section 3. Use the accompanying Transparency Activity Master. L2 ELL

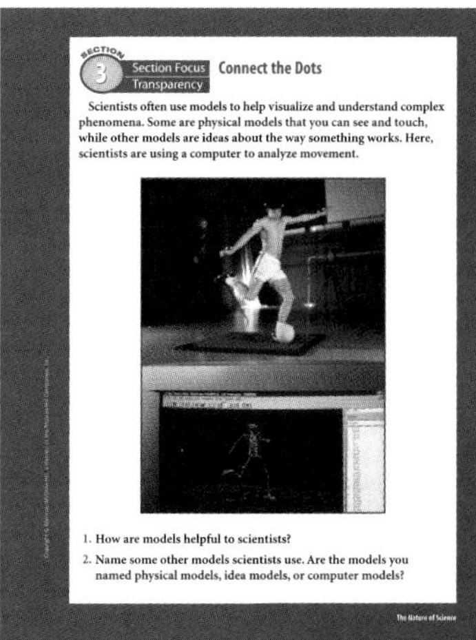

Section 3 Section Focus Transparency **Connect the Dots**

Scientists often use models to help visualize and understand complex phenomena. Some are physical models that you can see and touch, while other models are ideas about the way something works. Here, scientists are using a computer to analyze movement.

1. How are models helpful to scientists?
2. Name some other models scientists use. Are the models you named physical models, idea models, or computer models?

The Nature of Science

Tie to Prior Knowledge

Ask students whether they've ever described an event to someone and had a hard time doing it. To make things easier, they may try to act out the event. If it was the winning shot in a basketball game, for example, they may have begun "Okay, there's the basket and you're the player guarding me. . . " Tell them that if they did this, they made a model of the event.

2 Teach

Why are models necessary?

Use an Analogy

When you practice playing a sport, you are making a model. Good coaches know the kinds of plays another team uses and will simulate those plays in practice to prepare the players. This is a type of physical model.

Types of Models

Earth Science INTEGRATION

A topographic map shows areas of water and includes contour lines that show changes in the elevation of the land. Show students a topographic map with contour lines. Suggest an appropriate contour interval for your school grounds. You also might encourage students to draw a topographic map of their state that shows the largest features such as mountains, lakes, and rivers.

Fun Fact

Pilots and astronauts receive some of their most critical flight training without ever leaving the ground. They use complicated, realistic flight simulators that allow them to practice emergency procedures without risking an accident in the air.

✔ Reading Check

Answer show things that occur too slowly or too quickly to be seen and show motions and positions of things that would take hours or days to calculate by hand or using a calculator

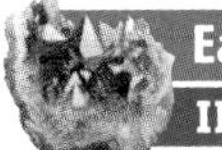

Earth Science INTEGRATION

A basic type of map used to represent an area of land is the topographic map. It shows the natural features of the land, in addition to artificial features such as political boundaries. Draw a topographic map of your school grounds in your Science Journal. Indicate both physical features and boundaries.

Types of Models

Most models fall into three basic types—physical models, computer models, and idea models. Depending on the reason that a model is needed, scientists can choose to use one or more than one type of model.

Physical Models Models that you can see and touch are called physical models. Examples include things such as a tabletop solar system, a globe of Earth, the inside of a cell, or the structure of a chemical's composition. Models show how parts relate to one another. They also can be used to show how things appear when they change position or how they react when an outside force acts on them.

Computer Models Computer models are built using computer software. You can't touch them, but you can view them on a computer screen. Some computer models can model events that take a long time or take place too quickly to see. For example, a computer can show plant growth that you couldn't observe, even by staring at a plant for several months.

Computers also can model motions and positions of things that would take hours or days to calculate by hand or even using a calculator. They can also predict the effect of different systems or forces. **Figure 18** shows how computer models are used by scientists to help predict the weather based on the motion of air currents in the atmosphere.

✔ Reading Check *What can computer models do?*

Figure 18
A weather map is a computer model showing weather patterns over large areas. Scientists can use this information to predict the weather and to alert people to potentially dangerous weather on the way.

Curriculum Connection

Social Studies You may have heard that a TV program is the number one rated show, but what exactly does that mean? Have students find out and report on how TV viewing statistics are obtained. TV viewing statistics are obtained by selecting a scientifically identified representative sample (a model) of the entire country's population. These households' viewing habits are monitored by special boxes on their sets and the results extended to the whole country. In the United States, about 25,000 homes rate the viewing habits of the entire country. L3 LS **Linguistic** P

Figure 19
Models can be created using various types of tools.

Idea Models Some models are ideas or concepts that describe how someone thinks about something in the natural world. Albert Einstein is famous for his theory of relativity, which involves the relationship between matter and energy. One of the most famous models Einstein used for this theory is the mathematical equation $E = mc^2$. This explains that mass, m, can be changed into energy, E. Einstein's idea models never could be built as physical models, because they are basically ideas.

Making Models

The process of making a model is something like a sketch artist at work, as shown in **Figure 19.** The sketch artist attempts to draw a picture from the description given by someone. The more detailed the description is, the better the picture will be. Like a scientist who studies data from many sources, the sketch artist can make a sketch based on more than one person's observation. The final sketch isn't a photograph, but if the information is accurate, the sketch should look realistic. Scientific models are made much the same way. The more information a scientist gathers, the more accurate the model will be. The process of constructing a model of King Tutankhamun, who lived more than 3,000 years ago, is shown in **Figure 20.**

Reading Check *How are sketches like scientific models?*

Using Models

When you think of a model, you might think of a model airplane or a model of a building. Not all models are for scientific purposes. You use models, and you might not realize it. Drawings, maps, recipes, and globes are all examples of models.

Thinking Like a Scientist

Procedure
1. Pour 15 mL of **water** into a **test tube.**
2. Slowly pour 5 mL of **vegetable oil** into the test tube.
3. Add two drops of **food coloring** and observe the liquid for 5 min.

Analysis
1. Examine what happened to the drops of food coloring.
2. Infer a scientific explanation for your observations.

Making Models

Quick Demo

A star chart is a type of physical model. Obtain a star chart and demonstrate how it can be used to make predictions of the night sky on different days of the year. L2 LS **Visual-Spatial**

Reading Check

Answer The more detailed the information used to make the model or the sketch, the better it will be.

Purpose Students use scientific thinking as they make observations and draw inferences. L2 LS **Kinesthetic**

Materials water, vegetable oil, graduated cylinder, test tube, food coloring, watch or clock

Teaching Strategies Before they do the experiment, explain to students that some liquids do not mix with each other. Tell students to remember the phrase "like dissolves like."

Troubleshooting Have students keep the test tubes as still as possible.

Analysis
1. The drops remain intact in the oil and sit on the oil/water border for several seconds until they push through the layer. Once in the water, the food dye explodes into swirls of color.
2. Food coloring does not mix with oil. Food coloring mixes with water because it is like water and "like dissolves like."

Process Have students suggest ways in which the observations made in this activity could be used to design an experiment that determines the identity of a substance. Use **Performance Assessment in the Science Classroom,** p. 95.

Resource Manager 

Chapter Resources Booklet
Transparency Activity, p. 50
MiniLAB, p. 5
Enrichment, p. 35
Directed Reading for Content Mastery, p. 23

NATIONAL GEOGRAPHIC

Visualizing the Modeling of King Tut

Have students examine the pictures and read the captions. Then ask the following questions.

Why might scientists want to make a model of the face of a person from a skull? Possible answer: to help discover the identity of victims of accidents, fires, plane crashes, war, or murder.

How is the model of King Tut like other models used by scientists? Like other models, it is used by scientists to describe things they cannot see directly. Models can help scientists explain data and predict outcomes.

Activity

Have small groups of students make models of objects or ideas related to science. After the models are complete, have each group present and explain its model to the class. Discuss the accuracy of each model and how well it serves its purpose.

Extension

Have students research how forensic anthropologists use the technique described in this feature to identify skeletal remains. Students could present their information in written or oral reports.

NATIONAL GEOGRAPHIC VISUALIZING THE MODELING OF KING TUT

Figure 20

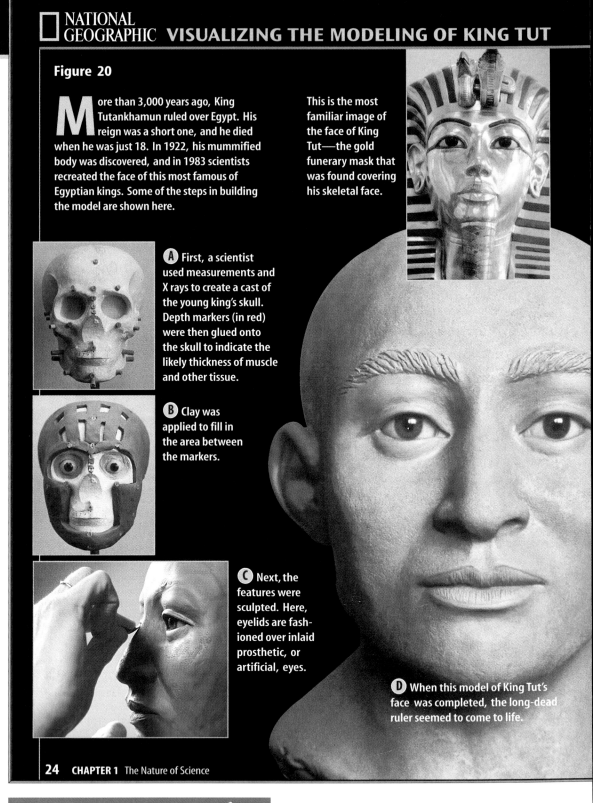

More than 3,000 years ago, King Tutankhamun ruled over Egypt. His reign was a short one, and he died when he was just 18. In 1922, his mummified body was discovered, and in 1983 scientists recreated the face of this most famous of Egyptian kings. Some of the steps in building the model are shown here.

This is the most familiar image of the face of King Tut—the gold funerary mask that was found covering his skeletal face.

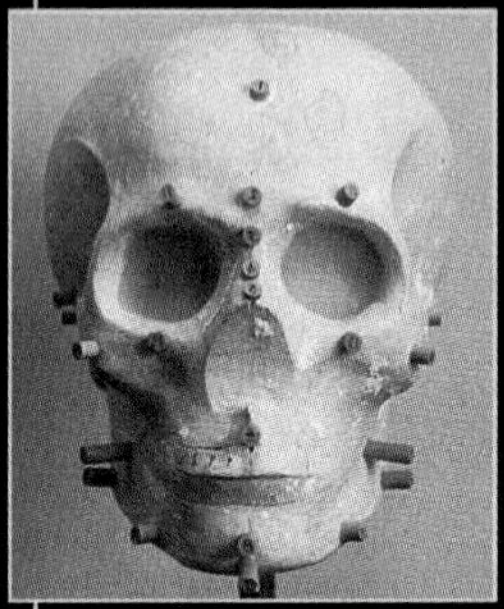

A First, a scientist used measurements and X rays to create a cast of the young king's skull. Depth markers (in red) were then glued onto the skull to indicate the likely thickness of muscle and other tissue.

B Clay was applied to fill in the area between the markers.

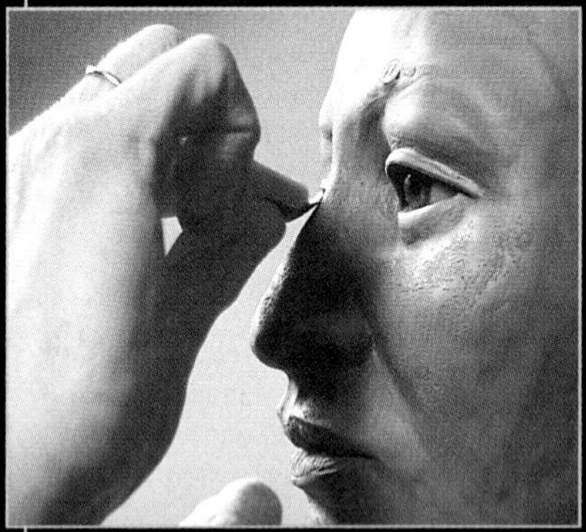

C Next, the features were sculpted. Here, eyelids are fashioned over inlaid prosthetic, or artificial, eyes.

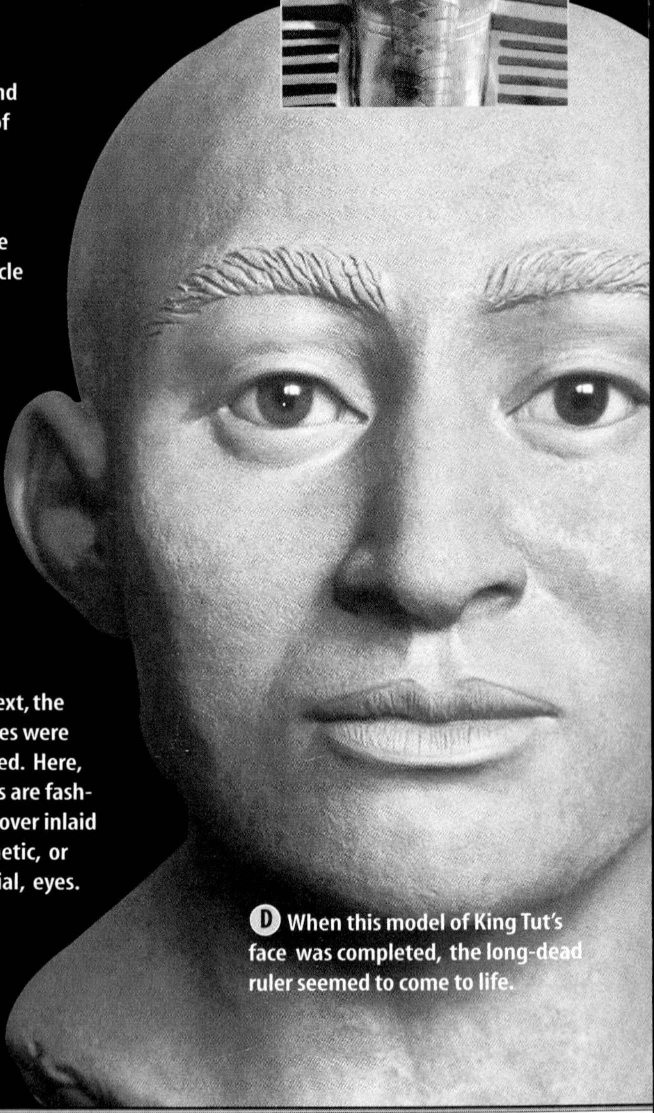

D When this model of King Tut's face was completed, the long-dead ruler seemed to come to life.

24 CHAPTER 1 The Nature of Science

Resource Manager 

Chapter Resources Booklet
Reinforcement, p. 31
Lab Activity, pp. 15–18

Science Inquiry Labs, p. 47

Models Communicate Some models are used to communicate observations and ideas to other people. Often, it is easier to communicate ideas you have by making a model instead of writing your ideas in words. This way others can visualize them, too.

Models Test Predictions Some models are used to test predictions. Ms. Clark's class predicted that a box with a stapler in it would have characteristics similar to their mystery box. To test this prediction, the class made a model. Automobile and airplane engineers use wind tunnels to test predictions about how air will interact with their products.

Models Save Time, Money, and Lives Other models are used because working with and testing a model can be safer and less expensive than using the real thing. Some of these models are shown in **Figure 21.** For example, crash-test dummies are used in place of people when testing the effects of automobile crashes. To help model the weightlessness of space, NASA has built a special airplane. This airplane flies in a parabolic arc that creates 20 to 25 s of low gravity. Making several trips in the airplane is easier, safer, and less expensive than making a trip into space.

Figure 21
Models are a safe and relatively inexpensive way to test ideas.

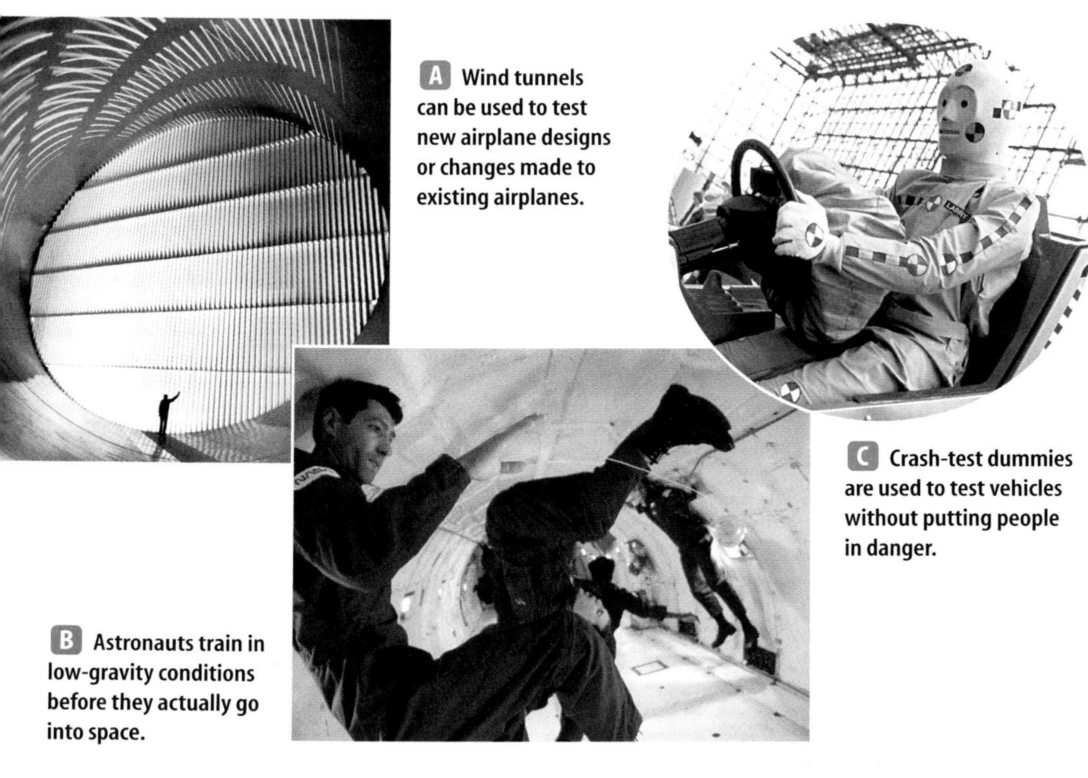

A **Wind tunnels can be used to test new airplane designs or changes made to existing airplanes.**

B **Astronauts train in low-gravity conditions before they actually go into space.**

C **Crash-test dummies are used to test vehicles without putting people in danger.**

Teacher FYI

The "weightless wonder" plane used to train NASA astronauts is a very busy machine. Most of the time, it is being used by scientists doing microgravity research. Also, when the Space Shuttle is being transported back to the Kennedy Space Center, it flies fifteen minutes ahead of the 747 plane carrying the shuttle to warn of the possibility of bad weather that might damage the shuttle's delicate tiles.

Using Models

Make a Model

Have students make models of the classroom. Have some draw pictures or take photographs of the room. Have others make paper cut outs or use blocks to represent the different classroom structures, paying close attention to scale. Ask which model would better represent the classroom to someone who hadn't seen it and which would better assist in making predictions about how the classroom could be arranged differently. L2 LS **Kinesthetic**

Teacher FYI

Before computerized animation, the models used to put special effects in movies had to be creative and diverse. To film a tornado scene in one early movie, for example, a string of muslin stockings was sewn together, stuffed, and swirled above a small-scale version of the movie set. For close-up views of the tornado, the filmmakers used a dust-filled burlap bag that released dark clouds when beaten.

Limitations of Models

Visual Learning

Figure 22 Have students consider the Earth-centered and Sun-centered models. **Standing here on Earth, is there any reason not to believe Earth is at the center of things?** Not really; we don't feel any motion and there is no way of proving just by sight that Earth is moving. L2 LS **Logical-Mathematical**

3 Assess

Reteach

Ask students which type of model, physical, computer, or idea, they'd use to represent the following: how a building will look when it's completed; the relationship between mass and gravity; how Earth's landscape has changed over time. physical or computer, idea, computer. L2

LS **Logical-Mathematical**

Challenge

Have students use a video camera to model a special effect in a motion picture. Possible effects might include someone flying, a giant, or a tornado. L3

LS **Visual-Spatial**

✔Assessment

Process Students probably had some knowledge of models before reading the section. Have them write in their Science Journals how their ideas about models have changed since reading the section. Use **Performance Assessment in the Science Classroom,** p. 157.

Resource Manager

Chapter Resources Booklet

Transparency Activity, p. 51

Directed Reading for Content Mastery, pp. 23, 24

Reading and Writing Skill Activities, p. 43

Figure 22
The model of Earth's solar system changed as new information was gathered.

A An early model of the solar system had Earth in the center with everything revolving around it.

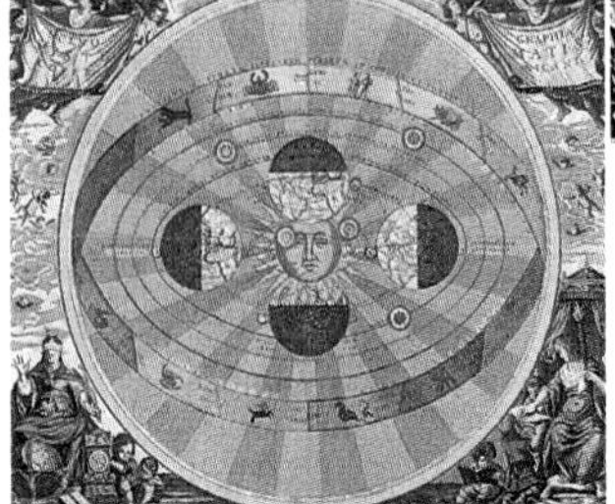

B Later on, a new model had the Sun in the center with everything revolving around it.

Limitations of Models

The solar system is too large to be viewed all at once, so models are made to understand it. Many years ago, scientists thought that Earth was the center of the universe and the sky was a blanket that covered the planet.

Later, through observation, it was discovered that the objects you see in the sky are the Sun, the Moon, stars, and other planets. This new model explained the solar system differently. Earth was still the center, but everything else orbited around it.

Models Change Still later, through more observation, it was discovered that the Sun was the center of the solar system. Earth, along with the other planets, orbited the Sun. In addition, it was discovered that other planets also had moons that orbited around them. A new model, shown in **Figure 22,** was developed to show this.

Earlier models of the solar system were not meant to be misleading. Scientists made the best models they could with the information they had. More importantly, their models gave future scientists information to build upon. Models are not necessarily perfect, but they provide a visual tool to learn from.

Section  Assessment

1. What type of model is a weather map? How can it be used?
2. How are models used in science?
3. What information can consumer testing services provide for safety at home and in vehicles?
4. Make a table describing three types of models, their advantages and limitations.
5. **Think Critically** Explain how some models are better than others for certain situations.

Skill Builder Activities

6. **Concept Mapping** Develop a concept map to explain models and their uses in science. How is this concept map a model? **For more help, refer to the Science Skill Handbook.**
7. **Using Proportions** On a map of a state, the scale shows that one inch is approximately 21 miles. If the distance between two cities is 1.7 inches on the map, how many miles separate them? **For more help, refer to the Math Skill Handbook.**

Answers to Section Assessment

1. A weather map is a computer model. It can be used to make predictions and look for patterns.
2. to study things that are too big, too small, take too long, or happen too quickly to observe easily and to make predictions.
3. They can tell how much weight a ladder, for example, could hold without breaking. They also can suggest at what speed a car crash would cause the most damage.
4. physical model—can be handled but can take a while to make and be difficult to modify; computer model—can show slow or fast changes and can be run many times. but can't show spatial relations very well; idea model—can show relationships between abstract concepts but can be hard to understand
5. Possible response: It would be difficult to make a physical model of weather changes because there are too many factors to consider.
6. Concept maps should include the different types of models and note their ability to communicate data, make predictions, and save time, lives, and money. The concept map is like a model because it is a representation of ideas.
7. 1.7 inches × 21 miles/inch = 35.7 miles

26 CHAPTER 1 The Nature of Science

SECTION 4

Evaluating Scientific Explanation

Believe it or not?

Look at the photo in **Figure 23.** Do you believe what you see? Do you believe everything you read or hear? Think of something that someone told you that you didn't believe. Why didn't you believe it? Chances are you looked at the facts you were given and decided that there wasn't enough proof to make you believe it. What you did was evaluate, or judge the reliability of what you heard. When you hear a statement, you ask the question "How do you know?" If you decide that what you are told is reliable, then you believe it. If it seems unreliable, then you don't believe it.

Critical Thinking When you evaluate something, you use critical thinking. **Critical thinking** means combining what you already know with the new facts that you are given to decide if you should agree with something. You can evaluate a scientific explanation by breaking it down into two parts. First you can look at and evaluate the observations made during the scientific investigation. Do you agree with what the scientists saw? Then you can evaluate the inferences—or conclusions made about the observations. Do you agree with what the scientists think their observations mean?

As You Read

***What* You'll Learn**

- **Evaluate** scientific explanations.
- **Evaluate** promotional claims.

Vocabulary

critical thinking

***Why* It's Important**

You will learn how to evaluate scientific claims to make better decisions.

Figure 23
In science, observations are not always agreed upon by everyone.
Do you see the same things your classmates see in this photo?

SECTION

Evaluating Scientific Explanation

1 Motivate

Bellringer Transparency

Display the Section Focus Transparency for Section 4. Use the accompanying Transparency Activity Master. L2 ELL

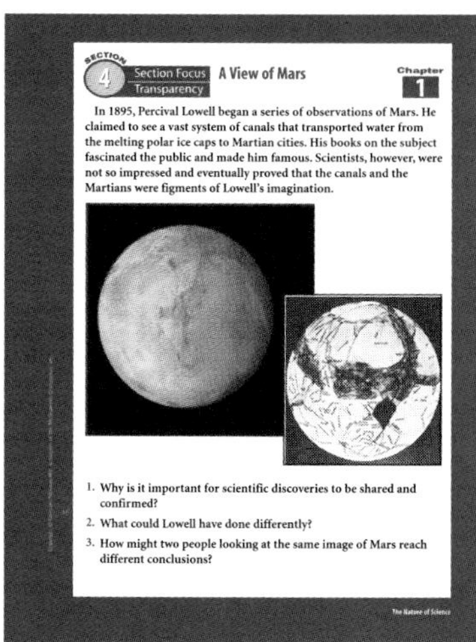

Section Focus Transparency 4 — A View of Mars — Chapter 1

In 1895, Percival Lowell began a series of observations of Mars. He claimed to see a vast system of canals that transported water from the melting polar ice caps to Martian cities. His books on the subject fascinated the public and made him famous. Scientists, however, were not so impressed and eventually proved that the canals and the Martians were figments of Lowell's imagination.

1. Why is it important for scientific discoveries to be shared and confirmed?
2. What could Lowell have done differently?
3. How might two people looking at the same image of Mars reach different conclusions?

The Nature of Science

Tie to Prior Knowledge

Ask students whether they believe everything they hear. People usually don't, especially if they don't trust the source of the information. Explain that the fact that someone says something is supported by science also doesn't mean you should believe it without question. To be a smart consumer, you need to know how to evaluate the evidence.

Section Assessment Planner

PORTFOLIO
Assessment, p. 30

PERFORMANCE ASSESSMENT
Skill Builder Activities, p. 30
See page 38 for more options.

CONTENT ASSESSMENT
Section, p. 30
Challenge, p. 30
Chapter, pp. 38–39

2 Teach

Believe it or not?

Caption Answer

Figure 23 Answers will vary.

Discussion

Have students discuss different advertisements they've heard on the radio or seen on TV. **Do any of these ads use scientific evidence to back up their claims?** Students may mention ads that say "Four out of five doctors prefer . . ." or "Hospitals recommend . . ." **Do you trust this evidence?** Answers will vary.

Evaluating the Data

Activity

Ask students to express the data given in **Table 2** as percentages. **What percent of the people surveyed preferred pizza?** $37 \div (37 + 28) \times 100\% = 57\%$ **What percent preferred hamburgers?** $28 \div (37 + 28) \times 100\% = 43\%$ **How many people in this survey would make up 50% of the people surveyed?** $x \div (37 + 28) \times 100\% = 50\%$; $x = 50\% \times (37 + 28) \div 100\% = 32.5$ Point out that the statement "More people surveyed preferred pizza than preferred hamburgers" would be true if anywhere from 33 to 65 people in the survey preferred pizza. L2 LS **Logical-Mathematical**

Caption Answer

Figure 24 It will increase the reliability of their data, because they will be less likely to forget something important.

Table 2 Favorite Foods

People's Preference	Tally	Frequency
pepperoni pizza	卌 卌 卌 卌 卌 卌 卌 II	37
hamburgers with ketchup	卌 卌 卌 卌 卌 III	28

Evaluating the Data

A scientific investigation always contains observations—often called data. These might be descriptions, tables, graphs or drawings. When evaluating a scientific claim, you might first look to see if any data are given. You should be cautious about believing any claim that is not supported by data.

Are the data specific? The data given to back up a claim should be specific. That means they need to be exact. What if your friend tells you that many people like pizza more than they like hamburgers? What else do you need to know before you agree with your friend? You might want to hear about a specific number of people rather than unspecific words like *many* and *more*. You might want to know how many people like pizza more than hamburgers. How many people were asked about which kind of food they liked more? When you are given specific data a statement is more reliable and you are more likely to believe it. An example of data in the form of a frequency table is shown in **Table 2.** A frequency table shows how many times types of data occur. Scientists must back up their scientific statements with specific data.

Take Good Notes Scientists must take thorough notes at the time of an investigation, like the scientists shown in **Figure 24.** Important details can be forgotten if you wait several hours or days before you write down your observations. It is also very important for you to write down every observation, including ones that you don't expect. Often, great discoveries are made when something unexpected happens in an investigation.

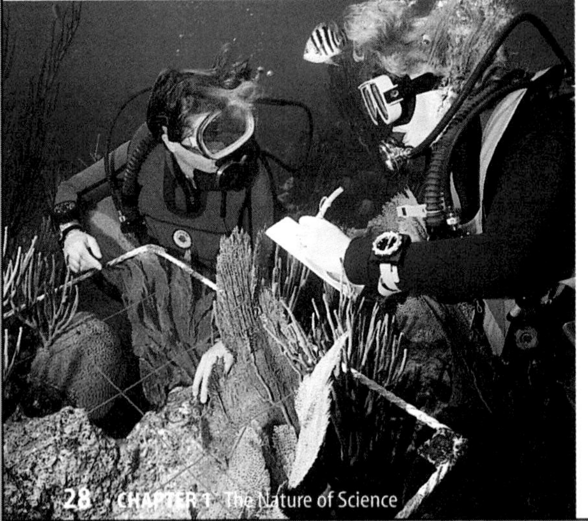

Figure 24
These scientists are writing down their observations during their investigation rather than waiting until they are back on land. *Do you think this will increase or decrease the reliability of their data?*

Visual Learning

Figure 23 Many times it's no accident that pictures of supposed UFOs appear out of focus. **Why might this make the claim more believable?** Because the object is blurry, you can't say for sure that it's not a UFO. **How is this similar to using words like many and most?** The words *many* and *most* sometimes blur ideas like a camera's lens can blur an object. L2 LS **Visual-Spatial**

Your Science Journal During this course, you will be keeping a science journal. You will write down what you do and see during your investigations. Your observations should be detailed enough that another person could read what you wrote and repeat the investigation exactly as you had performed it. Instead of writing "the stuff changed color," you might say, "the clear liquid turned to bright red when I added a drop of food coloring." Detailed observations written down during an investigation are more reliable than sketchy observations written from memory. Practice your observation skills by describing what you see in **Figure 25.**

Can the data be repeated? If your friend told you he could hit a baseball 100 m, but couldn't do it when you were around, you probably wouldn't believe him. Scientists also require repeatable evidence. When a scientist describes an investigation, as shown in **Figure 26,** other scientists should be able to do the investigation and get the same results. The results must be repeatable. When evaluating scientific data, look to see if other scientists have repeated the data. If not, the data might not be reliable.

Evaluating the Conclusions

When you think about a conclusion that someone has made you can ask yourself two questions. First, does the conclusion make sense? Second, are there any other possible explanations? Suppose you hear on the radio that your school will be running on a two-hour delay that morning because of snow. You look outside. The roads are clear of snow. Does the conclusion that snow is the cause for the delay make sense? What else could cause the delay? Maybe it is too foggy or icy for the buses to run. Maybe there is a problem with the school building. The original conclusion is not very reliable unless the other possible explanations are proven unlikely.

Figure 25
Detailed observations are important in order to get reliable data.
Write down at least five sentences describing what you see in this photo.

Figure 26
Working together is an important part of science. Several scientists must repeat an experiment and obtain the same results before data are reliable.

Caption Answer

Figure 25 A spiral shaped copper-colored metal is in a blue solution. Sparkly silver stuff is also in the blue solution. It looks like the sparkly stuff is coming from the metal.

Evaluating the Conclusions

Discussion

Tell students that, when doing experiments, scientists often run multiple trials of the same test and average the results. **How does this affect the way you evaluate the scientists' data?** Because the results are based on the averages of repeated trials, they are more likely to be repeatable and reliable. L2 LS **Logical-Mathematical**

Evaluating Promotional Materials

Activity

Have students look at the products used in their homes and write down five claims made on the packaging. Ask students to share the claims with the class and describe which claims they believe and which they do not believe and why. L2 LS **Logical-Mathematical**

Teacher FYI

Most of the time, advertisers do not intend to defraud the consumer, but some advertisers go too far. If you feel you've been the victim of false advertising, you can contact the Federal Trade Commission in Washington, D.C. Last year the FTC logged more than 60,000 complaints from consumers who didn't get what had been promised to them in ads. Make sure students understand that they also need to be cautious of advertising they see on the Internet.

Resource Manager

Chapter Resources Booklet
Transparency Activity, p. 51
Directed Reading, pp. 23, 24
Enrichment, p. 36

Life Science Critical Thinking/Problem Solving, p. 4

Evaluating Promotional Materials, continued

Caption Answer

Figure 27 answers will vary

3 Assess

Reteach

Read to students a list of ten items such as the names of cities. Ask students to recite these back to you in the order you gave them. **How does this demonstrate the importance of writing down data?** Possible response: It's hard to remember many specific things, even when you've just heard them. L2 LS **Auditory-Musical**

Challenge

Have students read product reviews for several specific products from a noncommercial consumer magazine. Then tell them to compare the reviews to advertisements for the products. Ask them to write short essays in their Science Journals discussing the accuracy of the ads. L2 LS **Linguistic**

Performance Have each student write an advertisement for a household product. The ad should be upbeat and complimentary, but not make any false claims. Use **PASC**, p. 157. P

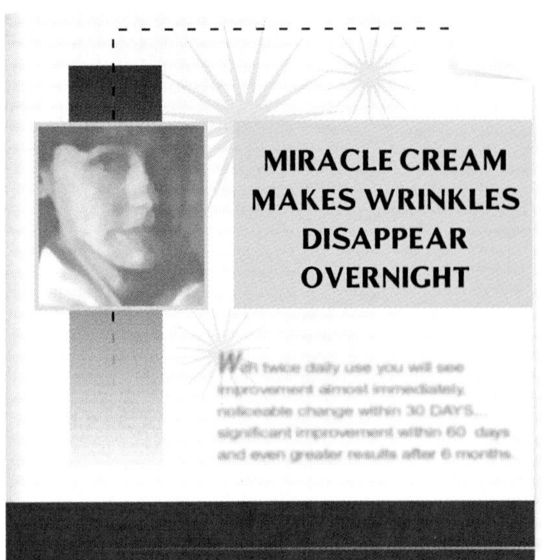

Figure 27
All material should be read with an analytical mind. *What does this advertisement mean?*

Evaluating Promotional Materials

Scientific processes are not used only in the laboratory. Suppose you saw an advertisement in the newspaper like the one in **Figure 27.** What would you think? First, you might ask, "Does this make sense?" It seems unbelievable. You would probably want to hear some of the scientific data supporting the claim before you would believe it. What does the word *virtually* mean? How is the amount of wrinkling in skin measured? You might also want to know if an independent laboratory repeated the results. An independent laboratory is one that is not hired by or related in any way to the company that is selling the product or service. It has nothing to gain from the sales of the product. Results from an independent laboratory usually are more reliable than results from a laboratory paid by the selling company. Advertising materials are designed to get you to buy a product or service. It is important that you carefully evaluate advertising claims and the data that support them before making a quick decision to spend your money.

Section  4 Assessment

1. Explain what is meant by critical thinking and give an example.
2. What types of scientific claims should be verified?
3. Name two parts of a scientific explanation. Give examples of ways to evaluate each part.
4. How can vague claims in advertising be misleading?
5. **Think Critically** An advertisement on a food package claims it contains Glistain, a safe, taste enhancer. Make a list of at least ten questions you would ask when evaluating the claim.

Skill Builder Activities

6. **Classifying** Watch three television commercials and read three magazine advertisements. In your Science Journal, record the claims that each advertisement made. Classify each claim as being vague, misleading, reliable, and/or scientific. **For more help, refer to the Science Skill Handbook.**
7. **Researching Information** Visit the your school library and choose an article from a news magazine. Pick one that deals with a scientific claim. Perform research on that claim and evaluate it using the scientific process. **For more help, refer to the Science Skill Handbook.**

Answers to Section Assessment

1. Critical thinking is combining what you already know with any new facts to decide whether you should believe something. You know that hitting a baseball 100 m is not easy to do. If someone tells you he or she can do it, you use critical thinking to decide whether you believe him or her.
2. All scientific claims should be verified by some kind of specific data.
3. Data given should be exact. Instead of using words such as *many* or *more,* try using specific numbers that can be confirmed. In addition, data should be repeatable. That means other scientists should be able to do the same investigation and get the same results.
4. Vague claims are misleading because they contain terms that can have more than one meaning.
5. Possible questions include: What is Glistain? Has Glistain been tested? What were the results? Has it been tested on humans? Over how long a period of time was it tested? Was it tested by an independent lab?
6. Answers will vary. Make sure students select ads from each medium.
7. Answers will vary.

Activity

What is the right answer?

Scientists sometimes develop more than one explanation for observations. Can more than one explanation be correct? Do scientific explanations depend on judgment?

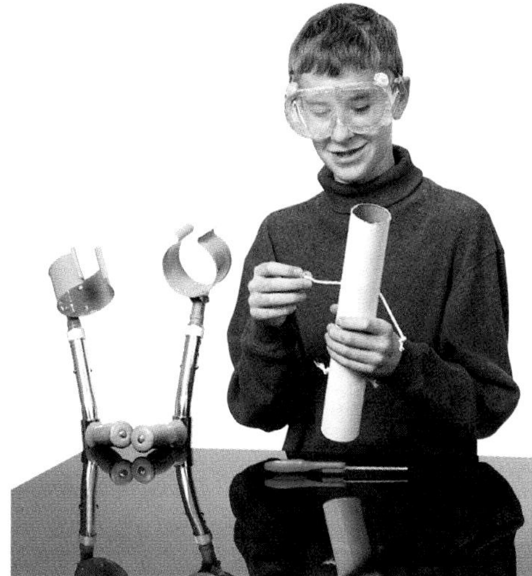

What You'll Investigate

Can more than one explanation apply to the same observation?

Materials

cardboard mailing tubes
*empty shoe boxes
length of rope
scissors

*Alternate Materials

Goals

- **Make a hypothesis** to explain an observation.
- **Construct** a model to support your hypothesis.
- **Refine** your model based on testing.

Safety Precautions  

WARNING: *Be careful when punching holes with sharp tools.*

Procedure

1. You will be shown a cardboard tube with four ropes coming out of it, one longer than the others. Your teacher will show you that when any of the three short ropes—A, C, or D—is pulled, the longer rope, B, gets shorter. Pulling on rope B returns the other ropes to their original lengths.
2. Make a hypothesis as to how the teacher's model works.
3. **Sketch** a model of a tube with ropes based on your hypothesis. Check your sketch to be sure that your model will do what you expect. Revise your sketch if necessary.
4. Using a cardboard tube and two lengths of rope, build a model according to your design. Test your model by pulling each of the ropes. If it does not perform as planned, modify your hypothesis and your model to make it work like your teacher's model.

Conclude and Apply

1. **Compare** your model with those made by others in your class.
2. Can more than one design give the same result? Can more than one explanation apply to same observation? Explain.
3. Without opening the tube, can you tell which model is exactly like your teacher's?

Communicating Your Data

Make a display of your working model. Include sketches of your designs. **For more help, refer to the Science Skill Handbook.**

Activity

BENCH TESTED

Purpose Students show that multiple explanations sometimes can apply to the same observations L2 LS **Kinesthetic**

Process Skills forming a hypothesis, designing an experiment to test a hypothesis, controlling variables, observing, inferring, predicting, recognizing cause and effect, communicating

Time Required 45 minutes

Alternate Materials empty shoe boxes with lids

Teaching Strategies Demonstrate a way in which one rope may affect another rope.

Answers to Questions

1. Have students note differences and similarities in their designs. Have them demonstrate that all models work.
2. Yes; yes; if you see two identical cars traveling at the same speed, you can't say they both have the same engine.
3. No

Content Students can show their rope trick to students in lower grades and see whether younger students can determine how it works. Encourage students to act like magicians presenting a magic trick, but to clearly explain how it works when they are finished. Use **PASC,** p. 143.

Resource Manager 

Chapter Resources Booklet
Activity Worksheet, pp. 7–8
Reinforcement, p. 32
Reading and Writing Skill Activities, p. 47

Communicating Your Data

Suggest that students draw different designs and show how they can act similarly. If students have access to a computer animation program, encourage them to make animated drawings of the inside of the tube.

Activity

BENCH TESTED

What You'll Investigate

Purpose

Students identify the steps of a scientific investigation.

Process Skills

recognizing cause and effect, observing, inferring, making and using graphs

Time Required

45 minutes

Procedure

Teaching Strategies

Write the steps of the scientific method on the board for students to use as a reference as they complete this activity.

Expected Outcome

Students should see that fertilizer B gave the best results. They should also see that, after starting out more slowly, fertilizer A did produce about the same results from week to week as did fertilizer B.

Activity

Identifying Parts of an Investigation

Science investigations follow many different steps. How can you identify the various parts of an investigation?

What You'll Investigate

What are the various parts of an experiment to test which fertilizer helps a plant grow best?

Materials

description of fertilizer experiment
data table from the fertilizer experiment

Goals

- **Identify** parts of the fertilizer experiment.
- **Identify** constants, variables, and controls in the experiment.
- **Graph** the results of the experiment and draw appropriate conclusions.

Procedure

1. **Read** the description of the fertilizer experiment.
2. **List** factors that remained constant in the experiment.
3. **Identify** any variables in the experiment.
4. **Identify** the control in the experiment.
5. **Identify** one possible hypothesis that the gardener could have tested in her investigation.
6. **Describe** how the gardener went about testing her hypothesis using different types of fertilizers.
7. **Graph** the data that the gardener collected in a line graph.

Resource Manager

Chapter Resources Booklet
Activity Worksheet, pp. 9–10

Home and Community Involvement, p. 32

Lab Management and Safety, p. 71

A gardener was interested in helping her plants grow faster. When she went to the nursery, she found three fertilizers available for her plants. One of those fertilizers, fertilizer A, was recommended to her. However, she decided to conduct a test to determine which of the three fertilizers, if any, helped her plants grow fastest. The gardener planted four seeds, each in a separate pot. She used the same type of pot and the same type of soil in each pot. She fertilized one seed with fertilizer A, one with fertilizer B, and one with fertilizer C. She did not fertilize the fourth seed. She placed the four pots near one another in her garden. She made sure to give each plant the same amount of water each day. She measured the height of the plants each week and recorded her data. After eight weeks of careful observation and record-keeping, she had the following table of data.

Plant Height (cm)				
Week	Fertilizer A	Fertilizer B	Fertilizer C	No Fertilizer
1	0	0	0	0
2	2	4	1	1
3	5	8	5	4
4	9	13	8	7
5	14	18	12	10
6	20	24	15	13
7	27	31	19	16
8	35	39	22	20

Conclude and Apply

1. **Describe** the results indicated by your graph. What part of an investigation have you just done?
2. Based on the results in the table and your graph, which fertilizer do you think the gardener should use if she wants her plants to grow the fastest? What part of an investigation have you just done?
3. Suppose the gardener told a friend who also grows these plants about her results. What is this an example of?
4. Suppose fertilizer B is much more expensive than fertilizers A and C. Would this affect which fertilizer you think the gardener should buy? Why or why not?
5. Does every researcher need the same hypothesis for an experiment? What is a second possible hypothesis for this experiment (different from the one you wrote in step 5 in the Procedure section)?
6. Did the gardener conduct an adequate test of her hypothesis? Explain why or why not.

Compare your conclusions with those of other students in your class. **For more help, refer to the Science Skill Handbook.**

Conclude and Apply

1. The graph shows that the plant grew the most with fertilizer B, that it grew only slightly better with fertilizer C than with no fertilizer, and that with fertilizer A the plant started slowly, but then grew as fast as the plant with fertilizer B. This step is analyzing data.
2. She'd use fertilizer B. This is hypothesizing, or making a guess based on data.
3. This is communicating results.
4. Probably; if the gardener cannot afford the extra money she should buy fertilizer A because it helps the plant almost as much as fertilizer B.
5. Answers will depend on the students' initial hypotheses. One possible hypothesis is that fertilizers stop having an effect after eight weeks.
6. She worked hard to control variables and she did her experiment over a good period of time. To confirm her results, she could try the experiment more times and for longer periods of time.

Error Analysis

Other factors might have affected the rate of plant growth. There may have been some problem with the soil in fertilizer C's pot. Maybe the seed in fertilizer A just didn't grow as much.

Assessment

Performance Have students act out the gardener going to buy the fertilizer, the store clerk's comments to her, and her comments back to the store clerk after her investigation. Make sure each character argues using scientific evidence. Use **Performance Assessment in the Science Classroom,** p. 147.

Students can use a computer graphing program to make their graphs look more professional. The programs also may allow them to predict seed growth in upcoming weeks. Using these predictions, students can argue for or against a specific fertilizer.

Content Background

All three women featured on these pages made sacrifices to work in their chosen fields. Maria Goepport Mayer often had to work "under" or "for" men in order to make her famous discovery. After earning her doctorate in theoretical physics in 1930, Mayer was not immediately considered for a position as a faculty member until Sarah Lawrence College hired her as a lecturer in 1939. While there, she also worked for Harold Urey at the S.A.M. lab where he assigned her secondary projects that helped to back up the findings of men. Finally in 1959, she received a full professorship at the University of Chicago, and was finally considered more than just the wife of a professor who had a hobby in Physics.

Politics and geography inhibited Montalcini's work. In 1936 Mussolini issued the "Manifesto per la Difesa della Razza," signed by ten Italian 'scientists.' The manifesto was followed by laws barring non-Aryan Italian citizens from holding academic and professional jobs. In order to continue her work, Montalcini built a research unit in her bedroom.

TIME SCIENCE AND HISTORY

SCIENCE CAN CHANGE THE COURSE OF HISTORY!

Women in Science

Nobel prizes are given every year in many areas of science.

Is your family doctor a man or a woman? To your great-grandparents, such a question would likely have seemed odd. Why? Because 100 years ago, there were only a handful of women in scientific fields such as medicine. Women then weren't encouraged to study science as they are today. But that does not mean that there were no female scientists back in your great-grandparents' day. Many women managed to overcome great barriers and, like the more recent Nobel prizewinners featured in this article, made discoveries that changed the world.

34

Resources for Teachers and Students

Nobel Prize Winners (Women in Profile Service), by Carlotta Hacker. Crabtree Publishing, 1998.

Nobel Prize Women in Science: Their Lives, Struggles, and Momentous Discoveries, by Sharon Bertschi McGrayne, Kensington Pub. Corp., 1998.

Maria Goeppert Mayer

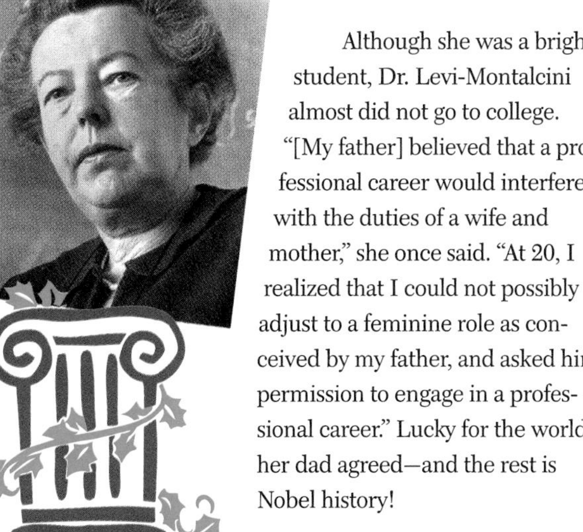

Dr. Maria Goeppert Mayer won the Nobel Prize in Physics in 1963 for her work on the structure of an atom. An atom is made up of protons, neutrons, and electrons. The protons and neutrons exist in the nucleus, or center, of the atom. The electrons orbit the nucleus in shells. Mayer proposed a similar shell model for the protons and neutrons inside the nucleus. This model greatly increased human understanding of atoms, which make up all forms of matter. About the Nobel prize, she said, "To my surprise, winning the prize wasn't half as exciting as doing the work itself. That was the fun—seeing it work out."

Rita Levi-Montalcini

In 1986, the Nobel Prize in Medicine went to Dr. Rita Levi-Montalcini, a biologist from Italy, for her discovery of growth factors. Growth factors regulate the growth of cells and organs in the body. Because of her work, doctors are better able to understand why tumors form and wounds heal.

Although she was a bright student, Dr. Levi-Montalcini almost did not go to college. "[My father] believed that a professional career would interfere with the duties of a wife and mother," she once said. "At 20, I realized that I could not possibly adjust to a feminine role as conceived by my father, and asked him permission to engage in a professional career." Lucky for the world, her dad agreed—and the rest is Nobel history!

Rosalyn Sussman Yalow

In 1977, Dr. Rosalyn Sussman Yalow, a nuclear physicist, was awarded the Nobel Prize in Medicine for discovering a way to measure substances in the blood that are present in tiny amounts, such as hormones and drugs.

The discovery made it possible for doctors to diagnose problems that they could not detect before. Upon winning the prize, Yalow spoke out against discrimination of women. She said, "The world cannot afford the loss of the talents of half its people if we are to solve the many problems which beset us."

CONNECTIONS Research **Write short biographies about recent Nobel prizewinners in physics, chemistry, and medicine. In addition to facts about their lives, explain why the scientists were awarded the prize. How did their discoveries impact their scientific fields or people in general?**

SCIENCE *Online*
For more information, visit science.glencoe.com

Discussion

What was an obstacle one of these scientists had to overcome in pursuing her field of choice? Possible Answer: Rita Levi-Montalcini's father thought a professional career stood in the way of her role as a wife and mother.

Historical Significance

Focusing on women in science is one way of turning attention to important scientific discoveries made by the three women discussed. It is also a way to inform students that women have not always been considered capable of such rigorous pursuits. Engage students in a discussion about the ways women have been excluded from many disciplines through history. As examples, tell them that the first woman senator, Hattie Wyatt Caraway, was not elected into office until 1938. In 2001, only 13 of the 100 U.S. senators were women. Historical data such as this exist for all disciplines and are relatively easy to find. Suggest students research prominent women pioneers in disciplines other than science. Have students determine what types of obstacles these women overcame in order to become the pioneers they are considered today. Useful reference materials include encyclopedias, Internet resources, and "Who's Who" type reference books.

CONNECTIONS Some students might be interested in researching recent winners whose work expands on the discoveries of one of the women featured in the in this article.

SCIENCE *Online*

Internet Addresses

Explore the Glencoe Science Web site at **science.glencoe.com** to find out more about topics in this feature.

Chapter 1 Study Guide

Reviewing Main Ideas

Preview

Students can answer the questions in their Science Journals. Discuss the answers as you go through the chapter. **LS Linguistic**

Review

Students can write their answers, then compare them with those of other students. **LS Interpersonal**

Reteach

Students can look at the illustrations and describe details that support the main ideas of the chapter. **LS Visual-Spatial**

Answers to Chapter Review

Section 1

4. Possible answers include: The lake, trees, and mountain are structures; the water cycle is a cycle that occurs in this system; evaporation and precipitation are processes that occur in this system.

Section 3

3. to find directions and distances between two places

Chapter 1 Study Guide

Reviewing Main Ideas

Section 1 What is science?

1. Science is a way of learning more about the natural world. It can provide only possible explanations for questions.
2. A scientific law describes a pattern in nature.
3. A scientific theory attempts to explain patterns in nature.
4. Systems are a collection of structures, cycles, and processes that interact. *Can you identify structures, cycles, and processes in this system?*

5. Science can be divided into three branches—life science, Earth science, and physical science.
6. Technology is the application of science.

Section 2 Science in Action

1. Science involves using a collection of skills.
2. A hypothesis is a reasonable guess based on what you know and observe.
3. An inference is a conclusion based on observation.
4. Controlled experiments involve changing one variable while keeping others constant.
5. You should always obey laboratory safety symbols. You should also wear and use appropriate gear in the laboratory.

Section 3 Models in Science

1. A model is any representation of an object or an event used as a tool for understanding the natural world.
2. There are physical, computer, and idea models.
3. Models can communicate ideas; test predictions; and save time, money, and lives. *How is this model used?*

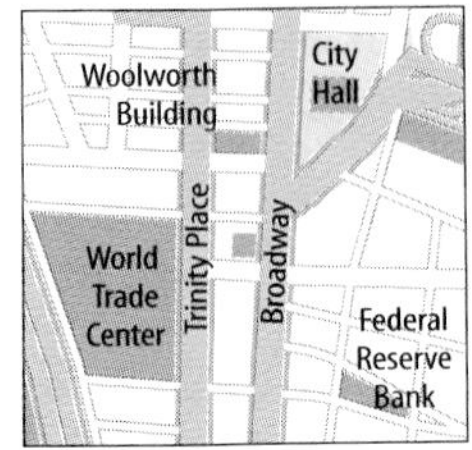

4. Models change as more information is learned.

Section 4 Evaluating Scientific Explanations

1. An explanation can be evaluated by looking at the observations and the conclusions in an experiment.
2. Reliable data is specific and repeatable by other scientists.
3. Detailed notes must be taken *during* an investigation.
4. To be reliable, a conclusion must make sense and be the most likely explanation.

FOLDABLES Reading & Study Skills — After You Read

Without looking at the chapter or at your Foldable, write what you learned about science on the *Learned* fold of your Know-Want-Learn Study Fold.

FOLDABLES Reading & Study Skills — After You Read

After students have read the chapter and completed the Foldable described in Before You Read, have them do the activity on the student page.

Dinah Zike

Chapter 1 Study Guide

Visualizing Main Ideas

Complete the following concept map.

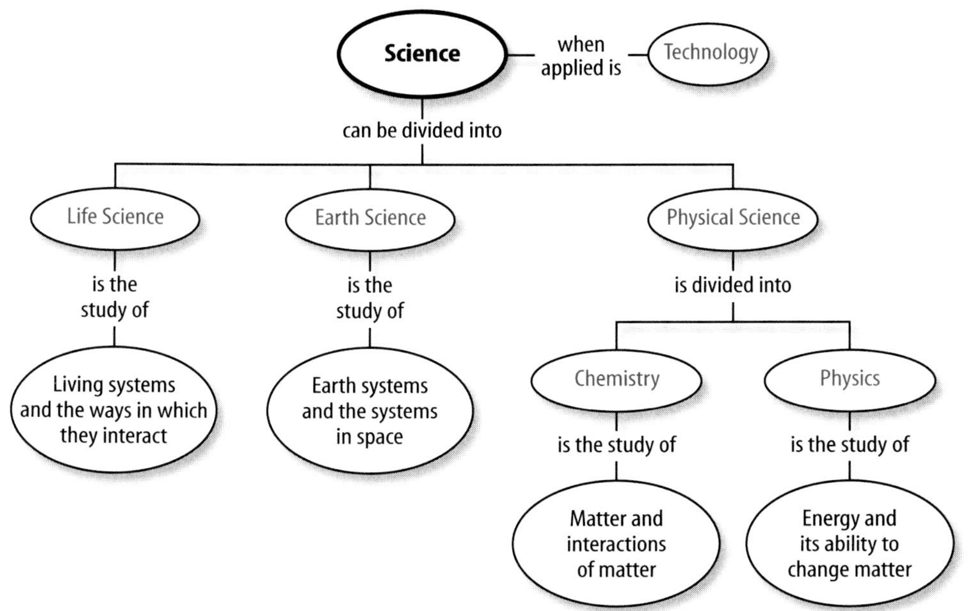

Vocabulary Review

Vocabulary Words

a. constant
b. controlled experiment
c. critical thinking
d. Earth science
e. hypothesis
f. infer
g. life science
h. model
i. physical science
j. science
k. scientific law
l. scientific theory
m. system
n. technology
o. variable

THE PRINCETON REVIEW — Study Tip

Make a note of anything you don't understand so that you'll remember to ask your teacher about it.

Using Vocabulary

Explain the relationship between the words in the following sets.

1. hypothesis, scientific theory
2. constant, variable
3. science, technology
4. science, system
5. Earth science, physical science
6. critical thinking, infer
7. scientific law, observation
8. model, system
9. controlled experiment, variable
10. scientific theory, scientific law

Chapter 1 Study Guide

Visualizing Main Ideas

See student page.

Vocabulary Review

Using Vocabulary

1. A hypothesis is a guess scientists make based upon what they observe. A scientific theory is an attempt to explain a pattern seen repeatedly in the natural world.
2. Variables are the parts of an experiment that change. A constant is the one variable in an experiment that does not change.
3. Science is a way of learning about the world. Technology is the use of this knowledge.
4. Science is a way of learning about the world. A system is a collection of structures, cycles, or processes in the world that relate to one another.
5. Earth science is the study of Earth systems and the systems in space. Physical science is the study of matter and energy and their relationships.
6. Critical thinking is used to evaluate evidence. To infer is used to draw a conclusion based on that evidence.
7. A scientific law is a rule that describes some pattern seen in nature. An observation can be anything you notice about the natural world.
8. A model is any representation of an object or event. A system is a collection of processes, cycles, or structures in the world. You can make a model of a system.
9. A controlled experiment is an experiment in which everything but one part of it stays the same. Variables are the things in a controlled experiment that can change.
10. A scientific theory is an explanation of why something happens in the world. A scientific law is a statement of some regularity about something seen in the world.

Chapter 1 Assessment

Checking Concepts

1. B
2. A
3. B
4. C
5. C
6. C
7. C
8. A
9. A
10. C

Thinking Critically

11. Answers may vary. Possible answer: No; a play review shows your personal feelings. Science cannot answer questions about what is good and bad.
12. You repeat an experiment to be sure that the results always will be the same. You have to be sure that the results you get are the results everyone will get if they do the experiment exactly the same way you did it.
13. You know that a rock is hard. You take this knowledge and use it to drive a nail. Technology is the use of science, the study of the natural world.
14. You need to record data accurately so you can be sure of the results of your experiment when you go back later to draw your conclusions.
15. Physical models most likely would be used. Young children can understand physical models without knowing how to read or use a computer.

Chapter 1 Assessment

Checking Concepts

Choose the word or phrase that best answers the question.

1. What does infer mean?
   A) make observations **C)** replace
   B) draw a conclusion **D)** test
2. Which is an example of technology?
   A) a squirt bottle **C)** a cat
   B) a poem **D)** physical science
3. Which branch of science includes the study of weather?
   A) life science **C)** physical science
   B) Earth science **D)** engineering
4. What explains something that takes place in the natural world?
   A) scientific law **C)** scientific theory
   B) technology **D)** experiments
5. Which of the following cannot protect you from splashing acid?
   A) goggles **C)** fire extinguisher
   B) apron **D)** gloves
6. If the results from your investigation do not support your hypothesis, what should you do?
   A) Do nothing.
   B) You should repeat the investigation until it agrees with the hypothesis.
   C) Modify your hypothesis.
   D) Change your data to fit your hypothesis.
7. Which of the following is NOT an example of a scientific hypothesis?
   A) Earthquakes happen because of stresses along continental plates.
   B) Some animals can detect ultrasound frequencies caused by earthquakes.
   C) Paintings are better than sculptures.
   D) Lava takes different forms depending on how it cools.
8. An airplane model is an example of what type of model?
   A) physical **C)** idea
   B) computer **D)** mental
9. Using a computer to make a three-dimensional picture of a building is a type of which of the following?
   A) model **C)** constant
   B) hypothesis **D)** variable
10. Which of the following will increase the reliability of a scientific explanation?
    A) vague statements
    B) notes taken after the investigation
    C) repeatable supporting data
    D) several likely explanations

Thinking Critically

11. Is evaluating a play in English class science? Explain.
12. Why is it a good idea to repeat an experiment a few times and compare results? Explain.
13. How is using a rock hammer an example of technology? Explain.
14. Why is it important to record and measure data accurately during an experiment?
15. What type of model would most likely be used in science classrooms with young children? Explain.

Developing Skills

16. **Comparing and Contrasting** How are scientific theories and laws similar? How are they different?

Chapter Assessment Planner

Portfolio Encourage students to place in their portfolios one or two items of what they consider to be their best work. Examples include:

- Assessment, p. 8
- Active Reading, p. 16
- Curriculum Connection, p. 22
- Assessment, p. 30

Performance Additional performance assessments, Performance Task Assessment Lists, and rubrics for evaluating these activities can be found in Glencoe's **Performance Assessment in the Science Classroom.**

17. **Drawing Conclusions** When scientists study how well new medicines work, one group of patients receives the medicine. A second group does not. Why?

18. **Forming Hypotheses** Make a hypothesis about the quickest way to get to school in the morning. How could you test your hypothesis?

19. **Making Operational Definitions** How does a scientific law differ from a state law? Give examples of both types of laws.

20. **Making and Using Tables** Mohs hardness scale measures how easily an object can be scratched. The higher the number is, the harder the material is. Use the table below to identify which material is the hardest and which is the softest.

Hardness	
Object	**Mohs Scale**
copper	3.5
diamond	10
fingernail	2.5
glass	5.5
quartz	7
steel file	6.5

Performance Assessment

21. **Write a Story** Write a story illustrating what science is and how it is used to investigate problems.

Technology

Go to the Glencoe Science Web site at **science.glencoe.com** or use the **Glencoe Science CD-ROM** for additional chapter assessment.

THE PRINCETON REVIEW Test Practice

Sally and Rafael have just learned about the solar system in science class. They decided to build a large model to better understand it.

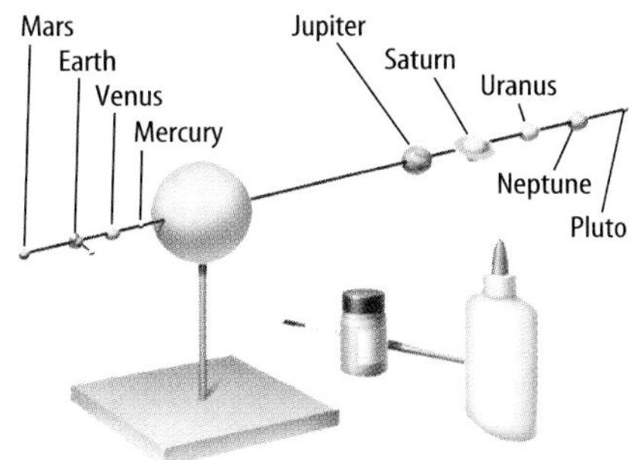

Study the diagram and answer the following questions.

1. According to this information, Rafael and Sally's model of the solar system best represents which kind of scientific model?
   A) idea
   B) computer
   C) physical
   D) realistic

2. In this model, all of the following are represented EXCEPT _____.
   F) the Sun
   G) the Moon
   H) planets
   J) stars

Assessment Resources

Reproducible Masters

Chapter Resources Booklet
Chapter Review, pp. 41–42
Chapter Tests, pp. 43–46
Assessment Transparency Activity, p. 55

Glencoe Science Web site
Interactive Tutor
Chapter Quizzes

Glencoe Technology
Assessment Transparency
Interactive CD-ROM Chapter Quizzes
ExamView Pro Test Bank
Vocabulary PuzzleMaker Software
MindJogger Videoquiz DVD/VHS

Chapter 1 Assessment

THE PRINCETON REVIEW Test Practice

The Test-Taking Tip was written by The Princeton Review, the nation's leader in test preparation.

1. C
2. J

Developing Skills

16. Both scientific theories and scientific laws are generalizations. A scientific theory explains why something happens, but a scientific law only says that something happens.
17. By not giving the medicine to one group of patients, scientists can see the effects of that medicine on the other group.
18. You could test the hypothesis by timing your method and comparing it to the times it takes to get to school using other methods.
19. A state law tells you what you are forbidden to do. A scientific law just tells you that things happen. A state law could forbid a driver to turn right at a red light. A scientific law would tell the driver that the force of gravity keeps the car on the road.
20. Diamond is the hardest and a fingernail is the softest.

Performance Assessment

21. Check students' stories to see that they address the topic reasonably. Use **PASC**, p. 155.

Section/Objectives	Standards		Activities/Features
	National	State/Local	
Chapter Opener	See p. 5T for a Key to Standards.		**Explore Activity:** Measure length, p. 41 **Before You Read,** p. 41
Section 1 Description and Measurement 3 sessions 1.5 blocks 1. **Determine** how reasonable a measurement is by estimating. 2. **Identify** and use the rules for rounding a number. 3. **Distinguish** between precision and accuracy in measurements.	National Content Standards: UCP3, A1, B1		**Chemistry Integration,** p. 43 **MiniLAB:** Measuring Accurately, p. 44 **Visualizing Precision and Accuracy,** p. 46 **Science Online,** p. 47 **Math Skills Activity:** Rounding, p. 48
Section 2 SI Units 3 sessions 1.5 blocks 1. **Identify** the purpose of SI. 2. **Identify** the SI units of length, volume, mass, temperature, time, and rate.	National Content Standards: UCP3, A1, B1		**Astronomy Integration,** p. 51 **MiniLAB:** Measuring Volume, p. 52 **Activity:** Scale Drawing, p. 55
Section 3 Drawings, Tables, and Graphs 4 sessions 2 blocks 1. **Describe** how to use pictures and tables to give information. 2. **Identify** and use three types of graphs. 3. **Distinguish** the correct use of each type of graph.	National Content Standards: UCP3, A1, B1		**Science Online,** p. 58 **Activity:** Pace Yourself, pp. 60–61 **Science Stats:** Heights and Measurements, pp. 62–63

Activity Materials	Reproducible Resources	Section Assessment	Technology
Explore Activity: items of various sizes to measure in hand-widths	**Chapter Resources Booklet** Foldables Worksheet, p. 13 Directed Reading Overview, p. 15 Note-taking Worksheets, pp. 29–31	GLENCOE'S ASSESSMENT ADVANTAGE	
MiniLAB: several measuring devices—clock or watch that indicates seconds, graduated cylinder or measuring cup, metric ruler, meterstick, spring scale	**Chapter Resources Booklet** Transparency Activity, p. 40 MiniLAB, p. 3 Enrichment, p. 26 Reinforcement, p. 23 Directed Reading, p. 16 **Cultural Diversity,** p. 29 **Physical Science Critical Thinking/Problem Solving,** p. 11	Portfolio Science Journal, p. 45 Performance MiniLAB, p. 44 Math Skills Activity, p. 48 Skill Builder Activities, p. 49 Content Section Assessment, p. 49	Section Focus Transparency Interactive CD-ROM/DVD Guided Reading Audio Program
MiniLAB: transparent measuring cup, water, solid object that will fit in cup, pencil **Activity:** 1-cm graph paper, pencil, metric ruler, meterstick	**Chapter Resources Booklet** Transparency Activity, p. 41 MiniLAB, p. 4 Enrichment, p. 27 Reinforcement, p. 24 Directed Reading, pp. 16, 17 Activity Worksheet, pp. 5–6 Lab Activity, pp. 9–10, 11–12 Transparency Activity, pp. 43–44 **Reading and Writing Critical Thinking/Problem Solving,** p. 13	Portfolio Assessment, p. 54 Performance MiniLAB, p. 52 Skill Builder Activities, p. 54 Content Section Assessment, p. 54	Section Focus Transparency Teaching Transparency Interactive CD-ROM/DVD Guided Reading Audio Program
Activity: meterstick, stopwatch or watch with a second hand	**Chapter Resources Booklet** Transparency Activity, p. 42 Enrichment, p. 28 Reinforcement, p. 25 Directed Reading, pp. 17, 18 Activity Worksheet, pp. 7–8 **Lab Management and Safety,** pp. 70, 71	Portfolio Assessment, p. 59 Performance Skill Builder Activities, p. 59 Content Section Assessment, p. 59	Section Focus Transparency Interactive CD-ROM/DVD Guided Reading Audio Program

Need materials? Contact Science Kit at 1-800-828-7777 or www.sciencekit.com on the Internet.

End of Chapter Assessment

GLENCOE'S ASSESSMENT ADVANTAGE

Blackline Masters	Technology	Professional Series
Chapter Resources Booklet Chapter Review, pp. 33–34 Chapter Tests, pp. 35–38 **Standardized Test Practice by The Princeton Review,** pp. 11–14	MindJogger Videoquiz CD-ROM Explorations and Quizzes Vocabulary Puzzle Makers ExamView Pro Test Bank Interactive Lesson Planner Interactive Teacher's Edition	Performance Assessment in the Science Classroom (PASC)

Transparencies

Section Focus

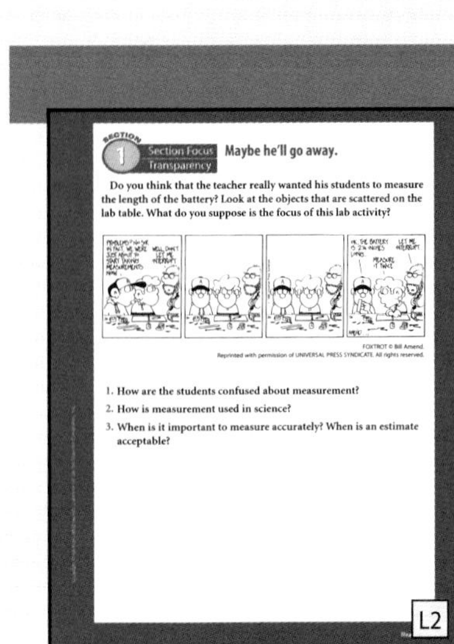
Section 1 Section Focus Transparency — Maybe he'll go away.

Do you think that the teacher really wanted his students to measure the length of the battery? Look at the objects that are scattered on the lab table. What do you suppose is the focus of this lab activity?

FOXTROT © Bill Amend. Reprinted with permission of UNIVERSAL PRESS SYNDICATE. All rights reserved.

1. How are the students confused about measurement?
2. How is measurement used in science?
3. When is it important to measure accurately? When is an estimate acceptable?

L2

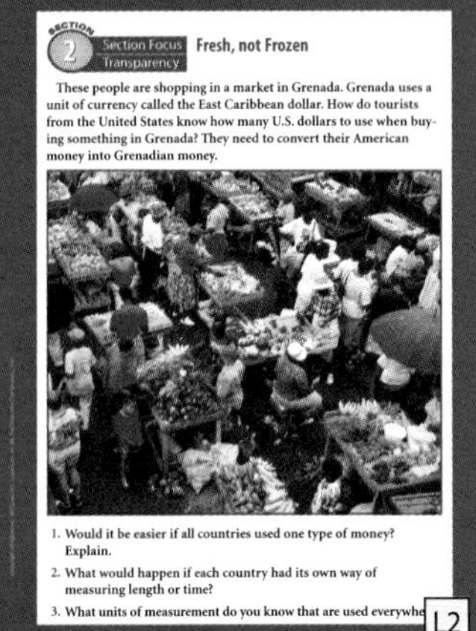
Section 2 Section Focus Transparency — Fresh, not Frozen

These people are shopping in a market in Grenada. Grenada uses a unit of currency called the East Caribbean dollar. How do tourists from the United States know how many U.S. dollars to use when buying something in Grenada? They need to convert their American money into Grenadian money.

1. Would it be easier if all countries used one type of money? Explain.
2. What would happen if each country had its own way of measuring length or time?
3. What units of measurement do you know that are used everywhe[re]

L2

Section 3 Section Focus Transparency — Different Views

This house, called Fallingwater, was designed by Frank Lloyd Wright as a weekend home. Along with photograph, you also see a plan for the main floor.

1. What could you learn about a house by looking at a floor plan?
2. Could you get the same information from a photograph? Explain.
3. What information do you need to build a house? What is the be[st] way to communicate that information?

L2

This is a representation of key blackline masters available in the Teacher Classroom Resources. See Resource Manager boxes within the chapter for additional information.

Assessment

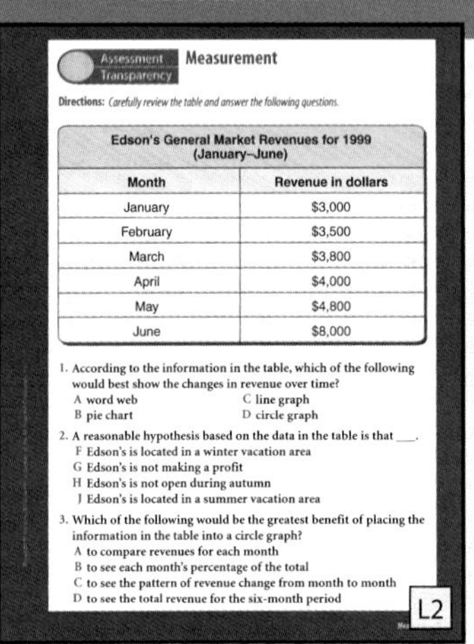
Assessment Transparency — Measurement

Directions: Carefully review the table and answer the following questions.

Edson's General Market Revenues for 1999 (January–June)	
Month	**Revenue in dollars**
January	$3,000
February	$3,500
March	$3,800
April	$4,000
May	$4,800
June	$8,000

1. According to the information in the table, which of the following would best show the changes in revenue over time?
   A word web
   B pie chart
   C line graph
   D circle graph
2. A reasonable hypothesis based on the data in the table is that ___.
   F Edson's is located in a winter vacation area
   G Edson's is not making a profit
   H Edson's is not open during autumn
   J Edson's is located in a summer vacation area
3. Which of the following would be the greatest benefit of placing the information in the table into a circle graph?
   A to compare revenues for each month
   B to see each month's percentage of the total
   C to see the pattern of revenue change from month to month
   D to see the total revenue for the six-month period

L2

Teaching

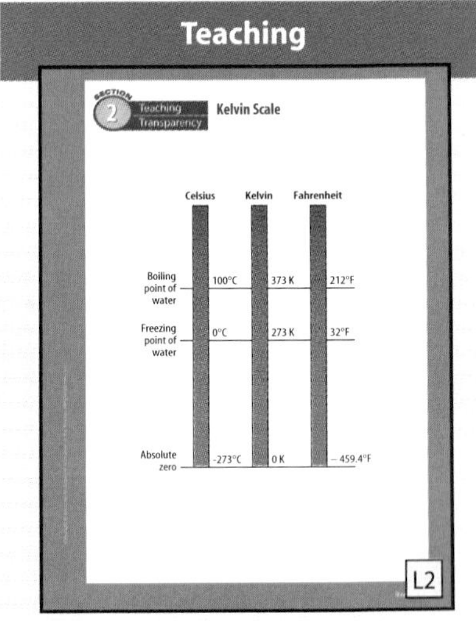
Section 2 Teaching Transparency — Kelvin Scale

L2

Key to Teaching Strategies

The following designations will help you decide which activities are appropriate for your students.

- **L1** Level 1 activities should be appropriate for students with learning difficulties.
- **L2** Level 2 activities should be within the ability range of all students.
- **L3** Level 3 activities are designed for above-average students.
- **ELL** ELL activities should be within the ability range of English Language Learners.
- **COOP LEARN** Cooperative Learning activities are designed for small group work.
- **LS** Multiple Learning Styles logos, as described on page 22T, are used throughout to indicate strategies that address different learning styles.
- **P** These strategies represent student products that can be placed into a best-work portfolio.

Hands-on Activities

Activity Worksheets

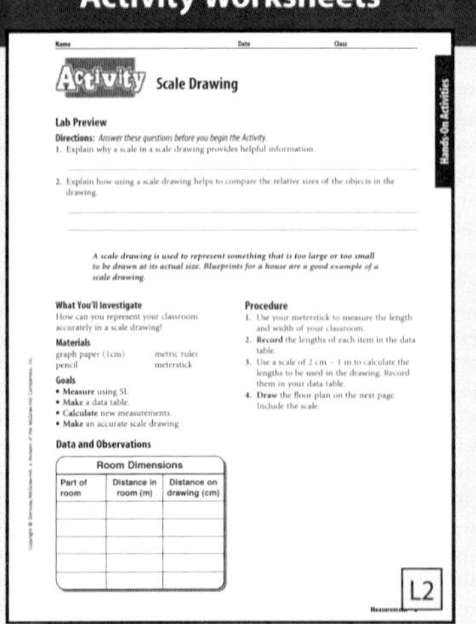
Activity — Scale Drawing

Lab Preview

What You'll Investigate

Materials

Goals

Procedure

Data and Observations

Room Dimensions		
Part of room	Distance in room (m)	Distance on drawing (cm)

L2

Laboratory Activity

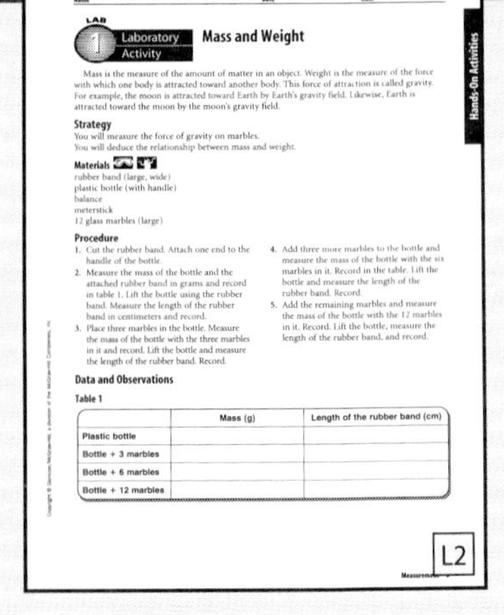
Lab 1 Laboratory Activity — Mass and Weight

Strategy

Materials

Procedure

Data and Observations

Table 1

	Mass (g)	Length of the rubber band (cm)
Plastic bottle		
Bottle + 3 marbles		
Bottle + 6 marbles		
Bottle + 12 marbles		

L2

Meeting Different Ability Levels

Content Outline

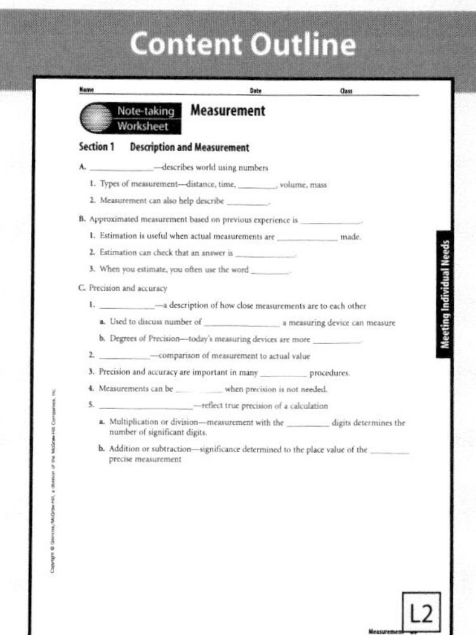

Reinforcement

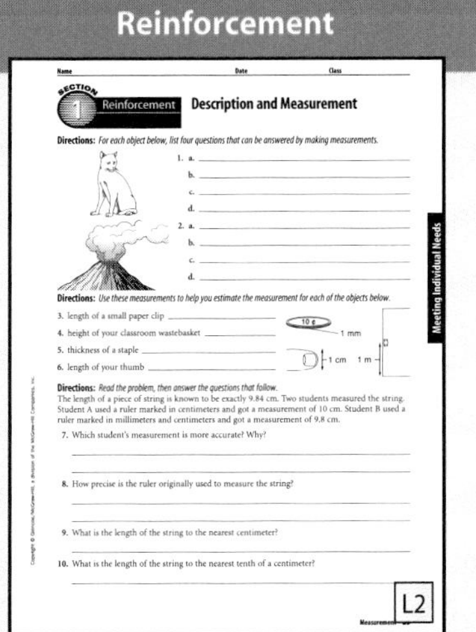

Directed Reading

Assessment

Chapter Tests

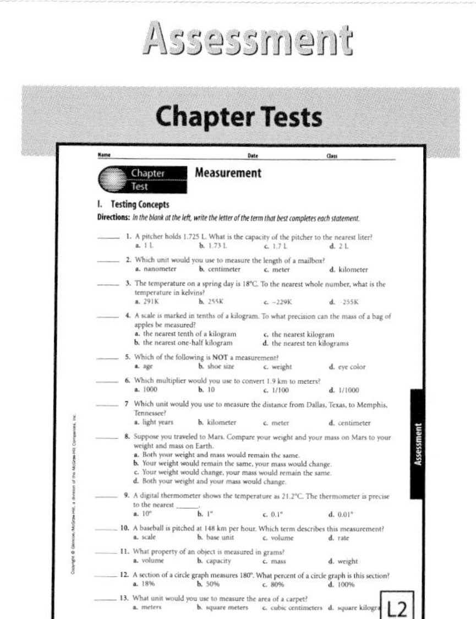

Enrichment

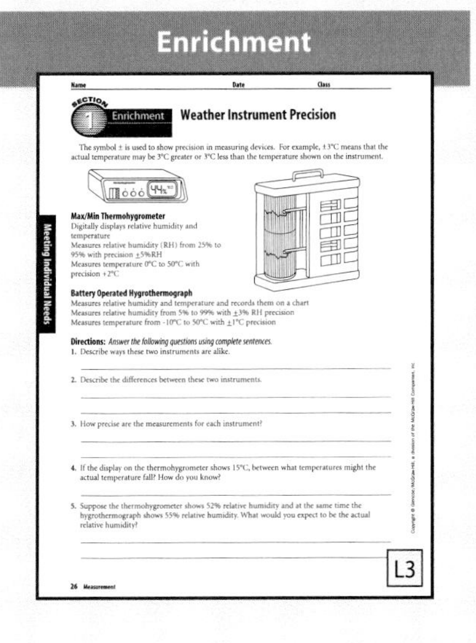

Spanish Directed Reading

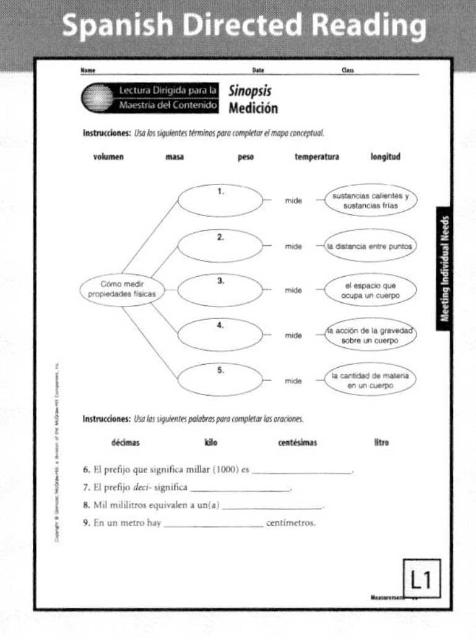

Test Practice Workbook

Chapter Review

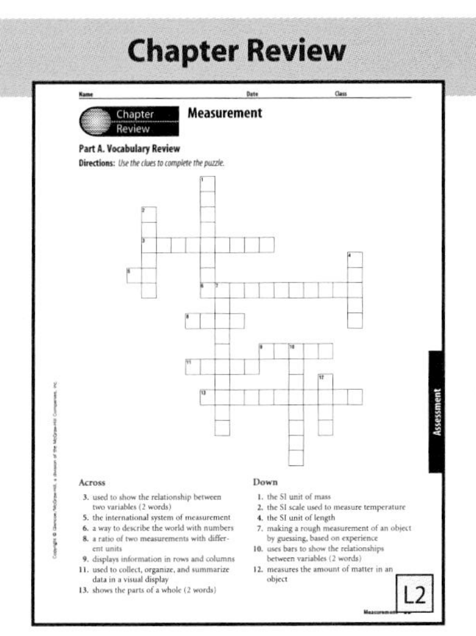

Science Content Background

SECTION 1 Description and Measurement

Degrees of Precision

Scientists use physical and chemical properties to describe matter. Measurement describes properties with numbers, which is known as quantifying. It describes features such as how long, how far, and how many.

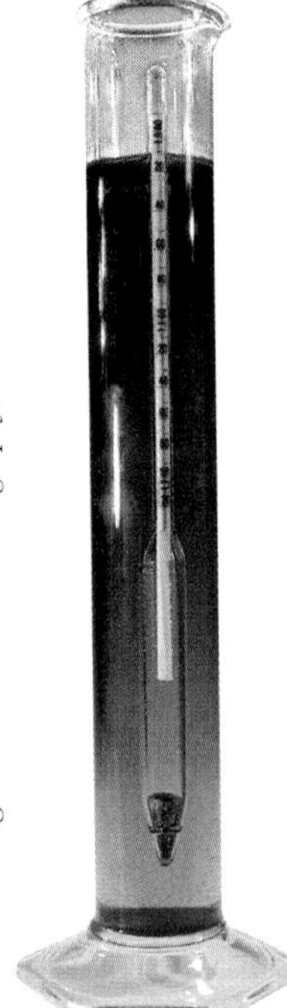
Runk/Schoenberger/Grant Heilman Photography, Inc.

Precision and Accuracy

Precision is related to the degree of exactness that is used to measure an item. A measurer can make adjustments by using tools or methods that refine the results of measuring. Precision can improve with more sophisticated tools. Although measurements of 4.2 and 4.20 may seem to be the same, the 4.20 measurement shows that it is a more precise measurement. When numbers are rounded off in calculations, they are rounded to show the precision of the measuring instruments.

SECTION 2 SI Units

The International System

The initials SI stand for *Systéme Internationalv*—the International System of Units for measurement. These units are used all over the world for science, commerce, and communication. The U.S. Bureau of Standards determines standards for measurements in the United States.

SI standards are based on key measurement units such as meter, liter, and kilograms. These units are further defined by the prefixes, of which the most commonly used are *kilo-*, *centi-*, and *milli-*. All units differ by factors of ten, so to convert the same unit with different prefixes simply requires the sliding of the decimal point to the left or right. To convert between units, use dimensional analysis, also called unit analysis. Cancel units the same way you cancel numbers.

- 3 km × (1,000m/1 km) = 3,000 m
- 45 cm (1 m/100 cm) = 0.45 m

In the classroom, SI length is measured with a metric ruler or a meterstick. A meterstick or a graduated cylinder is used to measure volume.

Length

Old units of length students might have heard of include the cubit and the roman mile. Accurate length measurement was important for ancient engineering projects such as the Nazca lines, pyramids in Central America and Africa, and the great public buildings found in many cultures.

Mass

Mass and weight are often confused. Moving an object to different locations, the mass is constant while the weight—a measure of the amount of gravity on an object—can change. Because the force of gravity is nearly constant on Earth's surface, mass and weight are often used interchangeably. The weight on the Earth is found by multiplying the mass by the acceleration due to gravity, which averages 9.8 m/s2.

SECTION 3

Drawings, Tables, and Graphs

Scientific Illustrations

Each science develops a visual language, a standard way to illustrate and communicate important information. A geologist, for example, will learn to "read," or interpret, illustrations of geological strata as part of his or her training. Meteorologists learn to interpret images captured by satellites.

Tables and Graphs

A line graph is used to show the relationship between two numerical variables. As a rule, the independent variable is on the horizontal axis and the dependent variable is on the vertical axis. For example, distance traveled depends on time. While it is common to use the left and bottom sides of a grid as axes, the top or right side can also be used. Bar graphs and circle graphs often are used to present the results of opinion polls.

For additional content background on this topic, go to the Glencoe Science Web site at science.glencoe.com.

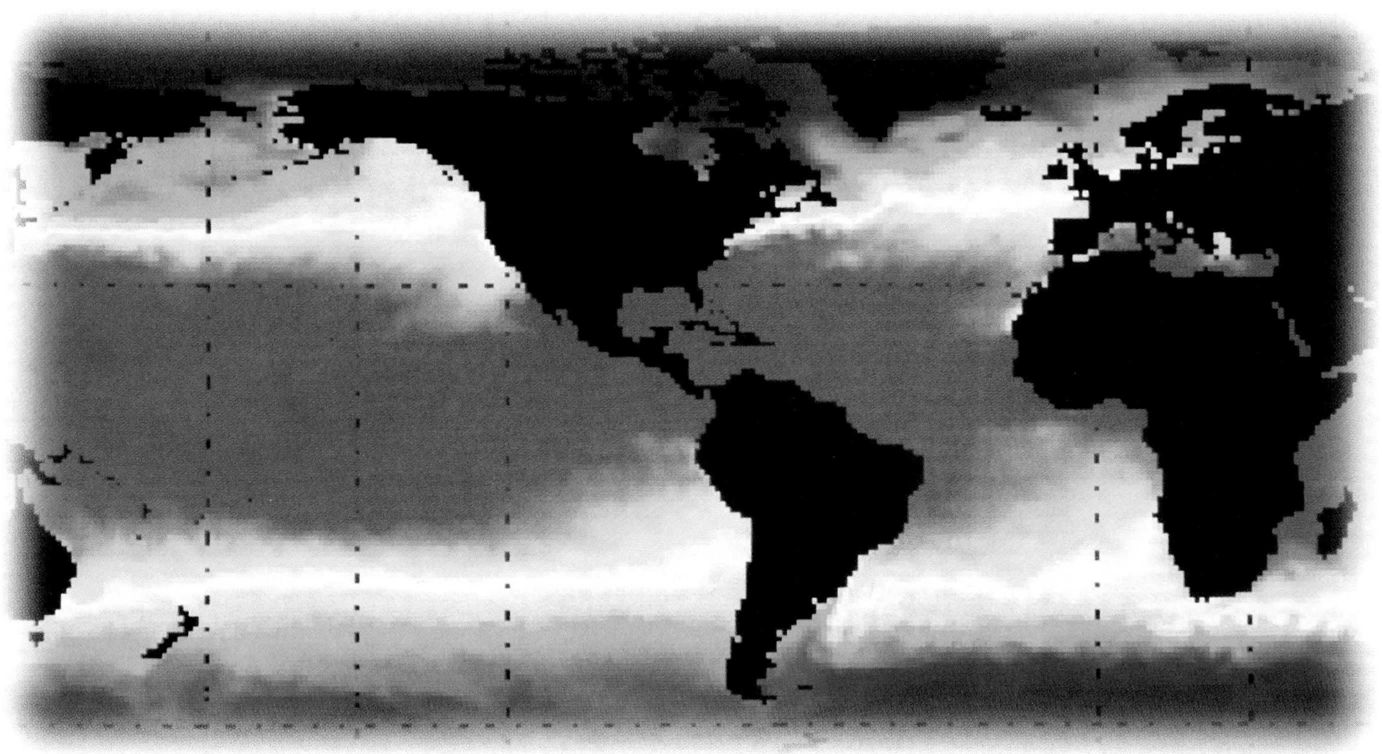

Warren Faidley/International Stock

Measurement

Chapter Vocabulary

measurement
estimation
precision
accuracy
SI
meter
mass
kilogram
kelvin
rate
table
graph
line graph
bar graph
circle graph

What do you think?

Science Journal The photograph shows a stopwatch. This stopwatch measures time in 0.10 S.

CHAPTER 2

Measurement

Does the expression "winning by a nose" mean anything to you? If you have ever "won by a nose," that means the race was close. Sometimes horse races, such as this one, are so close the winner has to be determined by a photograph. But there is more to measure than just how close the race was. How fast did the horse run? Did he break a record? In this chapter, you will learn how scientists measure things like distance, time, volume, and temperature. You also will learn how to use illustrations, pictures, and graphs to communicate measurements.

What do you think?

Science Journal Look at the picture below with a classmate. Discuss what you think this might be. Here's a hint: *How fast did you come up with an answer?* Write your answer or best guess in your Science Journal.

40

Theme Connection

Systems and Interactions The SI system is used throughout the world. Because it is based on powers of 10, it is easy to convert between units and do calculations.

You make measurements every day. If you want to communicate those measurements to others, how can you be sure that they will understand exactly what you mean? Using vague words without units won't work. Do the Explore Activity below to see the confusion that can result from using measurements that aren't standard.

Measure length

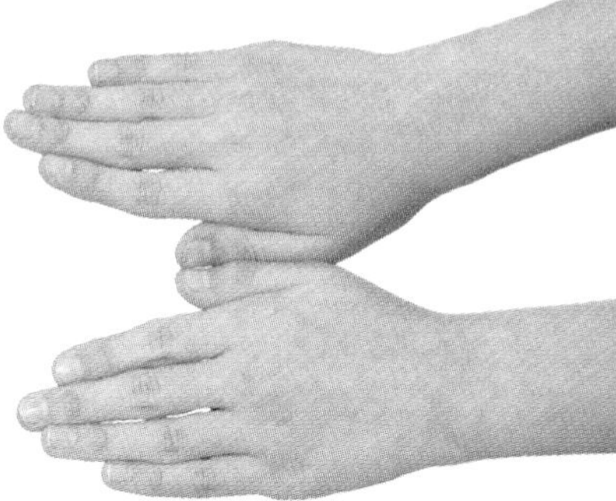

1. Measure several items using the width of your hand.
2. About how many hands long is your arm from shoulder to fingertip? How wide is this book?
3. Now measure two other objects in the classroom using the width of your hand.

Observe

Is your hand the same width as your classmates' hands? Discuss in your Science Journal why it is better to switch from using hands to using units of measurement that are the same all the time.

Before You Read

Making an Organizational Study Fold **When information is grouped into clear categories, it is easier to understand what you are learning. Before you begin reading, make the following Foldable to help you organize your thoughts about measurements.**

1. Place a sheet of paper in front of you so the short side is at the top. Fold the paper in half from the left side to the right side two times. Unfold all the folds.
2. Fold the paper from top to bottom in equal thirds and then in half. Unfold all the folds.
3. Trace over all the fold lines and label the table you created. Label the columns: *Estimate It, Measure It,* and *Round It,* as shown. Label the rows: *Length of ______, Volume of ______, Mass of ______, Temperature of ______,* and *Rate of ______,* as shown.
4. Before you read the chapter, select objects to measure and estimate their measurements. As you read the chapter, complete the *Measure It* column.

41

EXPLORE ACTIVITY

Purpose Students discover what happens when measurements aren't standardized. L1 ELL COOP LEARN LS **Kinesthetic**

Preparation Before doing this activity, practice using your hand as a unit of length and measure the length of several objects.

Materials something to measure, such as a tabletop, a bookshelf, and a door, in addition to smaller objects

Teaching Strategy Model for the students by measuring your arm or desk with your hand.

Observe

No; because hands vary in size, a more standard unit of measurement is needed.

Process Have students work in pairs. Each pair should choose a limb of the body, then use it to measure the length of something. Have each student of the pair do the measurement using his or her own limb, then have students compare their measurements with one another. Use **Performance Assessment in the Science Classroom,** p. 169.

Before You Read

FOLDABLES Reading & Study Skills

Dinah Zike Study Fold

Purpose Students make and use a Foldable table to practice measuring the length, volume, mass, temperature and rates of different objects. The Foldable table will also provide practice in estimating measurements, recording exact measurements, and rounding measurements.

For additional help, see Foldables Worksheet, p. 13 in **Chapter Resources Booklet,** or go to the Glencoe Science Web site at **science.glencoe.com.** See After You Read in the Study Guide at the end of this chapter.

SECTION

Description and Measurement

1 Motivate

Bellringer Transparency

Display the Section Focus Transparency for Section 1. Use the accompanying Transparency Activity Master. L2 ELL

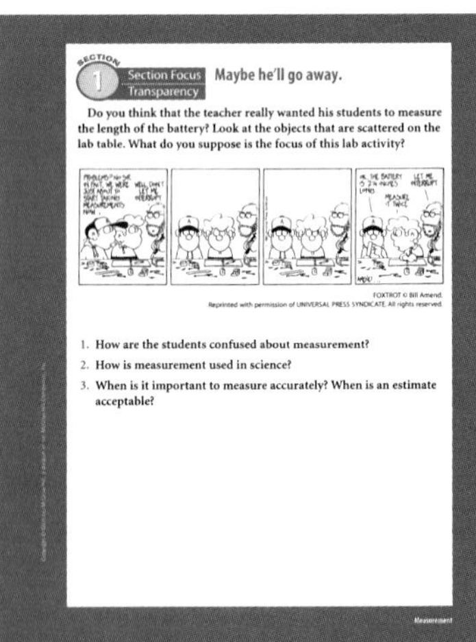

Section Focus Transparency 1 Maybe he'll go away.

Do you think that the teacher really wanted his students to measure the length of the battery? Look at the objects that are scattered on the lab table. What do you suppose is the focus of this lab activity?

1. How are the students confused about measurement?
2. How is measurement used in science?
3. When is it important to measure accurately? When is an estimate acceptable?

Tie to Prior Knowledge

Discuss with students times when they have used measuring tools such as rulers or scales.

SECTION 1

Description and Measurement

As You Read

***What* You'll Learn**

- **Determine** how reasonable a measurement is by estimating.
- **Identify** and use the rules for rounding a number.
- **Distinguish** between precision and accuracy in measurements.

Vocabulary

measurement, estimation, precision, accuracy

***Why* It's Important**

Measurement helps you communicate information and ideas.

Measurement

How would you describe what you are wearing today? You might start with the colors of your outfit, and perhaps you would even describe the style. Then you might mention sizes—size 7 shoes, size 14 shirt. Every day you are surrounded by numbers. **Measurement** is a way to describe the world with numbers. It answers questions such as how much, how long, or how far. Measurement can describe the amount of milk in a carton, the cost of a new compact disc, or the distance between your home and your school. It also can describe the volume of water in a swimming pool, the mass of an atom, or how fast a penguin's heart pumps blood.

The circular device in **Figure 1** is designed to measure the performance of an automobile in a crash test. Engineers use this information to design safer vehicles. In scientific endeavors, it is important that scientists rely on measurements instead of the opinions of individuals. You would not know how safe the automobile is if this researcher turned in a report that said, "Vehicle did fairly well in head-on collision when traveling at a moderate speed." What does "fairly well" mean? What is a "moderate speed?"

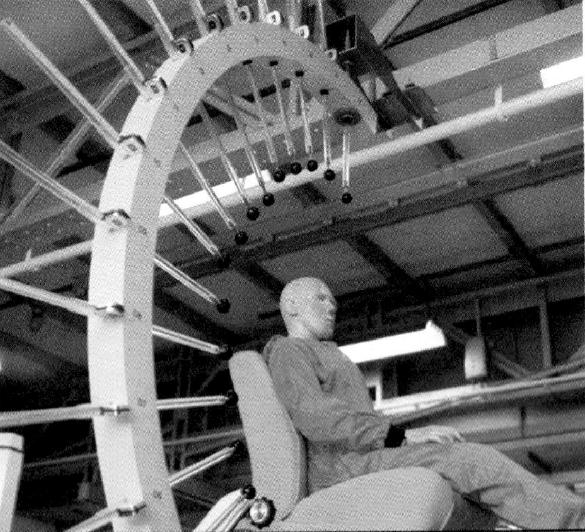

Figure 1
This device measures the range of motion of a seat-belted mannequin in a simulated accident.

Section Assessment Planner

PORTFOLIO
Science Journal, p. 45

PERFORMANCE ASSESSMENT
MiniLAB, p. 44
Math Skills Activity, p. 48
Skill Builder Activities, p. 49
See page 66 for more options.

CONTENT ASSESSMENT
Section, p. 49
Challenge, p. 49
Chapter, pp. 66–67

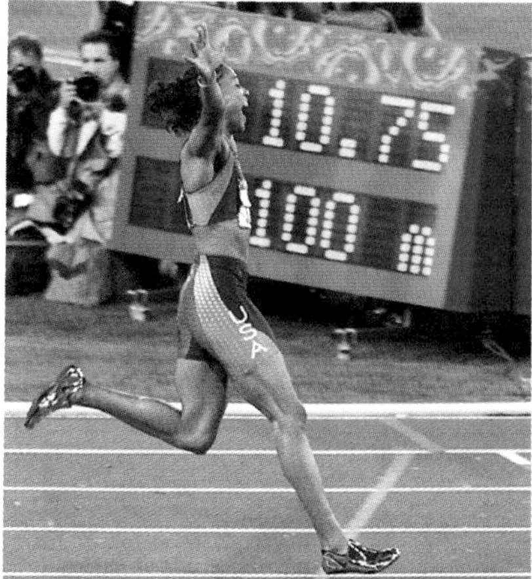

Figure 2
Accurate measurement of distance and time is important for competitive sports like track and field. *Why wouldn't a clock that measured in minutes be accurate enough for this race?*

Describing Events Measurement also can describe events such as the one shown in **Figure 2.** In the 1956 summer Olympics, sprinter Betty Cuthbert of Australia came in first in the women's 200-m dash. She ran the race in 23.4 s. In the 2000 summer Olympics, Marion Jones of the United States won the 100-m dash in a time of 10.75 s. In this example, measurements convey information about the year of the race, its length, the finishing order, and the time. Information about who competed and in what event are not measurements but help describe the event completely.

Estimation

What happens when you want to know the size of an object but you can't measure it? Perhaps it is too large to measure or you don't have a ruler handy. **Estimation** can help you make a rough measurement of an object by guessing. When you estimate, you can use your knowledge of the size of something familiar to estimate the size of a new object. Estimation is a skill based on previous experience and is useful when you are in a hurry and exact numbers are not required. Estimation is a valuable skill that improves with experience, practice, and understanding.

✔ Reading Check ***When should you not estimate a value?***

How practical is the skill of estimation? In many instances, estimation is used on a daily basis. A caterer prepares for each night's crowd based on an estimation of how many will order each entree. When a chef makes her prize-winning chili, she doesn't measure the cumin; she adds "just that much." Firefighters estimate how much hose to pull off the truck when they arrive at a burning building.

Chemistry INTEGRATION

A description of matter that does not involve measurement is *qualitative.* For example, water is composed of hydrogen and oxygen. A *quantitative* description uses measurement. For example, one water molecule is composed of one oxygen atom and two hydrogen atoms. Research another compound containing hydrogen and oxygen—hydrogen peroxide. Infer a qualitative and quantitative description of hydrogen peroxide in your Science Journal.

2 Teach

Measurement

Activity

Have students measure a common item to the nearest 0.1 cm using a ruler. Ask them to share the measurements and to discuss possible reasons for variations. differences in the rulers, differences in the way students align the ruler with the object, differences in the angle at which they look at the ruler L1 ELL LS **Kinesthetic**

Caption Answer

Figure 2 Olympic runners win by fractions of a second.

Possible answers: quantitative: two hydrogen and two oxygen atoms, it has more oxygen atoms than water has; qualitative: hydrogen peroxide is made up of hydrogen atoms and oxygen atoms.

Estimation

Make a Model

Collect commonly used containers such as one- and two-liter bottles. Pour given amounts of water into each bottle. Use a permanent ink marker to draw a line at the water level and to mark metric amounts on the outside of the bottle. For example, pour 100mL of water into a two-liter bottle, draw a line around the container at the water level, and write 100 mL above the line. Have students estimate where the 200-mL mark would be on each bottle. L2 ELL LS **Visual-Spatial**

✔ Reading Check

Answer when you need to know the exact measurement

Resource Manager

Chapter Resources Booklet

Transparency Activity, p. 40

Directed Reading for Content Mastery, pp. 15, 16

Curriculum Connection

History Length was once measured using units such as the width of the palm or the length of the foot. A cubit is the distance from the elbow to the tip of the middle finger. A pace is the length of a walking step from one heel to another. Have students measure a distance of ten paces, and compare their results. L2 ELL LS **Kinesthetic**

Estimation, continued

Caption Answer

Figure 3 About 4.5 meters (15 feet); accept all reasonable estimates.

Purpose Students will practice measurement skills with various instruments. L1 ELL LS **Kinesthetic**

Materials graduated cylinder, spring scale, meterstick, clock with a second hand

Teaching Strategies

- Demonstrate that when measuring volume with a graduated cylinder you need to read the volume from the bottom of the meniscus.
- Demonstrate and discuss measuring to the nearest gram, millimeter, centimeter, or meter.
- Show students how to find a pulse. Place the fingers on the neck just below the edge of the jaw.

Analysis

1. Possible answers: air temperature, body weight, volume of food or liquid (with measuring spoon or cup), length of objects, time (hours, minutes, seconds)
2. A balance or meterstick may be too small for some objects; a graduated cylinder can't be used for some solid objects; it can be difficult to keep track of seconds and impossible to measure tenths of seconds on an analog clock.

Oral Have students work in small groups to define measurement and show how it is done. Have students demonstrate and present their results to the class. Use **PASC,** p. 143.

Figure 3
This student is about 1.5 m tall. *Estimate the size of the tree in the photo.*

Using Estimation You can use comparisons to estimate measurements. For example, the tree in **Figure 3** is too tall to measure easily, but because you know the height of the student next to the tree, you can estimate the height of the tree. When you estimate, you often use the word *about.* For example, doorknobs are about 1 m above the floor, a sack of flour has a mass of about 2 kg, and you can walk about 5 km in an hour.

Estimation also is used to check an answer that seems unreasonable. Suppose you calculate your friend's running speed as 47 m/s. You are familiar with how long a second is and how long a meter is. Think about it. Can your friend really run a 50-m dash in 1 s? Estimation tells you that 47 m/s is unrealistically fast and you need to check your work.

Mini LAB

Measuring Accurately

Procedure

1. Choose **several measuring devices** in the classroom to practice measuring.
2. Measure two things with each device. For example, you might measure pulse rate using a clock, volume of a cup using a graduated cylinder, or the height of the door using a meterstick.
3. Record your data and observations about the measuring equipment in your **Science Journal.**

Analysis

1. What measurements could you easily make at home?
2. What limitations does each piece of equipment have?

Precision and Accuracy

One way to evaluate measurements is to determine whether they are precise. **Precision** is a description of how close measurements are to each other. Suppose you measure the distance between your home and your school five times with an odometer. Each time, you determine the distance to be 2.7 km. Suppose a friend repeated the measurements and measured 2.7 km on two days, 2.8 km on two days, and 2.6 km on the fifth day. Because your measurements were closer to each other than your friend's measurements, yours were more precise. The term precision is also used when discussing the number of decimal places a measuring device can measure. A clock with a second hand is considered more precise than one with only an hour hand.

Inclusion Strategies

Learning Disabled Make sure that learning disabled students handle measuring equipment and make measurements, rather than just reading and observing. Check that they are using the correct scale and starting their measurement at the zero position.

Resource Manager

Chapter Resources Booklet
MiniLAB, p. 3
Note-taking Worksheets, pp. 29–31

Earth Science Critical Thinking/Problem Solving, p. 11

Degrees of Precision The timing for Olympic events has become more precise over the years. Events that were measured in seconds 100 years ago are measured to the hundredth of a second today. Today's measuring devices are more precise. **Figure 4** shows an example of measurements of time with varying degrees of precision.

Accuracy When you compare a measurement to the real, actual, or accepted value, you are describing **accuracy.** A watch with a second hand may be more precise than one with only an hour hand, but if it is not properly set, the readings could be off by an hour or more. Therefore, the watch is not accurate. On the other hand, measurements of 1.03 m, 1.04 m, and 1.06 m compared to an actual value of 1.05 m are accurate, but not precise. **Figure 5** illustrates the difference between precision and accuracy.

Reading Check *What is the difference between precision and accuracy?*

Figure 4
Each of these clocks provides a different level of precision. *Which of the three could you use to be sure to make the 3:35 bus?*

B **For centuries, analog clocks—the kind with a face—were the standard.**

A **Before the invention of clocks, as they are known today, a sundial was used. As the Sun passed through the sky, its shadow moved around the dial.**

C **Digital clocks are now as common as analog ones.**

Precision and Accuracy

Discussion

Discuss with students timekeeping tools used at school and at home. These include a stopwatch, clock, kitchen timer, alarm clock, and timer on a microwave oven. **What are some of the limitations of these tools for timing an event?** Possible answers: Many timers read only to the second and sometimes it is necessary to measure tenths or hundredths of seconds. The time it takes a timekeeper to start and stop a stopwatch affects its precision. L2 LS **Linguistic**

Reading Check

Answer Precision describes the exactness of a measure. Accuracy compares a measurement to the actual or accepted value.

Caption Answer

Figure 4 the analog and digital clocks

Visual Learning

Figure 4 Have small groups discuss ways each of the clocks could be used. Possible answers: sundial to see if it is before or after noon; analog clock to make it on time for school or for after-school activities; digital stopwatch to measure speed of a reaction during a science experiment or to measure how fast a student runs in a race L2 ELL COOP LEARN LS **Interpersonal**

Science Journal

Using Measurements In their Science Journals, have students describe a situation in which both accuracy and precision in measurement is necessary. Have students share examples in a small group. Sample answers: measure the distance from first to second base on a baseball diamond, or measure the length of a down in football L2 LS **Linguistic** P

Teacher FYI

The cesium atomic clock uses the radiation generated by the transition between two states of cesium-133 atoms to operate a clock that is both precise and accurate. The clock is used for the basic unit of time in the International System of Units. It has an error of plus or minus one second in one million years.

Visualizing Precision and Accuracy

Have students examine the pictures and read the captions. Then ask the following questions.

How would you describe the accuracy and the precision of a basketball player who makes 97 out of 100 free throws? good accuracy and good precision

How would you describe the accuracy and precision of a basketball player who has 99 out of 100 free throws hit the front rim of the basket and bounce off? good precision, poor accuracy

How would you describe the accuracy and precision of a basketball player who makes 33 out of 100 free throws, while the others miss the basket completely? poor precision, poor accuracy

Activity

Have small groups of students select another sport and make a similar display that illustrates precision and accuracy. Have each group present its display to the class. L2 ELL COOP LEARN **LS Visual-Spatial and Interpersonal**

Extension

Ask students to write paragraphs explaining whether they think it is possible for experimental data to have good accuracy but poor precision. Encourage them to explain their reasoning. L2 ELL COOP LEARN **LS Linguistic and Logical-Mathematical**

Figure 5

From golf to gymnastics, many sports require precision and accuracy. Archery—a sport that involves shooting arrows into a target—clearly shows the relationship between these two factors. An archer must be accurate enough to hit the bull's-eye and precise enough to do it repeatedly.

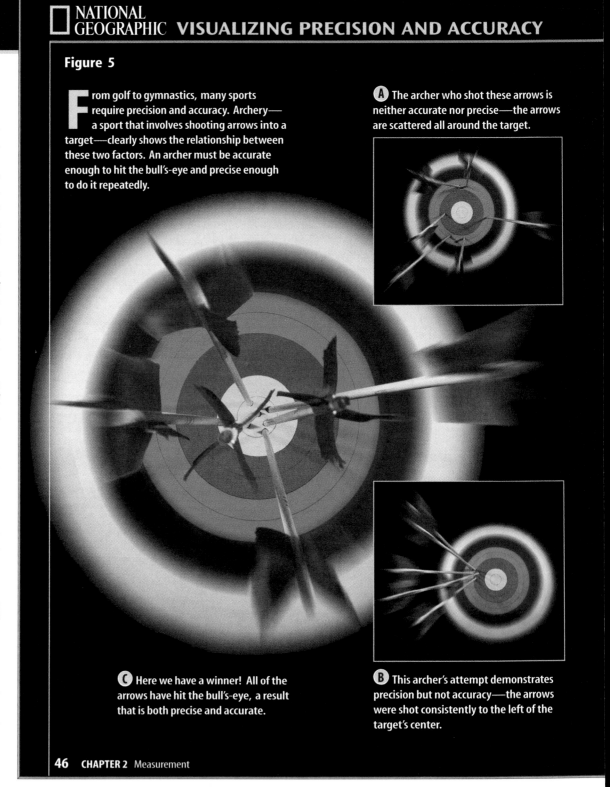

(A) The archer who shot these arrows is neither accurate nor precise—the arrows are scattered all around the target.

(B) This archer's attempt demonstrates precision but not accuracy—the arrows were shot consistently to the left of the target's center.

(C) Here we have a winner! All of the arrows have hit the bull's-eye, a result that is both precise and accurate.

Resource Manager

Chapter Resources Booklet

Enrichment, p. 26

Cultural Diversity, p. 29

Precision and accuracy are important in many medical procedures. One of these procedures is the delivery of radiation in the treatment of cancerous tumors. Because radiation damages cells, it is important to limit the radiation to only the cancerous cells that are to be destroyed. A technique called Stereotactic Radiotherapy (SRT) allows doctors to be accurate and precise in delivering radiation to areas of the brain. The patient makes an impression of his or her teeth on a bite plate that is then attached to the radiation machine. This same bite plate is used for every treatment to position the patient precisely the same way each time. A CAT scan locates the tumor in relation to the bite plate, and the doctors can pinpoint with accuracy and precision where the radiation should go.

Rounding a Measurement Not all measurements have to be made with instruments that measure with precision like the scale in **Figure 6.** Suppose you need to measure the length of the sidewalk outside your school. You could measure it to the nearest millimeter. However, you probably would need to know the length only to the nearest meter or tenth of a meter. So, if you found that the length was 135.841 m, you could round off that number to the nearest tenth of a meter and still be considered accurate. How would you round this number? To round a given value, follow these steps:

1. Look at the digit to the right of the place being rounded to.
   - If the digit to the right is 0, 1, 2, 3, or 4, the digit being rounded to remains the same.
   - If the digit to the right is 5, 6, 7, 8, or 9, the digit being rounded to increases by one.
2. The digits to the right of the digit being rounded to are deleted if they are also to the right of a decimal. If they are to the left of a decimal, they are changed to zeros.

Look back at the sidewalk example. If you want to round the sidewalk length of 135.841 to the tenths place, you look at the digit to the right of the 8. Because that digit is a 4, you keep the 8 and round it off to 135.8 m. If you want to round to the ones place, you look at the digit to the right of the 5. In this case you have an 8, so you round up, changing the 5 to a 6, and your answer is 136 m.

SCIENCE Online

Research Visit the Glencoe Science Web site at **science.glencoe.com** for more information about measurement. Communicate to your class what you learn.

Figure 6
This laboratory scale measures to the nearest hundredth of a gram.

Precision and Accuracy, continued

Teacher FYI

Twenty-four Global Positioning System (GPS) satellites orbit Earth. Each satellite measures time precisely and accurately using four atomic clocks, and continuously broadcasts toward Earth a coded signal telling the time, the satellite's location, and other data. The signals are picked up by GPS receivers that can measure their distance from any GPS satellite based on the time the signal took to arrive. The receiver compares data from four different satellites to calculate its own latitude, longitude, and elevation, as well as the correct time. If the receiver is moving, it can also determine its own velocity.

Health INTEGRATION

Ask students to identify which parts of the procedure make the measurement precise and which make it accurate. Precise: the instruments and the techniques used make measurements with a high degree of exactness; also, the bite plate positions the patient exactly the same way each time. Accurate: the CAT scan locates the tumor accurately.

Curriculum Connection

History The first chemists were the alchemists of ancient Egypt, China, Greece, and Rome, and of medieval Arabia and Europe. Have students find out what alchemists did and what kinds of systems they used for measurement. Alchemists tried to change metals into gold and helped develop perfumes, cosmetics and the gilding of metals. They did not have precise tools or a standard measuring system.

Internet Addresses

Explore the Glencoe Science Web site at **science.glencoe.com** to find out more about topics in this section.

Precision and Accuracy, continued

Math Skills Activity

National Math Standards

Correlation to Mathematics Objectives

1,4,6

Teaching Strategies

To round to a certain place, remember to ignore all of the numbers more than one place to the right.

Answer to Practice Problem

6.9; 20.2

Extension

Discuss this example with your students. The mass of a substance is determined to be 0.0045 kilograms. **How many significant digits are in this measurement?** There are two significant digits. The zeros in 0.0045 are used to show only the place value of the decimal and are not counted as significant digits.

Precision and Number of Digits Do you always need to be absolutely precise? Suppose you want to divide a 2-L bottle of soda equally among seven people. When you divide 2 by 7, your calculator display reads as shown in **Figure 7.** Will you measure exactly 0.285 714 285 7 L for each person? Of course not. All you need to know is that each person gets about 0.3 L of soda.

Using Precision and Significant Digits The number of digits that truly reflect the precision of a measurement are called the significant digits or significant figures. They are figured as follows:

- Digits other than zero are always significant.
- Final zeros after a decimal point (6.54600 g) are significant.
- Zeros between any other digit (507.0301) are significant.
- Zeros before any other digit (0.0002030) are NOT significant.
- Zeros in a whole number (1650) may or may not be significant.
- An exact number such as the number of people in a room or the number of meters in a kilometer has infinite significant digits.

Math Skills Activity

Rounding

Example Problem

The mass of one object is 6.941 g. The mass of a second object is 20.180 g. You need to know these values only to the nearest whole number to solve a problem. What are the rounded values?

Solution

1. *This is what you know:* mass of first object = 6.941; mass of second object = 20.180
2. *This is what you need to know:* the number to the right of the one's place; first object: 9, second object: 1
3. *This is what you need to use:* digits 0, 1, 2, 3, 4 remain the same; for digits 5, 6, 7, 8, 9, round up
4. *Solution:* first object: 9 makes the 6 round up = 7; second object: 1 makes the 0 remain the same = 20

Practice Problem

What are the rounded masses of the objects to the nearest tenth of a unit?

For more help, refer to the Math Skill Handbook.

Cultural Diversity

Social Time While time's passage can be accurately measured, its perceived importance, or social time, varies from culture to culture. In the U.S., people call and apologize if they expect to be late. In Latin American and Arab countries, people may arrive an hour late with no apology expected or given. One study of social time rated Japan highest and the U.S. second in accuracy of bank clocks and pace of life.

Resource Manager

Chapter Resources Booklet
Reinforcement, p. 23

Physical Science Critical Thinking/Problem Solving, p. 11

Following the Rules In the soda example you have an exact number, seven, for the number of people. This number has infinite significant digits. You also have the number two, for how many liters of soda you have. This has only one significant digit.

There are also rules to follow when deciding the number of significant digits in the answer to a calculation. They depend on what kind of calculation you are doing.

- For multiplication and division, you determine the number of significant digits in each number in your problem. The significant digits of your answer is determined by the number with fewer digits.

$$6.14 \times 5.6 = \boxed{34}.384$$

3 digits 2 digits 2 digits

- For addition and subtraction, you determine the place value of each number in your problem. The significant digits of the answer is determined by the number that is least precise.

6.14	to the hundredths
+ 5.6	to the tenths
$\boxed{11.7}$4	to the tenths

Therefore, in the soda example you are dividing and the limiting number of digits is determined by the amount of soda, 2 L. There is one significant digit there; therefore, your answer has one.

What determines the number of significant digits in the answer to an addition problem?

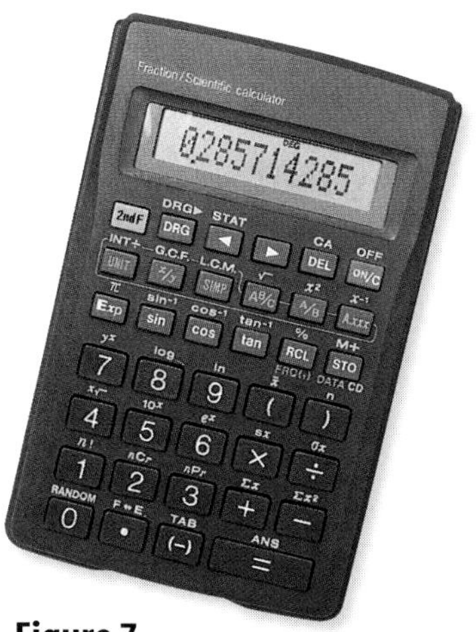

Figure 7
Sometimes considering the size of each digit will help you realize they are unneeded. In this calculation, the seven ten-thousandths of a liter represents just a few drops of soda.

Section 1 Assessment

1. Estimate the distance between your desk and your teacher's desk. Explain the method you used.
2. Measure the height of your desk to the nearest half centimeter.
3. Sarah's garden is 11.72 m long. Round to the nearest tenth of a meter.
4. John's puppy has chewed on his ruler. Will John's measurements be accurate or precise?
5. **Think Critically** Would you use half centimeters or millimeters to measure the following: *a thin wire, a book, a spoon,* and *a staple?*

Skill Builder Activities

6. **Using Precision and Significant Digits** Perform the following calculations and express the answer using the correct number of significant digits: 42.35 + 214; 225/12. **For more help, refer to the Math Skill Handbook.**
7. **Communicating** Describe your backpack in your Science Journal. Include in your description one set of qualities that have no measurements, such as color and texture, and one set of measured quantities, such as width and mass. **For more help, refer to the Science Skill Handbook.**

Reading Check

Answer the number that is least precise

3 Assess

Reteach

Obtain measuring tools and items to measure. Have students describe how they can use the tools to collect data that are accurate and precise. L2 **Visual-Spatial**

Challenge

Use a math textbook or other reference book to locate information about estimation. **Are there specific rules given? Will the method give accurate results?** Example: Front-end estimation is done by retaining the number in the largest place and rewriting all other digits as 0. Thus 7899 becomes 7000. The result is precise according to this method, but the result is not accurate; it is 899 smaller than the original number. L3 **Logical-Mathematical**

Performance Have each student make a poster that shows the difference between estimation and precise measurement. Students should present their posters to a small group of students or to the class. Use **Performance Assessment in the Science Classroom,** p. 145.

Answers to Section Assessment

1. Possible answer: About 3 m; it looks like two students could almost lie down head to toe in the space.
2. Check students' work.
3. 11.7 m
4. John's measurements will not be precise in the area in which measuring lines have been destroyed by the dog. They may still be accurate, depending on what he's measuring and what the dog destroyed.
5. A thin wire would be measured in millimeters, a book in centimeters, a spoon in centimeters, and a staple in millimeters.
6. 256; 19
7. Answers will vary. Qualities might include color, fabric, or design. Measurements might include dimensions, mass, or number of pockets.

SECTION

SI Units

1 Motivate

Bellringer Transparency

Display the Section Focus Transparency for Section 2. Use the accompanying Transparency Activity Master. L2 ELL

Section Focus Transparency 2 — Fresh, not Frozen

These people are shopping in a market in Grenada. Grenada uses a unit of currency called the East Caribbean dollar. How do tourists from the United States know how many U.S. dollars to use when buying something in Grenada? They need to convert their American money into Grenadian money.

1. Would it be easier if all countries used one type of money? Explain.
2. What would happen if each country had its own way of measuring length or time?
3. What units of measurement do you know that are used everywhere?

Tie to Prior Knowledge

Recall from the previous section the importance of using precise tools. In this section, students will learn about the tools and units used for scientific measurement.

Reading Check

Answer to provide a worldwide standard of physical measurement for science, industry, and commerce

SECTION

SI Units

As You Read

What You'll Learn

- **Identify** the purpose of SI.
- **Identify** the SI units of length, volume, mass, temperature, time, and rate.

Vocabulary

SI, meter, mass, kilogram, kelvin, rate

Why It's Important

The SI system is used throughout the world, allowing you to measure quantities in the exact same way as other students around the world.

The International System

Can you imagine how confusing it would be if people in every country used different measuring systems? Sharing data and ideas would be complicated. To avoid confusion, scientists established the International System of Units, or **SI,** in 1960 as the accepted system for measurement. It was designed to provide a worldwide standard of physical measurement for science, industry, and commerce. SI units are shown in **Table 1.**

Reading Check *Why was SI established?*

The SI units are related by multiples of ten. Any SI unit can be converted to a smaller or larger SI unit by multiplying by a power of 10. For example, to rewrite a kilogram measurement in grams, you multiply by 1,000. The new unit is renamed by changing the prefix, as shown in **Table 2.** For example, one millionth of a meter is one *micro*meter. One thousand grams is one *kilo*gram. **Table 3** shows some common objects and their measurements in SI units.

Table 1 Examples of SI Units

Quantity	Unit	Symbol
length	meter	m
volume	cubic meter	m^3
mass	kilogram	kg
temperature	kelvin	K
time	second	s
weight	newton	N

Table 2 SI Prefixes

Prefix	Multiplier
giga-	1,000,000,000
mega-	1,000,000
kilo-	1,000
hecto-	100
deca-	10
[unit]	1
deci-	0.1
centi-	0.01
milli-	0.001
micro-	0.000 001
nano-	0.000 000 001

Section Assessment Planner

PORTFOLIO
Assessment, p. 54

PERFORMANCE ASSESSMENT
Try at Home MiniLAB, p. 52
Skill Builder Activities, p. 54
See page 66 for more options.

CONTENT ASSESSMENT
Section, p. 54
Challenge, p. 54
Chapter, pp. 66–67

Length

Length is defined as the distance between two points. Lengths measured with different tools can describe a range of things from the distance from Earth to Mars or the thickness of a human hair. In your laboratory activities, you usually will measure length with a metric ruler or meterstick.

The **meter** (m) is the SI unit of length. One meter is about the length of a baseball bat. The size of a room or the dimensions of a building would be measured in meters. For example, the height of the Washington Monument in Washington D.C. is 169 m.

Smaller objects can be measured in centimeters (cm) or millimeters (mm). The length of your textbook or pencil would be measured in centimeters. A twenty dollar bill is 15.5 cm long. You would use millimeters to measure the width of the words on this page. To measure the length of small things such as blood cells, bacteria, or viruses, scientists use micrometers (millionths of a meter) and nanometers (billionths of a meter).

A Long Way Sometimes people need to measure long distances, such as the distance a migrating bird travels or the distance from Earth to the Moon. To measure such lengths, you use kilometers. Kilometers might be most familiar to you as the distance traveled in a car or the measure of a long-distance race, as shown in **Figure 8.** The course of a marathon is measured carefully so that the competitors run 42.2 km. When you drive from New York to Los Angeles, you cover 4,501 km.

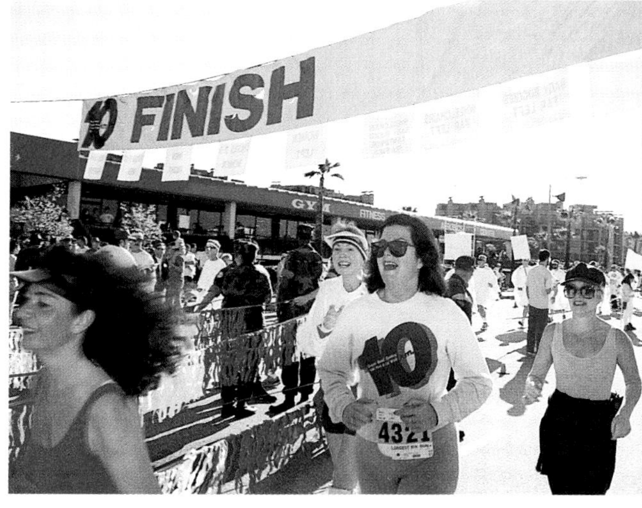

Figure 8
These runners have just completed a 10 kilometer race—known as a 10K. *About how many kilometers is the distance between your home and your school?*

Astronomy INTEGRATION

How important are accurate measurements? In 1999, the *Mars Climate Orbiter* disappeared as it was to begin orbiting Mars. NASA later discovered that a unit conversion error caused the flight path to be incorrect and the orbiter to be lost. Research the error and infer whether SI units were being used.

Table 3 Common Objects in SI Measurements

Object	Type of Measurement	Measurement
can of soda	volume	355 cm^3
bag of potatoes	mass	4.5 kg
fluorescent tube	length	1.2 m
refrigerator	temperature	276 K

2 Teach

The International System

Fun Fact

SI stands for Le Système Internationale d'Unités, which is the French term for International System of units.

Caption Answer

Figure 8 Answers will vary. Have students explain how they arrived at their answers.

Use Science Words

Word Origin The prefix *centi-*, the word *percent*, and our unit of money cent all derive from the same French and Latin root, which means 100. **Can you think of other ways we use the root word *cent*?** centimeter, century, centigrade, centipede L2 **Linguistic**

Astronomy INTEGRATION

The error occurred because the common unit pound • seconds was used instead of the SI unit Newton • seconds in the computer program that determined trajectories of the orbiter.

Length

Activity

Have students use rulers to measure the length of a small item on their desks while sitting with their backs against the backs of their chairs. Then have them remeasure the item while looking directly at it from above. Discuss which measurement is more accurate. The measurement made while looking directly at it from above is more accurate. L2 ELL **Kinesthetic**

Resource Manager

Chapter Resources Booklet
- Transparency Activity, p. 42
- Directed Reading for Content Mastery, pp. 16, 17
- Lab Activity, pp. 9–10

Visual Learning

Tables 1 and 2 Have students use the information in the tables to determine the meaning of the following units: kilogram—1,000 grams; centimeter—1/100 meter; millimeter—1/1,000 meter. Have pairs take turns using the prefixes to make their own units and identifying their meanings. sample answer: centimeter—one-hundredth of a meter L2 ELL **Logical-Mathematical**

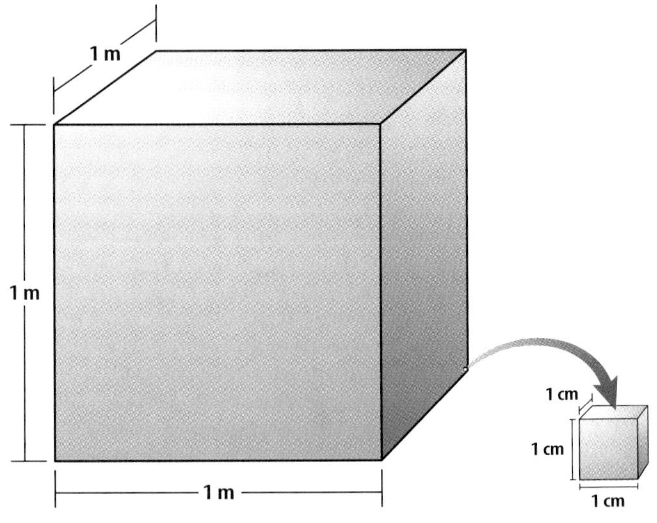

Figure 9
A cubic meter equals the volume of a cube 1 m by 1 m by 1 m. *How many cubic centimeters are in a cubic meter?*

Volume

The amount of space an object occupies is its volume. The cubic meter (m^3), shown in **Figure 9,** is the SI unit of volume. You can measure smaller volumes with the cubic centimeter (cm^3 or cc). To find the volume of a square or rectangular object, such as a brick or your textbook, measure its length, width, and height and multiply them. What is the volume of a compact disc case?

You are probably familiar with a 2-L bottle. A liter is a measurement of liquid volume. A cube 10 cm on a side holds 1 L (1,000 cm^3) of water. A cube 1 cm on a side holds 1 mL (1 cm^3) of water.

Volume by Immersion Not all objects have an even, regular shape. How can you find the volume of something irregular like a rock or a piece of metal?

Have you ever added ice cubes to a nearly full glass of soda only to have the soda overflow? Why did the soda overflow? Did you suddenly have more soda? The volume of soda did not increase at all, but the soda was displaced when the ice cubes were added. Each ice cube takes up space or has volume. Therefore, the new level of soda in the glass reflects the volume of the ice cubes and the soda. The difference in the volume before and after the addition equals the volume of the ice cubes.

The ice cubes took up space and caused the total volume in the glass to increase. When you measure the volume of an irregular object, you do the same thing. You start with a known volume of water and drop in, or immerse, the object. The increase in the volume of water is the volume of the object.

TRY AT HOME Mini LAB

Measuring Volume

Procedure

1. Fill a plastic or glass **liquid measuring cup** until half full with **water.** Measure the volume.
2. Find an **object,** such as a rock, that will fit in your measuring cup.
3. Carefully lower the object into the water. If it floats, push it just under the surface with a **pencil.**
4. Record in your **Science Journal** the new volume of the water.

Analysis

1. How much space does the object occupy?
2. If 1 mL of water occupies exactly 1 cm^3 of space, what is the volume of the object in cm^3?

Volume

Caption Answer

Figure 9 There are 1,000,000 cubic centimeters in a cubic meter.

Quick Demo

Units of metric measurement can be understood using common items that students are familiar with. Show students that a meter is about the height of a doorknob, a centimeter is about the width of their little fingertip, and a millimeter is about the thickness of a dime.

Text Question Answer

A compact disc case is about 1 cm × 12.5 cm × 14.2 cm. Its volume is 177.5 cm^3.

Purpose to measure volume by immersion

Materials transparent measuring cup, water, small object

Teaching Strategies

- Make sure students do not spill water from the measuring cup when lowering the object into the water.
- Do not use an object that floats, since pushing will cause errors.

Analysis

1. The difference between the first volume of water and the second.
2. Check students' work.

Process Have students redo the MiniLAB using a small rectangular solid then measure the sides of the object and calculate its volume. Are the two volumes the same? Use **Performance Assessment in the Science Classroom,** p. 89.

Inclusion Strategies

Learning Disabled While presenting information about measurement, use physical models as you discuss each concept. For example, a meterstick and centimeter ruler should be shown while learning about length, a pan balance or digital scale should be shown while discussing mass, and a stopwatch should be shown while discussing rate. L2 ELL LS **Visual-Spatial**

Teacher FYI

An international measurement system was originally established during the French Revolution by representatives from seventeen nations, including the United States. The U.S. adopted the decimal system only for currency. In 1902, a law requiring the United States to use the metric system was defeated by one vote.

52 CHAPTER 2 Measurement

Figure 10
A triple beam balance compares an unknown mass to known masses. This is not the same as weight.

Mass

The **mass** of an object measures the amount of matter in the object. The **kilogram** (kg) is the SI unit for mass. One liter of water has a mass of about 1 kg. Smaller masses are measured in grams (g). One gram is about the mass of a large paper clip.

You can measure mass with a triple beam balance, shown in **Figure 10.** The balance compares an object to a known mass. It is balanced when the object on the pan is equal to the known standard mass of the slides on the balance.

Why use the word *mass* instead of *weight?* Weight and mass are not the same. Mass depends only on the amount of matter in an object. If you ride in an elevator in the morning and then ride in the space shuttle later that afternoon, your mass is the same. Mass does not change when only your location changes.

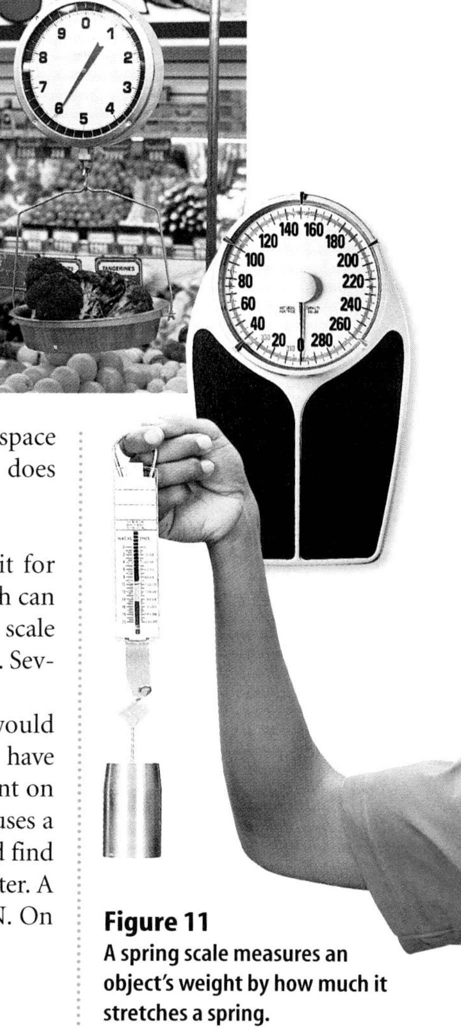

Figure 11
A spring scale measures an object's weight by how much it stretches a spring.

Weight Weight is a measurement of force. The SI unit for weight is the newton (N). Weight depends on gravity, which can change depending on where the object is located. A spring scale measures how a planet's gravitational force pulls on objects. Several spring scales are shown in **Figure 11.**

If you were to travel to other planets, your weight would change, even though you would still be the same size and have the same mass. This is because gravitational force is different on each planet. If you could take your bathroom scale, which uses a spring, to each of the planets in this solar system, you would find that you weigh much less on Mars and much more on Jupiter. A mass of 75 pounds, or 34 kg, on Earth is a weight of 332 N. On Mars, the same mass is 126 N, and on Jupiter it is 782 N.

What does weight measure?

Resource Manager

Chapter Resources Booklet
MiniLAB, p. 4
Enrichment, p. 27

Reading and Writing Critical Thinking/ Problem Solving, p. 13

Science Journal

Rates Have students use the information in the student text to write several rates. Possible answers: kilometers per hour, kilometers per liter of gas. Ask them to explain how these rates are used. L2 LS **Logical-Mathematical**

Mass

Discussion

Have students discuss what would happen to their mass and weight if they visited the moon. What might happen if they tried jumping while on the moon? They would have the same mass but less weight, so they would be able to jump higher and farther. L2
LS **Logical-Mathematical**

Use Science Words

Word Usage Have students use the words mass and weight in sentences describing how the concepts are different. Possible answer: Mass is the amount of matter in an object; it is not affected by gravity. Weight is a measure of the force of gravity; it changes with the force of gravity.
L2 ELL LS **Linguistic**

Use an Analogy

A pan balance is like a seesaw. When the weights on each side are equal, it is balanced.

Reading Check

Answer the force of gravity on an object

Temperature

Teacher FYI

Temperature is a measure of the kinetic energy of molecules and atoms. The temperature 0 K is also called absolute zero. Scientists believe that absolute zero is the lowest temperature possible because at this temperature all molecular and atomic motion stops.

3 Assess

Reteach

Collect a set of measurement tools. Display each tool and have a student volunteer tell the class its name, what it measures, and the unit(s) it uses. L1 ELL LS **Visual-Spatial**

Challenge

Have each student make a chart to organize the information they learned in this section. The chart should include a title with International System in it. It should also include pictures and information about measuring length, volume, mass, temperature, and time. L2 ELL LS **Visual-Spatial**

Process Ask each student to make an illustration of a spring scale, showing how it works. Use **Performance Assessment in the Science Classroom,** p. 127. P

Figure 12
The kelvin scale starts at 0 K. In theory, 0 K is the coldest temperature possible in nature.

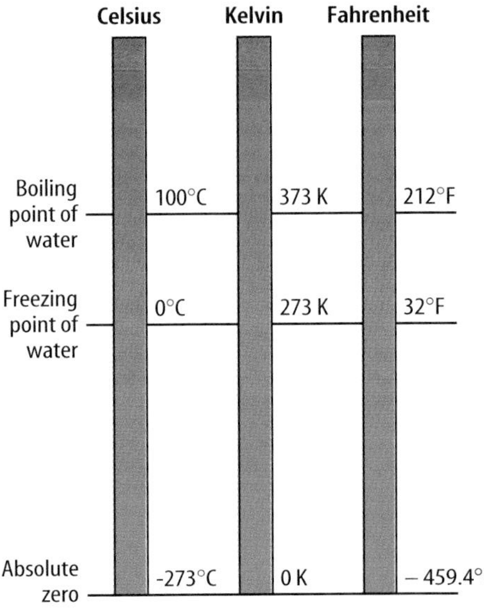

Temperature

The physical property of temperature is related to how hot or cold an object is. Temperature is a measure of the kinetic energy, or energy of motion, of the particles that make up matter.

The Fahrenheit and Celsius temperature scales are two common scales used on thermometers. Temperature is measured in SI with the **kelvin** scale. A 1-K difference in temperature is the same as a 1°C difference in temperature, as shown in **Figure 12.** However, the two scales do not start at the same point.

Time and Rates

Time is the interval between two events. The SI unit of time is the second (s). Time is also measured in hours (h). Although the hour is not an SI unit, it is easier to use for long periods of time. Can you imagine hearing that a marathon was run in 7,620 s instead of 2 h and 7 min?

A **rate** is the amount of change of one measurement in a given amount of time. One rate you are familiar with is speed, which is the distance traveled in a given time. Speeds often are measured in kilometers per hour (km/h).

The unit that is changing does not necessarily have to be an SI unit. For example, you can measure the number of cars that pass through an intersection per hour in cars/h. The annual rate of inflation can be measured in dollars/y.

Section  Assessment

1. Describe a situation in which different units of measure could cause confusion.
2. What type of quantity does the cubic meter measure?
3. How would you change a measurement in centimeters to kilometers?
4. What SI unit replaces the pound? What does this measure?
5. **Think Critically** You are told to find the mass of a metal cube. How will you do it?

Skill Builder Activities

6. **Measuring in SI** Measure the length, volume, and mass of your textbook in SI units. Describe any tools or calculations you use. **For more help, refer to the Science Skill Handbook.**
7. **Converting Units** A block of wood is 0.2 m by 0.1 m by 0.5 m. Find its dimensions in centimeters. Use these to find its volume in cubic centimeters. Show your work. **For more help, refer to the Math Skill Handbook.**

Answers to Section Assessment

1. Possible answer: Someone thinks a temperature is given in Fahrenheit degrees, but it is actually in Celsius degrees.
2. volume
3. divide by 100,000
4. newton; the force of gravity on an object
5. Use a pan balance or scale. The description should provide step-by-step instructions for using the instrument.
6. Answers will vary, but length should be measured in centimeters, volume in cubic centimeters, and mass in grams.
7. 20 cm × 10 cm × 50 cm = 10,000 cm^3

Activity

Scale Drawing

A scale drawing is used to represent something that is too large or too small to be drawn at its actual size. Blueprints for a house are a good example of a scale drawing.

What You'll Investigate

How can you represent your classroom accurately in a scale drawing?

Materials

1-cm graph paper
pencil
metric ruler
meterstick

Goals

- **Measure** using SI.
- **Make** a data table.
- **Calculate** new measurements.
- **Make** an accurate scale drawing.

Procedure

1. Use your meterstick to measure the length and width of your classroom. Note the locations and sizes of doors and windows.
2. **Record** the lengths of each item in a data table similar to the one below.
3. Use a scale of 2 cm = 1 m to calculate the lengths to be used in the drawing. Record them in your data table.
4. **Draw** the floor plan. Include the scale.

Room Dimensions

Part of Room	Distance in Room (m)	Distance on Drawing (cm)
Front right corner to door	1.5	3
Across door	1.0	2

Conclude and Apply

1. How did you calculate the lengths to be used on your drawing? Did you put a scale on your drawing?
2. What would your scale drawing look like if you chose a different scale?
3. **Sketch** your room at home, estimating the distances. Compare this sketch to your scale drawing of the classroom. When would you use each type of illustration?
4. What measuring tool simplifies this task?

Communicating Your Data

Measure your room at home and compare it to the estimates on your sketch. Explain to someone at home what you did and how well you estimated the measurements. **For more help, refer to the Science Skill Handbook.**

Resource Manager

Chapter Resources Booklet
Reinforcement, p. 24
Lab Activity, pp. 11–12
Activity Worksheet, pp. 5–6

Communicating Your Data

Have students use a drawing to discuss scale and features with a small group or the class, in addition to explaining these things to someone at home.

Activity

BENCH TESTED

Purpose To learn how to make and use a scale drawing L2 ELL COOP LEARN LS **Visual-Spatial**

Process Skills comparing and contrasting, interpreting data, making and using tables, using numbers, making models

Time Required one 45-minute period to measure the classroom, one 30-minute period to draw the room to scale (could be homework)

Teaching Strategies

- Discuss where to start measuring, and whether to measure from the inner or outer edge of doors and window frames.
- Demonstrate how to draw the length of a wall to scale.

Answers to Questions

1. Length was measured with a meterstick. The scale of 2 cm/1 m should be noted on the drawing.
2. The shape of the drawing would remain the same, but it would be larger or smaller, depending on the new scale chosen.
3. Check students' work. A rough sketch might be used to give an idea of how to design a room. A scale drawing might be used to determine if the furniture will actually fit in the space available.
4. Possible tools to use: meterstick, tape measure, retractable metal tape measure, measuring wheel

Assessment

Portfolio Have students add to their work a detailed explanation of how to make and use a scale drawing. Use **PASC,** p. 177.

SECTION 3

Drawings, Tables, and Graphs

1 Motivate

Bellringer Transparency

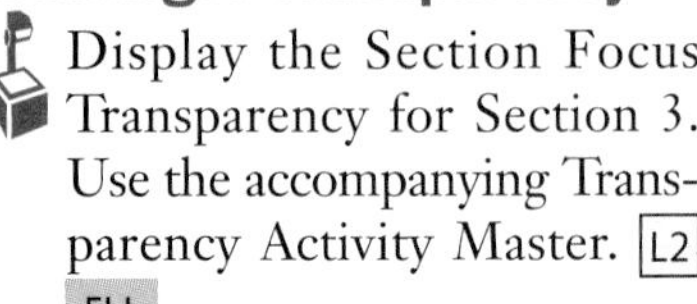

Display the Section Focus Transparency for Section 3. Use the accompanying Transparency Activity Master. L2 ELL

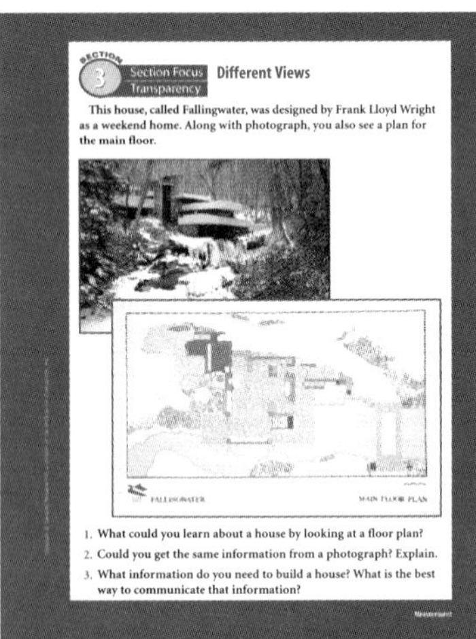

Section Focus Transparency 3 Different Views

This house, called Fallingwater, was designed by Frank Lloyd Wright as a weekend home. Along with photograph, you also see a plan for the main floor.

1. What could you learn about a house by looking at a floor plan?
2. Could you get the same information from a photograph? Explain.
3. What information do you need to build a house? What is the best way to communicate that information?

Tie to Prior Knowledge

Ask students to recall publications other than science books in which they have seen graphs and charts. Newspapers and news magazines are good sources of examples.

SECTION 3

Drawings, Tables and Graphs

As You Read

***What* You'll Learn**

- **Describe** how to use pictures and tables to give information.
- **Identify** and use three types of graphs.
- **Distinguish** the correct use of each type of graph.

Vocabulary

table
graph
line graph
bar graph
circle graph

***Why* It's Important**

Illustrations, tables, and graphs help you communicate data about the world around you in an organized and efficient way.

Scientific Illustrations

Most science books include pictures. Photographs and drawings model and illustrate ideas and sometimes make new information more clear than written text can. For example, a drawing of an airplane engine shows how all the parts fit together much better than several pages of text could describe it.

Drawings A drawing is sometimes the best choice to show details. For example, a canyon cut through red rock reveals many rock layers. If the layers are all shades of red, a drawing can show exactly where the lines between the layers are. The drawing can emphasize only the things that are necessary to show.

A drawing also can show things you can't see. You can't see the entire solar system, but drawings show you what it looks like. Also, you can make quick sketches to help model problems. For example, you could draw the outline of two continents to show how they might have fit together at one time.

A drawing can show hidden things, as well. A drawing can show the details of the water cycle, as in **Figure 13.** Architects use drawings to show what the inside of a building will look like. Biologists use drawings to show where the nerves in your arm are found.

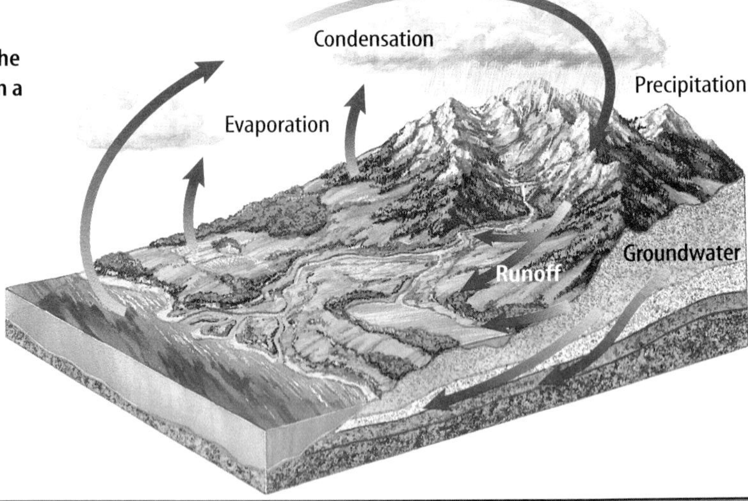

Figure 13
This drawing shows details of the water cycle that can't be seen in a photograph.

Section Assessment Planner

Portfolio
Make a Model, p. 57

Performance Assessment
Skill Builder Activities, p. 59
See page 66 for more options.

Content Assessment
Section, p. 59
Challenge, p. 59
Chapter, pp. 66–67

Photographs A still photograph shows an object exactly as it is at a single moment in time. Movies show how an object moves and can be slowed down or speeded up to show interesting features. In your schoolwork, you might use photographs in a report. For example, you could show the different types of trees in your neighborhood for a report on ecology.

Tables and Graphs

Everyone who deals with numbers and compares measurements needs an organized way to collect and display data. A **table** displays information in rows and columns so that it is easier to read and understand, as seen in **Table 4.** The data in the table could be presented in a paragraph, but it would be harder to pick out the facts or make comparisons.

A **graph** is used to collect, organize, and summarize data in a visual way. The relationships between the data often are seen more clearly when shown in a graph. Three common types of graphs are line, bar, and circle graphs.

Line Graph A **line graph** is used to show the relationship between two variables. A variable is something that can change, or vary, such as the temperature of a liquid or the number of people in a race. Both variables in a line graph must be numbers. An example of a line graph is shown in **Figure 14.** One variable is shown on the bottom line, or horizontal axis, of the graph. The other variable is placed along the vertical axis. A line on the graph shows the relationship between the two variables.

Table 4 Endangered Species in the United States

Year	Number of Endangered Species
1980	174
1982	179
1984	192
1986	213
1988	245
1990	263
1992	284
1994	321
1996	324
1998	357

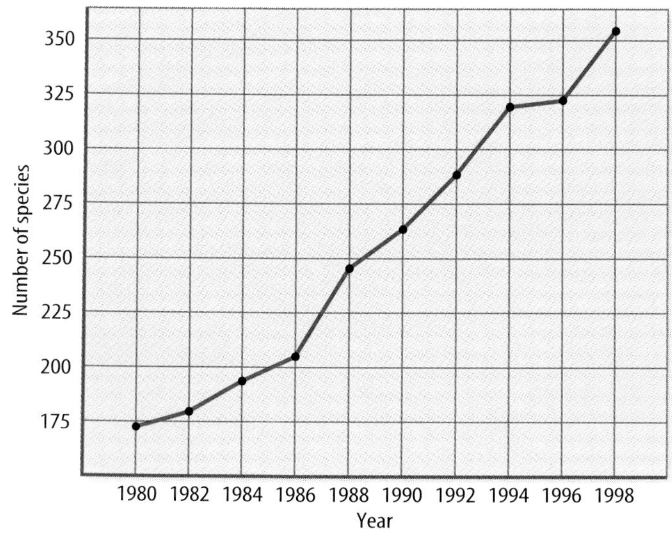

Figure 14
To find the number of endangered species in 1988, find that year on the x-axis and see what number corresponds to it on the y-axis.

2 Teach

Scientific Illustrations

Activity

Ask each student to choose an area of science in which he or she is interested. The student should locate a drawing that shows a cross section of an item related to that science. Examples may include the bones inside the arm, the inner structure of a plant, or the gears inside a watch. Students can show and explain their drawings to the class. L3
LS **Visual-Spatial** P

Teacher FYI

When books were hand-copied, illustrations were few. Illustrations often lost all useful meaning after they had been copied several times, as important details were changed or deleted. The invention of woodcuts for printing books made accurate reproduction of illustrations possible.

Resource Manager

Chapter Resources Booklet
Transparency Activity, p. 42
Directed Reading for Content Mastery, pp. 17, 18
Enrichment, p. 28

LAB DEMONSTRATION

Purpose to show how to collect information and organize it as a table and a line graph

Materials graph paper, ten books (some thick, some thin), centimeter ruler, meterstick

Preparation Set up a table on the board for data collected in this demonstration.

Procedure Measure and record the height of one book placed on a table. Add books one at a time, and measure and record the height of the stack after each addition. Finally, demonstrate how to use the data to make a line graph.

Expected Outcome The graph shows that the height of the stack of books increases.

Assessment

What does the graph tell about the relationship between the number of books and the height of the stack? The height of the stack increases with each additional book, but the rate of increase is not even.

Tables and Graphs

Caption Question Answer

Figure 15A birds

Answer In a line graph both variables must be numbers. In a bar graph one variable must be a number but the other one does not have to be a number.

Quick Demo

On the board draw two line graphs of the same data using two different scales for the *y*-axis. Point out to students that one of the lines looks much steeper than the other. Have students study the units on the axes of the graphs to see that the information in both graphs is the same. L2 LS **Visual-Spatial**

Explore the Glencoe Science Web site at **science.glencoe.com** to find out more about topics in this section.

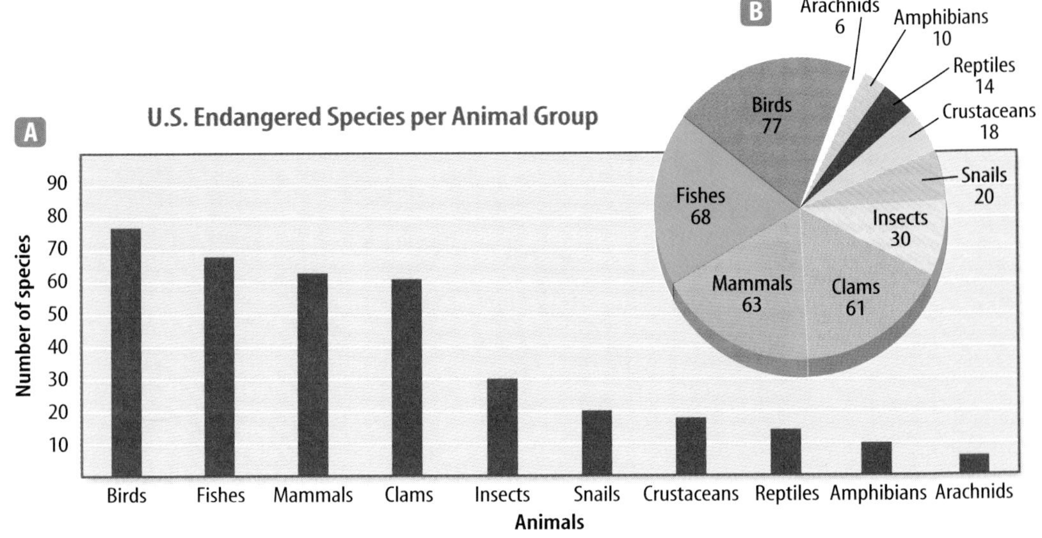

Figure 15
A Bar graphs allow you to picture the results easily. *Which category of animals has the most endangered species?* **B On this circle graph, you can see what part of the whole each animal represents.**

Bar Graph A **bar graph** uses rectangular blocks, or bars, of varying sizes to show the relationships between variables. One variable is divided into parts. It can be numbers, such as the time of day, or a category, such as an animal. The second variable must be a number. The bars show the size of the second variable. For example, if you made a bar graph of the endangered species data from **Figure 14,** the bar for 1990 would represent 263 species. An example of a bar graph is shown in **Figure 15A.**

Reading Check *How are the variables in line and bar graphs different?*

Circle Graph Suppose you want to show the relationship between the types of endangered species. A **circle graph** shows the parts of a whole. Circle graphs are sometimes called pie graphs. Each piece of pie visually represents a percentage of the total. Looking at the circle graph in **Figure 15B,** you see quickly which animals have the highest number of endangered species by comparing the sizes of the pieces of pie.

To make a circle graph, you first find the percent for each part. A percent is found by dividing the part by the whole and multiplying by 100. In the example given, 63 of the 367 endangered species (63 divided by 367 and multiplied by 100), or 17.2 percent, are mammals. Next, you multiply the percent by 360° and divide by 100 to find the angle measure of that part. If you multiply 17.2 percent by 360 and divide by 100, the answer is 61.9. A 61.9° section represents the 63 species of endangered mammals. Each part of the whole is calculated in this way.

SCIENCE Online

Research Visit the Glencoe Science Web site at **science.glencoe.com** for more information about scientific illustrations. Communicate to your class what you learn.

Active Reading

Metacognition Journal In this strategy, each student analyzes his or her own thought processes. Have students divide the paper in half. On the left, have them record what they have learned about a topic. On the right, have them record the reason they learned it. Have students write a Metacognition Journal about graphs.

Resource Manager

Chapter Resources Booklet
- Reinforcement, p. 25
- Activity Worksheet, pp. 7–8

Lab Management and Safety, pp. 70, 71

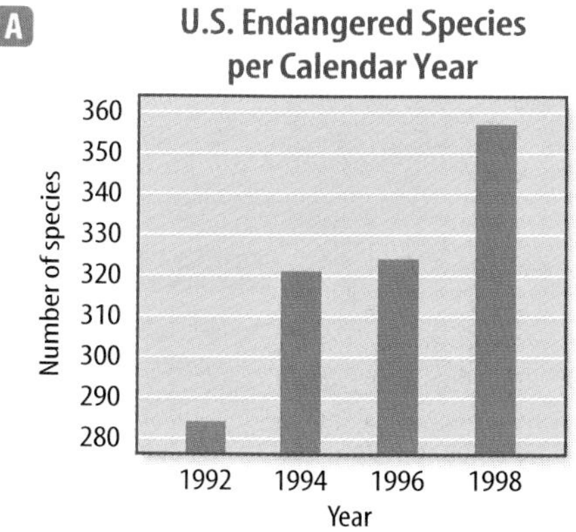

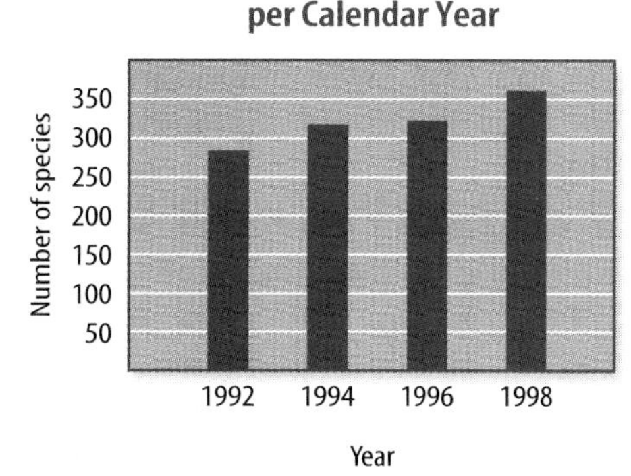

Reading Graphs When you are using or making graphs to display data, be careful—the scale of a graph can be misleading. The way the scale on a graph is marked can create the wrong impression, as seen in **Figure 16A.** Until you look at the scale, it appears that the number of endangered species has quadrupled in just six years.

This is called a broken scale and is used to highlight small but significant changes, just as an inset on a map draws attention to a small area of a larger map. **Figure 16B** shows the same data on a graph that does not have a broken scale. The number of species has only increased 22 percent from 1980 to 1986. Both graphs have correct data, but must be read carefully. Always analyze the measurements and graphs that you come across. If there is a surprising result, look closer at the scale.

Figure 16
Careful reading of graphs is important. A This graph does not start at zero, which makes it appear that the number of species has more than quadrupled from 1980 to 1986. B The actual increase is about 22 percent as you can see from this full graph. The broken scale must be noted in order to interpret the results correctly.

Section  Assessment

1. Describe a time when an illustration would be helpful in everyday activities.
2. Explain how to use **Figure 16** to find the number of endangered species in 1998.
3. Explain the difference between tables and graphs.
4. Suppose your class surveys students about after-school activities. What type of graph would you use to display your data? Explain.
5. **Think Critically** How are line, bar, and circle graphs the same? How are they different?

Skill Builder Activities

6. **Making and Using Graphs** Record the amount of time you spend reading each day for the next week. Then make a graph to display the data. What type of graph will you use? Could more than one kind of graph be used? **For more help, refer to the Science Skill Handbook.**
7. **Using an Electronic Spreadsheet** Use a spreadsheet to display how the total mass of a 500-kg elevator changes as 50-kg passengers are added one at a time. **For more help, refer to the Technology Skill Handbook.**

3 Assess

Reteach

Have each student make a chart of the different types of graphs defined in the section. Then have them write the key words that define each under the type of graph. line graph: shows relationship between two number variables; bar graph: shows relationship between a number variable and a number or category variable; circle graph: shows relationship among parts of a whole L2 LS **Visual-Spatial**

Challenge

Have students collect tables and graphs from newspapers or magazines. Display their information on a bulletin board with the following headings: table, line graph, bar graph, circle graph, other graphs, misleading graphs. Ask students to place their graphs in the appropriate category. Discuss placement of each or some of the graphs. L2 COOP LEARN LS **Visual-Spatial**

Performance Have students collect weather data for a week and display it in a table and a graph. Use **Performance Assessment in the Science Classroom,** p. 111. P

Answers to Section Assessment

1. Answers will vary. Possible response: directions showing how to assemble a new toy.
2. Possible answer: Find the bar for 1998. Use a ruler or visually align the top of the bar with the Time scale. This tells you the number of endangered species for that year.
3. A table displays data in rows and columns so that it's easy to read. A graph presents data in a visual way.
4. A bar graph or a circle graph would be appropriate. A circle graph would show the percent of students who prefer each activity. A bar graph would show the number of students who prefer each activity.
5. All show numerical data in ways that make it easier to interpret. A line graph shows the relationship between two numbers. A bar graph displays the relationship between a number and either another number or a category. A circle graph shows the relationship among the parts of a whole.
6. The graph should show reading time (number of minutes or hours) compared to days of the week. A bar graph or a line graph would be appropriate.
7. Mass should start at 500 kg and increase by 50 kg with each passenger added.

Activity BENCH TESTED

Recognize the Problem

Purpose

Students apply the concepts of precision, measurement, and graphing to a specific problem.
L2 ELL Kinesthetic

Process Skills

designing an experiment, forming a hypothesis, communicating, observing and inferring, making and using tables, interpreting data

Time Required

45 minutes each to plan and do the experiment

Materials

meterstick, stopwatch

Alternate Materials

clock with a second hand

Safety Precautions

Work in an area where it is safe to run. If this is not possible, measure walking speed only. Check that students do not have health problems that could prevent them from exercising. Allow students to decline running if it is physically uncomfortable or embarrassing for them.

Form a Hypothesis

Possible Hypotheses

A course on a flat, straight surface will be the most accurately measurable with the given tools. Accuracy will be better if more than one group member times each walker or runner.

Activity Design Your Own Experiment

Pace Yourself

In a track meet, you complete a distance that has been measured precisely. Officials watch the start of the race to be sure that all of the participants begin at the same time. The finish line is observed carefully—the clock is stopped at the moment you cross the line. Your time is measured by the officials as precisely as possible. The participant taking the shortest time to cover that distance wins. The rate or speed is calculated as a distance per unit of time.

Recognize the Problem

How will you measure the speed of each person in your group? How will you display these data?

Form a Hypothesis

Think about the information you have learned about precision, measurement, and graphing. In your group, make a hypothesis about a technique that will provide you with the most precise measurement of each person's pace.

Goals

- **Design** an experiment that allows you to measure speed for each member of your group accurately.
- **Display** data in a table and a graph.

Possible Materials

meterstick
stopwatch
*watch with a second hand
*Alternate materials

Safety Precautions

Work in an area where it is safe to run. Participate only if you are physically able to exercise safely.

Test Your Hypothesis

Possible Procedures

Measure the distance to be walked. Mark the starting and ending points for the walk. For each student, use a stopwatch to measure walking time to the nearest tenth of a second. Record each student's time on a data table. Graph the results. Repeat these steps, replacing the walk with a run.

Time to Walk and Run 18 m

Student	Walking time	Running time	Walking speed	Running speed
Carlos	21.3 s	10.6 s	0.845 m/s	1.70 m/s
Brianna	19.6 s	10.9 s	0.918 m/s	1.65 m/s

Test Your Hypothesis

Plan

1. As a group, decide what materials you will need.
2. How far will you travel? How will you measure that distance? How precise can you be?
3. How will you measure time? How precise can you be?
4. List the steps and materials you will use to test your hypothesis. Be specific. Will you try any part of your test more than once?
5. Before you begin, create a data table. Your group must decide on its design. Be sure to leave enough room to record the results for each person's time. If more than one trial is to be run for each measurement, include room for the additional data.

Do

1. Make sure that your teacher approves your plan before you start.
2. Carry out the experiment as planned and approved.
3. Be sure to record your data in the data table as you proceed with the measurements.

Analyze Your Data

1. **Graph** your data. What type of graph would be best?
2. Are your data table and graph easy to understand? Explain.
3. How do you know that your measurements are precise?
4. Do any of your data appear to be out of line with the rest?

Draw Conclusions

1. How is it possible for different members of a group to find different times while measuring the same event?
2. What tools would help you collect more precise data?
3. What other data displays could you use? What are the advantages and disadvantages of each?

Communicating Your Data

Make a larger version of your graph to display in your classroom with the graphs of other groups. **For more help, refer to the Science Skill Handbook.**

Teaching Strategy

Demonstrate to students how to use the meterstick to measure walking/running distance and how to stop, start, and reset the stopwatch.

Expected Outcome

Most results will show students moving at different speeds from each other. Often, two students recording the same event will measure different times.

Analyze Your Data

1. bar graph
2. Check students' work. A person unfamiliar with the experiment should be able to quickly grasp the results.
3. Students should explain their efforts to measure precisely.
4. Students should use their bar graphs to answer this question.

Error Analysis

Have students compare their results and their hypotheses and explain why differences occurred.

Draw Conclusions

1. People's reaction times with the stopwatch may be different, people watching the race from different angles may see the runner pass the finish line at slightly different times, and the stopwatches may vary.
2. Possible answers: global positioning data, a timer that used infrared or laser light to determine start and stop times
3. Possible answers: Graph with a different scale or bar graph or data table comparing average time for male students versus average time for female students; each arranges the information in different ways, so more relationships can be seen.

Assessment

Performance Ask students to design a method to measure another speed, such as the speed of a person swimming two laps in a pool. Use **Performance Assessment in the Science Classroom,** p. 95.

Communicating Your Data

Have each group use its graph to explain its data to the class.

Science Stats

Content Background

The rafflesia is a parasitic plant that grows in the mountains of Malaysia. This plant has adapted to feed off of the roots of large vines that are in the grape family. The large, fleshy flower remains open for five to seven days. The flower emits a very strong offensive odor that attracts carrion-feeding flies. It is thought that the flies are the source of pollination.

The eruption of Krakatau in 1883 was so loud that the explosion was heard 4,800 km (3,000 mi) away. A series of eruptions discharged so much ash and dust into the air that the area surrounding the volcano was plunged into darkness for days. The massive eruption set off a series of tsunamis and tidal waves that killed thousands of people in the nearby islands.

Discussion

Students may not have a good grasp of the magnitude of these features. Make the conversion calculations to English units on the board as a class to give students a better idea of how large these items are. Useful conversion factors (numbers are rounded off): 1 kg = 2.2 lbs; 1 m = 3.3 ft. Converted Numbers: 11 kg = 24.2 lbs; 1 m = 39.37 in; 1,800 m = 5,940 ft; 110 m = 363 ft; 452 m = 1,492 ft; 442 m = 1,459 ft; 33.5 m = 110.6 ft; 1.65 m = 5.45 ft.

Extension

Have students find out more about the blue whale, including its diet and habitat. Suggest students record their findings in their Science Journals.

Science Stats

Biggest, Tallest, Loudest

Did you know...

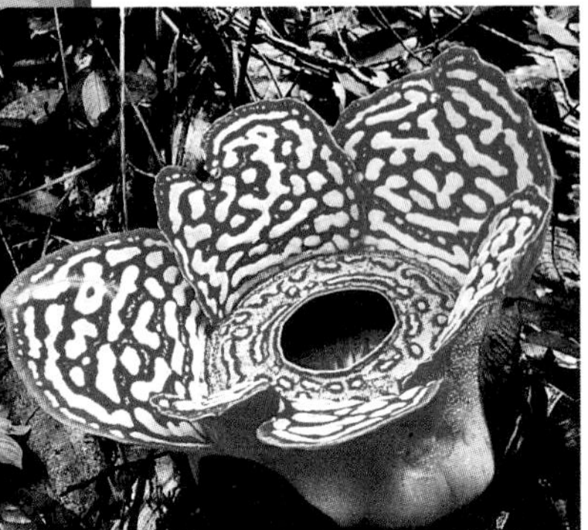

... The world's most massive flower belongs to a species called rafflesia (ruh FLEE zhee uh) and has a mass of up to 11 kg. The diameter, or the distance across the flower's petals, can measure up to 1 m.

... The world's tallest building is the Petronus Towers in Kuala Lumpur, Malaysia. It is 452 m tall. The tallest building in the United States is Chicago's Sears Tower, shown here, which measures 442 m.

... The Grand Canyon is so deep— as much as 1,800 m—that it can hold more than four Empire State Buildings stacked on top of one another.

... The world's tallest tree is a coast redwood in the Humboldt Redwoods State Park in California. The tree stands 110 m high.

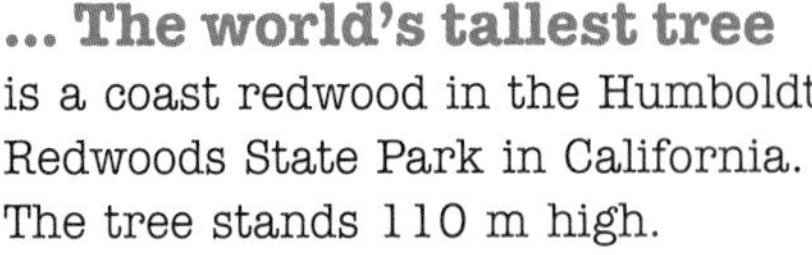

Internet Addresses

Explore the Glencoe Science Web site at **science.glencoe.com** to find out more about topics in this feature.

Connecting To Math

...The largest animal on Earth is the blue whale. It can grow to be 33.5 m long. If 20 people who are each 1.65 m tall were lying head to toe, it would equal this length.

How do they measure up?

...One of the loudest explosions on Earth was the 1883 eruption of Krakatau (krah kuh TAHEW), an Indonesian volcano.

Do the Math

1. How many of the largest rafflesia petals would you have to place side by side to equal the length of a blue whale?
2. When Krakatau erupted, it ejected 18,000 km^3 of ash and rock. Other large eruptions released the following: Mount Pinatubo—7,000 km^3, Mount Katmai—13,000 km^3, Tambora—30,000 km^3, Vesuvius—5,000 km^3. Make a bar graph to compare the sizes of these eruptions.
3. Use the information provided about the Grand Canyon to calculate how many Sears Towers would have to stand end to end to equal the depth of the canyon.

Go Further

Do research on the Internet at **science.glencoe.com** to find facts that describe some of the shortest, smallest, or fastest things on Earth. Create a class bulletin board with the facts you and your classmates find.

Connecting To Math

Do the Math

Teaching Strategies

- Discuss which units should be used to mark the y-axis on the bar graph for the second question in the Do the Math.
- Provide graph paper to assist the students with question two in the Do the Math.

Answers

1. 33.5 or 34
2. Check student's graph.
3. over 4

Go Further

A good source of information for this may be The Guiness Book of World Records.

Visual Learning

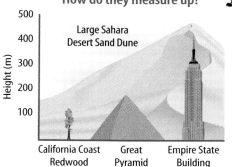

How do they measure up? Approximately how tall is the Great Pyramid? 200 m How tall is the Great Pyramid in feet? about 660 feet What is the difference in height of The Large Sahara Desert Sand Dune and the Great Pyramid? about 300 m

Chapter 2 Study Guide

Reviewing Main Ideas

Preview

Students can answer the questions in their Science Journals. Discuss the answers as you go through the chapter. LS **Linguistic**

Review

Students can write their answers, then compare them with those of other students. LS **Interpersonal**

Reteach

Students can look at the illustrations and describe details that support the main ideas of the chapter. LS **Visual-Spatial**

Answers to Chapter Review

Section 1

4. neither

Section 2

2. length

Section 3

2. San Francisco, CA

Chapter 2 Study Guide

Reviewing Main Ideas

Section 1 Description and Measurement

1. Measurements such as length, volume, mass, temperature, and rates are used to describe objects and events.
2. Estimation is used to make an educated guess at a measurement.
3. Accuracy describes how close a measurement is to the true value.
4. Precision describes how close measurements are to each other. *Are the shots accurate or precise on the basketball hoop shown?*

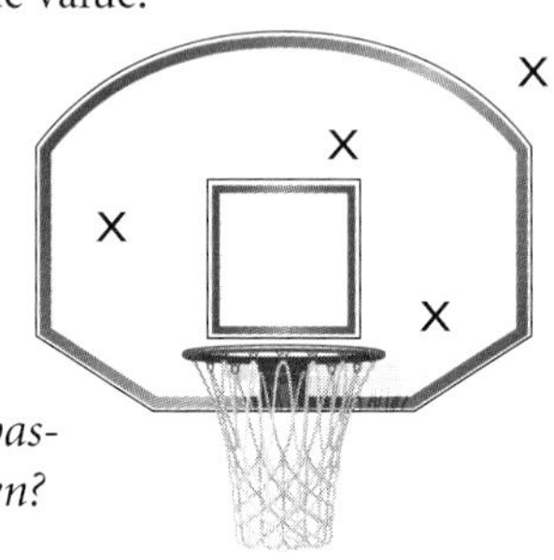

Section 2 SI Units

1. The international system of measurement is called SI. It is used throughout the world for communicating data.
2. The SI unit of length is the meter. Volume—the amount of space an object occupies—can be measured in cubic meters. The mass of an object is measured in kilograms. The SI unit of temperature is the kelvin. *What type of measurement is being made according to the sign shown?*

Section 3 Communicating Data

1. Tables, photographs, drawings, and graphs can sometimes present data more clearly than explaining everything in words. Scientists use these tools to collect, organize, summarize, and display data in a way that is easy to use and understand.
2. The three common types of graphs are line graphs, bar graphs, and circle graphs. *Which city on the line graph shown is the coldest in the fifth month?*

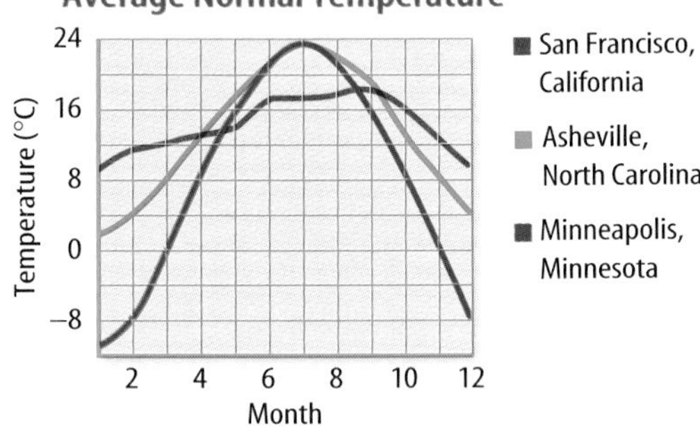

3. Line graphs show the relationship between two variables that are numbers on an *x*-axis and a *y*-axis. Bar graphs divide a variable into parts to show a relationship. Circle graphs show the parts of a whole like pieces of a pie.

Foldables Reading & Study Skills — After You Read

Fill in the *Round It* column on your Foldable. Explain when it is acceptable and appropriate for scientists to round measurements.

Foldables Reading & Study Skills — After You Read

After students have read the chapter and completed the Foldable described in Before You Read, have them do the activity on the student page.

Dinah Zike

Visualizing Main Ideas

Complete the following concept map.

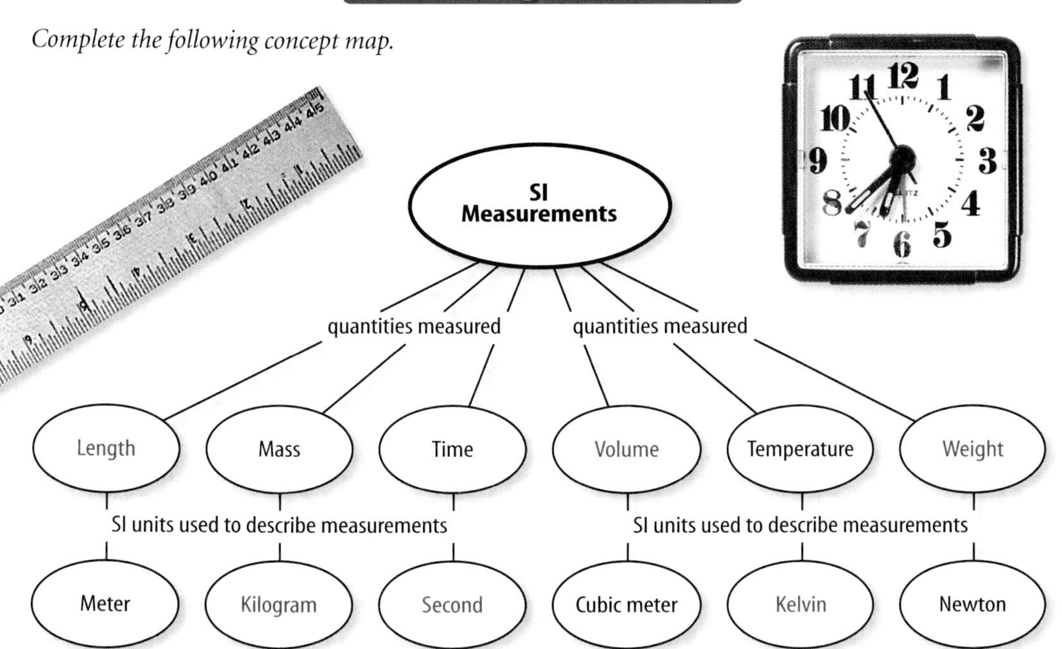

Vocabulary Review

Vocabulary Words

a. accuracy
b. bar graph
c. circle graph
d. estimation
e. graph
f. kelvin
g. kilogram
h. line graph
i. mass
j. measurement
k. meter
l. precision
m. rate
n. SI
o. table

Study Tip

When you encounter new vocabulary, write it down in your Science Journal. This will help you understand and remember them.

Using Vocabulary

Each phrase below describes a vocabulary word. Write the word that matches the phrase describing it.

1. the SI unit for length
2. a description with numbers
3. a method of making a rough measurement
4. the amount of matter in an object
5. a graph that shows parts of a whole
6. a description of how close measurements are to each other
7. the SI unit for temperature
8. an international system of units

Chapter 2 Study Guide

Visualizing Main Ideas

See student page.

Vocabulary Review

Using Vocabulary

1. meter
2. measurement
3. estimation
4. mass
5. circle graph
6. precision
7. kelvin
8. SI

Chapter 2 Assessment

Checking Concepts

1. D
2. D
3. C
4. A
5. B
6. C
7. A
8. C
9. D
10. B

Thinking Critically

11. Multiply its length times its width times its height.
12. The SI system of measurement is understood internationally, while the English system is understood in only a limited number of countries.
13. 1 mm, 100 mm, 1 m, 10 km
14. Accept any reasonable answer. Sample answer: to show distance traveled versus time of travel; no, you cannot use a bar graph for this.
15. Sample response: to allow for precision and reproducibility in design and printing; for example, ads for a given product all use exactly the same colors.

Chapter 2 Assessment

Checking Concepts

Choose the word or phrase that best answers the question.

1. The measurement 25.81 g is precise to the nearest what?
   A) gram
   B) kilogram
   C) tenth of a gram
   D) hundredth of a gram
2. What is the SI unit of mass?
   A) kilometer **C)** liter
   B) meter **D)** kilogram
3. What would you use to measure length?
   A) graduated cylinder
   B) balance
   C) meterstick
   D) spring scale
4. The cubic meter is the SI unit of what?
   A) volume **C)** mass
   B) weight **D)** distance
5. Which of the following can improve with practice?
   A) length **C)** rounding
   B) estimation **D)** mass
6. Which is a temperature scale?
   A) volume **C)** Celsius
   B) mass **D)** mercury
7. Which is used to organize data?
   A) table **C)** precision
   B) rate **D)** meterstick
8. To show the number of wins for each football team in your district, which of the following would you use?
   A) photograph **C)** bar graph
   B) line graph **D)** SI
9. What organizes data in rows and columns?
   A) bar graph **C)** line graph
   B) circle graph **D)** table
10. To show 25 percent on a circle graph, the section must measure what angle?
    A) 25° **C)** 180°
    B) 90° **D)** 360°

Thinking Critically

11. How would you estimate the volume your backpack could hold?
12. Why do scientists in the United States use SI rather than the English system (feet, pounds, pints, etc.) of measurement?
13. List the following in order from smallest to largest: 1 m, 1 mm, 10 km, 100 mm.
14. Describe an instance when you would use a line graph. Can you use a bar graph for the same purpose?
15. Computer graphics artists can specify a color by using numbers for the amount of each color of ink to be used at each point in a picture. Why was this method of describing color invented?

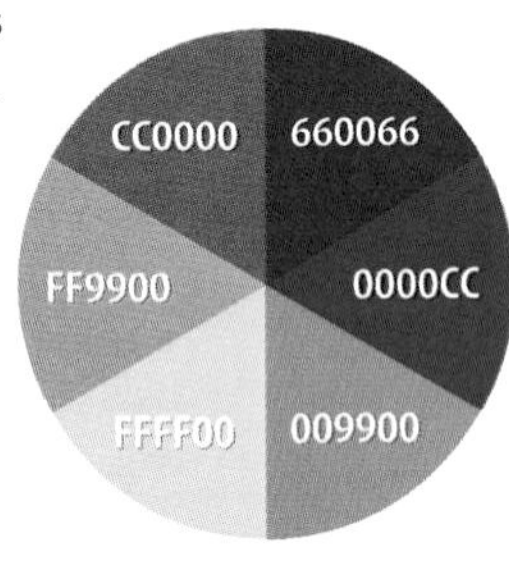

Developing Skills

16. **Measuring in SI** Make a fist. Use a centimeter ruler to measure the height, width, and depth of your fist.
17. **Comparing and Contrasting** How are volume, length, and mass similar? How are they different? Give several examples of units that are used to measure each quantity. Which units are SI?

Chapter Assessment Planner

Portfolio Encourage students to place in their portfolios one or two items of what they consider to be their best work. Examples include:
- Science Journal, p. 45
- Performance Assessment, p. 48
- Activity Assessment, p. 55
- Make a Model, p. 57

Performance Additional performance assessments, Performance Task Assessment Lists, and rubrics for evaluating these activities can be found in Glencoe's **Performance Assessment in the Science Classroom.**

18. **Making and Using Graphs** The table shows the area of several bodies of water. Make a bar graph of the data.

Areas of Bodies of Water

Body of Water	Area (km^2)
Currituck Sound (North Carolina)	301
Pocomoke Sound (Maryland/Virginia)	286
Chincoteague Bay (Maryland/Virginia)	272
Core Sound (North Carolina)	229

19. **Interpreting Scientific Illustrations** What does the figure show? How has this drawing been simplified?

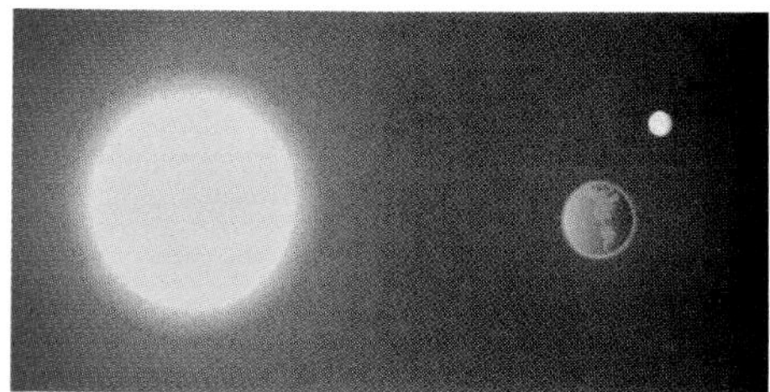

Performance Assessment

20. **Poster** Make a poster to alert the public about the benefits of using SI units.
21. **Newspaper Search** Look through a week's worth of newspapers and evaluate any graphs or tables that you find.

Technology

Go to the Glencoe Science Web site at **science.glencoe.com** or use the **Glencoe Science CD-ROM** for additional chapter assessment.

Test Practice

Some students in Mrs. Olsen's science class measured their masses during three consecutive months. They placed their results in the following table. Study the table and answer the following questions.

Student Masses: Sept. – Nov. 1999

Student	September	October	November
Domingo	41.13 kg	40.92 kg	42.27 kg
Latoya	35.21 kg	35.56 kg	36.07 kg
Benjamin	45,330 g	45,680 g	45,530 g
Poloma	31.78 kg	31.55 kg	31.51 kg
Frederick	50,870 g	51,880 g	51,030 g
Fiona	37.62 kg	37.71 kg	37.85 kg

1. According to the table, which shows how much Frederick weighs in kilograms for the three months?
   A) 5.087, 5.118, 5.103
   B) 50.87, 51.88, 51.03
   C) 508.7, 511.8, 510.3
   D) 5,087, 5,118, 5,103
2. According to this information, which lists the students from lightest to heaviest during November?
   F) Poloma, Benjamin, Domingo, Frederick
   G) Domingo, Latoya, Frederick, Benjamin
   H) Fiona, Domingo, Benjamin, Frederick
   J) Frederick, Benjamin, Domingo, Poloma

Chapter 2 Assessment

Test Practice

THE PRINCETON REVIEW

The Test-Taking Tip was written by The Princeton Review, the nation's leader in test preparation.

1. B
2. H

Developing Skills

16. Answers will vary. Check students' work.
17. Volume, length, and mass are all properties that can be measured. Volume is the amount of space an object occupies; length is the distance between two points; mass is the amount of matter in an object. Sample units: cubic meter (volume); meter (length); kilogram (mass). These are all SI units.
18. Check students' graphs.
19. It shows Earth, the moon, and the Sun. Size and distance are not to scale, and the inner planets are missing.

Performance Assessment

20. Use **Performance Assessment in the Science Classroom,** p. 145.
21. Use **Performance Assessment in the Science Classroom,** p. 99.

Assessment Resources

Reproducible Masters

Chapter Resources Booklet
Chapter Review, pp. 33–34
Chapter Tests, pp. 35–38
Assessment Transparency Activity, p. 45

Glencoe Science Web site
Interactive Tutor
Chapter Quizzes

Glencoe Technology
Assessment Transparency
Interactive CD-ROM Chapter Quizzes
ExamView Pro Test Bank
Vocabulary PuzzleMaker Software
MindJogger Videoquiz DVD/VHS

Standardized Test Practice

Reading Comprehension

Question 1: B

Students must use information in the passage in order to identify the best supported conclusion.

- **Choice A** No; this is not supported by the passage.
- **Choice B** Yes; this is supported by the passage.
- **Choice C** No; this is not supported by the passage.
- **Choice D** No; this is not supported by the passage.

Question 2: H

Students must determine, based on the reading passage, which of the answer choices is appropriate in describing ancient measurements.

- **Choice F** No; they were not precise.
- **Choice G** No; they were correct for those who used them.
- **Choice H** Yes; they were reasonable estimates.
- **Choice J** No; this term is judgmental.

All questions written and validated by The Princeton Review.

Standardized Test Practice

Reading Comprehension

Read the passage carefully. Then read each question that follows the passage. Decide which is the best answer to each question.

History of Measurement Units

In modern society, units of measurement that have been defined and agreed upon by international scientists are used. In ancient times, people were just beginning to invent and use units of measurement. For example, thousands of years ago, a cabinetmaker would build one cabinet at a time and measure the pieces of wood needed relative to the size of the other pieces of that cabinet. Today, factories manufacture many of the same products. Ancient cabinetmakers rarely made two cabinets that were exactly the same. Eventually, it became obvious that units of measurement had to mean the same thing to everybody.

Measurements, such as the inch, foot, and yard, began many years ago as fairly crude units. For example, the modern-day inch began as "the width of one's thumb." The foot originally was defined as "the length of one's foot." The yard was defined as "the distance from the tip of one's nose to the end of one's arm."

Although using these units of measurement was easier than not using any units of measurement, these ancient units were confusing. Human beings come in many different sizes and shapes, and one person's foot can be much larger than another person's foot. So, whose foot defines a foot? Who's thumb width defines an inch? Ancient civilizations used these kinds of measurements for thousands of years. Over time, these units were redefined and standardized, eventually becoming the exact units of measurement that you know today.

Test-Taking Tip After you read and think about the passage, write one or two sentences that summarize the most important points. Read your sentences out loud.

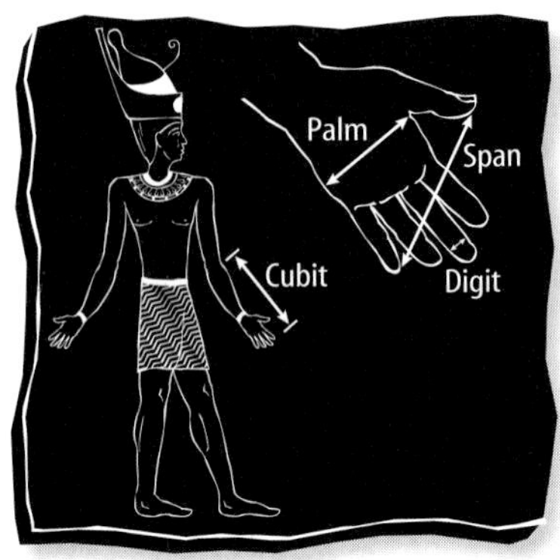

Ancient people created units of measurement.

1. Based on the passage, the reader can conclude that _____.
   A) ancient cultures had no concept of measurement
   B) standards of measurement developed over a long period of time
   C) ancient people were probably good at communicating exacts units of measurement
   D) units of measurement are needed only in modern and technologically advanced societies

2. According to the passage, which of these best describes ancient units of measurement?
   F) precise
   G) incorrect
   H) approximate
   J) irresponsible

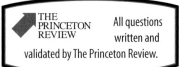

Standardized Test Practice

Reasoning and Skills

Read each question and choose the best answer.

1. All of these are things that can be measured accurately EXCEPT _____.
   A) the temperature of a human body
   B) the space that a couch takes up in a living room
   C) the beauty in a piece of artwork
   D) the mass of a rock from the Moon

Test-Taking Tip Think about the reasons why people use measurement and the kinds of things that can and cannot be measured.

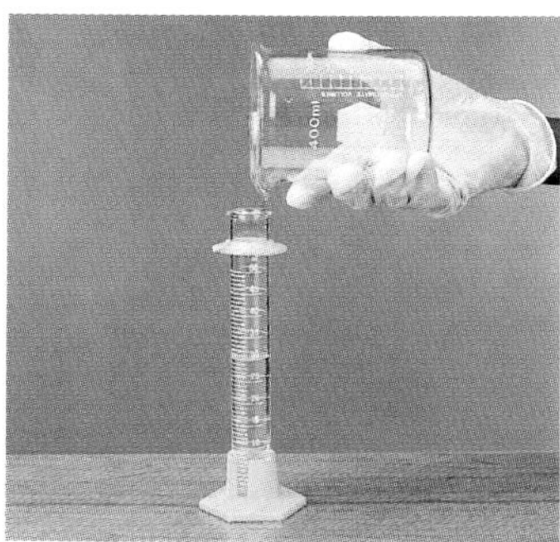

2. Jodie and William are using the graduated cylinder pictured above to measure the volume of liquid in milliliters. What multiple of a liter is a milliliter?
   F) 1,000
   G) 0.01
   H) 0.001
   J) 0.000 001

Test-Taking Tip Consider the prefixes used in SI units, as well as the amount of liquid shown.

Group S
• How does this medication work to reduce a fever?
• Why do tides occur?
• What is the melting point of iron?
• What was Earth's climate like in the past?

Group T
• Who would make the best class president?
• Is it right to compliment a friend's new shirt if you don't like the shirt?
• Shouldn't everyone like cauliflower, broccoli, turnips, and spinach?
• Why is a sunset beautiful?

3. The questions in Group S are different from the questions in Group T because only the questions in Group S _____.
   A) cannot be answered by science
   B) will have answers that are solely opinions
   C) can be answered with absolute certainty
   D) can be answered by science

Test-Taking Tip Think about the kinds of questions that scientists try to and are able to answer.

Consider this question carefully before writing your answer on a separate sheet of paper.

4. Suppose you decide to investigate this problem: Which brand of fertilizer produces the most tomatoes per plant? Identify the independent and dependent variables. List the constants in your investigation.

Test-Taking Tip Think about the procedures that scientists must go through in order to discover and explain.

Standardized Test Practice

Reasoning and Skills

QUESTION 1: C

Students must understand the difference between objective and subjective measurements (also known as fact and opinion).

- **Choice A** Yes; this can be measured.
- **Choice B** Yes; this can be measured.
- **Choice C** No; this can not be measured. It is an opinion.
- **Choice D** Yes; this can be measured.

QUESTION 2: H

Students must know that the prefix *milli-* means one-thousandth.

QUESTION 3: D

Students must consider the information in the two groups.

- **Choice A** No; the questions in Group T, not Group S, cannot be answered by science.
- **Choice B** No; the questions in Group T, not Group S, will have answers that are opinions.
- **Choice C** No; although the questions in Group S are fact-based and can be answered by science, they may only be answered by scientific hypothesis, which are not absolute certainties.
- **Choice D** Yes; the questions in Group S are looking for facts and, therefore, can be answered by science.

QUESTION 4: Answers will vary.

Students should design a controlled experiment with the brand of fertilizer as the independent (tested) variable. All other factors, including kind of plant, soil, water, temperature, and light, would have to be kept constant to insure valid results.

Teaching Tip

Have students review SI prefixes and their meanings.

Unit Contents

✔ Pre-Reading Activity

Have students look through the chapters and find and compare models of atoms.

UNIT 2 Matter

How Are Refrigerators & Frying Pans Connected?

In the late 1930s, scientists were experimenting with a gas that they hoped would work as a new coolant in refrigerators. They filled several metal canisters with the gas and stored the canisters on dry ice. Later, when they opened the canisters, they were surprised to find that the gas had disappeared and that the inside of each canister was coated with a slick, powdery white solid. The gas had undergone a chemical change. That is, the chemical bonds in its molecules had broken and new bonds had formed, turning one kind of matter into a completely different kind of matter. Strangely, the mysterious white powder proved to be just about the slipperiest substance that anyone had ever encountered. Years later, a creative Frenchman obtained some of the slippery stuff and tried applying it to his fishing tackle to keep the lines from tangling. His wife noticed what he was doing and suggested putting the substance on the inside of a frying pan to keep food from sticking. He did, and nonstick cookware was born!

70

Teacher to Teacher

"Multicolored modeling clay is an inexpensive and reusable material for middle school students to use to visualize science concepts. Students use their creativity to make 'atoms' that have touchable protons, neutrons, and electrons."

Petrolia Moss, Teacher
North Heights Junior High
Texarkana, AK

NATIONAL GEOGRAPHIC

Introducing the Unit

How Are Refrigerators & Frying Pans Connected?

It was Roy Plunkett who first discovered polytetrafluoroethylene (PTFE) in 1938. It was used to protect metal equipment from corrosion during World War II. It was 1960 when the first nonstick cookware was released. PTFE is an organic polymer known for its strength, toughness, and slippery surface. It is almost completely indifferent to attack by all chemicals, and retains its physical properties at high temperatures. These qualities make it ideal for use in gaskets, bearings, cooking utensils, and numerous other products.

SCIENCE CONNECTION

PHYSICAL AND CHEMICAL CHANGES Working in teams of 3 or 4, look up and write down the definitions of "physical change" and "chemical change." Then brain-storm to compile a list of 10 physical and 10 chemical changes that you might encounter in everyday life. Make flashcards from your list. On each card, write a description of the change on one side and the type of change on the other side. Pair up with another team and use your flashcards to quiz each other.

SCIENCE CONNECTION

Activity

Ask students to further classify their physical and chemical changes from the Science Connection. Possible subcategories for physical changes might include a change in state, a change in quantity, and change in appearance. Possible sub-categories for chemical changes include reactions that release energy (exothermic) vs. reactions that absorb energy (endothermic) and slow reactions vs. fast reactions. Have students support their selections with the information presented in the unit.

SCIENCE Online

Internet Addresses

____

____

____

____

Explore the Glencoe Science Web site at **science.glencoe.com** to find out more about topics in this unit.

Section/Objectives	Standards		Activities/Features
	National	State/Local	
Chapter Opener	See p. 5T for a Key to Standards.		**Explore Activity:** Observe matter, p. 73 **Before You Read,** p. 73
Section 1 Structure of Matter 4 sessions 2 blocks 1. **Describe** characteristics of matter. 2. **Identify** what makes up matter. 3. **Identify** the parts of an atom. 4. **Compare** the models that are used for atoms.	National Content Standards: UCP1, A1, A2, B1		**MiniLAB:** Making a Model, p. 76 **Science Online,** p. 78 **Physics Integration**, p. 80
Section 2 The Simplest Matter 4 sessions 2 blocks 1. **Describe** the relationship between elements and the periodic table. 2. **Explain** the meaning of atomic mass and atomic number. 3. **Identify** what makes an isotope. 4. **Contrast** metals, metalloids, and nonmetals.	National Content Standards: UCP2, A1, A2, B1		**Science Online,** p. 83 **Visualizing the Periodic Table,** p. 84 **Activity:** Elements and the Periodic Table, p. 88
Section 3 Compounds and Mixtures 5 sessions 2.5 blocks 1. **Identify** the characteristics of a compound. 2. **Compare and contrast** different types of mixtures.	National Content Standards: UCP2, A1, A2, B1, G1, G3		**MiniLAB:** Comparing Compounds, p. 90 **Problem-Solving Activity:** What's the best way to desalt ocean water?, p. 91 **Life Science Integration,** p. 92 **Science Online,** p. 92 **Earth Science Integration,** p. 93 **Activity:** Mystery Mixture, p. 94 **Science and History:** Ancient Views of Matter, p. 96

Activity Materials	Reproducible Resources	Section Assessment	Technology
Explore Activity: dry paper towel or tissue, tape, plastic cup, bowl or sink, water	**Chapter Resources Booklet** Foldables Worksheet, p. 13 Directed Reading Overview, p. 15 Note-taking Worksheets, pp. 29–31	GLENCOE'S ASSESSMENT ADVANTAGE	
MiniLAB: sealed shoe box, one or more items *Need materials?* Contact Science Kit at 1-800-828-7777 or www.sciencekit.com on the Internet.	**Chapter Resources Booklet** Transparency Activity, p. 40 MiniLAB, p. 3 Enrichment, p. 26 Reinforcement, p. 23 Directed Reading, p. 16 Transparency Activity, pp. 43–44 **Reading and Writing Skill Activities,** p. 41 **Mathematics Skill Activities,** p. 39	Portfolio Activity, p. 78 Performance MiniLAB, p. 76 Skill Builder Activities, p. 81 Content Section Assessment, p. 81	Section Focus Transparency Teaching Transparency Interactive CD-ROM/DVD Guided Reading Audio Program
Activity: colored markers, large index cards, Merck index, encyclopedia, large bulletin board, 8 1/2- × 14-inch paper, thumbtacks	**Chapter Resources Booklet** Transparency Activity, p. 41 Enrichment, p. 27 Reinforcement, p. 24 Directed Reading, p. 17 Activity Worksheet, pp. 5–6 **Physical Science Critical Thinking/Problem Solving,** p. 13 **Science Inquiry Labs,** p. 25 **Earth Science Critical Thinking/ Problem Solving,** p. 2	Portfolio Extension, p. 85 Performance Skill Builder Activities, p. 87 Content Section Assessment, p. 87	Section Focus Transparency Interactive CD-ROM/DVD Guided Reading Audio Program
MiniLAB: sugar, rubbing alcohol, salad oil, spoon, glasses, hot water **Activity:** 4 test tubes, cornstarch, sugar, baking soda, mystery mixture, 3 small scoops, 2 dropper bottles, iodine solution, white vinegar, hot plate, 250-mL beaker, water, test-tube holder, small pie pan, matches	**Chapter Resources Booklet** Transparency Activity, p. 42 MiniLAB, p. 4 Enrichment, p. 28 Reinforcement, p. 25 Directed Reading, pp. 17, 18 Activity Worksheet, pp. 7–8 Lab Activities, pp. 9–10, 11–12 **Lab Management and Safety,** p. 44	Portfolio Curriculum Connection, p. 92 Performance MiniLAB, p. 90 Problem-Solving Activity, p. 91 Skill Builder Activities, p. 93 Content Section Assessment, p. 93	Section Focus Transparency Interactive CD-ROM/DVD Guided Reading Audio Program

End of Chapter Assessment

GLENCOE'S ASSESSMENT ADVANTAGE

Blackline Masters	Technology	Professional Series
Chapter Resources Booklet Chapter Review, pp. 33–34 Chapter Tests, pp. 35–38 **Standardized Test Practice by The Princeton Review,** pp. 15–18	MindJogger Videoquiz CD-ROM Explorations and Quizzes Vocabulary Puzzle Makers ExamView Pro Test Bank Interactive Lesson Planner Interactive Teacher's Edition	Performance Assessment in the Science Classroom (PASC)

Transparencies

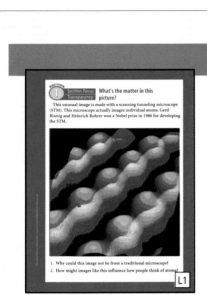

Section Focus

SECTION 1 Section Focus Transparency **What's the matter in this picture?**

This unusual image is made with a scanning tunneling microscope (STM). This microscope actually images individual atoms. Gerd Binnig and Heinrich Rohrer won a Nobel prize in 1986 for developing the STM.

1. Why could this image not be from a traditional microscope?
2. How might images like this influence how people think of atoms?

L1

SECTION 2 Section Focus Transparency **Some call it quicksilver.**

This element is a liquid at room temperature. It is probably best known as the liquid in traditional thermometers; however, it is so toxic that people often choose digital thermometers that do not contain this element.

1. Describe what you see in the picture. What characteristics does this element have?
2. Which element do you think this is? Do you know of any other uses for it?
3. Which elements most resemble this element, according to the periodic table?

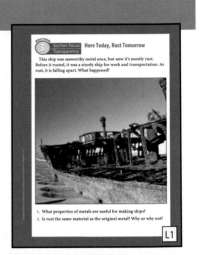

L1

SECTION 3 Section Focus Transparency **Here Today, Rust Tomorrow**

This ship was seaworthy metal once, but now it's mostly rust. Before it rusted, it was a sturdy ship for work and transportation. As rust, it is falling apart. What happened?

1. What properties of metals are useful for making ships?
2. Is rust the same material as the original metal? Why or why not?

L1

This is a representation of key blackline masters available in the Teacher Classroom Resources. See Resource Manager boxes within the chapter for additional information.

Assessment

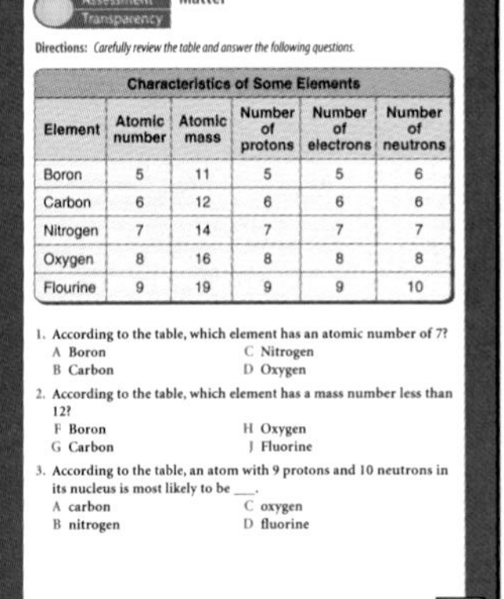

Assessment Transparency **Matter**

Directions: *Carefully review the table and answer the following questions.*

Characteristics of Some Elements					
Element	Atomic number	Atomic mass	Number of protons	Number of electrons	Number of neutrons
Boron	5	11	5	5	6
Carbon	6	12	6	6	6
Nitrogen	7	14	7	7	7
Oxygen	8	16	8	8	8
Flourine	9	19	9	9	10

1. According to the table, which element has an atomic number of 7?
   A Boron C Nitrogen
   B Carbon D Oxygen
2. According to the table, which element has a mass number less than 12?
   F Boron H Oxygen
   G Carbon J Fluorine
3. According to the table, an atom with 9 protons and 10 neutrons in its nucleus is most likely to be ___.
   A carbon C oxygen
   B nitrogen D fluorine

L1

Teaching

Key to Teaching Strategies

The following designations will help you decide which activities are appropriate for your students.

L1 Level 1 activities should be appropriate for students with learning difficulties.

L2 Level 2 activities should be within the ability range of all students.

L3 Level 3 activities are designed for above-average students.

ELL ELL activities should be within the ability range of English Language Learners.

COOP LEARN Cooperative Learning activities are designed for small group work.

LS Multiple Learning Styles logos, as described on page 22T, are used throughout to indicate strategies that address different learning styles.

P These strategies represent student products that can be placed into a best-work portfolio.

Hands-on Activities

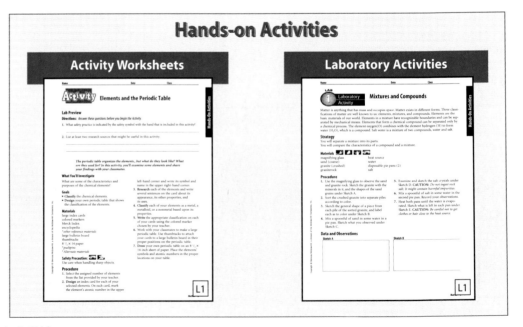

Activity Worksheets

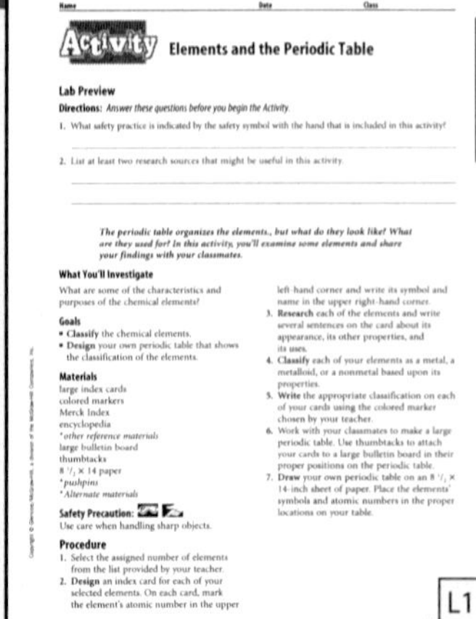

Name Date Class

Activity **Elements and the Periodic Table**

Hands-On Activities

Lab Preview

Directions: *Answer these questions before you begin the Activity.*

1. What safety practice is indicated by the safety symbol with the hand that is included in this activity?
2. List at least two research sources that might be useful in this activity.

The periodic table organizes the elements., but what do they look like? What are they used for? In this activity, you'll examine some elements and share your findings with your classmates.

What You'll Investigate

What are some of the characteristics and purposes of the chemical elements?

Goals
- **Classify** the chemical elements.
- **Design** your own periodic table that shows the classification of the elements.

Materials

large index cards
colored markers
Merck Index
encyclopedia
**other reference materials*
large bulletin board
thumbtacks
8 1/2 × 14 paper
**pushpins*
**Alternate materials*

Safety Precaution:
Use care when handling sharp objects.

Procedure
1. Select the assigned number of elements from the list provided by your teacher.
2. **Design** an index card for each of your selected elements. On each card, mark the element's atomic number in the upper left-hand corner and write its symbol and name in the upper right-hand corner.
3. **Research** each of the elements and write several sentences on the card about its appearance, its other properties, and its uses.
4. **Classify** each of your elements as a metal, a metalloid, or a nonmetal based upon its properties.
5. **Write** the appropriate classification on each of your cards using the colored marker chosen by your teacher.
6. Work with your classmates to make a large periodic table. Use thumbtacks to attach your cards to a large bulletin board in their proper positions on the periodic table.
7. **Draw** your own periodic table on an 8 1/2 × 14-inch sheet of paper. Place the elements' symbols and atomic numbers in the proper locations on your table.

L1

Laboratory Activities

Name Date Class

LAB 1 Laboratory Activity **Mixtures and Compounds**

Hands-On Activities

Matter is anything that has mass and occupies space. Matter exists in different forms. Three classifications of matter are well known to us: elements, mixtures, and compounds. Elements are the basic materials of our world. Elements in a mixture have recognizable boundaries and can be separated by mechanical means. Elements that form a chemical compound can be separated only by a chemical process. The element oxygen(O) combines with the element hydrogen (H) to form water (H_2O), which is a compound. Salt water is a mixture of two compounds, water and salt.

Strategy

You will separate a mixture into its parts.
You will compare the characteristics of a compound and a mixture.

Materials

magnifying glass
sand (coarse)
granite (crushed)
graniterock
heat source
water
disposable pie pans (2)
salt

Procedure
1. Use the magnifying glass to observe the sand and granite rock. Sketch the granite with the minerals in it, and the shapes of the sand grains under Sketch A.
2. Sort the crushed granite into separate piles according to color.
3. Sketch the general shape of a piece from each pile of the sorted granite, and label each as to color under Sketch B.
4. Mix a spoonful of sand in some water in a pie pan. Sketch what you observed under Sketch C.
5. Examine and sketch the salt crystals under Sketch D. **CAUTION:** *Do not ingest rock salt. It might contain harmful impurities.*
6. Mix a spoonful of salt in some water in the second pie pan. Record your observations.
7. Heat both pans until the water is evaporated. Sketch what is left in each pan under Sketch E. **CAUTION:** *Be careful not to get clothes or hair close to the heat source.*

Data and Observations

Sketch A

Sketch B

L1

Meeting Different Ability Levels

Content Outline

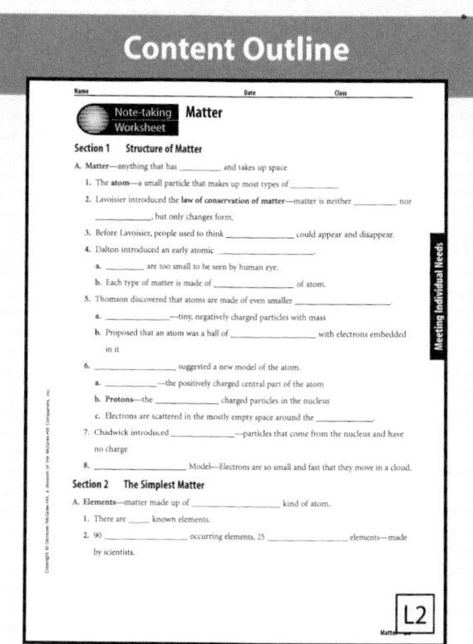

Reinforcement

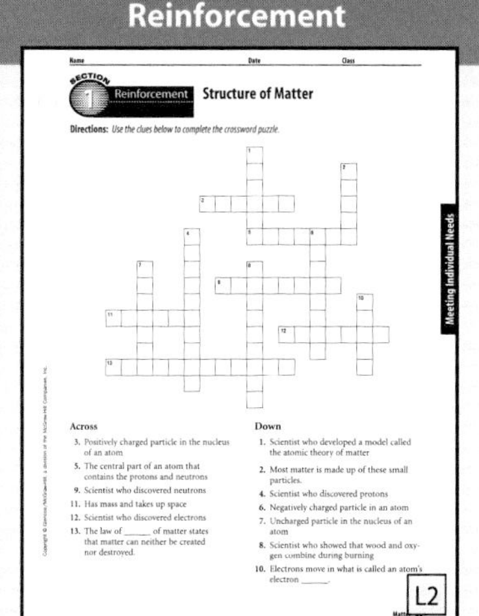

Directed Reading

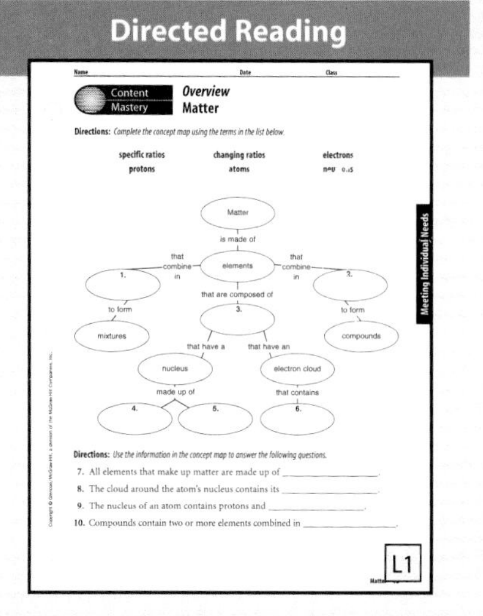

Enrichment

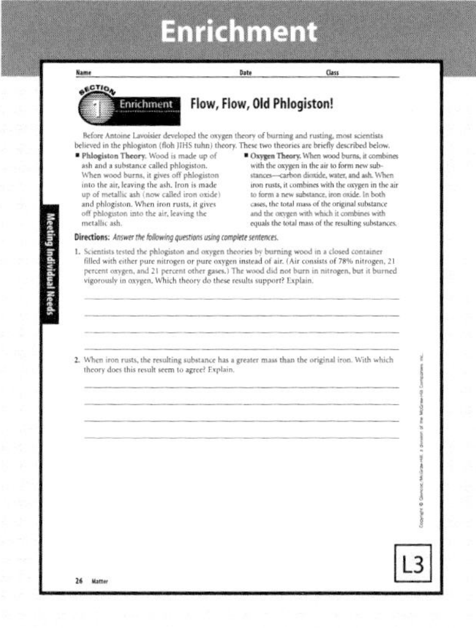

Spanish Directed Reading

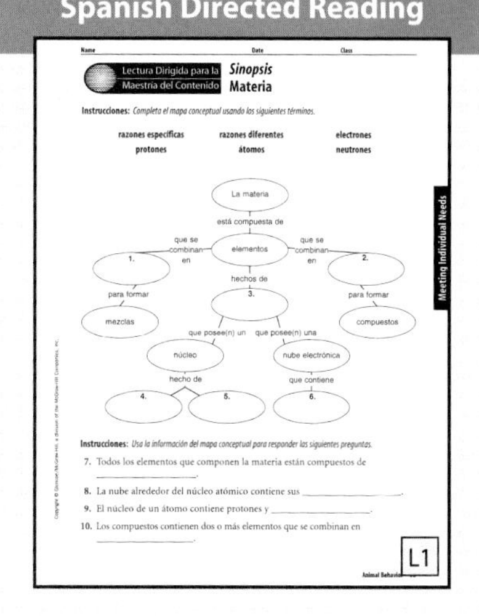

Assessment

Chapter Tests

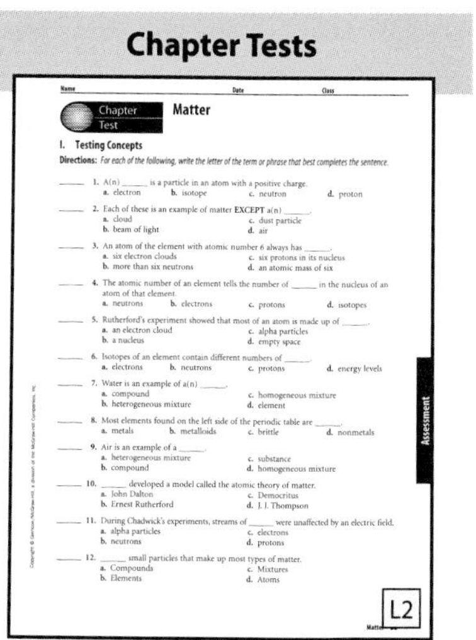

Test Practice Workbook

Chapter Review

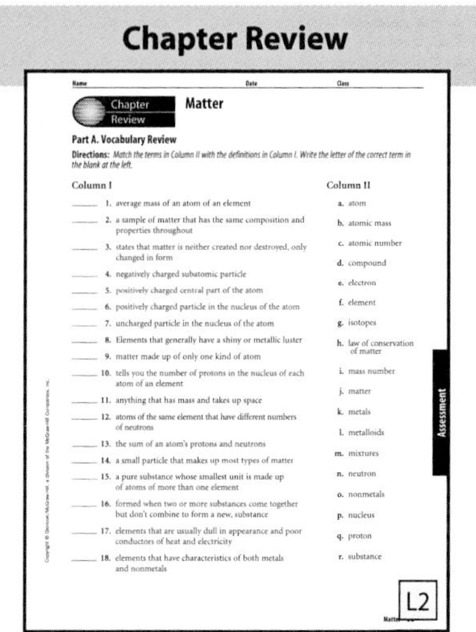

Science Content Background

SECTION 1 Structure of Matter

Matter Basics

Solids, liquids, and gases are matter—they take up space and have mass. The amount of space an object occupies is its volume. The mass of an object refers to the amount of matter it contains. On Earth the amount of mass is directly proportional to the weight of the object. Dividing matter into smaller pieces reduces its volume and mass, and because the mass is reduced, so is the weight. Although the pieces get so small you can't feel them pressing on your hand, they still have weight.

Student Misconception

Objects have weight only if you can feel them. If you keep dividing matter into smaller pieces, you will eventually get small pieces with no weight.

Refer to the facing page for teaching strategies to address this misconception. Refer to pages 74–76 for content related to this topic.

Ions

Many substances are ionic. That is, they are made up of charged particles called ions rather than neutral atoms. For example, sodium chloride is made up of sodium ions that have 1+ charges and chloride ions that have 1- charges. A sodium ion is formed when a sodium atom loses one of its 11 electrons. A chloride ion is formed when a chlorine atom gains an additional electron to go with the 17 it had as an atom.

Plasma

Plasma, another fluid state of matter, is a gaslike state of negatively charged electrons and positively charged ions. Most matter in the universe is plasma. Stars are mostly plasma, and the hydrogen ions that occur in interstellar space exist in the plasma state.

SECTION 2 The Simplest Matter

Elements

The arrangement of electrons in the energy levels and sublevels in the atoms of an element determines the properties of that element. Elements whose atoms have identical arrangements of electrons in their highest energy levels have similar properties and make up a family of elements on the periodic table.

SECTION 3 Compounds and Mixtures

Compounds

Electron sharing is called covalent bonding. Covalent bonding between atoms of different elements produces molecular compounds. The molecules of molecular compounds attract each other to varying degrees. In the solid state, these attractions sometimes lead to an orderly arrangement of molecules called a molecular crystal. In other cases, the molecules have random arrangements and produce amorphous solids.

When atoms react by losing or gaining electrons, called ionic bonding, ions are formed. The formula for an ionic compound such as sodium chloride ($NaCl$) is called an empirical formula and gives the simplest ratio of ions in the compound, not the formula for a molecule. The strong attractions between ions in an ionic compound result in a crystalline structure in the solid state.

Mixtures

Solid solutions, made up of uniform mixtures of metals and sometimes nonmetals, are called alloys. Brass and stainless steel are common alloys.

For additional content background on this topic, go to the Glencoe Science Web site at science.glencoe.com.

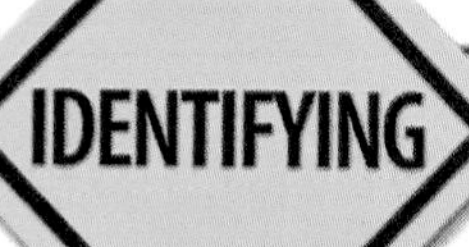

Misconceptions

Find Out What Students Think

Students may think that . . .

- **Objects have weight only if you can feel them.**
- **If you keep dividing matter, you will eventually get small pieces with no weight.**

Students may have these misconceptions because they are relying on their senses. In this case they are relying on their sense of touch. They may think that if an object does not press down on their hands and feel heavy, it has no weight.

Demonstration

Hold up a plastic foam cup, and ask students if the cup has weight. Establish that it does. Break a chunk off the cup, and ask how the weight of this part of the cup compares with the weight of the original cup. Establish that it has less weight. Give pieces of the cup to four different students sitting in different parts of the classroom. Ask students to break their pieces and hold up the biggest piece of cup that has no weight. When they hold these up ask other students if they agree that the pieces have no weight. Have students explain why they agree or disagree.

Promote Understanding

Activity

Divide the class into groups. Give foam cup to each group. Have them discuss whether the cup is matter. Establish that it is because it has mass and takes up space. Explain that on Earth, the mass of a cup is directly proportional to its weight. This means that if a cup has a large mass, it has a large weight, and if it has a small mass, it has a small weight. Have students do the following:

- Using a scale that can measure mass to at least 0.1 g, measure the mass of the cup.
- Draw a picture of the cup, and write its mass.
- Use scissors to cut the cup exactly in half.
- Draw a picture of the half cup, calculate its mass (original mass divided by two), and write the new mass by the picture.
- Take one half of the cup and cut it into two equal parts.
- Draw a picture of one of the new pieces, and write its mass next to it.
- Repeat this procedure four more times, each time cutting the piece in half, drawing it, and calculating its mass.
- Make a graph of the data. The x-axis should be mass in grams. It should start with zero and have a range that includes the mass of the whole cup. The y-axis should be labeled "Fraction of Cup." It should begin with 1/64th of a cup and go up in the following increments: 1/32, 1/16, 1/8, 1/4, 1/2, and 1.

Instruct students to examine their data and discuss whether they will ever get a piece of cup that has absolutely no mass. Make sure students understand that as pieces get smaller and smaller, their masses and their weights get smaller and smaller, but the pieces always have some mass.

Assess

After completing the chapter, see *Identifying Misconceptions* in the Study Guide.

CHAPTER 3

Atoms, Elements, and the Periodic Table

Chapter Vocabulary

matter
atom
law of conservation of matter
electron
nucleus
proton
neutron
element
atomic number
isotope
mass number
atomic mass
metal
nonmetal
metalloid
substance
compound
mixture

What do you think?

Science Journal The photograph shows pieces of a model kit. Scientists use models to examine things that are too small to be seen such as atoms, or too large to work with, such as the atmosphere.

CHAPTER 3

Atoms, Elements, and the Periodic Table

The sky is clear and the breeze is light—perfect conditions for a hot-air balloon ride. You lift off and soar above the treetops. During your flight, you look up inside the balloon. What is keeping you airborne? Is it the air, the heat, or the balloon? It has something to do with matter, but how can you tell what is matter and what isn't?

What do you think?

Science Journal Look at the picture below with a classmate. Discuss what this might be. Here's a hint: *It's a small version of the real thing.* Write your answer or best guess in your Science Journal.

72

Theme Connection

Scale and Structure Tiny particles called atoms make up elements. Elements are the building blocks of all matter.

You've just finished playing basketball. You're hot and thirsty. You reach for your bottle of water and take a drink. Releasing your grip, you notice that the bottle is nearly empty. Is the bottle really almost empty? According to the dictionary, *empty* means "containing nothing." When you have finished all the water in the bottle, will it be empty or full?

Observe matter

1. Wad up a dry paper towel or tissue and tape it to the inside of a plastic cup as shown.
2. Fill a bowl or sink with water. Turn the cup upside down and slowly push the cup straight down into the water as far as you can.
3. Slowly raise the cup straight up and out of the water. Remove the paper towel or tissue paper and examine it.

Observe

In your Science Journal, describe the activity and its results. Explain what you think happened. Was anything in the cup besides the paper? If so, what was it?

Before You Read

Making a Main Ideas Study Fold **Before you read the chapter, make the following Foldable to help you identify the main ideas about atoms, elements, compounds, and mixtures.**

1. Place a sheet of paper in front of you so the long side is at the top. Fold the paper in half from the left side to the right side and then unfold.
2. Fold each side in to the centerfold line to divide the paper into fourths.
3. Fold the paper in half from top to bottom and unfold again. Label each area *Atoms, Elements, Compounds* and *Mixtures,* as shown.
4. Through the top thickness of paper, cut along both of the middle fold lines to form four tabs, as shown.
5. As you read the chapter, record information about each on the back of the four tabs.

Before You Read

Dinah Zike Study Fold

Purpose Use this activity to determine what students know about the four states of matter before reading the chapter. Students can use the resulting Foldable for recording and organizing notes as they read.

For additional help, see Foldables Worksheet, p. 13 in **Chapter Resources Booklet,** or go to the Glencoe Science Web site at **science.glencoe.com.** See After You Read in the Study Guide at the end of this chapter.

Explore Activity

Purpose Use the Explore Activity to help students discover that air is matter because it occupies space. L2 ELL LS **Kinesthetic**

Preparation Obtain water if sinks are not available in your classroom. The sink or bowl used in the activity must be deep enough for the cup to be submerged in water.

Materials paper towel or tissue, plastic cup, sink or bowl, water, tape

Teaching Strategy In Step 2, remind students to *slowly* push the cup into the water to avoid spills.

Observe

Students should observe that the paper towel was dry when removed from the cup. They should infer that air in the cup took up space and did not allow water to enter.

Process Have students work in small groups to make a mini picture book that explains to third graders how air is matter. Use **Performance Assessment in the Science Classroom,** p. 129.

SECTION

Structure of Matter

1 Motivate

Bellringer Transparency

Display the Section Focus Transparency for Section 1. Use the accompanying Transparency Activity Master. L2 ELL

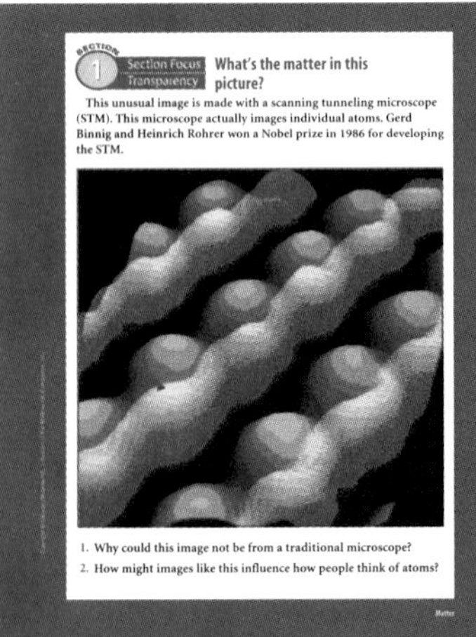

Tie to Prior Knowledge

Have students recall what they know about gases. Then demonstrate that air has mass. Tie an inflated balloon to each end of a meterstick. Balance the meterstick on top of a ring stand or on your fingertip, and pop one of the balloons.

SECTION

Structure of Matter

As You Read

What **You'll Learn**

- **Describe** characteristics of matter.
- **Identify** what makes up matter.
- **Identify** the parts of an atom.
- **Compare** the models that are used for atoms.

Vocabulary

matter
atom
law of conservation of matter
electron
nucleus
proton
neutron

Why **It's Important**

Matter makes up almost everything we see—and much of what we can't see.

What is matter?

Is a glass with some water in it half empty or half full? Actually, neither is correct. The glass is completely full—half full of water and half full of air. What is air? Air is a mixture of several gases, including nitrogen and oxygen, which are kinds of matter. **Matter** is anything that has mass and takes up space. So, even though you can't see it or hold it in your hand, air is matter. What about all the things you can see, taste, smell, and touch? They are made of matter, too. Look at the things in **Figure 1** and determine which of them are matter.

What isn't matter?

You can see the words on this page because of the light from the Sun or from a fixture in the room. Does light have mass or take up space? What about the warmth from the Sun or the heat from the heater in your classroom? Light and heat do not take up space, and they have no mass. Therefore, they are not forms of matter. Emotions, thoughts, and ideas are not matter either. Does this information change your mind about the items in **Figure 1**?

✔ Reading Check *Why is air matter, but light is not?*

Figure 1
A rainbow is formed when light filters through the raindrops, a plant grows from a seed in the ground, and a statue is sculpted from bronze. *Which are matter?*

Section ✔Assessment Planner

Portfolio
Activity, p. 78

Performance Assessment
MiniLAB, p. 76
Skill Builder Activities, p. 81
See page 100 for more options.

Content Assessment
Section, p. 81
Challenge, p. 81
Chapter, pp. 100–101

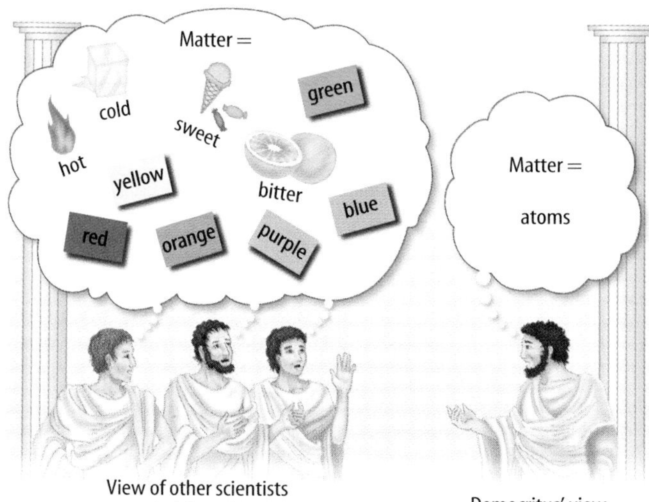

Figure 2
Democritus argued with other philosophers who thought that matter could be explained only by descriptive terms. In his view, all of the descriptions of matter were secondary to the identity of the atoms making it up.

What makes up matter?

Suppose you cut a chunk of wood into smaller and smaller pieces. Do the pieces seem to be made of the same matter as the large chunk you started with? If you could cut a small enough piece, would it still have the same properties as the first chunk? Would you reach a point where the last cut resulted in a piece that no longer resembled the first chunk? Is there a limit to how small a piece can be? For centuries, people have asked questions like these and wondered what matter is made of.

An Early Idea Democritus, who lived from about 460 B.C. to 370 B.C., was a Greek philosopher who thought the universe was made of empty space and tiny bits of stuff. He believed that the bits of stuff were so small they could no longer be divided into smaller pieces. He called these tiny pieces atoms. The term *atom* comes from a Greek word that means "cannot be divided." Today an **atom** is defined as a small particle that makes up most types of matter. In **Figure 2** the difference between Democritus's ideas and those of other scientists and philosophers of the time is pictured. Democritus thought that different types of atoms existed for every type of matter and that the atom's identity explained the characteristics of each type of matter. Democritus' ideas about atoms were a first step toward understanding matter. However, his ideas were not accepted for over 2,000 years. It wasn't until the early 1800s that scientists build upon the concept of atoms to form the current atomic theory of matter.

2 Teach

What is matter?

Activity

Take students outside to make a list of all the things they observe. Return to the classroom and have them classify the items as "Matter" and "Not Matter." **What is matter?** Possible answers: Matter is anything that has mass and takes up space and includes things that we see, taste, smell, and touch. **What isn't matter?** Possible answers: Emotions, thoughts, ideas, and light are not matter because they do not have mass and do not take up space. L2

What isn't matter?

Answer Air has mass and takes up space; light does not.

Caption Answer

Figure 1 The sculpture and pumpkin are matter; the drops the light filters through to make the rainbow are matter, but the rainbow itself is light, and thus not matter.

What makes up matter?

Students may think that objects have weight only if you can feel them. Refer to page 72F for teaching strategies that address this misconception.

Resource Manager

Chapter Resources Booklet
Note-taking Worksheets, pp. 29–31
Transparency Activity, p. 40

Directed Reading for Content Mastery, pp. 15, 16

What makes up matter?, continued

Caption Answer

Figure 3 the air

Models of the Atom

Purpose Students infer the number and types of objects in a sealed box to model how scientists study atoms. L2

LS **Logical-Mathematical**

Materials sealed shoe box containing various items (eraser, coin, paper clip, ruler)

Teaching Strategy Emphasize that students should not open the box.

Analysis

1. Answers will vary depending on items in the box.
2. Scientists perform experiments on matter to make models of the atom, but they cannot actually see inside an atom to verify that their models are correct.

Process Have students open the box and examine the items contained inside. Ask them to infer why some objects were easier to identify than others. Use **PASC,** p. 89.

Figure 3
When wood burns, matter is not lost. The total mass of the wood and the oxygen it combines with during a fire equals the total mass of the water vapor, carbon dioxide, other gases, and ashes produced. *When you burn wood in a fireplace, what is the source of oxygen?*

Lavoisier's Contribution Lavoisier (la VWAH see ay), a French chemist who lived about 2,000 years after Democritus, also was curious about matter—especially when it changed form. Before Lavoisier, people thought matter could appear and disappear because of the changes they saw as matter burned or rusted. You might have thought that matter can disappear if you've ever watched wood burn in a fireplace or at a bonfire. However, Lavoisier showed that wood and the oxygen it combines with during burning have the same mass as the ash, water, carbon dioxide, and other gases that are produced, as shown in **Figure 3.** In a similar way, an iron bar and oxygen have the same mass as the rust that forms when they interact. From Lavoisier's work came the **law of conservation of matter,** which states that matter is not created or destroyed—it only changes form.

Making a Model

Procedure

1. Your teacher will give you a **sealed shoe box** that contains **one or more items.**
2. Try to find out how many and what kinds of items are inside the box. You cannot look inside the box. The only observations you can make are by handling the box.

Analysis

1. How many items do you infer are in the box? Sketch the apparent shapes of the items and identify them if you can.
2. Compare your procedure with how scientists perform experiments and make models to find out more about the atom.

Models of the Atom

Models are often used for things that are too small or too large to be seen and observed or that are too difficult to be understood easily. One way to make a model is to make a smaller version of something large. If you wanted to design a new sailboat, would you build a full-sized boat and hope it would float? It would be more effective, less expensive, and safer to build and test a smaller version first. Then, if it didn't float, you could change your design and build another model. You could keep trying until the model works.

In the case of atoms, scientists use large models to explain something that is too small to be looked at. Throughout history, scientists have constructed and changed models to learn more about what atoms are made of and how they act.

Resource Manager

Chapter Resources Booklet
MiniLAB, p. 3
Enrichment, p. 26
Mathematics Skill Activities, p. 39

Visual Learning

Figure 3 Why could being in a closed space with a fire be hazardous, even if you are in no danger of being burned? As the fuel burns, it consumes oxygen and produces smoke. Thus, being confined with a fire can lead to suffocation, not only from lack of oxygen, but also from smoke inhalation.

Dalton's Atomic Model In the early 1800s, an English schoolteacher and chemist named John Dalton studied the experiments of Lavoisier and others. Dalton thought he could design an atomic model that explained the results of those experiments. His model later became known as the atomic theory of matter. Dalton's atomic model was a set of ideas—not a physical object. Dalton believed that matter was made of atoms that were too small to be seen by the human eye. He also thought that each type of matter was made of only one kind of atom. For example, gold atoms make up a gold nugget and give a gold ring its shiny appearance. Likewise, iron atoms make up an iron bar and give it unique properties, and so on.

Sizes of Atoms Atoms are so small it would take about 1 million of them lined up in a row to equal the thickness of a human hair. For another example of how small atoms are, look at **Figure 4.** Imagine you are holding an orange in your hand. If you wanted to be able to see the individual atoms on the orange's surface, the size of the orange could be increased to the size of Earth. Then, imagine the Earth-sized orange covered with billions and billions of marbles. Each marble would represent one of the atoms on the skin of the orange. No matter what kind of model you use to picture it, the result is the same—an atom is an extremely small particle of matter.

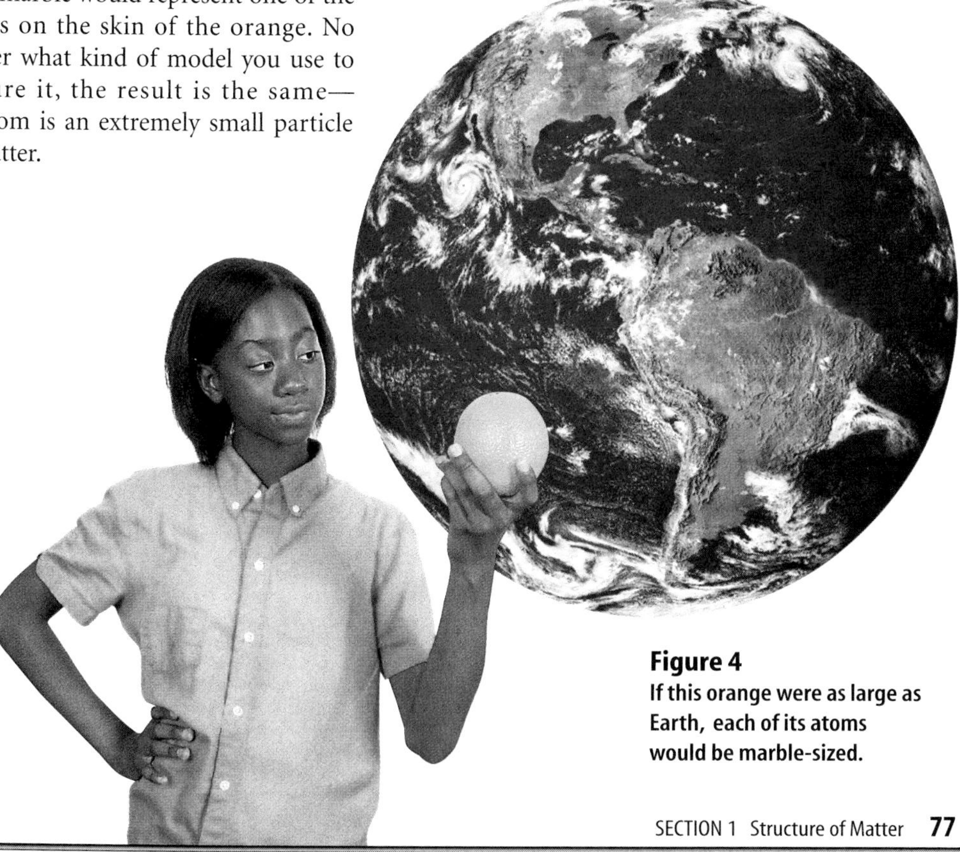

Figure 4
If this orange were as large as Earth, each of its atoms would be marble-sized.

Discussion

Show students several educational models. Examples include plant, solar system, or anatomy models. **How can models be helpful?** Models can help us understand the structure of things and how they behave. L1

Extension

Have students find out more about the people involved in the discovery of the parts of the atom—where they lived and worked, when they made their discoveries, how the discoveries were made, and other scientists they worked with. Have them combine their reports to make a class newspaper called "Great Moments in Atomic History." L2 COOP LEARN LS **Linguistic**

LAB DEMONSTRATION

Purpose to demonstrate that matter is neither created nor destroyed

Materials fine steel wool, heatproof mitt, safety goggles, crucible tongs, burner, pan balance

Preparation Wear goggles and heatproof mitt while performing this activity.

Procedure Obtain the mass of a piece of steel wool. Hold the steel wool in a burner flame using tongs. After a few fibers burn, ask question 1. After students have responded, obtain the mass of the burned steel wool and then ask question 2.

Expected Outcome Mass increases after burning.

Assessment

Will what's left have a mass greater or less than the original? Most students will likely think the mass has decreased. **Why is there a gain in mass?** The iron in the wool reacted with O_2 in the air to form iron oxide, so the mass of the O_2 has been added to the original mass.

Models of the Atom, continued

Caption Answer

Figure 5 The rays would straighten.

Quick Demo

Demonstrate the presence and shape of a magnetic field by putting iron filings on a sheet of transparency plastic and placing the plastic over a bar magnet on an overhead projector.

Use Science Words

Word Usage Have students use the word *electron* in a sentence describing its characteristics. Sentences should include that an electron has a small mass, a negative charge, and is found outside the atomic nucleus. L2

Reading Check

Answer The particles in the rays were charged, and thus were affected by the magnet's magnetic field.

Activity

Have students fold a piece of paper into four sections. Instruct them to write one of the following terms in each box: electron, nucleus, proton, neutron. As you read and discuss this section, have students illustrate and write key facts for each part of the atom. Illustrations will vary. Key facts should include: electron–negatively charged particles scattered outside the nucleus; nucleus–positively charged central part of the atom; proton–positively charged particle located in the nucleus; neutron–a particle with no charge found in the nucleus of the atom. P

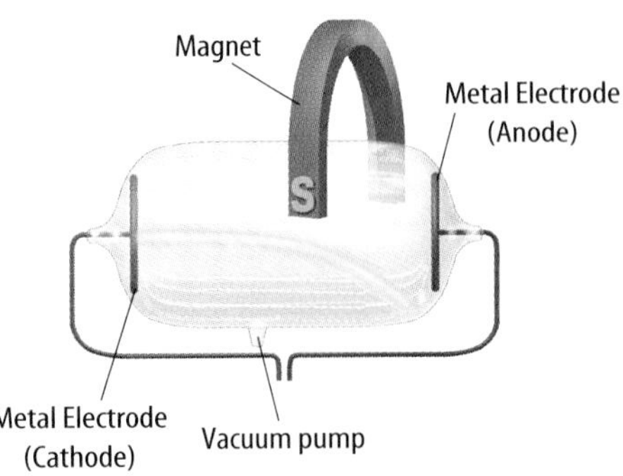

Figure 5
In Thomson's experiment, the magnet caused the cathode rays inside the tube to bend. *What do you think would happen to the cathode rays if the magnet were removed?*

Discovering the Electron One of the many pioneers in the development of today's atomic model was J.J. Thomson, an English scientist. He conducted experiments using a cathode ray tube, which is a glass tube sealed at both ends out of which most of the air has been pumped. Thomson's tube had a metal plate at each end. The plates were connected to a high-voltage electrical source that gave one of the plates—the anode—a positive charge and the other plate—the cathode—a negative charge. During his experiments, Thomson observed rays that traveled from the cathode to the anode. These cathode rays were bent by a magnet, as seen in **Figure 5,** showing that the rays were made up of particles that had mass. Thomson knew that like charges repel each other and opposite charges attract each other. When he saw that the rays traveled toward a positively charged plate, he concluded that the cathode rays were made up of negatively charged particles. These invisible, negatively charged particles are called **electrons.**

Collect Data Visit the Glencoe Science Web site at **science.glencoe.com** for more information about electron energy levels in atoms. Display your data in a table.

Reading Check *Why were the cathode rays in Thomson's cathode ray tube bent by a magnet?*

Try to imagine Thomson's excitement at this discovery. He had shown that atoms are not too tiny to divide after all. Rather, they are made up of even smaller subatomic particles. Other scientists soon built upon Thomson's results and found that the electron had a small mass. In fact, an electron is 1/1,837 the mass of the lightest atom, the hydrogen atom. In 1906, Thomson received the Nobel Prize in Physics for his work on the discovery of the electron.

Matter that has an equal amount of positive and negative charge is said to be neutral—it has no net charge. Because most matter is neutral, Thomson pictured the atom as a ball of positive charge with electrons embedded in it. It was later determined that neutral atoms contained an equal number of positive and negative charges.

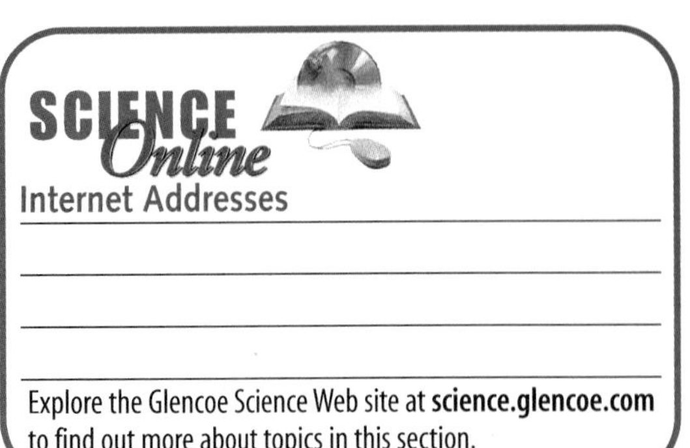

Internet Addresses
Explore the Glencoe Science Web site at science.glencoe.com to find out more about topics in this section.

Inclusion Strategies

Learning Disabled Have students make-up new lyrics to a familiar tune using the vocabulary and definitions from the chapter. The song can focus on one concept, such as the parts of an atom, or cover the entire chapter's content. Some examples for the familiar tune are "Row, Row, Row Your Boat," "Old McDonald," and "Itsy Bitsy Spider." LS **Auditory-Musical**

Thomson's Model Thomson's model, shown in **Figure 6,** can be compared to chocolate chips spread throughout a ball of cookie dough. However, the model did not provide all the answers to the questions about atoms that puzzled scientists.

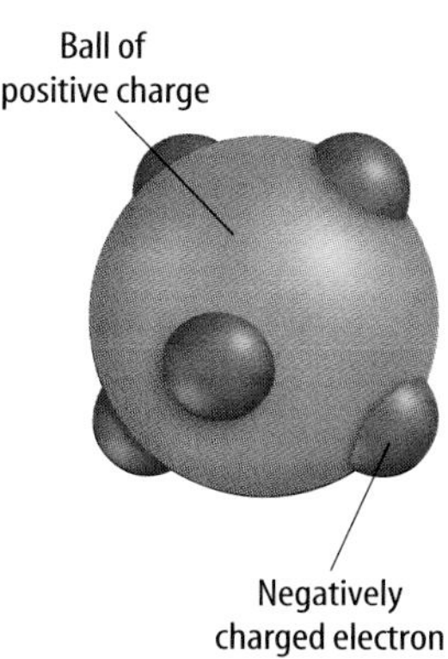

Figure 6
Thomson's model shows the atom as electrons embedded in a ball of positive charge. *How did Thomson know that atoms contain positive and negative charges?*

Rutherford—The Nucleus Scientists still had questions about how the atom was arranged and about the presence of positively charged particles. In 1909, a team of scientists led by Ernest Rutherford began their work on these questions. In their experiment, they bombarded an extremely thin piece of gold foil with alpha particles. Alpha particles are tiny, high-energy, positively charged particles. Most of the particles passed straight through the foil as if it were not there at all. However, other particles changed direction, and some even bounced back. Rutherford thought the result was so remarkable that he later said, "It was almost as incredible as if you had fired a 15-inch shell at a piece of tissue paper, and it came back and hit you."

Positive Center Rutherford concluded that because so many of the alpha particles passed straight through the gold foil, the atoms must be made of mostly empty space. However, because some of the alpha particles bounced off of something, the gold atoms must contain some positively charged object concentrated in the midst of this empty space. Rutherford called the positively charged, central part of the atom the **nucleus** (NEW klee us). He named the positively charged particles in the nucleus **protons.** He also suggested that electrons were scattered in the mostly empty space around the nucleus, as shown in **Figure 7.**

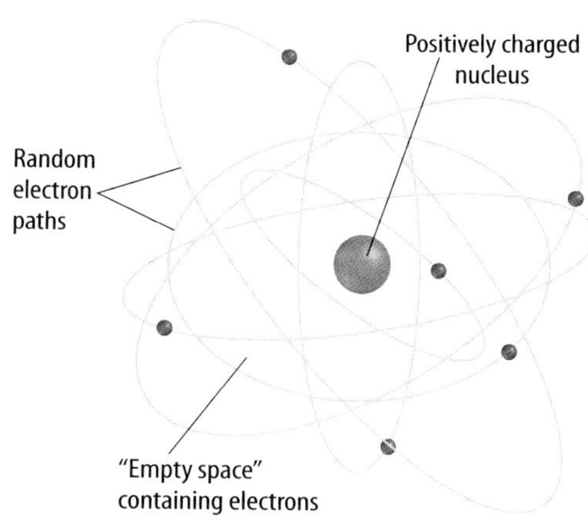

Figure 7
Rutherford concluded that the atom must be mostly empty space in which electrons travel in random paths around the nucleus. He also thought the nucleus of the atom must be small and positively charged. *Where is most of the mass of the atom concentrated?*

Discussion

How are protons and neutrons similar and how are they different? Protons and neutrons are both found in atomic nuclei. Both particles are small but massive, and their masses are nearly equal. The proton is positively charged, while the neutron has no charge.

Visual Learning

Figures 6 and 7 Have students compare Thomson's model with Rutherford's model. **How are they the same?** Both are spherical and contain particles. **How are they different?** Thomson's model is like a solid ball, while Rutherford's is mostly empty space, like a cloud.

Caption Answers

- **Figure 6** Because matter is neutral, if it contains particles with negative charges, it must also contain particles with positive charges.
- **Figure 7** in the nucleus

Resource Manager

Chapter Resources Booklet
Transparency Activity, pp. 43–44
Cultural Diversity, p. 59
Reading and Writing Skill Activities, p. 41

Teacher FYI

An alpha particle consists of two protons and two neutrons and is identical to the nucleus of a helium atom. Alpha particles are emitted by many radioactive nuclei, such as the ones that Rutherford used in his experiment.

Improving the Atomic Model

Make a Model

Students may find this abstract information difficult to understand unless models and visual examples are used during reading and discussion. Have students construct a teaching model by using a standard paper plate as the electron cloud. Have them use different colors for electrons (negative symbols) and protons (positive symbols).

L1 LS **Kinesthetic**

Students may think that atoms and their structures are two-dimensional or flat because the models and illustrations are flat. In fact, an atom is a three-dimensional object in which the electrons travel in a random pattern within a given distance around the nucleus.

Quantum theory was originated by Max Planck, who won the Nobel Prize for this idea in 1918. It was further refined by Erwin Schrodinger and his work in quantum mechanics. The work of these scientists and others, including Einstein, Dirac, and Heisenberg, lead to the idea of quantum mechanics, a branch of physics that deals with the behavior of matter and light on the atomic scale. Quantum mechanics attempts to describe the properties of subatomic particles, including the interactions of the particles with one another and with electromagnetic radiation.

Physicists in the 1920s began to think that electrons—like light—have a wave/particle nature. This is called quantum field theory. Research which two scientists introduced this theory. In your Science Journal, infer how thoughts about atoms changed.

Discovering the Neutron Rutherford had been puzzled by one observation from his experiments with alpha particles. After the collisions, the alpha particles seemed to be heavier. Where did this extra mass come from? James Chadwick, a student of Rutherford's, answered this question. The alpha particles themselves were not heavier, but the atoms that had been bombarded had given off new particles. Chadwick experimented with these new particles and found that, unlike electrons, the paths of these particles were not affected by an electric field. To explain his observations, he said that these particles came from the nucleus and had no charge. Chadwick called these uncharged particles **neutrons.** His proton-neutron model of the atomic nucleus is still accepted today.

Improving the Atomic Model

Early in the twentieth century, a scientist named Niels Bohr found evidence that electrons in atoms are arranged in energy levels. The lowest energy level is closest to the nucleus and can hold only two electrons. Higher energy levels are farther from the nucleus and can contain more electrons. To explain these energy levels, some scientists thought that the electrons might orbit an atom's nucleus in paths that are specific distances from the nucleus, as shown in **Figure 8.** This is similar to how the planets orbit the Sun.

The Modern Atomic Model As a result of continuing research, scientists now realize that because electrons are so small and move so fast, their energy levels are not defined, planetlike orbits around the nucleus. Rather, it seems most likely that electrons move in what is called the atom's electron cloud, as shown in **Figure 9.**

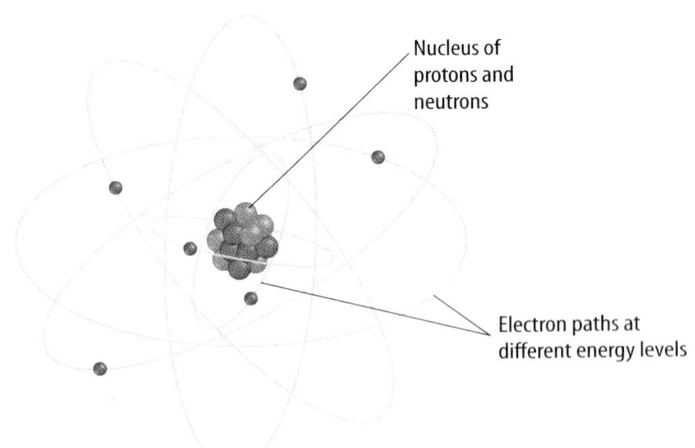

Figure 8
This simplified model shows a nucleus of protons and neutrons and electron paths based on energy levels. *How is this similar to our solar system?*

80 CHAPTER 3 Atoms, Elements, and the Periodic Table

Resource Manager

Chapter Resources Booklet
Reinforcement, p. 23
Science Inquiry Labs, p. 47

Caption Answers

- **Figure 8** The nucleus represents the Sun and the electrons represent the planets. The electrons orbit the nucleus much like our planets orbit the Sun.
- **Figure 9** The electrons are more likely to be close to the nucleus.

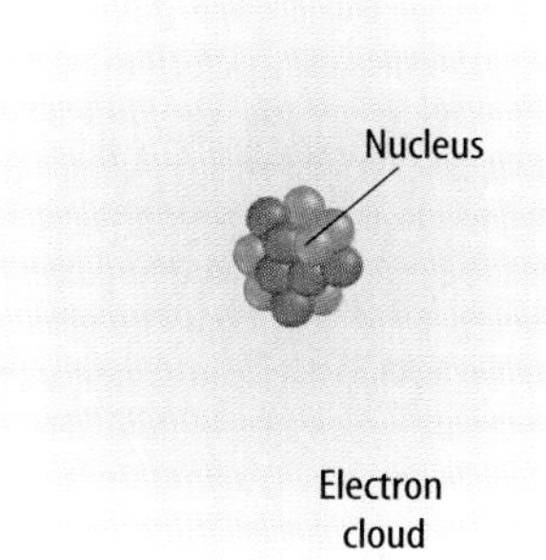

Figure 9
This model of the atom pictures the electrons moving around the nucleus in a region called an electron cloud. The concentration of color represents places where the electron is more likely to be found. *What does the intensity of color near the nucleus suggest?*

The Electron Cloud The electron cloud is a spherical cloud of varying density surrounding the nucleus. The varying density shows where an electron is more or less likely to be. Atoms with electrons in higher energy levels have additional electron clouds of different shapes that also show where those electrons are likely to be.

Further Research Today, scientists called physicists continue to study the basic parts of atoms. They have succeeded in breaking down protons and neutrons into even smaller particles called quarks. These particles can combine to make other kinds of tiny particles, too. The six types of quarks are *up, down, strange, charmed, top,* and *bottom.* Research will continue as new discoveries are made about the structure of matter.

Section 1 Assessment

1. List five examples of matter and five examples that are not matter. Explain your answers.
2. Why was the word *atom* an appropriate term for Democritus's ideas?
3. Name and describe the parts of an atom.
4. List each scientist who contributed to today's understanding of the atom along with his contribution.
5. **Think Critically** When neutrons were discovered, were these neutrons created in the experiment? How does Lavoisier's work help answer this question?

Skill Builder Activities

6. **Classifying** Look at your list from question 4. Classify the information according to the type of discovery each scientist made. Explain why you grouped certain scientists together. **For more help, refer to the Science Skill Handbook.**
7. **Evaluating Others' Data and Conclusions** Analyze and critique Thompson's "cookie dough" theory. Identify strengths and weaknesses of the theory based on Rutherford's gold foil experiment. **For more help, refer to the Science Skill Handbook.**

3 Assess

Reteach

Have students make a labeled diagram of an atom. Diagrams should include the nucleus, protons, neutrons, and electrons. Labels should include brief definitions. L1
LS **Visual-Spatial**

Challenge

Have students use common materials to make models that correspond to today's model of the atom. Have a contest and award prizes to the models that are judged the most accurate or creative. L2 ELL COOP LEARN
LS **Kinesthetic**

Assessment

Performance Have students work in small groups to create presentations that illustrate the basic structure of matter. Use **Performance Assessment in the Science Classroom,** p. 143.

Answers to Section Assessment

1. Possible answers: matter: things that have mass and occupy space; not matter: ideas, emotions, light
2. *Atom* means cannot be divided. Democritus thought the universe was made of empty space and tiny bits of indivisible stuff.
3. A massive center or nucleus consists of positively charged protons and neutral neutrons; negatively charged electrons move in a cloud-like area outside the nucleus.
4. Democritus: matter made of bits of stuff called atoms; Lavoisier: law of conservation of matter; Dalton: atomic theory of matter; Thompson: negatively charged particles (electrons); Rutherford: positively charged particles (protons) in nucleus, electrons scattered around nucleus; Chadwick: neutral particles in nucleus (neutrons)
5. No; Lavoisier's law of the conservation of matter said that the neutron cannot be created or destroyed because it is matter.
6. Classification schemes will vary. Students could group scientists by theories or by particles.
7. Thompson: atom is ball of positive charge with electrons embedded in it. Rutherford: atom is mostly empty space with electrons scattered around small nucleus. Strength: shows atom is divisible and composed of charged particles. Weakness: does not show atom is mostly space and has "structure."

SECTION

The Simplest Matter

1 Motivate

Bellringer Transparency

Display the Section Focus Transparency for Section 2. Use the accompanying Transparency Activity Master. L2

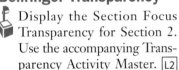

ELL

Section 2 Section Focus Transparency **Some call it quicksilver.**

This element is a liquid at room temperature. It is probably best known as the liquid in traditional thermometers; however, it is so toxic that people often choose digital thermometers that do not contain this element.

1. Describe what you see in the picture. What characteristics does this element have?
2. Which element do you think this is? Do you know of any other uses for it?
3. Which elements most resemble this element, according to the periodic table?

Tie to Prior Knowledge

Many students are familiar with the chemical formula for water, H_2O. Ask whether they know what the symbols H and O represent. H represents the element hydrogen; O represents the element oxygen. Have students list the names and symbols of any other elements they know.

SECTION

The Simplest Matter

As You Read

What **You'll Learn**

- **Describe** the relationship between elements and the periodic table.
- **Explain** the meaning of atomic mass and atomic number.
- **Identify** what makes an isotope.
- **Contrast** metals, metalloids, and nonmetals.

Vocabulary

element
atomic number
isotope
mass number
atomic mass
metal
nonmetal
metalloid

Why **It's Important**

Everything on Earth is made of the elements that are listed on the periodic table.

The Elements

Have you watched television today? TV sets are common, yet each one is a complex system. The outer case is made mostly of plastic, and the screen is made of glass. Many of the parts that conduct electricity are metals or combinations of metals. Other parts in the interior of the set contain materials that barely conduct electricity. All of the different materials have one thing in common. They are made up of even simpler materials. In fact, if you had the proper equipment, you could separate the plastics, glass, and metals into these simpler materials.

One Kind of Atom Eventually, though, you would separate the materials into groups of atoms. At that point, you would have a collection of elements. An **element** is matter made of only one kind of atom. More than 115 elements are known and 90 of them occur naturally on Earth. These elements make up gases in the air, minerals in rocks, and liquids such as water. Examples of the 90 naturally occurring elements include the oxygen and nitrogen in the air you breathe and the metals gold, silver, aluminum, and iron. The other 25 elements are known as synthetic elements. These elements have been made by scientists with machines like the one shown in **Figure 10.** Some synthetic elements have important uses in medical testing and are found in smoke detectors and heart pacemaker batteries.

Figure 10
The Tevatron has a circumference of 20 km—a distance that allows particles to accelerate to high speeds. A 30-km linear accelerator is being planned for even higher-speed collisions. These high-speed collisions can create synthetic elements.

Section Assessment Planner

PORTFOLIO
Extension, p. 85

PERFORMANCE ASSESSMENT
Skill Builder Activities, p. 87
See page 100 for more options.

CONTENT ASSESSMENT
Section, p. 87
Challenge, p. 87
Chapter, pp. 100–101

Figure 11
When you look for information in the library, a system of organization called the Dewey Decimal Classification system helps you find a book quickly and efficiently.

Dewey Decimal Classification System	
000	Computers, information, and general reference
100	Philosophy and psychology
200	Religion
300	Social sciences
400	Language
500	Science
600	Technology
700	Arts and recreation
800	Literature
900	History and Geography

The Periodic Table

Suppose you go to a library, like the one shown in **Figure 11,** to look up information for a school assignment. How would you find the information? You could look randomly on shelves as you walk up and down rows of books, but the chances of finding your book would be slim. Not only that, you also would probably become frustrated in the process. To avoid such haphazard searching, many libraries use the Dewey Decimal Classification System to categorize and organize their volumes and to help you find books quickly and efficiently.

Charting the Elements When scientists need to look up information about an element or select one to use in the laboratory, they need to be quick and efficient, too. Chemists have created a chart called the periodic table of the elements to help them organize and display the elements. **Figure 12** shows how scientists changed their model of the periodic table over time.

When you walk into a laboratory or science classroom, you often see the modern version of this chart on the wall. Each element is represented by a chemical symbol that contains one to three letters. The symbols are a form of chemical shorthand that chemists use to save time and space—on the periodic table as well as in written formulas. The symbols are an important part of an international system that is understood by scientists everywhere.

The elements represented by the symbols on the periodic table are placed purposely in their position on the table. There are rows and columns that represent relationships between the elements. The rows in the table are called periods. Elements in a period have the same number of energy levels. The columns are called groups. The elements in each group have similar properties related to their structure. They also tend to form similar bonds.

SCIENCE Online

Data Update For an online update of the number of elements, visit the Glencoe Science Web site at **science.glencoe.com** and select the appropriate chapter.

2 Teach

The Elements

IDENTIFYING Misconceptions

Students may think that all aspects of the structure and building blocks of matter are completely known. Point out that much remains to be learned about atoms and elements.

The Periodic Table

Activity

Have students skim the periodic table for symbols and names of familiar elements. Have them share with the class the things that these elements with similar properties are found in. Example: Ca—calcium is found in milk and other food products. L2

LS **Interpersonal**

Use an Analogy

Describe a month's calendar as being like the periodic table. The days are arranged from left to right, as periods of elements are arranged from left to right. Days with the same name are arranged in columns, as groups of elements are arranged in the table.

Teacher FYI

Elements such as gold, silver, tin, copper, lead, and mercury have been known since ancient times. As more elements were discovered, people began to recognize patterns in their properties. Later, scientists used the patterns to classify the elements.

Internet Addresses

Explore the Glencoe Science Web site at **science.glencoe.com** to find out more about topics in this section.

Resource Manager 

Chapter Resources Booklet

Transparency Activity, p. 41

Directed Reading for Content Mastery, p. 27

Visualizing the Periodic Table

Have students examine the pictures and read the captions. Then ask the following questions.

Why do you think the periodic table is so useful to scientists? It helps them organize and understand the chemical properties of the elements.

One difference between Mendeleev's table and the one used today is that his table lacks the column containing the elements helium through radon. Why do you think this is? None of the elements in that column had been discovered in Mendeleev's time. This is because they are not common and they don't readily undergo chemical reactions.

Activity

Divide the class into eighteen groups. Assign each group a different group of elements from the periodic table. Have them research the similarities and differences among the elements in their respective groups and make a poster illustrating the properties of these elements. L2

COOP LEARN **LS Interpersonal**

Extension

Have students research the following questions: How were alchemists' ideas about matter different from modern ideas? How is this reflected in their version of the periodic table? How did modern chemistry develop from the methods of alchemy? Ask students to share their findings with the class. L3

LS Linguistic

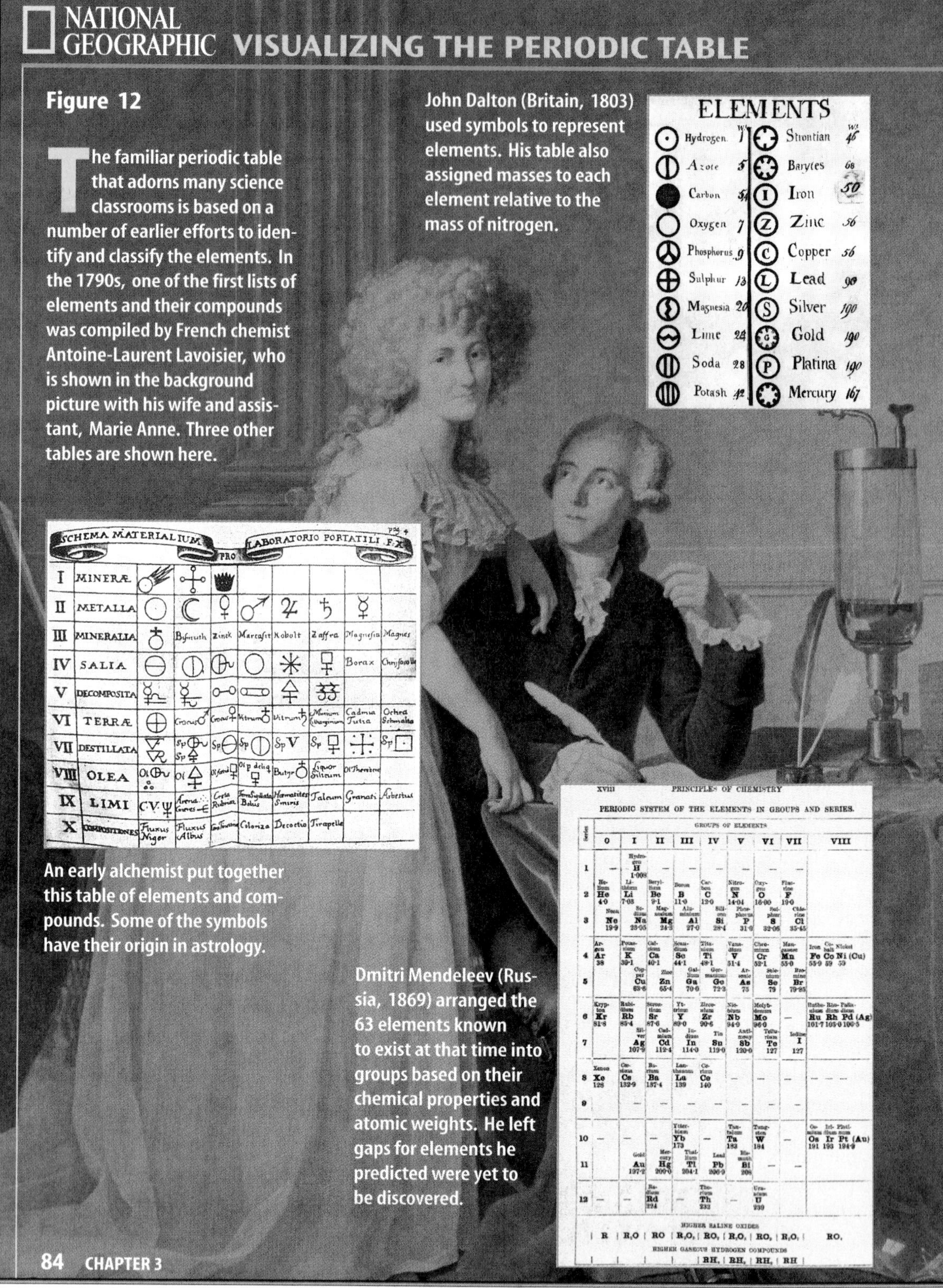

NATIONAL GEOGRAPHIC VISUALIZING THE PERIODIC TABLE
Figure 12
The familiar periodic table that adorns many science classrooms is based on a number of earlier efforts to identify and classify the elements. In the 1790s, one of the first lists of elements and their compounds was compiled by French chemist Antoine-Laurent Lavoisier, who is shown in the background picture with his wife and assistant, Marie Anne. Three other tables are shown here.
John Dalton (Britain, 1803) used symbols to represent elements. His table also assigned masses to each element relative to the mass of nitrogen.
ELEMENTS
Hydrogen 1
Azote 5
Carbon 5½
Oxygen 7
Phosphorus 9
Sulphur 13
Magnesia 20
Lime 24
Soda 28
Potash 42
Strontian 46
Barytes 68
Iron 50
Zinc 56
Copper 56
Lead 90
Silver 190
Gold 190
Platina 190
Mercury 167
SCHEMA MATERIALIUM PRO LABORATORIO PORTATILI
I MINERÆ
II METALLA
III MINERALIA
IV SALIA
V DECOMPOSITA
VI TERRÆ
VII DESTILLATA
VIII OLEA
IX LIMI
X COMPOSITIONES
An early alchemist put together this table of elements and compounds. Some of the symbols have their origin in astrology.
PRINCIPLES OF CHEMISTRY
PERIODIC SYSTEM OF THE ELEMENTS IN GROUPS AND SERIES.
Dmitri Mendeleev (Russia, 1869) arranged the 63 elements known to exist at that time into groups based on their chemical properties and atomic weights. He left gaps for elements he predicted were yet to be discovered.
84 CHAPTER 3

Teacher FYI

In 1869, Dmitri Mendeleev published a periodic table based on his recognition of patterns in the properties and atomic masses of 60 known elements. In trying to extend the patterns, he made a card for each element. Each card contained the element's symbol, atomic mass, and its characteristic chemical and physical properties. By arranging the cards on a table, in order of increasing atomic mass, and by grouping elements of similar properties together, the resultant "periodic table" showed vertical, horizontal, and diagonal relationships. Although Mendeleev left gaps in his table for the discovery of unknown elements, he was able to predict their chemical and physical properties in detail.

Identifying Characteristics

Each element is different and has unique properties. These differences can be described in part by looking at the relationships between the atomic particles in each element. The periodic table contains numbers that describe these relationships.

Number of Protons and Neutrons Look up the element chlorine on the periodic table found on the inside back cover of your book. Cl is the symbol for chlorine, as shown in **Figure 13,** but what are the two numbers? The top number is the element's **atomic number.** It tells you the number of protons in the nucleus of each atom of that element. Every atom of chlorine, for example, has 17 protons in its nucleus.

What are the atomic numbers for Cs, Ne, Pb, and U?

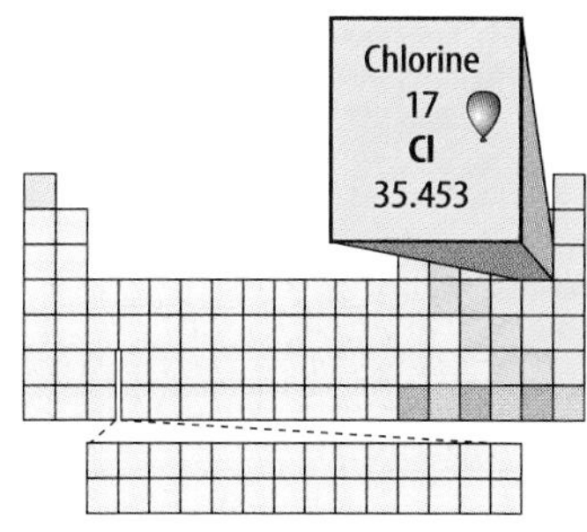

Figure 13
The periodic table block for chlorine shows its symbol, atomic number, and atomic mass. *Are chlorine atoms more or less massive than carbon atoms?*

Isotopes Although the number of protons changes from element to element, every atom of the same element has the same number of protons. However, the number of neutrons can vary even for one element. For example, some chlorine atoms have 18 neutrons in their nucleus while others have 20. These two types of chlorine atoms are chlorine-35 and chlorine-37. They are called **isotopes** (I suh tohps), which are atoms of the same element that have different numbers of neutrons.

You can tell someone exactly which isotope you are referring to by using its mass number. An atom's **mass number** is the number of protons plus the number of neutrons it contains. The numbers 35 and 37, which were used to refer to chlorine, are mass numbers. Hydrogen has three isotopes with mass numbers of 1, 2, and 3. They are shown in **Figure 14.** Each hydrogen atom always has one proton, but in each isotope the number of neutrons is different.

Figure 14
Three isotopes of hydrogen are known to exist. They have zero, one, and two neutrons in addition to their one proton. Protium, with only the one proton, is the most abundant isotope.

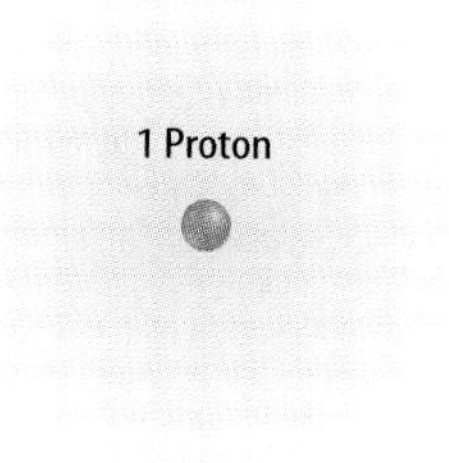

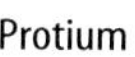

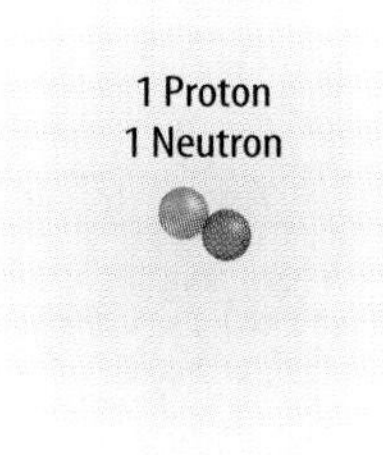

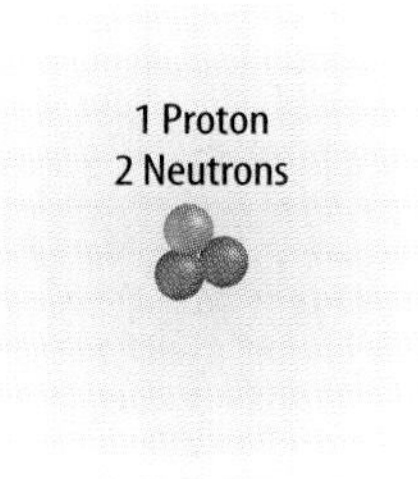

Identifying Characteristics

Caption Answer

Figure 13 more massive

Extension

Have students read the labels on their favorite breakfast cereals and list the elements found in the cereals. Then have students research and make a poster describing the use of these elements by the human body. L2 IS **Linguistic** P

Fun Fact

To get an idea of how small the mass of an atom is, consider that there are roughly 6.5 sextillion (6,500,000,000,000,000,000,000) atoms of hydrogen and oxygen combined in one drop of water.

Reading Check

Answer Cs–55; Ne–10; Pb–82; U–92

Visual Learning

Figure 14 Have students identify the differences among the three isotopes of hydrogen. Then explain that almost all elements have some isotopes. As an extension, have students research the isotopes of some elements and draw the different nuclei. Carbon is an example: C-12: 6 p, 6 n; C-13: 6 p, 7 n; C-14; 6 p, 8 n. Remind students that all of the isotopes of one element have the same number of protons.

Inclusion Strategies

Learning Disabled While presenting information about the atom and its structure, use colored markers to illustrate the parts of the atom and their location on an overhead projector. For example, protons are purple and neutrons are in green in **Figure 14.** Remind students that these parts are not really colored.

Resource Manager

Chapter Resources Booklet
Enrichment, p. 27

Classification of Elements

Activity

Mendeleev grouped elements based on their atomic masses. Have students find three pairs of elements on the periodic table at the back of the book that would have been switched in Mendeleev's table based on atomic masses. Cobalt is element 9 and has an average mass of 58.933; nickel is element 10 and has an average mass of 58.693. Other pairs of elements that would have been switched on Mendeleev's table are iodine and tellurium, and argon and potassium. L2

LS **Logical-Mathematical**

Discussion

Have students use the information on these pages to explain how cobalt and nickel got their current positions on the periodic table. Position on the current periodic table is based on the atomic number of an element. L2

Circle Graph Showing Abundance of Chlorine Isotopes

Average atomic mass = 35.453 u

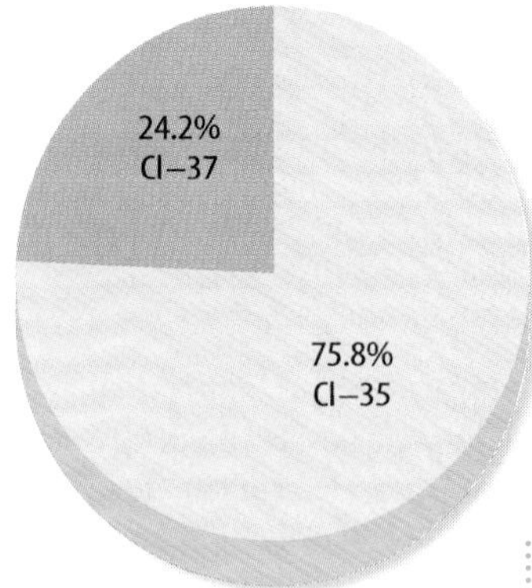

Figure 15
If you have 1,000 atoms of chlorine, about 758 will be chlorine-35 and have a mass of 35 u each. About 242 will be chlorine-37 and have a mass of 37 u each. The total mass of the 1,000 atoms is 35,484 u, so the average mass of one chlorine atom is 35.484 u.

Atomic Mass The **atomic mass** is the weighted average atomic mass of all the known isotopes of an element. The atomic mass is the number found below the element symbol in **Figure 12.** The unit that scientists use for atomic mass is called the atomic mass unit, which is given the symbol u. It is defined as 1/12 the mass of a carbon-12 atom.

The calculation of atomic mass takes into account the different isotopes of the element. Chlorine's atomic mass of 35.453 u could be confusing because there aren't any chlorine atoms that have that exact mass. About 76 percent of chlorine atoms are chlorine-35 and about 24 percent are chlorine-37, as shown in **Figure 15.** The official average mass of all chlorine atoms is 35.453 u.

Classification of Elements

Elements fall into three general categories—metals, metalloids (MET ul oydz), and nonmetals. The elements within a category have similar properties.

Metals generally have a shiny or metallic luster and are good conductors of heat and electricity. All metals, except mercury, are solids at room temperature. Metals are malleable (MAL yuh bul), which means they can be bent and pounded into various shapes. The beautiful form of the shell-shaped basin in **Figure 16** is a result of this characteristic. Metals are also ductile, which means they can be drawn into wires without breaking. If you look at the periodic table, you can see that most of the elements are metals.

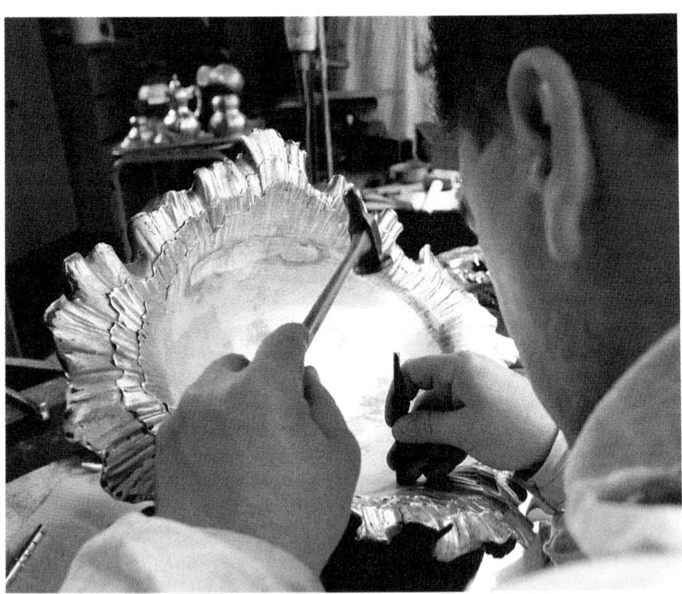

Figure 16
The artisan is chasing, or chiseling, the malleable metal into the desired form.

Science Journal

Medical Uses of Isotopes Have students research and write essays on isotopes that are used to diagnose and treat diseases. Some isotopes students might research include ^{67}Cu, ^{111}In, ^{186}Re, ^{82}Sr, ^{68}Ge, ^{153}Sm, and ^{103}Pd. L3

Resource Manager

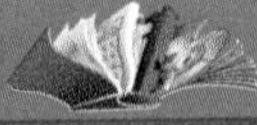

Chapter Resources Booklet
Reinforcement, p. 25

Science Inquiry Labs, p. 25

Earth Science Critical Thinking/Problem Solving, p. 2

Other Elements **Nonmetals** are elements that are usually dull in appearance. Most are poor conductors of heat and electricity. Many are gases at room temperature, and bromine is a liquid. The solid nonmetals are generally brittle, meaning they cannot change shape easily without breaking. The nonmetals are essential to the chemicals of life. About 96 percent of your body is made up of various nonmetals, as shown in **Figure 17.** You can see that, except for hydrogen, the nonmetals are found on the right side of the periodic table.

Metalloids are elements that have characteristics of metals and nonmetals. On the periodic table, metalloids are found between the metals and nonmetals. All metalloids are solids at room temperature. Some metalloids are shiny and many are conductors, but they are not as good at conducting heat and electricity as metals are. Some metalloids, such as silicon, are used to make the electronic circuits in computers, televisions, and other electronic devices.

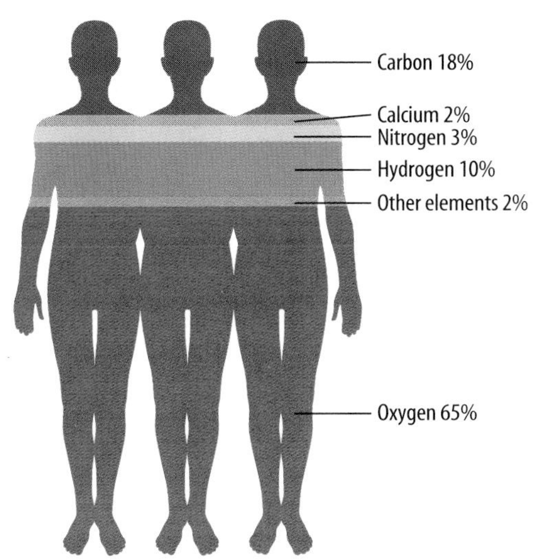

Figure 17
You are made up of mostly nonmetals.

Reading Check *What is a metalloid?*

Section 2 Assessment

1. What is an element?
2. Describe the difference between atomic number and atomic mass.
3. What are isotopes? How are two isotopes of an element different?
4. Explain some of the uses of metals based on their properties.
5. **Think Critically** Hector is new to your class today. He missed the lesson on how to use the periodic table to find information about the elements. Describe how you would teach Hector to find the atomic number for the element oxygen. Explain what this information tells him about oxygen.

Skill Builder Activities

6. **Interpreting Data** Look up the atomic mass of the element boron in the periodic table inside the back cover of this book. The naturally occurring isotopes of boron are boron-10 and boron-11. Which of the two isotopes is more abundant? Explain your reasoning. **For more help, refer to the Science Skill Handbook.**
7. **Solving One-Step Equations** An atom of niobium has a mass number of 93. How many neutrons are in the nucleus of this atom? An atom of phosphorus has 15 protons and 15 neutrons in its nucleus. What is the mass number of this isotope? **For more help, refer to the Math Skill Handbook.**

Reading Check

Answer an element with characteristics of both metals and nonmetals

3 Assess

Reteach

Write all the information found on the periodic table for one element on the board. Have students tell what each symbol or number represents. L2

 **Visual-Spatial**

Challenge

Have small groups of students classify classroom objects as being made mostly of metals or nonmetals and record their answers on a chart. Then have students write a statement that can be used to determine if their chart is correct.

Possible Answers:

Metal	Nonmetal
File cabinet	Carpet
Chair legs	Plastic seat

Metal items are shiny, solid at room temperature, conduct heat and electricity, and can be pounded into different shapes without breaking. Nonmetals do not have those properties.

Oral Name elements on the periodic table at random. Ask students to tell whether each selected element is a metal, a metalloid, or a nonmetal. Use **PASC,** p. 143.

Answers to Section Assessment

1. a material that cannot be broken down into simpler materials by ordinary means
2. atomic number: the number of protons in the nucleus of each atom of an element; mass number: the sum of an atom's protons and neutrons
3. Isotopes are atoms of the same element that contain different numbers of neutrons.
4. good conductors of heat and electricity (electrical circuits and cookware), malleable (formed into tools), ductile (drawn into wires)
5. Hector should locate oxygen on the periodic table. Oxygen's atomic number (8) is the large number in the element's box and means that every atom of oxygen contains eight protons in its nucleus.
6. Boron-11; boron's atomic mass is 10.811, which is closer to 11 than 10. Thus it is likely that boron -11 is more abundant.
7. $93 - 41 = 52$ n; 15 p $+ 15$ n $= 30$

Activity

BENCH TESTED

Purpose Students classify elements and build a periodic table that shows their classifications. L2 LS **Visual-Spatial**

Process Skills classifying, comparing and contrasting, making and using tables, interpreting data, predicting

Time Required 2 to 3 class periods

Teaching Strategy Because a large amount of information is available for most elements, advise students to focus their efforts and collect only key information.

Answers to Questions

1. The table students make will look like the periodic table, but only certain elements will be present.
2. This element should be shiny in the solid state, have such metallic characteristics as high electrical and thermal conductivities, and be reactive with nonmetals to form compounds.

✔Assessment

Portfolio Take a photograph of the class periodic table and have a copy made for each student. Have students include the index cards for their elements and the photograph of the class periodic table in their portfolios. Use **Performance Assessment in the Science Classroom,** pp. 135, 169.

Activity

Elements and the Periodic Tab

The periodic table organizes the elements, but what do they look like? What are they used for? In this activity, you'll examine some elements and share your findings with your classmates.

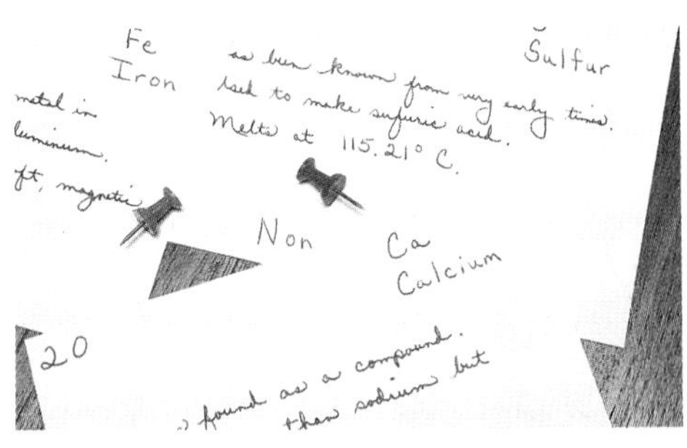

What You'll Investigate

What are some of the characteristics and purposes of the chemical elements?

Goals

- **Classify** the chemical elements.
- **Design** your own periodic table that shows the classification of the elements.

Materials

colored markers	large bulletin board
large index cards	$8^1/_2 \times 14$ inch paper
Merck Index	thumbtacks
encyclopedia	**pushpins*
**other reference materials*	**Alternate materials*

Safety Precaution

Use care when handling sharp objects.

Procedure

1. Select the assigned number of elements from the list provided by your teacher.
2. **Design** an index card for each of your selected elements. On each card, mark the element's atomic number in the upper left-hand corner and write its symbol and name in the upper right-hand corner.
3. **Research** each of the elements and write several sentences on the card about its appearance, its other properties, and its uses.
4. **Classify** each of your elements as a metal, a metalloid, or a nonmetal based upon its properties.
5. **Write** the appropriate classification on each of your cards using the colored marker chosen by your teacher.
6. Work with your classmates to make a large periodic table. Use thumbtacks to attach your cards to a bulletin board in their proper positions on the periodic table.
7. **Draw** your own periodic table. Place the elements' symbols and atomic numbers in the proper locations on your table.

Conclude and Apply

1. **Interpret** the class data and classify the elements into the categories metal, metalloid, and nonmetal. Highlight each category in a different color on your periodic table.
2. **Predict** the properties of a yet-undiscovered element located directly under francium on the periodic table.

Communicating Your Data

Compare and contrast your table with that of a friend. Discuss the differences. **For more help, refer to the** **Science Skill Handbook.**

Communicating Your Data

Have students use a database program to display their results. The printed database can be shared with a small group or with the class.

Resource Manager

Chapter Resources Booklet
Activity Worksheet, pp. 5–6

Physical Science Critical Thinking/Problem Solving, p. 13

SECTION 3

Compounds and Mixtures

Substances

Scientists classify matter in several ways that depend on what it is made of and how it behaves. For example, matter that has the same composition and properties throughout is called a **substance.** A bar of gold is a substance. Elements—listed on the periodic table—are substances. When different elements combine, other substances are formed.

Compounds What do you call the colorless liquid that flows from the kitchen faucet? You probably call it water, but maybe you've seen it written H_2O. The elements hydrogen and oxygen exist as separate, colorless gases at room temperature. However, these two elements can combine, as shown in **Figure 18,** to form the compound water that is different from the elements that make it. A **compound** is a substance whose smallest unit is made up of atoms of more than one element bonded together.

Compounds often have properties that are different from the elements that make them up. Water is distinctly different from the gases that make it up. It is also different from another compound made from the same elements. Have you ever used hydrogen peroxide (H_2O_2) to disinfect a cut? This compound is a different combination of hydrogen and oxygen and has different properties.

Water is a nonirritating liquid that is used for bathing, drinking, cooking, and much more. In contrast, hydrogen peroxide carries warnings on its labels such as *Keep Hydrogen Peroxide Out of the Eyes.* Although it is useful in solutions for cleaning contact lenses, it is not safe for your eyes directly from the bottle.

As You Read

***What* You'll Learn**

- **Identify** the characteristics of a compound.
- **Compare and contrast** different types of mixtures.

Vocabulary

substance
compound
mixture

***Why* It's Important**

The food you eat, the materials you use, and all matter can be classified by these terms.

Figure 18
A space shuttle is powered by the reaction between liquid hydrogen and liquid oxygen. The reaction produces a large amount of energy and a single compound, water.
Why would a car that burns hydrogen rather than gasoline be friendly to the environment?

Section Assessment Planner

PORTFOLIO
Curriculum Connection, p. 92

PERFORMANCE ASSESSMENT
Try at Home MiniLAB, p. 90
Problem-Solving Activity, p. 91
Skill Builder Activities, p. 93
See page 100 for more options.

CONTENT ASSESSMENT
Section, p. 93
Challenge, p. 93
Chapter, pp. 100–101

SECTION 3

Compounds and Mixtures

1 Motivate

Bellringer Transparency

Display the Section Focus Transparency for Section 3. Use the accompanying Transparency Activity Master. L2 ELL

Tie to Prior Knowledge

Have students recall chemical formulas for substances such as water or salt. H_2O and NaCl Show a periodic table and point out that these substances represent a combination of elements from the periodic table.

Caption Answer

Figure 18 It would produce water rather than pollution.

2 Teach

Substances

Make a Model

While discussing the law of definite proportions, have students make models of the compounds in **Figure 19** using materials such as gumdrops and toothpicks. Have them share their models with the class. L1 ELL LS **Kinesthetic**

Purpose Students observe and compare the properties of three compounds. L2 ELL LS **Visual-Spatial**

Materials sugar, rubbing alcohol, salad oil, 3 glasses, hot water

Teaching Strategy Warn students to use hot tap water, not boiling water, in Step 3.

Analysis

1. Rubbing alcohol is colorless; salad oil is golden, and sugar is white in color. Sugar is a solid; rubbing alcohol and the oil are liquids. Salad oil is more viscous than alcohol. Rubbing alcohol has a strong chemical smell; the other substances have little or no odor. Sugar and rubbing alcohol dissolve easily in water, but salad oil floats on the water.
2. The number of atoms of each type of element and their arrangement account for the different properties.

Content Have students draw pictures showing how the substances mix with each other in the MiniLAB. Use **PASC**, p. 127.

Figure 19
The elements hydrogen and oxygen can form two compounds—water and hydrogen peroxide. Note the differences in their structure.

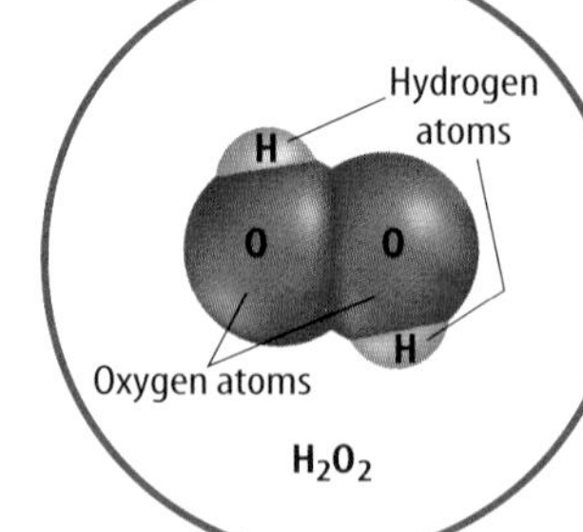

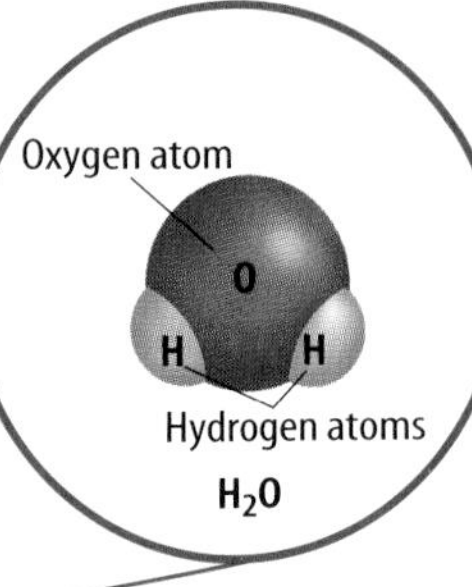

TRY AT HOME Mini LAB

Comparing Compounds

Procedure

1. Collect the following substances—granular **sugar, rubbing alcohol,** and **salad oil.**
2. Observe the color, appearance, and state of each substance. Note the thickness or texture of each substance.
3. Stir a spoonful of each substance into separate **glasses** of **hot water** and observe.

Analysis

1. Compare the different properties of the substances.
2. The formulas of the three substances are made of only carbon, hydrogen, and oxygen. Infer how they can have different properties.

Compounds Have Formulas What's the difference between water and hydrogen peroxide? H_2O is the chemical formula for water, and H_2O_2 is the formula for hydrogen peroxide. The formula tells you which elements make up a compound as well as how many atoms of each element are present. Look at **Figure 19.** The subscript number written below and to the right of each element's symbol tells you how many atoms of that element exist in one unit of that compound. For example, hydrogen peroxide has two atoms of hydrogen and two atoms of oxygen. Water is made up of two atoms of hydrogen and one atom of oxygen.

Carbon dioxide, CO_2, is another common compound. Carbon dioxide is made up of one atom of carbon and two atoms of oxygen. Carbon and oxygen also can form the compound carbon monoxide, CO, which is a gas that is poisonous to all warm-blooded animals. As you can see, no subscript is used when only one atom of an element is present. A given compound always is made of the same elements in the same proportion. For example, water always has two hydrogen atoms for every oxygen atom, no matter what the source of the water is. No matter what quantity of the compound you have, the formula of the compound always remains the same. If you have 12 atoms of hydrogen and six atoms of oxygen, the compound is still written H_2O, but you have six molecules of H_2O ($6\ H_2O$), not $H_{12}O_6$. The formula of a compound communicates its identity and makeup to any scientist in the world.

Reading Check *Propane has three atoms of carbon and eight atoms of hydrogen. What is propane's chemical formula?*

Visual Learning

Figure 19 Ask students to write the formula for hydrogen peroxide. (H_2O_2) Point out how much easier it is to write the chemical formulas than it is to write out all of the words.

Resource Manager

Chapter Resources Booklet

Transparency Activity, p. 42
Directed Reading for Content Mastery, pp. 17, 18
MiniLAB, p. 4
Enrichment, p. 28

Mixtures

When two or more substances (elements or compounds) come together but don't combine to make a new substance, a **mixture** results. Unlike compounds, the proportions of the substances in a mixture can be changed without changing the identity of the mixture. For example, if you put some sand into a bucket of water, you have a mixture of sand and water. If you add more sand or more water, it's still a mixture of sand and water. Its identity has not changed. Air is another mixture. Air is a mixture of nitrogen, oxygen, and other gases, which can vary at different times and places. Whatever the proportion of gases, it is still air. Even your blood is a mixture. When placed in a machine called a centrifuge, the parts of blood separate, as shown in **Figure 20.**

Reading Check *How do the proportions of a mixture relate to its identity?*

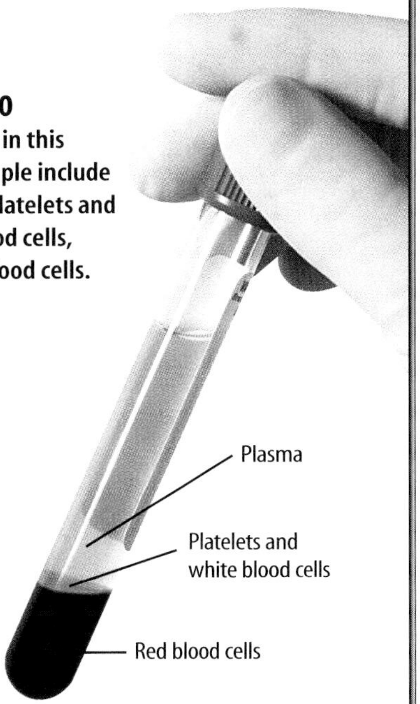

Figure 20
The layers in this blood sample include plasma, platelets and white blood cells, and red blood cells.

Plasma
Platelets and white blood cells
Red blood cells

Problem-Solving Activity

What's the best way to desalt ocean water?

You can't drink ocean water because it contains salt and other suspended materials. Or can you? In many areas of the world where drinking water is in short supply, methods for getting the salt out of salt water are being used to meet the demand for fresh water. Use your problem solving skills to find the best method to use in a particular area.

Methods for Desalting Ocean Water

Process	Amount of Water a Unit Can Desalt in a Day (m^3)	Special Needs	Number of People Needed to Operate
Distillation	1,000 to 200,000	lots of energy to boil the water	many
Electrodialysis	10 to 4,000	stable source of electricity	1 to 2 persons

Identifying the Problem

The table above compares desalting methods. In distillation, the ocean water is heated. Pure water boils off and is collected, and the salt is left behind. Electrodialysis uses electric current to pull salt particles out of water.

Solving the Problem

1. What method(s) might you use to desalt the water for a large population where energy is plentiful? What method(s) would you chose to use in a single home?

Reading Check

Answer C_3H_8

Mixtures

Discussion

Remind students that a compound is a pure substance whose smallest unit is made up of atoms of more than one element. **What compounds do you use in your daily activities?** Examples include table salt, water, and sugar.

Reading Check

Answer They can change without changing the identity of a mixture.

Problem-Solving Activity

National Math Standards

Correlation to Mathematics Objectives

6, 8, 9

Answer

1. Distillation would be best to use for a large population. Although the unit needs many operators and lots of energy, it produces the largest amount of fresh water. Electrodialysis and reverse osmosis work in a home or small resort hotel. These methods produce smaller amounts of fresh water and do not require many skilled operators. They only need a stable source of electricity.

Cultural Diversity

Ocher Ocher, a naturally occuring iron oxide (Fe_2O_3), is formed by the weathering of rocks. Historically, ocher has been used to produce rock paintings and continues to be used for artwork today. It comes in a variety of colors, depending on the percentage of iron oxide present. Hematite ore, one source of ocher that can be ground to produce a bright red color, appears to have been mined in Swaziland, Africa, as early as 44,000 years ago. Ocher has also been found in burial plots in Rome, Mayan caves, the great pyramids in Egypt, and with the Aborigines in Australia. Have students find out the other colors produced by iron oxide ores. Other colors produced include black (magnetite), yellow (limonite), and brown (siderite and pyrite).

Whole blood is often separated into plasma and packed cells. The plasma component contains substances that dissolve in water.

Extension

Use labels from popular food items and work with students to determine whether each of the ingredients is an element, a compound, or a mixture. L3 ELL COOP LEARN

SCIENCE Online

Internet Addresses

Explore the Glencoe Science Web site at **science.glencoe.com** to find out more about topics in this section.

Use Science Words

Word Usage Ask students to classify these mixtures as heterogeneous or homogeneous: clear apple juice homogeneous; oil and vinegar heterogeneous. L2

Figure 21
Mixtures are part of your everyday life.

SCIENCE Online

Research Visit the Glencoe Science Web site at **science.glencoe.com** for more information about separating mixtures.

Your blood is a mixture made up of elements and compounds. It contains white blood cells, red blood cells, water, and a number of dissolved substances. The different parts of blood can be separated and used by doctors in different ways. The proportions of the substances in your blood change daily, but the mixture does not change its identity.

Separating Mixtures Sometimes you can use a liquid to separate a mixture of solids. For example, if you add water to a mixture of sugar and sand, only the sugar dissolves in the water. The sand then can be separated from the sugar and water by pouring the mixture through a filter. Heating the remaining solution will separate the water from the sugar.

At other times, separating a mixture of solids of different sizes might be as easy as pouring them through successively smaller sieves or filters. A mixture of marbles, pebbles, and sand could be separated in this way.

Curriculum Connection

Art Have students make collages that demonstrate the difference between a homogeneous mixture and a heterogeneous mixture. Have them search through magazines to collect illustrations for their collages. Images could include: homogenous—any type of solution; heterogeneous: strawberry ice cream, salad, chocolate chip cookie. L1 P

Resource Manager

Chapter Resources Booklet
Activity Worksheet, pp. 7–8
Lab Activity, pp. 9–10, 11–12

Lab Management and Safety, p. 44

Homogeneous or Heterogeneous Mixtures, such as the ones shown in **Figure 21,** can be classified as homogeneous or heterogeneous. *Homogeneous* means "the same throughout." You can't see the different parts in this type of mixture. In fact, you might not always know that homogeneous mixtures are mixtures because you can't tell by looking. Which mixtures in **Figure 21** are homogeneous? No matter how closely you look, you can't see the individual parts that make up air or the parts of the mixture called brass in the lamp shown. Homogeneous mixtures can be solids, liquids, or gases.

A heterogeneous mixture has larger parts that are different from each other. You can see the different parts of a heterogeneous mixture, such as sand and water. How many heterogeneous mixtures are in the figure? A pepperoni and mushroom pizza is a tasty kind of heterogeneous mixture. Other examples of this kind of mixture include tacos, vegetable soup, a toy box full of toys, or a tool box full of nuts and bolts.

Earth Science INTEGRATION

Scientists called geologists study rocks and minerals. A mineral is composed of a pure substance. Rocks are mixtures and can be described as being homogeneous or heterogeneous. Research to learn more about rocks and minerals and note some examples of homogeneous and heterogeneous rocks in your Science Journal.

Section 3 Assessment

1. List three examples of compounds and three examples of mixtures. Explain your choices.
2. How can you tell that a substance is a compound by looking at its formula?
3. Which kind of mixture is sometimes difficult to distinguish from a compound? Why?
4. What is the difference between homogeneous and heterogeneous mixtures?
5. **Think Critically** Was your breakfast a compound, a homogeneous mixture, or a heterogeneous mixture? Explain.

Skill Builder Activities

6. **Comparing and Contrasting** Compare and contrast compounds and mixtures based on what you have learned from this section. **For more help, refer to the Science Skill Handbook.**
7. **Using a Database** Use a computerized card catalog or database to find out about one element from the periodic table. Include information about the properties and uses of the mixtures and/or compounds the element is found in. **For more help, refer to the Technology Skill Handbook.**

Mixtures, continued

Earth Science INTEGRATION

Strictly speaking, the term *rocks* applies to the solid materials that make up Earth's crust. These materials are not homogeneous and have no definite chemical composition. *Minerals,* on the other hand, have more or less definite chemical compositions, crystal structures, and properties.

3 Assess

Reteach

Ask a medical technologist to make a class presentation explaining the different parts of the mixture known as human blood and describing how these parts can be separated by physical means. L1

Challenge

Have students develop a demonstration that differentiates between homogeneous and heterogeneous mixtures. Possible answer: Homogeneous mixtures can include substances such as tea or carbonated soft drinks. Heterogeneous mixtures can include substances such as a tossed salad, a pizza with toppings, or fruit salad.

Process Have students design an experimental procedure that they could use to separate a mixture of white sand and sugar. Use **PASC,** p. 95.

Answers to Section Assessment

1. Possible answers: Compounds— water, carbon dioxide, table salt; mixtures— air, ocean water, brass; mixtures can be separated by physical means; compounds can't.
2. The formula includes more than one element.
3. Homogeneous mixtures; the mixture is the same throughout.
4. Homogeneous: cannot see individual parts; heterogeneous: can see different parts.
5. Answers will vary, but most breakfasts, such as orange juice and cold cereal with milk, will be heterogeneous mixtures.
6. Possible answer: Compounds are pure substances whose properties vary from the original elements that they are made from. Mixtures are made from different parts and can be separated.
7. Sample answer: Carbon is found in the Sun, stars, comets, and atmospheres of most planets. It is present as carbon dioxide in the atmosphere and dissolved in water. It is a component of rocks as carbonates of calcium (limestone), magnesium, and iron. Fossil fuels are chiefly hydrocarbons. Organic chemistry is the study of most carbon compounds.

Activity

BENCH TESTED

What You'll Investigate

Purpose

Students test for certain compounds and decide which are present in a mystery mixture. L2 ELL LS **Logical-Mathematical**

Process Skills

forming a hypothesis, communicating, observing and inferring, recognizing cause and effect, separating and controlling variables, interpreting data

Time Required

45 minutes

Materials

Compounds used are cornstarch, powdered sugar, and baking soda. Combine any two of these compounds to make the mystery mixture. Prepare iodine test solution by adding 7 g of iodine and 5 g of potassium iodide to 5 mL of water, then diluting to 100 mL with denatured alcohol.

Safety Precautions

- Students must wear goggles and aprons. Remind students that while heating the test tube, the opening of the tube should never be pointed at themselves or others.
- Iodine is poisonous and will stain clothing.
- Remind students that test tubes should not be touched while they are hot.

Activity

Mystery Mixture

You will encounter many compounds that look alike. For example, a laboratory stockroom is filled with white powders. It is important to know what each is. In a kitchen, cornstarch, baking powder, and powdered sugar are compounds that look alike. To avoid mistaking one for another, you can learn how to identify them. Different compounds can be identified by using chemical tests. For example, some compounds react with certain liquids to produce gases. Other combinations produce distinctive colors. Some compounds have high melting points. Others have low melting points.

What You'll Investigate

How can the compounds in an unknown mixture be identified by experimentation?

Goals

- **Test** for the presence of certain compounds.
- **Decide** which of these compounds are present in an unknown mixture.

Materials

test tubes (4)
cornstarch
sugar
baking soda
mystery mixture
small scoops (3)
dropper bottles (2)
iodine solution
white vinegar
hot plate
250-ml beaker
water (125 ml)
test-tube holder
small pie pan
matches

Safety Precautions

Use caution when handling hot objects. Substances could stain or burn clothing. Be sure to point the test tube away from your face and your classmates while heating.

Inclusion Strategies

Learning Disabled Assist students in completing the activity using a skill sequence—model one skill at a time and have students perform the skill immediately after it is observed. Copy the Data Table for students and distribute. Model Step 2 and have students perform Step 2. Continue to model each step and have students perform the task(s). Write students' responses to questions on the board.

Active Reading

Reflective Journal Have students write reflective journals about their experiences in this activity. Have students divide sheets of paper into several columns and record their thoughts under headings such as "What I Did," "What I Learned," "What Questions I Have," "What Surprises I Experienced," and "Overall Response." Suggest that volunteers share their reflections with the class.

Procedure

1. Copy the data table into your Science Journal. Record your results for each of the following steps.
2. Place a small scoopful of cornstarch on the pie pan. Do the same for the sugar and baking soda. Add a drop of vinegar to each. Wash and dry the pan after you record your observations.
3. Place a small scoopful of cornstarch, sugar, and baking soda on the pie pan. Add a drop of iodine solution to each one.
4. Place a small scoopful of each compound in a separate test tube. Hold the test tube with the test-tube holder and with an oven mitt. Gently heat the test tube in a beaker of boiling water on a hot plate.
5. Follow steps 2 through 4 to test your mystery mixture for each compound.

Identifying Presence of Compounds

Substance to Be Tested	Fizzes with Vinegar	Turns Blue with Iodine	Melts When Heated
Cornstarch	No	Yes	No
Sugar	No	No	Yes
Baking soda	Yes	No	No
Mystery mix	Answers will vary		

Conclude and Apply

1. Use your observations to form a hypothesis about compounds in your mystery mixture. Describe how you arrived at your conclusion.
2. How would you be able to tell if all three compounds were not in your mystery mixture sample?
3. What would you conclude if you tested baking powder from your kitchen and found that it fizzed with vinegar, turned blue with iodine, and did not melt when heated?

Communicating Your Data

Make a different data table to display your results in a new way. **For more help, refer to the Science Skill Handbook.**

Performance After students have determined the two compounds that were present in the mystery mixture, have them determine other possible two-material combinations and explain how the combinations would react when tested. Use **Performance Assessment in the Science Classroom,** p. 89.

Students could use illustrations, chemical symbols, or color to revise their data table.

Procedure

Teaching Strategies

- In Steps 2 and 3, have students use only sufficient amounts of the solids to produce satisfactory test results. Test your scoops to determine how much to use.
- In Step 4, have students use only enough solid to fill the bottom rounded portion of the test tubes.

Expected Outcome

Cornstarch will react with iodine to make a blue color. Sugar will melt when heated. Baking soda will fizz in the presence of vinegar.

Conclude and Apply

1. Answers will vary depending on the two compounds used for the mystery mixture. In describing their conclusions, students should include the data they gathered.
2. If all three compounds were absent from the mystery mixture, the mixture would not turn blue in the presence of iodine, it would not melt when heated, and it would not fizz with vinegar.
3. It contained baking soda and cornstarch.

Error Analysis

If students let their experiments run together or do not clean their equipment, they may get erroneous results. Have students compare their results to the results of other groups. If results differ, discuss errors that could have caused the differences.

Content Background

Since ancient times, Indian philosophers have thought that, except for Akash (ether), all the elements were physically palpable and hence comprised of miniscule particles of matter. The last tiny particle of matter, which could not be subdivided further, was termed Parmanu. The word *Parmanu* is a coupling of *Param*, meaning "beyond," and *any* meaning "atom." In essence, the term Parmanu is suggestive of the possibility that, at least at an abstract level, Indian philosophers had conceived the possibility of splitting an atom. This Indian concept was developed independently and prior to the development of the idea in the Greco-Roman world.

Pinyin WU XING (Chinese: Five Elements) in ancient Chinese cosmogony are the five basic components of the physical universe: earth, wood, metal, fire, and water. These elements were thought to destroy and succeed one another in an immutable cycle and were correlated with the cardinal directions, seasons, colors, musical tones, and bodily organs. The Wu Xing cycle served as a broad explanatory principle in Chinese history, philosophy, and medicine; the sage-alchemist Tsou Yen first linked it to dynastic history in the third 3rd century B.C.

TIME **SCIENCE** AND HISTORY

SCIENCE CAN CHANGE THE COURSE OF HISTORY!

Ancient Views

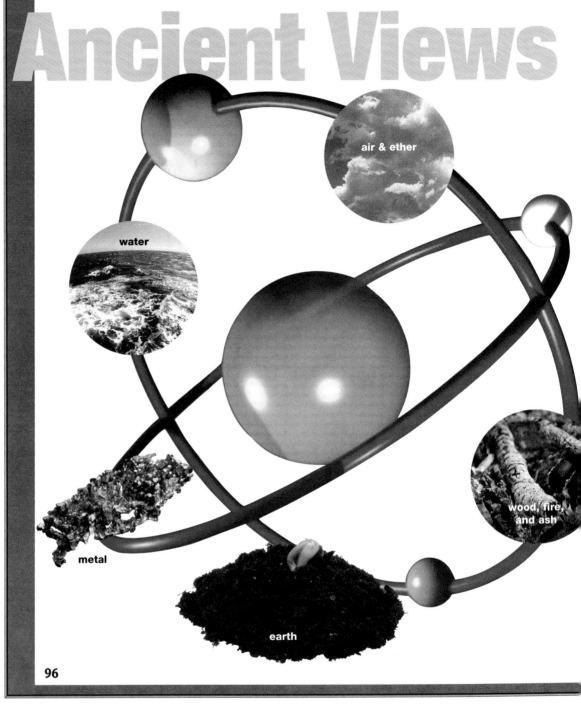

96

Resources for Teachers and Students

Chemistry in Action by Nina Morgan, Oxford University Press, 1995.

The Periodic Kingdom by P.W. Atkins, Basic Books, 1995.

# of Matter

Two cultures observed the world around them differently

The world's earliest scientists were people who were curious about the world around them and who tried to develop explanations for the things they observed. This type of observation and inquiry flourished in ancient cultures such as those found in India and China. In some cases, their views of the world weren't so different from ours. Matter, for example, is defined today as anything that has mass and takes up space. Read on to see how the ancient Indians and Chinese defined matter.

Indian Ideas

To Indians living about 3,000 years ago, the world was made up of five elements: fire, air, earth, water, and ether, which they thought of as an unseen substance that filled the heavens. Building upon this concept, the early Indian philosopher Kashyapa (kah SHI ah pah) proposed that the five elements could be broken down into smaller units called parmanu (par MAH new). Parmanu were similar to atoms in that they were too small to be seen but still retained the properties of the original element. Kashyapa also believed that each type of parmanu had unique physical and chemical properties.

Parmanu of earth elements, for instance, were heavier than parmanu of air elements. The different properties of the parmanu determined the characteristics of a substance. Kashyapa's ideas about matter are similar to those of the Greek philosopher Democritus, who lived centuries after Kashyapa. Historians are unsure as to whether the two men developed their views separately, or whether trade and communication with India influenced Greek thought.

Chinese Ideas

Ancient Chinese also broke matter down into five elements: fire, wood, metal, earth, and water. Unlike the early Indians, however, the Chinese believed that the elements constantly changed form. For example, wood can be burned and thus changes to fire. Fire eventually dies down and becomes ashes, or earth. Earth gives forth metals from the ground. Dew or water collects on these metals, and the water then nurtures plants that grow into trees, or wood.

This cycle of constant change was explained in the fourth century B.C. by the philosopher Tsou Yen. Yen, who is known as the founder of Chinese scientific thought, wrote that all changes that took place in nature were linked to changes in the five elements. In his writings, Yen also developed a classification system for matter.

CONNECTIONS Research **Write a brief paragraph that compares and contrasts the ancient Indian and Chinese views of matter. How are they different? Similar? Which is closer to the modern view of matter? Explain.**

SCIENCE Online

For more information, visit science.glencoe.com

Discussion

Kashyapa's notions were later compared to a modern day philosophy. What was one possible theory concerning how the theory was handed down and to whom? Possible Answer: It was possibly passed along through communication and trade to the Greeks; however, according to this text, this has never been proven.

Historical Significance

Historically, both the Chinese and Indian philosophies presented here have roots reaching back even further in history. For example, the first Indian philosopher who formulated ideas about the atom in a systematic manner was Kanada, who lived in the sixth century B.C. Pakudha Katyayana, who also lived in the sixth century B.C. and was a contemporary of Gautama Buddha, also propounded ideas about the atomic constitution of the material world. Encourage students to choose a current scientific theory and use a variety of research tools to trace the idea back to its earliest notions. This activity will help students become aware that our modern theories have a long history of development.

CONNECTIONS As a prewriting activity, have students call out similarities and differences in the two theories presented here. Select a volunteer to record suggestions. Encourage students to use this information in their paragraphs, and to reexamine it as they compare the historical perspectives with the modern view of matter. Remind students that the modern view of the atom was presented earlier in the chapter.

SCIENCE Online

Internet Addresses

Explore the Glencoe Science Web site at **science.glencoe.com** to find out more about topics in this feature.

Chapter 3 Study Guide

Reviewing Main Ideas

Preview

Students can answer the questions in their Science Journals. Discuss the answers as you go through the chapter. **LS Linguistic**

Review

Students can write their answers, then compare them with those of other students. **LS Interpersonal**

Reteach

Students can look at the illustrations and describe details that support the main ideas of the chapter. **LS Visual-Spatial**

Answers to Chapter Review

Section 1

3. electrons

Section 2

4. metal

Section 3

2. heterogeneous mixture

Chapter 3 Study Guide

Reviewing Main Ideas

Section 1 Structure of Matter

1. Matter is anything that occupies space and has mass. It includes all the things that you can see, touch, taste, or smell. Matter does not include light, sound, heat, thoughts, or emotions.
2. Matter is made up of atoms of different kinds.
3. Atoms are made of smaller parts called protons, neutrons, and electrons. *Which particle was discovered using an apparatus like the one pictured?*

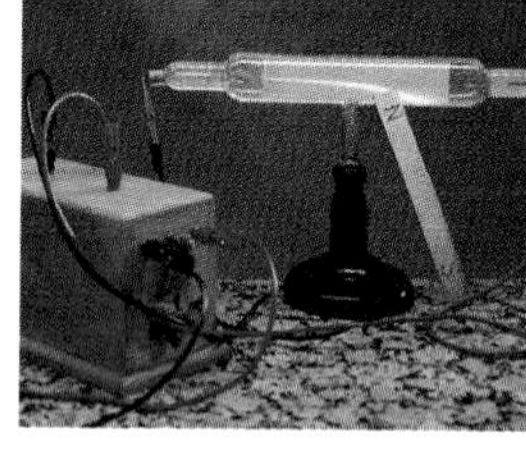

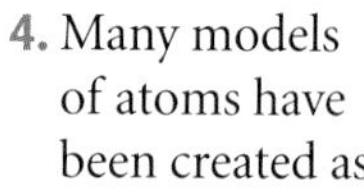

4. Many models of atoms have been created as scientists try to discover and define the atom's internal structure. Today's model has a central nucleus with the protons and neutrons, and an electron cloud surrounding it that contains the electrons.

Section 2 The Simplest Matter

1. Elements are the basic building blocks of matter.
2. An element's atomic number tells how many protons its atoms contain, and its atomic mass tells how heavy its atoms are. The chemical symbol for each element is understood by scientists everywhere. Information about elements is displayed on the periodic table.
3. Isotopes are two or more atoms of the same element that have different numbers of neutrons.
4. Each element has a unique set of properties and is generally classified as a metal, metalloid, or nonmetal. *How would you classify the spool of wire in the picture?*

Section 3 Compounds and Mixtures

1. Compounds are substances that are produced when elements combine. Compounds contain specific proportions of the elements that make them up. A compound's properties are different from those of the elements from which it is formed.
2. Mixtures are combinations of compounds and elements that have not formed new substances. Their proportions can change. Homogeneous mixtures contain individual parts that cannot be seen. However, you can see the individual parts of heterogeneous mixtures. *Is the orange juice pictured a homogeneous or heterogeneous mixture?*

FOLDABLES Reading & Study Skills — After You Read

Under each tab of your Foldable, list several everyday examples of the atoms, elements, compounds and mixtures.

FOLDABLES Reading & Study Skills — After You Read

After students have read the chapter and completed the Foldable described in Before You Read, have them do the activity on the student page.

Dinah Zike

98 CHAPTER STUDY GUIDE

Visualizing Main Ideas

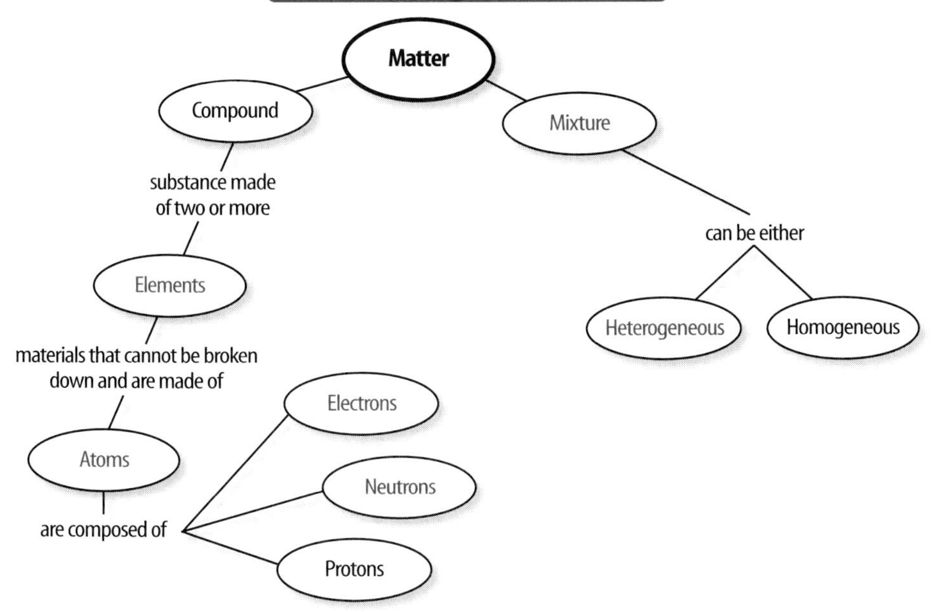

Vocabulary Review

Vocabulary Words

a. atom
b. atomic mass
c. atomic number
d. compound
e. electron
f. element
g. isotope
h. law of conservation of matter
i. mass number
j. matter
k. metal
l. metalloid
m. mixture
n. neutron
o. nonmetal
p. nucleus
q. proton
r. substance

THE PRINCETON REVIEW Study Tip

Find out what concepts, objectives, or standards are being tested well before the test. Keep these concepts in mind as you answer the questions.

Using Vocabulary

Replace the underlined word or phrase with the correct vocabulary word.

1. The <u>neutron</u> is the particle in the nucleus of the atom that carries a positive charge and is counted to identify the atomic number.
2. The new substance formed when elements combine chemically is a <u>mixture</u>.
3. Anything that has mass and takes up space is <u>metal</u>.
4. The particles in the atom that account for most of the mass of the atom are protons and <u>electrons</u>.
5. Elements that are shiny, malleable, ductile, good conductors of heat and electricity, and make up most of the periodic table are <u>nonmetals</u>.

IDENTIFYING Misconceptions

Assess

Use the assessment as follow-up to page 72F after students have completed the chapter.

Materials 50 mL graduated cylinder, beaker, water, droppers, pan balance

Procedure Find the mass of the empty graduated cylinder, then pour 50 mL of water into it and find the mass again. Use the dropper to decrease the volume of water by one half and calculate the mass of the water. Repeat this process three more times to obtain volumes of 50 mL, 25 mL, 12.5 mL, 6.25 mL, and 3.125 mL. Will you ever get a drop of water that has no mass?

Expected Outcome No matter how small the volume, the water has mass and therefore weight.

Visualizing Main Ideas

See student page.

Vocabulary Review

Using Vocabulary

1. proton
2. compound
3. matter
4. neutrons
5. metals

Chapter 3 Assessment

Checking Concepts

1. D
2. C
3. B
4. C
5. D
6. B
7. C
8. A
9. B
10. C

Thinking Critically

11. one sulfur atom to two oxygen atoms
12. An atom with seven protons is nitrogen. The number of protons determines the identity of an atom.
13. The element loses its characteristics and a new substance is formed.
14. Cobalt-60 and cobalt-59 are isotopes because they both have 27 protons in their nuclei. The numbers of neutrons in the two types of atoms are different; therefore, they have different mass numbers.
15. Rutherford's gold foil experiment told scientists that the atom contains a small, dense, positively charged structure. Rutherford called this structure the nucleus.

Chapter 3 Assessment

Checking Concepts

Choose the word or phrase that best answers the question.

1. What is a solution an example of?
   A) element
   B) heterogeneous mixture
   C) compound
   D) homogeneous mixture
2. The nucleus of one atom contains 12 protons and 12 neutrons, while the nucleus of another atom contains 12 protons and 16 neutrons. What are the atoms?
   A) two different atoms
   B) two different elements
   C) two isotopes of an element
   D) negatively charged
3. What is a compound?
   A) a mixture of chemicals and elements
   B) a combination of two or more elements
   C) anything that has mass and occupies space
   D) the building block of matter
4. What does the atom consist of?
   A) electrons, protons, and alpha particles
   B) neutrons and protons
   C) electrons, protons, and neutrons
   D) elements, protons, and electrons
5. In an atom, where is an electron located?
   A) in the nucleus with the proton
   B) on the periodic table of the elements
   C) with the neutron
   D) in a cloudlike formation surrounding the nucleus
6. How is matter defined?
   A) the negative charge in an atom
   B) anything that has mass and occupies space
   C) the mass of the nucleus
   D) sound, light, and energy
7. What are two atoms that have the same number of protons called?
   A) metals **C)** isotopes
   B) nonmetals **D)** metalloids
8. What are the majority of the elements on the periodic table called?
   A) metals **C)** nonmetals
   B) metalloids **D)** compounds
9. Which element is a metalloid?
   A) bromine **C)** potassium
   B) silicon **D)** iron
10. Which is a heterogeneous mixture?
    A) air **C)** a salad
    B) brass **D)** a soft drink

Thinking Critically

11. A chemical formula is written to indicate the makeup of a compound. What is the ratio of sulfur atoms to oxygen atoms in SO_2?
12. An atom contains seven electrons and seven protons. What element is this atom? Explain your answer.
13. What happens to an element when it becomes part of a compound?
14. Cobalt-60 and cobalt-59 are isotopes. How can they be the same element but have different mass numbers?
15. What did Rutherford's gold foil experiment tell scientists about atomic structure?

Developing Skills

16. **Predicting** Suppose Rutherford had bombarded aluminum foil with alpha particles instead of the gold foil he used in his experiment. What observations do you predict Rutherford would have made? Explain your prediction.

Chapter Assessment Planner

Portfolio Encourage students to place in their portfolios one or two items of what they consider to be their best work. Examples include:
- Activity, p. 78
- Extension, p. 85
- Curriculum Connection, p. 92

Performance Additional performance assessments, Performance Task Assessment Lists, and rubrics for evaluating these activities can be found in Glencoe's **Performance Assessment in the Science Classroom.**

17. Comparing and Contrasting Aluminum is close to carbon on the periodic table. Explain why aluminum is a metal and carbon is not.

18. Drawing Conclusions You are shown two samples of phosphorus. One is white and burns if exposed to air. The other is red and burns if lit. Infer why the properties of two samples of the same element differ.

19. Interpreting Scientific Illustrations Look at the two carbon atoms below. Explain whether or not the atoms are isotopes.

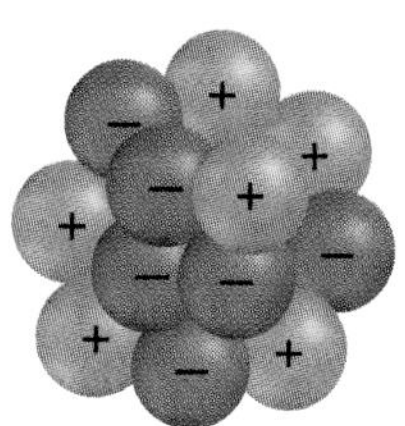

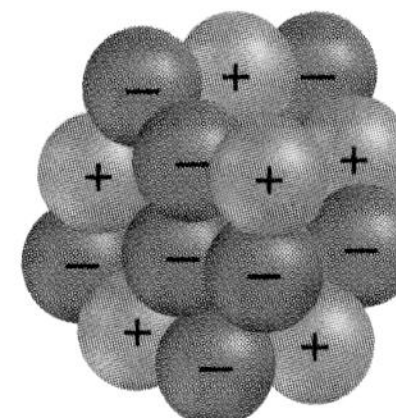

Performance Assessment

20. Newspaper Article Research the source, composition, and properties of asbestos. Why was it used in the past? Why is it a health hazard now? What is being done about it? Write a newspaper article to share your findings.

TECHNOLOGY

Go to the Glencoe Science Web site at **science.glencoe.com** or use the **Glencoe Science CD-ROM** for additional chapter assessment.

THE PRINCETON REVIEW Test Practice

A researcher is analyzing four different compounds in the laboratory. The formulas for the compounds are listed below.

H_2O	H_2O_2
Water	**Hydrogen peroxide**
H_2SO_4	SO_2
Sulfuric acid	**Sulfur dioxide**

Study the formulas and answer the following questions.

1. Which of the compounds contains the most oxygen atoms?
   A) water
   B) sulfur dioxide
   C) sulfuric acid
   D) hydrogen peroxide

2. What is the ratio of oxygen to hydrogen in sulfuric acid?
   F) 2 to 1
   G) 4 to 2
   H) 1 to 1
   J) 2 to 4

3. What is the ratio of hydrogen to oxygen in a hydrogen peroxide?
   A) 2 to 1
   B) 4 to 2
   C) 1 to 1
   D) 2 to 4

Assessment Resources

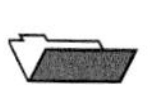 **Reproducible Masters**

Chapter Resources Booklet
Chapter Review, pp. 33–34
Chapter Tests, pp. 35–38
Assessment Transparency Activity, p. 45

Glencoe Science Web site
Interactive Tutor
Chapter Quizzes

Glencoe Technology
Assessment Transparency
Interactive CD-ROM Chapter Quizzes
ExamView Pro Test Bank
Vocabulary PuzzleMaker Software
MindJogger Videoquiz DVD/VHS

Chapter 3 Assessment

THE PRINCETON REVIEW Test Practice

The Test-Taking Tip was written by The Princeton Review, the nation's leader in test preparation.

1. C
2. J
3. C

Developing Skills

16. The cause of nitrogen fixing is lightning and legumes. The effect is the production of nitrogen compounds that plants can use.
17. Aluminum is shiny, solid at room temperature, and can be pounded into different shapes without breaking. Carbon is dull and a poor conductor of electricity.
18. The two samples of phosphorus are allotropes—different forms of the same element. Since allotropes have different molecular structures, their respective properties will differ.
19. The atoms are isotopes because they differ in their number of neutrons. The atom on the left has 6p + 6n whereas the one on the right has 6p + 8n.

Performance Assessment

20. Asbestos is a hydrous magnesium silicate—$Mg_3Si_2O_5(OH)_4$. It occurs as fibers, which are spun into yarn or mixed with other materials to form cement board or other fireproof building materials. When asbestos fibers become airborne, they can be inhaled. The sharp fibers penetrate the lungs, and can cause a form of lung cancer. Use **PASC**, p. 141.

Section/Objectives	Standards		Activities/Features
	National	State/Local	
Chapter Opener	See p. 5T for a Key to Standards.		**Explore Activity:** Experiment with a freezing liquid, p. 103 **Before You Read,** p. 103
Section 1 Matter 3 sessions 1.5 blocks 1. **Recognize** that matter is made of particles in constant motion. 2. **Relate** the three states of matter to the arrangement of particles within them.	National Content Standards: UCP1, B1		**Earth Science Integration,** p. 106 **Science Online,** p. 107
Section 2 Changes of State 3 sessions 1.5 blocks 1. **Define and compare** thermal energy and temperature. 2. **Relate** changes in thermal energy to changes of state. 3. **Explore** energy and temperature changes on a graph.	National Content Standards: UCP3, A1, B1, B3		**Physics Integration,** p. 110 **Visualizing States of Matter,** p. 112 **Science Online,** p. 113 **Problem-Solving Activity:** How can ice save oranges?, p. 113 **MiniLAB:** Explaining What You Feel, p. 114 **Science Online,** p. 115 **Activity:** A Spin Around the Water Cycle, p. 117
Section 3 Behavior of Fluids 5 sessions 2.5 blocks 1. **Explain** why some things float but others sink. 2. **Describe** how pressure is transmitted through fluids.	National Content Standards: UCP3, A1, B1, D1, G2		**MiniLAB:** Observing Bernoulli's Principle, p. 121 **Math Skills Activity:** Calculating Density, p. 123 **Science Online,** p. 125 **Activity:** Design Your Own Ship, pp. 126–127 **Oops! Accidents in Science:** The Incredible Stretching Goo, pp. 128–129

Activity Materials	Reproducible Resources	Section Assessment	Technology
Explore Activity: test tubes containing unidentified liquid, test tube rack, thermometer	**Chapter Resources Booklet** Foldables Worksheet, p. 15 Directed Reading Overview, p. 17 Note-taking Worksheets, pp. 31–33	GLENCOE'S ASSESSMENT ADVANTAGE	
Need materials? Contact Science Kit at 1-800-828-7777 or www.sciencekit.com on the Internet.	**Chapter Resources Booklet** Transparency Activity, p. 42 Enrichment, p. 28 Reinforcement, p. 25 Directed Reading, p. 18 Transparency Activity, pp. 45–46 Lab Activity, pp. 9–10	Portfolio Extension, p. 105 Assessment, p. 108 Performance Skill Builder Activities, p. 108 Content Section Assessment, p. 108	Section Focus Transparency Teaching Transparency Interactive CD-ROM/DVD Guided Reading Audio Program
MiniLAB: dropper, rubbing alcohol **Activity:** hot plate, ice cubes, Celsius thermometer, wall clock or watch with second hand, stirring rod, 250-mL beaker	**Chapter Resources Booklet** Transparency Activity, p. 43 MiniLAB, p. 3 Enrichment, p. 29 Reinforcement, p. 26 Directed Reading, p. 19 Activity Worksheet, pp. 5–6 Lab Activity, pp. 11–13 **Earth Science Critical Thinking/ Problem Solving,** p. 10 **Physical Science Critical Thinking/ Problem Solving,** p. 10 **Reading and Writing Skill Activities,** p. 17	Portfolio Extension, p. 111 Performance Problem-Solving Activity, p. 113 MiniLAB, p. 114 Skill Builder Activities, p. 116 Content Section Assessment, p. 116	Section Focus Transparency Interactive CD-ROM/DVD Guided Reading Audio Program
MiniLAB: piece of string, plastic spoon, faucet **Activity:** balance, 2 small plastic cups, graduated cylinder, metric ruler, scissors, cupful of marbles, sink or basin	**Chapter Resources Booklet** Transparency Activity, p. 44 MiniLAB, p. 4 Enrichment, p. 30 Reinforcement, p. 27 Directed Reading, pp. 19, 20 Activity Worksheet, pp. 7–8 **Lab Management and Safety,** p. 71 **Mathematics Skill Activities,** p. 31	Portfolio Science Journal, p. 119 Performance MiniLAB, p. 121 Math Skills Activity, p. 123 Skill Builder Activities, p. 125 Content Section Assessment, p. 125	Section Focus Transparency Interactive CD-ROM/DVD Guided Reading Audio Program

End of Chapter Assessment

GLENCOE'S ASSESSMENT ADVANTAGE

Blackline Masters	Technology	Professional Series
Chapter Resources Booklet Chapter Review, pp. 35–36 Chapter Tests, pp. 37–40 **Standardized Test Practice by The Princeton Review,** pp. 19–22	MindJogger Videoquiz CD-ROM Explorations and Quizzes Vocabulary Puzzle Makers ExamView Pro Test Bank Interactive Lesson Planner Interactive Teacher's Edition	Performance Assessment in the Science Classroom (PASC)

Transparencies

Section Focus

Section 1 Section Focus Transparency Bummer

If you found a rock like one of these, what would you think? A lot of people would think they had found gold. Unfortunately, this rock is really a mineral called pyrite, or fool's gold.

1. What can you determine about pyrite from this picture?
2. How is pyrite similar to gold? How might pyrite and gold differ?

L2

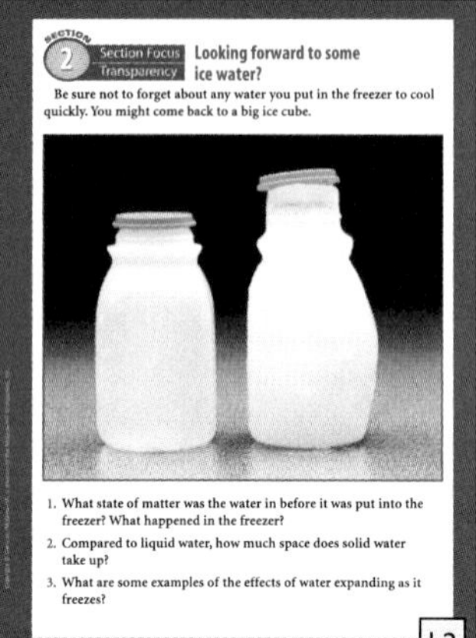
Section 2 Section Focus Transparency Looking forward to some ice water?

Be sure not to forget about any water you put in the freezer to cool quickly. You might come back to a big ice cube.

1. What state of matter was the water in before it was put into the freezer? What happened in the freezer?
2. Compared to liquid water, how much space does solid water take up?
3. What are some examples of the effects of water expanding as it freezes?

L2

Section 3 Section Focus Transparency Up or down?

Submarines have the ability to float on top of the ocean as well as dive beneath the surface. They accomplish this by taking water into ballast tanks to dive and releasing it to surface

1. The shape of a submarine is similar to an airplane's body. Why is this so?
2. From the context above, what do you think "ballast" means?
3. How are submarines and hot air balloons similar in the way they ascend and descend?

L2

This is a representation of key blackline masters available in the Teacher Classroom Resources. See Resource Manager boxes within the chapter for additional information.

Assessment

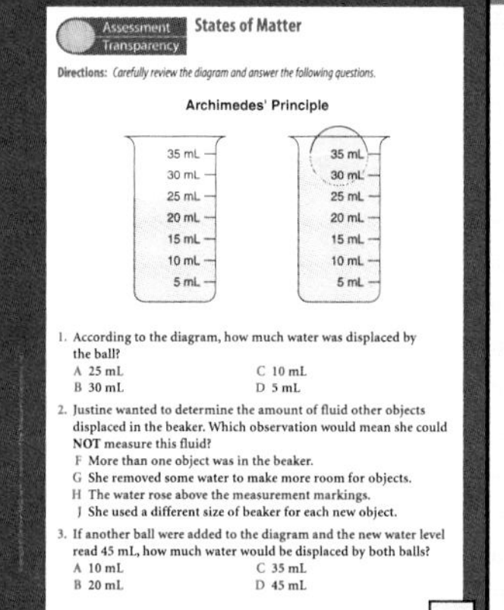
Assessment Transparency States of Matter

Directions: *Carefully review the diagram and answer the following questions.*

1. According to the diagram, how much water was displaced by the ball?
   A 25 mL C 10 mL
   B 30 mL D 5 mL
2. Justine wanted to determine the amount of fluid other objects displaced in the beaker. Which observation would mean she could NOT measure this fluid?
   F More than one object was in the beaker.
   G She removed some water to make more room for objects.
   H The water rose above the measurement markings.
   J She used a different size of beaker for each new object.
3. If another ball were added to the diagram and the new water level read 45 mL, how much water would be displaced by both balls?
   A 10 mL C 35 mL
   B 20 mL D 45 mL

L2

Teaching

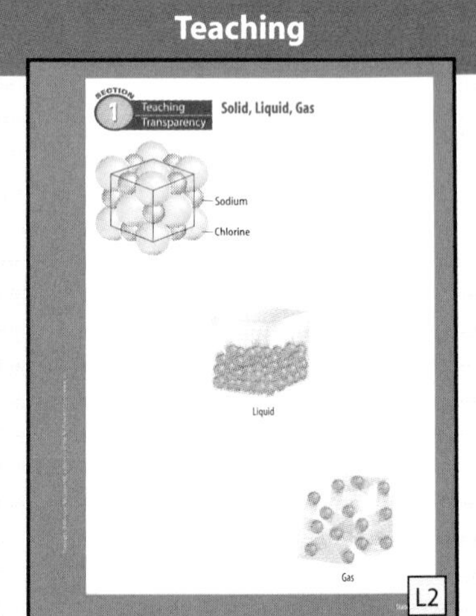
Section 1 Teaching Transparency Solid, Liquid, Gas

L2

Key to Teaching Strategies

The following designations will help you decide which activities are appropriate for your students.

- L1 Level 1 activities should be appropriate for students with learning difficulties.
- L2 Level 2 activities should be within the ability range of all students.
- L3 Level 3 activities are designed for above-average students.
- ELL ELL activities should be within the ability range of English Language Learners.
- COOP LEARN Cooperative Learning activities are designed for small group work.
- LS Multiple Learning Styles logos, as described on page 22T, are used throughout to indicate strategies that address different learning styles.
- P These strategies represent student products that can be placed into a best-work portfolio.

Hands-on Activities

Activity Worksheets

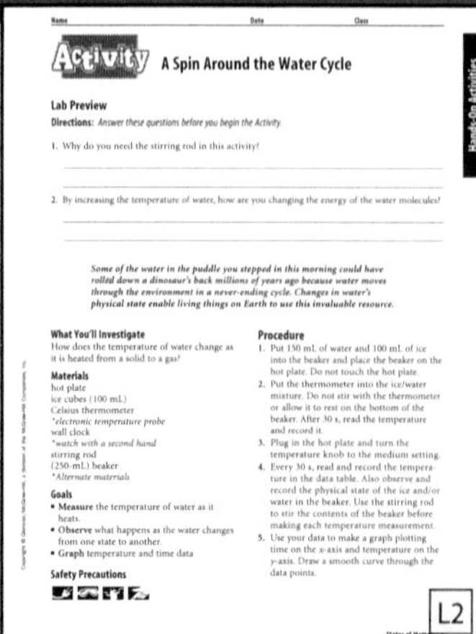
Name Date Class

Activity A Spin Around the Water Cycle

Lab Preview

Directions: *Answer these questions before you begin the Activity.*

1. Why do you need the stirring rod in this activity?
2. By increasing the temperature of water, how are you changing the energy of the water molecules?

Some of the water in the puddle you stepped in this morning could have rolled down a dinosaur's back millions of years ago because water moves through the environment in a never-ending cycle. Changes in water's physical state enable living things on Earth to use this invaluable resource.

What You'll Investigate
How does the temperature of water change as it is heated from a solid to a gas?

Materials
hot plate
ice cubes (100 mL)
Celsius thermometer
**electronic temperature probe*
wall clock
**watch with a second hand*
stirring rod
(250-mL) beaker
**Alternate materials*

Goals
- **Measure** the temperature of water as it heats.
- **Observe** what happens as the water changes from one state to another.
- **Graph** temperature and time data

Safety Precautions

Procedure
1. Put 150 mL of water and 100 mL of ice into the beaker and place the beaker on the hot plate. Do not touch the hot plate.
2. Put the thermometer into the ice/water mixture. Do not stir with the thermometer or allow it to rest on the bottom of the beaker. After 30 s, read the temperature and record it.
3. Plug in the hot plate and turn the temperature knob to the medium setting.
4. Every 30 s, read and record the temperature in the data table. Also observe and record the physical state of the ice and/or water in the beaker. Use the stirring rod to stir the contents of the beaker before making each temperature measurement.
5. Use your data to make a graph plotting time on the x-axis and temperature on the y-axis. Draw a smooth curve through the data points.

Hands-On Activities

L2

Laboratory Activities

Name Date Class

Lab 1 Laboratory Activity **States of Matter**

Three common states of matter are solid, liquid, and gas. A fourth state of matter, the plasma state, exists only at extremely high temperatures. Differences among the physical states depend on the distance between the atoms or molecules and on the rate of movement of the atoms or molecules. Pressure and temperature control these two factors.

Strategy
You will observe the characteristics of a solid.
You will change a gas to a liquid.
You will compare the characteristics of a solid, a liquid, and a gas.

Materials
beaker (1000-mL)
ice cubes (frozen from 500 mL of water)
ice cube tray
plastic drinking glass (cold or add an ice cube)
water

Procedure
1. Mark the level of the top of the ice cubes while they are still in the tray. Remove the ice cubes and place them in the beaker. Record the characteristics of ice in Table 1.
2. Let the ice cubes melt. Record the characteristics of the resulting water in Table 1.
3. Pour the water back into the tray. Mark the level of the top of the water on the tray. Under "Other characteristics" in Table 1, record whether this level is higher or lower than that of the ice.
4. Place the cold glass in a warm area. After a few minutes, record your observations in Table 1.
5. Place an ice cube in the beaker of water. Observe whether or not it floats. Record your observations in Table 1.

Data and Observations

Table 1

Material	State of matter	Takes shape of container (yes or no)	Other characteristics
Ice cubes			floats: yes or no
Water			higher or lower in tray than ice

Material	Observations
Glass	
Beaker with ice	

Hands-On Activities

L2

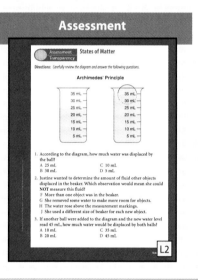

Meeting Different Ability Levels

Content Outline

Note-taking Worksheet — States of Matter

L2

Reinforcement

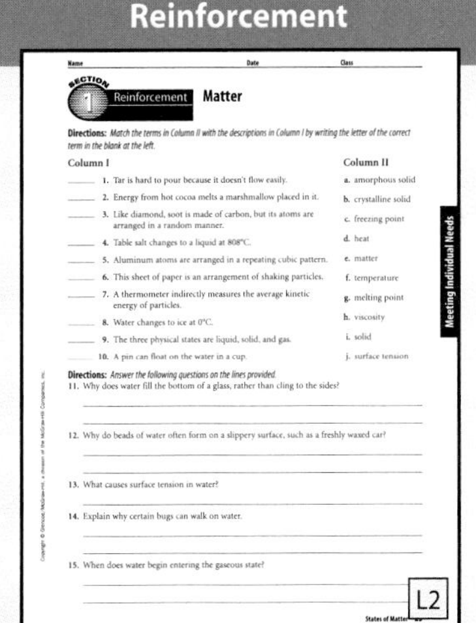

Section 1 Reinforcement — Matter

L2

Directed Reading

Directed Reading for Content Mastery — Overview: States of Matter

L1

Enrichment

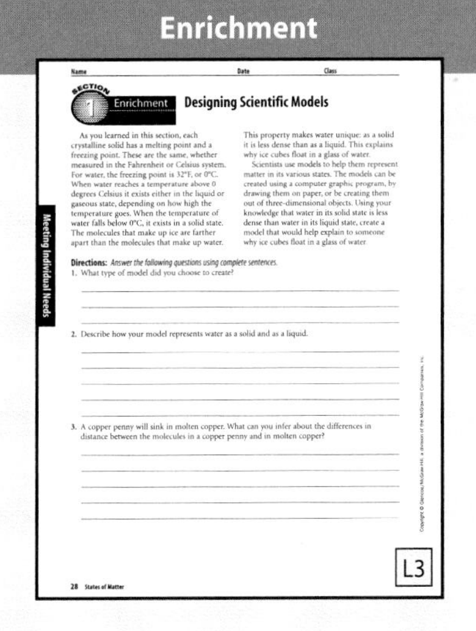

Section 1 Enrichment — Designing Scientific Models

L3

Spanish Directed Reading

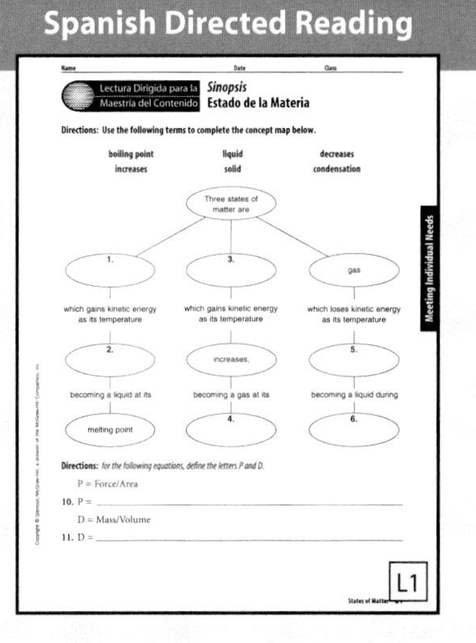

Lectura Dirigida para la Maestría del Contenido — Sinopsis: Estado de la Materia

L1

Assessment

Chapter Tests

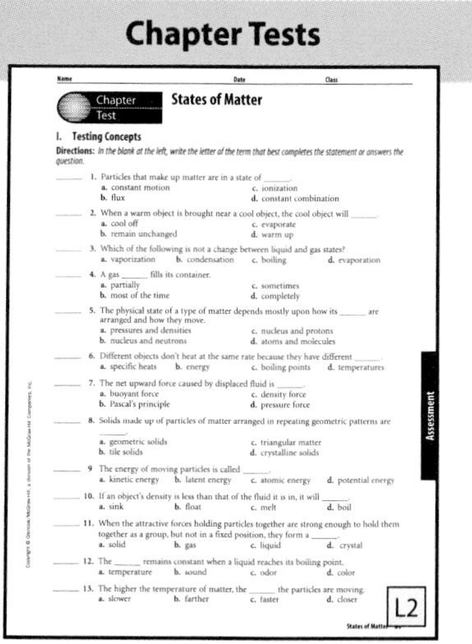

Chapter Test — States of Matter

L2

Test Practice Workbook

Chapter Review

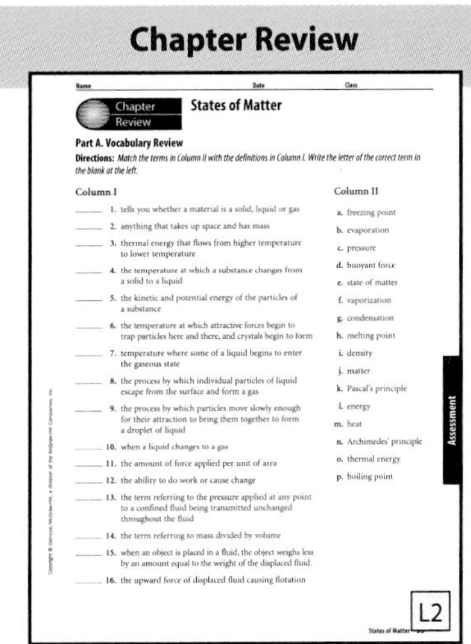

Chapter Review — States of Matter

L2

Science Content Background

SECTION 1

Matter

Understanding Matter

Matter is made of tiny moving particles separated by space. The three states of matter that people mainly encounter are gases, liquids, and solids. In gases, the separation of the particles is the greatest because these particles are moving the fastest. Decreasing the spaces between gas molecules by decreasing the temperature or increasing the pressure can turn gases into liquids and liquids into solids.

Student Misconception

Matter does not include liquids or gases; matter includes energy such as heat and light.

Refer to the facing page for teaching strategies to address this misconception. Refer to pages 110–111 for content related to this topic.

Temperature

The Kelvin temperature scale is an absolute scale. It begins at absolute zero, or 0 K. Each degree on the Kelvin scale is the same magnitude as a degree on the Celsius temperature scale. The freezing point of water on the Celsius scale is 0°C; the freezing point of water on the Kelvin scale is 273 K. The average kinetic energy of the particles that make up a substance is directly proportional to its Kelvin temperature. Although particles should not be moving at absolute zero, they have a small amount of motion called the zero point energy.

Takehide Kazami/Peter Arnold, Inc.

Heat

Heat is energy transferred from matter at a higher temperature to matter at a lower temperature. Objects do not contain heat; they contain internal energy, which is the sum of the kinetic and potential energies of their particles. Heat can be transferred three ways: radiation is the emission of electromagnetic waves, conduction is the transfer of heat by direct contact, and convection is heat transfer by warmer matter flowing into regions of colder matter.

SECTION 2

Changes of State

Forces Between Molecules

When a liquid is poured into a container such as a glass test tube, the liquid's surface is called the meniscus. The shape of the meniscus depends on the relative strength of the cohesive forces between liquid particles and the adhesive forces between particles of the liquid and the container. If the adhesive forces are greater, the meniscus is concave. An example is water in a glass tube has a concave meniscus. If the cohesive forces are greater, the meniscus is convex. Mercury in a glass tube has a convex meniscus.

SECTION 3

Behavior of Fluids

Atmospheric Pressure

Air pressure decreases rapidly with altitude. At the top of Mount Everest, 8.84 km above sea level, the pressure is only 33% of atmospheric pressure at sea level. This difference in pressure demonstrates how effectively gravity contains Earth's atmosphere.

For additional content background on this topic, go to the Glencoe Science Web site at science.glencoe.com.

Misconceptions

Find Out What Students Think

Students may think that . . .

- **Matter does not include liquids or gases.**
- **Forms of energy such as heat and light are matter.**

Since solids are easy to see and feel, students usually understand easily that these materials are matter. Most gasses are not directly observed, either through vision or other senses, so students may have difficulty categorizing gases as matter. Some students, however, may have too inclusive a view of matter. They fail to realize that energy may affect particles but is not composed of particles. These misunderstandings about matter can interfere with acquisition of new concepts.

Discussion

Ask students to divide a page in their Science Journals into two columns, one headed "Matter" and the other headed "Not Matter". Read the following terms, and have students write each one in the appropriate column: *oxygen gas, orange juice, science book, pencil, electricity, carbon dioxide gas, water, heat,* and *light*.

Superstock

Promote Understanding

Demonstration

Explain that matter is composed of molecules.

- Hold up an ice cube, and establish that it is matter and is made of H_2O molecules.
- Allow the ice cube to melt. Point to the water. Is this matter? Establish that it is matter and that it is still made of H_2O molecules.
- Boil the water on a hot plate to produce steam. Is the steam matter? Establish that it is and that it is still made of H_2O molecules. Matter includes solids, liquids, and gases.
- Move your hand over the hot plate, and say that it feels warm. Is heat matter? Let students discuss this.
- Does heat have particles? Make sure students realize that heat affects particles but is not composed of particles. Heat is a form of energy, just as light and X rays are forms of energy. Energy is not matter.

Have students go back to their charts and move any terms that are not in the proper columns.

Assess

After completing the chapter, see *Identifying Misconceptions* in the Study Guide.

States of Matter

Chapter Vocabulary

matter
solid
liquid
gas
temperature
heat
melting
freezing
vaporization
condensation
pressure
buoyant force
Archimedes' principle
density
Pascal's principle

What do you think?

Science Journal The photograph shows rain drops as they deflect off of an umbrella in a downpour. Rain is water in the liquid state.

CHAPTER

States of Matter

Ah-h-h-h, a good hot soak on a cold, snowy day! This Asian monkey called a macaque is experiencing one of the properties of matter—it can transfer thermal energy. In this case, thermal energy is transferred from a warmer object (the hot spring water) to a colder object (the macaque monkey). In this chapter, you will learn about other properties of solids, liquids, gases, and plasma—the four states of matter.

What do you think?

Science Journal Look at the picture below with a classmate. Discuss what you think is happening. Here's a hint: *Several of these bring flowers in May.* Write your answer or best guess in your Science Journal.

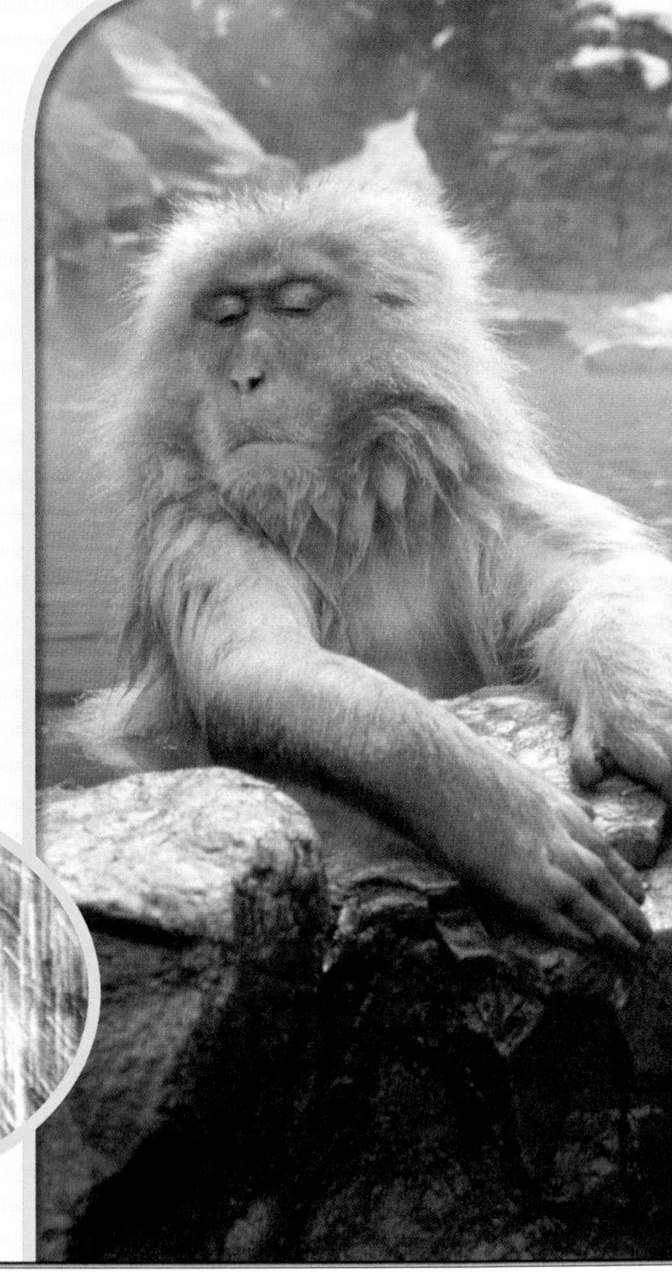

102

Theme Connection

Systems and Interactions The structure and motion of particles of matter can be analyzed to explain many properties of systems containing huge numbers of particles. Powerful changes can be caused when energy is absorbed or released by these systems. Earth's weather offers many examples of changes involving the absorption or release of energy.

Explore Activity

In a few short months, the lake that is now the solid surface supporting you on ice skates will be a liquid in which you can swim. Many substances, such as water, change as they become warm or cool.

Experiment with a freezing liquid

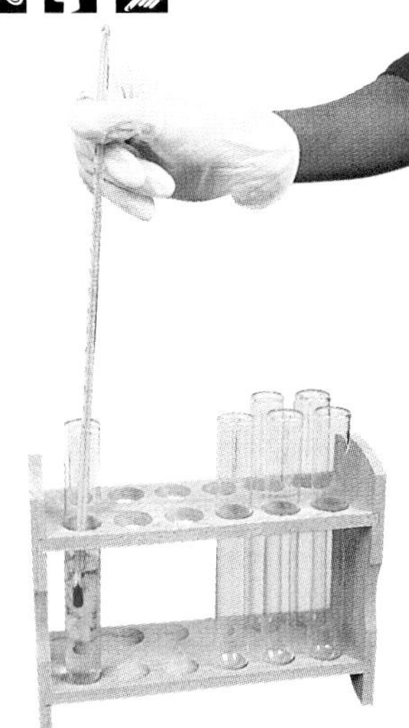

1. Obtain a test tube containing an unknown liquid from your teacher. Place the test tube in a rack. Make a table to record temperature and appearance.
2. Insert a thermometer into the liquid. **WARNING:** *Do not allow the thermometer to touch the bottom of the test tube.* Starting immediately, observe and record the substance's temperature and appearance every 30 s.
3. Continue making measurements and observations until you're told to stop.

Observe

In your Science Journal, describe your investigation and observations. Did anything unusual happen while you were observing? If so, what?

Before You Read

FOLDABLES Reading & Study Skills

Making an Organizational Study Fold **Make the following Foldable to help you organize your thoughts into clear categories about states of matter.**

1. Place a sheet of paper in front of you so the short side is at the top. Fold the paper in half from the left side to the right side two times. Unfold all the folds.
2. Fold the paper in half from top to bottom. Then fold it in half again. Unfold all the folds and trace over all the fold lines.
3. Label the rows *Liquid Water, Water as a Vapor,* and *Water as a Solid (Ice).* Label the columns *Define States,* + *Heat,* and −*Heat* as shown. As you read the chapter, define the states of matter listed on your Foldable in the *Define States* column.

	Define States	+ Heat	− Heat
Liquid Water			
Water as a Vapor			
Water as a Solid (Ice)			

Before You Read

FOLDABLES Reading & Study Skills

Dinah Zike Study Fold

Purpose Students will make and use a Foldable table to collect information about the states of matter and the changes these states experience when heat is added or taken away.

For additional help, see Foldables Worksheet, p. 15 in **Chapter Resources Booklet,** or go to the Glencoe Science Web site at **science.glencoe.com.** See After You Read in the Study Guide at the end of this chapter.

Explore Activity

Purpose Use the Explore Activity to help students discover that temperature remains constant as a substance freezes. L2 COOP LEARN IN **Kinesthetic**

Preparation When students arrive, have test tubes half-filled with molten stearic acid sitting in a hot water bath at a temperature of approximately 70°C.

Materials laboratory-grade stearic acid, glass test tube, Celsius thermometer, watch or clock with a second hand, test-tube rack or jar

Teaching Strategy Suggest that student groups divide the responsibilities of tracking time, taking temperature readings, and recording data. Students then can graph and analyze the data individually.

Observe

The liquid's temperature fell gradually, remained the same as the liquid formed a white solid, then fell again. Heat was given off by the freezing liquid.

Performance Have students predict what would happen if they were given twice as much of the unknown liquid. Use **PASC,** p. 89.

SECTION

Matter

1 Motivate

Bellringer Transparency

Display the Section Focus Transparency for Section 1. Use the accompanying Transparency Activity Master. L2 ELL

SECTION 1 Section Focus Transparency **Bummer**

If you found a rock like one of these, what would you think? A lot of people would think they had found gold. Unfortunately, this rock is really a mineral called pyrite, or fool's gold.

1. What can you determine about pyrite from this picture?
2. How is pyrite similar to gold? How might pyrite and gold differ?

States of Matter

Tie to Prior Knowledge

Ask what happens to ice that is left out of a freezer. It melts. Explain that when ice melts, its state of matter changes. The effect of this change on the particles in the water will be explored in this section.

Caption Answer

Figure 1 solid ice; liquid water; gaseous air; plasma in the Sun

SECTION

Matter

As You Read

***What* You'll Learn**

- **Recognize** that matter is made of particles in constant motion.
- **Relate** the three states of matter to the arrangement of particles within them.

Vocabulary

matter, solid, liquid, gas

***Why* It's Important**

Everything you can see, taste, and touch is matter. Without matter—well, nothing would matter!

What is matter?

Take a look at the beautiful scene in **Figure 1.** What do you see? Perhaps you notice the water and ice. Maybe you are struck by the Sun in the background. All of these images show examples of matter. **Matter** is anything that takes up space and has mass. Matter doesn't have to be visible—even air is matter.

All matter is made up of tiny particles, such as atoms, molecules, or ions. These particles attract one another. In other words, each particle pulls the other particles toward itself. The strength of the attraction determines whether the particles are held close together or are spread far apart.

States of Matter There are three familiar physical states of matter—solid, liquid, and gas. The arrangement and attraction of particles within a sample of matter determine whether the matter is a solid, liquid, or gas.

A fourth state of matter known as plasma occurs only at very high temperatures. Plasma is found in the Sun and in lightning. Although plasma is common in the universe, it is not common on Earth. For that reason, this chapter will focus on the three states of matter that are common on Earth.

Figure 1
Matter exists in all four states in this scene. *Identify the solid, liquid, gas, and plasma in this photograph.*

Section Assessment Planner

PORTFOLIO
Extension, p. 105
Assessment, p. 108

PERFORMANCE ASSESSMENT
Skill Builder Activities, p. 108
See page 132 for more options.

CONTENT ASSESSMENT
Section, p. 108
Challenge, p. 108
Chapter, pp. 132–133

Solids

You are sitting on solid matter right now. Chairs, floors, rocks, trees, and ice cubes are a few examples of matter in the solid state. **Solid** objects have definite shapes and volumes, which means that solid matter does not change shape when you move it from one place to another. Consider a baseball, for example. Suppose you pick up a baseball from the ground and place it in a bucket. The ball doesn't change shape when you touch it. Instead, the ball will keep its shape and volume no matter what type of container you place it in.

A solid keeps its shape and volume because the particles of a solid are packed closely together, as shown in **Figure 2.** The attractions between the particles in a solid are strong enough to hold the particles in almost fixed positions. The particles move by vibrating in place.

Figure 2
The particles in a solid vibrate in place, maintaining a constant shape and volume.

Reading Check *What motion do solid particles have?*

Crystalline Solids In some solids, the particles are arranged in a repeating, three-dimensional pattern called a crystal. These solids are called crystalline solids. In **Figure 3** you can see the arrangement of particles in a crystal of sodium chloride, which is table salt. The particles in the crystal are arranged in the shape of a cube. Diamond, another crystalline solid, is made entirely of carbon atoms that form crystals that look more like pyramids. Sugar, sand, and snow are other crystalline solids.

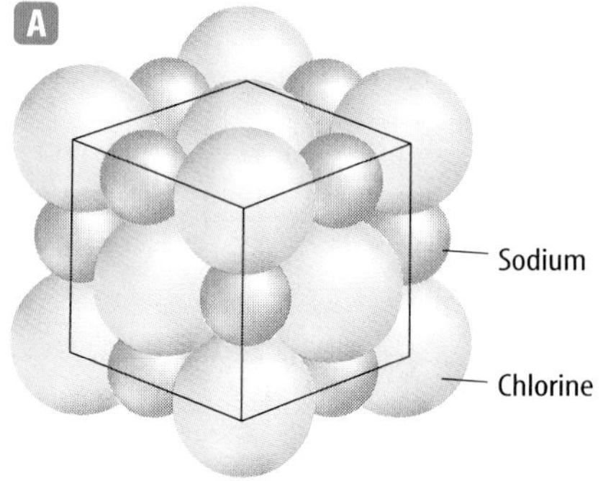

Figure 3
A The particles in a crystal of sodium chloride (NaCl) are arranged in an orderly pattern. B This magnified image shows the cubic shape of sodium chloride crystals.

Resource Manager

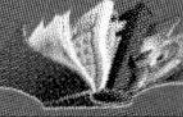

Chapter Resources Booklet
- Transparency Activity, p. 42
- Directed Reading for Content Mastery, p. 18
- Note-taking Worksheets, pp. 31–33

2 Teach

What is matter?

Extension

Have students find out what plasma consists of and how it forms. Have them write a paragraph about what they find. Plasma consists of ions, electrons, and atomic nuclei that have lost all their electrons. Plasma forms at temperatures greater than 5,000°C. L3 ELL
LS **Linguistic** P

Solids

Teacher FYI

The arrangement of atoms and molecules in a solid determines its properties. For example, diamond and graphite are two forms of carbon in which the atoms are arranged differently. In diamonds, each carbon atom is bonded to four others to form a pyramid-like crystal. Because this structure is extremely strong, the diamond is very hard. In graphite, the carbon atoms form layers of hexagonal rings that are held together by weak forces. Because these bonds are easily broken, the graphite layers can be made to slide easily past one another. Such inherent slipperiness makes graphite an excellent lubricant.

Reading Check

Answer a vibratory motion

Make a Model

Have groups of students use **Figure 3** as a reference to make models of the sodium chloride crystal lattice. Provide colored marshmallows of different sizes and toothpicks. Discuss the features of the shape formed. L2
ELL COOP LEARN LS **Visual-Spatial**

Solids, continued

Use an Analogy

The particles in a crystalline solid occupy defined spaces, like eggs in an egg carton. In an amorphous solid the particles are in a random arrangement, more like lemons in a bowl.

Answer The particles in amorphous solids have a random arrangement instead of an ordered arrangement as in a crystalline solid.

Explain to students that more than 97% of Earth's water is salt water found in the oceans. Have students make circle graphs showing the proportion of salt water to freshwater on Earth. L2

LS **Logical-Mathematical**

Liquids

Fun Fact

The physics department of the University of Queensland, Australia, has a funnel of pitch—the black, sticky material used in blacktopping roads and waterproofing basements—that is so viscous it takes about ten years for a drop to drip. Students can view it at the Glencoe Science Web site.

About 85 percent of Earth's freshwater is in the form of solid ice. Most of the remaining freshwater, about 14.9 percent, exists as a liquid in lakes, rivers, and in the ground. A small fraction, less than 0.5 percent, of Earth's freshwater can be found in the air as water vapor, which is the gas state of water. Create a circle graph showing the states of Earth's freshwater.

Amorphous Solids Some solids come together without forming crystal structures. These solids often consist of large particles that are not arranged in a repeating pattern. Instead, the particles are found in a random arrangement. These solids are called amorphous (uh MOR fuhs) solids. Rubber, plastic, glass, and wood are examples of amorphous solids.

Reading Check *How is a crystalline solid different from an amorphous solid?*

Liquids

From the orange juice you drink with breakfast to the water you use to brush your teeth at night, matter in the liquid state is familiar to you. How would you describe the characteristics of a liquid? Is it hard like a solid? Does it keep its shape? A **liquid** is matter that has a definite volume but no definite shape. When you pour a liquid from one container to another, the liquid takes the shape of the container. The volume of a liquid, however, is the same no matter what the shape of the container. If you pour 50 mL of juice from a carton into a pitcher, the pitcher will contain 50 mL of juice. If you then pour that same juice into a glass, its shape will change again but its volume will not.

Free to Move The reason that a liquid can have different shapes is because the particles in a liquid move more freely, as shown in **Figure 4,** than the particles in a solid. The attractive forces between particles in a liquid are strong enough to keep them close together, but not strong enough to hold them in fixed positions.

Figure 4
The particles in a liquid stay close together, although they are free to move past one another.

Inclusion Strategies

Learning Disabled Have students make their own vocabulary flash cards. Using index cards, the students should write the word on one side of the card and the definition on the other side. English language learners may want to use both their native language and English initially. Students should save these cards and use them to study for chapter, unit, and semester exams. L1

ELL LS **Linguistic**

Resource Manager

Chapter Resources Booklet
- Enrichment, p. 28
- Reinforcement, p. 25
- Transparency Activity, pp. 45–46
- Lab Activity, pp. 9–10

Viscosity Do all liquids flow the way water flows? You know that honey flows more slowly than water and you've probably heard the phrase "slow as molasses." Some liquids flow more easily than others. A liquid's resistance to flow is known as the liquid's viscosity. Honey has a high viscosity. Water has a lower viscosity. The slower a liquid flows, the higher its viscosity is. The viscosity results from the strength of the attraction between the particles of the liquid. For many liquids, viscosity increases as the liquid becomes colder.

Surface Tension If you're careful, you can float a needle on the surface of water. This is because attractive forces cause the particles on the surface of a liquid to pull themselves together and resist being pushed apart. You can see in **Figure 5A** that particles beneath the surface of a liquid are pulled in all directions. Particles at the surface of a liquid are pulled toward the center of the liquid and sideways along the surface. No liquid particles are located above to pull on them. The uneven forces acting on the particles on the surface of a liquid are called surface tension. Surface tension causes the liquid to act as if a thin film were stretched across its surface. As a result you can float a needle on the surface of water. For the same reason, the water strider in **Figure 5B** can move around on the surface of a pond or lake. When a liquid is present in small amounts, surface tension causes the liquid to form small droplets, as shown in **Figure 5C.**

SCIENCE Online

Research Visit the Glencoe Science Web site at **science.glencoe.com** for more information about the states of matter. How does the fourth state of matter, plasma, differ from the others? Make a poster that describes and gives examples of the four states of matter.

Figure 5
A These arrows show the forces pulling on the particles of a liquid. Surface tension exists because the particles at the surface experience different forces than those at the center of the liquid. B Surface tension allows this strider to float on water as if the water had a thin film. C Water drops form on these leaves due to surface tension.

Visual Learning

Figure 5 Explain the forces that are in effect in each photo and ask why surface tension is not a property of solids. The particles in solids are rigidly held in place and are not free to move. L2

IS **Logical-Mathematical**

Use an Analogy

One force of attraction that causes particles to pull toward each other is called cohesion. Cohesion between particles is similar to the force of gravity that pulls inward to produce the spherical shape of the planets and sun.

Internet Addresses

Explore the Glencoe Science Web site at **science.glencoe.com** to find out more about topics in this section.

LAB DEMONSTRATION

Purpose to show how temperature affects the viscosity of a liquid

Materials 2 jars, syrup or molasses, refrigerator, 2 small beakers, stopwatch

Preparation Add 10 mL of syrup to each jar. Place one jar in a refrigerator overnight, and allow the other to stand at room temperature.

Procedure Have one student pour all the cold syrup into one beaker while another student pours all the room-temperature syrup into the other beaker. Have remaining students record the time it takes to empty each jar.

Expected Outcome The cold syrup takes longer to pour.

Why does the cold syrup have higher viscosity than the warmer syrup? The particles in the cold syrup are closer together and exert a stronger force upon each other than do the warmer particles.

Gases

Reading Check

Answer The helium will move out of the balloon in all directions to fill the room.

Quick Demo

Demonstrate that gases spread out to fill all available space by spraying a small amount of air freshener in one corner of the room. Have students raise their hands when they first smell the scent. Have students explain the movement of the particles.

3 Assess

Reteach

Blow up a balloon and tie it closed at the neck. Use the balloon to illustrate to students that a gas can be compressed. Ask students what happens to the gas in the balloon if you twist the balloon at the center. Some gas moves into each end of the balloon, where it is compressed into a smaller space. L1 LS **Visual-Spatial**

Challenge

Have students explain why motor oil is made in a wide range of viscosities. Motor oil must remain fluid enough to protect a car engine in a wide range of weather conditions. L2 LS **Logical-Mathematical**

Content Have students prepare posters that compare and contrast the properties of solids, liquids, and gases. Use **PASC**, p. 145. P

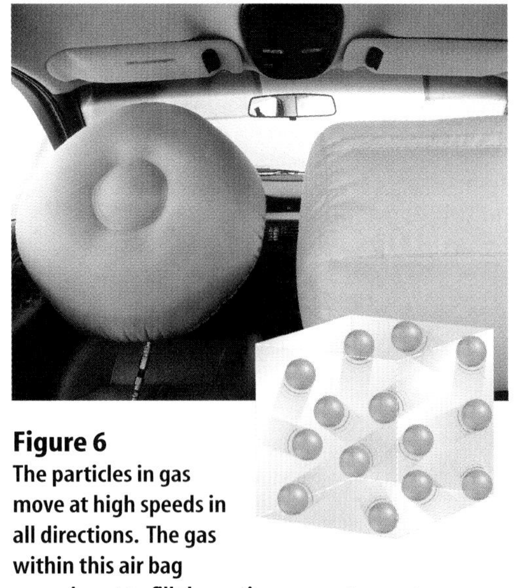

Figure 6
The particles in gas move at high speeds in all directions. The gas within this air bag spreads out to fill the entire volume of the bag.

Gases

Unlike solids and liquids, most gases are invisible. The air in the air bag shown in **Figure 6** and the helium in some balloons are examples of gases. **Gas** is matter that does not have a definite shape or volume. The particles in gas are much farther apart than those in a liquid or solid. Gas particles move at high speeds in all directions. They will spread out evenly, as far apart as possible. If you poured a small volume of a liquid into a container, the liquid would stay in the bottom of the container. However, if you poured the same volume of a gas into a container, the gas would fill the container completely. A gas can expand or be compressed. Decreasing the volume of the container squeezes the gas particles closer together.

Reading Check *How will the shape and volume of helium gas change when it escapes from a balloon?*

You sometimes will hear the term *vapor* applied to gases. A vapor is matter that exists in the gas state but is generally a liquid or solid at room temperature. Water, for example, is a liquid at room temperature. Steam, the gas state of water, is called water vapor.

Section 1 Assessment

1. Define matter in your own words and provide at least three examples.
2. Describe the movement of particles within solids, liquids, and gases.
3. Why do liquids flow?
4. A scientist places 25 mL of a yellow substance into a 50-mL container. The substance quickly fills the entire container. In what state of matter is the substance? Why?
5. **Think Critically** Two of the three common states of matter can be grouped together. Which two states share a similar property? Explain your reasoning.

Skill Builder Activities

6. **Venn Diagram** Using what you have read, draw a Venn diagram in your Science Journal and fill in the characteristics of the states of matter. Add information that you've gained from experience. **For more help, refer to the Science Skill Handbook.**
7. **Communicating** You are surrounded by solids, liquids, and gases all the time. In your Science Journal, make a table with three columns. List several examples of each state of matter. **For more help, refer to the Science Skill Handbook.**

Answers to Section Assessment

1. Matter is anything that takes up space and has mass. It is composed of tiny particles. Salt, water, and oxygen are three examples of matter.
2. Solids: particles are very close together and vibrate back and forth; liquids: particles are farther apart and individual particles can flow past each other; gases: particles are very far apart and move quickly in all directions.
3. The attraction between the particles is strong enough to hold them together, but not strong enough to hold them in fixed positions, so the liquid can flow. The attraction between the particles pulls additional particles along.
4. Gas state; the particles take the shape and volume of their container.
5. Liquids and gases both take the shape of their containers.
6. Diagrams should show that a solid has a definite shape and a gas has no definite volume. Both solid and liquid have definite volume. Both liquid and gas have no definite shape.
7. Check students' work.

SECTION 2

Changes of State

Thermal Energy and Heat

Shards of ice fly from the sculptor's chisel. As the crowd looks on, a swan slowly emerges from a massive block of ice. As the day wears on, however, drops of water begin to fall from the sculpture. Drip by drip, the sculpture is transformed into a puddle of liquid water. What makes matter change from one state to another? To answer this question, you need to take another look at the particles that make up matter.

Energy Simply stated, energy is the ability to do work or cause change. The energy of motion is called kinetic energy. Particles within matter are in constant motion. The amount of motion of these particles depends on the kinetic energy they possess. Particles with more kinetic energy move faster and farther apart. Particles with less energy move more slowly and stay closer together.

The total energy of all the particles in a sample of matter is called thermal energy. Thermal energy depends on the number of particles in a substance as well as the amount of energy each particle has. If either the number of particles or the amount of energy each particle in a sample has increases, the thermal energy of the sample increases. The hot water and snow in **Figure 7** have different amounts of energy.

As You Read

***What* You'll Learn**

- **Define and Compare** thermal energy and temperature.
- **Relate** changes in thermal energy to changes of state.
- **Explore** energy and temperature changes on a graph.

Vocabulary

temperature
heat
melting
freezing
vaporization
condensation

***Why* It's Important**

Matter changes state as it heats up or cools down.

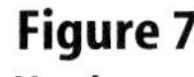

Figure 7
You know how it feels to be hot and cold. This hot spring, for example, feels much hotter than the snow around it. *How is hot matter different from cold matter?*

SECTION 2

Changes of State

1 Motivate

Bellringer Transparency

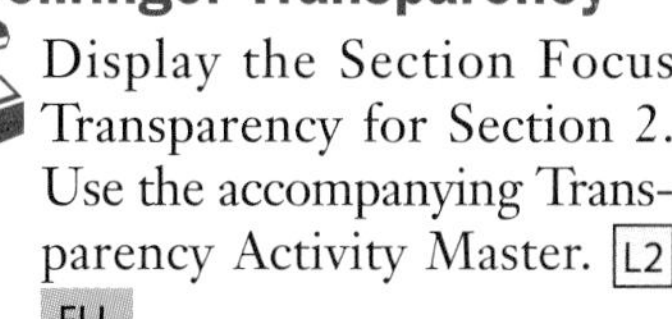

Display the Section Focus Transparency for Section 2. Use the accompanying Transparency Activity Master. L2 ELL

Section 2 Section Focus Transparency **Looking forward to some ice water?**

Be sure not to forget about any water you put in the freezer to cool quickly. You might come back to a big ice cube.

1. What state of matter was the water in before it was put into the freezer? What happened in the freezer?
2. Compared to liquid water, how much space does solid water take up?
3. What are some examples of the effects of water expanding as it freezes?

States of Matter

Tie to Prior Knowledge

Remind students of the differences in particle arrangement and movement in solids, liquids, and gases.

Caption Answer

Figure 7 Hot matter has more kinetic energy than cold matter.

Section Assessment Planner

PORTFOLIO
Extension, p. 111

PERFORMANCE ASSESSMENT
MiniLAB, p. 114
Skill Builder Activities, p. 116
See page 132 for more options.

CONTENT ASSESSMENT
Section, p. 116
Challenge, p. 116
Chapter, pp. 132–133

Resource Manager

Chapter Resources Booklet
Transparency Activity, p. 43
Directed Reading for Content Mastery, p. 19

2 Teach

Thermal Energy and Heat

IDENTIFYING Misconceptions

Students may think that matter does not include liquids or gases. They may also think that forms of energy, such as heat and light, are matter. Refer to page 102F for teaching strategies that address these misconceptions.

Physics INTEGRATION

Possible answer: mechanical energy used in riding bike, chemical energy in digesting food, electrical energy in flashlight batteries

Reading Check

Answer When a substance is heated, it gains thermal energy; therefore, its particles move faster and its temperature rises.

Figure 8
The particles in hot tea move faster than those in iced tea. The temperature of hot tea is higher than the temperature of iced tea.

Physics INTEGRATION

Thermal energy is one of several different forms of energy. Other forms include the chemical energy in chemical compounds, the electrical energy used in appliances, the electromagnetic energy of light, and the nuclear energy stored in the nucleus of an atom. Make a list of examples of energy that you are familiar with.

Temperature Not all of the particles in a sample of matter have the same amount of energy. Some have more energy than others. The average kinetic energy of the individual particles is the **temperature** of the substance. You can find an average by adding up a group of numbers and dividing the total by the number of items in the group. For example, the average of the numbers 2, 4, 8, and 10 is $(2 + 4 + 8 + 10) \div 4 = 6$. Temperature is different from thermal energy because thermal energy is a total and temperature is an average.

You know that the iced tea is colder than the hot tea, as shown in **Figure 8.** Stated differently, the temperature of iced tea is lower than the temperature of hot tea. You also could say that the average kinetic energy of the particles in the iced tea is lower than the average kinetic energy of the particles in the hot tea.

Heat When a warm object is brought near a cooler object, thermal energy will be transferred from the warmer object to the cooler one. The movement of thermal energy from a substance at a higher temperature to one at a lower temperature is called **heat.** When a substance is heated, it gains thermal energy. Therefore, its particles move faster and its temperature rises. When a substance is cooled, it loses thermal energy, which causes its particles to move more slowly and its temperature to drop.

Reading Check *How is heat related to temperature?*

Science Journal

Thermal Energy on the Move Ask students to pay attention to the transfer of thermal energy around them and record all the examples they observe in one 24-hour period. Have them write their observations in their Science Journals, including for each example where the thermal energy came from and where it went. L2 LS **Naturalist**

Teacher FYI

Two systems at the same temperature can have different amounts of thermal energy. For example, a cup of boiling water and a pot of boiling water may have the same temperature, but the pot of water has more thermal energy and can transfer more heat.

Specific Heat

If you walk from the grass to the pavement on a hot summer day, you know that the pavement is much hotter than the grass. Both surfaces were heated by the Sun and therefore received the same amount of thermal energy. Why does the temperature of one rise higher than the temperature of the other? The reason is that each surface has a different specific heat. The specific heat of a substance is the amount of heat needed to raise the temperature of 1 g of a substance 1°C.

Substances that have a low specific heat, such as most metals, heat up quickly because they require only small amounts of heat to cause their temperatures to rise. A substance with a high specific heat, such as the water in **Figure 9,** heats up slowly because a much larger quantity of heat is required to cause its temperature to rise by the same amount.

Figure 9
The water in this lake is much colder than the surrounding sand because the specific heat of water is higher than that of sand.

Changes Between the Solid and Liquid States

Matter can change from one state to another when thermal energy is absorbed or released. A change from one physical state of matter to another is known as change of state. The graph in **Figure 11** shows the changes in temperature and thermal energy that occur as you gradually heat a beaker of water.

Figure 10
Rather than melting into a liquid, glass gradually softens. Glass blowers use this characteristic to shape glass into beautiful vases while it is hot.

Melting As the ice in **Figure 11** is heated, it absorbs thermal energy and its temperature rises. At some point, the temperature stops rising and the ice changes into liquid water. The change from the solid state to the liquid state is called **melting.** The temperature at which a substance changes from a solid to a liquid is called the melting point. The melting point of water is 0°C.

Amorphous solids, such as rubber and glass, don't melt in the same way as crystalline solids. Because they don't have crystal structures to break down, these solids get softer and softer as they are heated, as you can see in **Figure 10.**

Specific Heat

Extension

Between 0°C and 100°C the specific heat of water is about 1 calorie/(g × °C). Ask students to find the specific heats of several metals and compare them with the specific heat of water. Have them make a table from their findings. The specific heat of silver between these temperatures is 0.056 calories/(g × °C), between 20°C and 100°C the specific heat of aluminum is 0.219 calories/(g × °C), the specific heat of copper is 0.093 calories/(g × °C), and the specific heat of iron is 0.119 calories/(g × °C). These range from about one-twentieth that of water to about one-fifth that of water. L3

LS **Logical-Mathematical** P

Changes Between the Solid and Liquid States

IDENTIFYING Misconceptions

Students may think particles of a substance can change state only at the melting point or boiling point of the substance. In fact, at any temperature different particles of a substance have different amounts of kinetic energy and may have enough energy to change state. Melting and boiling occur when the number of particles with enough energy to change state is great enough that the average kinetic energy of the particles is at the melting point or the boiling point of the substance.

Resource Manager

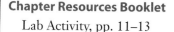

Chapter Resources Booklet

Lab Activity, pp. 11–13

Earth Science Critical Thinking/Problem Solving, p. 10

Curriculum Connection

Geography Earth's temperature has increased during the past few decades. Have students research how this increase could cause changes in the state of water and the effects these changes could have on a specific geographic region. For example, melting of the polar ice caps is causing erosion along coastlines. L3 LS **Linguistic**

Visualizing States of Matter

Have students examine the pictures and read the captions. Then ask the following questions.

During the melting and vaporization process the temperature remains constant. Look at the graph and identify which factor continues to increase. thermal energy

What changes in molecular attraction occur as water goes from a solid to a liquid to a gas? As a solid, the molecules have the most attraction for each other. As a liquid, the molecular attraction has decreased. As a gas, the particles are very far apart and are moving quickly enough to completely overcome the attractive forces.

During condensation, what must be removed from the gas in order for the gas to become a liquid? thermal energy

Activity

Have students write poems about the life of a water molecule as it goes from a solid to a gas. The poems should contain information about changes in molecular attraction and thermal energy. L2 LS **Linguistic**

Extension

Challenge students to research the energy changes that occur during the refrigeration cycle. Have them also find the properties of good refrigerants and share the information that they find with the class. L3 LS **Linguistic**

Figure 11

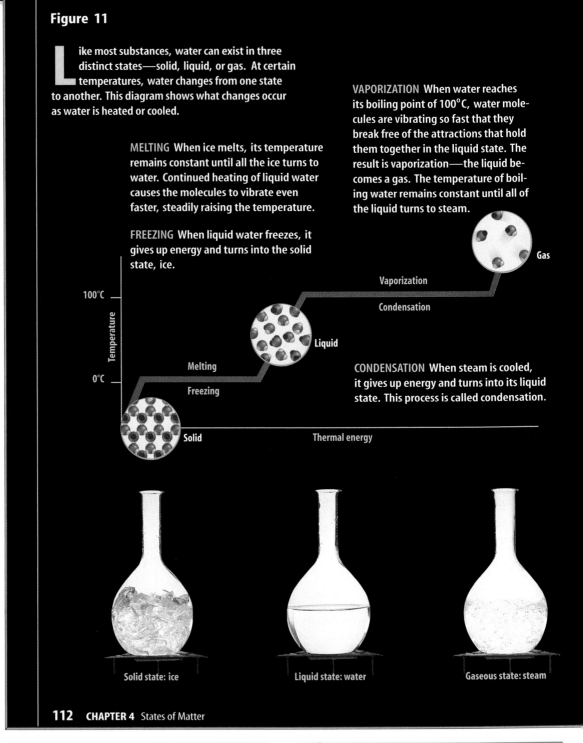

Like most substances, water can exist in three distinct states—solid, liquid, or gas. At certain temperatures, water changes from one state to another. This diagram shows what changes occur as water is heated or cooled.

MELTING When ice melts, its temperature remains constant until all the ice turns to water. Continued heating of liquid water causes the molecules to vibrate even faster, steadily raising the temperature.

FREEZING When liquid water freezes, it gives up energy and turns into the solid state, ice.

VAPORIZATION When water reaches its boiling point of 100°C, water molecules are vibrating so fast that they break free of the attractions that hold them together in the liquid state. The result is vaporization—the liquid becomes a gas. The temperature of boiling water remains constant until all of the liquid turns to steam.

CONDENSATION When steam is cooled, it gives up energy and turns into its liquid state. This process is called condensation.

100°C
0°C
Temperature
Melting
Freezing
Vaporization
Condensation
Solid
Liquid
Gas
Thermal energy

Solid state: ice

Liquid state: water

Gaseous state: steam

112 CHAPTER 4 States of Matter

Resource Manager

Chapter Resources Booklet
Enrichment, p. 29

Physical Science Critical Thinking/Problem Solving, p. 10

Active Reading

Quickwrites This strategy will help students identify what they already know about thermal energy, temperature, and changes in state. Have students list ideas about these topics, and then share their ideas with the class. Students can write their ideas freely in a paragraph and share them with the class during or after a learning experience on the states of matter.

Freezing The process of melting a crystalline solid can be reversed if the liquid is cooled. As the liquid cools, it loses thermal energy. As a result, its particles slow down and come closer together. Attractive forces begin to trap particles, and the crystals of a solid begin to form. The change from the liquid state to the solid state is called **freezing**. As you can see in **Figure 11,** freezing and melting are opposite processes.

The temperature at which a substance changes from the liquid state to the solid state is called the freezing point. The freezing point of the liquid state of a substance is the same temperature as the melting point of the solid state. For example, solid ice melts at 0°C and liquid water freezes at 0°C.

As in the case of freezing, the temperature of a substance remains constant while all the liquid changes to a solid. During the change, the energy lost during freezing is used for changing the arrangement of the particles rather than lowering the temperature. Then, after all of the liquid has become a solid, the temperature continues to drop.

Research Visit the Glencoe Science Web site at **science.glencoe.com** for more information about freezing. Make a list of several substances and the temperatures at which they freeze. Find out how the freezing point affects how the substance is used. Share your findings with the class.

Problem-Solving Activity

How can ice save oranges?

During the spring, Florida citrus farmers carefully watch the fruit when temperatures drop close to freezing. When the temperatures fall below 0°C, the juice in the sacs of oranges can freeze, then expand and break the sacs. The juice spreads into the orange making the crop useless for sale. To prevent this, farmers spray the oranges with water just before the temperature reaches 0°C. How does spraying oranges with water protect them?

Identifying the Problem

Using the diagram at the left, consider what is happening to the water at 0°C. Two things occur. What are they?

Solving the Problem

1. What change of state and what energy changes occur when water freezes?
2. How does the formation of ice on the orange help the orange?

Teacher FYI

The field of low-temperature physics is called cryogenics. Scientists working in this area have been able to cool down rubidium atoms to 170 billionths of a degree above absolute zero (0 K) Scientists believe that at absolute zero all molecular motion stops.

Discussion

Since temperature doesn't change as a substance is freezing, the kinetic energy of its particles doesn't change. But the substance is losing energy. **What kind of energy is the substance losing?** It is losing the potential energy of the attraction between the particles. L3 LS **Logical-Mathematical**

Problem-Solving Activity

Teaching Strategies

Show students an orange that has been frozen below 0°C (-2.2°C) and one that has not been frozen. The layer of ice around the orange protects it from cold air temperatures. Point out that this is also what occurs when a lake freezes over. The ice on top protects the water beneath, so fish can survive.

Answers

1. The two changes that occur are the phase change from water to ice and the loss of energy (exothermic) when the phase change occurs.
2. The ice forms at 0°C, coating the orange and acting as insulation against the colder air temperature. Some of the energy that is released when the ice forms goes into the orange.

SCIENCE Online

Internet Addresses

Explore the Glencoe Science Web site at **science.glencoe.com** to find out more about topics in this section.

Inclusion Strategies

Learning Disabled Help students analyze the questions posed in the Problem-Solving Activity by breaking down the process that occurs as the water sprayed on the oranges freezes. Draw diagrams and use arrows to show the energy transfers involved and relate them to the graphs on the previous page. L2 LS **Logical-Mathematical**

Changes Between the Liquid and Gas States

Purpose Students observe that a liquid absorbs heat from its surroundings as it evaporates. L1 IS **Kinesthetic**

Materials dropper, rubbing alcohol

Teaching Strategy Prevent waste by providing students with small amounts of alcohol.

Safety Precautions Students should wear goggles when performing this MiniLAB. Alcohol is flammable. There should be no open flames in the lab.

Analysis

1. The alcohol evaporated.
2. The hand felt cool where the alcohol was located. The alcohol removed heat from the skin as it evaporated, and then the hand warmed up again.

Assessment

Content Explain how the body is cooled by perspiration. Heat from the body is absorbed as perspiration evaporates from the skin. Use **Performance Assessment in the Science Classroom,** p. 89. L2

Visual Learning

Figure 12 Discuss with students the difference between evaporation and boiling. **Could both occur at the same time?** Yes; while some particles are becoming gas inside the liquid, others gas particles can escape from the surface. L2 IS **Logical-Mathematical**

Explaining What You Feel

Procedure

1. Use a **dropper** to place five drops of **rubbing alcohol** on the back of your hand.
2. Describe how your hand feels during the next 2 min.
3. Wash your hands.

Analysis

1. What changes in the appearance of the rubbing alcohol did you notice?
2. What sensation did you feel during the 2 min? How can you explain this sensation?

Changes Between the Liquid and Gas States

After an early morning rain, you and your friends enjoy stomping through the puddles left behind. But later that afternoon when you head out to run through the puddles once more, the puddles are gone. The liquid water in the puddles changed into a gas. Matter changes between the liquid and gas states through vaporization and condensation.

Vaporization As liquid water is heated, its temperature rises until it reaches 100°C. At this point, liquid water changes into water vapor. The change from a liquid to a gas is known as **vaporization** (vay puhr uh ZAh shun). You can see in **Figure 11** that the temperature of the substance does not change during vaporization. However, the substance absorbs thermal energy. The additional energy causes the particles to move faster until they have enough energy to escape the liquid as gas particles.

Two forms of vaporization exist. Vaporization that takes place below the surface of a liquid is called boiling. When a liquid boils, bubbles form within the liquid and rise to the surface. The temperature at which a liquid boils is called the boiling point. The boiling point of water is 100°C.

Vaporization that takes place at the surface of a liquid is called evaporation. Evaporation, which occurs at temperatures below the boiling point, explains how puddles dry up. Imagine that you could watch individual water molecules in a pot of water, as shown in **Figure 12.** You would notice that the molecules move at different speeds. Although the temperature of the water is constant, remember that temperature is a measure of the average kinetic energy of the molecules. Some of the fastest-moving molecules overcome the attractive forces of other molecules and escape from the surface of the water.

Figure 12
During vaporization, particles near the surface of a liquid that have enough energy can escape the liquid and enter the gas state. As a result, the volume and temperature of the remaining liquid decrease.

Resource Manager

Chapter Resources Booklet
MiniLAB, p. 3

Reading and Writing Skill Activities, p. 17

Teacher FYI

At a given temperature, the motions of the particles in a substance vary according to a well-defined distribution of particle speeds called the Maxwell-Boltzmann distribution. This distribution looks similar to a bell curve but is not as symmetrical. The limit on the fastest speeds is the speed of light, while zero is the lowest speed a particle can have.

Figure 13
The drops of water on these glasses and pitcher of lemonade were formed when water vapor in the air lost enough energy to return to the liquid state. This process is called condensation.

Location of Molecules It takes more than speed for water molecules to escape the liquid state. These faster molecules also must be near the surface, heading in the right direction, and they must avoid hitting other water molecules as they leave.

With the faster particles evaporating from the surface of a liquid, the particles that remain are the slower, cooler ones. Evaporation cools the liquid and anything the liquid touches. You experience this cooling effect when perspiration evaporates from your skin.

Condensation Pour a nice, cold glass of lemonade and place it on the table for a half hour on a warm day. When you come back to take a drink, the outside of the glass will be covered by drops of water, as shown in **Figure 13.** What happened? As a gas cools, its particles slow down. When particles move slowly enough for their attractions to bring them together, droplets of liquid form. This process, which is the opposite of vaporization, is called **condensation.** As a gas condenses to a liquid, it releases the thermal energy it absorbed to become a gas. During this process, the temperature of the substance does not change. The decrease in energy changes the arrangement of particles. After the change of state is complete, the temperature continues to drop, as you saw in **Figure 11.**

✔ Reading Check *What energy change occurs during condensation?*

Condensation formed the droplets of water on the outside of your glass of lemonade. In the same way, water vapor in the atmosphere condenses to form the liquid water droplets in clouds. When the droplets become large enough, they fall to the ground as rain.

SCIENCE Online

Research Visit the Glencoe Science Web site at **science.glencoe.com** for more information about how condensation is involved in weather. Find out how condensation is affected by the temperature as well as the amount of water in the air.

Visual Learning

Figure 13 Have students describe the various places that heat transfer is occurring in **Figure 13.** L2 LS **Visual-Spatial**

SCIENCE Online

Internet Addresses

Explore the Glencoe Science Web site at **science.glencoe.com** to find out more about topics in this section.

✔ Reading Check

Answer During condensation, a gas releases energy as its particles become more ordered.

Curriculum Connection

Geography Have students research how changes of state contribute to the formation of deserts near the Tropic of Cancer. Ask students to make posters with diagrams illustrating their findings. Human overuse of land and water as well as droughts cause water from top soil to evaporate. Then the dry winds that blow in those areas increase the amount of water that evaporates into the air. L2 LS **Linguistic**

Changes Between the Solid and Gas States

3 Assess

Reteach

Have students explain the difference between evaporation and boiling. Boiling occurs when particles below the surface of a liquid change from liquid to gas. Evaporation occurs when particles at the surface of a liquid change from liquid to gas. L1 **LS Logical-Mathematical**

Challenge

If you have an automatic ice-cube maker in your freezer, you may have noticed that the older ice cubes at the bottom of the tray are much smaller than the newer cubes at the top. Use what you have learned to explain why. The faster molecules on the surface of an ice cube can escape from the cube and become a gas. Over time, the ice cube will completely sublimate away. L2 **LS Logical-Mathematical**

Performance Have students hypothesize what would happen if the unknown substance from the Explore Activity were reheated. The substance would melt at the same temperature at which it froze. The temperature would remain constant while the substance was melting, then increase gradually. Use **PASC,** p. 93.

Figure 14
The solid dry ice at the bottom of this beaker of water is changing directly into gaseous carbon dioxide. This process is called sublimation.

Changes Between the Solid and Gas States

Some substances can change from the solid state to the gas state without ever becoming a liquid. During this process, known as sublimation, the surface particles of the solid gain enough energy to become a gas. One example of a substance that undergoes sublimation is dry ice. Dry ice is the solid form of carbon dioxide. It often is used to keep materials cold and dry. At room temperature and pressure, carbon dioxide does not exist as a liquid. Therefore, as dry ice absorbs thermal energy from the objects around it, it changes directly into a gas. When dry ice becomes a gas, it absorbs thermal energy from water vapor in the air. As a result, the water vapor cools and condenses into liquid water droplets, forming the fog you see in **Figure 14.**

Section  Assessment

1. How are thermal energy and temperature similar? How are they different?
2. How does a change in thermal energy cause matter to change from one state to another? Give an example.
3. During which three changes of state is energy absorbed?
4. What are two types of vaporization?
5. **Think Critically** How can the temperature of a substance remain the same even if the substance is absorbing thermal energy?

Skill Builder Activities

6. **Making and Using Graphs** Using the data you collected in the Explore Activity, plot a temperature-time graph. Describe your graph. At what temperature does the graph level off? What was the liquid doing during this time period? **For more help, refer to the Science Skill Handbook.**
7. **Communicating** In your Science Journal, explain why you can step out of the shower into a warm bathroom and begin to shiver. **For more help, refer to the Science Skill Handbook.**

Answers to Section Assessment

1. Thermal energy is the total amount of energy contained in a body whereas temperature measures the average kinetic energy of the particles in the body. Both deal with the amount of energy something has.
2. As thermal energy changes, the kinetic energy of the particles changes. If their kinetic energy increases, particles can overcome the attractive forces holding them together. If their kinetic energy decreases, particles can become subject to the forces pulling them together. Examples will vary.
3. melting, vaporization, and sublimation
4. boiling and evaporation
5. The temperature remains the same because the absorbed energy is being used to break attractive forces between the particles of a substance as it changes state.
6. Check students' work. The temperature should level off as the material changes from a liquid to a solid.
7. The water on your skin absorbs heat from your body and evaporates, cooling the skin and causing you to shiver.

Activity

A Spin Around the Water Cycle

Some of the water in the puddle you stepped in this morning could have rolled down a dinosaur's back millions of years ago because water moves through the environment in a never-ending cycle. Changes in water's physical state enable living things on Earth to use this invaluable resource.

What You'll Investigate

How does the temperature of water change as it is heated from a solid to a gas?

Materials

hot plate
ice cubes (100 mL)
Celsius thermometer
*electronic temperature probe
wall clock
*watch with second hand
stirring rod
250-mL beaker
*Alternate materials

Goals

- **Measure** the temperature of water as it heats.
- **Observe** what happens as the water changes from one state to another.
- **Graph** the temperature and time data.

Safety Precautions

Procedure

1. Copy the data table shown.
2. Put 150 mL of water and 100 mL of ice into the beaker and place the beaker on the hot plate. Do not touch the hot plate.
3. Put the thermometer into the ice/water mixture. Do not stir with the thermometer or allow it to rest on the bottom of the beaker. After 30 s, read the temperature and record it in your data table.

Characteristics of Water Sample

Time (min)	Temperature (°C)	Physical State
0.0		
0.5		
1.0	Answers will vary.	
1.5		
2.0		

4. Plug in the hot plate and turn the temperature knob to the medium setting.
5. Every 30 s, read and record the temperature in the data table. Also observe and record the physical state of the ice and/or water in the beaker. Use the stirring rod to stir the contents of the beaker before making each temperature measurement.
6. Use your data to make a graph plotting time on the *x*-axis and temperature on the *y*-axis. Draw a smooth curve through the data points.

Conclude and Apply

1. How did the temperature of the ice/water mixture change as you heated the beaker?
2. How did the state of water change as you heated the beaker?
3. **Describe** the shape of the graph during any changes of state.

Communicating Your Data

Add captions to your graph. Use the detailed graph to explain to your class how water changes state. **For more help, refer to the Science Skill Handbook.**

Resource Manager

Chapter Resources Booklet
Reinforcement, p. 26
Activity Worksheet, pp. 5–6

Communicating Your Data

Encourage students to compare graphs with other students and discuss possible reasons for inconsistent data.

Activity

BENCH TESTED

Purpose Students observe the solid and liquid states of water. L1 LS **Kinesthetic**

Process Skills measuring, observing, making and using tables, using numbers, making and using graphs, inferring

Time 30 minutes

Alternate Materials electronic temperature probe

Safety Precautions Caution students not to use the thermometer as a stirrer or allow it to rest on the bottom of the beaker during heating.

Teaching Strategy Crushed ice or small pieces will give quicker results.

Answers to Questions

1. The temperature increased, stayed the same for a period of time, then increased again.
2. The ice changed from the solid state to the liquid state.
3. During changes of state, the graph leveled off.

Performance How would the graphs change if twice as much ice were used? The temperature would rise more slowly and the plateau would be longer. Use **Performance Assessment in the Science Classroom,** p. 101. L2 LS **Logical-Mathematical**

SECTION

Behavior of Fluids

1 Motivate

Bellringer Transparency

Display the Section Focus Transparency for Section 3. Use the accompanying Transparency Activity Master. L2 ELL

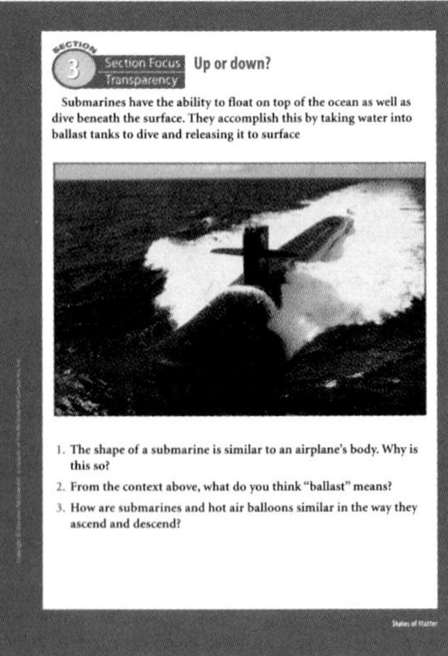

SECTION 3 Section Focus Transparency **Up or down?**

Submarines have the ability to float on top of the ocean as well as dive beneath the surface. They accomplish this by taking water into ballast tanks to dive and releasing it to surface

1. The shape of a submarine is similar to an airplane's body. Why is this so?
2. From the context above, what do you think "ballast" means?
3. How are submarines and hot air balloons similar in the way they ascend and descend?

States of Matter

Tie to Prior Knowledge

Ask students whether they have ever pumped up bicycle tires. Have a volunteer describe what happens during the process. More and more air molecules are pushed into the tire, increasing the pressure inside. Explain that in this section students will explore how the motion of particles of matter is related to different kinds of pressure occurring in fluids.

SECTION

Behavior of Fluids

As You Read

***What* You'll Learn**

- **Explain** why some things float but others sink.
- **Describe** how pressure is transmitted through fluids.

Vocabulary

pressure
buoyant force
Archimedes' principle
density
Pascal's principle

***Why* It's Important**

Pressure enables you to squeeze toothpaste from a tube, and buoyant force helps you float in water.

Pressure

It's a beautiful summer day when you and your friends go outside to play volleyball, much like the kids in **Figure 15.** There's only one problem—the ball is flat. You pump air into the ball until it is firm. The firmness of the ball is the result of the motion of the air particles in the ball. As the air particles in the ball move, they collide with one another and with the inside walls of the ball. As each particle collides with the inside walls, it exerts a force, pushing the surface of the ball outward. A force is a push or a pull. The forces of all the individual particles add together to make up the pressure of the air.

Pressure is equal to the force exerted on a surface divided by the total area over which the force is exerted.

$$(P)\text{ pressure} = (F)\text{ force}/(A)\text{ area}$$

When force is measured in newtons (N) and area is measured in square meters (m^2), pressure is measured in newtons per square meter (N/m^2). This unit of pressure is called a pascal (Pa). A more useful unit of pressure is the kilopascal (kPa), which is 1,000 pascals.

Figure 15
Without the pressure of air inside this volleyball, the ball would be flat.

Section Assessment Planner

Portfolio
Science Journal, p. 119

Performance Assessment
Try at Home MiniLAB, p. 121
Skill Builder Activities, p. 125
See page 132 for more options.

Content Assessment
Section, p. 125
Challenge, p. 125
Chapter, pp. 132–133

Figure 16
The force of the dancer's weight on pointed toes results in a higher pressure than the same force on flat feet. *Why is the pressure different?*

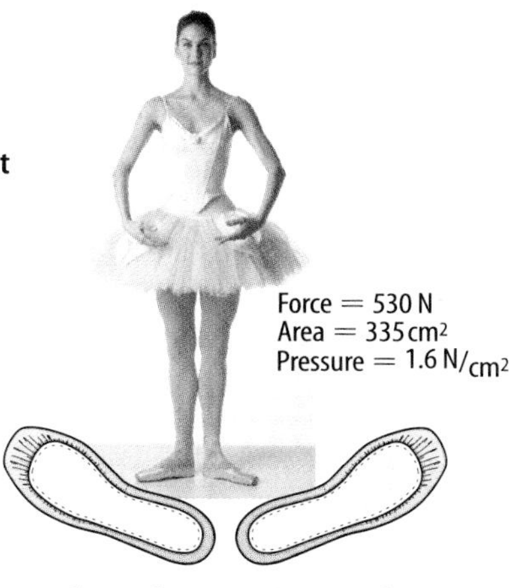

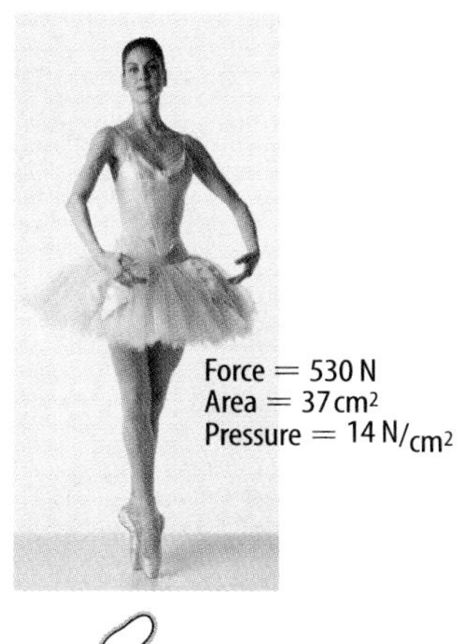

Force and Area You can see from the equation on the opposite page that pressure depends on how much force there is and how large an area you're working with. As the force increases over the same area, pressure increases. If the force decreases, the pressure will decrease. However, if the area changes, the same amount of force can result in different pressure. **Figure 16** shows that if the force of the ballerina's weight is exerted over a smaller area, the pressure increases. If instead the force is exerted over a larger area, the pressure will decrease.

Reading Check *What variables does pressure depend on?*

Atmospheric Pressure You can't see it and you usually can't feel it, but the air around you presses on you with tremendous force. The pressure of air also is known as atmospheric pressure because air makes up the atmosphere around Earth. Atmospheric pressure is 101.3 kPa at sea level. This means that air exerts a force of about 101,000 N on every square meter it touches. This is approximately equal to the weight of a large truck.

It might be difficult to think of air as having pressure when you don't notice it. However, you often take advantage of air pressure without even realizing it. Air pressure, for example, enables you to drink from a straw. When you first suck on a straw, you remove the air from it. As you can see in **Figure 17,** air pressure pushing down on the liquid in your glass then forces air up into the straw. If you tried to drink through a straw inserted into a sealed, airtight container, you would not have any success because the air would not be able to push down on the surface of the drink.

Figure 17
The downward pressure of air pushes the juice up into the straw.

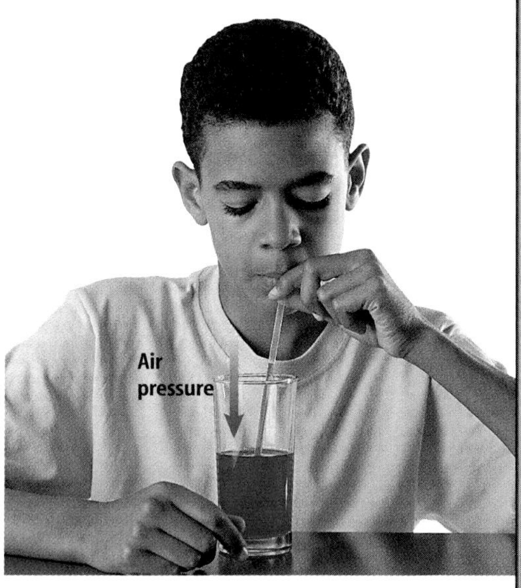

2 Teach

Pressure

Caption Answer

Figure 16 The area is smaller.

Extension

Some bicycle tires are inflated to a pressure of 90 lb/in^2. Have students convert this pressure to kilopascals. There are 9.8 N in 1 kg, and 2.2 lb in 1 kg. Therefore, there are 9.8 ÷ 2.2 = 4.45 N in 1 lb. In 90 lb there are 4.45 × 90 = 400.5 N. There are 0.0254 m in 1 in. so there are 0.000645 m^2 in 1 in^2. Therefore 90 lb/in^2 = 400.5 N ÷ 0.000645 m^2 = 620,930 Pa = 621 kPa. L2 **Logical-Mathematical**

Reading Check

Answer force and area

Visual Learning

Figure 17 Have students explain how a drinking straw works. Sucking on the straw creates a difference between the air pressure on the liquid in the cup and the air pressure on the liquid in the straw. The higher pressure outside the straw pushes the liquid up the straw. L2 **Visual-Spatial**

Discussion

How does using snow skis or snowshoes enable a person to ski or walk on soft snow? The skis or snowshoes distribute the force of the person's weight over a larger area, decreasing the pressure exerted on the surface of the snow. L2 **Logical-Mathematical**

Resource Manager

Chapter Resources Booklet
- Transparency Activity, p. 44
- Directed Reading for Content Mastery, pp. 19, 20

Science Journal

Pressure Applied Have each student make a drawing of a sports ball in his or her Science Journal and show the molecular forces that are keeping the ball inflated. Ask students to include captions that explain why the ball stays inflated. After completing the section, have students compare their drawings and explanations with **Figure 15.** L2 **Visual-Spatial** P

Pressure, continued

Use Science Words

Word Meaning The word *atmosphere* is formed from the word parts *atmos*, which is Greek for "vapor," and *sphaera*, the Latin word for "sphere." Ask students to explain how these word parts are related to the meaning of *atmosphere*. The atmosphere is the gases (or vapors) that surround Earth (a spherical body). L2 LS **Linguistic**

Extension

Changes in atmospheric pressure cause problems for people who climb high mountains such as Mount Everest. Have students find out what mountain climbers do to adjust to the situation. Mountain climbers rest a few days at camps at successively higher altitudes to allow their bodies time to adjust. L3 LS **Linguistic**

Discussion

Suppose that instead of a balloon you had a sealed box of air. **What would happen to the particles of air as you carried the box up the mountain? Explain.** Nothing would happen as long as the box was sealed, because the rigid walls of the box would keep the particles in the box isolated from the changes in air pressure outside the box. L3 LS **Logical-Mathematical**

Figure 18
The pressure pushing up on the dancer's leg is balanced by the pressure pushing down on it. As a result, she doesn't feel the tremendous force from air.

Balanced Pressure If air is so forceful, why don't you feel it? The reason is that pressure can be balanced. For example, when the dancer in **Figure 18** extends her leg, air pressure is exerted downward on her leg. However, air pressure also is exerted upward. The air pressure pushing down on her leg is equal to the pressure pushing up on it so the effects cancel each other. Air and fluids within your body exert pressure, as well.

Variations in Atmospheric Pressure Atmospheric pressure changes with altitutde. Altitude is the height above sea level. As altitude increases atmospheric pressure decreases. This is because fewer air particles are found in a given volume. Fewer particles have fewer collisions and, therefore, exert less pressure. This idea was first tested in the seventeenth century by a French physician named Blaise Pascal. He designed an experiment in which he filled a balloon only partially with air. He then had the balloon carried to the top of a mountain. **Figure 19** shows that as Pascal predicted, the balloon expanded while being carried up the mountain. Although the amount of air inside the balloon stayed the same, the air pressure pushing in on it from the outside decreased. Consequently, the particles of air inside the balloon were able to spread out further.

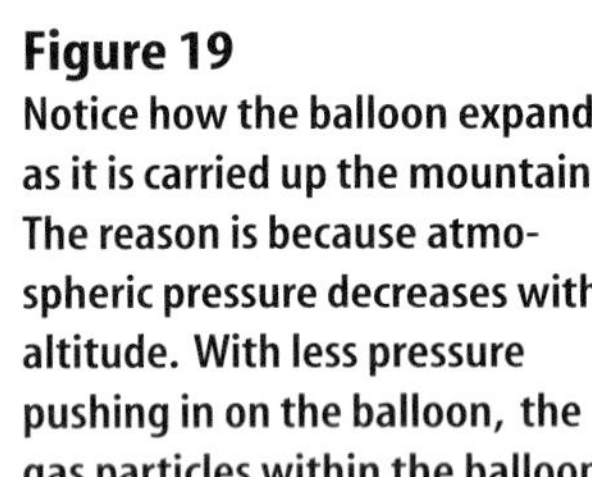

Figure 19
Notice how the balloon expands as it is carried up the mountain. The reason is because atmospheric pressure decreases with altitude. With less pressure pushing in on the balloon, the gas particles within the balloon are free to expand.

Visual Learning

Figure 19 Discuss with students how the balloon would change if the amount of air pressure exerted on it were increased. The gas inside the balloon would be compressed as it was squeezed by increased air pressure acting on the balloon. This would make the balloon get smaller. L2 LS **Logical-Mathematical**

Teacher FYI

Blaise Pascal lived from 1623 to 1662. As part of his work with fluids, he formulated Pascal's principle, which will be studied later in this chapter. The unit of pressure, the pascal, was named for him.

The Pressure in a Moving Fluid

What happens to the pressure in a fluid if the fluid is moving? Try the following experiment. Place an empty soda can on the desktop and blow to the right of the can, as shown in **Figure 20.** How would you expect the can to move?

When you blow to the right of the can, the can moves to the right, toward the moving air. The air pressure exerted on the right side of the can, where the air is moving, is less than the air pressure on the left side of the can, where the air is not moving. As a result, the force exerted by the air pressure on the left side is greater than the force exerted on the right side, and the can is pushed to the right.

Figure 20
By blowing on one side of the can, you decrease the air pressure on that side. Because the air pressure on the opposite side is now greater, the can moves to the side you're blowing on.

Bernoulli's Principle

The surprising behavior of the can is an example of Bernoulli's Principle, which was discovered by the Swiss scientist Daniel Bernoulli in the eighteenth century. According to **Bernoulli's principle,** when the speed of a fluid increases, the pressure exerted by the fluid decreases. When you blew across the side of the can, the pressure exerted by the air on that side of the can decreased because the air was moving faster than on the other side. As a result, the can was pushed toward the side you blew across.

Damage From High Winds You might have seen photographs of people preparing for a hurricane by closing shutters or nailing boards across the outside of windows. In a hurricane, the high winds blowing outside the house cause the pressure outside the house to be less than the pressure inside. This difference in pressure can be large enough to cause windows to be pushed out and shatter.

Hurricanes and other high winds can sometimes blow roofs from houses. When wind blows across the roof of a house, the pressure outside the roof decreases. If the wind outside is blowing fast enough, the outside pressure can become so low that the roof can be pushed off the house by the higher pressure inside.

How are roofs pulled off of houses during hurricanes?

Observing Bernoulli's Principle

Procedure

1. Tie a **piece of string** to the handle of a **plastic spoon.**
2. Turn on a **faucet** to make a stream of water.
3. Holding the string, bring the spoon close to the stream of water.

Analysis

Use Bernoulli's principle to explain the motion of the spoon.

The Pressure in a Moving Fluid

Students may think that only liquids are fluids. Remind them that gases are also fluids.

Bernoulli's Principle

Purpose Students observe an application of Bernoulli's principle.

Materials string, plastic spoon, water faucet

Teaching Strategy If a water faucet is not available, students can use a stream of water poured from a container. The convex side of the spoon should face the water.

Troubleshooting Students should use a small, lightweight plastic spoon.

Analysis

The moving water and the moving air beside it cause pressure to decrease. The greater air pressure on the other side of the spoon moves the spoon toward the water.

Portfolio Have students draw the results of the activity using arrows to show motion and labels to show areas of high and low pressure. Use **PASC,** p. 127.

Reading Check

Answer by a decrease in pressure outside the roof

Resource Manager

Chapter Resources Booklet
MiniLAB, p. 4

Physical Science Critical Thinking/Problem Solving, p. 3

Teacher FYI

Bernoulli's principle only applies along lines parallel to the direction the fluid is flowing. It also only applies to a fluid that is flowing with a constant speed.

Bernoulli's Principle, continued

Extension

A special case of the Bernoulli principle is known as the Venturi effect. When fluids are forced to flow through narrow spaces, such as tunnels, the speed of the fluid increases. Have students describe how this effect explains why large cities are so windy. Wind speed increases as the wind flows between large skyscrapers.

Activity

Students can demonstrate the Bernoulli principle using table-tennis balls hanging from a string. Have students tape about 30 cm of string to each of the balls. Next, have them tie the balls to a dowel or pencil so that the balls hang side-by-side, about 5 cm apart. One student should hold the dowel as another student blows slowly between the balls. As the air flow between the balls increases, the pressure between them drops and the balls move toward one another. LS **Visual-Spatial**

Float or Sink

Discussion

What do you think will happen if the buoyant force in a fluid is equal to the weight of an object in it? The object will remain suspended in the fluid, neither rising nor falling. L3
LS **Logical-Mathematical**

Figure 21
The air moving past the chimney causes the pressure above the chimney to be lower than it is inside the house. This forces more smoke up the chimney.

Chimneys and Bernoulli's Principle In a fireplace, the hotter, less dense air above the fire is pushed upward by the cooler air in the room. Wind outside the house can increase the rate at which the smoke rises. Look at **Figure 21.** Air moving across the top of the chimney causes the air pressure above the chimney to decrease, according to Bernoulli's principle. As a result, more smoke is pushed upward by the higher pressure of the air in the room.

Float or Sink

You may have noticed that you feel lighter in water than you do when you climb out of it. While you are under water, you experience water pressure pushing on you in all directions. Just as air pressure increases as you walk down a mountain, water pressure increases as you swim deeper in water. Water pressure increases with depth. As a result, the pressure pushing up on the bottom of an object is greater than the pressure pushing down on it because the bottom of the object is deeper than the top.

The difference in pressure results in an upward force on an object immersed in a fluid, as shown in **Figure 22.** This force is known as the **buoyant force.** If the buoyant force is greater than the weight of an object, the object will float. If the buoyant force is less than the weight of an object, the object will sink.

Figure 22
A The pressure pushing up on an object is greater than the pressure pushing down on it. This difference results in the buoyant force. B Weight is a force in the downward direction. The buoyant force is in the upward direction. An object will float if the upward force is greater than the downward force.

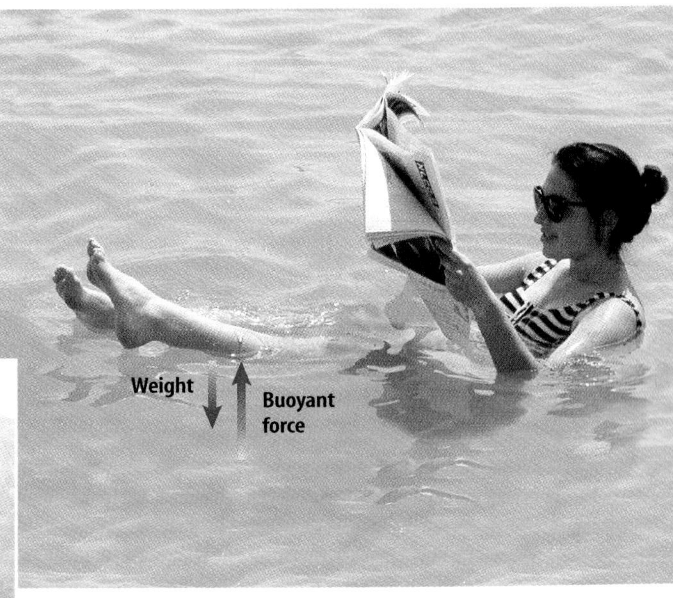

Inclusion Strategies

Gifted Have students construct a neutrally buoyant helium balloon and gondola—one that has the same density as air. When you test the balloon, make sure there are no drafts in the room. Students will have succeeded if the balloon and gondola remain stationary between the ceiling and floor of a room for several minutes or if they ascend or descend slowly.
L3 LS **Kinesthetic**

Curriculum Connection

Architecture The homes of prairie dogs are a maze of underground tunnels. The entrances to the tunnels are at different levels, and the higher openings are exposed to stronger wind than the lower openings. Have students use Bernoulli's principle to infer the direction of wind flow through the prairie dogs' tunnels. from lower openings to higher openings

Archimedes' Principle What determines the buoyant force? According to **Archimedes'** (ar kuh MEE deez) **principle,** the buoyant force on an object is equal to the weight of the fluid displaced by the object. In other words, if you place an object in a beaker that already is filled to the brim with water, some water will spill out of the beaker, as in **Figure 23.** If you weigh the spilled water, you will find the buoyant force on the object.

Density Understanding density can help you predict whether an object will float or sink. **Density** is mass divided by volume.

$$\text{density} = \frac{\text{mass}}{\text{volume}}$$

An object will float in a fluid that is more dense than itself and sink in a fluid that is less dense than itself. If an object has the same density as the fluid, the object will neither sink nor float but instead stay at the same level in the fluid. An iceberg floats in water because the density of ice is less than the density of water. A helium balloon floats in air because the density of helium is less than the density of air.

Figure 23
When the golf ball was dropped in the large beaker, it displaced some of the water into the smaller beaker. *What do you know about the weight and the volume of the displaced water?*

Math Skills Activity

Calculating Density

Example Problem

You are given a sample of a solid that has a mass of 10.0 g and a volume of 4.60 cm^3. Will it float in liquid water, which has a density of 1.00 g/cm^3?

Solution

1. *This is what you know:* mass = 10.0 g; volume = 4.60 cm^3; density of water = 1.00 g/cm^3

   A sample will float in a substance that is more dense than itself.
2. *This is what you need to find:* the density of the sample
3. *This is the equation you need to use:* density = mass/volume
4. *Substitute in the known values:* density = 10.0 g/4.60 cm^3 = 2.17 g/cm^3

   The density of the sample is greater than the density of water. The sample will sink.

Practice Problem

A 7.40-cm^3 sample of mercury has a mass of 102 g. Will it float in water?

For more help, refer to the Math Skill Handbook.

Caption Answer

Figure 23 The volume of the displaced water equals the volume of the golf ball. The weight of the displaced water is less that the weight of the golf ball.

Activity

Obtain unopened aluminum cans of regular and diet versions of a soft drink. Show the class that the volumes of the cans are equal. Have students predict what will happen when the cans are placed in a sink or aquarium filled with water. Place the cans into the water and observe. The can of diet drink floats, while the can of regular sinks. Divide the class in half and have each group measure the masses of the cans with a balance. Ask how the masses compare. The regular drink is heavier. Discuss with students the idea that equal volumes of different substances can have different masses. Explain that the difference in mass is due to sugar. L2

ELL IN **Kinesthetic**

Math Skills Activity

National Math Standards

Correlation to Mathematics Objectives

6, 8, 9

Teaching Strategy

This is what you know: mass = 102 g; volume = 7.40 cm^3, density of water = 1.00g/cm^3

This is what you need to find: density of the sample.

This is the equation you need to use: density = mass/volume

Substitute in the known values: density = 102 g/7.40 cm_3 = 1.36 cm_3

Answer

No; the density of mercury is greater than the density of water.

Resource Manager

Chapter Resources Booklet
Enrichment, p. 30

Mathematics Skill Activities, p. 31

Performance Assessment in the Science Classroom, p. 39

Curriculum Connection

History Archimedes was one of history's most gifted mathematicians. He very nearly invented calculus, but did not have the notation to describe his ideas. He came to an unfortunate end when he yelled at an invading Roman soldier for ruining calculations he was writing in the dirt. The unappreciative soldier killed him with his sword. Have students find out when Archimedes lived. 287–212 B.C. L2

Pascal's Principle

Teacher FYI

Pascal's principal led to the development of hydraulics, in which a small force is multiplied to create a much larger force that can be used to lift heavy objects, such as an automobile in a repair shop. Pressure is the same throughout the hydraulic fluid. Because you cannot derive more work from a system than you put into the system, the small force must be applied over a greater distance.

Visual Learning

Figure 25 Review with students the process shown in this figure. Remind students that work equals force times distance. In a hydraulic lift, the force applied to the smaller piston is small, but it is applied over a long distance, so the work done on each side of the lift is the same. L2

LS **Visual-Spatial**

Discussion

Challenge students to use Pascal's principle to explain why their ears may hurt when they swim to the bottom of the deepest part of a swimming pool. The weight of the water above makes the pressure at the bottom of the pool greater than that at the surface. L2

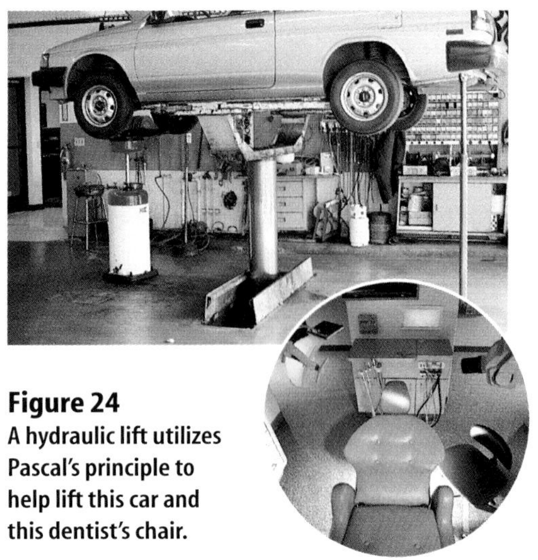

Figure 24
A hydraulic lift utilizes Pascal's principle to help lift this car and this dentist's chair.

Pascal's Principle

What happens if you squeeze a plastic container filled with water? If the container is closed, the water has nowhere to go. As a result, the pressure in the water increases by the same amount everywhere in the container—not just where you squeeze or near the top of the container. When a force is applied to a confined fluid, an increase in pressure is transmitted equally to all parts of the fluid. This relationship is known as **Pascal's principle.**

Hydraulic Systems You witness Pascal's principle when a car is lifted up to have its oil changed or if you are in a dentist's chair as it is raised or lowered, as shown in **Figure 24.** These devices, known as hydraulic (hi DRAW lihk) systems, use Pascal's principle to increase force. Look at the tube in **Figure 25.** The force applied to the piston on the left increases the pressure within the fluid. That increase in pressure is transmitted to the piston on the right. Recall that pressure is equal to force divided by area. You can solve for force by multiplying pressure by area.

$$\text{pressure} = \frac{\text{force}}{\text{area}} \quad \text{or} \quad \text{force} = \text{pressure} \times \text{area}$$

If the two pistons have the same area, the force will be the same on both pistons. If, however, the piston on the right has a greater surface area than the piston on the left, the resulting force will be greater. The same pressure multiplied by a larger area equals a greater force. Hydraulic systems enable people to lift heavy objects using relatively small forces.

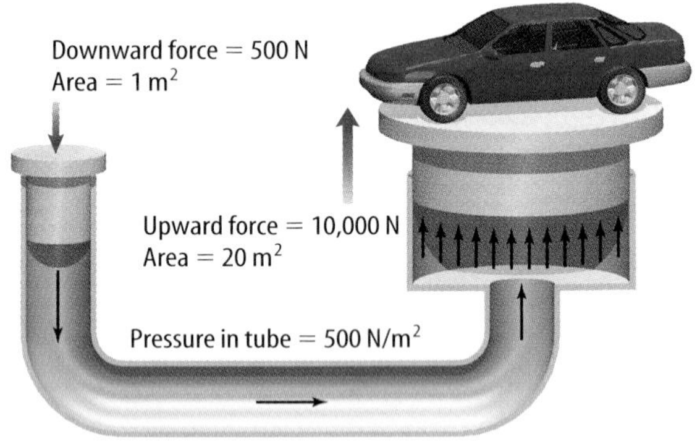

Figure 25
By increasing the area of the piston on the right side of the tube, you can increase the force exerted on the piston. In this way a small force pushing down on the left piston can result in a large force pushing up on the right piston. The force can be great enough to lift a car.

Resource Manager

Chapter Resources Booklet
- Reinforcement, p. 27
- Activity Worksheet, pp. 7–8

Lab Management and Safety, p. 71

Cultural Diversity

Force Pumps Simple piston-type force pumps were known throughout the ancient world. The more efficient double-acting piston bellows was developed by the Chinese in the fourth century B.C., and did not reach Europe until the 1500s. In this device, fluid is pulled in through intake valves on either side and pushed out through a nozzle on both strokes of the piston.

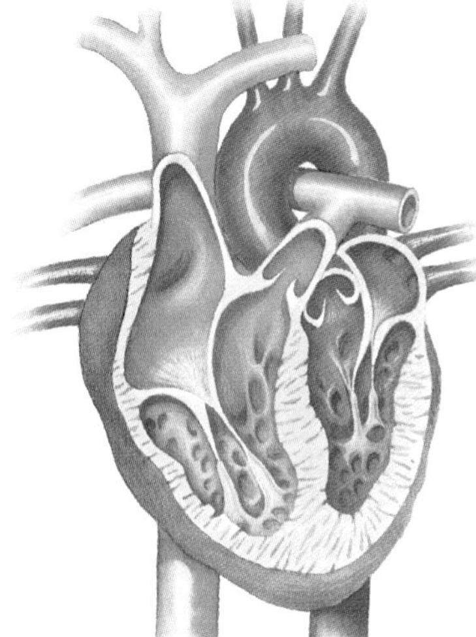

Figure 26
The heart is responsible for moving blood throughout the body. Two force pumps work together to move blood to and from the lungs and to the rest of the body.

Force Pumps If an otherwise closed container has a hole in it, any fluid in the container will be pushed out the opening when you squeeze it. This arrangement, known as a force pump, makes it possible for you to squeeze toothpaste out of a tube or mustard from a plastic container.

Your heart has two force pumps. One pump pushes blood to the lungs, where it picks up oxygen. The other force pump pushes the oxygen-rich blood to the rest of your body. Identify the pumps in **Figure 26.**

SCIENCE Online

Research Visit the Glencoe Science Web site at **science.glencoe.com** for more information about blood pressure. Find out what the term means, how it changes throughout the human body, and why it is unhealthy to have high blood pressure. Communicate to your class what you learn.

Section  Assessment

1. What happens to pressure as the force exerted on a given area increases?
2. How does atmospheric pressure change as altitude increases?
3. State Pascal's principle in your own words.
4. An object floats in a fluid. What do you know about the buoyant force on the object? How does the density of the object compare with the density of the fluid?
5. **Think Critically** All of the air is removed from a sealed metal can. After the air has been removed, the can looks as if it were crushed. Why?

Skill Builder Activities

6. **Recognizing Cause and Effect** On a hot summer day, you buy a bunch of balloons in a store. But when you take the balloons out of the air-conditioned store, some of them pop. How can you explain this? **For more help, refer to the Science Skill Handbook.**
7. **Solving One-Step Equations** What pressure is created when 5.0 N of force are applied to an area of 2.0 m^2? How does the pressure change if the force is increased to 10.0 N? What about if instead the area is decreased to 1.0 m^2? **For more help, refer to the Math Skill Handbook.**

Internet Addresses

Explore the Glencoe Science Web site at **science.glencoe.com** to find out more about topics in this section.

3 Assess

Reteach

Organize the class into five groups. Assign each group pressure, density, Archimedes' principle, Bernoulli's principle, or Pascal's principle. Have each group present to the class its understanding of the assigned term. Each group should be able to define the term and give examples illustrating it. L2 COOP LEARN **Interpersonal**

Challenge

Have students predict what would happen if a rock punched a small hole in the bottom of an airtight compartment in a ship. As long as no air escaped, the pressure of the air in the compartment would allow little water into the compartment. L3 **Logical-Mathematical**

Process Place a beaker of water, a beaker of alcohol, and a beaker of ethylene glycol in front of the class. Challenge students to use buoyancy to put the liquids in order from lowest density to highest density. Students may immerse objects in the liquids to determine the relative densities of the liquids. Use **PASC,** p. 97.

Answers to Section Assessment

1. Pressure increases.
2. Atmospheric pressure decreases.
3. When a force is applied to a confined fluid, an increase in pressure is transmitted equally to all parts of the fluid.
4. The buoyant force is greater than the weight of the object. The density of the object is less than the density of the fluid.
5. After the air is removed, the atmospheric pressure on the outside of the can is greater than the pressure on the inside of the can, so the can collapses.
6. As the temperature increased, the movement of the gas particles in the balloons increased, which increased the pressure inside the balloons and caused them to pop.
7. 2.5 Pa; the pressure increases to 5 Pa. If the force is 5.0 N and the area is decreased to 1.0 m^2 the pressure increases to 5 Pa.

Activity

Design Your Own Experiment

Design Your Own Ship

It is amazing to watch ships that are taller than buildings float easily on water. Passengers and cargo are carried on these ships in addition to the tremendous weight of the ship itself. How can you figure out how much cargo a ship can carry before it sinks? Can you design a ship to hold a specific amount of cargo?

Cargo Ship

Recognize the Problem

How can you determine the size of a ship needed to keep a certain mass of cargo afloat?

Form a Hypothesis

Think about Archimedes' principle and how it relates to buoyant force. Form a hypothesis about how the volume of water displaced by a ship relates to the mass of cargo the ship can carry.

Goals

- **Design** an experiment that uses Archimedes' principle to determine the size of ship needed to carry a given amount of cargo in such a way that the top of the ship is even with the surface of the water.

Possible Materials

balance
small plastic cups (2)
graduated cylinder
metric ruler
scissors
marbles (cupful)
sink
**basin, pan, or bucket*
**Alternate materials*

Safety Precautions

Activity

BENCH TESTED

Recognize the Problem

Purpose

Students apply Archimedes' principle to shipbuilding. L2

ELL COOP LEARN

LS Logical-Mathematical

Process Skills

observing and inferring, designing an experiment to test a hypothesis, interpreting data, separating and controlling variables, predicting, using numbers

Time Required

90 minutes

Materials

balance, 2 small plastic cups, graduated cylinder into which the cups will fit, metric ruler, scissors, marbles, sink

Alternate Materials

basin, pan, or bucket

Form a Hypothesis

Possible Hypothesis

Students might hypothesize that a boat floats when the displaced water weighs the same as or more than the boat and its cargo.

Test Your Hypothesis

Possible Procedure

Find the mass of the cup and the marbles. Use the density of water (1.00 g/mL) to calculate the volume of water that has the same mass as the cup and marbles, which is the volume of water the boat must displace. Fill the cup with the amount of water that has the same mass as the cup and marbles or submerge the cup so that it displaces this volume. Draw a line around the cup at the water line, trim the cup to size, and dry the cup. Put the cup into the water in the sink or basin and carefully load the marbles and the trimmed pieces of cup into the floating cup.

Test Your Hypothesis

Plan

1. Obtain a set of marbles or other items from your teacher. This is the cargo that your ship must carry. Think about the type of ship you will design. Consider the types of materials you will use. Decide how your group is going to test your hypothesis.
2. **List** the steps you need to follow to test your hypothesis. Include in your plan how you will measure the mass of your ship and cargo, calculate how much water your ship must displace in order to float with its cargo, and measure the volume and mass of the displaced water. Also explain how you will design your ship so that it will float with its cargo at the surface of the water.
3. **Prepare** a data table in your Science Journal so that it is ready to use as your group collects data.

Do

1. Make sure your teacher approves your plan before you start.
2. Carry out your experiment as planned. Be sure to follow all proper safety procedures. In particular, clean up any spilled water immediately.
3. While doing the experiment, record your observations carefully and complete the data table in your Science Journal.

Analyze Your Data

1. **Write** your calculations showing how you determined the volume of displaced water needed to make your ship and cargo float.
2. Did your ship float at the water's surface, sink, or float above the water's surface? Draw a diagram of your ship in the water.

Draw Conclusions

1. If your ship sank, how would you change your experiment or calculations to correct the problem? What changes would you make if your ship floated too high in the water?
2. What does the density of a ship's cargo have to do with the volume of cargo the ship can carry? What about the density of the water?

Compare your results with other students' data. Prepare a combined data table or summary showing how the calculations affect the success of the ship. **For more help, refer to the** **Science Skill Handbook.**

Teaching Strategies

- Before conducting the experiment, review density and its relationship to buoyancy.
- Students should not put the marbles into the boats until they are ready to test their boats.

Expected Outcome

Students' data tables should include spaces for the mass of the cup and marbles, the volume of water the cup must displace, measurements of the cup, any calculations of the cup's volume, and the results of the experiment.

Analyze Your Data

1. Typical calculations will involve relating the mass of the cargo and boat to the volume of the water displaced.
2. Results will vary.

Error Analysis

Students should explain why the boat sank or floated too high in the water and identify the problems.

Draw Conclusions

1. Answers will vary. Either way, students should check their measurements and calculations.
2. A ship can carry only a certain mass of cargo safely. Therefore, the ship can carry less high-density cargo than low-density cargo.

Assessment

Oral Have students explain why a ship designer always designs ships to be taller than needed to just float the anticipated cargo. If the ship has no excess height, waves could wash over the ship's side easily or excess cargo could be loaded onto the ship, sinking the ship. Use **Performance Assessment in the Science Classroom,** p. 89. L2

Communicating Your Data

Suggest students use a spreadsheet program for preparing combined data tables.

Oops! Accidents in SCIENCE

SOMETIMES GREAT DISCOVERIES HAPPEN BY ACCIDENT!

Content Background

Silicon is the second most abundant element in Earth's crust. Rubber is a natural carbon-based polymer that comes from trees. Polymers are large molecules made from many small molecules linked together. During World War II, scientists were trying to replace carbon in organic molecules such as rubber with silicon. Silicones are polymers made up of silicon atoms linked to oxygen atoms. Various organic compounds are often attached to the polymer to control and change its physical properties. Some silicones form rubbery elastic compounds, while others are designed to act as lubricants.

Discussion

Why wasn't the goo a good substitute for synthetic rubber? Possible answer: If strong pressure is applied, the goo breaks apart and rubber doesn't. For that reason, it wouldn't work well on vehicle tires.

Why do you think the toy maker decided to package the goo in plastic eggs? Possible answers: It could easily be shipped to toy stores in egg cartons, which are inexpensive and were readily available.

The Incredible

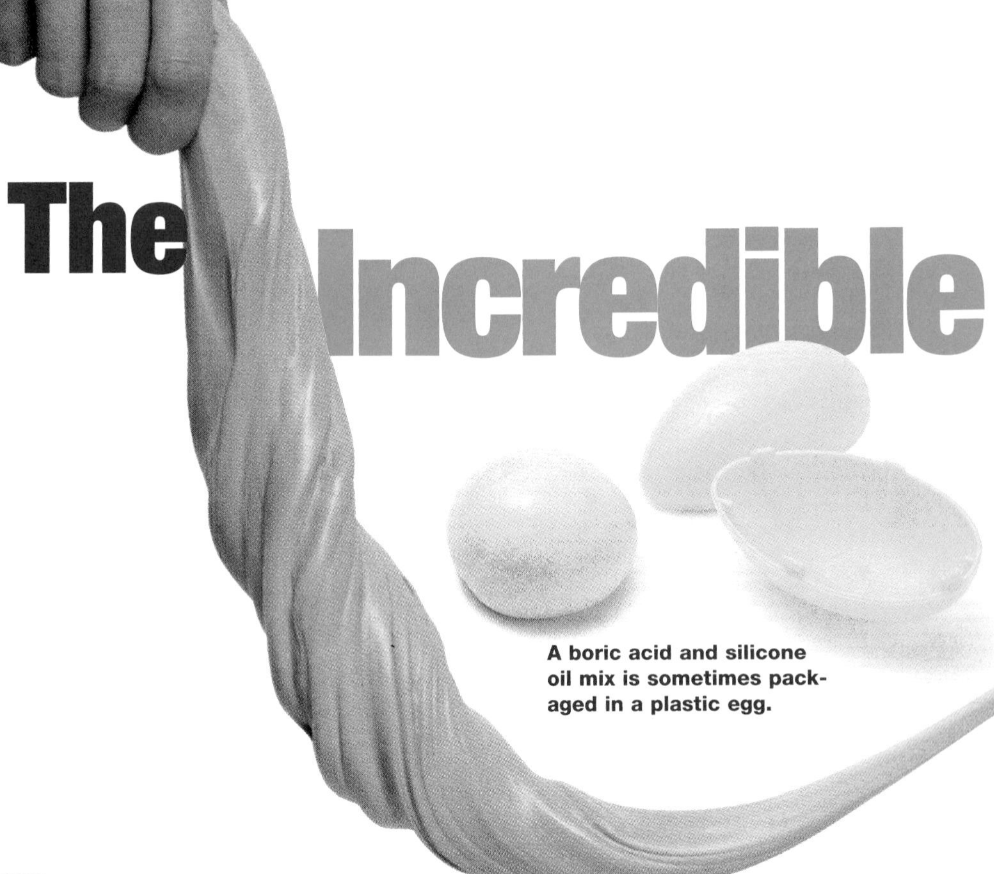

A boric acid and silicone oil mix is sometimes packaged in a plastic egg.

During World War II, when natural resources were scarce and needed for the war effort, the U.S. government asked an engineer to come up with an inexpensive alternative to synthetic rubber. While researching the problem and looking for solutions, the engineer dropped boric acid into silicone oil. The result of these two substances mixing together was—a goo!

Because of its molecular structure, the goo could bounce and stretch in all directions. The engineer also discovered the goo could break into pieces. When strong pressure is applied to the substance, it reacts like a solid and breaks apart. Even though the combination was versatile—and quite amusing, the U.S. government decided the new substance wasn't a good substitute for synthetic rubber.

128

Resources for Teachers and Students

They All Laughed...From Light Bulbs to Lasers: The Fascinating Stories Behind Great Inventions That Have Changed Our Lives, by Ira Flatow, Harper Perennial, 1992.

Super Science Concoctions, by Jill Frankel Hauser, Williamson Publishing, 1997.

A serious search turns up a toy

Stretching Goo

A few years later, the recipe for the stretch material fell into the hands of a businessperson, who saw the goo's potential—as a toy. The toymaker paid $147 for rights to the boric acid and silicone oil mixture. And in 1949 it was sold at toy stores for the first time. The material was packaged in a plastic egg and it took the U.S. by storm. Today, the acid and oil mixture comes in a multitude of colors and almost every child has played with it at some time.

The substance can be used for more than child's play. Its sticky consistency makes it good for cleaning computer keyboards and removing small specks of lint from fabrics. People use it to make impressions of newspaper print or comics. Athletes strengthen their grips by grasping it over and over. Astronauts use it to anchor tools on spacecraft in zero gravity. All in all, a most eggs-cellent idea!

CONNECTIONS Research As a group, examine a sample of the colorful, sticky, stretch toy made of boric acid and silicone oil. Then brainstorm some practical—and impractical—uses for the substance.

SCIENCE Online For more information, visit science.glencoe.com

Activity

Allow small groups of students to investigate how the addition of a compound can change the properties of a polymer. Dissolve 2 mL of borax in 125 mL of water in a beaker. Have students pour 15 mL of white glue (a polymer) into a paper cup. Then have them add 15 mL of the borax solution to the glue and stir it with a craft stick. The borax cross-links the glue polymers, making the resulting compound thicker and more rubbery. Tell students to remove the polymer from the cup and knead it for a few minutes. As a class, discuss the properties of the new polymer. L2 LS **Kinesthetic**

Analyze the Event

Ask students to brainstorm possible reasons scientists tried unusual experiments when working to come up with an inexpensive alternative to synthetic rubber.

CONNECTIONS Ask students in each group to describe the list of uses they came up with for the goo. Ask students in other groups to comment on whether or not they think the proposed uses would actually work. If possible, allow students to demonstrate some of the uses they brainstormed.

SCIENCE Online

Internet Addresses

Explore the Glencoe Science Web site at **science.glencoe.com** to find out more about topics in this feature.

Chapter 4 Study Guide

Reviewing Main Ideas

Preview

Students can answer the questions in their Science Journals. Discuss the answers as you go through the chapter. LS **Linguistic**

Review

Students can write their answers, then compare them with those of other students. LS **Interpersonal**

Reteach

Students can look at the illustrations and describe details that support the main ideas of the chapter. LS **Visual-Spatial**

Answers to Chapter Review

Section 1

3. Liquids take the shape of their containers.

Section 2

1. the pot

Section 3

4. Squeezing the tube transfers pressure throughout the tube. Since the tube has an opening, toothpaste is pushed out.

Chapter 4 Study Guide

Reviewing Main Ideas

Section 1 Matter

1. All matter, which includes anything that takes up space and has mass, is composed of tiny particles that are in constant motion.
2. In the solid state, the attractive forces between particles hold them in place to vibrate. Solids have definite shapes and volumes.
3. Particles in the liquid state have defined volumes and are free to move about within the liquid. *What property of liquids is shown in the photo?*

4. Particles in the gas state move about freely and completely fill their containers. Gases have neither definite shapes nor volumes.

Section 2 Changes of State

1. Thermal energy is the total energy of the particles in a sample of matter. The average kinetic energy of the particles is temperature. *Which of these samples has a greater amount of thermal energy?*

2. For a change of state to occur, matter must gain or lose thermal energy.
3. An object gains thermal energy during melting when it changes from a solid to a liquid or during vaporization when it changes from a liquid to a gas.
4. An object loses thermal energy during condensation when it changes from a gas into a liquid or during freezing when it changes from a liquid to a solid.

Section 3 Behavior of Fluids

1. Pressure is force divided by area.
2. Fluids exert a buoyant force in the upward direction on objects immersed in them. Archimedes' principle states that the buoyant force on an object is equal to the weight of the fluid displaced by the object.
3. An object will float in a fluid that is more dense than itself. Density is equal to mass divided by volume.
4. Pressure applied to a liquid is transmitted evenly throughout the liquid. This is known as Pascal's principle. *How does Pascal's principle relate to this tube of toothpaste?*

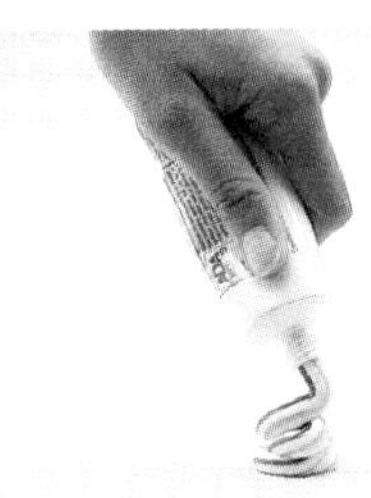

FOLDABLES Reading & Study Skills — **After You Read**

Use what you learned to write about what happens when heat is added to or lost from the three states of matter on your Organizational Study Fold.

FOLDABLES Reading & Study Skills — **After You Read**

After students have read the chapter and completed the Foldable described in Before You Read, have them do the activity on the student page.

Dinah Zike

Visualizing Main Ideas

Complete the following concept map on matter.

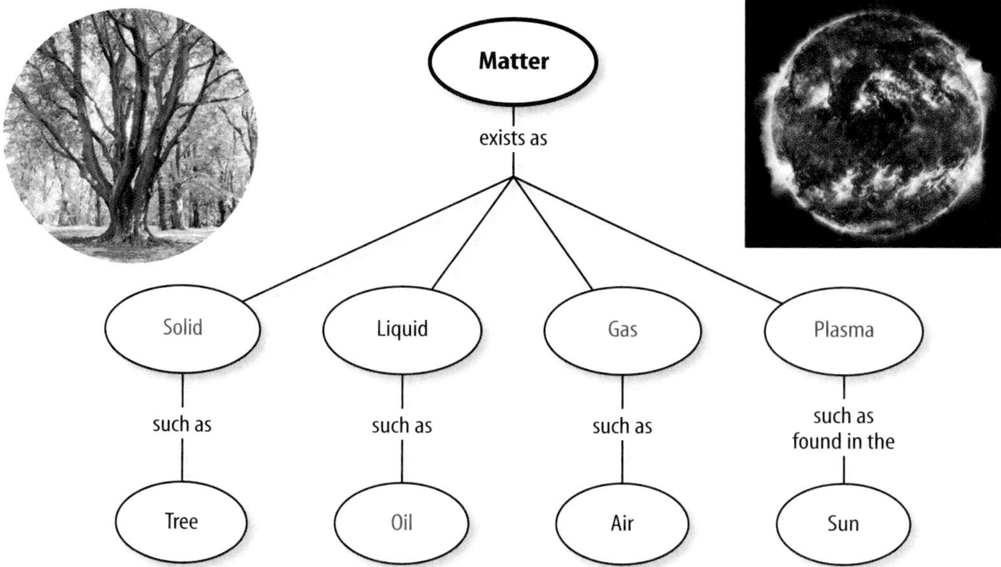

Vocabulary Review

Vocabulary Words

a. Archimedes' principle
b. buoyant force
c. condensation
d. density
e. freezing
f. gas
g. heat
h. liquid
i. matter
j. melting
k. Pascal's principle
l. pressure
m. solid
n. temperature
o. vaporization

Using Vocabulary

Replace the underlined words with the correct vocabulary words.

1. A liquid can change shape and volume.
2. A solid has a different shape but the same volume in any container.
3. Matter is thermal energy moving from one substance to another.
4. Heat is a measure of the average kinetic energy of the particles of a substance.
5. A substance changes from a gas to a liquid during the process of melting.
6. A liquid becomes a gas during freezing.
7. Pressure is mass divided by volume.
8. Density is force divided by area.

THE PRINCETON REVIEW **Study Tip**

Find a quiet place to study, whether at home or school. Turn off the television or radio, and give your full attention to your lessons.

IDENTIFYING Misconceptions

Assess

Use the assessment as follow-up to page 102F after students have completed the chapter.

Materials paper, pencil

Procedure Have students work in groups to make cartoon posters of sporting events in which the Matter Team plays the Non-Matter Team. Students should choose a team sport and create each team. For instance in a baseball game there can be an Iron Infielder and Plastic Pitcher on the Matter Team and Light Left fielder and Kinetic Energy Catcher on the Non-Matter Team.

Expected Outcome Students should realize that matter includes solids, liquids, and gases and does not include types of energy.

Chapter 4 Study Guide

Visualizing Main Ideas

See student page.

Vocabulary Review

Using Vocabulary

1. gas
2. liquid
3. Heat
4. Temperature
5. condensation
6. vaporization
7. Density
8. Pressure

Chapter 4 Assessment

Checking Concepts

1. A
2. B
3. C
4. D
5. B
6. C
7. D
8. B
9. A
10. B

Thinking Critically

11. Steam has more thermal energy than boiling water.
12. The general shape of the graph would remain the same. However, the temperature would rise more slowly and the time required for melting and boiling would increase.
13. Some of the hot water from the shower evaporates into the air. It condenses on the mirror because the mirror is cooler than the air.
14. As air pressure decreases, the boiling point decreases.
15. No; $1{,}800 \div 110 = 16.3$; the crown is not dense enough to be pure gold.

Chapter 4 Assessment

Checking Concepts

Choose the word or phrase that best answers the question.

1. Which description best describes a solid?
   A) It has a definite shape and volume.
   B) It has a definite shape but not a definite volume.
   C) It adjusts to the shape of its container.
   D) It can flow.

2. Which of these is a crystalline solid?
   A) glass **C)** rubber
   B) sugar **D)** plastic

3. What property enables you to float a needle on water?
   A) viscosity **C)** surface tension
   B) temperature **D)** crystal structure

4. What happens to an object as its kinetic energy increases?
   A) It holds more tightly to nearby objects.
   B) Its mass increases.
   C) Its particles move more slowly.
   D) Its particles move faster.

5. During which process do particles of matter lose energy?
   A) melting **C)** evaporation
   B) freezing **D)** boiling

6. How does water vapor in air form clouds?
   A) melting **C)** condensation
   B) evaporation **D)** sublimation

7. Which is a unit of pressure?
   A) N **C)** g/cm^3
   B) kg **D)** N/m^2

8. Which change results in an increase in gas pressure inside a container?
   A) decrease in temperature
   B) decrease in volume
   C) increase in volume
   D) increase in altitude

9. In which case will an object float on a fluid?
   A) Buoyant force is greater than weight.
   B) Buoyant force is less than weight.
   C) Buoyant force equals weight.
   D) Buoyant force equals zero.

10. Which is equal to the buoyant force on an object?
    A) volume of the object
    B) weight of the displaced fluid
    C) weight of object
    D) volume of fluid

Thinking Critically

11. Why does steam cause more severe burns than boiling water?

12. How would this graph change if a greater volume of water were heated? How would it stay the same? Explain.

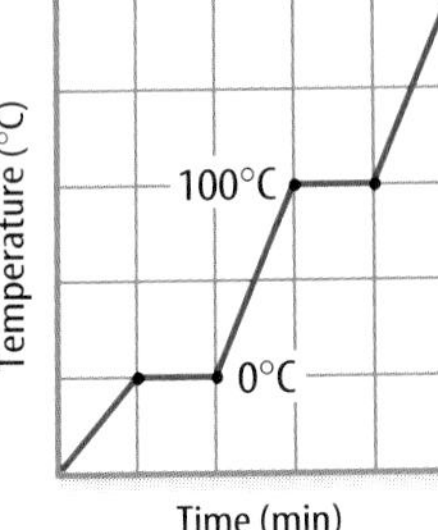

13. Why does the bathroom mirror become fogged while you are taking a shower?

14. The boiling point of a substance decreases as altitude increases. Based on this information, infer the relationship between boiling point and air pressure. Draw a graph.

15. A king's crown has a volume of 110 cm^3 and a mass of 1,800 g. The density of gold is 19.3 g/cm^3. Is the crown pure gold?

Developing Skills

16. **Forming Operational Definitions** Write operational definitions that explain the properties of and differences among solids, liquids, and gases.

Chapter Assessment Planner

Portfolio Encourage students to place in their portfolios one or two items of what they consider to be their best work. Examples include:
- Extension, p. 105
- Assessment, p. 108
- Extension, p. 111
- Science Journal, p. 119

Performance Additional performance assessments, Performance Task Assessment Lists, and rubrics for evaluating these activities can be found in Glencoe's **Performance Assessment in the Science Classroom.**

17. **Concept Mapping** Prepare a sequence chart to show the events that occur as a solid changes into a liquid and then into a gas.

18. **Drawing Conclusions** Why do some balloons pop when they are left in the Sun for too long?

19. **Calculating** A hydraulic device has two pistons. How much force do you have to apply to the piston with an area of 10 cm^2 to lift an object weighing 2,000 N on a piston with an area of 50 cm^2?

20. **Making and Using Graphs** In May of 1997, Francesco Ferraras of Cuba dove to a depth of 150 m without any scuba equipment. Make a depth-pressure graph for the data below. Based on your graph, how does water pressure vary with depth? Note: The pressure at sea level, 101.3 kPa, is called one atmosphere (atm).

Water Pressure

Depth (m)	Pressure (atm)	Depth (m)	Pressure (atm)
0	1.0	100	11.0
25	3.5	125	13.5
50	6.0	150	16.0
75	8.5	175	18.5

Performance Assessment

21. **Storyboard** Create a visual-aid storyboard to show ice changing to steam. There should be a minimum of five frames.

Technology

Go to the Glencoe Science Web site at **science.glencoe.com** or use the **Glencoe Science CD-ROM** for additional chapter assessment.

THE PRINCETON REVIEW Test Practice

Seth is studying the forces exerted on objects in water and has drawn the following illustration of his experiment.

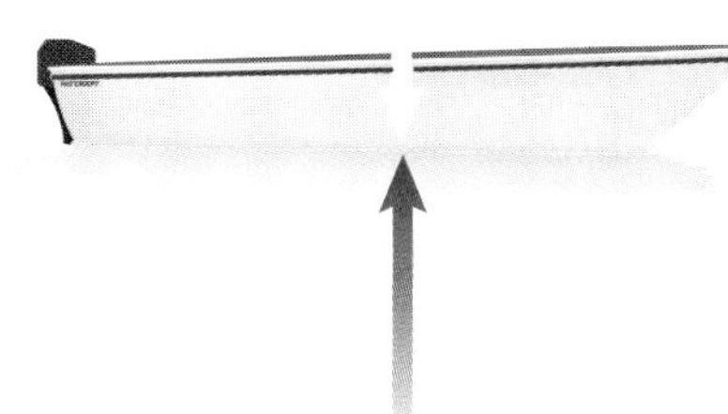

Study the diagram and answer the following questions:

1. The most likely reason the boat is floating rather than sinking is that
   A) gravity is pushing it down.
   B) gravity is stronger than the buoyant force.
   C) the buoyant force is stronger than gravity.
   D) gravity is equal to the buoyant force.

2. Seth wanted to find out how shape affects buoyancy. To compare these two variables, he should
   F) use boats of different sizes.
   G) use different-shaped objects of the same weight.
   H) use similarly shaped objects of different weights.
   J) use objects with different textures.

Assessment Resources

Reproducible Masters

Chapter Resources Booklet
Chapter Review, pp. 35–36
Chapter Tests, pp. 37–40
Assessment Transparency Activity, p. 47

Glencoe Science Web site
Interactive Tutor
Chapter Quizzes

Glencoe Technology
Assessment Transparency
Interactive CD-ROM Chapter Quizzes
ExamView Pro Test Bank
Vocabulary PuzzleMaker Software
MindJogger Videoquiz DVD/VHS

THE PRINCETON REVIEW Test Practice

The Test-Taking Tip was written by The Princeton Review, the nation's leader in test preparation.

1. C
2. G

Developing Skills

16. Solids are materials with particles that are very close together. Solids have a definite shape and volume and can be crystalline or amorphous. Liquids are materials in which particles are farther apart than in solids. The individual particles in liquids can flow past each other and have an attraction to each other that gives liquids viscosity and surface tension. Liquids have a definite volume and take the shape of their containers. Gases have particles that are very far apart, move quickly, and lack an attraction to each other. Gases have no definite shape or volume.
17. Check student work.
18. The pressure of the gas inside the balloon increases as the air in the balloon heats up.
19. one-fifth of the force upward on the object on the 50 cm^2 piston = 2,000n/5 = 400n
20. Water pressure increases as the depth increases.

Performance Assessment

21. Ice should change first to liquid water, then to steam as heat is added to the system and the water molecules move faster. Use **PASC**, p. 135.

CHAPTER 5 PROPERTIES AND CHANGES OF MATTER

Section/Objectives	Standards: National	Standards: State/Local	Activities/Features
Chapter Opener	See p. 5T for a Key to Standards.		**Explore Activity:** Compare characteristics, p. 135 **Before You Read,** p. 135
Section 1 Physical Properties 3 sessions 1.5 blocks 1. **Describe** the physical properties of matter. 2. **Explain** how to find the density of a substance. 3. **Compare and contrast** the properties of acids and bases.	National Content Standards: UCP2, A1, B1		**Math Skills Activity:** Determining the Density of a Material, p. 137 **MiniLAB:** Classifying Properties, p. 138 **Health Integration,** p. 139 **Science Online,** p. 140
Section 2 Chemical Properties 1 session 1 block 1. **Describe** chemical properties of matter. 2. **Explain** the chemical properties of acids and bases. 3. **Explain** how a salt is formed.	National Content Standards: UCP2, B1		
Section 3 Physical and Chemical Changes 5 sessions 2.5 blocks 1. **Identify** physical and chemical changes. 2. **Exemplify** how physical and chemical changes affect the world you live in.	National Content Standards: UCP2, UCP3, UCP4, A1, B1, E2, F5, G3		**MiniLAB:** Comparing Chemical Changes, p. 147 **Science Online,** p. 148 **Environmental Science Integration,** p. 150 **Activity:** Sunset in a Bag, p. 151 **Activity:** Homemade pH Scale, pp. 152–153 **Science and History:** Crumbling Monuments, pp. 154–155

Activity Materials	Reproducible Resources	Section Assessment	Technology
Explore Activity: table-tennis ball, golf ball, bowl, water	**Chapter Resources Booklet** Foldables Worksheet, p. 15 Directed Reading Overview, p. 17 Note-taking Worksheets, pp. 31–33	GLENCOE'S ASSESSMENT ADVANTAGE	
MiniLAB: 3 different sized blocks of the same type of wood, metric ruler, balance	**Chapter Resources Booklet** Transparency Activity, p. 42 MiniLAB, p. 3 Lab Activity, pp. 9–10 Enrichment, p. 28 Reinforcement, p. 25 Directed Reading, p. 18 **Physical Science Critical Thinking/Problem Solving,** p. 15	Portfolio Science Journal, p. 138 Performance Math Skills Activity, p. 137 MiniLAB, p. 138 Skill Builder Activities, p. 140 Content Section Assessment, p. 140	Section Focus Transparency Interactive CD-ROM/DVD Guided Reading Audio Program
Need materials? Contact Science Kit at 1-800-828-7777 or www.sciencekit.com on the Internet.	**Chapter Resources Booklet** Transparency Activity, p. 43 Enrichment, p. 29 Reinforcement, p. 26 Directed Reading, p. 18 Transparency Activity, pp. 45–46 **Science Inquiry Labs,** pp. 17, 57	Portfolio Assessment, p. 144 Performance Skill Builder Activities, p. 144 Content Section Assessment, p. 144	Section Focus Transparency Teaching Transparency Interactive CD-ROM/DVD Guided Reading Audio Program
MiniLAB: fine steel wool, tap water, salt water, paper plate **Activity:** baking soda, calcium chloride, phonol red solution, water, 2 teaspoons, resealable plastic bag, graduated cylinder **Activity:** vials of pH paper (1–14), pH color chart, distilled water, fruit juices, vinegar, salt, sugar, soft drinks, household cleaners, soaps and detergents, antacids	**Chapter Resources Booklet** Transparency Activity, p. 44 MiniLAB, p. 4 Lab Activity, pp. 11–13 Enrichment, p. 30 Reinforcement, p. 27 Directed Reading, pp. 19, 20 Activity Worksheets, pp. 5–6, 7–8 **Reading and Writing Skill Activities,** p. 17 **Lab Management and Safety,** p. 38	Portfolio Activity, p. 148 Performance MiniLAB, p. 147 Skill Builder Activities, p. 150 Content Section Assessment, p. 150	Section Focus Transparency Interactive CD-ROM/DVD Guided Reading Audio Program

End of Chapter Assessment

GLENCOE'S ASSESSMENT ADVANTAGE

Blackline Masters	Technology	Professional Series
Chapter Resources Booklet Chapter Review, pp. 35–36 Chapter Tests, pp. 37–40 **Standardized Test Practice by The Princeton Review,** pp. 23–26	MindJogger Videoquiz CD-ROM Explorations and Quizzes Vocabulary Puzzle Makers ExamView Pro Test Bank Interactive Lesson Planner Interactive Teacher's Edition	Performance Assessment in the Science Classroom (PASC)

Transparencies

Section Focus

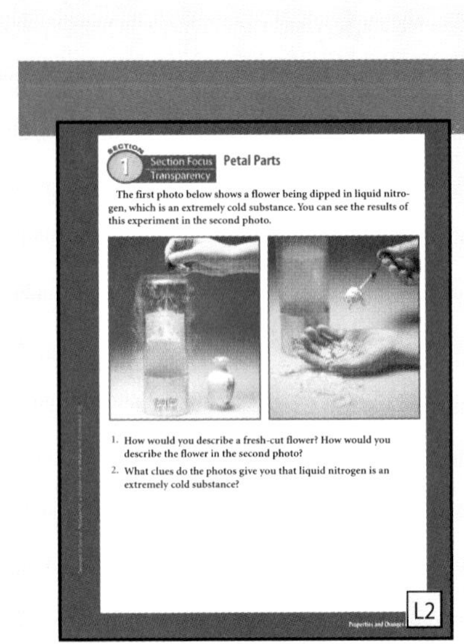
Section 1 Section Focus Transparency Petal Parts

The first photo below shows a flower being dipped in liquid nitrogen, which is an extremely cold substance. You can see the results of this experiment in the second photo.

1. How would you describe a fresh-cut flower? How would you describe the flower in the second photo?
2. What clues do the photos give you that liquid nitrogen is an extremely cold substance?

L2

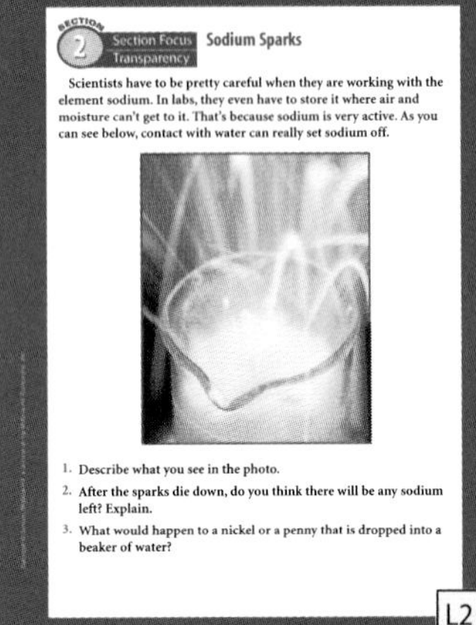
Section 2 Section Focus Transparency Sodium Sparks

Scientists have to be pretty careful when they are working with the element sodium. In labs, they even have to store it where air and moisture can't get to it. That's because sodium is very active. As you can see below, contact with water can really set sodium off.

1. Describe what you see in the photo.
2. After the sparks die down, do you think there will be any sodium left? Explain.
3. What would happen to a nickel or a penny that is dropped into a beaker of water?

L2

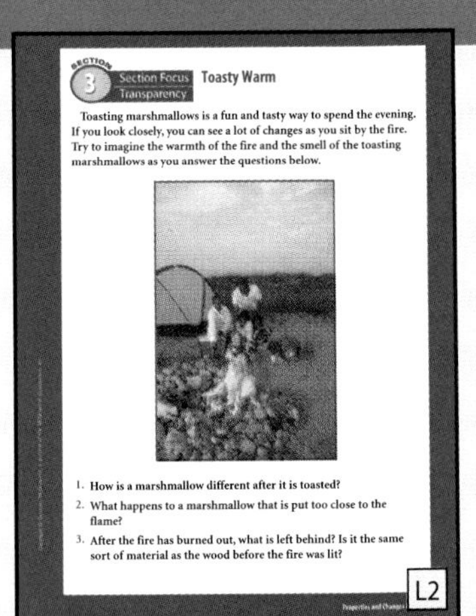
Section 3 Section Focus Transparency Toasty Warm

Toasting marshmallows is a fun and tasty way to spend the evening. If you look closely, you can see a lot of changes as you sit by the fire. Try to imagine the warmth of the fire and the smell of the toasting marshmallows as you answer the questions below.

1. How is a marshmallow different after it is toasted?
2. What happens to a marshmallow that is put too close to the flame?
3. After the fire has burned out, what is left behind? Is it the same sort of material as the wood before the fire was lit?

L2

This is a representation of key blackline masters available in the Teacher Classroom Resources. See Resource Manager boxes within the chapter for additional information.

Assessment

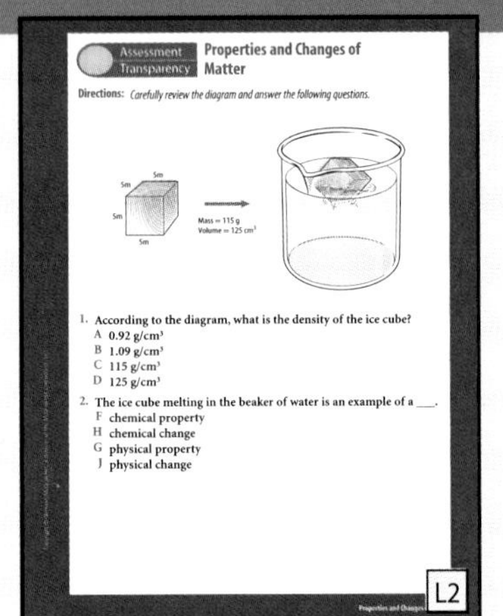
Assessment Transparency Properties and Changes of Matter

Directions: *Carefully review the diagram and answer the following questions.*

1. According to the diagram, what is the density of the ice cube?
   A 0.92 g/cm³
   B 1.09 g/cm³
   C 115 g/cm³
   D 125 g/cm³
2. The ice cube melting in the beaker of water is an example of a ___.
   F chemical property
   H chemical change
   G physical property
   J physical change

L2

Teaching

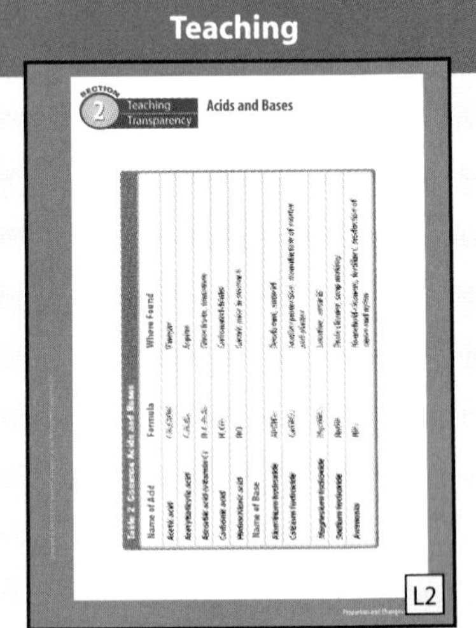
Section 2 Teaching Transparency Acids and Bases

L2

Key to Teaching Strategies

The following designations will help you decide which activities are appropriate for your students.

- L1 Level 1 activities should be appropriate for students with learning difficulties.
- L2 Level 2 activities should be within the ability range of all students.
- L3 Level 3 activities are designed for above-average students.
- ELL ELL activities should be within the ability range of English Language Learners.
- COOP LEARN Cooperative Learning activities are designed for small group work.
- LS Multiple Learning Styles logos, as described on page 22T, are used throughout to indicate strategies that address different learning styles.
- P These strategies represent student products that can be placed into a best-work portfolio.

Hands-on Activities

Activity Worksheets

Activity Sunset in a Bag

L2

Laboratory Activities

Activity (continued)

L2

Meeting Different Ability Levels

Content Outline

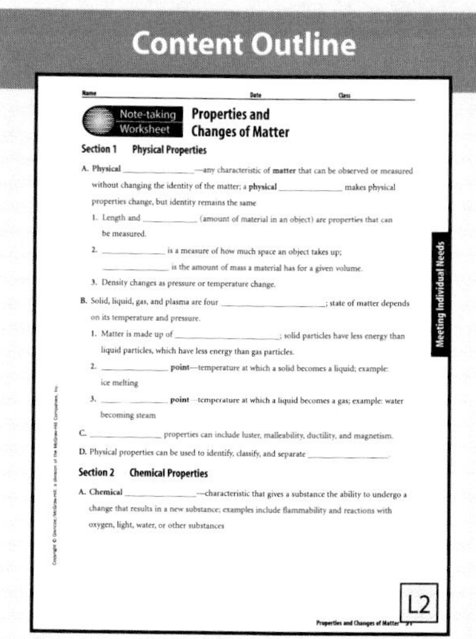

Name Date Class

Note-taking Worksheet **Properties and Changes of Matter**

Section 1 Physical Properties

A. Physical ______________—any characteristic of matter that can be observed or measured without changing the identity of the matter; a physical ______________ makes physical properties change, but identity remains the same

1. Length and ______________ (amount of material in an object) are properties that can be measured.
2. ______________ is a measure of how much space an object takes up; ______________ is the amount of mass a material has for a given volume.
3. Density changes as pressure or temperature change.

B. Solid, liquid, gas, and plasma are four ______________; state of matter depends on its temperature and pressure.

1. Matter is made up of ______________; solid particles have less energy than liquid particles, which have less energy than gas particles.
2. ______________ point—temperature at which a solid becomes a liquid; example: ice melting
3. ______________ point—temperature at which a liquid becomes a gas; example: water becoming steam

C. ______________ properties can include luster, malleability, ductility, and magnetism.

D. Physical properties can be used to identify, classify, and separate ______________.

Section 2 Chemical Properties

A. Chemical ______________—characteristic that gives a substance the ability to undergo a change that results in a new substance; examples include flammability and reactions with oxygen, light, water, or other substances

Meeting Individual Needs

L2

Reinforcement

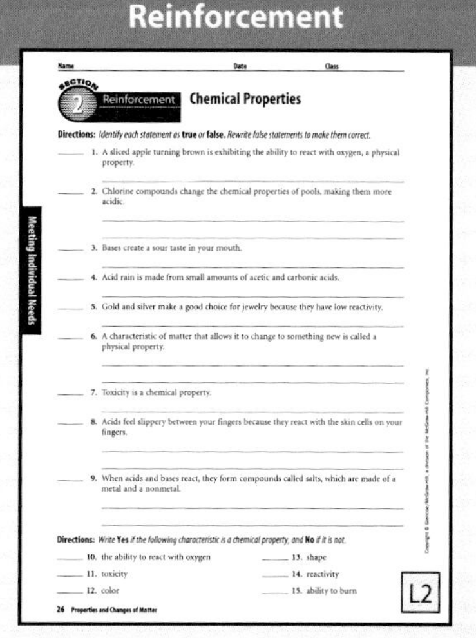

Name Date Class

Section 2 Reinforcement **Chemical Properties**

Directions: *Identify each statement as* **true** *or* **false.** *Rewrite false statements to make them correct.*

____ 1. A sliced apple turning brown is exhibiting the ability to react with oxygen, a physical property.

____ 2. Chlorine compounds change the chemical properties of pools, making them more acidic.

____ 3. Bases create a sour taste in your mouth.

____ 4. Acid rain is made from small amounts of acetic and carbonic acids.

____ 5. Gold and silver make a good choice for jewelry because they have low reactivity.

____ 6. A characteristic of matter that allows it to change to something new is called a physical property.

____ 7. Toxicity is a chemical property.

____ 8. Acids feel slippery between your fingers because they react with the skin cells on your fingers.

____ 9. When acids and bases react, they form compounds called salts, which are made of a metal and a nonmetal.

Directions: *Write* **Yes** *if the following characteristic is a chemical property, and* **No** *if it is not.*

____ 10. the ability to react with oxygen ____ 13. shape

____ 11. toxicity ____ 14. reactivity

____ 12. color ____ 15. ability to burn

Meeting Individual Needs

L2

Directed Reading

Name Date Class

Directed Reading for Content Mastery *Overview* **Properties and Changes of Matter**

Directions: *Complete the concept map using the terms in the list below.*

physical properties, rot, length, change color, density, chemical properties, volume, burn

Matter — has two properties — 1. / 2.; including 3. 4. 5.; include the ability to 6. 7. 8.

Directions: *Answer the following questions on the lines provided.*

9. List three size-dependent properties.
10. List three size-independent properties.
11. What is the pH range of an acid?

Meeting Individual Needs

L1

Assessment

Chapter Tests

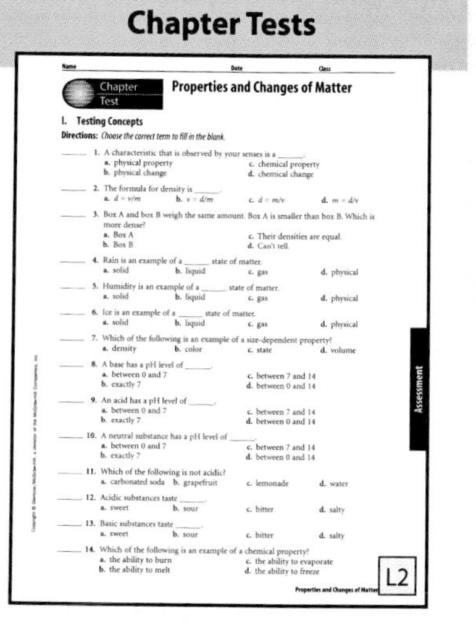

Name Date Class

Chapter Test **Properties and Changes of Matter**

I. Testing Concepts

Directions: *Choose the correct term to fill in the blank.*

____ 1. A characteristic that is observed by your senses is a ______. a. physical property b. physical change c. chemical property d. chemical change

____ 2. The formula for density is ______.

____ 3. Box A and box B weigh the same amount. Box A is smaller than box B. Which is more dense? a. Box A b. Box B c. Their densities are equal. d. Can't tell.

____ 4. Rain is an example of a ______ state of matter. a. solid b. liquid c. gas d. physical

____ 5. Humidity is an example of a ______ state of matter. a. solid b. liquid c. gas d. physical

____ 6. Ice is an example of a ______ state of matter. a. solid b. liquid c. gas d. physical

____ 7. Which of the following is an example of a size-dependent property? a. density b. color c. state d. volume

____ 8. A base has a pH level of ______. a. between 0 and 7 b. exactly 7 c. between 7 and 14 d. between 0 and 14

____ 9. An acid has a pH level of ______. a. between 0 and 7 b. exactly 7 c. between 7 and 14 d. between 0 and 14

____ 10. A neutral substance has a pH level of ______. a. between 0 and 7 b. exactly 7 c. between 7 and 14 d. between 0 and 14

____ 11. Which of the following is not acidic? a. carbonated soda b. grapefruit c. lemonade d. water

____ 12. Acidic substances taste ______. a. sweet b. sour c. bitter d. salty

____ 13. Basic substances taste ______. a. sweet b. sour c. bitter d. salty

____ 14. Which of the following is an example of a chemical property? a. the ability to burn b. the ability to melt c. the ability to evaporate d. the ability to freeze

Assessment

L2

Enrichment

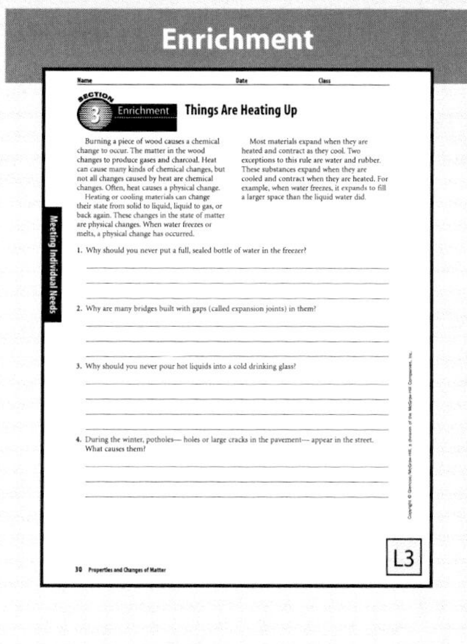

Name Date Class

Section 3 Enrichment **Things Are Heating Up**

Burning a piece of wood causes a chemical change to occur. The matter in the wood changes to produce gases and charcoal. Heat can cause many kinds of chemical changes, but not all changes caused by heat are chemical changes. Often, heat causes a physical change. Heating or cooling materials can change their state from solid to liquid, liquid to gas, or back again. These changes in the state of matter are physical changes. When water freezes or melts, a physical change has occurred.

Most materials expand when they are heated and contract as they cool. Two exceptions to this rule are water and rubber. These substances expand when they are cooled and contract when they are heated. For example, when water freezes, it expands to fill a larger space than the liquid water did.

1. Why should you never put a full, sealed bottle of water in the freezer?
2. Why are many bridges built with gaps (called expansion joints) in them?
3. Why should you never pour hot liquids into a cold drinking glass?
4. During the winter, potholes—holes or large cracks in the pavement—appear in the street. What causes them?

Meeting Individual Needs

L3

Spanish Directed Reading

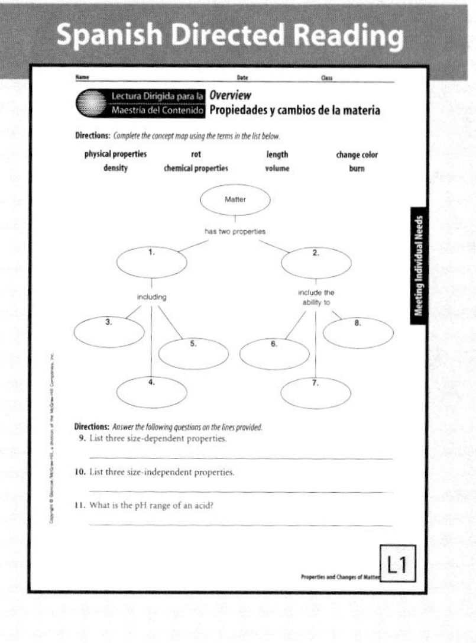

Name Date Class

Lectura Dirigida para la Maestría del Contenido *Overview* **Propiedades y cambios de la materia**

Directions: *Complete the concept map using the terms in the list below.*

physical properties, rot, length, change color, density, chemical properties, volume, burn

Matter — has two properties — 1. / 2.; including 3. 4. 5.; include the ability to 6. 7. 8.

Directions: *Answer the following questions on the lines provided.*

9. List three size-dependent properties.
10. List three size-independent properties.
11. What is the pH range of an acid?

Meeting Individual Needs

L1

Test Practice Workbook

Chapter Review

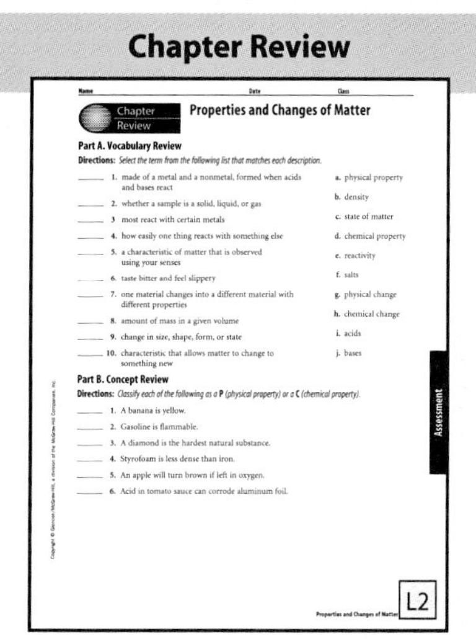

Name Date Class

Chapter Review **Properties and Changes of Matter**

Part A. Vocabulary Review

Directions: *Select the term from the following list that matches each description.*

____ 1. made of a metal and a nonmetal, formed when acids and bases react — a. physical property

____ 2. whether a sample is a solid, liquid, or gas — b. density

____ 3. most react with certain metals — c. state of matter

____ 4. how easily one thing reacts with something else — d. chemical property

____ 5. a characteristic of matter that is observed using your senses — e. reactivity

____ 6. taste bitter and feel slippery — f. salts

____ 7. one material changes into a different material with different properties — g. physical change

____ 8. amount of mass in a given volume — h. chemical change

____ 9. change in size, shape, form, or state — i. acids

____ 10. characteristic that allows matter to change to something new — j. bases

Part B. Concept Review

Directions: *Classify each of the following as a* **P** *(physical property) or a* **C** *(chemical property).*

____ 1. A banana is yellow.

____ 2. Gasoline is flammable.

____ 3. A diamond is the hardest natural substance.

____ 4. Styrofoam is less dense than iron.

____ 5. An apple will turn brown if left in oxygen.

____ 6. Acid in tomato sauce can corrode aluminum foil.

Assessment

L2

Science Content Background

SECTION 1

Physical Properties

Physical Properties

The physical properties of substances are primarily collected using the senses. For instance, a physical property of table salt is it is a white, crystalline solid. Both of these properties can be observed. The freezing point, boiling point, and density are physical properties too, and they require simple measurements to obtain.

Fun Fact

Of the top 100 chemical products produced in the United States, seven are acids, three are bases, and twelve are salts.

Geometric formulas can be used to find the volume for regularly shaped solid objects such as those shaped like cubes or rectangular prisms. The volume of an irregularly shaped, insoluble object can be measured by finding the volume of water the object will displace. The mass of the object is found by using a laboratory balance. Once the volume and mass are known density is found by dividing mass by volume.

SECTION 

Chemical Properties

A Complete Description

Unlike physical properties, the chemical properties of a substance cannot be found by observation of the substance alone. The chemical properties of a substance describe its chemical behavior with other substances. For instance, the fact that sodium will react with chlorine to form a salt is a chemical property of sodium.

Acids and Bases

Classes of substances such as acids and bases have chemical properties too. For example, acids react with bases in a neutralization reaction that forms water and a salt.

The definition of an acid and base varies slightly depending upon which theory is used. This table summarizes the Arrhenis, Bronsted-Lowry, and Lewis definitions of acids and bases. These theories are not discussed in this chapter but they may be helpful in making some explanations.

Barry Runk/Grant Heilman Photography, Inc.

Summary of Acid-Base Theories

Theory	Acid Definition	Base Definition
Arrhenius	Any substance that releases $H+$ ion in water solution	Any substance that releases $OH-$ ions in water solution
Bronsted-Lowry	Any substance that donates a proton	Any substance that accepts a proton
Lewis	Any substance that can accept an electron pair	Any substance that can donate an electron pair

Runk/Schoenberger/Grant Heilman Photography, Inc.

Rudi Von Briel/PhotoEdit

SECTION 3

Physical and Chemical Changes

Chemical Changes

In physical changes, the original materials can be easily recovered by ordinary means because a chemical reaction has not taken place. After a chemical change, the original materials can only be recovered by another chemical reaction because new materials have been formed.

Chemical and Physical Changes in Nature

The plant pigments that are responsible for the yellow, brown, and orange colors of leaves are called carotenoids. Chlorophyll and carotenoids are present in green leaves throughout the growing season. The pigments responsible for red and purple colors, called anthocyanins, are not present in green leaves. Anthocyanins are made in autumn. Anthocyanins change color depending on the acidity of the cell sap in the plant. The brightest colors usually occur when there is a succession of sunny days and cool nights.

Fun Fact

Sulfuric acid is used commercially in so many chemical processes that its annual consumption can be used to estimate a country's extent of industrialization.

For additional content background on this topic, go to the Glencoe Science Web site at science.glencoe.com.

Properties and Changes of Matter

Chapter Vocabulary
physical property
density
state of matter
chemical property
reactivity
salts
physical change
chemical change

What do you think?
Science Journal This is a time-lapsed photograph of a popcorn kernel popping.

CHAPTER 5

Properties and Changes of Matter

This iceberg once was part of an Antarctic ice shelf. Ice, like all matter, has physical and chemical properties and can undergo changes. Density is a physical property. Ice floats in water because it is less dense than water. It underwent a physical change when it became an iceberg. In this chapter you'll learn about chemical properties and changes and other physical properties and changes.

What do you think?
Science Journal Look at the picture below with a classmate. Discuss what you think might be happening. Here's a hint: *This change makes a tasty snack.* Write your answer or best guess in your Science Journal.

134

Theme Connection
Stability and Change Matter can be described by its physical and chemical properties. Matter is capable of undergoing physical and chemical changes based upon these properties.

Using your senses to observe characteristics of matter will help you classify, or categorize, it. Classifying different types of matter helps you understand what the types of matter are and can help you identify unknown types of matter. In this activity, you will observe and compare the characteristics of two items that you might be familiar with.

Compare characteristics

1. Obtain a table-tennis ball and a golf ball from your teacher.
2. How are the two balls similar?
3. Which sample is heavier?
4. Compare the surfaces of the table-tennis ball and the golf ball. How are their surfaces different?
5. Place each ball in water and observe.

Observe

If you were to create a classification system to classify different kinds of balls, which characteristics might you use? Describe your classification system in your Science Journal.

FOLDABLES Reading & Study Skills

Before You Read

Making a Classify Study Fold **Make the following Foldable to help you organize types of properties and changes into groups based on their common features.**

1. Place a sheet of paper in front of you so the short side is at the top. Fold the paper in half from the left side to the right side.
2. Now fold the paper in half from top to bottom. Then fold it in half again top to bottom. Unfold the last two folds.
3. Through the top thickness of paper, cut along each of the fold lines to form four tabs as shown.
4. Label the four sections *Physical Properties, Chemical Properties, Physical Change,* and *Chemical Change* as shown.
5. Before you read the chapter, list examples of each type of property and each type of change.
6. As you read the chapter, add to or correct what you have written under each tab.

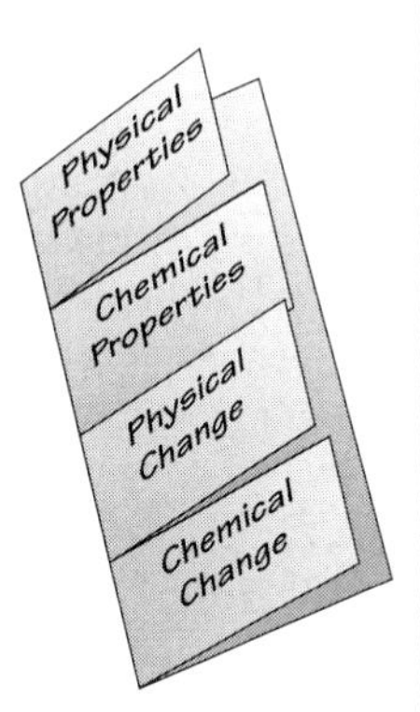

EXPLORE ACTIVITY

Purpose Use the Explore Activity to help students begin to observe and record physical properties of objects. L2

LS **Kinesthetic**

Preparation Obtain enough table-tennis balls and golf balls to allow each student to have a set. These balls may be borrowed from the athletic department at your school.

Materials golf ball, table-tennis ball, large container or beaker, water.

Teaching Strategy Remind students to observe characteristics such as color, texture, and coverings.

Observe

Answers will vary. Possible characteristics include mass, surface, ability to bounce, and color. Check students' classification systems.

Oral Ask students to write paragraphs comparing and contrasting the physical characteristics of the golf ball and the table-tennis ball. Use **Performance Assessment in the Science Classroom,** p. 159.

FOLDABLES Reading & Study Skills

Before You Read

Dinah Zike Study Fold

Purpose Students each make a Foldable to help them determine what they know about the physical and chemical properties of matter and physical and chemical changes before they read the chapter. They then use the Foldable for recording and organizing notes about these topics as they read.

For additional help, see Foldables Worksheet, p. 15 in **Chapter Resources Booklet,** or go to the Glencoe Science Web site at **science.glencoe.com.** See After You Read in the Study Guide at the end of this chapter.

SECTION 1

Physical Properties

1 Motivate

Bellringer Transparency

Display the Section Focus Transparency for Section 1. Use the accompanying Transparency Activity Master. L2 ELL

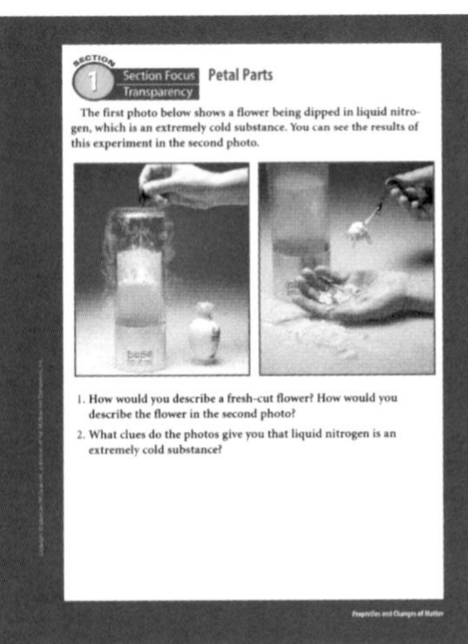

Section 1 Section Focus Transparency **Petal Parts**

The first photo below shows a flower being dipped in liquid nitrogen, which is an extremely cold substance. You can see the results of this experiment in the second photo.

1. How would you describe a fresh-cut flower? How would you describe the flower in the second photo?
2. What clues do the photos give you that liquid nitrogen is an extremely cold substance?

Properties and Changes of Matter

Tie to Prior Knowledge

Although they may not have used the terms *physical properties* and *chemical properties*, students frequently use characteristics of items to describe them. Display a large rock, a beaker of baking soda, and a beaker of water for students to see. Ask students to write a description of each substance. Explain that their descriptions include the physical characteristics of the substances.

SECTION 1

Physical Properties

As You Read

What You'll Learn

- **Describe** the physical properties of matter.
- **Explain** how to find the density of a substance.
- **Compare and contrast** the properties of acids and bases.

Vocabulary

physical property
density
state of matter

Why It's Important

When you learn about physical properties, you can better describe the world around you.

Physical Properties

Have you ever been asked by a teacher to describe something that you saw on a field trip? How would you describe the elephant in the exhibit shown in **Figure 1?** What features can you use in your description—color, shape, size, and texture? These features are all properties, or characteristics, of the elephant. Scientists use the term *physical property* to describe a characteristic of matter that you can detect with your senses. A **physical property** is any characteristic of matter that can be observed without changing the identity of the material. All matter, such as the elephant, has physical properties.

Common Physical Properties You probably are familiar with some physical properties, such as color, shape, smell, and taste. You might not be as familiar with others, such as mass, volume, and density. Mass is the amount of matter in an object. A golf ball has more mass than a table tennis-ball. Volume is the amount of space that matter takes up. A swimming pool holds a larger volume of water than a paper cup does. **Density** is the amount of mass in a given volume. A golf ball is more dense than a table-tennis ball. Density is determined by finding the mass of a sample of matter and dividing this mass by the volume of the sample.

$$\text{Density (g/cm}^3\text{)} = \text{mass (g)/volume (cm}^3\text{)}$$

Figure 1
This large gray African elephant is displayed on the main floor of the National Museum of Natural History in Washington, D.C.

136

Section Assessment Planner

Portfolio
Science Journal, p. 138

Performance Assessment
Math Skills Activity, p. 137
Skill Builder Activities, p. 140
See page 158 for more options.

Content Assessment
Section, p. 140
Challenge, p. 140
Chapter, pp. 158–159

Density A table-tennis ball and a golf ball are about the same volume. When you decided which had a higher density, you compared their masses. Because they are about the same volume, the one with more mass had the higher density. Suppose you were asked if all the bowling balls in **Figure 2** were identical. They appear to be the same size, shape, and color, but do they all have the same mass? If you could pick up these bowling balls, you would discover that their masses differ. You also might notice that the heavier balls strike the pins harder. Although the volumes of the balls are nearly identical, the densities of the bowling balls are different because their masses are different.

Identifying Unknown Substances In some cases, density also can be used to identify unknown compounds and elements. The element silver, for example, has a density of 10.5 g/cm^3 at 20°C. Suppose you want to know whether or not a ring is pure silver. You can find the ring's density by dividing the mass of the ring by its volume. If the density of the ring is determined to be 11.3 g/cm^3, then the ring is not pure silver.

Figure 2
These bowling balls look the same but have different densities.

Math Skills Activity

Determining the Density of a Material

Example Problem

An antique dealer decided to use density to help determine the material used to make a figurine. The volume of the figurine is 1,000 cm^3 and the mass is 8,470 g. What is its density?

Solution

1. *This is what you know:* density = mass/volume = M/V; M = 8,470 g, V = 1,000 cm^3
2. *This is what you need to find:* density needed: D
3. *This is the equation you need to use:* $D = M/V$
4. *Substitute the known values into the equation:* $D = M/V$ = 8,470 g/1,000 cm^3 = 8.470 g/cm^3

Check your answer by substituting it and the known values back into the original equation.

Practice Problem

If a candlestick has a mass of 8,509 g and a volume of 955 cm^3, what is its density?

For more help, refer to the Math Skill Handbook.

2 Teach

Physical Properties

Quick Demo

Write the formula for finding density on the board, Density = mass/volume. Using a balance, measure out 10 g of clay. Pour water into a 100-mL graduated cylinder to the 50-mL mark. Shape the clay to fit into the graduated cylinder. Cut a piece of string and attach it to the clay. Use the string to lower the clay into the graduated cylinder. Be careful not to splash out any water. Explain that the volume of the clay is the volume of the clay + water minus 50 mL. Using this value for the clay's volume, calculate the clay's density. Remind the students that 1 mL = 1 cm^3, so the clay's density can be expressed in g/cm^3. L2 ELL LS **Visual-Spatial**

Use Science Words

Word Usage Have students use the term *physical property* as they describe an object in their backpacks or desks. Possible answer: My ruler has the physical properties of being shaped long, narrow, and thin. L2 ELL LS **Linguistic**

Math Skills Activity

National Math Standards

Correlation to Mathematics Objectives

2, 6

Answer to Practice Problem

8.91 g/cm^3

Resource Manager

Chapter Resources Booklet

- Transparency Activity, p. 42
- Directed Reading for Content Mastery, pp. 17, 18
- Note-taking Worksheets, pp. 31–33

Mathematics Skill Activities, p. 9

Inclusion Strategies

Visually Impaired Ask these students to describe nonvisual physical properties that can be used to identify objects. Possible answers: solid—shape, size, texture, weight, smell; liquid—thickness, slipperiness, smell; gas—smell L2 LS **Kinesthetic**

Physical Properties, continued

Purpose Students measure wooden blocks and calculate their density. L2 ELL
LS **Kinesthetic**

Materials 3 different-sized wooden blocks, ruler, balance

Teaching Strategies Make sure the blocks are made from the same type of wood.

Analysis

1. length, width, height, mass, and volume
2. density

Process Have students find the density of balsa wood using the same methods used in the Minilab. Students should compare the results. The density of balsa wood is approximately 0.11 g/cm^3. Use **Performance Assessment in the Science Classroom,** p. 97.

Activity

Unit analysis is a good way to check that a problem has been set up correctly. Explain that when doing unit analysis, you set up a problem using only the units, cancel appropriately, and see whether the answer is in the desired units. Have students do a unit analysis using mass and volume to find density. If mass is in grams and volume is in milliliters, unit analysis says mass/volume = g/mL = density, whose units are g/mL. L2
LS **Logical-Mathematical**

Figure 3
All three states of water are present here—solid, liquid, and gas.

State of Matter State of matter is another physical property. The **state of matter** tells you whether a sample of matter is a solid, a liquid, or a gas. This property depends on the temperature and pressure of the matter. For example, water exists in the solid state below 0°C. Water exists in the liquid state between 0°C and 100°C. It also exists as a gas above 100°C. In each case, each molecule of water is the same—two hydrogen atoms and one oxygen atom. But water appears to be different because it exists in different states, as shown in **Figure 3.**

Size-Dependent and Size-Independent Properties Some physical properties change when the size of an object changes. These properties are called size-dependent properties. For example, a wooden block might have a volume of 30 cm^3 and a mass of 20 g. A larger block might have a volume of 60 cm^3 and a mass of 40 g. The volume and mass of the block change when the size of the block changes. However, the density of both blocks is 0.67 g. Density does not change with a change in size. Density is an example of a size-independent property. Other examples of size-dependent and size-independent properties are shown in **Table 1.**

Mini LAB

Classifying Properties

Procedure

1. Obtain three different-sized **blocks** of the same type of wood.
2. Write all of your observations of each block in your **Science Journal** as you make your measurements.
3. Measure the length, width, height, and mass of each block. Calculate the volume and density of each block.

Analysis

1. Which properties were size-dependent?
2. Which properties were size-independent?

Table 1 Physical Properties

Type of Property	Property
Size-dependent properties	length, width, height, volume, mass
Size-independent properties	density, color, state

Science Journal

A fourth state of matter is called plasma. Have students research the plasma state and record their findings in their Science Journals. Plasma is made up of ions, electrons, and atomic nuclei completely stripped of electrons. Plasma forms at temperatures above 5,000°C. L3 LS **Linguistic** P

Resource Manager

Chapter Resources Booklet
MiniLAB, p. 3
Enrichment, p. 28
Reinforcement, p. 25
Lab Activity, pp. 9–10

Home and Community Involvement, p. 36

Physical Properties of Acids and Bases

One way to describe matter is to classify it as either an acid or a base. The strength of an acid or base can be determined by finding the pH of the sample. The pH scale has a range of 0 to 14. Acids have a pH between 0 and 7. Bases have a pH between 7 and 14. A sample with a pH of exactly 7 is neutral—neither acidic nor basic. Pure water is a substance with a pH of exactly 7.

Properties of Acids What do you think of when you hear the word *acid?* Do you picture a dangerous chemical that can burn your skin, make holes in your clothes, and even destroy metal? Some acids, such as hydrochloric acid, are like that. But not all acids are harmful. One example is shown in **Figure 4.** Carbonated soft drinks contain acids. Every time you eat a citrus fruit such as an orange or a grapefruit, you eat citric and ascorbic (uh SOR bihk) acids. What properties do these and other acids have in common?

Imagine the sharp smell of a freshly sliced lemon. That scent comes from the citric acid in the fruit. Take a big bite out of the fruit shown in **Figure 5** and you would immediately notice a sour taste. If you then rubbed your molars back and forth, your teeth would squeak. All of these physical properties are common in acids.

Reading Check *What are two examples of foods that contain acids?*

Figure 4
When you sip a carbonated soft drink, you drink carbonic and phosphoric (faws FOR ihk) acids.

Figure 5
All citrus fruits contain citric and ascorbic acids, which is why these fruits taste sour.

Health INTEGRATION

Vitamin C and alpha-hydroxy acids are found in fruits and are the active ingredient in some anti-aging skin creams. It is believed that these ingredients slow down the aging process. Research safety issues regarding these products as well as how these ingredients work.

Physical Properties of Acids and Bases

Reading Check

Answer Possible answers: tomatoes and all citrus fruits.

Discussion

Explain to students that a base is also called an alkali. *Alkali* comes from the Arabic term for "the ashes" *(al qaliy)*. *Acid* comes from the Latin word for "sour" *(acidus)*. How do these word origins relate to the physical properties of acids and bases? Bases are slippery like ashes. Acids taste sour. L2 **Logical-Mathematical**

Health INTEGRATION

The safety and benefits of alphahydroxy acids and vitamin C are still under debate. Some scientists believe alphahydroxy acids can actually cause skin to age more rapidly. The FDA recommends that consumers use adequate sun protection while using alphahydroxy acids because it is suspected that they cause the skin to be more sensitive to UV radiation.

Teacher FYI

Acids and bases dissociate in water to form ions. Strong acids and bases dissociate more than weak acids and bases. pH is a measure of the amount of ionization a particular acid or base undergoes.

Internet Addresses

Explore the Glencoe Science Web site at **science.glencoe.com** to find out more about topics in this section.

Visual Learning

Figure 4 Ask students what states of matter are present in the glass of soft drink. Answers should include: solid (ice cubes, liquid (soft drink), and gas (bubbles). L2 **Visual-Spatial**

Physical Properties of Acids and Bases, continued

Reading Check

Answer Possible answers include any cleaner containing ammonia or any soap.

3 Assess

Reteach

Ask each student to select a rectangular solid and calculate its volume and density. They can do this by measuring the length, width, and height of the object and using the formula $V = l \times w \times h$ to calculate volume. Have them then determine the object's mass and calculate its density with the formula $D = m/v$. L2 LS **Logical-Mathematical**

Challenge

The particles that make up matter move differently in solids, liquids, and gases. Have students find out how the motion differs and draw diagrams illustrating their findings. The particles in a solid move back and forth in place. The particles in a liquid move faster and can slide past one another. The particles in a gas move faster still and move independently of one another in straight lines until they hit something. L3 LS **Visual-Spatial**

Assessment

Oral Is a liquid with a pH of 12 an acid or base? base **Is a liquid with a pH of 6 an acid or base?** acid **Is a liquid with a pH of 7 an acid or base?** neutral Use **PASC,** p. 101.

Figure 6
Soaps are bases, which is why they are slippery.

SCIENCE Online

Research Visit the Glencoe Science Web site at **science.glencoe.com** for information about the common and industrial uses of acids and bases. Communicate to your class what you learn.

Physical Properties of Bases Bases have physical properties that are different from acids. A familiar example of a base is ammonia (uh MOH nyuh), often used for household cleaning. If you got a household cleaner that contained ammonia on your fingers and then rubbed your fingers together, they would feel slippery. Another familiar base is soap, shown in **Figure 6,** which also has a slippery feel. You shouldn't taste soap, but if you accidentally did, you'd notice a bitter taste. A bitter taste and a slippery feel are physical properties of bases.

Reading Check *What are two examples of products that contain bases?*

The physical properties of acids and bases are different and can be used to classify them. But it is important to note that you should never taste, touch, or smell anything in a lab.

Section  Assessment

1. Define the term *physical property* and describe the physical properties of salt.
2. Define the term *density,* describe how it is determined, and explain why it is a size-independent property.
3. What are two physical properties of acids?
4. What are two physical properties of bases?
5. **Think Critically** How could you identify a pure metal if you have a balance, a graduated cylinder, and a table of densities for metals?

Skill Builder Activities

6. **Solving One-Step Equations** What is the density of a substance with a mass of 65.7 g and volume of 3.40 cm^3? **For more help, refer to the Math Skill Handbook.**
7. **Making and Using Tables** Make a table and list ten things in your home. On the table, include the following physical properties for each item: *color, state of matter, shape,* and *hardness.* **For more help, refer to the Science Skill Handbook.**

Answers to Section Assessment

1. A physical property is any characteristic of matter that can be observed without changing the identity of the material. Table salt is white and is a solid.
2. Density is the amount of mass in a given volume. Density is determined by dividing the mass of an object by its volume. Density is size independent because it doesn't change as the size of the object changes.
3. a sharp smell and a sour taste
4. a slippery feel and a bitter taste
5. Calculate the density of the metal and compare it to the densities of metals given in the table.
6. Density equals: $65.7\ g/3.40\ cm^3 = 19.3\ g/cm^3$
7. Answers will vary.

SECTION

Chemical Properties

A Complete Description

You've observed that the density of a table-tennis ball is less than the density of a golf ball. You also have noticed the state of water in an ice cube and a lake. You've noticed the taste of acid in a lemon and the slippery feel of a base such as ammonia. However, a description of something using only physical properties is not complete. What type of property describes how matter behaves?

Common Chemical Properties If you strike a match on a hard, rough surface, the match probably will start to burn. The element phosphorus (FAWS for us) and the wood in the match combine with oxygen in the air to form new materials. Why does that happen? The phosphorus and the wood have the ability to burn. The ability to burn is a chemical property. A **chemical property** is a characteristic of something that allows it to change to something new.

Reading Check *What is a chemical property?*

You see an example of a chemical property when you leave a half-eaten apple on your desk, and the exposed part turns brown. The property you observe is the ability to react with oxygen. Two other chemical properties are shown in **Figure 7.**

As You Read

What You'll Learn

- **Describe** chemical properties of matter.
- **Explain** the chemical properties of acids and bases.
- **Explain** how a salt is formed.

Vocabulary

chemical property
reactivity
salts

Why It's Important

Chemical properties can help you predict how matter will change.

Figure 7
The chemical properties of a material often require a warning about its careful use.

A Gasoline is flammable. Gas pumps warn customers not to get near them with anything that might start the gasoline burning.

B Toxicity (tahk SIH suh tee) indicates how poisonous something is. Workers who use toxic chemicals have to wear protective clothing.

SECTION

Chemical Properties

1 Motivate

Bellringer Transparency

Display the Section Focus Transparency for Section 2. Use the accompanying Transparency Activity Master. L2 ELL

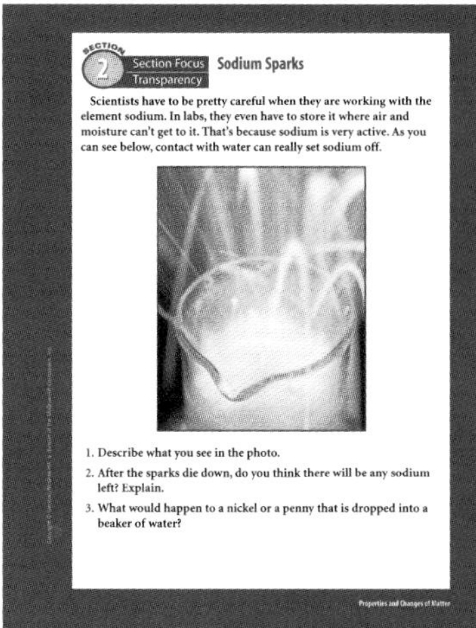

Section 2 Section Focus Transparency **Sodium Sparks**

Scientists have to be pretty careful when they are working with the element sodium. In labs, they even have to store it where air and moisture can't get to it. That's because sodium is very active. As you can see below, contact with water can really set sodium off.

1. Describe what you see in the photo.
2. After the sparks die down, do you think there will be any sodium left? Explain.
3. What would happen to a nickel or a penny that is dropped into a beaker of water?

Properties and Changes of Matter

Tie to Prior Knowledge

Ask students if they have ever seen soured milk. Soured milk is a result of a chemical reaction that occurs in fresh milk. Point out that the properties of the milk before the chemical reaction are different from the properties of the milk after the chemical reaction.

Section Assessment Planner

PORTFOLIO
Assessment, p. 144

PERFORMANCE ASSESSMENT
Skill Builder Activities, p. 144
See page 158 for more options.

CONTENT ASSESSMENT
Section, p. 144
Challenge, p. 144
Chapter, pp. 158–159

Resource Manager

Chapter Resources Booklet
Transparency Activity, p. 43
Directed Reading for Content Mastery, p. 18

2 Teach

A Complete Description

✔ Reading Check

Answer a characteristic of a something that allows it to change into something else

Activity

The chemical properties of a substance depend on the ways the molecules of the substance interact with molecules of other substances. Tell students that a water molecule contains two hydrogen atoms and one oxygen atom. Explain that two water molecules can decompose to form two molecules of hydrogen gas and one molecule of oxygen gas. A molecule of hydrogen gas contains two hydrogen atoms, and a molecule of oxygen gas contains two oxygen atoms. Have students use gumdrops and toothpicks to make models of several water molecules and then use the models to simulate the decomposition of water. L3 ELL COOP LEARN LS **Visual-Spatial**

Extension

Ask students to find out what chemical property makes hard water different from soft water. Hard water contains minerals that react chemically with soap to form solids. Soft water does not contain these compounds. L3 LS **Linguistic**

✔ Reading Check

Answer Reactivity is how easily one thing reacts with something else.

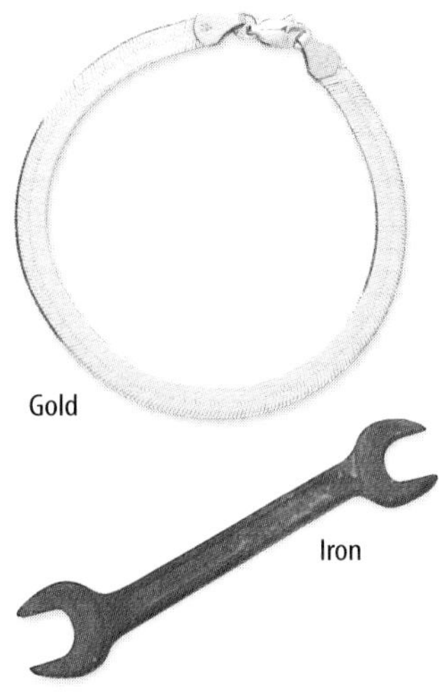

Figure 8
Gold and iron have different chemical properties that make them suitable for different uses.

Choosing Materials Look at **Figure 8.** Would you rather wear a bracelet made of gold or one made of iron? Why? Iron is less attractive and less valuable than gold. It also has an important chemical property that makes it unsuitable for jewelry. Think about what happens to iron when it is left out in moist air. Iron rusts easily because of its high reactivity (ree ak TIH vuh tee) with oxygen and moisture in the air. **Reactivity** is how easily one thing reacts with something else. The low reactivity of silver and gold, in addition to their desirable physical properties, makes those metals good choices for jewelry.

✔ Reading Check *What is reactivity?*

Chemical Properties and Pools Did you ever wonder why chlorine is added to swimming pools? Chlorine compounds change the chemical properties of the pool water. They make it more acidic and kill bacteria, insects, algae, and plants. The person in **Figure 9** is testing the pool water to see whether it has the correct amount of chlorine.

Any time you have standing water, mosquitoes and other insects can lay eggs in it. Various plants and algae can turn a sparkling blue pool into a slimy green mess. Bacteria are another problem. When you go swimming, you bring along millions of uninvited guests—the normal bacteria that live on your skin. The chlorine compounds kill the bacteria—as well as insects, algae, and plants that might be in the pool.

Chlorine makes the water more acidic, and this acidity can cause problems as well. Have your eyes ever burned after swimming in a pool? The chlorinated water can irritate the skin and eyes of swimmers.

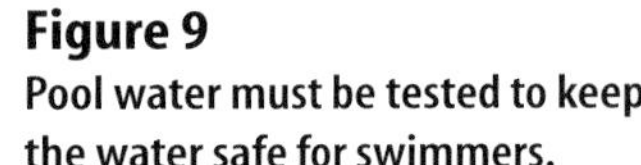

Figure 9
Pool water must be tested to keep the water safe for swimmers.

Inclusion Strategies

Learning Disabled Have students gather pictures from magazines and newspapers that show items containing acids or bases. Have them use the pictures to create one mobile or collage for acids and one for bases. They also can use labels containing the properties of acids and bases in their mobiles and collages. L2 LS P

Resource Manager

Chapter Resources Booklet
Enrichment, p. 29
Reinforcement, p. 26
Transparency Activity, pp. 45–46

Chemical Properties of Acids and Bases You have learned that acids and bases have physical properties that make acids taste sour and bases taste bitter and feel slippery. The chemical properties of acids and bases are what make them both useful but sometimes harmful. Several acids and bases are shown in **Table 2.**

Acids Many acids react with, or corrode, certain metals. Have you ever used aluminum foil to cover leftover spaghetti or tomato sauce? **Figure 10** shows what you might see the next day. You might see small holes in the foil where it has come into contact with the tomatoes in the sauce. The acids in tomato sauce, oranges, carbonated soft drinks, and other foods won't hurt you. However, many acids can damage plant and animal tissue. Small amounts of nitric (NITE rihk) acid and sulfuric (sulf YER ihk) acid are found in rain. This rain, called acid rain, harms plant and animal life in areas where acid rain falls. Sulfuric acid that has no water mixed with it is useful in many industries because it removes water from certain materials. However, that same property causes burns on skin that touches sulfuric acid.

Figure 10
Aluminum reacts easily with acids, which is why acidic food, such as tomatoes, should not be cooked or stored in aluminum.

Table 2 Common Acids and Bases

Name of Acid	Formula	Where Found
Acetic acid	CH_3COOH	Vinegar
Acetylsalicylic acid	$C_9H_8O_4$	Aspirin
Ascorbic acid (vitamin C)	$H_2C_6H_6O_6$	Citrus fruits, tomatoes
Carbonic acid	H_2CO_3	Carbonated drinks
Hydrochloric acid	HCl	Gastric juice in stomach
Name of Base		
Aluminum hydroxide	$Al(OH)_3$	Deodorant, antacid
Calcium hydroxide	$Ca(OH)_2$	Leather protection, manufacture of mortar and plaster
Magnesium hydroxide	$Mg(OH)_2$	Laxative, antacid
Sodium hydroxide	NaOH	Drain cleaner, soap making
Ammonia	NH_3	Household cleaners, fertilizer, production of rayon and nylon

Chemical Properties of Acids and Bases

Visual Learning

Table 2 What element do all of the acids have in common? hydrogen **What pair of elements do all of the bases except ammonia have in common?** hydrogen and oxygen L2 **Visual-Spatial**

Extension

Ask students to find out what types of crops grow well in acidic or basic soils. Then ask them to find information from a local horticulturist or lawn and garden store about plants that grow well in your area. Ask students to use this information to infer whether the soil in your area is acidic or basic. L3 **Naturalist**

Teacher FYI

The term *pH* means "potential of hydrogen." In water, hydrogen ions combine with water to form hydronium ions (H_3O^+). pH is a measure of the concentration of hydronium ions in a solution. The pH scale is logarithmic, not linear. A solution with a pH of 8 has ten times as many hydronium ions as a solution with a pH of 9.

Quick Demo

Show students that acids react with metals. Pour colorless, carbonated soft drink into a cup and drop in an iron nail. Have students observe the results the next day. L1 ELL **Visual-Spatial**

Cultural Diversity

Tasty Properties The ability to taste varies from person to person. Some of the variation is genetic. A dominant gene controls a person's ability to taste PTC (phenylthiocarbamide). To people who can taste it, PTC is bitter. PTC-like substances are found in foods such as buttermilk, spinach, and turnips, so tasters and nontasters have different responses to these foods. Some poisonous plants also contain PTCs, so being a taster would be useful to a food gatherer living where these plants grow. The ability to taste PTC varies from population to population. In sub-Saharan Africa, only 5 percent of the genes are for tasting; in Denmark, 57 percent are.

3 Assess

Reteach

Ask each student to write the name of something on a slip of paper. Collect the slips of paper and put them into a container. Draw them one at a time and have students name a physical and chemical property for each item. L1 LS **Interpersonal**

Challenge

Molecules of bases usually contain an –OH group. Ammonia, NH_3, does not contain an –OH group. Have students find out why ammonia is classified as a base. Like other bases, ammonia forms OH^- ions in water. L3 LS **Logical-Mathematical**

Portfolio Choose an item or material in the classroom. Ask students to write a fiction story about it, describing all the chemical and physical properties of it that they can. Examples of items or materials include water, fabric, wood, plastic, and lab chemicals. Use **Performance Assessment in the Science Classroom,** p. 155. P

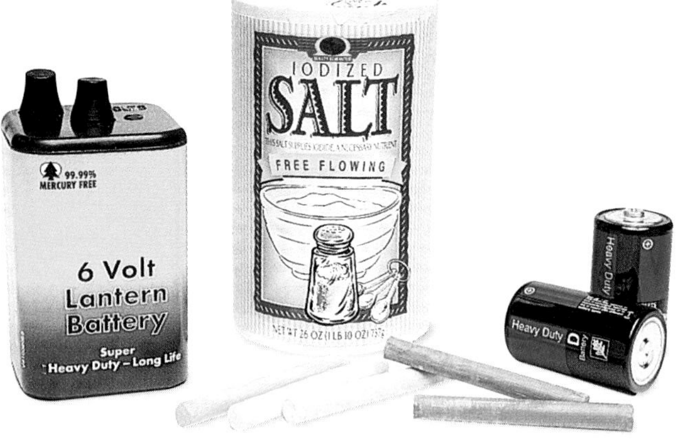

Figure 11
These everyday items contain salts.

Bases A strong base is just as dangerous as a strong acid. A base, such as sodium hydroxide (hi DRAHK side) can damage living tissue. It is not uncommon for someone who smells strong ammonia to get a bloody nose or to get a burn if a strong base is touched. Ammonia feels slippery to the touch because the base reacts with fat that lies under the top layer of skin cells in your fingertips, which results in damaged tissue.

Salts What happens in reactions between acids and bases? Acids and bases often are studied together because they react with each other to form water and other useful compounds called salts. **Salts** are compounds made of a metal and nonmetal that are formed when acids and bases react. Look at **Figure 11.** That white solid in your salt shaker—table salt—is the most common salt. Table salt, sodium chloride, can be formed by the reaction between the base sodium hydroxide and hydrochloric acid. Other useful salts are calcium carbonate, which is chalk, and ammonium chloride, which is used in some types of batteries.

Section  Assessment

1. Define the term *chemical property* and give an example of a chemical property of a substance.
2. Describe at least two chemical properties of an acid.
3. Describe at least two chemical properties of a base.
4. Describe what is formed when an acid and a base react.
5. **Think Critically** Think about safety precautions you take around your home. Which ones are based upon physical properties and which ones are based upon chemical properties? Explain.

Skill Builder Activities

6. **Classifying** Classify each of the following properties as being physical or chemical. **For more help, refer to the Science Skill Handbook.**
   - **a.** Iron will rust when left out in the air.
   - **b.** Lye feels slippery.
   - **c.** Iodine is poisonous.
   - **d.** Solid sulfur shatters when struck.
   - **e.** Copper statues turn green.
7. **Communicating** In your Science Journal, write a poem describing the physical and chemical properties of an acid or a base. **For more help, refer to the Science Skill Handbook.**

Answers to Section Assessment

1. A chemical property is a characteristic of something that allows it to change to something new. A chemical property of wood is that it will burn.
2. Acids can kill bacteria, insects, algae, and plants; acids react with bases to form salts.
3. Strong bases can damage living tissue. Strong bases react with the fat in the top layer of skin cells when touched; bases react with acids to form salts.
4. a salt and water
5. Physical properties—Use a safe ladder when placing items on high shelves. Wet floors are slippery. Chemical properties—Store all chemicals and cleaners away from small children. Store all flammable liquids away from an open flame such as a pilot light.
6. physical b, d. chemical a, c, e.
7. Answers will vary.

144 CHAPTER 5 Properties and Changes of Matter

SECTION 3

Physical and Chemical Changes

Physical Change

The crowd gathers at a safe distance and the cameras from the news media are rolling. A sense of excitement, fear, and anticipation fills the air. The demolition experts are making their final inspections. Then, in just a few seconds, a large building becomes a pile of rubble. The appearance of this building changed—a physical change.

What is physical change? Most matter can undergo physical change. A **physical change** is any change in size, shape, form, or state where the identity of the matter stays the same. Only the physical properties change. The building in **Figure 12** underwent a physical change. It went from a tall, stately building to a pile of steel and concrete. The materials are the same; they just look different.

Reading Check *What is a physical change?*

As You Read

What You'll Learn

- **Identify** physical and chemical changes.
- **Exemplify** how physical and chemical changes affect the world you live in.

Vocabulary

physical change
chemical change

Why It's Important

Many of the changes around you are chemical changes.

Figure 12
This building underwent a physical change—its form changed.

Section Assessment Planner

PORTFOLIO
Activity, p. 148

PERFORMANCE ASSESSMENT
Try At Home MiniLAB, p. 147
Skill Builder Activities, p. 150
See page 158 for more options.

CONTENT ASSESSMENT
Section, p. 150
Challenge, p. 150
Chapter, pp. 158–159

SECTION 3

Physical and Chemical Changes

1 Motivate

Bellringer Transparency

Display the Section Focus Transparency for Section 3. Use the accompanying Transparency Activity Master. L2 ELL

SECTION 3 Section Focus Transparency **Toasty Warm**

Toasting marshmallows is a fun and tasty way to spend the evening. If you look closely, you can see a lot of changes as you sit by the fire. Try to imagine the warmth of the fire and the smell of the toasting marshmallows as you answer the questions below.

1. How is a marshmallow different after it is toasted?
2. What happens to a marshmallow that is put too close to the flame?
3. After the fire has burned out, what is left behind? Is it the same sort of material as the wood before the fire was lit?

Properties and Changes of Matter

Tie to Prior Knowledge

Review with students some of the physical and chemical properties of matter about which they have learned. Explain that these properties can change when matter undergoes physical and chemical changes.

Resource Manager

Chapter Resources Booklet
Transparency Activity, p. 44
Directed Reading for Content Mastery, pp. 19, 20

2 Teach

Physical Change

Reading Check

Answer any change in size, shape, form, or state in which the identity of the matter stays the same

Identifying Misconceptions

When students see a substance such as water change state, they may think there has been a chemical change, creating a different substance. Point out that ice, water, and steam (water vapor) all have the same chemical makeup and formula, H_2O.

Visual Learning

Figure 13 Mention to students that all the changes of state shown have specific names. The four changes shown are melting, freezing, condensation, and evaporation, respectively. L2 ELL LS **Visual-Spatial**

Teacher FYI

Another change of state is sublimation. Sublimation is a change of a solid directly to a gas or a gas directly to a solid, without going through the liquid state. Sublimation is used to make freeze-dried food products. The element iodine is a solid that sublimes at room temperature, as is dry ice (solid carbon dioxide).

Examples of Physical Changes How can you recognize a physical change? Just look to see whether or not the matter has changed size, shape, form, or state. If you cut a watermelon into chunks, the watermelon has changed size and shape. That's a physical change. If you pop one of those chunks into your mouth and bite it, you have changed the watermelon's size and shape again.

Change of State Matter can undergo a physical change in another way, too. It can change from one state to another. Suppose it's a hot day. You and your friends decide to make snow cones. A snow cone is a frozen, solid mixture of water, sugar, food coloring, and flavoring. The water in the snow cone is solid, but in the hot sunshine, it begins to warm. When the temperature of the water reaches its melting point, the solid water begins to melt. The chemical composition of the water—two hydrogens and one oxygen—does not change. However, its form changes. This is an example of a physical change. The solid water becomes a liquid and drips onto the sidewalk. As the drops of liquid sit in the sunshine, the water changes state again, evaporating to become a gas. Water also can change from a solid to liquid by boiling. Other examples of change of state are shown in **Figure 13.**

Figure 13
The four most common changes of state are shown here.

A A solid will melt, becoming a liquid.

B As it cools, this liquid metal will become solid steel.

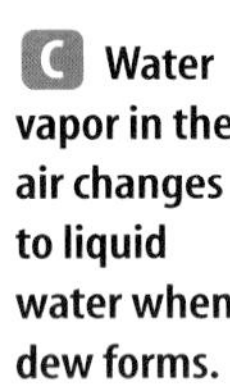

C Water vapor in the air changes to liquid water when dew forms.

D Liquid water in perspiration changes to a gas when it evaporates from your skin.

146

Curriculum Connection

Geography The Grand Canyon was formed over time by physical changes to the rock, as were the stone pillars in Bryce National Park. Have students look through several magazines that show remarkable landscapes. Have them explain how physical weathering could have formed some of these structures. L2 LS **Visual-Spatial**

Resource Manager

Chapter Resources Booklet
MiniLAB, p. 4
Reinforcement, p. 27

Figure 14
Chemical changes occur all around you.

A This unprotected car fender was exposed to salt which caused it to rust.

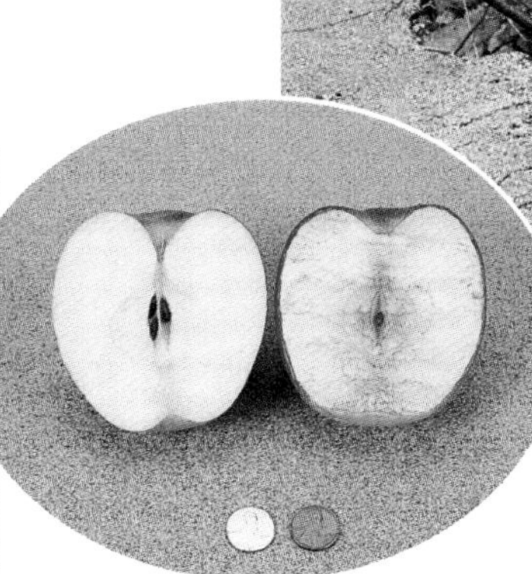

B Apples and pennies darken due to chemical changes.

C This bridge support will have to be repaired or replaced because of the rust damage.

Chemical Changes

Unprotected cars driven on salted roads and steel structures like the one shown in **Figure 14** can begin to rust after only a few winters. A shiny copper penny becomes dull and dark. An apple left out too long begins to rot. What do all these changes have in common? Each of these changes is a chemical change. A **chemical change** occurs when one material changes into a different material with different properties.

✔ Reading Check *What happens during a chemical change?*

Examples of Chemical Change Chemical changes are going on around you—and inside you—every day. Plants use photosynthesis to produce food—the product of chemical changes. When you eat fruits and vegetables produced by photosynthesis, these products must be chemically changed again so that the cells in your body can use them as food. There are many chemical changes occurring outside of your body, too. Paint drying, silver tarnishing, iron rusting, and petroleum products combusting are all examples of chemical changes that are occurring around you. Although these reactions may be occurring at different rates and producing different products, they are still examples of chemical changes.

TRY AT HOME Mini LAB

Comparing Chemical Changes

Procedure
1. Separate a piece of **fine steel wool** into two halves.
2. Dip one half in **tap water** and the other half in the same amount of **salt water.**
3. Place both pieces of steel wool on a **paper plate** and let them sit overnight. Observe any changes.

Analysis
1. What happened to the steel wool that was dipped in the salt water?
2. What might be a common problem with machinery that is operated near an ocean?

Chemical Changes

✔ Reading Check

Answer One material changes into another material with different properties.

TRY AT HOME Mini LAB

Purpose to observe the effect of salt on the reaction of steel wool with air L2 ELL
LS **Visual-Spatial**

Materials piece of fine steel wool, water, salt water, paper plate

Teaching Strategy Some steel wool is lightly coated with oil. Use steel wool that has neither soap nor oil.

Analysis
1. It rusted more than the other piece.
2. If not properly protected, salt from the ocean would speed rusting of the steel in the machinery.

✔ Assessment

Performance Ask students to infer the benefits and problems of using plastic for car bodies. Be sure they include whether problems are caused by physical properties or chemical properties. Have each student write a paragraph describing his or her conclusions. Use **PASC,** p. 157.

LAB DEMONSTRATION

Purpose to deomonstrate chemical and physical changes

Materials 2 pennies, rough surface, glass beaker, dilute hydrochloric acid, torch, tongs

Preparation CAUTION: *Wear a laboratory apron, gloves, and safety goggles.* Use the rough surface to scratch the edge of each penny, exposing the zinc center.

Procedure Place one penny in a small amount of dilute HCl in a beaker. Observe the reaction. Using tongs, grip the other penny and place it near a flame.

Expected Outcome In the acid, the zinc reacted with the acid while the copper did not. In the flame, the zinc melted and the copper did not.

Which change was a physical change and which was a chemical change? The reaction in hydrochloric acid was a chemical change and the melting of the zinc was a physical change.

Chemical Changes, continued

Reading Check

Answer New materials with new properties are formed.

Use an Analogy

During a chemical change, molecules are broken apart and their atoms are regrouped into new, different molecules, and therefore into new substances. As an analogy, imagine taking a car apart and reshaping and regrouping its components to make a lawn mower, two sofas, and a shed. What had been a car is now several entirely different things.

Fun Fact

Pizza is produced by a combination of chemical and physical changes. For example, the yeast in the dough reacts chemically with the sugar and other substances, causing the dough to rise while it bakes. The melting of the cheese is a physical change.

Activity

Have student groups make posters for the classroom about chemical change. Each poster should include a colorful illustration demonstrating one or more signs that a chemical change is occurring or has occurred. L1 ELL COOP LEARN LS Visual-Spatial P

Internet Addresses

Explore the Glencoe Science Web site at **science.glencoe.com** to find out more about topics in this section.

Figure 15
Chemical changes are common when food, such as cake, is cooked.

New Materials Are Formed Ice melts, paper is cut, metal is hammered into sheets, and clay is molded into a vase. Seeing signs of these physical changes is easy—something changes shape, size, form, or state.

The only sure way to know whether a chemical change has occurred is if new materials are formed that are chemically different from the starting materials. A chemical change cannot be reversed easily. For example, when wood burns, you see it change to ash and gases that have properties that are different from the wood and oxygen that burned. You can't put the ash and gases back together to make wood. When the cake shown in **Figure 15** is baked, changes occur that make the cake become solid. The chemical change that occurs when baking powder mixes with water results in bubbles that make the cake rise. Raw egg in the batter undergoes changes that make the egg solid. These changes cannot be reversed.

Research Visit the Glencoe Science Web site at **science.glencoe.com** for information about the chemical changes that make glowsticks glow when bent.

Reading Check *How can you be sure that a chemical change has occurred?*

Signs of Chemical Change In these examples, you know that a chemical change occurred because you can see that a new substance forms. It's not always easy to tell when new substances are formed. What are other signs of chemical change?

One sign of a chemical change is the release or absorption of energy in the form of light, heat, or sound. Release of energy is obvious when something burns—light and heat are given off. Sometimes an energy change is so small or slow that it is difficult to notice, like when something rusts. Another sign that indicates a chemical change is the formation of a gas or a solid that is not the result of a change of state.

Curriculum Connection

Art Leonardo da Vinci was one of the world's great artists, but only a few of his artworks remain. He experimented with using oil paint instead of watercolors to paint frescoes. Because of chemical changes caused by the interaction of the oil, paint, air, and plaster, *The Battle of Anghiari* was lost within ten years, and *The Last Supper* must be restored continuously.

Resource Manager

Chapter Resources Booklet
Enrichment, p. 30

Chemical and Physical Changes in Nature

Often, a color change is evidence of a chemical change, an example of which is shown in **Figure 16.** Leaves can contain yellow pigments that are masked, or hidden, by green chlorophyll. In the fall, a chemical change causes chlorophyll to break down, revealing these yellow pigments. In some leaves, chemical changes also produce red pigments.

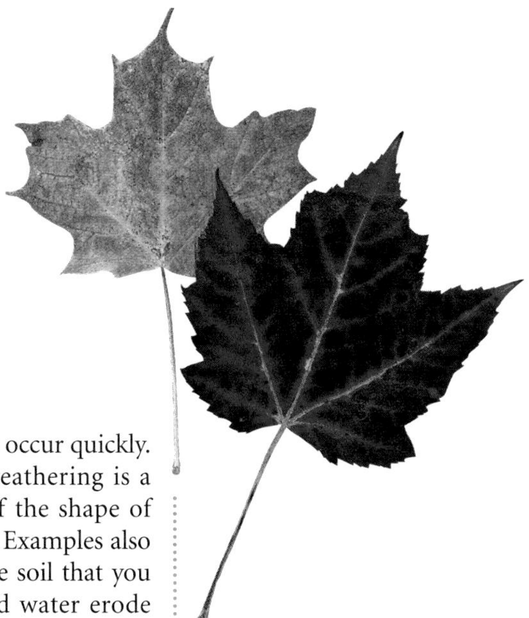

Figure 16 Chemical changes that occur in the fall bring about the color changes in these leaves.

Physical Weathering Some physical changes occur quickly. Others take place over a long time. Physical weathering is a physical change that is responsible for much of the shape of Earth's surface. Examples are shown in **Figure 17.** Examples also can be found in your own school yard. All of the soil that you see comes from physical weathering. Wind and water erode rocks, breaking them into small bits. Water fills cracks in rocks. When it freezes, the ice splits the rock into smaller pieces. No matter how small the pieces of rock are, they are made up of the same things that made up the bigger pieces of rock. The rock simply has undergone a physical change. Gravity, plants, animals, and the movement of land during earthquakes also help cause physical changes on Earth.

Figure 17 You can see dramatic examples of physical weathering caused by water and wind on rocky coastlines.

Chemical and Physical Changes in Nature

Visual Learning

Figure 17 What has caused the physical weathering along this coastline? The waves crashing against the rocks. L2 LS **Visual-Spatial**

Make a Model

Using simple materials, make a model of a chemical or physical change that occurs in nature. Possible models: volcano eruption and island formation, land or shoreline erosion, or glacier movement. L2 LS **Kinesthetic**

Activity

Have students choose a photograph of a scenic landscape and write a poem about the chemical and/or physical changes that have created the landscape. Students should share their poem with their class. L2 LS **Linguistic**

Environmental Science INTEGRATION

Other cave formations that can be found in Carlsbad Caverns include soda straws, drapery, flowstone, shelfstone, cave pearls, popcorn, helictites, and totem poles. All are products of the dissolution and subsequent deposition of minerals, mostly calcite. Temperature and whether water enters the cave by dripping, seeping, or splashing affect the types of cave formations formed.

Active Reading

Double Entry Journal In this strategy, the student takes notes and adds his or her own reflections while reading the student text. Students are encouraged to explore ideas, make responses, and take risks in giving opinions about the reading. Have them divide the paper in half. On the left, identify a particular passage or quotation of significance in the reading. The reader records anything luminous, enigmatic, stimulating, or disturbing. On the right, the reader responds, questions, elaborates, makes personal connections, evaluates, reflects, analyzes, or interprets. Have students make a Double Entry Journal for the discussion of physical and chemical changes in this section.

Reteach

Have students work in groups to name signs that indicate that a chemical change has occurred. Ask each group then to identify one situation in which one of these signs is present but in which no chemical change has occurred. Signs include the production of heat, light, smoke, color change, gas bubbles, sound, and the ease with which the change can be reversed. Gas bubbles are produced when water boils, but this is a physical change, not a chemical change. L2 LS **Logical-Mathematical**

Challenge

Fire is one chemical reaction that we sometimes want to stop quickly. Have students work in small groups to think of as many ways as they can to put out a fire. Ask each group to choose one and explain why it works. L2 COOP LEARN LS **Interpersonal**

Content Have students work in groups and use both physical and chemical changes to create works of art. Explain what each change is and how it contributes to the artwork. Use **Performance Assessment in the Science Classroom,** p. 127.

Figure 18
Over many years, acidic rainwater slowly reacts with layers of limestone rock. It forms caves and collects minerals that it later deposits as cave formations.

Environmental Science INTEGRATION

Carlsbad Caverns in New Mexico contains cave formations similar to the ones shown here. Stalagmites are cave formations that form on the floor of the cave and grow upward. Inside this cave you will find a stalagmite called the Giant Dome that is 19 m tall. Research and find out more information about this huge cave.

Chemical Weathering Cave formations like the one in **Figure 18** form by chemical weathering. As drops of water drip through the rocks above this cavern room, minerals become dissolved in the water. These icicle shapes, or stalactites, are formed when the water evaporates leaving the mineral deposits. There are instances of unnatural chemical weathering. For instance, the acid in acid rain can chemically weather marble buildings and statues, and other outdoor objects.

Section 3 Assessment

1. List five physical changes you can observe in your home. Explain how you decided that each change is physical.
2. When you cook an egg, what kind of change occurs? Explain.
3. Describe how physical changes can alter Earth's surface.
4. What are signs that a chemical change has occurred?
5. **Think Critically** Which of the following involves a chemical change: *combining an acid and base, ice melting,* and *souring milk.*

Skill Builder Activities

6. **Drawing Conclusions** When you mixed two substances together, you observed that heat, gas, and light were produced. Is this change chemical or physical? Explain. **For more help, refer to the Science Skill Handbook.**
7. **Developing Multimedia Presentations** Prepare a multimedia presentation that shows the steps in preparing, lighting, and extinguishing a wood fire. Identify each step as a physical or a chemical change. **For more help, refer to the Technology Skill Handbook.**

Answers to Section Assessment

1. Possible answers: shredding cheese, chopping onions, slicing apples, boiling water, and making ice cream. These are physical changes because the substances are the same before and after the change.
2. chemical changes because new substances with new properties are formed
3. Possible answers: erosion of soil by wind and water, drought or floods, freezing and thawing.
4. energy change, color change, formation of a gas or solid
5. combining an acid and base, souring milk
6. A chemical change occurred because there was an energy change and gas was given off.
7. Check students' work.

Activity

Sunset in a Bag

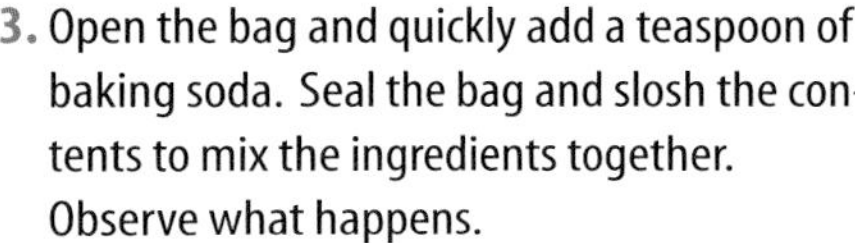

How do you know when a chemical change occurs? You'll see some signs of chemical change in this activity.

What You'll Investigate

What is evidence of a chemical change?

Goals

- **Observe** a chemical change.
- **Identify** some signs of chemical change.

Materials

baking soda
calcium chloride
phenol red solution
warm water
teaspoons (2)
resealable plastic bag
graduated cylinder

Safety Precautions

Procedure

1. Add 20 mL of warm water and 5 mL of phenol red solution to the plastic bag. Seal the bag and gently slosh the solution around to mix it.
2. Add a teaspoon of calcium chloride to the solution in the bag. Seal the bag and slosh the contents to mix the solution. Record any change in temperature.
3. Open the bag and quickly add a teaspoon of baking soda. Seal the bag and slosh the contents to mix the ingredients together. Observe what happens.

Conclude and Apply

1. What signs of chemical change did you observe?
2. Give an example of a chemical change that does not show an obvious energy change. How do you know a change occurs?

Communicating Your Data

Compare your conclusions with those of other students in your class. **For more help, refer to the Science Skill Handbook.**

ACTIVITY 151

Resource Manager

Chapter Resources Booklet
Activity Worksheet, pp. 5–6
Lab Activity, pp. 11–13

Communicating Your Data

Ask students to draw illustrations showing the changes that occurred in each step of this activity. Students can then compare their illustrations.

Activity

BENCH TESTED

Purpose Students observe a physical and chemical change. L2
LS **Kinesthetic**

Process Skills observing, inferring, recognizing cause and effect, measuring, recording observations, drawing conclusions

Time Required 45 minutes

Alternate Materials Many products sold to spread on icy pavement contain calcium chloride. The percentage of calcium chloride in these products varies. If you choose to use one of these products instead of laboratory calcium chloride, try the activity ahead of time to make sure the energy change can be noticed. If phenol red is not available, a purple solution made from cooked red cabbage leaves can be used, but the color change is less dramatic.

Teaching Strategy Caution students to be sure the bags are sealed before they slosh the contents. Caution students to open bags carefully away from their face.

Answers to Questions

1. A physical change occurred in steps 1 and 2. A chemical change occurred in step 3. Step 1 involved $CaCl_2$ dissolving in water. This is a physical process. Step 2 involved making a mixture ($CaCl_2$ and phenol red) also a physical process. Step 3 involved both a color change and the formation of bubbles. Two chemicals combined—a chemical change.
2. No; step 1 was a physical change but it still involved the production of heat.

Process Ask each student to write a lab report summarizing the procedures used and results obtained. Use **PASC,** p. 119.

Activity

BENCH TESTED

Recognize the Problem

Purpose

Students will determine the pH of various solutions and classify the solutions as acidic, basic, or neutral. L2 LS **Kinesthetic**

Process Skills

observing, classifying, using numbers, communicating, measuring, predicting, interpreting data, experimenting

Time Required

45 minutes

Materials

Clear fruit juices with little color, such as apple juice or white grape juice, work best. Use colorless soft drinks.

Safety Precautions

Do not use household cleaners that are dangerous to inhale or can irritate skin, such as strong ammonia solutions and drain and oven cleaners. Be sure to read and follow all caution statements on the labels. Be sure no cleaners are mixed together.

Form a Hypothesis

Possible Hypothesis

Fruit juices, vinegar, and soft drinks are acidic. Soaps and antacids are basic.

Activity — Design Your Own Experiment

Homemade pH Scale

The stronger an acid or base is, the more likely it is to be harmful to living organisms. A pH scale is used to measure how strong acids and bases are. A solution with a pH between 0 and 7 is acidic, a pH of 7 is neutral, and a pH of between 7 and 14 is basic. The strongest acids have a pH of 0, and the strongest bases have a pH of 14. In this activity, you will measure the pH of some things using treated paper. When it is dipped into a solution, this paper changes color. Check the color against the chart below to find the pH of the solution.

Recognize the Problem

How acidic or basic are some common household items?

Form a Hypothesis

Think about the properties of acids and bases. In your group, make a hypothesis about which kinds of solutions you are testing are acids and which kinds are bases.

Goals

- **Design** an experiment that allows you to test solutions to find the pH of each.
- **Classify** a solution as an acid or a base according to its pH.

Possible Materials

vial of pH paper, 1–14
pH color chart
distilled water
fruit juices
vinegar
salt
sugar
soft drinks
household cleaners
soaps and detergents
antacids

Safety Precautions

Never eat, taste, smell, or touch any chemical during a lab.

pH	Color	pH	Color
1		8	
2		9	
3		10	
4		11	
5		12	
6		13	
7		14	

pH of Solutions

Solution to Be Tested	pH	Acid, Base, or Neutral
dish-washing detergent	8	base
distilled water	7	neutral
apple juice	5	acid

Test Your Hypothesis

Possible Procedures

Dip a strip of pH paper into one solution. Compare the color of the test strip to the chart. Record the pH and whether the solution is acidic, basic, or neutral. Then test the remaining solutions.

Resource Manager

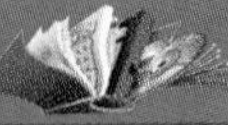

Chapter Resources Booklet
Activity Worksheet, pp. 7–8

Lab Management and Safety, p. 38

Test Your Hypothesis

Plan

1. As a group, decide which materials you will test. If a material is not a liquid, dissolve it in water so you can test the solution.
2. List the steps and materials that you need to test your hypothesis. Be specific. What parts of the experiment will you repeat, if any?
3. Before you begin, copy a data table like the one shown into your Science Journal. Be sure to leave room to record results for each solution tested. If there is to be more than one trial for each solution, include room for the additional trials.
4. Reread the entire experiment to make sure that all the steps are in logical order.

Do

1. Make sure your teacher approves your plan and data table. Be sure that you have included any suggested changes.
2. Carry out the experiment as planned and approved. Wash your hands when you are done.
3. **Record** the pH value of each solution in the data table as you complete each test. Determine whether each solution is acidic, basic, or neutral.

Analyze Your Data

1. Were any materials neither acids nor bases? How do you know?
2. Using your data table, conclude which types of materials are usually acidic and which are usually basic.
3. At what pH do you think acids become too dangerous to touch? Bases? Explain your answers.
4. What is the pH range of foods that you normally consume?

Draw Conclusions

Perhaps you have been told that you can use vinegar to dissolve hard-water deposits because vinegar is an acid. If you run out of vinegar, which of the following—lemon juice, ammonia, or water—could you most likely use instead of vinegar for this purpose?

Compare your findings with those of other student groups. Discuss why any differences in the data might have occurred.

Teaching Strategy

Demonstrate how to use the pH paper, following directions on the box.

Troubleshooting

If students need to dissolve a substance in water, they should make sure the resulting solutions are fairly concentrated. This will help them get definite readings wiht the pH paper. Different substance-to-water ratios might give different results.

Expected Outcome

Fruit juices, vinegar, soft drinks, and some cleaners will be acidic. Water, salt, and sugar will be neutral. Soaps, some household cleaners, and antacids will be basic.

Analyze Your Data

1. Water as well as solutions of salt and sugar were neutral because they gave pH readings of 7.
2. Fruit juices, vinegar, soft drinks, and some cleaners will be acidic. Water, salt, and sugar will be neutral. Soaps, some household cleaners, and antacids will be basic.
3. Answers will vary, but students can use their pH readings to support their answer.
4. See student results from lab to determine answer.

Error Analysis

Discuss with students things that might cause errors in their data. Ask how they could reduce the errors.

Draw Conclusions

lemon juice

✔Assessment

Process Have each student write his or her lab results on a poster, organized by pH. Students should include on their posters predicted properties of the solutions based on whether each is an acid or base. Use **Performance Assessment in the Science Classroom,** p. 145.

Suggest students use a spreadsheet program to make tables of their data.

TIME SCIENCE AND HISTORY

Content Background

When sulfur dioxide (SO_2) and various nitrogen oxides (NO_x) contact water in the atmosphere, they form acids of varying strengths. The strength of an acid is determined by its degree of ionization in solution. Acids in solution can be described as proton donors. A single proton is essentially a positive hydrogen ion (H^+). Ionized acids increase the H^+ concentration resulting in a lower pH. Bases are H^+ receptors and will lower the H^+ concentration and raise the pH.

When acids are flushed from the atmosphere by rain, they interact with any substance that will readily accept H^+ ions, such as bases and most metals. When they fall on materials that contain calcium carbonate, such as limestone, marble, and some sandstones, the reaction forms gypsum, CO_2, and water, The gypsum and water are easily washed away.

TIME
SCIENCE AND HISTORY
SCIENCE CAN CHANGE THE COURSE OF HISTORY!

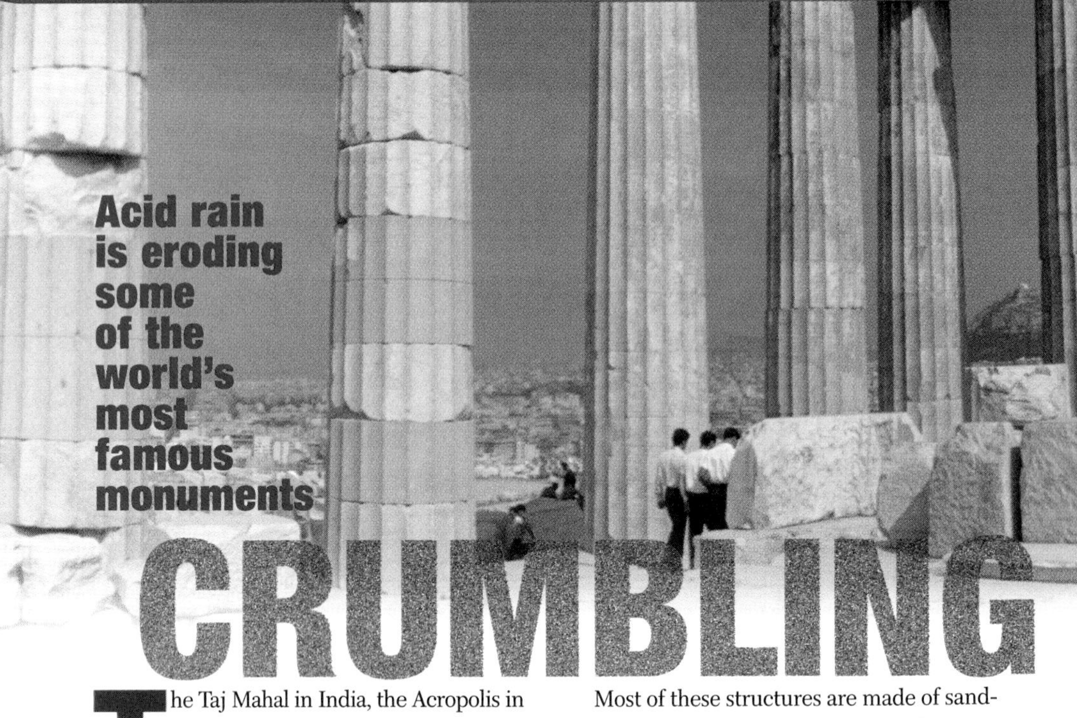

Acid rain is eroding some of the world's most famous monuments
CRUMBLING

The Taj Mahal in India, the Acropolis in Greece, and the Colosseum in Italy, have stood for centuries. They've survived wars, souvenir-hunters, and natural weathering from wind and rain. But now, something far worse threatens their existence—acid rain. Over the last few decades, this form of pollution has eaten away at some of history's greatest monuments.

Acid rain leads to health and environmental risks. It also harms human-made structures. Most of these structures are made of sandstone, limestone, and marble. Acid rain causes the calcium in these stones to form calcium sulfate, or gypsum. Gypsum's powdery little blotches are sometimes called "marble cancer." When it rains, the gypsum washes away, along with some of the surface of the monument. In many cases, acidic soot falls into the cracks of monuments. When rainwater seeps into the cracks, acidic water is formed, which further damages the structure.

Acid rain has not been kind to this Mayan figure.

Parts of India's Taj Mahal are turning yellow from pollutants.

Resources for Teachers and Students

US EPA, Clean Air Markets Division
1200 Pennsylvania Avenue, NW
Mail Code 6204N, Washington, DC 20460

National Park Service
Air Resources Division
1849 C Street NW, Washington, DC 20240
Phone: (202) 208-6843

U.S. Department of the Interior
U.S. Geological Survey
12201 Sunrise Valley Drive, Reston, VA 20192

An Introduction to Global Environmental Issues (2nd Ed.), by K. T. Pickering & L. A. Owen, London & NY. Routledge, 1997.

Greece's Parthenon is slowly being eaten away by acid rain.

MONUMENTS

In Agra, India, the smooth, white marble mausoleum called the Taj Mahal has stood since the seventeenth century. But acid rain is making the surface of the building yellow and flaky. The pollution is caused by hundreds of factories surrounding Agra that emit damaging chemicals.

What moisture, molds, and the roots of vegetation didn't do in 1,500 years, acid rain is doing in decades. It is destroying the Mayan ruins of Mexico. Pollution is causing statues to crumble and paintings on walls to flake off. The culprit is oil-burning refineries and exhaust from tour buses.

Acid rain is a huge problem affecting national monuments and treasures in just about every urban location in the world. These include the Capitol building in Washington, D.C., churches in Germany, and stained-glass windows in Sweden. Because of pollution, many corroding statues displayed outdoors have been brought inside museums. In London, acid rain has forced workers to repair and replace so much of Westminster Abbey that the structure is becoming a mere copy of the original.

Throughout the world, acid rain has weathered many structures more in the last 20 years than in the prior 2,000 years. This is one reason some steps have been taken in Europe and the United States to reduce emissions from the burning of fossil fuels. If these laws don't work, many irreplaceable art treasures could be gone forever.

CONNECTIONS Identify Which monuments and buildings represent the United States? Brainstorm a list with your class. Then choose a monument, and using your school's media center or the Glencoe Science Web site, learn more about it. Is acid rain affecting it in any way?

Science Online
For more information, visit science.glencoe.com

Discussion

Do we need to preserve historical monuments in order to learn about the past they represent? Why or why not? Some students may say that pictures in textbooks are sufficient for learning about a particular monument or the culture and events it represents. Other students may say that without the actual monument, people will learn less about the cultures and events the monument represents. L2 LS **Logical-Mathematical**

Historical Significance

As old or ancient structures deteriorate or disappear, the past tends to disappear with them. Students should understand that ancient buildings like the Parthenon and the Coliseum are tangible links to history that lead people to consider the events that occurred in and around them. The carvings on old temples and the images in ancient statues are indicators of the worldview of their creators that are much more immediate and lively than textbook descriptions of them. The more these images deteriorate, the more information is lost. Also, archaeologists, anthropologists, and other scientists analyze inanimate objects, including historic structures, in order to gain factual knowledge about them and the cultures that built them.

CONNECTIONS Suggest students also try to obtain information about the state of local monuments and how their community is dealing with acid rain damage if it is occurring.

Science Online

Internet Addresses

___

___

___

Explore the Glencoe Science Web site at **science.glencoe.com** to find out more about topics in this feature.

Chapter 5 Study Guide

Reviewing Main Ideas

Preview

Students can answer the questions in their Science Journals. Discuss the answers as you go through the chapter. **LS Linguistic**

Review

Students can write their answers, then compare them with those of other students. **LS Interpersonal**

Reteach

Students can look at the illustrations and describe details that support the main ideas of the chapter. **LS Visual-Spatial**

Answers to Chapter Review

Section 1

1. Answers will vary somewhat. The pinecone is solid and is about 17 cm long. It has a brown wood-like appearance. The pinecone has a center shaft with petal-like growths growing off of the shaft.

Section 2

2. Lemon juice and vinegar are acids. Ammonia and glass cleaner are bases.

Section 3

4. A gas has formed.

Chapter 5 Study Guide

Reviewing Main Ideas

Section 1 Physical Properties

1. A physical property can be observed without changing the makeup of the material. *What are the physical properties of the pinecone shown here?*

2. Acids and bases have physical properties. Acids have a sharp smell and a sour taste. Bases have a bitter taste and feel slippery.
3. Mass, volume, state of matter, and density are physical properties of a substance.

Section 2 Chemical Properties

1. A chemical property is a characteristic of a substance that allows it to change to a new substance.
2. Acids and bases are in many household products. *In the figure below, which substances are acids and which are bases?*

3. Acids and bases react with each other to produce water and a salt.

Section 3 Physical and Chemical Changes

1. A physical change is a change in the size, shape, form, or state of matter. The chemical makeup of the matter stays the same.
2. Water undergoes a change of state when it changes from a solid to a liquid or a liquid to a gas. The reverse processes are also physical changes.
3. In chemical changes, new materials are formed.
4. Evidence that a chemical change might have occurred includes a color or energy change or the formation of a gas or precipitate. *In the figure below, what evidence indicates that a chemical change has occurred?*

FOLDABLES Reading & Study Skills — After You Read

Under the tabs of your Classify Study Fold, write the definition of both types of properties and both types of changes.

FOLDABLES Reading & Study Skills — After You Read

After students have read the chapter and completed the Foldable described in Before You Read, have them do the activity on the student page.

Dinah Zike

Chapter 5 Study Guide

Visualizing Main Ideas

Complete the following concept map about matter.

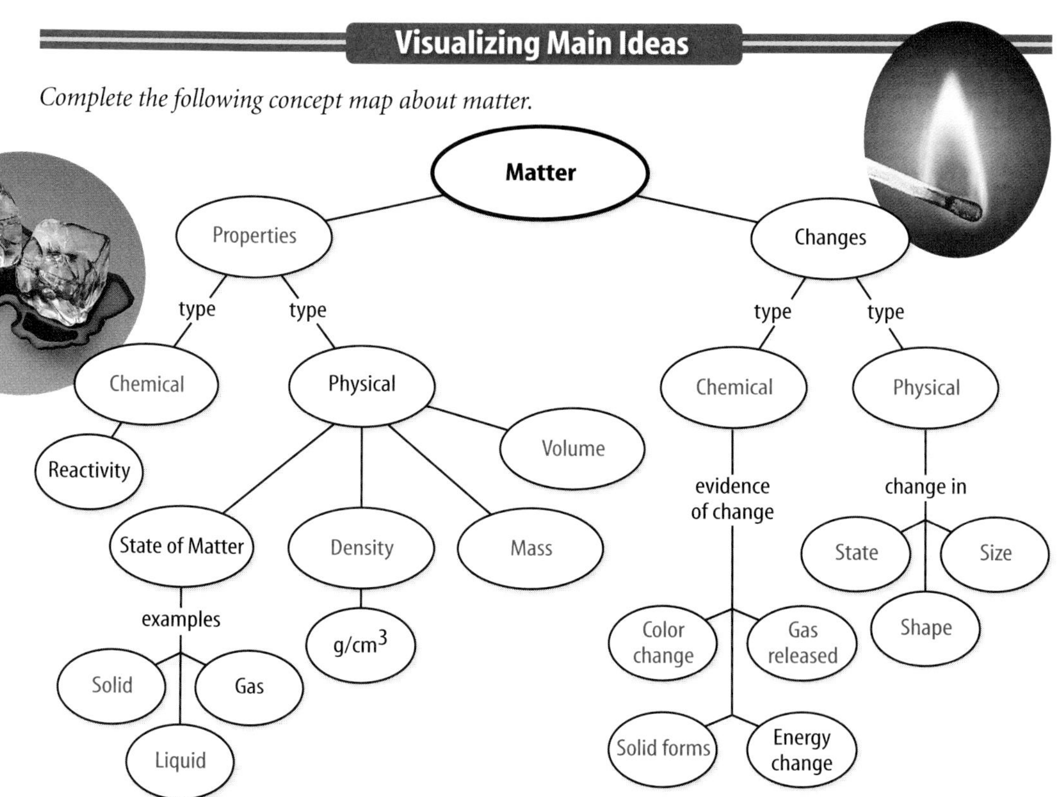

Vocabulary Review

Vocabulary Words

a. chemical change
b. chemical property
c. density
d. physical change
e. physical property
f. reactivity
g. salt
h. state of matter

Study Tip

After you've read a chapter, go back to the beginning and speed-read through what you've just read.

Using Vocabulary

Answer the following questions using complete sentences.

1. Mass divided by volume is the formula for which physical property?
2. Which type of properties include color, shape, size, and state?
3. Snow melting in sunshine is an example of which type of change?
4. Acid rain damaging marble statues is an example of which type of change?
5. Iron rusts quickly in moist air. Which chemical property is this?

Chapter 5 Study Guide

Visualizing Main Ideas

See student page.

Vocabulary Review

Using Vocabulary

1. Mass divided by volume is the formula for density.
2. Color, shape, size, and state are physical properties.
3. Snow melting is a physical change.
4. Acid rain damaging marble statues is an example of a chemical change.
5. Iron rusting in moist air is an example of the reactivity of iron.

CHAPTER STUDY GUIDE 157

Chapter 5 Assessment

Checking Concepts

1. D
2. B
3. A
4. D
5. B
6. D
7. C
8. A
9. D
10. D

Thinking Critically

11. No; feathers are much less dense than rocks.
12. It is a physical property because the compounds water and sugar remain unchanged in the solution.
13. carbon and hydrogen
14. a. physical; b. chemical; c. physical; d. chemical
15. a. physical; b. chemical; c. chemical

Chapter 5 Assessment

Checking Concepts

Choose the word or phrase that best answers the question.

1. Which of the following is a chemical property of a substance?
   A) density, 1.00 g/cm^3 **C)** mass, 5.00 g
   B) white powder **D)** reacts with HCl
2. Which item below is a sign of a chemical change?
   A) change of state
   B) release of energy
   C) change from a liquid to a solid
   D) change in physical properties
3. Which type of change listed below results in new compounds being formed?
   A) chemical **C)** seasonal
   B) physical **D)** state
4. Which answer below is another term for solid, liquid, and gas?
   A) physical changes
   B) physical properties of soil
   C) chemical changes
   D) three states of matter
5. Salts are formed when which of the following react?
   A) solids and gases **C)** bases and gases
   B) acids and bases **D)** acids and solids
6. Which term below would best describe the change that occurs when a window is broken?
   A) chemical **C)** neutral
   B) weathering **D)** physical
7. Which of the following physical properties does a base have?
   A) cold to touch
   B) gives off gas
   C) slippery and bitter taste
   D) sharp smell and sour taste
8. Which of the following changes when salt is added to water?
   A) physical properties of water
   B) chemical properties of water
   C) color of water
   D) formation properties of water
9. Which of the following clearly identifies a chemical change?
   A) cutting the substance into smaller pieces
   B) freezing the substance
   C) boiling the substance
   D) A new substance is formed.
10. Which of the following is NOT a sign that a chemical change occurred when two clear liquids were mixed?
    A) A color change occurred.
    B) Gas was released.
    C) A white solid settled to the bottom.
    D) The volume doubled.

Thinking Critically

11. Think about what you know about density. Could a bag of feathers have more mass than the same size bag of rocks? Explain.
12. Sugar dissolves in water. Is this a physical property or a chemical property of sugar?
13. When butane burns, it combines with oxygen in the air to form carbon dioxide and water. Which two elements must be present in butane?
14. Identify each of the following as either a physical property or a chemical property.
    a. Sulfur shatters when hit.
    b. Gasoline burns.
    c. Baking soda is a white powder.
    d. Newspaper turns brown when it is exposed to air and light.

Chapter Assessment Planner

Portfolio Encourage students to place in their portfolios one or two items of what they consider to be their best work. Examples include:
- Science Journal, p. 138
- Assessment, p. 144
- Activity, p. 148

Performance Additional performance assessments, Performance Task Assessment Lists, and rubrics for evaluating these activities can be found in Glencoe's **Performance Assessment in the Science Classroom.**

Chapter 5 Assessment

15. Identify each of the following as a physical change or a chemical change.
    a. Metal is drawn out into a wire.
    b. Sulfur in eggs tarnishes silver.
    c. Baking powder bubbles when water is added to it.

Developing Skills

16. Interpreting Scientific Illustrations Review the pictures below and determine whether each is a chemical change or a physical change.

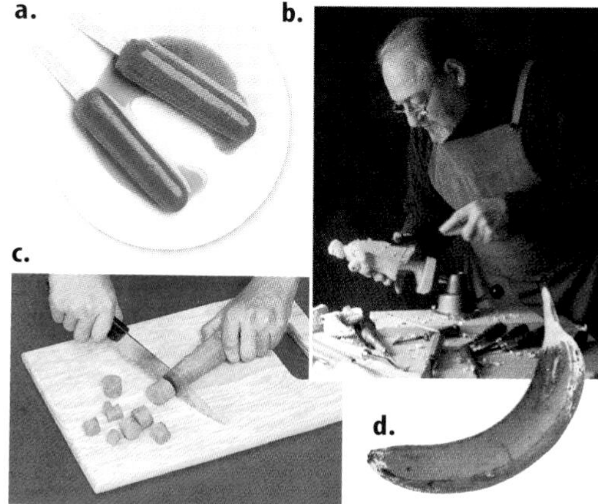

Performance Assessment

17. Display Create a display that demonstrates the characteristics of a chemical change. Be sure your display shows release of energy, change of color, and the formation of a solid.

TECHNOLOGY

Go to the Glencoe Science Web site at **science.glencoe.com** or use the **Glencoe Science CD-ROM** for additional chapter assessment.

THE PRINCETON REVIEW Test Practice

Russell used a triple-beam balance to determine that the mass of an aluminum cube was 337 g. Then he placed the cube in a beaker of water. His experiment is shown in the diagram below.

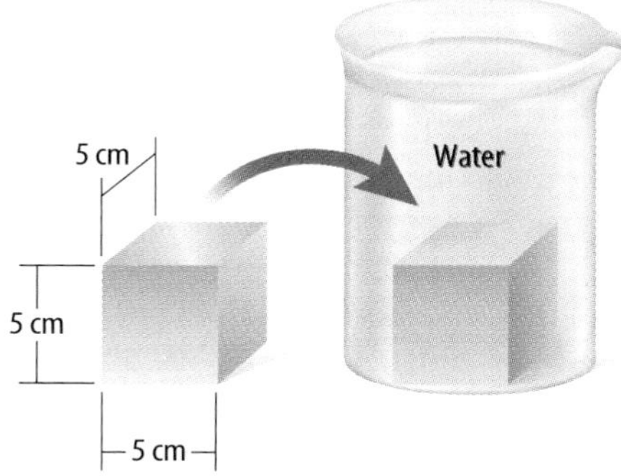

Mass = 337 g
Volume = 125 cm^3

Study the diagram and answer the following questions.

1. Using the information contained in the diagram, what is the density of the cube?
   A) 2.70 g/cm^3
   B) 0.371 g/cm^3
   C) 337 g/cm^3
   D) 125 g/cm^3
2. Cutting the cube into smaller pieces is an example of a _____.
   F) chemical property
   G) physical property
   H) chemical change
   J) physical change
3. According to the diagram, the aluminum cube _____.
   A) is more dense than water
   B) is less dense than water
   C) has more volume than the water
   D) floats in water

Chapter 5 Assessment

Test Practice

The Test-Taking Tip was written by The Princeton Review, the nation's leader in test preparation.

1. A
2. J
3. A

Developing Skills

16. a. physical
    b. physical
    c. physical
    d. chemical

Performance Assessment

17. Displays should make it clear that all of these characteristics do not happen with each chemical change. If students make displays that actually involve chemical reactions, check the plans for safety before students build the displays. Use **PASC,** p. 135.

Assessment Resources

Reproducible Masters

Chapter Resources Booklet
Chapter Review, pp. 35–36
Chapter Tests, pp. 37–40
Assessment Transparency Activity, p. 47

Glencoe Science Web site
Interactive Tutor
Chapter Quizzes

Glencoe Technology
Assessment Transparency
Interactive CD-ROM Chapter Quizzes
ExamView Pro Test Bank
Vocabulary PuzzleMaker Software
MindJogger Videoquiz DVD/VHS

Standardized Test Practice

Reading Comprehension

QUESTION 1: C

Students must recall chronology of events from the passage to identify which answer choice occurred first.

- **Choice A** No; this event occurred after Mendeleev made his predictions.
- **Choice B** No; this happened much later, in the 20th century.
- **Choice C** Yes; this event occurred first.
- **Choice D** No; this happened much later, in the 20th century.

Teaching Tip

Suggest students make a timeline to help them answer questions about sequence of events in a passage.

QUESTION 2: F

Students must use clues from the passage such as *made . . . in the laboratory* to identify that the best meaning of the underlined word *artificially* is choice F, *unnaturally*.

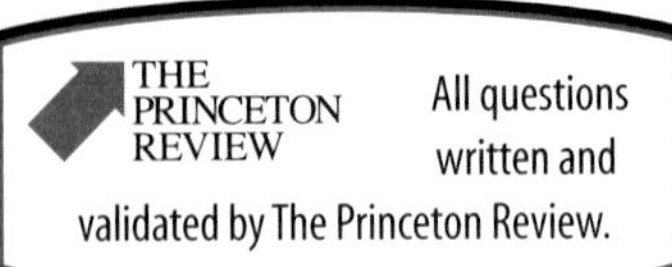

All questions written and validated by The Princeton Review.

Standardized Test Practice

Reading Comprehension

Read the passage. Then read each question that follows the passage. Decide which is the best answer to each question.

Grouping the Elements Using their Properties

By 1860, scientists had discovered a total of 63 chemical elements. Dmitri Mendeleev, a Russian chemist, thought that there had to be some order among the elements.

He made a card for each element. On the card, he listed the physical and chemical properties of the element, such as atomic mass, density, color, and melting point. He also wrote each element's combining power, or its ability to form compounds with other elements.

When he arranged the cards in order of increasing atomic mass, Mendeleev noticed that the elements followed a periodic, or repeating, pattern. After every seven cards, the properties repeated. He placed each group of seven cards in rows, one row under another. He noticed that the columns in his chart formed groups of elements that had similar chemical and physical properties.

In a few places, Mendeleev had to move a card one space to the left or right to maintain the similarities of his groups. This left a few gaps. He predicted that they would be filled with elements that were unknown. He even predicted their properties. Fifteen years later, three new elements were discovered and placed in the gaps of the periodic table. Their physical and chemical properties agreed with Mendeleev's predictions.

Today there are more than 100 known elements. An extra column has been added for the noble gases, a group of elements that were not yet discovered in Mendeleev's time. Members of this group almost never combine with other elements. As new elements are discovered or are made artificially, scientists can place them in their proper place on the periodic table thanks to Mendeleev.

Test-Taking Tip To answer questions about a sequence of events, make a time line of what happened in each paragraph of the passage.

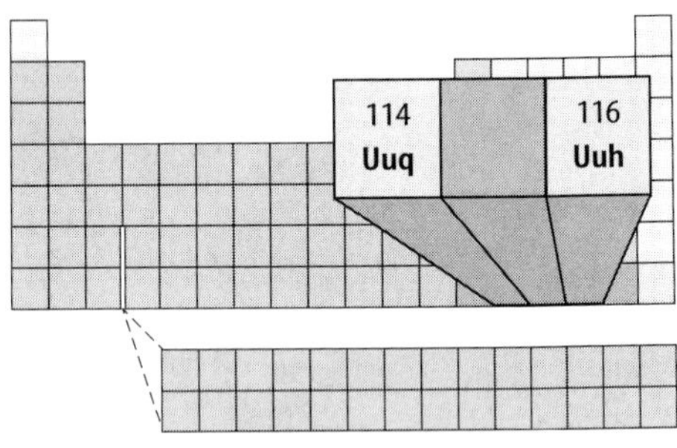

All elements can be organized according to their physical and chemical properties.

1. Which of the following occurred FIRST in the passage?

A) Three new elements were discovered 15 years after Mendeleev developed the periodic table.
B) The noble gases were discovered and added to the periodic table.
C) Mendeleev predicted properties of unknown elements.
D) New elements were made in the laboratory and added to the periodic table.

2. The word artificially in this passage means _____.

F) unnaturally
G) artistically
H) atomically
J) radioactively

Standardized Test Practice

Reasoning and Skills

Read each question and choose the best answer.

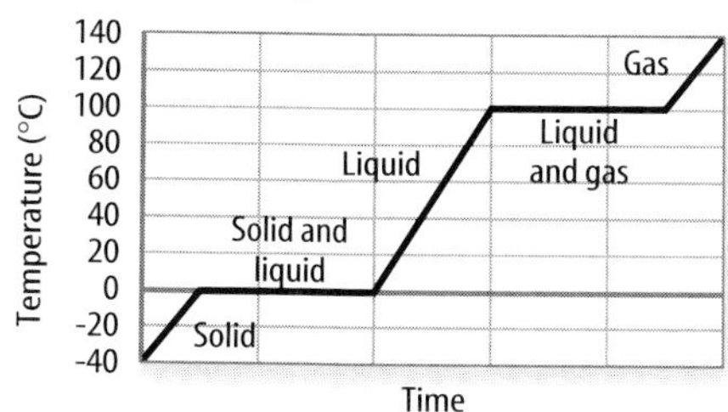

1. The graph shows the change in temperature that occurs as ice changes to water vapor. How much higher than the starting temperature is the boiling point?
   A) 40°C
   B) 100°C
   C) 140°C
   D) 180°C

Test-Taking Tip Boiling point is the flat section of the graph where liquid changes to gas.

2. What is being measured in the illustration?
   F) boiling point
   G) melting point
   H) density
   J) flammability

Test-Taking Tip Think about what you would measure with a thermometer in a liquid that you are heating.

Properties of Selected Pure Substances

Substance	Melting Point (°C)	Boiling Point (°C)	Color
Aluminum	660.4	2467	silver metallic
Argon	-189.2	-185.7	colorless
Mercury	-38.8	356.6	silver metallic
Water	0	100	colorless

3. Room temperature is about 20°C. In the table, which substance is a solid at room temperature?
   A) aluminum
   B) argon
   C) mercury
   D) water

Test-Taking Tip Remember that negative temperatures are below zero.

Read this question carefully before writing your answer on a separate sheet of paper.

4. The density of pure water is 1.00 g/cm^3. Ice floats on water, thus, the density of ice is *less* than that of water. Design an experiment to determine the density of an ice cube. List all the necessary steps.
   (Volume = Length × Width × Height;
   Density = Mass / Volume.)

Test-Taking Tip Consider all the information provided in the question.

Standardized Test Practice

Reasoning and Skills

QUESTION 1: C

Students must interpret the graph to identify the correct answer. Because the starting temperature was –40°C and the boiling point is 100°C, the correct answer is choice C, *140°C.*

QUESTION 2: F

Students must carefully examine the diagram. Because the substance in the beaker is already a liquid and appears to be boiling, the correct answer is choice F, *boiling point.*

QUESTION 3: A

Students must retrieve information from the table to identify the correct answer. Because there is only one substance with a melting point greater than 20°C, the correct answer is choice A, *aluminum.*

Teaching Tip

Review with students how to analyze the chart to determine at what temperature each substance changes from a solid to a liquid.

QUESTION 4: Answers will vary.

Answers should include measuring the length, width, and height of the ice cube with a metric ruler in order to find volume. In addition, the mass of the ice cube should be determined using a triple-beam balance. After these measurements have been determined, students should describe how to calculate volume and density.

UNIT 3

Unit Contents

Pre-Reading Activity

Have students look through the chapters for illustrations and photographs that depict motion and have them describe the motion.

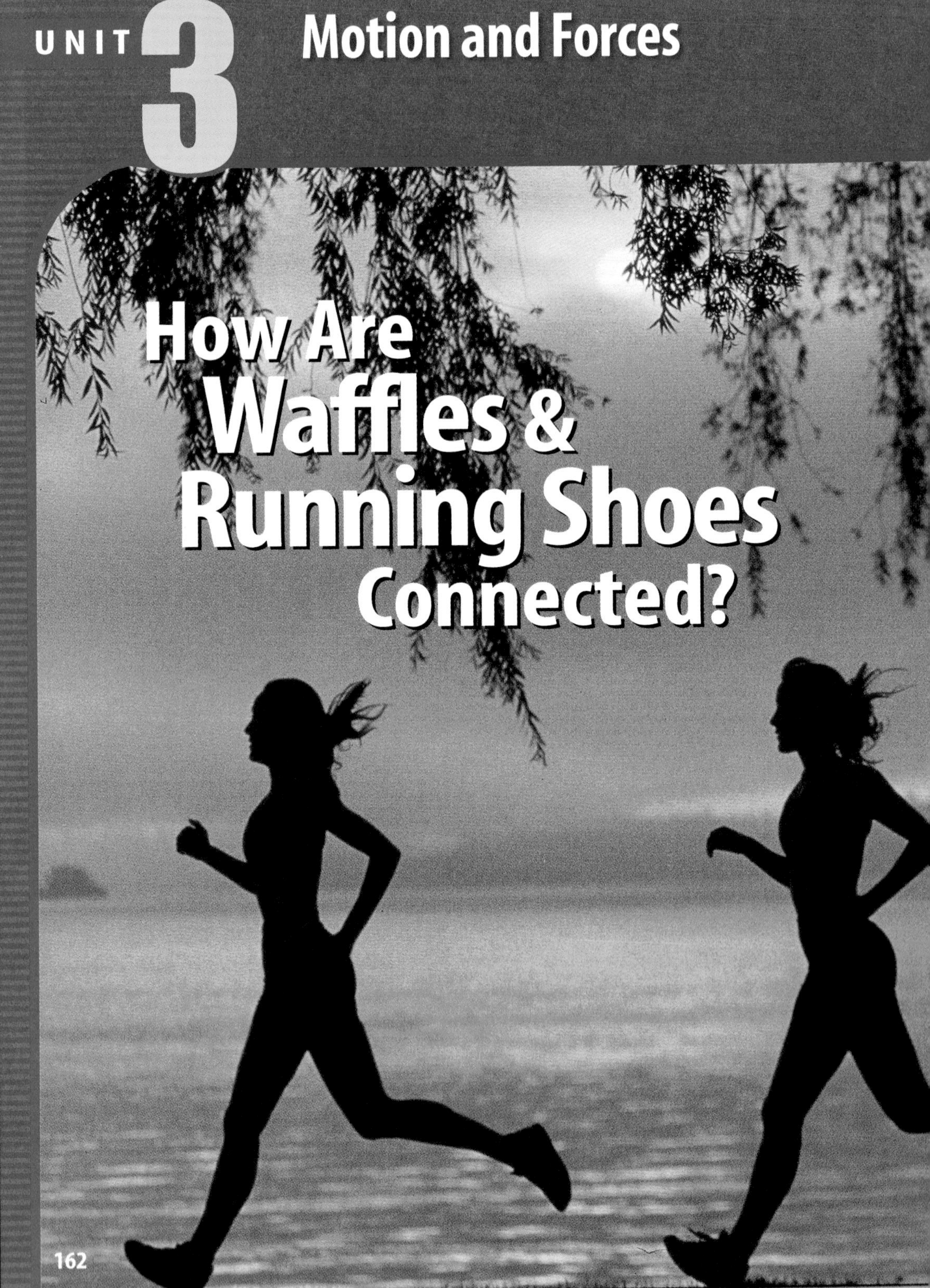

Teacher to Teacher

"Air resistance is a factor to consider with all moving objects on Earth. I have students identify where air resistance is purposefully increased or decreased as a result of design or function."

Kevin Finnegan, Teacher
McCord Middle School
Worthington, OH

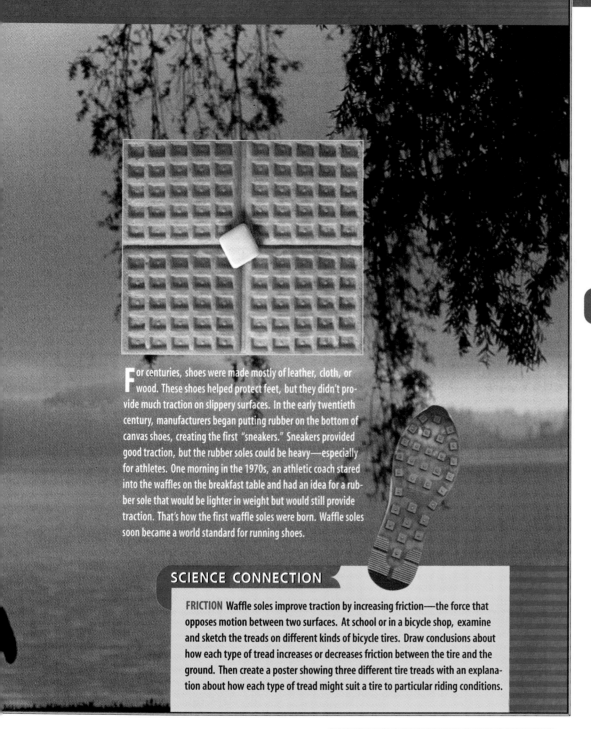

For centuries, shoes were made mostly of leather, cloth, or wood. These shoes helped protect feet, but they didn't provide much traction on slippery surfaces. In the early twentieth century, manufacturers began putting rubber on the bottom of canvas shoes, creating the first "sneakers." Sneakers provided good traction, but the rubber soles could be heavy—especially for athletes. One morning in the 1970s, an athletic coach stared into the waffles on the breakfast table and had an idea for a rubber sole that would be lighter in weight but would still provide traction. That's how the first waffle soles were born. Waffle soles soon became a world standard for running shoes.

SCIENCE CONNECTION

FRICTION Waffle soles improve traction by increasing friction—the force that opposes motion between two surfaces. At school or in a bicycle shop, examine and sketch the treads on different kinds of bicycle tires. Draw conclusions about how each type of tread increases or decreases friction between the tire and the ground. Then create a poster showing three different tire treads with an explanation about how each type of tread might suit a tire to particular riding conditions.

SCIENCE Online

Internet Addresses

Explore the Glencoe Science Web site at **science.glencoe.com** to find out more about topics in this unit.

Introducing the Unit

How Are Waffles & Running Shoes Connected?

Ask students how many of them have slipped when wearing an old pair of running or tennis shoes because the tread was worn.

Have students compare the tread pattern in several pairs of their shoes and hypothesize how each increases friction. Ask them how the intended surface affects what type of tread is on a shoe.

SCIENCE CONNECTION

Activity

Before students make their posters, have their conclusions confirmed by a bicycle expert. Pamphlets relating tread to riding conditions might also be available from tire or bicycle manufacturers. Encourage creativity, but be sure posters depict accurate relationships.

MOTION AND MOMENTUM

Section/Objectives	Standards		Activities/Features
	National	State/Local	
Chapter Opener	See p. 5T for a Key to Standards.		**Explore Activity:** Model collisions, p. 165 **Before You Read,** p. 165
Section 1 What is motion? 5 sessions 2.5 blocks 1. **Define** distance, speed, and velocity. 2. **Graph** motion.	National Content Standards: UCP3, A1, B2		**Science Online,** p. 166 **Life Science Integration,** p. 168 **Math Skills Activity:** Calculating Speed, p. 168 **MiniLAB:** Measuring Average Speed, p. 169 **Science Online,** p. 170
Section 2 Acceleration 3 sessions 1.5 blocks 1. **Define** acceleration. 2. **Predict** what effect acceleration will have on motion.	National Content Standards: UCP3, A1, B2		**Math Skills Activity:** Calculating Acceleration, p. 174 **MiniLAB:** Modeling Acceleration, p. 175
Section 3 Momentum 6 sessions 3 blocks 1. **Explain** the difference between mass and inertia. 2. **Define** momentum. 3. **Predict** motion using the law of conservation of momentum.	National Content Standards: UCP3, A1, B2, E1, F4, G1, G2, G3		**Life Science Integration,** p. 178 **Math Skills Activity:** Calculating Momentum, p. 178 **Visualizing Conservation of Momentum,** p. 181 **Activity:** Collisions, p. 183 **Activity:** Car Safety Testing, pp. 184–185 **Oops! Accidents in Science:** What Goes Around Comes Around—The Story of Boomerangs, pp. 186–187

Activity Materials	Reproducible Resources	Section Assessment	Technology
Explore Activity: 2 softballs, 2 tennis balls	**Chapter Resources Booklet** Foldables Worksheet, p. 17 Directed Reading Overview, p. 19 Note-taking Worksheets, pp. 33–34	GLENCOE'S ASSESSMENT ADVANTAGE	
MiniLAB: meterstick, stopwatch *Need materials?* Contact Science Kit at 1-800-828-7777 or www.sciencekit.com on the Internet.	**Chapter Resources Booklet** Transparency Activity, p. 44 MiniLAB, p. 3 Enrichment, p. 30 Reinforcement, p. 27 Directed Reading, p. 20 Lab Activity, pp. 9–11 Transparency Activity, pp. 47–48 **Physical Science Critical Thinking/Problem Solving,** pp. 2, 21 **Science Inquiry Labs,** p. 41	Portfolio Extension, p. 170 Performance Math Skills Activity, p. 168 MiniLAB, p. 169 Skill Builder Activities, p. 171 Content Section Assessment, p. 171	Section Focus Transparency Teaching Transparency Interactive CD-ROM/DVD Guided Reading Audio Program
MiniLAB: masking tape, meterstick	**Chapter Resources Booklet** Transparency Activity, p. 45 MiniLAB, p. 4 Enrichment, p. 31 Reinforcement, p. 28 Directed Reading, p. 20 Transparency Activity, pp. 47–48 Lab Activity, pp. 13–15	Portfolio Assessment, p. 176 Performance Math Skills Activity, p. 174 MiniLAB, p. 175 Skill Builder Activities, p. 176 Content Section Assessment, p. 176	Section Focus Transparency Teaching Transparency Interactive CD-ROM/DVD Guided Reading Audio Program
Activity: 5 small marbles, 2 large marbles, 2 metersticks, tape **Activity:** insulated foam meat trays or fast-food trays, insulated foam cups, straws, straight pins, tape, plastic eggs	**Chapter Resources Booklet** Transparency Activity, p. 46 Enrichment, p. 32 Reinforcement, p. 29 Directed Reading, pp. 21, 22 Activity Worksheet, pp. 5–6, 7–8 **Home and Community Involvement,** p. 48	Portfolio Currculum Connection, p. 178 Performance Math Skills Activity, p. 178 Skill Builder Activities, p. 182 Content Section Assessment, p. 182	Section Focus Transparency Interactive CD-ROM/DVD Guided Reading Audio Program

GLENCOE'S ASSESSMENT ADVANTAGE

End of Chapter Assessment

Blackline Masters	Technology	Professional Series
Chapter Resources Booklet Chapter Review, pp. 37–38 Chapter Tests, pp. 39–42 **Standardized Test Practice by The Princeton Review,** pp. 27–30	MindJogger Videoquiz CD-ROM Explorations and Quizzes Vocabulary Puzzle Makers ExamView Pro Test Bank Interactive Lesson Planner Interactive Teacher's Edition	Performance Assessment in the Science Classroom (PASC)

Transparencies

Section Focus

Section 1 Section Focus Transparency — How about a rematch?

In Aesop's fable "The Tortoise and the Hare," a tortoise and a hare have a race. The hare bounds far ahead of the tortoise and then, sure that he will win the race, lies down to rest under a tree. The tortoise passes the resting hare and wins the race.

1. Which animal ran faster?
2. Explain the difference between the average speed over the whole race and the speed at any one instant of the race.

L2

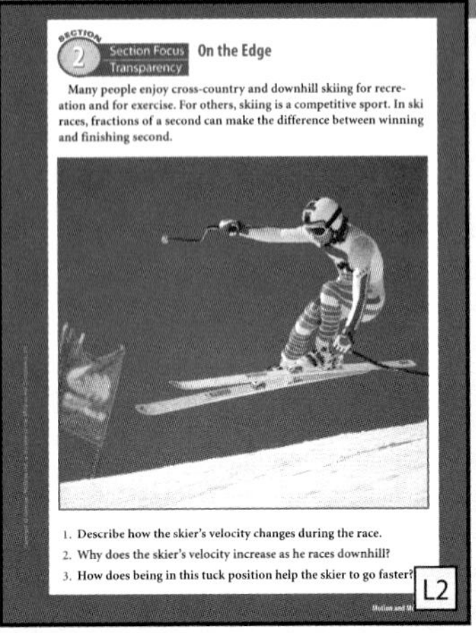
Section 2 Section Focus Transparency — On the Edge

Many people enjoy cross-country and downhill skiing for recreation and for exercise. For others, skiing is a competitive sport. In ski races, fractions of a second can make the difference between winning and finishing second.

1. Describe how the skier's velocity changes during the race.
2. Why does the skier's velocity increase as he races downhill?
3. How does being in this tuck position help the skier to go faster?

L2

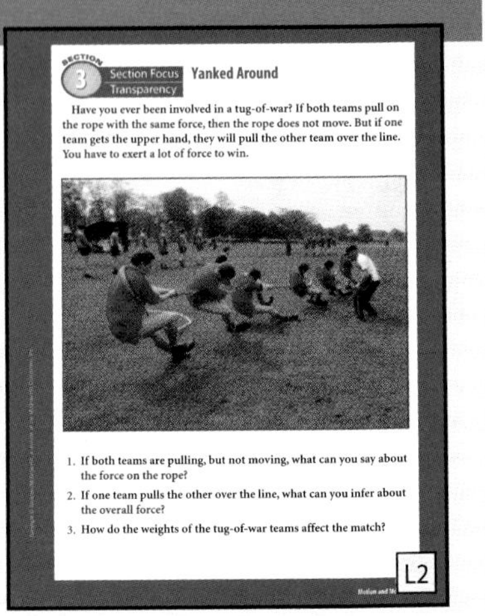
Section 3 Section Focus Transparency — Yanked Around

Have you ever been involved in a tug-of-war? If both teams pull on the rope with the same force, then the rope does not move. But if one team gets the upper hand, they will pull the other team over the line. You have to exert a lot of force to win.

1. If both teams are pulling, but not moving, what can you say about the force on the rope?
2. If one team pulls the other over the line, what can you infer about the overall force?
3. How do the weights of the tug-of-war teams affect the match?

L2

This is a representation of key blackline masters available in the Teacher Classroom Resources. See Resource Manager boxes within the chapter for additional information.

Assessment

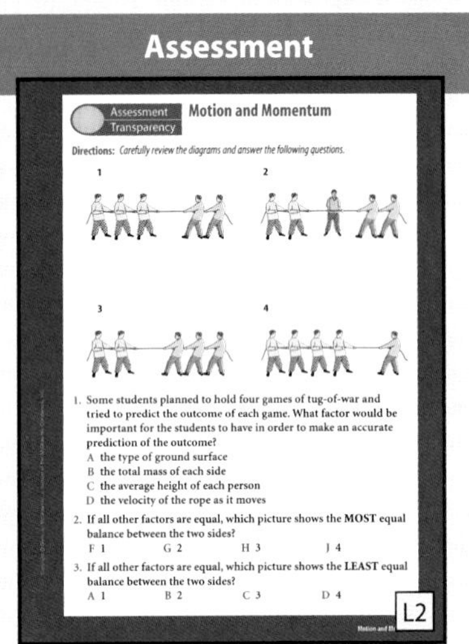
Assessment Transparency — Motion and Momentum

Directions: *Carefully review the diagrams and answer the following questions.*

1. Some students planned to hold four games of tug-of-war and tried to predict the outcome of each game. What factor would be important for the students to have in order to make an accurate prediction of the outcome?
   A the type of ground surface
   B the total mass of each side
   C the average height of each person
   D the velocity of the rope as it moves
2. If all other factors are equal, which picture shows the MOST equal balance between the two sides?
   F 1 G 2 H 3 J 4
3. If all other factors are equal, which picture shows the LEAST equal balance between the two sides?
   A 1 B 2 C 3 D 4

L2

Teaching

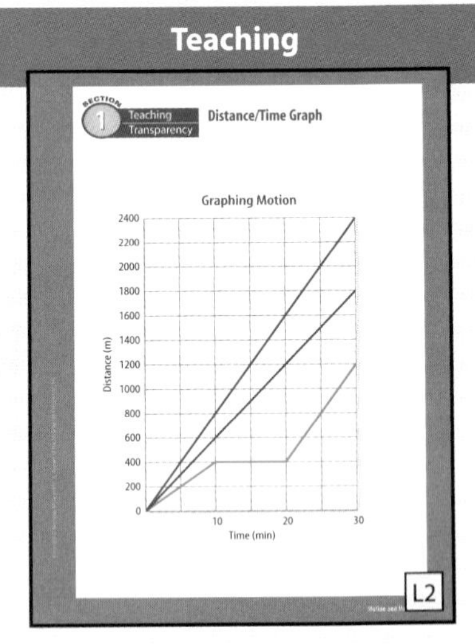
Section 1 Teaching Transparency — Distance/Time Graph

L2

Key to Teaching Strategies

The following designations will help you decide which activities are appropriate for your students.

- **L1** Level 1 activities should be appropriate for students with learning difficulties.
- **L2** Level 2 activities should be within the ability range of all students.
- **L3** Level 3 activities are designed for above-average students.
- **ELL** ELL activities should be within the ability range of English Language Learners.
- **COOP LEARN** Cooperative Learning activities are designed for small group work.
- **LS** Multiple Learning Styles logos, as described on page 22T, are used throughout to indicate strategies that address different learning styles.
- **P** These strategies represent student products that can be placed into a best-work portfolio.

Hands-on Activities

Activity Worksheets

Name Date Class

Activity — Force and Acceleration

Lab Preview

Directions: *Answer the following questions before you begin the Activity.*

1. Why do you think goggles are listed as a safety precaution for this activity?
2. According to Newton's first law of motion, what does it take to cause an object to begin moving from a state of rest?

If you stand at a stoplight, you will see cars stopping for red lights and then taking off when the light turns green. What makes the cars slow down? What makes them speed up? The cars accelerate because an unbalanced force is acting on them.

What You'll Investigate
How does an unbalanced force on a book affect its motion?

Materials
tape
paper clip
10-N spring scale
large book
this science book
triple beam balance
*electronic balance
*Alternate materials

Goals
- **Observe** the effect of force on the acceleration of an object.
- **Interpret** the data collected for each trial.

Safety Precautions
Proper eye protection should be worn at all times while performing this lab.

Procedure
1. With a piece of tape, attach the paper clip to your textbook so that the paper clip is just over the edge of the book.
2. Use Table 1 in the Data and Observations section to record your observations.
3. If available, use a large balance to find the mass of this science book.
4. Place the book on the floor or on the surface of a long table. Use the paper clip to hook the spring scale to the book.
5. Pull the book across the floor at a slow but constant velocity. While pulling, read the force you are pulling with on the spring scale and record it in your table.
6. Repeat step 5 two more times, once accelerating slowly and once accelerating quickly. Be careful not to pull too hard. Your spring scale will read only up to 10 N.
7. Place a second book on top of the first book and repeat steps 4 through 6.

L2

Laboratory Activities

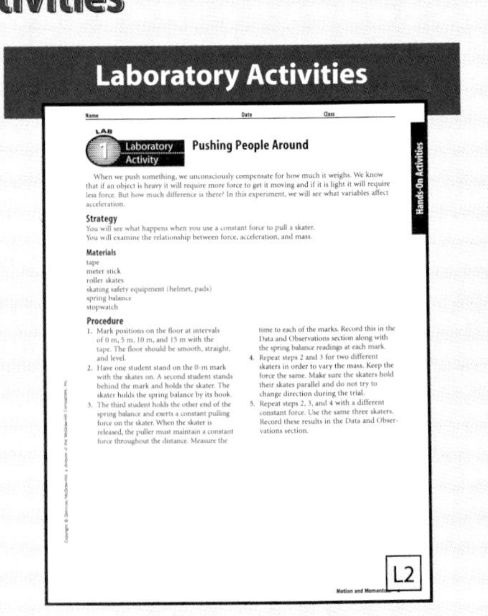
Name Date Class

Lab 1 Laboratory Activity — Pushing People Around

When we push something, we unconsciously compensate for how much it weighs. We know that if an object is heavy it will require more force to get it moving and if it is light it will require less force. But how much difference is there? In this experiment, we will see what variables affect acceleration.

Strategy
You will see what happens when you use a constant force to pull a skater.
You will examine the relationship between force, acceleration, and mass.

Materials
tape
meter stick
roller skates
skating safety equipment (helmet, pads)
spring balance
stopwatch

Procedure
1. Mark positions on the floor at intervals of 0 m, 5 m, 10 m, and 15 m with the tape. The floor should be smooth, straight, and level.
2. Have one student stand on the 0-m mark with the skates on. A second student stands behind the mark and holds the skater. The skater holds the spring balance by its hook.
3. The third student holds the other end of the spring balance and exerts a constant pulling force on the skater. When the skater is released, the puller must maintain a constant force throughout the distance. Measure the time to each of the marks. Record this in the Data and Observations section along with the spring balance readings at each mark.
4. Repeat steps 2 and 3 for two different skaters in order to vary the mass. Keep the force the same. Make sure the skaters hold their skates parallel and do not try to change direction during the trial.
5. Repeat steps 2, 3, and 4 with a different constant force. Use the same three skaters. Record these results in the Data and Observations section.

L2

Meeting Different Ability Levels

Content Outline

Name Date Class

Note-taking Worksheet **Motion and Momentum**

Section 1 What is Motion

A. __________—when an object changes its position relative to a reference point
1. __________—motion that is not obvious due to various possible reference points
2. __________—how far an object has moved
3. __________—distance and direction of an object's change in position from the starting point

B. __________—distance an object travels per unit of time
1. __________—any change over time
2. Calculation for speed: speed = distance / ______
3. Speed that doesn't change over time—__________ speed
4. Speed is usually not constant; usually an object has __________ speed.
5. __________—speed of motion when speed is changing; speed = total __________ / total travel time
6. __________—speed at any given point in time

C. A distance-time __________ displays motion of an object over time
1. Plot distance on a(n) __________ axis.
2. Plot time on a(n) __________ axis.

D. __________—speed and direction of an object's motion

E. Motion of Earth's crust—so __________ we don't notice

Meeting Individual Needs

L2

Motion and Momentum

Reinforcement

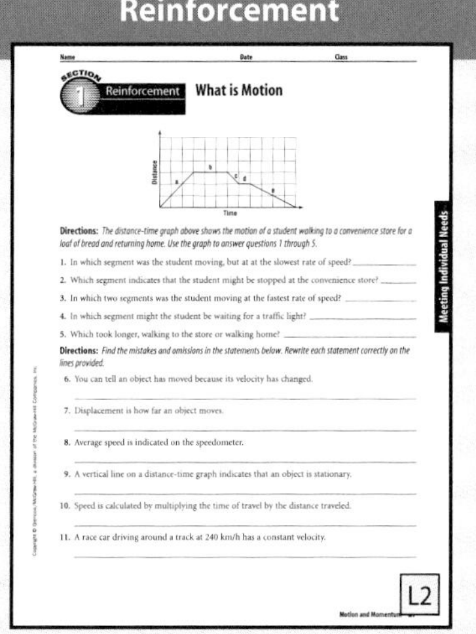

Name Date Class

Section 1 Reinforcement **What is Motion**

Directions: *The distance-time graph above shows the motion of a student walking to a convenience store for a loaf of bread and returning home. Use the graph to answer questions 1 through 5.*

1. In which segment was the student moving, but at the slowest rate of speed?
2. Which segment indicates that the student might be stopped at the convenience store?
3. In which two segments was the student moving at the fastest rate of speed?
4. In which segment might the student be waiting for a traffic light?
5. Which took longer, walking to the store or walking home?

Directions: *Find the mistakes and omissions in the statements below. Rewrite each statement correctly on the lines provided.*

6. You can tell an object has moved because its velocity has changed.
7. Displacement is how far an object moves.
8. Average speed is indicated on the speedometer.
9. A vertical line on a distance-time graph indicates that an object is stationary.
10. Speed is calculated by multiplying the time of travel by the distance traveled.
11. A race car driving around a track at 240 km/h has a constant velocity.

Meeting Individual Needs

L2

Motion and Momentum

Directed Reading

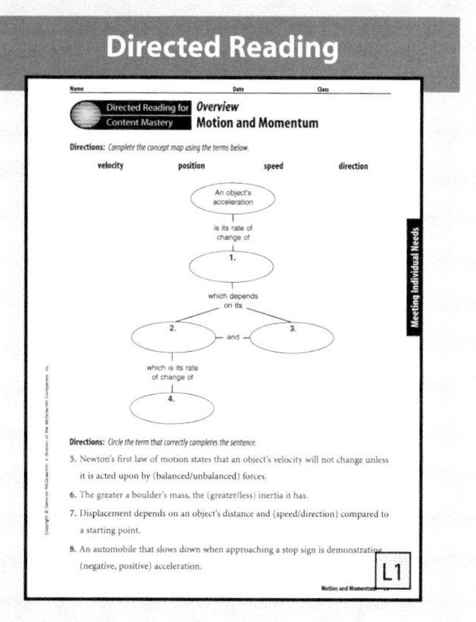

Name Date Class

Directed Reading for Content Mastery *Overview* **Motion and Momentum**

Directions: *Complete the concept map using the terms below.*

velocity position speed direction

Directions: *Circle the term that correctly completes the sentence.*

5. Newton's first law of motion states that an object's velocity will not change unless it is acted upon by (balanced/unbalanced) forces.
6. The greater a boulder's mass, the (greater/less) inertia it has.
7. Displacement depends on an object's distance and (speed/direction) compared to a starting point.
8. An automobile that slows down when approaching a stop sign is demonstrating (negative, positive) acceleration.

Meeting Individual Needs

L1

Motion and Momentum

Assessment

Chapter Tests

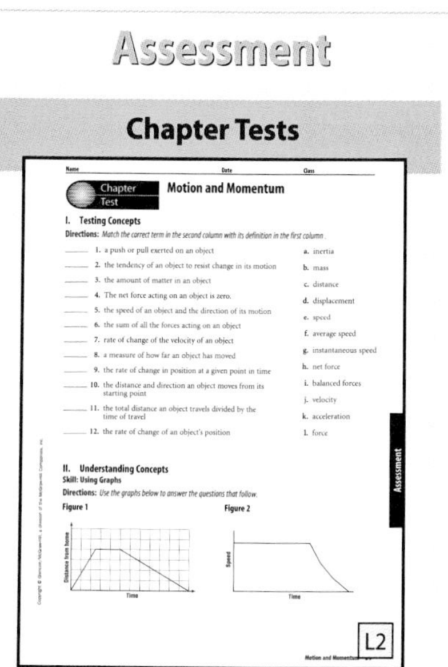

Name Date Class

Chapter Test **Motion and Momentum**

I. Testing Concepts

Directions: *Match the correct term in the second column with its definition in the first column.*

1. a push or pull exerted on an object — a. inertia
2. the tendency of an object to resist change in its motion — b. mass
3. the amount of matter in an object — c. distance
4. The net force acting on an object is zero. — d. displacement
5. the speed of an object and the direction of its motion — e. speed
6. the sum of all the forces acting on an object — f. average speed
7. rate of change of the velocity of an object — g. instantaneous speed
8. a measure of how far an object has moved — h. net force
9. the rate of change in position at a given point in time — i. balanced forces
10. the distance and direction an object moves from its starting point — j. velocity
11. the total distance an object travels divided by the time of travel — k. acceleration
12. the rate of change of an object's position — l. force

II. Understanding Concepts

Skill: Using Graphs

Directions: *Use the graphs below to answer the questions that follow.*

Figure 1 Figure 2

Assessment

L2

Motion and Momentum

Enrichment

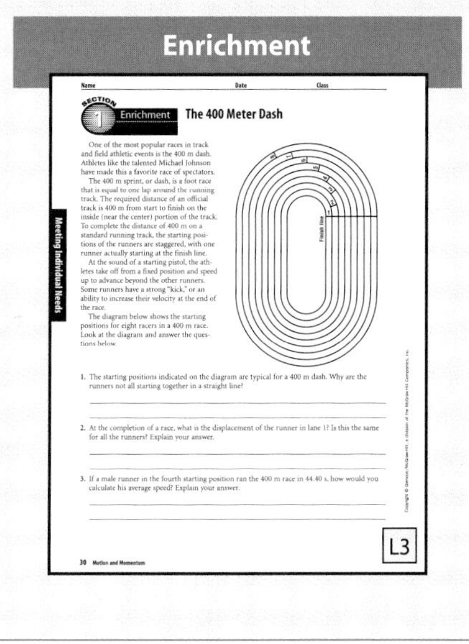

Name Date Class

Section 1 Enrichment **The 400 Meter Dash**

One of the most popular races in track and field athletic events is the 400 m dash. Athletes like the talented Michael Johnson have made this a favorite race of spectators.

The 400 m sprint, or dash, is a foot race that is equal to one lap around the running track. The required distance of an official track is 400 m from start to finish on the inside (near the center) portion of the track. To complete the distance of 400 m on a standard running track, the starting positions of the runners are staggered, with one runner actually starting at the finish line.

At the sound of a starting pistol, the athletes take off from a fixed position and speed up to advance beyond the other runners. Some runners have a strong "kick," or an ability to increase their velocity at the end of the race.

The diagram below shows the starting positions for eight racers in a 400 m race. Look at the diagram and answer the questions below.

1. The starting positions indicated on the diagram are typical for a 400 m dash. Why are the runners not all starting together in a straight line?
2. At the completion of a race, what is the displacement of the runner in lane 1? Is this the same for all the runners? Explain your answer.
3. If a male runner in the fourth starting position ran the 400 m race in 44.40 s, how would you calculate his average speed? Explain your answer.

Meeting Individual Needs

L3

30 Motion and Momentum

Spanish Directed Reading

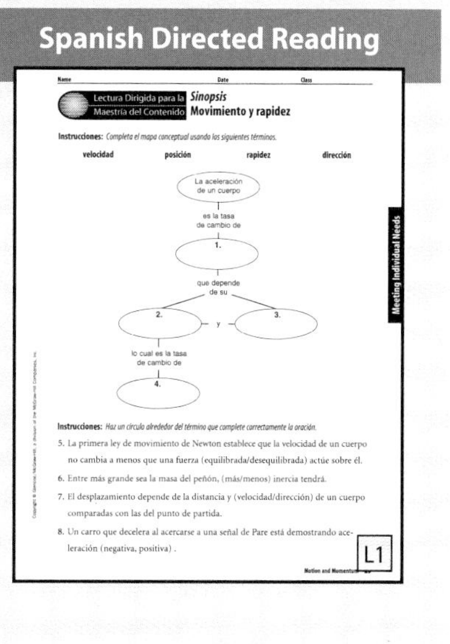

Nombre Fecha Clase

Lectura Dirigida para la Maestría del Contenido *Sinopsis* **Movimiento y rapidez**

Instrucciones: *Completa el mapa conceptual usando los siguientes términos.*

velocidad posición rapidez dirección

Instrucciones: *Haz un círculo alrededor del término que complete correctamente la oración.*

5. La primera ley de movimiento de Newton establece que la velocidad de un cuerpo no cambia a menos que una fuerza (equilibrada/desequilibrada) actúe sobre él.
6. Entre más grande sea la masa del peñón, (más/menos) inercia tendrá.
7. El desplazamiento depende de la distancia y (velocidad/dirección) de un cuerpo comparadas con las del punto de partida.
8. Un carro que decelera al acercarse a una señal de Pare está demostrando aceleración (negativa, positiva).

Meeting Individual Needs

L1

Motion and Momentum

Test Practice Workbook

Chapter Review

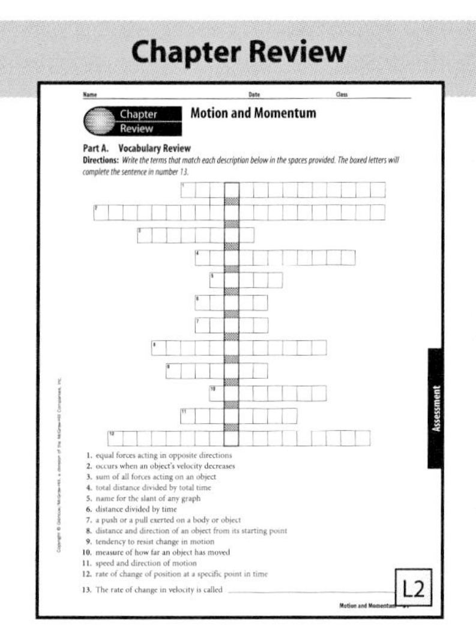

Name Date Class

Chapter Review **Motion and Momentum**

Part A. Vocabulary Review

Directions: *Write the terms that match each description below in the spaces provided. The boxed letters will complete the sentence in number 13.*

1. equal forces acting in opposite directions
2. occurs when an object's velocity decreases
3. sum of all forces acting on an object
4. total distance divided by total time
5. name for the slant of any graph
6. distance divided by time
7. a push or a pull exerted on a body or object
8. distance and direction of an object from its starting point
9. tendency to resist change in motion
10. measure of how far an object has moved
11. speed and direction of motion
12. rate of change of position at a specific point in time
13. The rate of change in velocity is called __________

Assessment

L2

Motion and Momentum

Science Content Background

What is motion?

Changing Position

Distance is a scalar quantity. This means it only has magnitude, such as 6 km. Displacement is a vector quantity; it has both magnitude and direction, such as 8 km south. A car or bike odometer displays distance not displacement.

> **Student Misconception**
>
> Distance and displacement are the same. Speed and velocity are the same.
>
> **Refer to the facing page for teaching strategies to address this misconception. Refer to pages 167–171 for content related to this topic.**

Speed

Speed, unlike displacement and velocity, is a scalar quantity because it depends only on the distance traveled. As the name implies, speedometers display speed, not velocity, so they do not indicate direction. Speedometers provide instantaneous speed, which helps you avoid going too fast or too slowly at a given moment. In planning a trip, however, average speed is more useful for determining the time required to travel.

Graphing Motion

A distance-time graph can never have a line with a negative slope, which means that the line showing motion can never go towards the x-axis. This is because it is impossible to travel a negative distance. A displacement-time graph can have a negative slope, which means the object is moving closer to its point of reference.

Acceleration

Acceleration and Motion

Acceleration is a measure of the rate of change of an object's velocity. If velocity is expressed as meters/second and time is given in seconds, then acceleration is expressed in units of meters per second. This is equivalent to m/s/s or (m/s × 1/s) or m/s^2.

When an object's velocity increases the object experiences positive acceleration. When its velocity decreases the object experiences negative acceleration. Both are acceleration because the object's speed changes. Acceleration also occurs when an object changes direction. For example, as Earth orbits the Sun it is accelerating. Although Earth travels at a relatively constant speed, its direction is constantly changing.

Momentum

Mass and Inertia

Astronauts in weightless conditions still have a harder time moving a massive object such as a bowling ball than moving a less massive object such as a table tennis ball. This is because the greater the mass of an object the greater is its inertia.

Momentum

In bowling, the greater the momentum of the ball the greater the chance of knocking down all the pins. A heavier ball has more mass but its mass may make it difficult to roll. Thus a player using a lighter ball may be able to give the ball more momentum by giving it a higher velocity.

For additional content background on this topic, go to the Glencoe Science Web site at science.glencoe.com.

Misconceptions

Find Out What Students Think

Students may think that . . .

- **Distance and displacement are the same.**
- **Speed and velocity are the same.**

One difficulty with the terms velocity and displacement is that they are both vector quantities, and students are much more familiar with scalar quantities. To confuse matters more, the term velocity is sometimes used in everyday language in a non-scientific way. Finally, the terms displacement and distance sound similar, and this may make it easier to confuse them.

Demonstration

After initially teaching the difference between distance and displacement, ask students whether the phrase, "as the crow flies," when estimating how far something is, is more like distance or more like displacement.

Promote Understanding

Activity

- Draw Figures 1 and 2 on the board. Explain that the distance-time graph and displacement-time graph both show Samantha's walking motion after she left her house.
- Ask students to supply a possible story to describe her motion. Ask them what she might be doing when the lines of both graphs are horizontal.

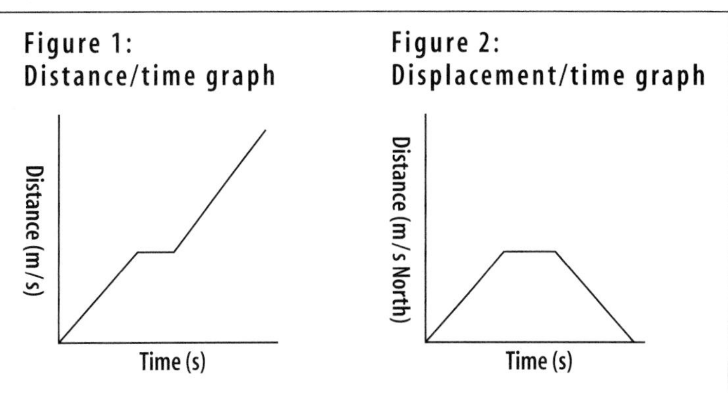

- Students should see that the distance-time graph and displacement-time graph for the same motion look very different. In this case the distance traveled is how far Samantha actually walked. Her displacement shows how far she is from her house.
- A plausible story for both graphs has Samantha walk with constant speed directly away from her house, then rest a bit, and then walk with constant speed directly back to her house.

Assess

After completing the chapter, see *Identifying Misconceptions* in the Study Guide.

Motion and Momentum

Chapter Vocabulary

speed
average speed
instantaneous speed
velocity
acceleration
mass
inertia
momentum
law of conservation of momentum

What do you think?

Science Journal The photo shows cars on a busy freeway at night. A slow shutter speed was used that causes the cars' lights to leave luminous trails on the image as the cars move.

CHAPTER

Motion and Momentum

Racers, like the ones shown here, want to know who is the fastest. How can you determine who's the fastest? What has to be measured to determine a racer's speed? How can you describe motion when speed is changing? In this chapter you will learn how to describe motion, including motion that is changing. You will also study how motion changes when objects collide.

What do you think?

Science Journal Look at the picture below with a classmate. Discuss what this might be or what is happening. Here's a hint: *You can see these almost everywhere, day or night.* Write your answer or your best guess in your Science Journal.

164

Theme Connection

Stability and Change An object can be in motion or at rest. If in motion, the motion can be constant or accelerated. If accelerated, the rate of acceleration can be constant or changing.

How is it possible for a 70-kg football player to knock down a 110-kg football player? The smaller player must be running much faster. Size and mass make a difference when two objects collide, but the speed of an object also matters. Explore the reactions of colliding objects during this activity.

Model collisions

1. Space yourself about 2 m away from a partner. Slowly roll a softball on the floor toward your partner, and have your partner roll a softball quickly into your ball.
2. Have your partner slowly roll a softball as you quickly roll a tennis ball into the softball.
3. You and your partner roll two tennis balls toward each other at the same speed.

Observe

Describe your observations of each of these collisions. In your Science Journal, write a paragraph discussing how the motion of the balls changed after the collision.

Before You Read

Making a Vocabulary Study Fold **Knowing the definition of vocabulary words is a good way to ensure you understand the content of the chapter.**

1. Place a sheet of notebook paper in front of you so the short side is at the top and the holes are on the right side. Fold the paper in half from the left side to the right side.
2. Through the top thickness of paper, cut along every third line from the outside edge to the fold, forming tabs.
3. Before you read, write the vocabulary words from each section in this chapter on the front of the tabs. Under each tab, write what you think the word means.
4. As you read the chapter, add to and correct your definitions.

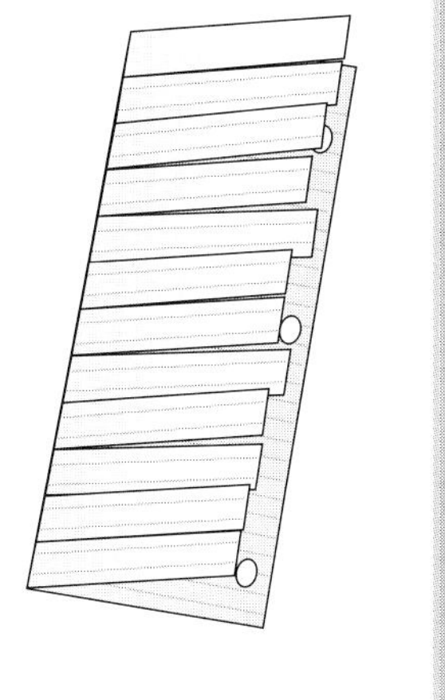

Explore Activity

Purpose Use the explore activity to introduce students to the way the speeds and masses of the objects in a collision affect the collision. L2 LS **Kinesthetic**

Preparation Ask students to bring in balls, or arrange to borrow them at your school.

Materials two softballs, two tennis balls

Alternate Materials Different types of balls can be used as long as the balls in each pair have identical masses.

Teaching Strategy Remind students of what they have observed in other collisions. For example, which ball is harder to catch?

Observe

In the first case, the slower ball reversed direction and increased speed after the collision. The speed of the faster ball decreased. In the second case, both balls reversed direction. Speeds depended on initial speeds. In the third case, the balls reversed direction when they collided, but moved off at about the same speed as before.

Assessment

Process Ask students to predict what would happen if a small child, running fast, ran into an adult who wasn't expecting it. In the collision, the child would slow down, and some of its motion would be transferred to the adult. Both would stumble in the direction the child was first moving, but at a slower speed. Use **PASC,** p. 89.

Before You Read

Foldables Reading & Study Skills

Dinah Zike Study Fold

Purpose Use this activity to determine what students know about the vocabulary words in this chapter before they read the chapter. The Foldable then provides space for students to add information they learn about the words as they read the chapter.

For additional help, see Foldables Worksheet, p. 17 in **Chapter Resources Booklet,** or go to the Glencoe Science Web site at **science.glencoe.com.** See After You Read in the Study Guide at the end of this chapter.

SECTION

What is motion?

1 Motivate

Bellringer Transparency

Display the Section Focus Transparency for Section 1. Use the accompanying Transparency Activity Master. L2 ELL

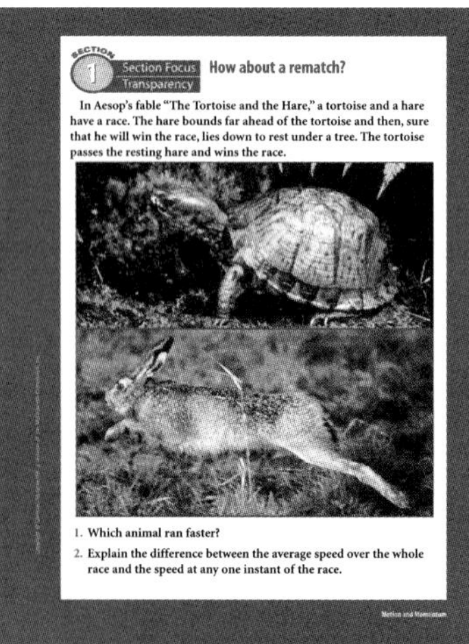

SECTION 1 Section Focus Transparency **How about a rematch?**

In Aesop's fable "The Tortoise and the Hare," a tortoise and a hare have a race. The hare bounds far ahead of the tortoise and then, sure that he will win the race, lies down to rest under a tree. The tortoise passes the resting hare and wins the race.

1. Which animal ran faster?
2. Explain the difference between the average speed over the whole race and the speed at any one instant of the race.

Tie to Prior Knowledge

Ask students to describe races they have watched or in which they have participated. Possibilities include running, swimming, bicycling, car racing, and horse racing, among others. Discuss what is being measured in each type of race

SECTION

What is motion?

As You Read

***What* You'll Learn**

- **Define** distance, speed, and velocity.
- **Graph** motion.

Vocabulary

speed
average speed
instantaneous speed
velocity

***Why* It's Important**

To be able to describe motion, you must understand the different parts of motion.

Matter and Motion

All matter in the universe is constantly in motion, from the revolution of Earth around the Sun to electrons moving around the nucleus of an atom. Plants grow. Lava flows from a volcano. Bees move from flower to flower as they gather pollen. Blood circulates through your body. These are all examples of matter in motion. How can the motion of these different objects be described?

Changing Position

To describe an object in motion, you must recognize first that the object is in motion. Something is in motion if it is changing position. It could be a fast-moving airplane, a leaf swirling in the wind, or water trickling from a hose. Even your school is moving through space attached to Earth. When an object moves from one location to another, it is changing position. The runners shown in **Figure 1** sprint from the start line to the finish line. Their positions change so they are in motion.

Research Visit the Glencoe Science Web site at **science.glencoe.com** for more information about early attempts to study motion. Make a table to show what you learn.

Figure 1
When running a race, you are in motion because your position changes.

Section Assessment Planner

PORTFOLIO
Extension, p. 170

PERFORMANCE ASSESSMENT
Math Skills Activity, p. 168
Try At Home MiniLAB, p. 169
Skill Builder Activities, p. 171
See page 190 for more options.

CONTENT ASSESSMENT
Section, p. 171
Challenge, p. 171
Chapter, pp. 190–191

Relative Motion Determining whether something changes position requires a point of reference. An object changes position if it moves relative to a reference point. To visualize this, picture yourself competing in a 100-m dash. You begin just behind the start line. When you pass the finish line, you are 100 m from the start line. If the start line is your reference point then your position has changed by 100 m relative to the start line, and motion has occurred. Look at **Figure 2.** How can you determine that the dog has been in motion?

Figure 2
The dog has moved relative to what object?

✔ **Reading Check** *How do you know if an object has changed position?*

Distance and Displacement Suppose you are to meet your friends at the park in five minutes. Can you get there on time by walking, or should you ride your bike? To help you decide, you need to know the distance you will travel to get to the park. This distance is the length of the route you will travel from your house to the park.

Suppose the distance you traveled from your house to the park was 200 m. When you get to the park, how would you describe your location? You could say that your location was 200 m from your house. To describe your location exactly, you also would have to tell in what direction you traveled. Did you travel 200 m east or 200 m west? Your final position would depend on whether you traveled east or west. To exactly describe your location, you would have to specify your displacement. Displacement includes the distance between the starting and stopping points, and the direction in which you travel. **Figure 3** shows the difference between distance and displacement.

Figure 3
Distance is how far you have walked. Displacement is the direction and difference in position between your starting point to your ending point.

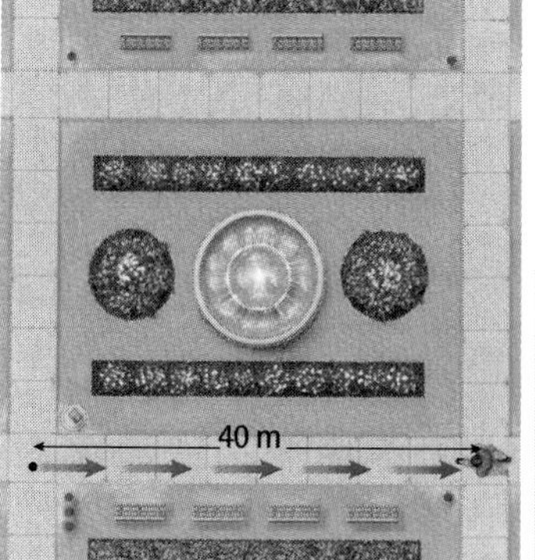

Distance: 40 m
Displacement: 40 m east

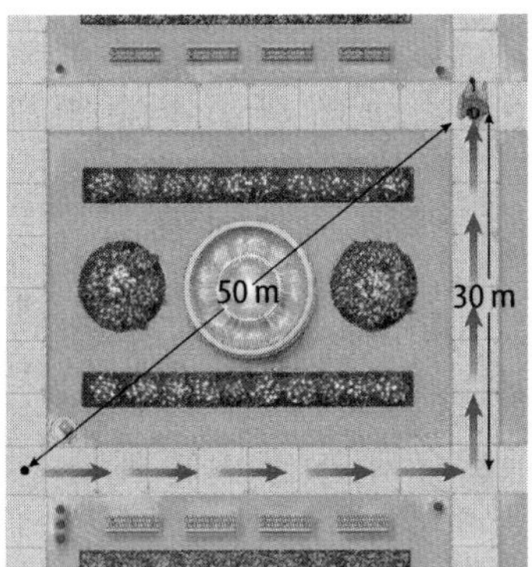

Distance: 70 m
Displacement: 50 m northeast

Distance: 140 m
Displacement: 0 m

2 Teach

Matter and Motion

Internet Addresses

Explore the Glencoe Science Web site at **science.glencoe.com** to find out more about topics in this section.

Changing Position

✔ **Reading Check**

Answer It has moved relative to a reference point.

Caption Answer

Figure 2 the bench

Activity

Have students work in pairs. Ask one student to walk forward while the other stands still. Then have the first student stand still while the other walks forward. Have students describe their motion relative to each other. L2 LS **Kinesthetic**

Quick Demo

Toss a ball to a student. Maintaining the same distance from the student, vary the toss. Throw the ball quickly and along a fairly flat path, bounce it, and toss it high in the air. Point out that the ball's displacement remains the same, but its total path varies. L2 LS **Visual-Spatial**

Cultural Diversity

Chinese Mapmaking By the second century A.D., Chang Heng, inventor of the seismograph, was applying uniform grids to maps to make it easier to calculate distances. This was eventually developed to the point where, by the 1300s, some maps eliminated the physical features and simply showed place names and grid lines, as a modern computer might model a map.

Resource Manager

Chapter Resources Booklet
- Transparency Activity, p. 44
- Note-Taking Worksheets, pp. 33–34
- Guided Reading for Content Mastery, pp. 19, 20

Speed

Answers will vary. Some characteristics might be a streamlined body shape to help swim, long legs to help run, and low body mass to help fly.

Activity

In the United States students are more likely to encounter speeds in miles per hour or feet per second. Give students practice problems to help them get accustomed to converting between these units. Have them convert 60 miles per hour to kilometers per hour; 97 km/h 35 miles per hour to kilometers per hour; 56 km/h 80 km per hour to miles per hour; 50 mi/h and 66 feet per second to meters per second. 20 m/s L2

LS **Logical-Mathematical**

IDENTIFYING Misconceptions

Students may think that distance and displacement are the same, and that speed and velocity are the same. See page 164F for teaching tips related to these misconceptions.

Math Skills Activity

National Math Standards

Correlation to Mathematics Objectives

1, 2, 4, 6, 8, 9

Answer to Practice Problem

In the first race the runner ran 400 m/43.9 s = 9.1 m/s. In the second race, runner ran 100 m/10.4s = 9.6 m/s. His speed was faster in the second race.

Different animals can move at different top speeds. What are some of the fastest animals? Research the characteristics that help animals run, swim, or fly at high speed.

Speed

When something is moving, knowing how fast it is moving can be important. The faster something is moving, the less time it takes to travel a certain distance. **Speed** is the distance traveled divided by the time taken to travel the distance. This definition can be written as the following equation:

$$\text{speed} = \frac{\text{distance}}{\text{time}}$$

For example, the fastest runners can run the 100-m dash in about 10 s. When sprinters run 100 m in 10 s, their speed is as follows:

$$\text{speed} = \frac{\text{distance}}{\text{time}} = \frac{100\text{ m}}{10\text{ s}} = 10\text{ m/s}$$

The units of speed are units of distance divided by units of time. In SI units, the units of speed are meters per second (m/s).

Math Skills Activity

Calculating Speed

Example Problem

Calculate the speed of a swimmer who swims 100 m in 56 s.

Solution

1. *This is what you know:* distance: 100 m; time: 56 s
2. *This is what you need to know:* speed
3. *This is the equation you need to use:* speed = distance/time
4. *Substitute the known values:* speed = (100 m)/(56 s); speed = 1.8 m/s

Check your answer by multiplying the calculated speed by the time. Did you calculate the distance that was given in the problem?

Practice Problem

A runner completes a 400-m race in 43.9 s. In a 100-m race, he finishes in 10.4 s. In which race was his speed faster?

For more help, refer to the Math Skill Handbook.

Curriculum Connection

Music Ask students to identify the units used to measure speed in music and to demonstrate how speed is used and depicted in music. Beats per minute are the units used. A rapid beat or slow beat affects the mood of a piece. L3 ELL LS **Auditory-Musical**

Teacher FYI

Before people had accurate timekeeping devices, they used pulse rate to keep time. Early musicians based the tempo of music on pulse rate, and Galileo analyzed the movement of a pendulum using his pulse.

Average Speed If a sprinter ran the 100-m dash in 10 s, she probably couldn't have run the entire race with a speed of 10 m/s. Consider that when the race started, the sprinter wasn't moving. Then, as she started running, she moved faster and faster, which increased her speed. During the entire race, the sprinter's speed could have been different from instant to instant. However, the sprinter's motion for the entire race can be described by her average speed which is 10 m/s. Average speed is found by dividing the total distance traveled by the time taken.

✔ **Reading Check** *How is average speed calculated?*

An object in motion can change speeds many times as it speeds up or slows down. The speed of an object at one instant of time is the object's **instantaneous speed.** To understand the difference between average and instantaneous speeds, think about walking to the library. If it takes you 0.5 h to walk 2 km to the library, your average speed would be as follows:

$$\text{speed} = \frac{\text{distance}}{\text{time}}$$

$$= \frac{2\text{ km}}{0.5\text{ h}} = 4\text{ km/h}$$

However, you might not have been moving at the same speed throughout the trip. At a crosswalk, your instantaneous speed might have been 0 km/h. If you raced across the street, your speed might have been 7 km/h. If you were able to walk at a steady rate of 4 km/h during the entire trip, you would have moved at a constant speed. Average speed, instantaneous speed, and constant speed are illustrated in **Figure 4.**

TRY AT HOME Mini LAB

Measuring Average Speed

Procedure

1. Measure the distance between two marks, such as two doorways.
2. Time yourself walking from one mark to the other.
3. Time yourself walking slowly, walking safely and quickly, and walking with a varying speed; for example, slow/fast/slow.

Analysis

1. Calculate your average speed in each case.
2. Compare the last average speed, when your actual speed varied. Which speed was it closest to?
3. Predict how long it would take you to walk 100 m slowly, at your normal speed, and quickly.

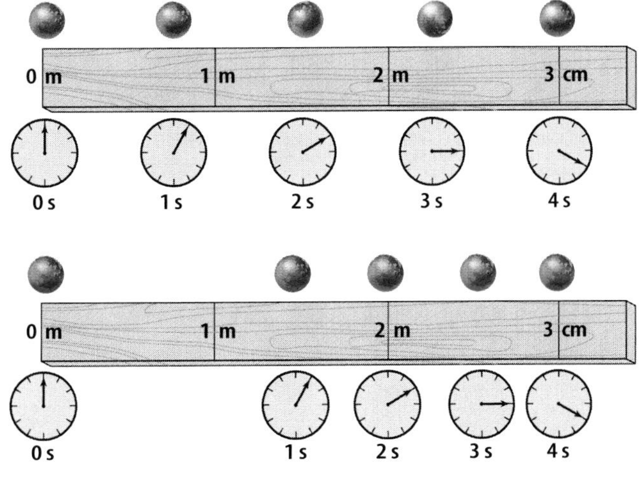

Figure 4
The average speed of each ball is the same from 0 s to 3 s.

A This ball is moving at a constant speed. In each time increment, the ball moves the same distance.

B This ball has a varying speed. Its instantaneous speed is fast between 0 and 1 s and slow between 2 s and 3 s.

✔ **Reading Check**

Answer by dividing the total distance traveled by the total time taken

Purpose Students measure distance and time and calculate speed. L2 IN **Kinesthetic**

Materials meterstick or other measuring device, watch with second hand

Teaching Strategy To give meaningful results, make sure the distance students move is at least 10 meters.

Analysis

1. Students should use distance ÷ time and include correct units.
2. Answers will vary. If their speed changed between slow and fast, the average speed should be between the average speeds for walking slowly and walking quickly.
3. Students should use the formula 100 m ÷ (measured speed for that pace) = predicted time.

✔ *Assessment*

Process Tell students an object moves 35 m in 15 s. Ask students to calculate the average speed, and then use the results to predict how long it would take the object to travel 250 m at that speed and how far the object would go at that speed in 20 minutes. Average speed = 2.3 m/s, it would take 109 s to travel 250 m; it would travel 2,760 m in 20 minutes. Use **PASC,** p. 101.

Visual Learning

Figure 4 Point out to students that this drawing illustrates motion over time. Tell them that photographers can take time-lapse photos to show the same thing. If the photographer knows the time between shots, he or she can find the average speed between any two positions. Ask students whether the motion shown in **A** or **B** is more like their trip to school. probably B

Resource Manager

Chapter Resources Booklet

MiniLAB, p. 3
Lab Activity, pp. 9–12
Transparency Activity, pp. 47–48

Graphing Motion

Activity

Tell students that to calculate speed from a distance-time graph, they must find the slope of the line. The slope is a measure of the steepness of the graph, and is found by dividing the rise, or vertical change, by the run, or horizontal change. In **Figure 5,** the slope of line A between 1 and 2 seconds is (2 m − 1 m) ÷ (2 s − 1 s) = 1 m/s. Have students find the slope of line B for that period of time. (1 m − 0.5 m) ÷ (2 s − 1 s) = 0.5 m/s

L3 LS **Logical-Mathematical**

Caption Answer

Figure 5 student A

Extension

The motion of groups of objects can be modeled using graph paper. Have students divide a sheet of graph paper into six regions to represent one-second intervals from 0 to 5 s. Have students use the graph paper to illustrate what happens to four objects moving at different speeds and directions at $t = 0$, 1, 2, 3, 4, and 5 s. Each graph should be like a photo of the objects' positions at that time. Then ask them to predict when and if various pairs of objects meet. L3 LS **Visual-Spatial** P

Graphing Motion

You can represent the motion of an object with a distance-time graph. For this type of graph, time is plotted on the horizontal axis and distance is plotted on the vertical axis. **Figure 5** shows the motion of two students who walked across a classroom, plotted on a distance-time graph.

SCIENCE Online

Research Visit the Glencoe Science Web site at **science.glencoe.com** for information about how the land speed record has changed over the past century. Make a chart showing what you learn.

Distance-Time Graphs and Speed The distance-time graph can be used to compare the speeds of objects. Look at the graph shown in **Figure 5.** According to the graph, after 1 s student A traveled 1 m. Her average speed during the first second is as follows:

$$\text{speed} = \frac{\text{distance}}{\text{time}} = \frac{1\text{ m}}{1\text{ s}} = 1\text{ m/s}$$

Student B, however, only traveled 0.5 m in the first second. His average speed is

$$\text{speed} = \frac{\text{distance}}{\text{time}} = \frac{0.5\text{ m}}{1\text{ s}} = 0.5\text{ m/s}$$

So student A traveled faster than student B. Now compare the steepness of the lines on the graph in **Figure 5.** The line representing the motion of student A is steeper than the line of student B. A steeper line on the distance-time graph represents a greater speed. A horizontal line on the distance-time graph means that no change in position occurs. Then the speed at any time shown on the graph is zero.

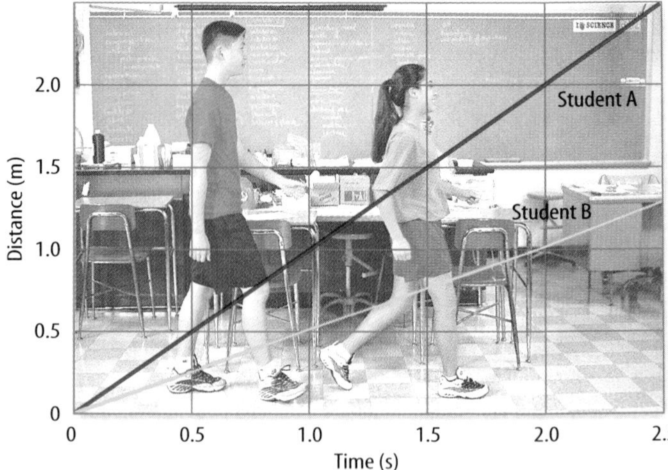

Figure 5
The motion of two students walking across a classroom is plotted on this distance-time graph.
Which student moved faster?

Curriculum Connection

Math The horizontal axis of a graph represents the independent variable; that is, the variable in which a change causes a change in the other variable. In distance-time graphs the independent variable is time. The vertical axis shows the dependent variable, in this case distance. The variables can be switched, but time is almost always the independent variable.

Resource Manager

Chapter Resources Booklet

Enrichment, p. 30

Reinforcement, p. 27

Velocity

If you are hiking in the woods, it is important to know in which direction you should walk in order to get back to camp. You want to know not only your speed, but also the direction in which you are moving. The **velocity** of an object is the speed of the object and direction of its motion. This is why a compass and a map, like the one shown in **Figure 6,** are useful to hikers. To get back to camp before nightfall, they need to know how far, how fast, and in what direction they need to travel. The map and the compass help the hikers to determine what their velocity must be. Velocity has the same units as speed, but it also includes the direction of motion.

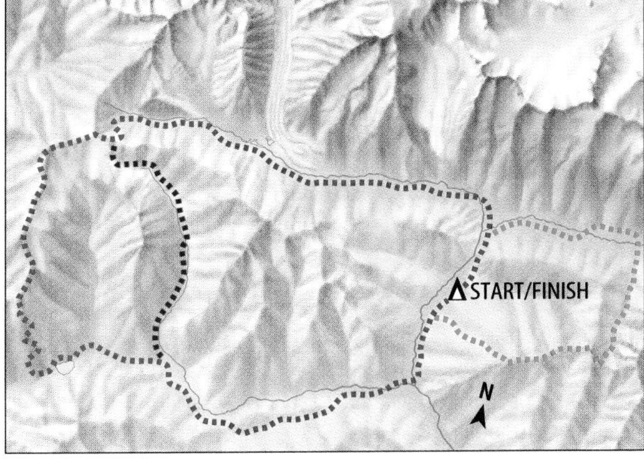

Figure 6
A map helps determine the direction in which you need to travel.

The velocity of an object can change if the object's speed changes, its direction of motion changes, or they both change. For example, suppose a car is traveling at a speed of 60 km/h north and then turns left at an intersection and continues on with a speed of 60 km/h. The speed of the car is constant at 60 km/h, but the velocity changes from 60 km/h north to 60 km/h west. Why can you say the velocity of a car changes as it comes to a stop at an intersection?

Section  Assessment

1. A dancer moves 5 m toward the left of the stage over the course of 15 s. What is her average velocity for this time?
2. If you know an object's velocity, do you know its speed? Explain.
3. An airplane flies a distance of 650 km at an average speed of 300 km/h. How long was the flight?
4. **Think Critically** A bee flies 25 m north of the hive, then 10 m east, 5 m west, and 10 m south. How far north and east of the hive is it now? Explain how you calculated your answer.

Skill Builder Activities

5. **Making and Using Graphs** You walk forward at 1.5 m/s for 8 s. Your friend decides to walk faster and starts out at 2.0 m/s for the first 4 s. But then she slows down and walks forward at 1.0 m/s for the next 4 s. Make a distance-time graph of your motion and your friend's motion. Who walked farther? **For more help, refer to the Science Skill Handbook.**
6. **Using a Database** Use a database to research the top speeds of different animals. Convert all data to units of m/s. **For more help, refer to the Technology Skill Handbook.**

Velocity

Discussion

Could you use a distance-time graph to show velocity? Why or why not? A distance-time graph could indicate the speed component of velocity but not the direction component. L2 **IN Logical-Mathematical**

Text Question Answer

because its speed changes

2 Teach

Reteach

Have a student start at the door and walk across the classroom in a straight line. Then move a few desks into the path and have the student repeat the test, dodging the desks. What was the distance in each case? The displacement? Was the speed constant or changing? The velocity? L2 ELL
IN Visual-Spatial

Challenge

Have each student make a distance-time graph of the following motion.

0 s to 4 s: walk at 0.8 m/s

4 s to 6 s: stopped

6 s to 10 s: run at 2.3 m/s

What was the average speed over the 10 s? 1.24 m/s L2
IN Logical-Mathematical

Assessment

Process Give students a distance-time graph showing the motions of three different people. Ask them to compare the motions. How did each person's speed and position change over time? Use **PASC,** p. 113.

Answers to Section Assessment

1. 5 m ÷ 15 s = 0.33 m/s left
2. Yes; velocity includes speed and direction.
3. 650 km ÷ 300 km/h = 2.17 h
4. 15 m north (25 − 10) and 5 m east (10 − 5)
5. The horizontal axis should be marked from 0 s to 8 s and the vertical axis should be marked from 0 m to 12 m. The graph of your motion is a diagonal line from (0, 0) to (8, 12). The graph of your friend's motion is a 2 part line, extending from (0, 0) to (4, 8) and from (4, 8) to (8, 12). You walked the same distance, 12 m.
6. Check students' work.

SECTION

Acceleration

1 Motivate

Bellringer Transparency

Display the Section Focus Transparency for Section 2. Use the accompanying Transparency Activity Master. L2 ELL

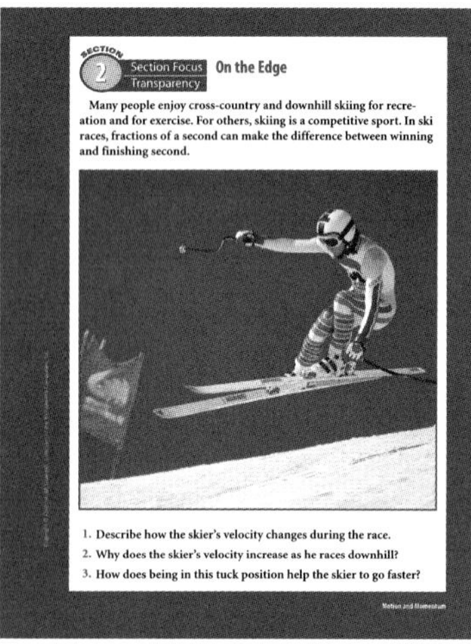

2 Section Focus Transparency **On the Edge**

Many people enjoy cross-country and downhill skiing for recreation and for exercise. For others, skiing is a competitive sport. In ski races, fractions of a second can make the difference between winning and finishing second.

1. Describe how the skier's velocity changes during the race.
2. Why does the skier's velocity increase as he races downhill?
3. How does being in this tuck position help the skier to go faster?

Tie to Prior Knowledge

Bring to class a car advertising statement like "goes from 0 to 60 in 8.3 s." Ask students to describe acceleration using this example. **What would it mean if the car reached a faster speed in 8.3 s?** higher acceleration **What would it mean if it took 12 s to reach 60 mi/h?** lower acceleration **What do people mean when they say a car has "no acceleration"?** That it won't increase its speed very rapidly.

SECTION

Acceleration

As You Read

What **You'll Learn**

- **Define** acceleration.
- **Predict** what effect acceleration will have on motion.

Vocabulary
acceleration

Why **It's Important**

Whenever an object changes its motion, it accelerates.

Acceleration and Motion

When you watch the first few seconds of a lift off, a rocket barely seems to move. With each passing second, however, you can see it move faster until it reaches an enormous speed. How could you describe the change in the rocket's motion? When an object changes its motion, it is accelerating. **Acceleration** is the change in velocity divided by the time it takes for the change to occur.

Like velocity, acceleration has a direction. If an object speeds up, the acceleration is in the direction that the object is moving. If an object slows down, the acceleration is opposite to the direction that the object is moving. What if the direction of the acceleration is at an angle to the direction of motion? Then the direction of motion will turn toward the direction of the acceleration.

Speeding Up You get on a bicycle and begin to pedal. The bike moves slowly at first, then it accelerates because its speed increases. When an object that is already in motion speeds up, it also is considered to be accelerating. Imagine that you are biking along a level path and you start pedaling harder. Your speed increases. When its speed is increasing, an object is accelerating.

Suppose a car is speeding up, as shown in **Figure 7.** Each second, the car moves at a greater speed and travels a greater distance than it did in the previous second. When the car stops accelerating, it will move in a straight line at the speed it reached when the acceleration stopped.

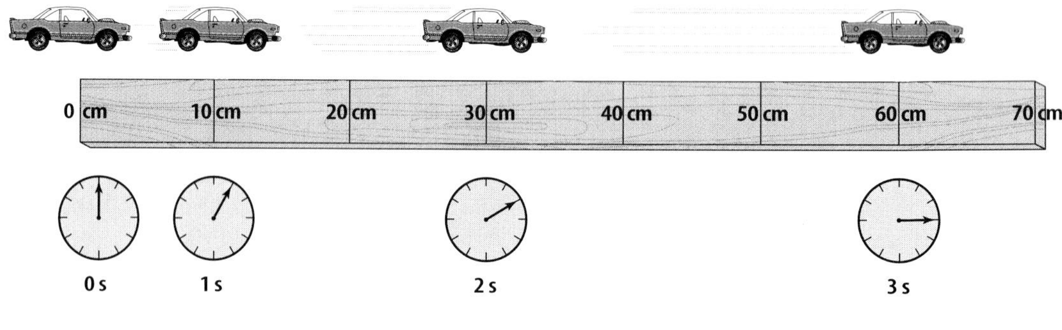

Figure 7
The car is accelerating to the right. The speed is increasing.

Section Assessment Planner

Portfolio
Assessment, p. 176

Performance Assessment
Math Skills Activity, p. 174
MiniLAB, p. 175
Skill Builder Activities, p. 176
See page 190 for more options.

Content Assessment
Section, p. 176
Challenge, p. 176
Chapter, pp. 190–191

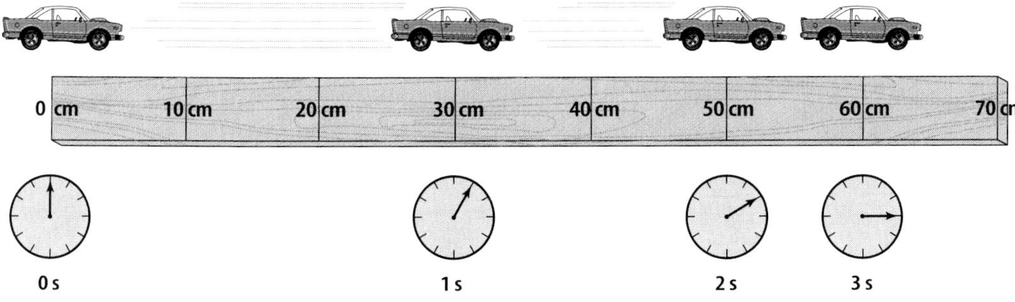

Slowing Down Now suppose you are biking at a speed of 4 m/s and you apply the brakes. This causes you to slow down. It might sound odd, but because your speed changes, you have accelerated. Acceleration occurs when an object slows down, as well as when it speeds up. The car in **Figure 8** is slowing down. During each time interval, the car travels a smaller distance, yet it still is considered to be accelerating.

In each of these examples, speed is changing, so acceleration must be occurring. Because speed is decreasing, the direction of the acceleration is opposite to the direction of motion. Any time an object slows down, its acceleration is in the opposite direction of its motion.

Figure 8
The car is moving to the right but accelerating to the left. In each time interval, it covers less distance and moves more slowly.

Changing Direction Motion is not always along a straight line. If the acceleration is at an angle to the direction of motion, the object will turn. At the same time, it might speed up, slow down, or have no change in speed.

Picture yourself again riding a bicycle. When you lean to one side and turn the handlebars, the bike turns. Because the direction of the bike's motion has changed, the bike has accelerated. The acceleration is in the direction that the bicycle turned.

Figure 9 shows another example of an object that is accelerating. The ball starts moving upward, but its direction of motion changes as its path turns downward. Here the acceleration is downward. The longer the ball accelerates, the more its path turns toward the direction of acceleration.

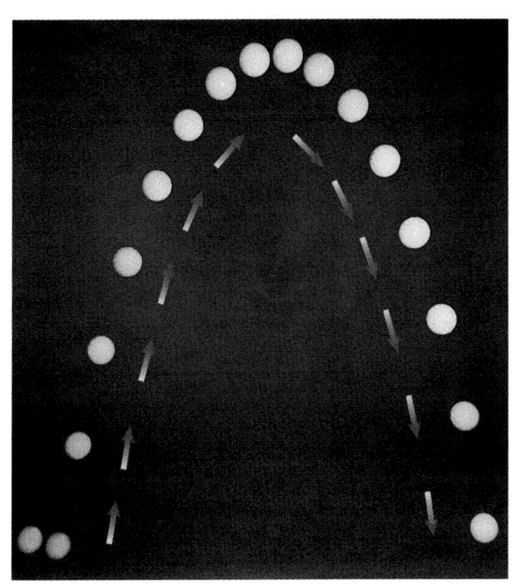

Figure 9
The ball starts out by moving forward and upward, but the acceleration is downward, so the ball's path turns in that direction.

2 Teach

Acceleration and Motion

Use Science Words

Word Origins Ask students to look up the origin of the word *accelerate* and explain how it relates to the scientific use of the word. Accelerate comes from the Latin prefix *ac-*, meaning "toward," the Latin root word *celer*, meaning "swift," and the Latin suffix *-ate*, meaning "cause to become." These together mean "cause to become swift toward." This covers one meaning, to get faster, of the scientific use of the word accelerate. It does not cover slowing down or turning. L3
LS **Linguistic**

Visual Learning

Figures 7 and 8 Review with students the accelerations shown in the figures. Ask students how else the car might accelerate. by changing direction

Accelerating to School Have students note each time they accelerate on their way to school and write their observations in their Science Journals. Make sure they include each time they stop, start, and turn on their journeys. L2
ELL LS **Linguistic**

Resource Manager

Chapter Resources Booklet
Transparency Activity, p. 45
Directed Reading, p. 20
Transparency Activity, pp. 47–48

Calculating Acceleration

Activity

Have students look at the equations on this page. **Why is acceleration measured in meters divided by seconds *squared*?** Velocity is measured in meters per second. To find acceleration, you divide velocity by time, so the final answer has distance divided by time (velocity) divided by time = m/s^2. L2

LS **Logical-Mathematical**

Extension

When doing calculations, students may be helped by doing unit analysis. In doing unit analysis, you write the initial problem with units included, and cancel appropriately to see what units the answer will be in. If the answer does not have the right units, the problem is set up incorrectly. Have students do a unit analysis of the problem of finding the time needed to accelerate from 3 m/s to 8 m/s at 2 m/s^2. Before they solve the problem mathematically, check that the units cancel leaving the unit of time, seconds. The change in velocity is 5 m/s. Rearrange the equation for acceleration to:

time = change in velocity ÷ acceleration unit analysis indicates that

$s = (m/s - m/s) \div m/s^2 = m/s \times s^2/m = s$

$t = (5\ m/s) \div (2\ m/s^2) = 2.5\ s$ L3

LS **Logical-Mathematical**

Math Skills Activity

National Math Standards

Correlation to Mathematics Objectives

2, 4, 6, 8, 9

Answer to Practice Problem

$(18\ m/s - 7\ m/s) \div 120\ s = 0.092\ m/s^2$

Calculating Acceleration

If an object is moving in a straight line, its acceleration can be calculated using this equation.

$$\text{acceleration} = \frac{\text{final speed} - \text{initial speed}}{\text{time}}$$

In this equation, the final speed is the speed at the end of the time period and the initial speed is the speed at the beginning of the time period. Also, time is the length of time over which the motion changes.

This equation also can be written in a simpler way by using symbols. Let a stand for acceleration and t stand for time. Then let s_f stand for the final speed and s_i stand for the initial speed. Then the above equation can be written as follows.

$$a = \frac{(s_f - s_i)}{t}$$

The unit of acceleration is distance divided by time squared. In SI units, acceleration has units meters per second squared (m/s^2).

Math Skills Activity

Calculating Acceleration

Example Problem

Calculate the acceleration of a bus whose speed changes from 5 m/s to 12 m/s over a period of 8 s.

1. *This is what you know:* initial speed: $s_i = 5$ m/s; final speed: $s_f = 12$ m/s; time: $t = 8$ s
2. *This is what you need to know:* acceleration: a
3. *This is the equation you need to use:* $a = (s_f - s_i)/t$
4. *Substitute the known values:* $a = (12\ m/s - 5\ m/s)/(8\ s) = (7\ m/s)/(8\ s) = 0.875\ m/s^2$

Check your answer by multiplying the calculated acceleration by the time. Then add the initial speed. Do you calculate the final speed given in the problem?

Practice Problem

A train's velocity increases from 7 m/s to 18 m/s over a period of 120 s. Calculate its acceleration.

For more help, refer to the Math Skill Handbook.

Inclusion Strategies

Learning Disabled Provide extra practice problems for students who have difficulty understanding the mathematics discussed on these pages. Make sure students understand the basic principles used both to set up and solve the problems.

Resource Manager

Chapter Resources Booklet

MiniLAB, p. 4
Enrichment, p. 30
Reinforcement, p. 28
Lab Activity, pp. 13–15

Figure 10
When skidding to a stop, you are slowing down. This means you have a negative acceleration.

Positive and Negative Acceleration An object is accelerating when it speeds up, and the acceleration is in the same direction as the motion. An object also is accelerating when it slows down, but the acceleration is in the direction opposite the motion, such as the bicycle in **Figure 10.** How else is acceleration different when an object is speeding up and slowing down?

Suppose you were riding your bicycle and speeded up from 4 m/s to 6 m/s in 5 s. You could calculate your acceleration from the equation on the previous page.

$$a = \frac{(s_f - s_i)}{t}$$

$$= \frac{(6 \text{ m/s} - 4 \text{ m/s})}{5 \text{ s}} = \frac{+2 \text{ m/s}}{5 \text{ s}}$$

$$= +0.4 \text{ m/s}^2$$

When you speed up, your final speed always will be greater than your initial speed. So subtracting the initial speed from the final speed always will give a positive number. As a result, acceleration always will be positive when an object is speeding up.

Suppose you slow down from a speed of 4 m/s to 2 m/s in 5 s. Now the final speed is less than the initial speed. You could calculate your acceleration as follows:

$$a = \frac{(s_f - s_i)}{t}$$

$$= \frac{(2 \text{ m/s} - 4 \text{ m/s})}{5 \text{ s}} = \frac{-2 \text{ m/s}}{5 \text{ s}}$$

$$= -0.4 \text{ m/s}^2$$

Because the final speed is less than the initial speed, acceleration is always negative when an object slows down.

Mini LAB

Modeling Acceleration

Procedure

1. Use **masking tape** to lay a course on the floor. Mark a starting point and place marks along a straight path at 10 cm, 40 cm, 90 cm, 160 cm, and 250 cm from the start.
2. Clap a steady beat. On the first beat, the person walking the course is at the starting point. On the second beat, the walker is on the first mark, and so on.

Analysis

1. Describe what happens to your speed as you move along the course. Infer what would happen if the course were extended farther.
2. Repeat step 2, starting at the other end. Are you still accelerating? Explain.

Mini LAB

Purpose Students observe constant acceleration. L2

Kinesthetic

Materials meter stick or other measuring device, masking tape

Teaching Strategy Explain to students that the actual time interval used doesn't matter, as long as it is constant—it could be 1 s–1 s–1s or 3 s–3 s–3 s, or any other regular time interval. Clapping steadily is easier than trying to watch the clock and the course at the same time.

Safety Precaution Suggest students leave space at the fast end of the course to slow to a stop.

Analysis

1. You speed up. You would go faster and faster with each clap.
2. Yes, your speed is changing. In this case you are slowing down.

Process Ask students to repeat the experiment using different steady beats—very slow or very fast. How does this affect the acceleration they experience? The faster the beat, the greater the acceleration, because the time between beats decreases. Use **PASC,** p. 97.

Curriculum Connection

History An early problem in the study of motion was to measure the acceleration of an object due to gravity. Did objects accelerate as they fell? At a constant or changing rate? What was that rate? Have students do research to find Galileo's contributions to understanding the answers to these problems. Galileo showed that all falling bodies fall at the same rate, regardless of mass. L3 **Linguistic**

Teacher FYI

A negative number multiplied by a positive number results in a negative number. Because time is always positive, a negative acceleration multiplied by a positive time will always give a negative change in velocity.

Calculating Acceleration, continued

Figure 11 What will the graph show if the car comes to a stop? The line will slope downward until it reaches the horizontal axis, which is zero velocity.

Reading Check

Answer by a horizontal line

3 Assess

Reteach

Draw the following speed-time graph on the board: straight line sloping up, flat line, straight line sloping partway down, another flat line, then a curving line down. **Where does the graph show positive acceleration?** sloping up **Negative acceleration?** sloping down **No acceleration?** flat **Constant acceleration?** any straight line L2

LS **Visual-Spatial**

Challenge

Ask students to draw a speed-time graph showing an object at a constant acceleration of 8 m/s² from rest for 10 s. Have them use points on this graph to calculate the average speed after 8 seconds and the distance traveled in 8 seconds. The average speed is (speed after 8 sec − initial speed) ÷ 2 = (64 m/s − 0 m/s) ÷ 2 = 32 m/s. The distance traveled in 8 seconds is 32 m/s × 8 = 256 m. L2

LS **Logical-Mathematical**

Assessment

Portfolio Ask students to make a speed-time graph for a possible trip from their homes to school. The graph should indicate where students speed up, slow down, or move at constant speed and give an idea of the comparative speeds and accelerations. Use **PASC**, p. 111. P

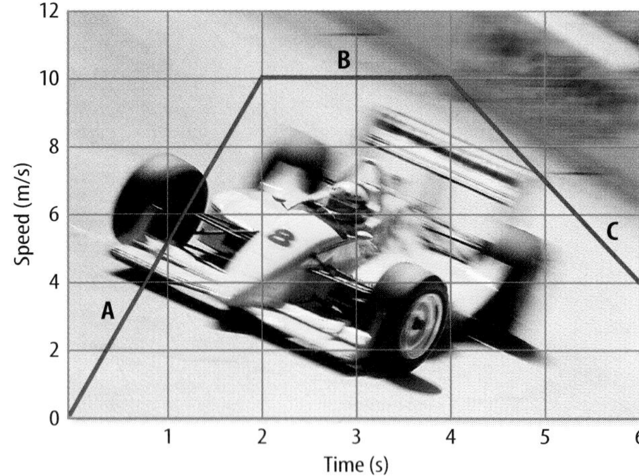

Figure 11
The speed-time graph can be used to find acceleration. When the line rises, the object is speeding up. When it is horizontal, the acceleration is zero. When the line falls, the object is slowing down.

Graphing Accelerated Motion

The motion of an object that is accelerating can be shown with a graph. For this type of graph, speed is plotted on the vertical axis and time on the horizontal axis. Take a look at **Figure 11.** On section A of the graph, the speed changes from 0 m/s to 10 m/s during the first 2 s. The acceleration over this time period is 5 m/s^2. The object is speeding up, so the acceleration is positive. Look at the line in section A. It slopes upward to the right. An object that is speeding up will always have a line on a speed-time graph that slopes upward.

Now look at section C. Between 4 s and 6 s the speed changes from 10 m/s to 4 m/s. The acceleration is –3 m/s^2. The object is slowing down, so the acceleration is negative. On the speed-time graph, the line in section C is sloping downward to the right. An object that is slowing down will always have a line on a speed-time graph that slopes downward.

On section B, where the line is horizontal, the change in speed is zero. So a horizontal line on the speed-time graph represents an acceleration of zero or constant speed.

How is an acceleration of zero represened on a speed-time graph?

Section 2 Assessment

1. A runner accelerates from 0 m/s to 3 m/s in 12 s. What was the acceleration?
2. A speed-time graph shows a line sloping downward. How was the speed changing?
3. In what three ways can acceleration change an object's motion?
4. An object falls with an acceleration of 9.8 m/s^2. What is its speed after 2 s?
5. **Think Critically** You start to roll backward down a hill on your bike, so you use the brakes to stop your motion. In what direction did you accelerate?

Skill Builder Activities

6. **Forming Operational Definitions** Give an operational definition of acceleration. **For more help, refer to the Science Skill Handbook.**
7. **Making and Using Graphs** A sprinter had the following speeds at different times during a race: 0 m/s at 0 s, 4 m/s at 2 s, 7 m/s at 4 s, 10 m/s at 6 s, 12 m/s at 8 s, and 10 ms at 10 s. Plot these data on a speed-time graph. During what time intervals is the acceleration positive? Negative? Is the acceleration ever zero? **For more help, refer to the Science Skill Handbook.**

Answers to Section Assessment

1. (3 m/s − 0 m/s) ÷ 12 s = 0.25 m/s²
2. Speed was decreasing.
3. slow it down, speed it up, or turn it
4. 9.8 m/s² × 2 s = 19.6 m/s
5. Against the motion; you accelerated uphill.
6. Acceleration is a change in the motion of an object.
7. Check students' graphs; positive: from 0 s to 8 s; negative: from 8 s to 10 s; the acceleration is zero for a split second as it changes from positive to negative between 8 and 10 s.

176 CHAPTER 6 Motion and Momentum

Momentum

Mass and Inertia

The world you live in is filled with objects in motion. How can you describe these objects? Objects have many properties such as color, size, and composition. One important property of an object is its mass. The **mass** of an object is the amount of matter in the object. In SI units the unit for mass is the kilogram.

Any object that is in motion has mass. What is different about the motion of objects that have different masses? Would you have to define velocity and acceleration differently for objects with different masses? The answer is no. Velocity and acceleration are defined the same way for all objects, regardless of their mass. However, objects with different mass are different in an important way.

Think about what happens when you try to stop someone who is rushing toward you. A small child is easy to stop. A large adult is hard to stop. The more mass an object has, the harder it is to slow it down, speed it up, or turn it. This tendency of an object to resist a change in its motion is called **inertia.** Objects with more mass have more inertia, as shown in **Figure 12.** The more mass an object has, the harder it is to change its motion.

As You Read

***What* You'll Learn**

- **Explain** the difference between mass and inertia.
- **Define** momentum.
- **Predict** motion using the law of conservation of momentum.

Vocabulary

mass
inertia
momentum
law of conservation of momentum

***Why* It's Important**

Objects in motion have momentum. The motion of objects after they collide depends on their momentum.

Figure 12
The more mass an object has, the greater its inertia is. A table-tennis ball responds to a gentle hit that would only slightly move a tennis ball.

Section Assessment Planner

Portfolio
Curriculum Connection, p. 178

Performance Assessment
Math Skills Activity, p. 178
Skill Builder Activities, p. 182
See page 190 for more options.

Content Assessment
Section, p. 182
Challenge, p. 182
Chapter, pp. 190–191

SECTION 3

Momentum

1 Motivate

Bellringer Transparency

Display the Section Focus Transparency for Section 3. Use the accompanying Transparency Activity Master. L2 ELL

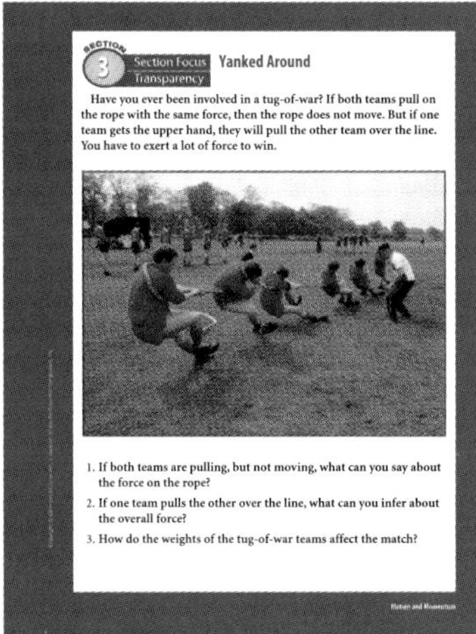

Section 3 Section Focus Transparency **Yanked Around**

Have you ever been involved in a tug-of-war? If both teams pull on the rope with the same force, then the rope does not move. But if one team gets the upper hand, they will pull the other team over the line. You have to exert a lot of force to win.

1. If both teams are pulling, but not moving, what can you say about the force on the rope?
2. If one team pulls the other over the line, what can you infer about the overall force?
3. How do the weights of the tug-of-war teams affect the match?

Tie to Prior Knowledge

Ask students if any of them have dogs they take for walks using a leash. Ask whether it is harder to hold back a charging German shepherd or a charging chihuahua. Tell students the larger dog has more inertia than the small dog and that they will be studying inertia in this section.

Resource Manager

Chapter Resources Booklet
Transparency Activity, p. 46
Directed Reading, pp. 21, 22

2 Teach

Mass and Inertia

Many people confuse mass and weight. Mass measures the amount of matter in an object. For a given object, mass is constant. Weight measures the force of gravity on an object. Weight changes when the force of gravity changes. On the Moon, which has one-sixth the gravity of Earth, your weight would be one-sixth its value on Earth, but your mass would stay the same.

Momentum

Life Science INTEGRATION

Predators often prey on animals that are smaller than they are. However, predators that hunt in groups may pursue game that is larger.

Math Skills Activity

National Math Standards

Correlation to Mathematics Objectives

1, 2, 4, 6, 8, 9

Answer to Practice Problem

p = mv = 10,000 kg × 15 m/s = 150,000 kg × m/s

Life Science INTEGRATION

A running animal has momentum. A small animal might be able to turn more quickly than a larger pursuing predator, because the smaller animal has less momentum. The larger an animal is and the faster it runs, the harder it is to turn or stop. Research the sizes of some predators and their usual prey.

Momentum

You know that the faster a bicycle moves, the harder it is to stop. Just as increasing the mass of an object makes it harder to stop, increasing the speed or velocity of an object also makes it harder to stop. The **momentum** of an object is a measure of how hard it is to stop the object. This depends on the object's mass and velocity. The momentum of an object can be calculated from this equation.

$$\text{momentum} = \text{mass} \times \text{velocity}$$

Momentum is usually symbolized by p. If m stands for mass and v stands for velocity, this equation can be written like this.

$$p = mv$$

According to this equation, the momentum increases if the mass of the object or its velocity increases. Mass is measured in kilograms and velocity has units meter per second, so momentum has units of kilograms multiplied by meters per second (kg·m/s). Also, because velocity includes a direction, momentum has a direction that is the same direction as its velocity.

Math Skills Activity

Calculating Momentum

Example Problem

Calculate the momentum of a 14 kg bicycle traveling north at 2 m/s.

Solution

1. *This is what you know:* mass: $m = 14$ kg; velocity: $v = 2$ m/s north
2. *This is what you need to find:* momentum: p
3. *This is the equation you need to use:* $p = mv$
4. *Substitute the known values:* $p = 14 \text{ kg} \times 2 \text{ m/s north}$ $= 28 \text{ kg·m/s north}$

Check your answer by dividing your momentum calculation by the mass of the bicycle. Do you calculate the velocity given in the problem?

Practice Problem

A 10,000-kg train is traveling east at 15 m/s. Calculate the momentum of the train.

For more help, refer to the Math Skill Handbook.

178 CHAPTER 6 Motion and Momentum

Curriculum Connection

Physical Education Momentum and inertia are part of all sports. Ask each student to choose a sport and prepare a poster illustrating how momentum and inertia are important in that sport. Possibilities include the inertia of a runner racing around an oval track, the momentum of a soccer ball going past a goalie, and the inertia of a wrestler. L2

LS Visual-Spatial P

Resource Manager

Chapter Resources Booklet

Enrichment, p. 32

Reinforcement, p. 29

Conservation of Momentum

If you've ever played billiards, you know that when the cue ball hits another ball, the motion of both balls changes. The cue ball slows down, and may change direction, so its momentum decreases. Meanwhile, the other ball starts moving, so its momentum increases. It seems as if momentum is transferred from the cue ball to the other ball.

In fact, during the collision the momentum lost by the cue ball was gained by the other ball. This means that the total momentum of both balls was the same just before and just after the collision. This is true for any collision, as long as no outside forces such as friction act on the objects and change their speeds after the collision. According to the **law of conservation of momentum,** the total momentum of objects that collide with each other is the same before and after the collision. This is true for the collisions of the billiard balls shown in **Figure 13,** as well as for atoms, cars, football players, or any other matter.

Figure 13
When the cue ball hits the other billiard balls, it slows down because it transfers part of its momentum to the other billiard balls. *What would happen to the speed of the cue ball if all of its momentum were transferred to the other billiard balls?*

Using Momentum Conservation

Outside forces such as gravity and friction are almost always acting on objects that are colliding. However, sometimes the effects of these forces are small enough that they can be ignored. The law of conservation of momentum can predict how the motions of objects will change after a collision.

There are many ways collisions can occur. Sometimes the objects that collide will bounce off each other, like the bowling ball and bowling pins in **Figure 14A.** In some collisions, objects will stick to each other after the collision, like the two football players in **Figure 14B.** In this type of collision, the law of conservation of momentum enables the speeds of the objects after the collision to be calculated.

Figure 14
In these collisions, the total momentum before the collision equals the total momentum after the collision.

A When the bowling ball hits the pins, some of its momentum is transferred to the pins. The ball and the pins move away from each other.

B When one player tackles the other they both change speeds, but momentum is conserved.

Conservation of Momentum

Caption Answer

Figure 13 It would drop to zero.

Use an Analogy

People sometimes use the word momentum to say things such as "The push for reform is gaining momentum." **How is this analogous to the use of the word momentum in physical science?** Both suggest motion and that as momentum increases, something becomes harder to stop. L2 **Linguistic**

Teacher FYI

There are two types of collisions. In an elastic collision, both momentum and mechanical energy are conserved. In an inelastic collision, momentum is conserved but kinetic energy is not. In some inelastic collisions the final kinetic energy is less than the initial kinetic energy because some of it is converted to heat energy in the collision. In other inelastic collisions, the final kinetic energy is greater because internal energy is released in the collision. In both cases, total energy is conserved.

Using Momentum Conservation

Make a Model

Have students model collisions using marbles in a pie pan. As more marbles are added or the marbles move faster, they collide more frequently. If students keep the pie pans moving at a steady rate, the speeds of the marbles even out over time as faster marbles transfer momentum to slower marbles in collisions. L2 ELL **Kinesthetic**

Inclusion Strategies

Learning Disabled Help these students follow conservation of momentum using physical models. Use sliding cups, each containing a number of pennies or other identical small units. When the cups collide, the pennies can be traded between cups, but they cannot be lost from the system or added from outside. L1 **Kinesthetic**

Visual Learning

Figure 14 Ask students to use the pictures as a guide and think of other examples of collisions in which objects rebound or stick together. rebound: ice cubes in a glass, billiard balls colliding, particles colliding; stick together: catching a ball, space dust landing on a spacecraft, jumping on a skateboard L2 **Visual-Spatial**

Using Momentum Conservation, continued

Discussion

Suppose two balls approach each other at 1 m/s from opposite directions. Their total momentum is zero. After the collision, they both zoom off at 1 m/s in opposite directions. **What is their momentum?** It is still zero. **What do you know about the masses of the two balls?** The masses of the two balls are the same. Otherwise, the larger one would have transferred some of its momentum to the smaller one. L2

LS **Logical-Mathematical**

Extension

Have students find out what happens to momentum if, when they catch a backpack, they are not on skates. As you catch the backpack, you use friction to brace your feet on the floor. You slow down the pack's motion with your arms, eventually bringing it to a stop. You have to use force to do that, so momentum is no longer conserved. In the end, both your momentum and the momentum of the backpack are zero. L3 LS **Logical-Mathematical**

A 

B 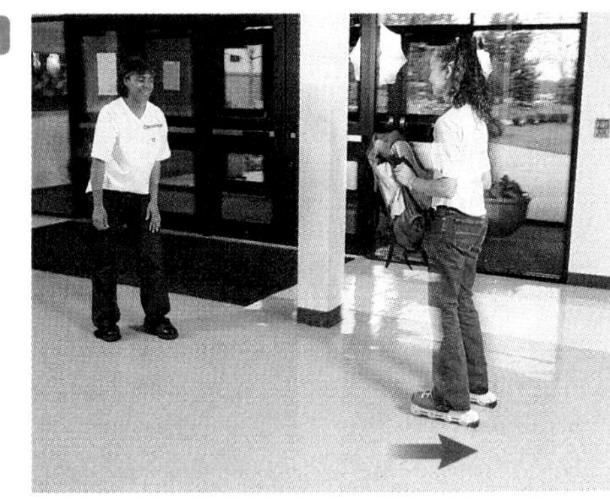

Figure 15
A Before the student and the backpack collide, she is not moving. B After the collision, the student and the backpack move together, at a slower speed than the backpack had before the collision.

Sticking Together Picture yourself standing on a pair of skates when someone throws a backpack to you, as in **Figure 15.** When you catch the backpack, you and the backpack continue to move in the same direction that the backpack was moving before the collision.

The law of conservation of momentum can be used to find your speed or velocity after you catch the backpack. Suppose a backpack with a mass of 2 kg is tossed at a speed of 5 m/s. You have a mass of 50 kg, and initially you are at rest. Then the total momentum before the collision would be

$$\begin{aligned}\text{total momentum} &= \text{momentum of backpack} + \text{your momentum}\\ &= 2\ \text{kg} \times 5\ \text{m/s} + 50\ \text{kg} \times 0\ \text{m/s}\\ &= 10\ \text{kg·m/s}\end{aligned}$$

After the collision, the total momentum remains the same and only one object is moving. It has a combined mass of you and the backpack. You can use the equation for momentum to find the new velocity.

$$\begin{aligned}\text{total momentum} &= (\text{mass of backpack} + \text{your mass}) \times \text{velocity}\\ 10\ \text{kg·m/s} &= (2\ \text{kg} + 50\ \text{kg}) \times \text{velocity}\\ 10\ \text{kg·m/s} &= (52\ \text{kg}) \times \text{velocity}\\ 0.2\ \text{m/s} &= \text{velocity}\end{aligned}$$

This is your velocity right after you catch the backpack. The final velocity in much less than the initial velocity of the backpack. The velocity decreases because the mass of you and the backpack together is much greater than the mass of the backpack alone.

As you continue to move on your skates, the force of friction between the ground and the skates slows you down. As a result, the momentum of you and the backpack together continually decreases until you come to a stop.

LAB DEMONSTRATION

Purpose to observe and measure momentum during an inelastic collision
Materials balance, 2 toy cars, 2 metersticks, timer
Preparation Set up a straight course bounded by two metersticks set end to end.
Procedure Measure the mass of each toy car. Write the numbers on the board. Place one car at the zero mark of the second meter stick. Push the other car so that it starts rolling at the zero mark of the first meterstick and hits the first car. Measure the time it takes the rolling car to reach the standing car, and measure the time and distance the two cars roll after the collision. Using your measurements, calculate momentum before and after the collision.

Assessment

Was momentum conserved in this collision? Answers will depend on experimental results, but momenta should be close. **If not, why not?** Some momentum was lost to heat in the collision.

Figure 16

The law of conservation of momentum can be used to predict the results of collisions between different objects, whether they are subatomic particles smashing into each other at enormous speeds, or the collisions of marbles, as shown on this page. What happens when one marble hits another marble initially at rest? The results of the collisions depend on the masses of the marbles.

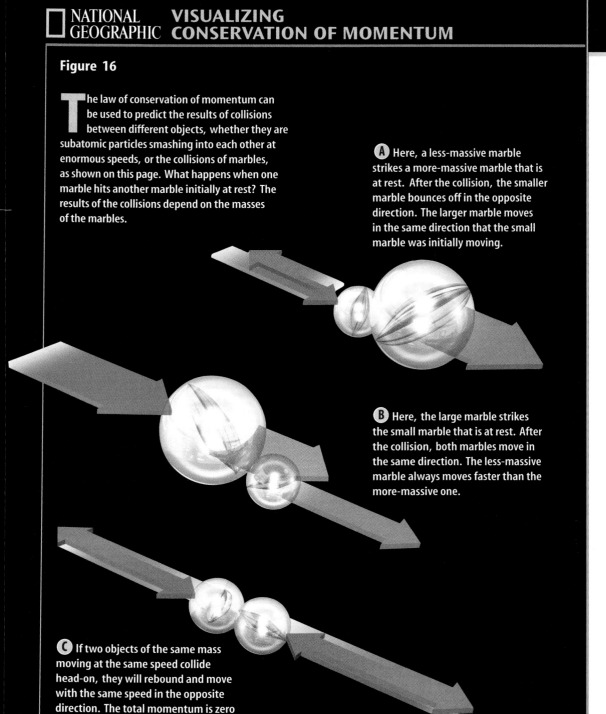

A Here, a less-massive marble strikes a more-massive marble that is at rest. After the collision, the smaller marble bounces off in the opposite direction. The larger marble moves in the same direction that the small marble was initially moving.

B Here, the large marble strikes the small marble that is at rest. After the collision, both marbles move in the same direction. The less-massive marble always moves faster than the more-massive one.

C If two objects of the same mass moving at the same speed collide head-on, they will rebound and move with the same speed in the opposite direction. The total momentum is zero before and after the collision.

Visualizing Conservation of Momentum

Have students examine the pictures and read the captions. Then ask the following questions.

If a small car is stopped at a traffic light and is hit from behind by a truck, what will happen? Both vehicles will move forward, with the car moving faster than the truck.

What will happen if two marbles of the same mass, traveling toward each other, collide? The marbles will collide and reverse directions, moving away from each other at the same speed as before the collision.

Activity

Have small groups of students tape two metersticks to a flat surface. The space between them should be wide enough to allow marbles to travel in the space. Have students form a ramp by placing one end of a grooved ruler on two or three books and the other end at one end of the track. They should place three marbles in the track and roll one marble down the ruler into the track and observe what happens. Ask students to repeat the procedure rolling two and three marbles down the ramp together. Ask them to explain their observations in terms of conservation of momentum. L2 IS **Kinesthetic**

Resource Manager

Chapter Resources Booklet
Activity Worksheet, pp. 5–6

Science Inquiry Labs, p. 27

3 Assess

Reteach

Toss a ping-pong ball, tennis ball, and basketball to students. Have the students compare the amounts of force they had to use to stop the three balls and the inertias of the three balls. It took the most force to stop the basketball, which had the most inertia. It took less force to stop the tennis ball, which had less inertia than the basketball. It took very little force to stop the ping-pong ball, which had the least inertia. L2

ELL LS **Kinesthetic**

Challenge

Kinetic energy, $0.5mv^2$, is also conserved in an elastic collision. Suppose a 10-kg ball moving 10 m/s hits a 1-kg ball at rest. **Can all the momentum be transferred to the second ball so the first is at rest and both momentum and kinetic energy are conserved?** No; the momentum before the collision is 10 kg × 10 m/s = 100 kg × m/s. Kinetic energy is 10 kg × 100 $m^2s^2/2$ = 500 kg × m^2/s^2. If the first ball stops, the velocity of the second ball has to be 100 m/s. In this case, kinetic energy will be 1 kg × 10,000 $m^2s^2/2$ = 5,000 kg × m^2/s^2. This does not equal the kinetic energy before the collision, which was 500 kg × m^2/s^2.

L3 LS **Logical-Mathematical**

Assessment

Process Ask students to design an experiment to demonstrate qualitatively what happens to velocity in different collisions. Use **PASC,** p. 95.

Figure 17
When bumper cars collide, they bounce off each other, and momentum is transferred.

Bouncing Off In some types of collisions the objects involved, like the bumper cars in **Figure 17,** bounce off each other when they collide. The law of conservation of momentum can be used to help determine how these objects move after they collide. The results of collisions between two objects of various masses are shown in **Figure 16.**

For example, what happens if two objects of the same mass moving with the same speed collide head on? The objects reverse their direction of motion after the collision but still move with the same speed. What happens when one object directly hits an object at rest and both have the same mass? The first object transfers all of its momentum to the object at rest and comes to a stop.

Section 3 Assessment

1. When a player uses a golf club to hit a ball, how is momentum transferred?
2. What is the momentum of a 0.1-kg mass moving at 5 m/s?
3. A system of two balls has a momentum of 1 kg·m/s. Ball A has a momentum of −3 kg·m/s. What is the momentum of ball B?
4. **Think Critically** You watch a film in which one billiard ball rolls forward and hits another. After the collision the second billiard ball rolls away and the first one is motionless. Can you tell whether the film is being shown forward or in reverse?

Skill Builder Activities

5. **Predicting** Two balls of the same mass move toward each other with equal speeds and in the opposite direction. Predict how the balls will move after the collision if they collide and then stick together. Explain your answer. **For more help, refer to the Science Skill Handbook.**
6. **Solving One-Step Equations** A 0.2-kg ball is moving left at 3 m/s. It strikes a 0.5-kg ball that is at rest. Immediately after the collision, the 0.2-kg ball comes to a stop. How fast is the 0.5-kg ball moving if the momentum is conserved? **For more help, refer to the Math Skill Handbook.**

Answers to Section Assessment

1. from club to ball
2. p = mv = 0.1 kg × 5 m/s = 0.5 kg × m/s
3. 4 kg × m/s
4. No, momentum could be transferred either way.
5. Momentum must be conserved. Before the collision, momentum is zero because $m_1v_1 = -m_2v_2$, so $m_1v_1 + m_2v_2 = 0$. After the collision momentum must be zero also. If the balls stick together, the only way for momentum to be zero is if the balls are at rest.
6. Before the collision momentum is 0.2 kg × 3 m/s + 0.5 kg × 0 = 0.6 kg × m/s left. After the collision, momentum must also be 0.6 kg × m/s left, so 0.5 kg × v = 0.6 kg × m/s left. v = 0.6 kg × m/s left/0.5 kg = 1.2 m/s left

Activity

Collisions

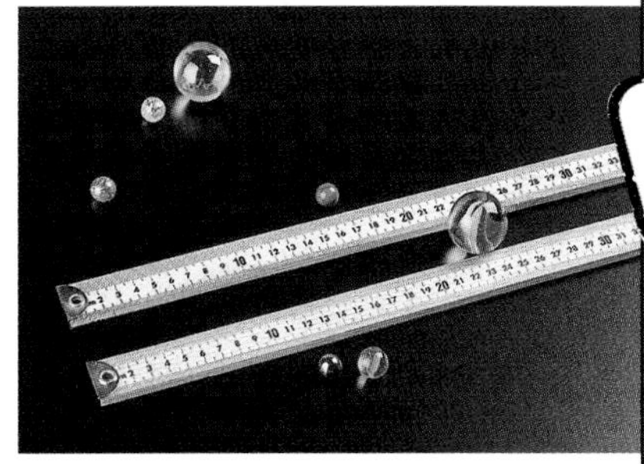

A collision occurs when a baseball bat hits a baseball, or a tennis racket hits a tennis ball. What would happen if you hit a baseball with a table-tennis paddle, or a table-tennis ball with a baseball bat? How do the masses of colliding objects change the results of collisions?

What You'll Investigate

How does changing the size and number of marbles in a collision affect the collision?

Materials

small marbles (5)
large marbles (2)
metersticks (2)
tape

Goals

- **Compare and contrast** different collisions.
- **Determine** how the speeds after a collision depend on the masses of the colliding objects.

Safety Precautions

Procedure

1. Tape the metersticks next to each other, slightly farther apart than the width of the large marbles. This limits the motion of the marbles to nearly a straight line.
2. Place a target marble in the center of the track formed by the metersticks. Place a small marble at one end of the track. Shoot this marble toward the target marble by flicking it with your finger. Describe the collision.
3. Repeat step 2, replacing the two small marbles with the two large marbles.
4. Repeat step 2, replacing the small shooter marble with a large marble.
5. Repeat step 2, replacing the small target marble with a large marble.
6. Repeat step 2, replacing the small target marble with four small marbles that are touching.
7. Place two small marbles at opposite ends of the metersticks. Shoot the marbles toward each other and describe the collision.
8. Place two large marbles at opposite ends of the metersticks. Shoot the marbles toward each other and describe the collision.
9. Place a small marble and a large marble at opposite ends of the metersticks. Shoot the marbles toward each other and describe the collision.

Conclude and Apply

1. **Compare and contrast** the results of the various types of collisions.
2. In which collisions did the shooter marble change direction? How did the mass of the target marble compare with the shooter marble in these collisions?

Communicating Your Data

Make a chart showing your results. You might want to make before-and-after sketches, with short arrows to show slow movement and long arrows to show fast movement. **For more help, refer to the Science Skill Handbook.**

Activity

BENCH TESTED

Purpose Students observe the change in momentum in different collisions. L2 LS **Kinesthetic**

Process Skills identifying and manipulating variables, observing and inferring, interpreting data, drawing conclusions

Time Required 50 minutes

Safety Precautions Make sure no loose marbles remain on the classroom floor when the experiment is done.

Teaching Strategy Caution students not to shoot the marbles so hard that they bounce or make the other marbles jump when they hit them.

Answers to Questions

1. When marbles are the same size, the momentum of the shooter is completely transferred to the other marble or to the last marble in a line of marbles. A large shooter slows down and sets the target moving. A small shooter stops and sets the target moving. Two small marbles rebound off each other at the same speed as before the collision.
2. The shooter changed direction when it hit a target marble with more mass than itself.

Assessment

Process Predict what will happen when a small shooter hits a line of five large target marbles. The shooter will stop, and the last target marble in line will be set in motion, with a velocity smaller than that of the shooter. Use **Performance Assessment in the Science Classroom,** p. 89.

Communicating Your Data

Students can work together on a large chart to be displayed as a class poster.

Activity BENCH TESTED

Recognize the Problem

Purpose

Students will construct a car that will protect an egg from a rapid deceleration. LS **Kinesthetic and Logical-Mathematical**

Time Required

approximately 70 minutes

Alternate Materials

The list for materials that can be used to make the car is nearly endless. Don't use items that are sharp or breakable.

Safety Precautions

Since the cars are intended to crash, students should wear safety goggles.

Form a Hypothesis

Possible Hypothesis

The egg will be most likely to survive in a car that gradually brings the egg to a stop, thus cushioning it.

Test Your Hypothesis

Possible Procedures

The car must roll freely to be fast. The egg must be protected or slowed gradually to a stop by some sort of layers or barriers or restraints.

Teaching Strategy

Students will often have elaborate, complex ideas that may be too difficult to be practical. Try to steer them clear of these without stifling their creativity.

Activity Design Your Own Experiment

Car Safety Testing

Imagine that you are a car designer. How can you create an attractive, fast car that is safe? When a car crashes, the passengers have inertia that can keep them moving. How can you protect the passengers from stops caused by sudden head-on impacts?

Recognize the Problem

How can you design a car to win a race and protect the passenger in a head-on crash at the end of the race?

Form a Hypothesis

Develop a hypothesis about how to design a car to quickly and safely deliver a plastic egg through a race course and a crash at the end.

Goals

- **Construct** a fast car.
- **Design** a safe car that will protect a plastic egg from the effects of inertia when the car crashes.

Safety Precautions

Protect your eyes from possible flying objects.

Possible Materials

insulated foam meat trays or fast food trays
insulated foam cups
straws
straight pins
tape
plastic eggs

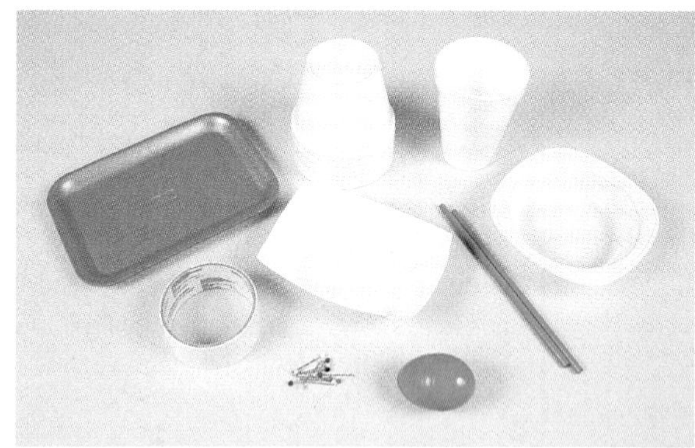

Inclusion Strategies

Learning Disabled Students who have learning challenges are sometimes good at manipulating or building things. Perhaps one student in a group could design an idea, and another could physically make it.

Resource Manager

Chapter Resources Booklet
Activity Worksheet, pp. 7–8
Cultural Diversity, p. 63

Using Scientific Methods

Test Your Hypothesis

Plan

1. Be sure your group has agreed on the hypothesis statement.
2. **Sketch** the design for your car. List the materials you will need.
3. As a group, make a detailed list of the steps you will take to test your hypothesis.
4. Gather the materials you will need to carry out your experiment.

Do

1. Make sure your teacher approves your plan before you start. Include any changes suggested by your teacher in your plans.
2. Carry out the experiment as planned.
3. **Write** any observations that you made while doing your experiment. Include suggestions for improving your design.

Analyze Your Data

1. **Compare** your car design to the designs of the other groups. What made the fastest car fast? What slowed the slowest car?
2. **Compare** your car's safety features to those of the other cars. What protected the eggs the best? How could you improve the unsuccessful designs?
3. What effect would decreasing the speed of your car have on the safety of the egg?

Draw Conclusions

1. How did the best designs protect the egg?
2. If you were designing cars, what could you do to better protect passengers from sudden stops?

Communicating Your Data

Write a descriptive paragraph on how a car could be designed to protect its passengers effectively. Include a sketch of your designs.

Expected Outcome

Cars that cushioned the egg will be most successful. Students should try to discover why some were successful and others weren't.

Analyze Your Data

1. Fast cars often were constructed better. They are often lighter, with less friction and resistance.
2. Eggs with layers of protection to gradually slow them to a stop work best.
3. Decreasing the speed would give the egg a better chance for survival because the egg would experience a smaller deceleration.

Error Analysis

Ask students to name features that allowed eggs to survive.

Draw Conclusions

1. The best designs protected the egg in the same way seat belts and airbags protect people.
2. Possible answer: provide devices to restrain people from being thrown as the car stops

Content Divide the class into groups and ask each group to develop and perform a short skit comparing the car with the egg to people in a real car. Use **PASC**, p. 147.

Active Reading

Syntheseis Journal In this strategy, students reflect on a project, a paper, or a performance in light of their own experiences and plan for personal application. Ask students to write a Synthesis Journal entry for this activity. Have each student divide a sheet of paper into three sections. For this activity, have them record "What I did," "What I learned," and "How I can use it."

To complete their writing, students could also briefly research how the automobile industry tests vehicle safety. Students may also find photos or videos of industry tests to incorporate into their writing.

Oops! Accidents in SCIENCE

SOMETIMES GREAT DISCOVERIES HAPPEN BY ACCIDENT!

Content Background

Not all boomerangs return to their throwers. A true boomerang is nothing more than a curved stick that is thrown. The early boomerangs used for hunting by peoples of many ancient cultures (including many tribes in the western United States) were much longer, straighter, and heavier than the more familiar returning types. Returning boomerangs are too light and thin to do much damage to any living thing. Returning boomerangs became popular primarily as playthings for Aborigines in Australia. Some hunters there used them to imitate hawks in flight and so serve as a decoy to drive other game birds into nets strung from trees.

Discussion

A returning boomerang is simple to make. **Why, then, do you think no one ever has found a very practical use for the returning boomerang?** Possible answers: They are probably difficult to throw accurately. Also, if you were to hit something with a returning boomerang, the boomerang probably wouldn't have enough momentum left to return to you. L2 LS **Logical-Mathematical**

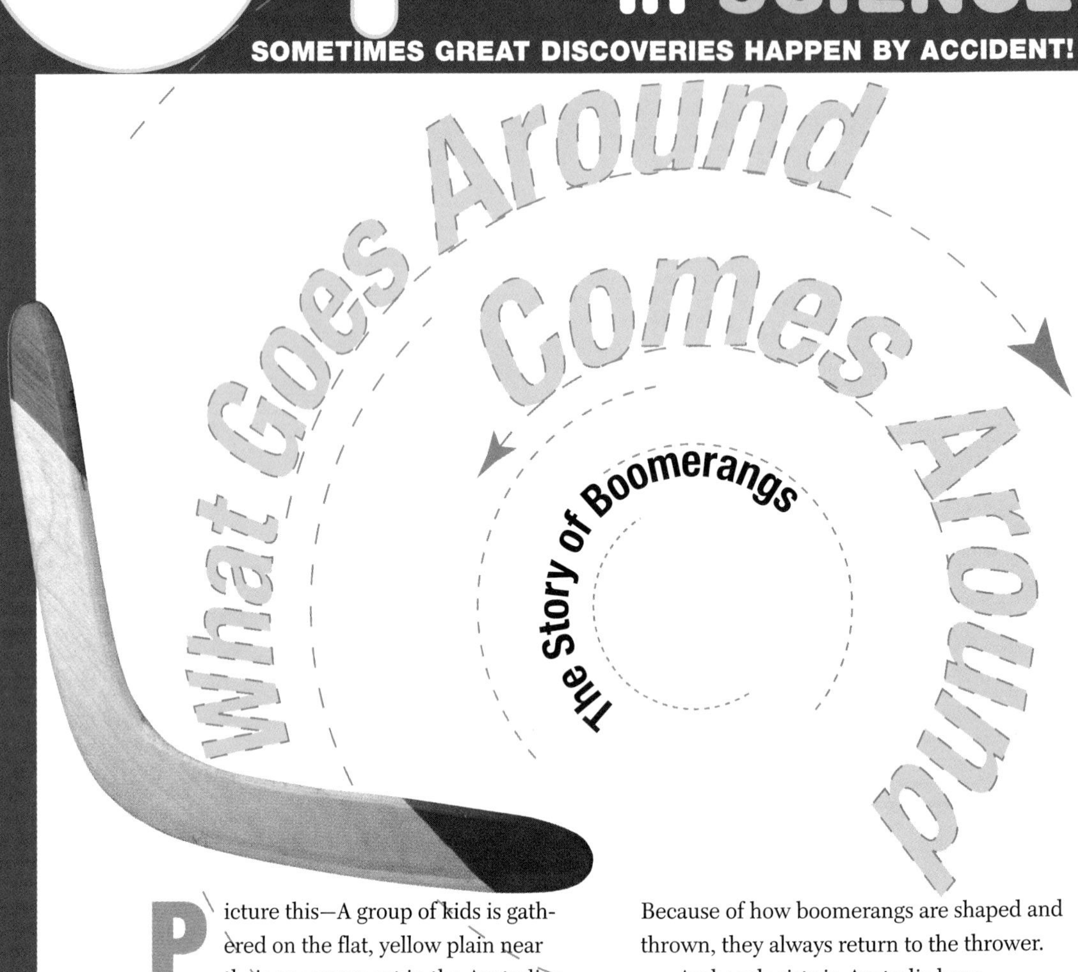

Picture this—A group of kids is gathered on the flat, yellow plain near their encampment in the Australian outback. One youth steps forward. With the flick of an arm, the youth flings a long, flat, angled stick that soars and spins into the sky. The stick's path curves until it returns—spinning right back into the thrower's hand. Another thrower steps forward with another stick. The contest goes on all afternoon.

That scene could be from today. Or, it could have taken place 10,000—or more—years ago. The kids were throwing boomerangs—elegantly curved sticks. Because of how boomerangs are shaped and thrown, they always return to the thrower.

Archaeologists in Australia have unearthed boomerangs from 15,000 years ago. The boomerang developed from simple clubs that early people threw to stun and kill prey animals. These people became very good throwers and probably soon discovered that clubs with different shapes had different properties in the air. They gradually refined their designs into a throwing stick resembling today's boomerangs. As boomerangs became more refined, they also might have been used for fun.

186

Resources for Teachers and Students

Boomerang: Behind an Australian Icon, by Philip Jones, Ten Speed Press, 1997.

Bout Boomerangs, America's Silent Sport: History, Heroes & How To, by Kelly B. Sagert, Plant Speak Products and Publications, 1996.

Many Happy Returns, Quarterly Newsletter of the United States Boomerang Association.

Modern boomerangs are made from many things—from paper to wood.

Making a Comeback

There are many different types of boomerangs, but they have a few things in common, each of which is related to how a boomerang works. First, boomerangs are flat on the bottom and rounded on the top. This provides lift, just like it does for an airplane wing. When you hold a boomerang to throw it, the flat side is against your palm and your fingers curl around the curved side.

Second, boomerangs are angled. This makes the boomerang spin in the air. When it is thrown correctly, a boomerang spins at right angles to the ground, not horizontally like the wings of an airplane.

Today, using boomerangs for fun is a popular sport. World-class boomerangers compete at the World Boomerang Championships. Throwers compete in events such as Time Aloft, in which they try to keep the boomerang up in the air as long as possible. In Team Terror, a grueling relay race, throwers perform difficult throws and trick catches, such as behind-the-back or under-the-leg. They use ultra-modern boomerangs—some of which look nothing like the old-style classic boomerang. But they carry on an ancient Australian tradition of competing for the best throw.

CONNECTIONS **Design** **Boomerangs are made from materials ranging from a piece of paper to expensive hardwood. Research at the library to find instructions for making boomerangs. After you and your friends build some boomerangs, have a competition of your own.**

SCIENCE Online
For more information, visit science.glencoe.com.

Activity

Take students outside and have volunteers throw boomerangs, first from a horizontal starting position and then from varying angles. Ask students what is different about the paths of the boomerangs. A boomerang thrown from a horizontal position flies off until it stops spinning and then falls. The boomerangs thrown at different angles curve. Explain to students that when a boomerang is thrown from an angle slightly different from the horizontal, the motions of its wings and speed through the air cause it to experience a force that makes it circle back to the thrower. L2 LS **Kinesthetic**

Analyze the Event

What characteristics in the flights of early, non-returning boomerangs do you think made people try to make returning boomerangs? Possible answers: They may have seen the boomerangs curving in flight. They also may have noticed how lighter and more curved sticks behaved differently in flight.

CONNECTIONS

Possible competition exercises might include the best catch, longest flight time, and greatest curvature achieved in flight. Students might also construct targets to hit or paper barriers to attempt to curve through on their return flights. Caution students that, although boomerangs are very light, they can hit hard when moving fast, so students should be careful when throwing them and wear protective goggles and gloves.

SCIENCE Online

Internet Addresses

Explore the Glencoe Science Web site at **science.glencoe.com** to find out more about topics in this feature.

Chapter 6 Study Guide

Reviewing Main Ideas

Preview

Students can answer the questions in their Science Journals. Discuss the answers as you go through the chapter. **LS Linguistic**

Review

Students can write their answers, then compare them with those of other students. **LS Interpersonal**

Reteach

Students can look at the illustrations and describe details that support the main ideas of the chapter. **LS Visual-Spatial**

Answers to Chapter Review

SECTION 1

5. object A

SECTION 2

4. The object speeds up during the second time interval when the slope is positive, and slows down during the first time interval when the slope is negative.

SECTION 3

3. measure the mass and velocity of each; no; conservation of momentum

Chapter 6 Study Guide

Reviewing Main Ideas

Section 1 What is motion?

1. An object is in motion if it is changing position.
2. Distance measures the length of the path that an object follows during its motion. Displacement is the change in position between the starting point and the ending point, as well as the direction from the start to end points.
3. Speed is a measure of how quickly the position of an object changes. Velocity includes the speed and direction of motion.
4. Speed can be calculated using the following equation:

$$\text{speed} = \frac{\text{distance}}{\text{time}}$$

5. A distance-time graph can be used to show motion. *Which object is moving the fastest?*

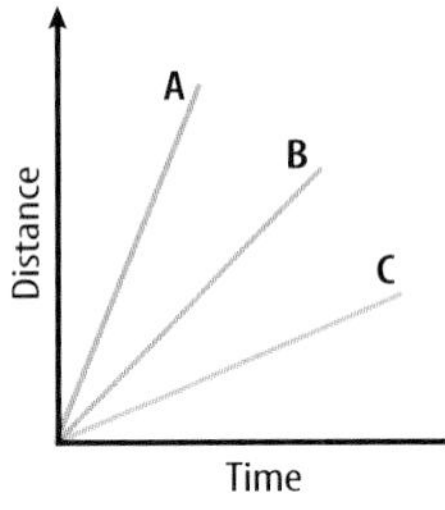

Section 2 Acceleration

1. Acceleration is a measure of how quickly velocity changes. It includes a direction.
2. Acceleration can cause an object to speed up, slow down, or turn.
3. When an object speeds up or slows down, its acceleration can be calculated by

$$a = \frac{(s_f - s_i)}{t}$$

4. An object's acceleration can be determined from the speed-time graph. *During what time intervals is the object speeding up? Slowing down? How can you tell?*

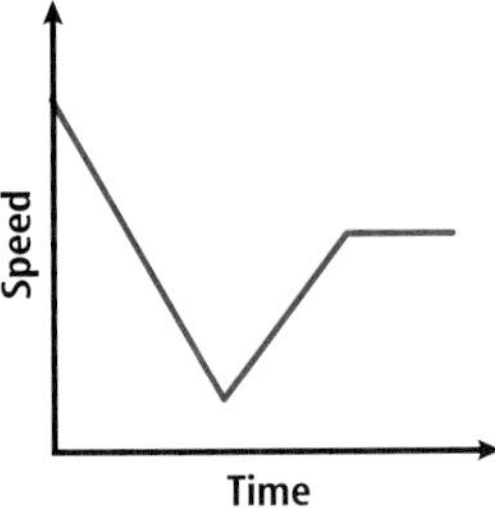

Section 3 Momentum

1. The momentum of an object is a measure of how hard it is to stop the object. Momentum is the product of mass and velocity. It has a direction.
2. Momentum is transferred from one object to another in a collision.
3. According to the law of conservation of momentum, the total amount of momentum of a group of objects does not change unless outside forces act on the objects. *How could you determine the total momentum of these balls? Would it change after they collide? Why or why not?*

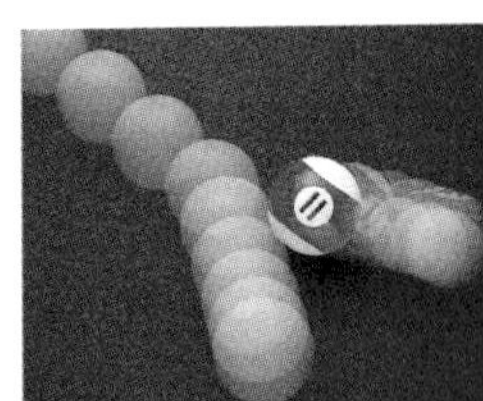

FOLDABLES Reading & Study Skills — After You Read

Use each vocabulary word on your Foldable in a sentence about motion and write it next to the definition of the word.

FOLDABLES Reading & Study Skills — After You Read

After students have read the chapter and completed the Foldable described in Before You Read, have them do the activity on the student page.

Dinah Zike

Chapter 6 Study Guide

Visualizing Main Ideas

Complete the following table comparing different descriptions of motion.

Describing Motion

Quantity	Definition	Direction?
Distance	change in position	no
Displacement	direction and amount of change in position	yes
Speed	rate of change in position	no
Velocity	rate of change in position and direction	yes
Acceleration	rate of change in velocity	yes
Momentum	mass times velocity	yes

Vocabulary Review

Vocabulary Words

a. acceleration
b. average speed
c. inertia
d. instantaneous speed
e. law of conservation of momentum
f. mass
g. momentum
h. speed
i. velocity

Using Vocabulary

Explain the relationship between each pair of words.

1. speed, velocity
2. velocity, acceleration
3. velocity, momentum
4. momentum, law of conservation of momentum
5. mass, momentum
6. mass, inertia
7. momentum, inertia
8. average speed, instantaneous speed

THE PRINCETON REVIEW Study Tip

Pay attention to the chapter's illustrations. Try to figure out exactly the main point each picture is trying to stress.

Chapter 6 Study Guide

Visualizing Main Ideas

See student page.

Vocabulary Review

Using Vocabulary

1. Both measure rate of change in position, but velocity includes a direction.
2. Both are rates of change in motion. Velocity is the rate of change in position, and acceleration is the rate of change in velocity.
3. Velocity is part of momentum, which is mass multiplied by velocity.
4. Momentum is the mass of an object times its velocity. The law of conservation of momentum states that the total momentum of a group of objects is the same before and after they collide unless some outisde force acts on the objects.
5. Mass is part of momentum, which is mass multiplied by velocity.
6. Mass is a measure of inertia.
7. An object always has inertia. It only has momentum when it is in motion.
8. Both measure rate of change in position. Instantaneous speed gives the speed at a moment in time; average speed gives the average of instantaneous speeds over a given time or distance interval.

IDENTIFYING Misconceptions

Assess

Use the assessment as follow-up to page 164F after students have completed the chapter.

Materials protractor, paper, ruler, string

Procedure Have each student use the protractor to draw a large circle and label four points 90 degrees apart A, B, C and D.

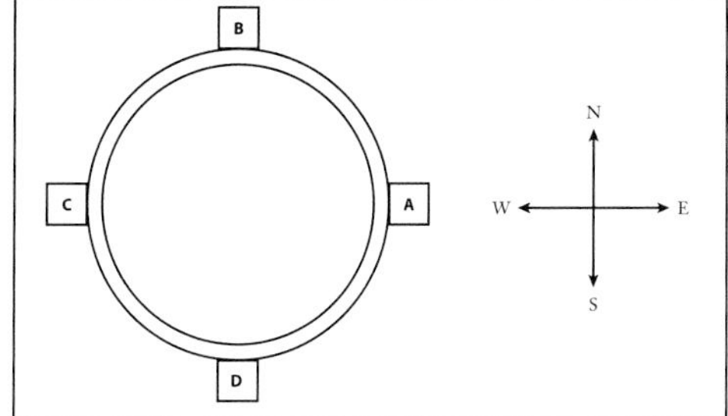

Have them place an object at point A, and tell them the object will travel around the circle. Their mission is to find the object's distance traveled and displacement at points B, C, and D. Tell them the top of the paper is north.

Expected Outcome Ways to find the distance traveled include using the string to measure the circle or using the formula for a perimeter of a circle.

Chapter 6 Assessment

Checking Concepts

1. D
2. B
3. A
4. A
5. C
6. B
7. D
8. B
9. C
10. D

Thinking Critically

11. It increases; when you divide by a smaller time, the speed increases.
12. No; displacement measures the shortest distance between A and B. The car may have driven a longer total distance than this displacement.
13. No; it is following a circular path around Earth, so its direction, and thus acceleration, is always changing.
14. It is very massive, so the momentum it transfers to the wall is large.

Chapter 6 Assessment

Checking Concepts

Choose the word or phrase that best answers the question.

1. What measures the quantity of matter?
   A) speed **C)** acceleration
   B) weight **D)** mass

2. A 2-kg ball has a momentum of 10 kg·m/s. What is its speed?
   A) 1 m/s **C)** 10 m/s
   B) 5 m/s **D)** 20 m/s

3. Which of the following is NOT an example of acceleration?
   A) a leaf falling at constant speed
   B) a car slowing down
   C) a skater spinning
   D) a dog running faster and faster

4. Speed measures change in which of the following?
   A) distance **C)** velocity
   B) momentum **D)** acceleration

5. A parked car is hit by a moving car, and the two cars stick together. How does the speed of the combined cars compare to the speed of the car before the collision?
   A) Combined speed is the same.
   B) Combined speed is greater.
   C) Combined speed is smaller.
   D) Any of these could be true.

6. A car travels for half an hour at 40 km/h. How far does it travel?
   A) 10 km **C)** 40 km
   B) 20 km **D)** 80 km

7. What is a measure of inertia?
   A) weight **C)** momentum
   B) gravity **D)** mass

8. What is 18 cm/h north an example of?
   A) speed **C)** acceleration
   B) velocity **D)** momentum

9. Ball A bumps into ball B. Which of the following is the same before and after the collision?
   A) the momentum of ball A
   B) the momentum of ball B
   C) the sum of the momentums
   D) the difference in the momentums

10. What measures the change in velocity?
    A) speed **C)** momentum
    B) force **D)** acceleration

Thinking Critically

11. You run 100 m in 25 s. If you later run the same distance in less time, does your average speed increase or decrease? Explain.

12. A car drives from point A to point B. Can its displacement be greater than the total distance that it traveled? Explain.

13. The Moon moves around Earth at close to constant speed. Does this mean it is not accelerating? Explain.

14. When a wrecking ball hits a wall, it is not moving fast. How can it have enough momentum to knock down a wall?

Developing Skills

15. **Predicting** A rocket accelerates at 12 m/s^2 for 8 s. If it starts at rest, what is its final speed?

16. **Measuring in SI** Measure the width of your desk. Time a pen rolling across the desk, and find the speed of the pen.

Chapter Assessment Planner

Portfolio Encourage students to place in their portfolios one or two items of what they consider to be their best work. Examples include:

- Extension, p. 170
- Assessment, p. 176
- Curriculum Connection, p. 180

Performance Additional performance assessments, Performance Task Assessment Lists, and rubrics for evaluating these activities can be found in Glencoe's **Performance Assessment in the Science Classroom.**

17. **Making Models** The molecules in a gas are modeled as colliding balls. If the molecules all have the same mass, explain what can happen when a fast-moving molecule hits a slow-moving molecule. Include a sketch.

18. **Recognizing Cause and Effect** Roll one marble into the end of a line of stationary marbles. What do you observe? Why do you think this happened?

19. **Making and Using Graphs** Use the speed-time graph below. What is the acceleration between $t = 0$ and $t = 3$?

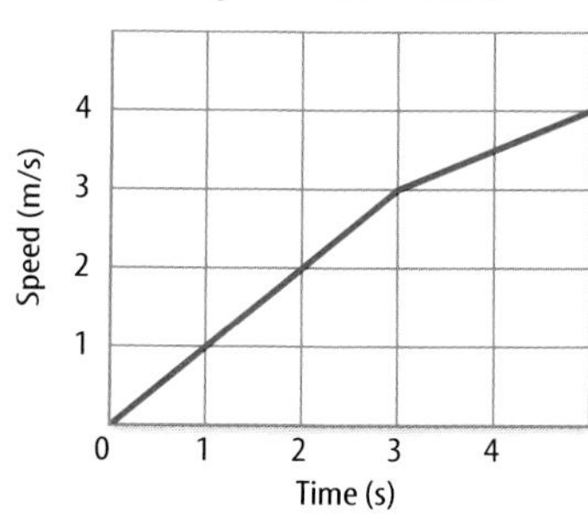

Performance Assessment

20. **Demonstration** Set up a racetrack and make rules for the type of motion allowed. Demonstrate how to measure distance, measure time, and calculate speed accurately.

21. **Poster** Make a poster showing how motion graphs represent acceleration and constant speed. Use both speed-time and distance-time graphs.

Technology

Go to the Glencoe Science Web site at **science.glencoe.com** or use the **Glencoe Science CD-ROM** for additional chapter assessment.

Test Practice

Two students are comparing the performance of different electric toy cars by measuring the top speed each car can reach. They also calculate the momentum of each car at its top speed. The table below summarizes their results.

Performance of Toy Cars

Car	Mass (kg)	Velocity (m/s)	Momentum (kg·m/s)
A	1.0	2	2.0
B	1.0	5	5.0
C	0.5	15	7.5
D	3.0	2	6.0
E	2.0	4	8.0

Study the table and answer the following questions.

1. According to the table, which statement best describes how the students calculated the momentum of the cars?
   A) momentum = mass + velocity
   B) momentum = mass − velocity
   C) momentum = mass × velocity
   D) momentum = mass/velocity

2. About how much greater is the momentum of the car with the least mass than that of the car with the greatest mass?
   F) 1.5 kg·m/s
   G) 4.0 kg·m/s
   H) 1.0 kg·m/s
   J) 0.5 kg·m/s

Chapter 6 Assessment

THE PRINCETON REVIEW **Test Practice**

The Test-Taking Tip was written by The Princeton Review, the nation's leader in test preparation.

1. C
2. F

Developing Skills

15. $12\ m/s^2 \times 8\ s = 96\ m/s$
16. Check students' work.
17. Momentum is transferred, so the faster molecule slows down and the slower molecule speeds up.
18. The final marble rolls away with the same momentum the incoming marble had. Momentum was transferred from one marble to the other, but was not lost.
19. $1\ m/s^2$

Performance Assessment

20. Check students' work. Use **PASC**, p. 97.
21. Check students' work. Use **PASC**, p. 145.

Assessment Resources

Reproducible Masters

Chapter Resources Booklet
Chapter Review, pp. 37–38
Chapter Tests, pp. 39–42
Assessment Transparency Activity, p. 49

Glencoe Science Web site
Interactive Tutor
Chapter Quizzes

Glencoe Technology
Assessment Transparency
Interactive CD-ROM Chapter Quizzes
ExamView Pro Test Bank
Vocabulary PuzzleMaker Software
MindJogger Videoquiz DVD/VHS

CHAPTER 7 FORCE AND NEWTON'S LAWS

Section/Objectives	Standards		Activities/Features
	National	State/Local	
Chapter Opener	See p. 5T for a Key to Standards.		**Explore Activity:** Analyze motion on a ramp, p. 193 **Before You Read,** p. 193
Section 1 Newton's First Law 3 sessions 1.5 blocks 1. **Identify** forces at work. 2. **Distinguish** between balanced and net forces. 3. **Demonstrate** Newton's first law of motion. 4. **Explain** how friction works.	National Content Standards: UCP3, A1, B2, E1		**Life Science Integration,** p. 195 **Science Online,** p. 197 **MiniLAB:** Observing Friction, p. 198
Section 2 Newton's Second Law 3 sessions 1.5 blocks 1. **Explain** Newton's second law of motion. 2. **Explain** why the direction of force is important.	National Content Standards: UCP3, B2, E1		**Astronomy Integration,** p. 201 **Math Skills Activity:** Calculating Force Using Newton's Second Law, p. 203
Section 3 Newton's Third Law 4 sessions 2 blocks 1. **Identify** the relationship between the forces that objects exert on each other.	National Content Standards: UCP3, A1, B2, E1, E2, F4, F5		**Science Online,** p. 208 **Visualizing Newton's Laws in Sports,** p. 209 **MiniLAB:** Measuring Force Pairs, p. 211 **Activity:** Balloon Races, p. 213 **Activity:** Modeling Motion in Two Directions, pp. 214–215 **Science and Society:** Air Bag Safety, pp. 216–217

Activity Materials	Reproducible Resources	Section Assessment	Technology
Explore Activity: 2 meter-sticks, 3 books, marble	**Chapter Resources Booklet** Foldables Worksheet, p. 17 Directed Reading Overview, p. 19 Note-taking Worksheets, pp. 33–35	Glencoe's Assessment Advantage	
MiniLAB: flat bar of soap, flat eraser, key, hard-sided notebook	**Chapter Resources Booklet** Transparency Activity, p. 44 MiniLAB, p. 3 Lab Activity, pp. 9–12 Enrichment, p. 30 Reinforcement, p. 27 Directed Reading, p. 20 Transparency Activity, pp. 47–48 **Home and Community Involvement,** p. 23	Portfolio Assessment, p. 198 Performance MiniLAB, p. 198 Skill Builder Activities, p. 199 Content Section Assessment, p. 199	Section Focus Transparency Teaching Transparency Interactive CD-ROM/DVD Guided Reading Audio Program
Need materials? Contact Science Kit at 1-800-828-7777 or www.sciencekit.com on the Internet.	**Chapter Resources Booklet** Transparency Activity, p. 45 Lab Activity, pp. 13–16 Enrichment, p. 31 Reinforcement, p. 28 Directed Reading, p. 21 Transparency Activity, pp. 47–48 **Mathematics Skill Activities,** p. 9	Portfolio Science Journal, p. 205 Performance Math Skills Activity, p. 203 Skill Builder Activities, p. 206 Content Section Assessment, p. 206	Section Focus Transparency Teaching Transparency Interactive CD-ROM/DVD Guided Reading Audio Program
MiniLAB: 2 spring scales **Activity:** balloons of different sizes and shapes, drinking straws, string, tape, meterstick, stopwatch **Activity:** masking tape, stop-watch, meterstick, 2 spring scales, plastic lid, golf ball	**Chapter Resources Booklet** Transparency Activity, p. 46 MiniLAB, p. 4 Enrichment, p. 32 Reinforcement, p. 29 Directed Reading, pp. 20, 22 Activity Worksheet, pp. 5–6, 7–8 Transparency Activity, pp. 47–48 **Lab Management and Safety,** p. 65	Portfolio Assessment, p. 211 Performance MiniLAB, p. 211 Skill Builder Activities, p. 212 Content Section Assessment, p. 212	Section Focus Transparency Teaching Transparency Interactive CD-ROM/DVD Guided Reading Audio Program

End of Chapter Assessment

Glencoe's Assessment Advantage

Blackline Masters	Technology	Professional Series
Chapter Resources Booklet Chapter Review, pp. 37–38 Chapter Tests, pp. 39–42 **Standardized Test Practice by The Princeton Review,** pp. 31–34	MindJogger Videoquiz CD-ROM Explorations and Quizzes Vocabulary Puzzle Makers ExamView Pro Test Bank Interactive Lesson Planner Interactive Teacher's Edition	Performance Assessment in the Science Classroom (PASC)

Transparencies

Section Focus

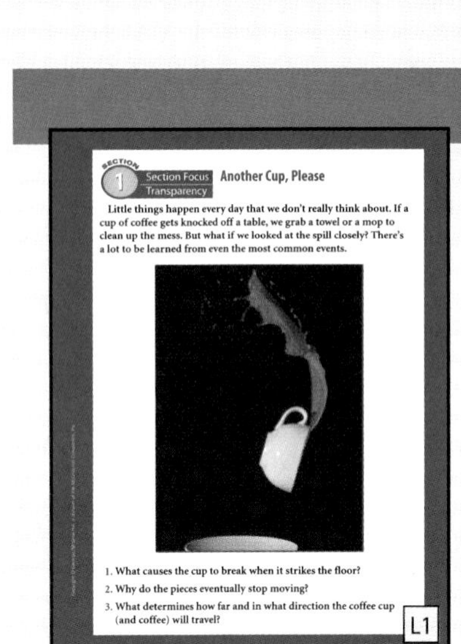
Section 1 Section Focus Transparency **Another Cup, Please**

Little things happen every day that we don't really think about. If a cup of coffee gets knocked off a table, we grab a towel or a mop to clean up the mess. But what if we looked at the spill closely? There's a lot to be learned from even the most common events.

1. What causes the cup to break when it strikes the floor?
2. Why do the pieces eventually stop moving?
3. What determines how far and in what direction the coffee cup (and coffee) will travel?

L1

Section 2 Section Focus Transparency **Loop D'loop**

Have you ever gone upside down on a roller coaster? What kept the car on the track? In the cartoon, Calvin is pulling the sled far up the hill so he can get a good start.

1. Does it make a difference where Calvin begins his descent? Why or why not?
2. How does friction figure into Calvin's scheme?
3. How will gravity affect Calvin if he makes it into the loop?

L1

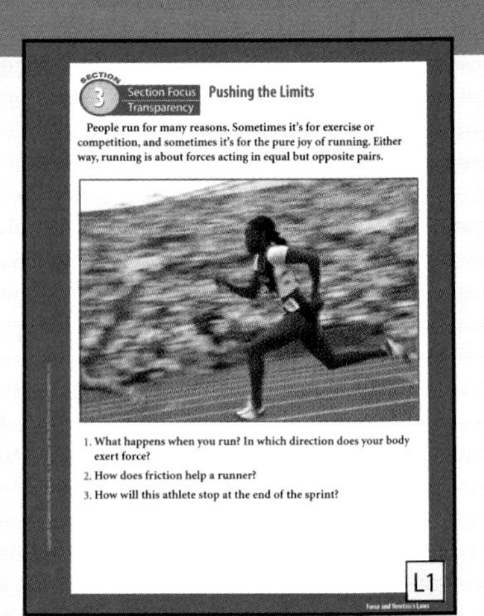
Section 3 Section Focus Transparency **Pushing the Limits**

People run for many reasons. Sometimes it's for exercise or competition, and sometimes it's for the pure joy of running. Either way, running is about forces acting in equal but opposite pairs.

1. What happens when you run? In which direction does your body exert force?
2. How does friction help a runner?
3. How will this athlete stop at the end of the sprint?

L1

This is a representation of key blackline masters available in the Teacher Classroom Resources. See Resource Manager boxes within the chapter for additional information.

Assessment

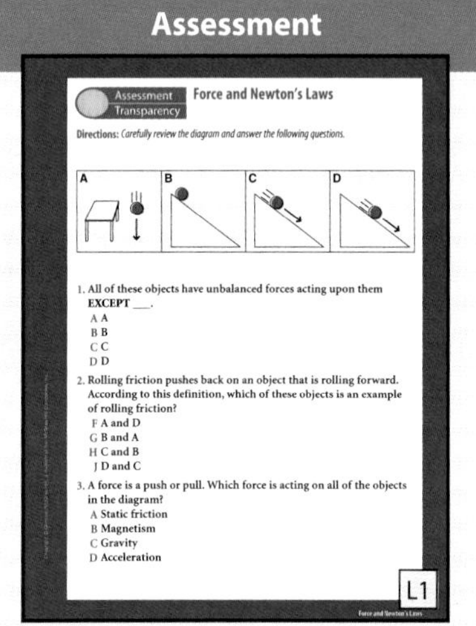
Assessment Transparency **Force and Newton's Laws**

Directions: *Carefully review the diagram and answer the following questions.*

1. All of these objects have unbalanced forces acting upon them EXCEPT ___.
   A A
   B B
   C C
   D D
2. Rolling friction pushes back on an object that is rolling forward. According to this definition, which of these objects is an example of rolling friction?
   F A and D
   G B and A
   H C and B
   J D and C
3. A force is a push or pull. Which force is acting on all of the objects in the diagram?
   A Static friction
   B Magnetism
   C Gravity
   D Acceleration

L1

Teaching

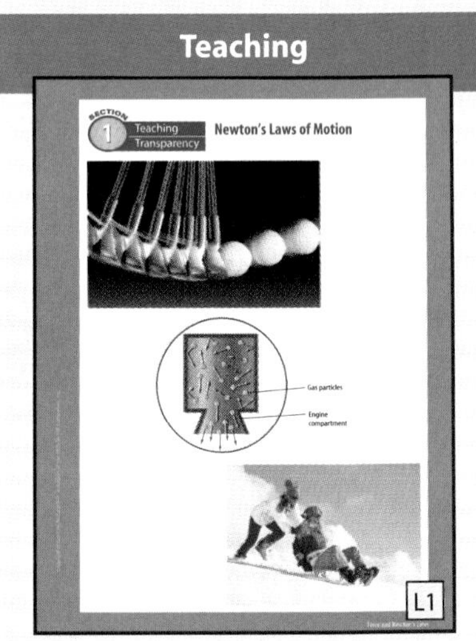
Section 1 Teaching Transparency **Newton's Laws of Motion**

L1

Key to Teaching Strategies

The following designations will help you decide which activities are appropriate for your students.

- **L1** Level 1 activities should be appropriate for students with learning difficulties.
- **L2** Level 2 activities should be within the ability range of all students.
- **L3** Level 3 activities are designed for above-average students.
- **ELL** ELL activities should be within the ability range of English Language Learners.
- **COOP LEARN** Cooperative Learning activities are designed for small group work.
- **LS** Multiple Learning Styles logos, as described on page 22T, are used throughout to indicate strategies that address different learning styles.
- **P** These strategies represent student products that can be placed into a best-work portfolio.

Hands-on Activities

Activity Worksheets

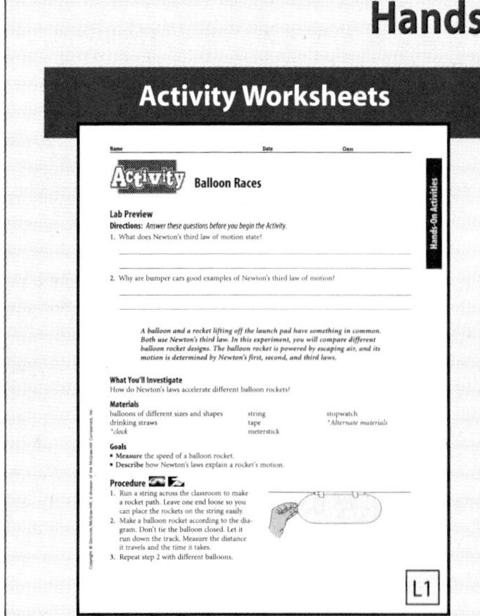
Name Date Class

Activity **Balloon Races**

Hands-On Activities

Lab Preview

Directions: *Answer these questions before you begin the Activity.*

1. What does Newton's third law of motion state?
2. Why are bumper cars good examples of Newton's third law of motion?

A balloon and a rocket lifting off the launch pad have something in common. Both use Newton's third law. In this experiment, you will compare different balloon rocket designs. The balloon rocket is powered by escaping air, and its motion is determined by Newton's first, second, and third laws.

What You'll Investigate

How do Newton's laws accelerate different balloon rockets?

Materials

balloons of different sizes and shapes, drinking straws, *clock, string, tape, meterstick, stopwatch

*Alternate materials

Goals

- **Measure** the speed of a balloon rocket.
- **Describe** how Newton's laws explain a rocket's motion.

Procedure

1. Run a string across the classroom to make a rocket path. Leave one end loose so you can place the rockets on the string easily.
2. Make a balloon rocket according to the diagram. Don't tie the balloon closed. Let it run down the track. Measure the distance it travels and the time it takes.
3. Repeat step 2 with different balloons.

L1

Laboratory Activities

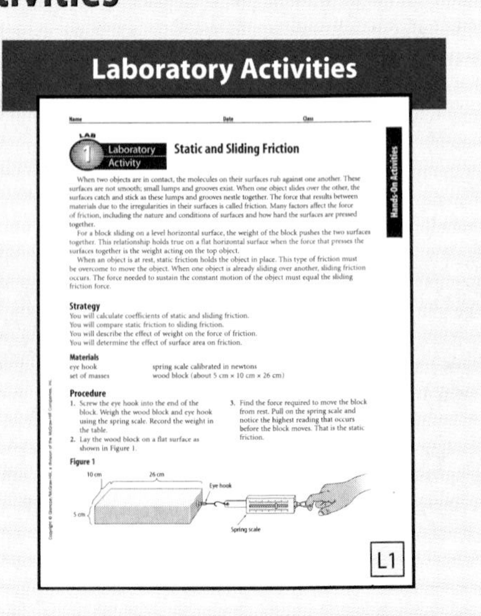
Name Date Class

LAB 1 Laboratory Activity **Static and Sliding Friction**

Hands-On Activities

When two objects are in contact, the molecules on their surfaces rub against one another. These surfaces are not smooth; small lumps and grooves exist. When one object slides over the other, the surfaces catch and stick as these lumps and grooves nestle together. The force that results between materials due to the irregularities in their surfaces is called friction. Many factors affect the force of friction, including the nature and conditions of surfaces and how hard the surfaces are pressed together.

For a block sliding on a level horizontal surface, the weight of the block pushes the two surfaces together. This relationship holds true on a flat horizontal surface when the force that presses the surfaces together is the weight acting on the top object.

When an object is at rest, static friction holds the object in place. This type of friction must be overcome to move the object. When one object is already sliding over another, sliding friction occurs. The force needed to sustain the constant motion of the object must equal the sliding friction force.

Strategy

You will calculate coefficients of static and sliding friction.
You will compare static friction to sliding friction.
You will describe the effect of weight on the force of friction.
You will determine the effect of surface area on friction.

Materials

eye hook, set of masses, spring scale calibrated in newtons, wood block (about 5 cm × 10 cm × 26 cm)

Procedure

1. Screw the eye hook into the end of the block. Weigh the wood block and eye hook using the spring scale. Record the weight in the table.
2. Lay the wood block on a flat surface as shown in Figure 1.
3. Find the force required to move the block from rest. Pull on the spring scale and notice the highest reading that occurs before the block moves. That is the static friction.

Figure 1

L1

Meeting Different Ability Levels

Content Outline

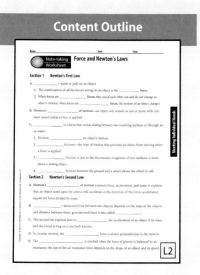

Note-taking Worksheet — Force and Newton's Laws

L2

Reinforcement

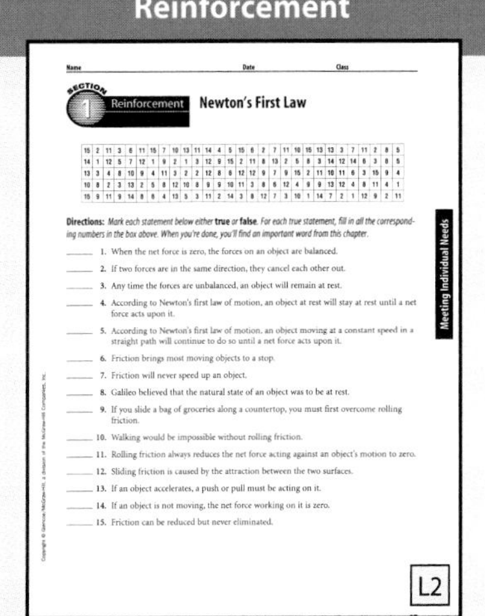

Reinforcement — Newton's First Law

L2

Directed Reading

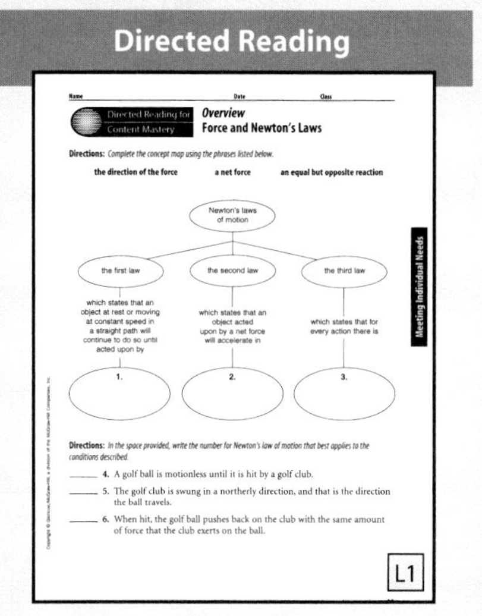

Directed Reading for Content Mastery — Overview: Force and Newton's Laws

L1

Enrichment

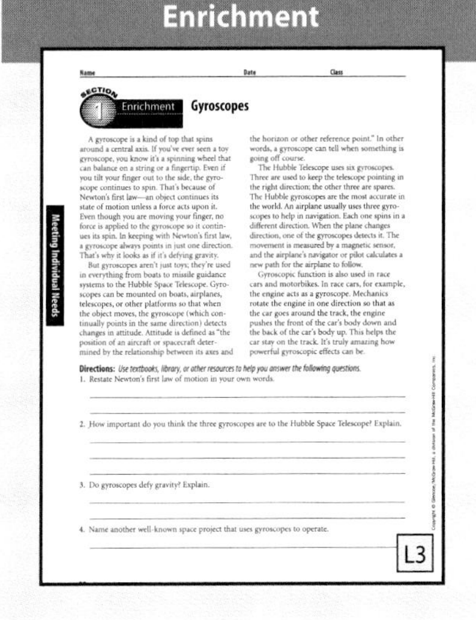

Enrichment — Gyroscopes

L3

Spanish Directed Reading

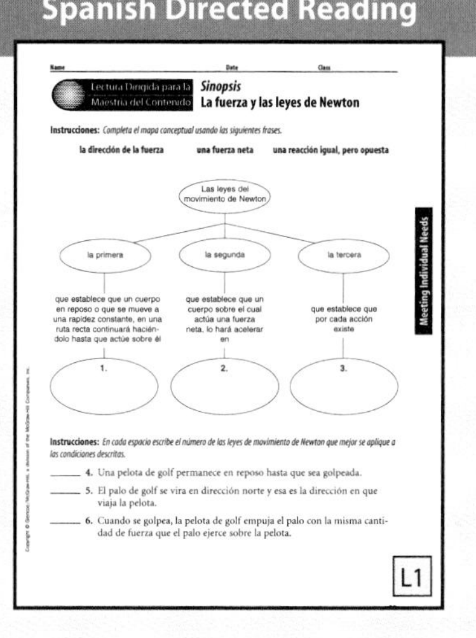

Lectura Dirigida para la Maestría del Contenido — Sinopsis: La fuerza y las leyes de Newton

L1

Assessment

Chapter Tests

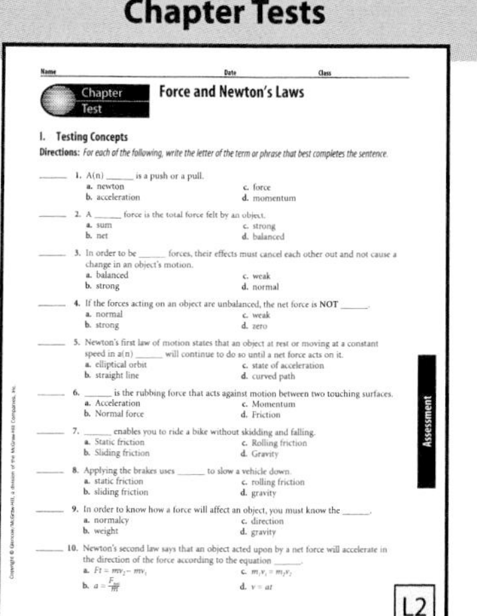

Chapter Test — Force and Newton's Laws

L2

Test Practice Workbook

L2

Chapter Review

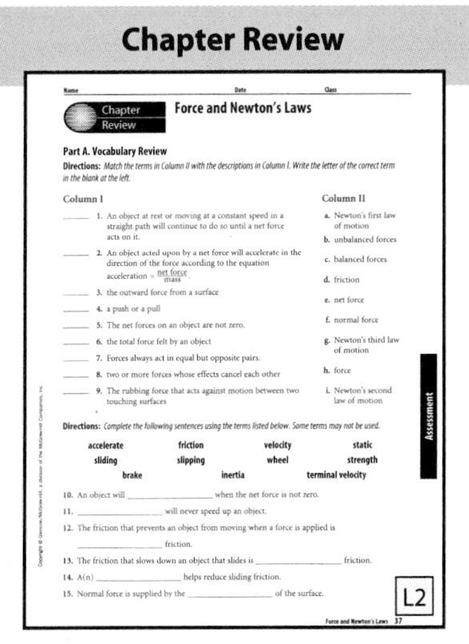

Chapter Review — Force and Newton's Laws

L2

Science Content Background

SECTION 1 Newton's First Law

Force

There are four fundamental forces. Gravity is the attraction between all matter. Electromagnetism is the attraction or repulsion due to electric and magnetic fields. The strong nuclear force holds neutrons and protons together in the nucleus. The weak nuclear force is involved in some types of radioactive decay—it can change a proton into a neutron and vice versa.

The examples of force in this chapter are mostly gravity and contact forces. A contact force is a force that exists because of the contact between objects. Gravity is a force that can act at a distance.

> **Student Misconception**
>
> An object at rest resists acceleration only because of friction.
>
> **Refer to the facing page for teaching strategies to address this misconception. Refer to pages 194–199 for content related to this topic.**

Newton's First Law of Motion

The idea that rest is natural and an object in motion must have a force to keep it moving is intuitive to many people. You might want to bring up examples such as a probe shot deep into space. If it doesn't come near any object (to attract it gravitationally), it can keep going without an engine propelling it. If students report seeing fictional spaceships on television come to a dead stop whenever the engine has problems, ask them to explain why this is problematic.

The fact that there is no difference between rest and uniform linear motion is a result of reference frames. If you are riding on a train at a constant velocity of 35 km/h west, to the passenger sitting opposite you, you appear to be still. To a driver in a car outside, your velocity is different, depending on the velocity of the car.

Friction

The friction force depends on the nature of the surfaces in contact. Different surfaces have different coefficients of fiction. Friction depends on the normal force exerted by a surface and is not affected by the area of the surfaces in contact.

SECTION 2 Newton's Second Law

Gravity

Gravity acts between all objects. The gravity exerted on one object by another is directly proportional to the masses of the two objects and inversely proportional to the square of the distance between them, as given in the equation $F = G\, m_1 m_2/d^2$. G is the universal gravitational constant, whose value is 6.67×10^{-11} N-m^2/kg^2. For objects on Earth, d is Earth's radius, and m_1 is Earth's mass.

SECTION 3 Newton's Third Law

Action and Reaction

It is important to understand that forces in a third law pair act on different objects. You can illustrate this in class with a ball. If two students push from opposite sides of the ball with the same force, it won't move. Both forces are applied to the same object. If the students toss the ball back and forth, there are action and reaction pairs between a student's hands and the ball when they throw and catch the ball. The push of the throw exerts a force on the ball and on the student.

For additional content background on this topic, go to the Glencoe Science Web site at science.glencoe.com.

Misconceptions

Find Out What Students Think

Students may think that . . .

- **An object at rest resists acceleration only because of friction.**

Students have probably learned about friction in the past and view it as the thing that works against motion.

Demonstration

Place a small cart or car on your desk. Give it a push and give a humorous grunt to show that it is hard work to get it going. Once it is moving make the pushing seem effortless. Ask students whether they have ever had to help push a stalled car. Did they notice that it takes a lot of effort to get the car going and less effort to keep it going?

Ask students why it takes a larger force to move a stopped car than it does to push a moving car. Give students a few minutes to think about the question. Then have them share their thoughts with a partner. Ask some of the pairs to share their answers with the whole class. Finally, see if the class can come to consensus about the correct answer to this question.

Promote Understanding

Activity

Give each group a cart, a hanging spring scale that reads force in Newtons, five objects with different masses, and string. Show them how to find the amount of force needed to pull the cart as shown in the diagram below.

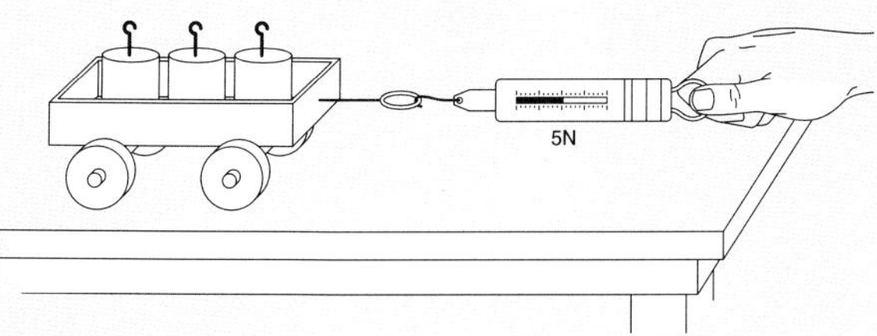

- Have students practice slowly pulling the cart and measuring the maximum force needed to get the cart moving. Then have them practice measuring the force needed to move the cart with constant velocity.

Once students are proficient in these techniques, ask them to investigate how increasing the cart's mass affects these two forces.

- They will need to know or measure the mass of the cart and the masses of each of the added objects.
- Suggest students graph their data with mass on the x-axis and force on the y-axis.

After students complete the activity, discuss with them the following questions:

- **What is the relationship between the mass of the cart and the maximum force needed to get the cart moving?** The greater the mass, the greater the force needed.
- **Why is a force needed to have the cart move with constant velocity?** to overcome friction
- **Why is the force needed to start the cart moving always greater than the force to keep it moving?** Once the cart is moving, its inertia is no longer keeping it from moving. At this point, the only force that needs to be overcome is friction.

Assess

After completing the chapter, see *Identifying Misconceptions* in the Study Guide.

Force and Newton's Laws

Chapter Vocabulary

force
net force
balanced forces
unbalanced forces
Newton's first law of motion
friction
Newton's second law of motion
weight
Newton's third law of motion
weightlessness

What do you think?

Science Journal The photograph shows a large rock balanced between rock faces. The rock doesn't move because it has no net force acting on it.

Force and Newton's Laws

This train can move! Japan's Shinkansen Bullet Train transports passengers at speeds of more than 260 km/h. It can move this fast because the engineers who built it understood the laws of motion that Isaac Newton first proposed more than 300 years ago. In this chapter, you'll learn about force and Newton's laws of motion. You'll learn why some objects move and why some stay still, and how objects exert forces on each other.

What do you think?

Science Journal Look at the picture below with a classmate. Discuss what this might be or what is happening. Here's a hint: *It's a delicate balancing act.* Write your answer or best guess in your Science Journal.

192

Theme Connection

Systems and Interactions Newton's laws of motion form a system that can be used to predict an object's future motions. Objects interacting with each other follow these laws. If you know the forces acting between objects, you can predict the objects' future motion.

Imagine being on a bobsled team speeding down an icy run. The force of gravity causes the sled to accelerate as it speeds down the course in a blur. You and your team use your bodies, brakes, and the steering mechanism to exert forces to change the sled's motion, causing it to slow down or turn. The motion of the sled as it speeds up, slows down, and turns can be explained with Newton's laws of motion. These laws tell how forces cause the motion of an object to change.

Analyze motion on a ramp

1. Lean two metersticks on three books as shown to the right. This is your ramp.
2. Tap a marble so it rolls up the ramp. Measure how far up the ramp it travels before rolling back.
3. Repeat step 2 using two books, one book, and zero books. The same person should tap with the same force each time.

Observe

Make a table to record the motion of the marble for each ramp height. What would happen if the ramp were perfectly smooth and level?

Before You Read

FOLDABLES Reading & Study Skills

Making an Organizational Study Fold **When information is grouped into clear categories, it is easier to make sense of what you are learning. Make the following Foldable to help you organize your thoughts about Newton's Three Laws of Motion.**

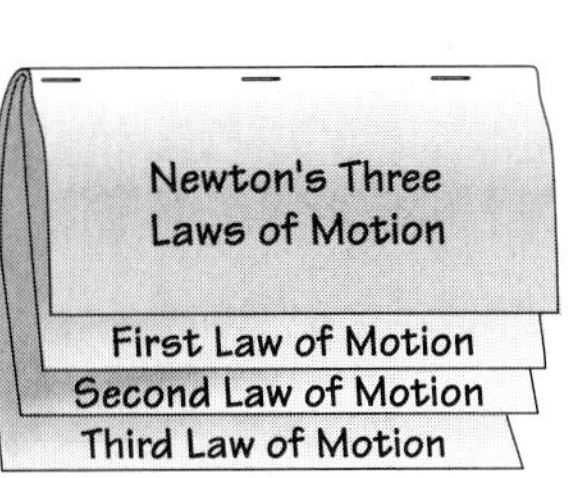

1. Stack two sheets of paper in front of you so the long side of both sheets is at the top.
2. Slide the top sheet up so that about four centimeters of the bottom sheet show.
3. Fold both sheets top to bottom to form four tabs and staple along the topfold as shown.
4. Label each flap *Newton's Three Laws of Motion, First Law of Motion, Second Law of Motion,* and *Third Law of Motion* as shown.
5. As you read the chapter, record what you learn about the laws of motion under the tabs.

193

Explore Activity

Purpose Use the Explore Activity to help students see the effect the steepness of a ramp has on the motion of a marble. L2 ELL LS **Kinesthetic**

Preparation Make sure that the books used are of similar thickness.

Materials 3 books, 2 metersticks, 1 marble

Teaching Strategies To make sure the initial velocity of the marble is constant always have the same person tap the marble.

Observe

Students' data should show that the steeper the incline, the shorter the distance traveled by the marble. If the ramp were perfectly smooth and level, the marble would slide forever.

Assessment

Oral Show students a picture of a bobsled track, ski run, or slide. Ask them to identify the points at which a rider would have maximum velocity. Ask students to write a sentence or two defending their choices. Use **Performance Assessment in the Science Classroom,** p. 159.

Before You Read

FOLDABLES Reading & Study Skills

Dinah Zike Study Fold

Purpose Students make and use a Foldable to collect and organize information on Newton's three laws of motion.

For additional help, see Foldables Worksheet, p. 17 in **Chapter Resources Booklet,** or go to the Glencoe Science Web site at **science.glencoe.com.** See After You Read in the Study Guide at the end of this chapter.

Newton's First Law

1 Motivate

Bellringer Transparency

Display the Section Focus Transparency for Section 1. Use the accompanying Transparency Activity Master. L2 ELL

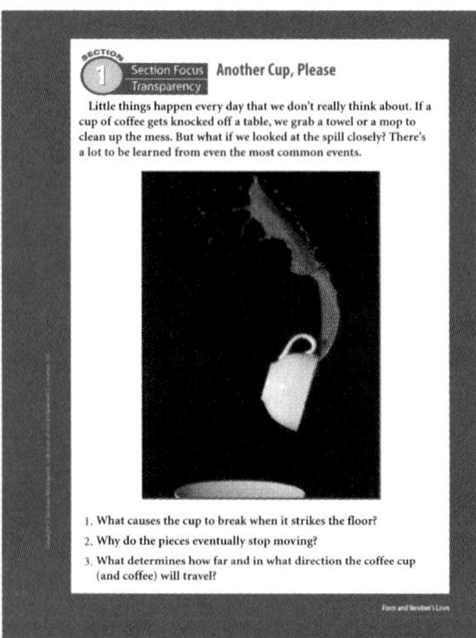

SECTION 1 Section Focus Transparency **Another Cup, Please**

Little things happen every day that we don't really think about. If a cup of coffee gets knocked off a table, we grab a towel or a mop to clean up the mess. But what if we looked at the spill closely? There's a lot to be learned from even the most common events.

1. What causes the cup to break when it strikes the floor?
2. Why do the pieces eventually stop moving?
3. What determines how far and in what direction the coffee cup (and coffee) will travel?

Force and Newton's Laws

Tie to Prior Knowledge

Push a book across your desk. Ask a volunteer to describe the motion of the book. Tell students that in this section they will learn to describe the motion of the book in terms of the forces acting on it and Newton's first law of motion.

Newton's First Law

As You Read

What You'll Learn

- **Identify** forces at work.
- **Distinguish** between balanced and net forces.
- **Demonstrate** Newton's first law of motion.
- **Explain** how friction works.

Vocabulary

force
net force
balanced forces
unbalanced forces
Newton's first law of motion
friction

Why It's Important

Newton's first law helps you understand why objects slow down and stop.

Force

A soccer ball sits on the ground, motionless, until you kick it. Your science book sits on the table until you pick it up. If you hold your book above the ground, then let it go, gravity pulls it to the floor. In every one of these cases, the motion of the ball or book was changed by something pushing or pulling on it. An object will speed up, slow down, or turn only if something is pushing or pulling on it.

A **force** is a push or a pull. Examples of forces are shown in **Figure 1.** Think about throwing a ball. Your hand exerts a force on the ball, and the ball accelerates forward until it leaves your hand. After the ball leaves your hand, gravity's force on it causes its path to curve downward. When the ball hits the ground, the ground exerts a force, stopping the ball.

A force can be exerted in different ways. For instance, a paper clip can be moved by the force a magnet exerts, Earth's gravity, or the force you exert when you pick it up. These are all examples of forces acting on the paper clip.

Figure 1
A force is a push or a pull.

B The magnet on the crane pulls the pieces of scrap metal upward.

A This golf club exerts a force by pushing on the golf ball.

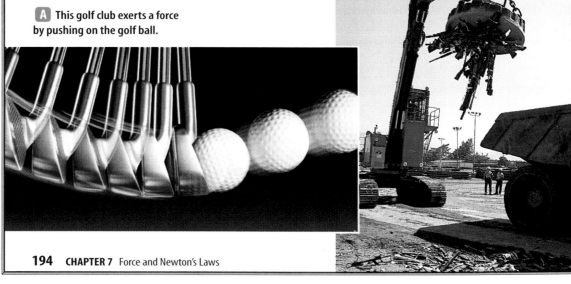

Section Assessment Planner

PORTFOLIO
Assessment, p. 198

PERFORMANCE ASSESSMENT
Try at Home MiniLAB, p. 198
Skill Builder Activities, p. 199
See page 220 for more options.

CONTENT ASSESSMENT
Section, p. 199
Challenge, p. 199
Chapter, pp. 220–221

A This door is not moving because the forces exerted on it are equal and in opposite directions.

B The door is closing because the force pushing the door closed is greater than the force pushing it open.

Figure 2
When a balanced force is applied, no change in motion occurs, but when an unbalanced force is applied, a change in motion does occur.

Combining Forces More than one force can act on an object at the same time. If you hold a paper clip near a magnet, you, the magnet, and gravity all exert forces on the paper clip. The combination of all the forces acting on an object is the **net force.** When more than one force is acting on an object, the net force determines the motion of the object. In this example, the paper clip is not moving, so the net force is zero.

How do forces combine to form the net force? If the forces are in the same direction, they add together to form the net force. If two forces are in opposite directions, then the net force is the difference between the two forces, and it is in the direction of the larger force.

Balanced and Unbalanced Forces A force can act on an object without causing it to accelerate if other forces cancel the push or pull of the force. Look at **Figure 2.** If you and your friend push on a door with the same force in opposite directions, the door does not move. Because you both exert forces of the same size in opposite directions on the door, the two forces cancel each other. Two or more forces exerted on an object are **balanced forces** if their effects cancel each other and they do not cause a change in the object's motion. If the forces on an object are balanced, the net force is zero. If the forces are **unbalanced forces,** their effects don't cancel each other. Any time the forces acting on an object are unbalanced, the net force is not zero and the motion of the object changes.

Life Science INTEGRATION

Whether you run, jump, or sit, forces are being exerted on different parts of your body. Biomechanics is the study of how the body exerts forces and how it is affected by forces acting on it. Research how biomechanics has been used to reduce job-related injuries. Write a paragraph on what you've learned in your Science Journal.

2 Teach

Force

Visual Learning

Figure 2 Point out to students the force arrows shown. Ask volunteers to identify the force represented by each arrow. L1 ELL LS Visual-Spatial

Use Science Words

Word Meaning The sum of the forces acting on an object is called the *net force*. Ask students to use a dictionary to find the meaning of the word *net*. Net is what remains after all deductions have been made. **What are other familiar uses of *net* in this sense?** Possible response: The net profit is the money earned after all expenses have been subtracted.

Life Science INTEGRATION

Researchers have used biomechanics to study such problems as repetitive strain injuries causing carpal tunnel syndrome and lower back pain.

Quick Demo

Use an equal arm balance to demonstrate the meanings of the terms *balanced* and *unbalanced*. Put materials of different mass on each side of the balance so that it is unbalanced. Then put equal masses on each side so it is balanced. L2 LS **Visual-Spatial**

Curriculum Connection

Art Mobiles are based on the principle of balanced forces. Have each student make a mobile with at least three arms. The only criterion students must follow is that each arm must be balanced. Hang students' mobiles in the classroom. L2 LS **Kinesthetic**

Resource Manager

Chapter Resources Booklet
- Transparency Activity, p. 44
- Directed Reading for Content Mastery, p. 20
- Note-taking Worksheets, pp. 33–35

IDENTIFYING Misconceptions

Some students may think that an object at rest resists acceleration only because of friction. See page 192F for teaching strategies related to this misconception.

Newton's First Law of Motion

Quick Demo

Place a cup of water on a skateboard and push it across the table to an assistant on the other side. Ask the assistant to stop the skateboard. Have paper towels handy. **What happens to the cup of water?** It keeps on moving, and it probably spills.
L2 LS **Visual-Spatial**

Activity

Have students roll a heavy ball across a large flat surface, such as the floor of the gymnasium. Have them roll the ball at different speeds and observe the motion. Ask them how they would change the path of the moving ball so that it arrived at a specified location. Make a hammer available to students so they can tap on the ball to test their plans. **How successful was your plan to direct the ball's motion?** Students often forget the tendency of the ball to stay in motion, so their efforts at redirecting it to a specific location are not successful. They may think a single tap on the side of the ball will send it to the new spot.
L2 ELL LS **Kinesthetic**

Friction

Quick Demo

Place a book on a board. Tilt the board slowly so the book does not move. Explain to students that friction is keeping the book from moving. Next, tilt the board far enough that the book begins to move. Explain that at this point the force of gravity pulling the book down is greater than the force of friction holding the book in place.
L2 ELL LS **Visual-Spatial**

Newton's First Law of Motion

If you stand on a skateboard and someone gives you a push, then you and your skateboard will start moving. You began to move when the force was applied. An object at rest—like you on your skateboard—remains at rest unless an unbalanced force acts on it and causes it to move.

Because a force had to be applied to make you move when you and your skateboard were at rest, you might think that a force has to be applied continually to keep an object moving. Surprisingly, this is not the case. An object can be moving even if the net force acting on it is zero.

Newton's first law of motion describes how an object moves when no net force is acting on it. According to **Newton's first law of motion,** if there is no net force acting on an object the object remains at rest, or if the object is already moving, it continues to move in a straight line with constant speed.

The Italian scientist Galileo Galilei, who lived from 1564 to 1642, was one of the first to understand that a force doesn't need to be constantly applied to an object to keep it moving. Galileo's ideas helped Isaac Newton to better understand the nature of motion. Newton was able to explain the motion of objects in three rules called Newton's laws of motion.

Friction

Galileo realized the motion of an object doesn't change until an unbalanced force acts on it. Every day you see moving objects come to a stop. The force that brings nearly everything to a stop is **friction,** which is the force that acts to resist sliding between two touching surfaces, as shown in **Figure 3.** Friction is why you never see objects moving with constant velocity unless a net force is applied. Friction is the force that eventually brings your skateboard to a stop unless you push it. Friction always acts on objects that are moving across surfaces or through air or water.

Figure 3
Friction acts against the motion between objects.

A Without friction, the rock climber would slide down the rock.

B Friction brings this sliding baseball player to a stop.

Teacher FYI

At the age of 42, Sir Isaac Newton published his *Principia Mathematica*, one of the most influential works of all time. It overturned Aristotle's ideas, which had prevailed for 2,000 years. Together, Galileo and Newton caused a revolution in our understanding of the world around us.

Curriculum Connection

Literature Bertold Brecht wrote the play *Galileo Galilei* about the arrest and trial of Galileo during the Inquisition. This play provides an interesting commentary on the relationship between science and the political climate in which it was studied. More advanced students might find this play of interest. L3 LS **Linguistic**

Opposing Sliding Although several different forms of friction exist, they all have one thing in common. If two objects are in contact, frictional forces always try to prevent one object from sliding on the other object. If you rub your hand against a tabletop, you can feel the friction push against the motion of your hand. If you rub the other way, you can feel the direction of friction change so it is again acting against your hand's motion. Friction always will slow an object down.

Reading Check ***What do the different forms of friction have in common?***

Older Ideas About Motion It took a long time for people to understand motion. One reason was that people did not understand the behavior of friction or understand that friction was a force. Because friction causes moving objects to stop, people thought the natural state of an object was to be at rest. For an object to be in motion, something had to be pushing or pulling it continuously. As soon as the force stopped, nature would bring the object to rest.

Galileo understood that an object in constant motion is as natural as an object at rest. It was usually the force of friction that made moving objects come to a stop. To keep an object moving, a force had to be applied to overcome the effects of friction. If friction could be removed, an object in motion would continue to move in a straight line with constant speed, as shown in **Figure 4.**

SCIENCE Online

Research Visit the Glencoe Science Web site at **science.glencoe.com** for more information about the lives of Galileo and Newton. Communicate to your class what you learn.

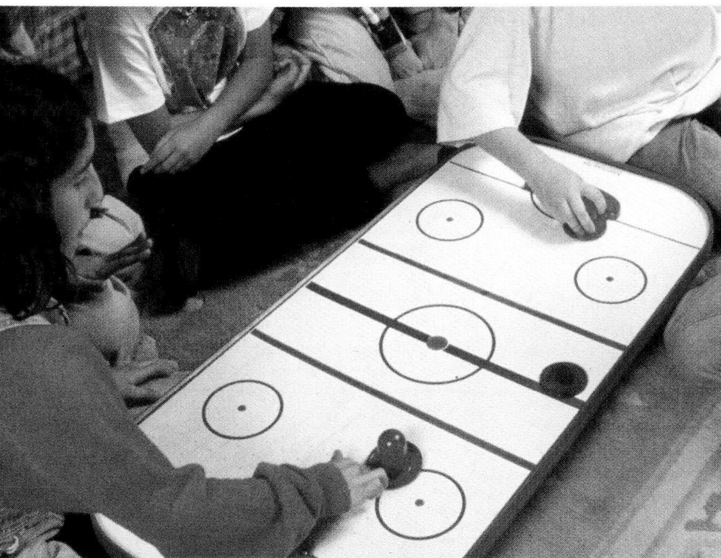

Figure 4
In an air hockey game, the puck floats on a layer of air, so that friction is almost eliminated. As a result, the puck moves in a straight line with nearly constant speed after it's been hit. *How would the puck move if there was no layer of air?*

Reading Check

Answer If two objects are in contact, frictional forces always try to prevent one object from sliding on the other object.

SCIENCE Online

Internet Addresses

Explore the Glencoe Science Web site at **science.glencoe.com** to find out more about topics in this section.

Activity

Have students investigate the sport of curling and the role friction plays in it. Curling is played on ice. Each player hurls a stone at fixed goals, and uses a broom to try to clear the path in front of the stone, thereby reducing the friction. L2 IS **Linguistic**

Extension

Physicists hypothesize there are only four fundamental forces of nature. Have students identify these forces and tell which kind friction is. The forces are gravitational force, electromagnetic force, the weak force, and the strong force. Friction is related to the electromagnetic forces between atoms and molecules. L3 IS **Logical-Mathematical**

Caption Answer

Figure 4 It would move in a straight line, but it would slow down and stop.

Inclusion Strategies

Physically Challenged If you have a student in your class who uses a wheelchair, ask the student to explain its braking system and the role friction plays in making it work. Have students compare pushing the chair with the brake off and with it on. L2 IS **Kinesthetic**

Resource Manager

Chapter Resources Booklet
- Enrichment, p. 30
- Lab Activity, pp. 9–12
- Transparency Activity, pp. 47–48

Purpose Students observe the static and sliding friction between various objects. L2 ELL LS **Kinesthetic**

Materials flat bar of soap, flat eraser, key, hard-sided notebook

Teaching Strategies Students should conduct the experiment several times. On occasion, one of the objects may abnormally stick, which could give misleading results if not rechecked.

Analysis

1. The eraser had the greatest static friction since it was the last to slide. The soap had the least since it was the first to slide.
2. The key slid the fastest, it has the least kinetic friction. The eraser slid the slowest, it had the most kinetic friction.
3. Increase the friction by pushing the surfaces together. Decrease the friction by placing a lubricant between the surfaces.

Process Ask students to explain why keeping a bicycle chain properly lubricated helps make the bicycle easier to ride. The lubricant decreases the friction between the links of the chain. Use **PASC**, p. 89.

Observing Friction

Procedure

1. Lay a **bar of soap,** a **flat eraser,** and a **key** side by side on one end of a **hard-sided notebook.**
2. At a constant rate, slowly lift the end of notebook with objects on it. Note the order in which the objects start sliding.

Analysis

1. For which object was static friction the greatest? For which object was it the smallest? Explain, based on your observations.
2. Which object slid the fastest? Which slid the slowest? Explain why there is a difference in speed.
3. How could you increase and decrease the amount of friction between two materials?

Static Friction If you've ever tried pushing something heavy, like a refrigerator, you might have discovered that nothing happened at first. Then as you push harder and harder, the object suddenly will start to move. When you first start to push, friction between the heavy refrigerator and the floor opposes the force you are exerting and the net force is zero. The type of friction that prevents an object from moving when a force is applied is called static friction.

Static friction is caused by the attraction between the atoms on the two surfaces that are in contact. This causes the surfaces to stick or weld together where they are in contact. Usually, as the surface gets rougher and the object gets heavier, the force of static friction will be larger. To move the object, you have to exert a force large enough to break the bonds holding two surfaces together.

Sliding Friction While static friction keeps an object at rest, sliding friction slows down an object that slides. If you push an object across a room, you notice the sliding friction between the bottom of the object and the floor. You have to keep pushing to overcome the force of sliding friction. Sliding friction is due to the microscopic roughness of two surfaces, as shown in **Figure 5.** A force must be applied to move the rough areas of one surface past the rough areas of the other. The brake pads in a car use sliding friction against the wheels to slow the car. Bicycle brakes, shown in **Figure 6A,** work the same way.

Reading Check ***What is the difference between static friction and sliding friction?***

Figure 5
Microscopic roughness, even on surfaces that seem smooth, such as the tray and metal shelf, causes sliding friction. *What do you think a lubricant does?*

Reading Check

Answer Static friction prevents two objects at rest from moving past one another; sliding friction slows down two objects moving against each other.

Caption Answer

Figure 5 It reduces the stickiness between two surfaces by putting a liquid between them.

Resource Manager

Chapter Resources Booklet

MiniLAB, p. 3

Reinforcement, p. 27

Home and Community Involvement, p. 23

Inclusion Strategies

Visually Impaired When these students do the MiniLAB, have them place the objects at the edge of the notebook by feel. Have a sighted student lift the end of the notebook while the first student puts his or her hand at the bottom of the notebook to catch the objects as they slide. Have students repeat the process several times, until they have had a chance to discover by feel the order in which the objects slide.

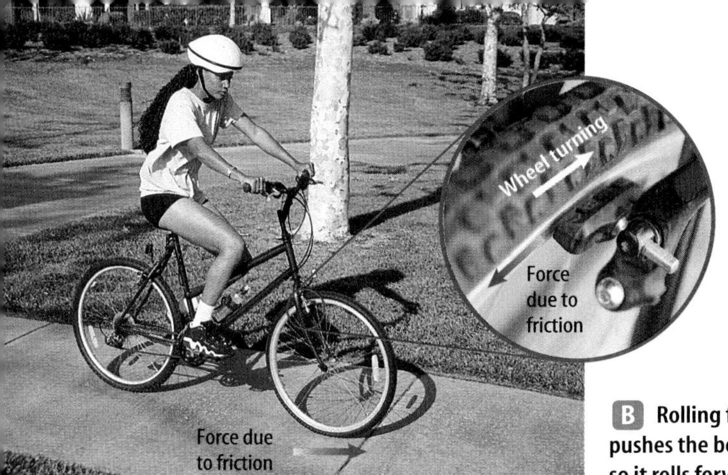

Figure 6
A bicycle uses sliding friction and rolling friction.

A **Sliding friction is used to stop this bicycle tire. Friction between the brake pads and the wheel brings the wheel to a stop.**

B **Rolling friction with the ground pushes the bottom of the bicycle tire, so it rolls forward.**

Rolling Friction Another type of friction, rolling friction, is needed to make a wheel or tire turn. Rolling friction occurs between the ground and the part of the tire touching the ground, as shown in **Figure 6B.** Rolling friction keeps the tire from slipping on the ground. If the bicycle tires are rolling forward, rolling friction exerts the force on the tires that pushes the bicycle forward.

It's usually easier to pull a load on a wagon or cart that has wheels rather than to drag the load along the ground. This is because rolling friction between the wheels and the ground is less than the sliding fiction between the load and the ground.

Section  Assessment

1. A car turns to the left at 20 km/h. Is a force acting on the car? Explain.
2. Explain why friction made it difficult to discover Newton's first law of motion.
3. If the net force on an object is zero, were the forces acting on it balanced or unbalanced? Explain.
4. What makes static friction increase?
5. **Think Critically** In the following situations, are the forces balanced or unbalanced? How can you tell?
   a. You push a box until it moves.
   b. You push a box at a constant rate.
   c. You stop pushing a box, and it stops.

Skill Builder Activities

6. **Comparing and Contrasting** Compare and contrast static friction, sliding friction, and rolling friction. **For more help, refer to the Science Skill Handbook.**
7. **Communicating** Most of the meteors that reach Earth's atmosphere burn up on the way down. Friction between the meteor and the atmosphere produces a great deal of heat. Research how the space shuttle is protected from friction when it reenters Earth's atmosphere. Report your findings in your Science Journal. **For more help, refer to the Science Skill Handbook.**

3 Assess

Reteach

Ask students to identify the type of friction in each of the following situations: a bicycle tire rolling along a road; rolling friction a basketball player slipping on a wet spot on the floor; sliding friction a car stuck in the mud. static friction

L2 LS **Logical-Mathematical**

Challenge

Have each student choose a part of an automobile that is affected by some form of friction. Have students state the type of friction, whether the friction decreases or increases the efficiency of the car, and how the friction can be increased or decreased to improve the performance of the car.

L3 LS **Logical-Mathematical**

✔Assessment

Process Ask each student to draw an events chain concept map illustrating why the space shuttle heats up to about 3,000°C when it re-enters the atmosphere. The friction of the atmosphere against the shuttle fuselage moving at 28,000 km/h heats it up to that temperature. Use **PASC,** p. 163. P

Answers to Section Assessment

1. Yes; a force is needed to change direction.
2. People could see that everything in motion eventually stopped, so they thought that rest was the natural state of matter.
3. Balanced; unbalanced forces cause motion.
4. Static friction increases if the surface is rougher or the object is heavier.
5. **a.** unbalanced, the box starts moving; **b.** balanced, box moves with constant velocity; **c.** unbalanced, box slows down
6. All three types of friction act against the direction an object moves. Static friction keeps an object from moving; sliding friction is the friction between two objects moving against each other; rolling friction is the static friction between the rolling object and the surface on which it is rolling.
7. The shuttle is covered with heat-resistant tiles that are made of silicate glass fibers.

SECTION

Newton's Second Law

1 Motivate

Bellringer Transparency

Display the Section Focus Transparency for Section 2. Use the accompanying Transparency Activity Master. L2 ELL

Section 2 Section Focus Transparency **Loop D'loop**

Have you ever gone upside down on a roller coaster? What kept the car on the track? In the cartoon, Calvin is pulling the sled far up the hill so he can get a good start.

CALVIN AND HOBBES © Watterson. Reprinted with permission of UNIVERSAL PRESS SYNDICATE. All rights

1. **Does it make a difference where Calvin begins his descent? Why or why not?**
2. **How does friction figure into Calvin's scheme?**
3. **How will gravity affect Calvin if he makes it into the loop?**

Tie to Prior Knowledge

Have students recall the definitions of mass and acceleration. In this section they will learn how the product of these gives the net force acting on an object.

Caption Answer

Figure 7 The cart with less food; it has less mass.

SECTION

Newton's Second Law

As You Read

***What* You'll Learn**

- **Explain** Newton's second law of motion.
- **Explain** why the direction of force is important.

Vocabulary

Newton's second law of motion
weight
weightlessness

***Why* It's Important**

Newton's second law of motion explains how any object, from a swimmer to a satellite, moves when acted on by forces.

Force and Acceleration

When you go shopping in a grocery store and push a cart, you exert a force to make the cart move. If you want to slow down or change the direction of the cart, a force is required to do this, as well. Would it be easier for you to stop a full or empty grocery cart suddenly, as in **Figure 7?** When the motion of an object changes, the object is accelerating. Acceleration occurs any time an object speeds up, slows down, or changes its direction of motion. Newton's second law describes how forces cause an object's motion to change.

Newton's second law of motion connects force, acceleration, and mass. According to the second law of motion, an object acted upon by a force will accelerate in the direction of the force. The acceleration is given by the following equation

$$\text{acceleration} = \frac{\text{net force}}{\text{mass}}$$

$$a = \frac{F_{net}}{m}$$

In this equation, a is the acceleration, m is the mass, and F_{net} is the net force. If both sides of the above equation are multiplied by the mass, the equation can be written this way:

$$F_{net} = ma$$

Reading Check *What is Newton's second law?*

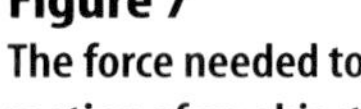

Figure 7
The force needed to change the motion of an object depends on its mass. *Which grocery cart would be easier to stop suddenly?*

Section Assessment Planner

PORTFOLIO
Science Journal, p. 205

PERFORMANCE ASSESSMENT
Math Skills Activity, p. 203
Skill Builder Activities, p. 206
See page 220 for more options.

CONTENT ASSESSMENT
Section, p. 206
Challenge, p. 206
Chapter, pp. 220–221

Units of Force Force is measured in newtons, abbreviated N. Because the SI unit for mass is the kilogram (kg) and acceleration has units of meters per second squared (m/s^2), 1 N also is equal to 1 kg·m/s^2. In other words, to calculate a force in newtons from the equation shown on the prior page, the mass must be given in kg and the acceleration in m/s^2.

Gravity

One force that you are familiar with is gravity. Whether you're coasting down a hill on a bike or a skateboard or jumping into a pool, gravity is at work pulling you downward. Gravity also is the force that causes Earth to orbit the Sun and the Moon to orbit Earth.

What is gravity? The force of gravity exists between any two objects that have mass. Gravity always is attractive and pulls objects toward each other. A gravitational attraction exists between you and every object in the universe that has mass. However, the force of gravity depends on the mass of the objects and the distance between them. The gravitational force becomes weaker the farther apart the objects are and also decreases as the masses of the objects involved decrease.

For example, there is a gravitational force between you and the Sun and you and Earth. The Sun is much more massive than Earth, but is so far away that the gravitational force between you and the Sun is too weak to notice. Only Earth has enough mass and is close enough to exert a noticeable gravitational force on you. The force of gravity between you and Earth is about 1,700 times greater than between you and the Sun.

A black hole is a star that has collapsed so that all its mass is compressed into a small region that may be less than 10 km in diameter. Near a black hole, the force of gravity is much stronger than the force of gravity near Earth. Research some of the unusual phenomena that occur near black holes.

Weight The force of gravity causes all objects near Earth's surface to fall with an acceleration of 9.8 m/s^2. By Newton's second law, the gravitational force on any object near Earth's surface is:

$$F = ma = m \times (9.8\ m/s^2)$$

This gravitational force also is called the weight of the object. Your **weight** on Earth is the gravitational force between you and Earth. Your weight would change if you were standing on a different planet than Earth, as shown in **Table 1**. Your weight on a different planet is the gravitational force between you and the planet.

Table 1 Weight of 60 kg Person on Various Planets

Place	Weight in Newtons If Your Mass Were 60 kg	Percent of Your Weight on Earth
Mars	223	38
Earth	588	100
Jupiter	1,470	250
Pluto	41	0.7

2 Teach

Force and Acceleration

✔ Reading Check

Answer An object acted upon by an unbalanced force will accelerate in the direction of the force according to $a = F_{net}/m$.

Gravity

Discussion

In the United States, people usually measure their weight in pounds. In European countries, people speak of their weight in kilograms. **When converting your weight to the metric system, should you convert it to kilograms or newtons? Why?** Convert it to newtons. Weight is a measure of the force of gravity, and newtons is the unit of force.

L2 LS **Logical-Mathematical**

Near the edge of a black hole, objects get pulled into strings of atoms. When gases come near a black hole, they form an accretion disk that is blue hot and emits ultraviolet and X rays.

Curriculum Connection

History Galileo was the first person to understand gravity's effect on objects. Have students learn more about Galileo and his understanding of gravity. Galileo discovered that the rate at which a body falls is independent of its weight or density, as long as air resistance can be neglected. He was also the first person to use mathematics to analyze his results. L2 LS **Linguistic**

Resource Manager

Chapter Resources Booklet

Transparency Activity, p. 45

Directed Reading for Content Mastery, p. 21

Lab Activity, pp. 13–16

Using Newton's Second Law

IDENTIFYING Misconceptions

The text states that the acceleration produced by a force must be in the direction of the force. This does not mean that every force produces an acceleration in the direction in which it is applied. All of the forces acting on an object are added together to determine the net force on the object. The object accelerates in the direction of this net force. So, for example, if one student pushes an object west while another student pushes it north, the net force on the object will be northwest, and will cause the object to move in that direction.

Discussion

$F = ma$ describes the relationship between force and acceleration. **What is the relationship between force and velocity?** A force causes a change in velocity. The magnitude of the change can be calculated if you know the velocity before the force acted, the velocity after the force acted, and how long the change took. L2 LS **Logical-Mathematical**

Figure 8
The girl is speeding up because she is being pushed in the same direction that she is moving.

Weight and Mass Weight and mass are different. Weight is a force, just like the push of your hand is a force, and is measured in newtons. When you stand on a bathroom scale, you are measuring the pull of Earth's gravity—a force. However, mass is the amount of matter in an object, and doesn't depend on location. A book with a mass of 1 kg has a mass of 1 kg on Earth or on Mars. However, the weight of the book would be different on Earth and Mars. The two planets would exert a different gravitational force on the book.

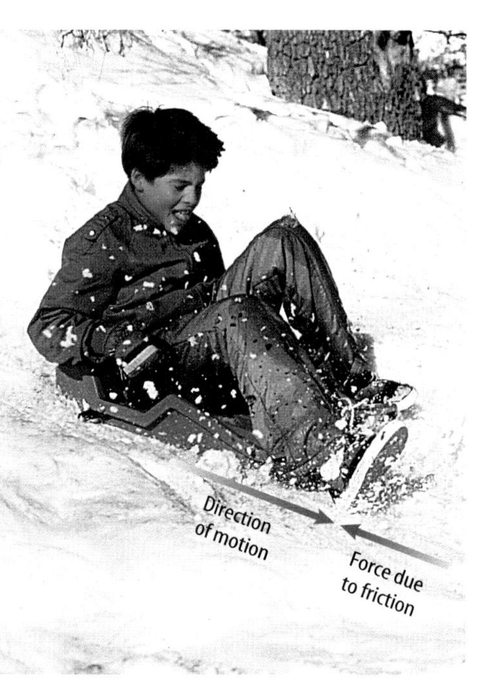

Figure 9
The boy is slowing down because the force exerted by his feet is in the opposite direction of his motion.

Using Newton's Second Law

How does Newton's second law determine how an object moves when acted upon by forces? The second law tells how to calculate the acceleration of an object if its mass and the forces acting on it are known. You may remember that the motion of an object can be described by its velocity. The velocity tells how fast an object is moving and in what direction. Acceleration tells how velocity changes. If the acceleration of an object is known, then the change in velocity can be determined.

Speeding Up Think about a soccer ball sitting on the ground. If you kick the ball, it starts moving. You exert a force on the ball, and the ball accelerates only while your foot is in contact with the ball. If you look back at all of the examples of objects speeding up, you'll notice that something is pushing or pulling the object in the direction it is moving, as in **Figure 8.** The direction of the push or pull is the direction of the force. It also is the direction of the acceleration.

Resource Manager

Mathematics Skill Activities, p. 9

Physical Science Critical Thinking/Problem Solving, p. 4

Visual Learning

Figure 9 Point out that the net force acting on the sled is a combination of the force of friction and the force of the boy's feet, both of which act to slow the sled. Have students calculate this net force if the boy stops the sled in 30 s, the boy's mass is 40 kg, and the sled's velocity when he starts slowing down is 10 km/h. Initial velocity = 10 km/h = 10,000 m/3600 s = 2.8 m/s; F = ma = 40 kg × (2.8 m/s − 0 m/s) ÷ 30 s = 3.7 N L2 LS **Logical-Mathematical**

Calculating Acceleration Newton's second law of motion can be used to calculate acceleration. For example, suppose you pull a 10-kg sled with a force of 5 N. The acceleration can be found as follows:

$$a = \frac{F_{net}}{m} = \frac{5\text{ N}}{10\text{ kg}} = 0.5\text{ m/s}^2$$

The sled keeps accelerating as long as you keep pulling on it. The acceleration does not depend on how fast the sled is moving. It depends only on the net force and the mass of the sled.

Slowing Down If you wanted to slow down an object, you would have to push or pull it against the direction it is moving. An example is given in **Figure 9.** Here the force is opposite to the velocity or the direction of motion.

Suppose you push a book so it slides across a tabletop. You exert a force on the book when your hand is in contact with it, and the book speeds up. Sliding friction also acts on the book as it starts to move. After the book is no longer in contact with your hand, friction acts in the opposite direction to the book's motion. This causes the book to slow down and come to a stop.

How does acceleration affect how you feel on a roller coaster? To find out more about acceleration and amusement park rides, see the **Amusement Park Rides Field Guide** at the back of the book.

Math Skills Activity

Calculating Force Using Newton's Second Law

Example Problem

A car with a mass of 1,500 kg has an acceleration of 3 m/s^2. Find the force acting on the car.

Solution

1. *This is what you know:* acceleration: $a = 3\text{ m/s}^2$; mass: $m = 1{,}500\text{ kg}$
2. *This what you need to find:* Force: F
3. *This is the equation you need to use:* $F = ma$
4. *Substitute the known values:* $F = (1{,}500\text{ kg}) \times (3\text{ m/s}^2) = 4{,}500\text{ N}$

Check your answer by dividing the force you calculate by the acceleration that was given. Do you calculate the same mass that was given?

Practice Problem

You throw a 150-g baseball so it has an acceleration of 80 m/s^2. Find the force you exerted on the baseball.

For more help, refer to the Math Skill Handbook.

Activity

Have students work in groups to demonstrate Newton's second law of motion. Have them measure the mass of a toy car, then roll it down a ramp. Have one student measure the distance the car rolled down the ramp, and have another student time how long it takes the car to get to the bottom of the ramp. Add some mass to the car and repeat. Change the mass 5 times. Then, ask students to use Newton's second law to calculate the net force acting on the car as it rolls down the ramp. $F = ma$; $a = v_{avg}/t$; v = distance traveled down the ramp ÷ time. L2 COOP LEARN **Kinesthetic**

Teacher FYI

The mathematics in this section explains how to calculate the acceleration of an object moving in a straight line. This is called the object's translational acceleration. Acceleration that causes an object to change direction is called rotational acceleration. Rotational acceleration is equal to v/r^2, where v is the speed of the object and r is the radius of the curve through which it moves. If the object is changing both speed and direction, its total acceleration takes into account both its translational acceleration and its rotational acceleration.

Math Skills Activity

National Math Standards

Correlation to Mathematics Objectives

1,2,4,9

Answer to Practice Problem

$F = ma = 0.15\text{ kg} \times 80\text{ m/s}^2 = 12\text{ N}$

Science Journal

Forces on You Ask students to calculate their mass in kilograms and write the results in their Science Journals. Then, ask them to calculate the amount of force it would take to accelerate them from standing still to a velocity of 10 km/h in 10 seconds. $a = (v_2 - v_1)/t$; v_2 = 10 km/h = 10,000 m/3,600 s = 2.8 m/s; $v_1 = 0$; therefore, $a = 2.8\text{ m/s} \div 10\text{ s} = 0.28\text{ m/s}^2$ $F = ma$, so the force needed will be the student's mass in kilograms times 0.28 m/s^2. L2 **Logical-Mathematical**

Using Newton's Second Law, continued

Visual Learning

Figure 10 Ask students to identify the forces acting on the ball as it is being thrown and while it is in the air. Ask them to describe the motion of the ball in both of these situations. The force of the hand accelerates the ball forward and up until it loses contact with the hand. Then only gravity acts on the ball, accelerating it downward. L2 **LS Visual-Spatial**

Discussion

Tell students to imagine throwing a baseball on Earth, and then throwing the ball with the same force on the Moon. **How would the paths of the ball differ? Why?** The ball would travel farther in the horizontal direction before falling to the ground on the Moon. The ball would have the same horizontal force acting on it, but the force pulling it down would be less on the Moon because of the Moon's lower gravity. L2 **LS Logical-Mathematical**

Circular Motion

Discussion

What is the centripetal force that keeps the Moon in orbit around Earth? gravity L2 **LS Logical-Mathematical**

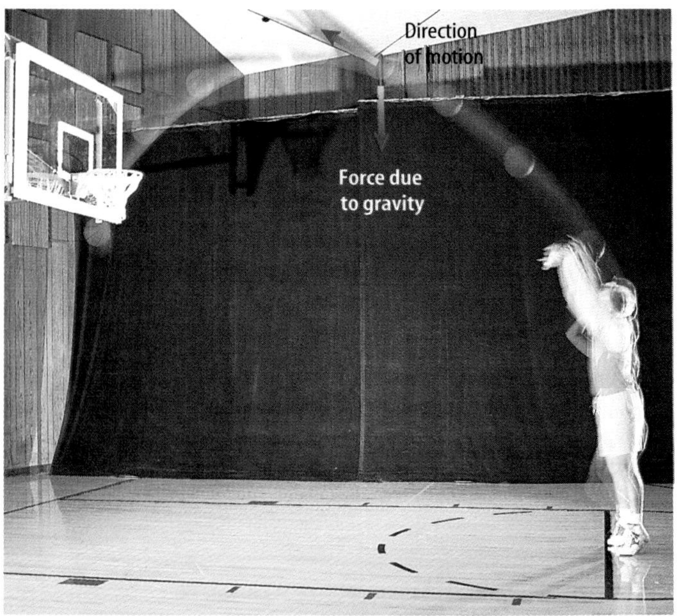

Figure 10
When the ball is thrown, it doesn't keep moving in a straight line. Gravity exerts a force downward that makes it move in a curved path.

Turning Sometimes forces and motion are not in a straight line. If a net force acts at an angle to the direction an object is moving, the object will follow a curved path. The object might be going slower, faster, or at the same speed after it turns.

For example, when you shoot a basketball, the ball doesn't continue to move in a straight line after it leaves your hand. Instead it starts to curve downward, as shown in **Figure 10.** The force of gravity pulls the ball downward. The ball's motion is a combination of its original motion and the downward motion due to gravity. This causes the ball to move in a curved path.

Circular Motion

A rider on a merry-go-round ride moves in a circle. This type of motion is called circular motion. If you are in circular motion, your direction of motion is constantly changing. This means you are constantly accelerating. According to Newton's second law of motion, if you are constantly accelerating, there must be a force acting on you the entire time.

Think about an object on the end of a string whirling in a circle. The force that keeps the object moving in a circle is exerted by the string. The string pulls on the object to keep it moving in a circle. The force exerted by the string is the centripetal force and always points toward the center of the circle. In circular motion the centripetal force is always perpendicular to the motion.

Active Reading

Jigsaw In this collaborative learning technique, individuals become experts on a portion of a text and share their expertise with a small group, called their home group. Everyone shares responsibility for learning the assigned reading. Assign each person in each home group an expert number (1 through 5, for example). Have students gather into the expert groups that correspond to the number they were assigned. Have them read, discuss, and master chapter concepts and determine how best to teach them to their home groups. Have students return to their home groups and share the content they learned in their expert groups. Have students use the Jigsaw strategy with the material on Newton's laws of motion covered in this chapter.

Satellite Motion Objects that orbit Earth are satellites of Earth. Satellites go around Earth in nearly circular orbits, with the centripetal force being gravity. If gravity is pulling satellites toward Earth, why doesn't a satellite fall to Earth like a baseball does? Actually, a satellite is falling to Earth just like a baseball.

Suppose Earth were perfectly smooth with no mountains or hills. Imagine you throw a baseball horizontally. Gravity pulls the baseball downward so it travels in a curved path. If the baseball is thrown faster, its path is less curved, and it travels farther before it hits the ground, as shown in **Figure 11.** If the baseball were traveling fast enough, as it fell, its curved path would follow the curve of Earth's surface. Then the baseball would never hit the ground. Instead, it would continue to fall around Earth.

Figure 11
The faster a ball is thrown, the farther it travels before gravity pulls it to Earth. If the ball is traveling fast enough, Earth's surface curves away from it as fast as it falls downward. Then the ball never hits the ground.

Satellites in orbit are being pulled toward Earth just as baseballs are. The difference is that satellites are moving so fast horizontally that Earth's surface curves downward at the same rate that the satellites are falling downward. The speed at which a object must move to go into orbit near Earth's surface is about 8 km/s, or about 29,000 km/h.

To place a satellite into orbit, a rocket carries the satellite to the desired height. Then the rocket fires again to give the satellite the horizontal speed it needs to stay in orbit.

Air Resistance

Whether you are walking, running, or biking, air is pushing against you. This push is air resistance. Air resistance is a form of friction that acts to slow down any object moving in the air. Air resistance gets larger as an object moves faster.

When an object falls it speeds up as gravity pulls it downward. At the same time, the force of air resistance pushing up on the object is increasing as the object moves faster. Finally, the upward air resistance force becomes large enough to equal the downward force of gravity.

When the air resistance force equals the weight, the net force on the object is zero. By Newton's second law, the object's acceleration then is zero, and its speed no longer increases. The constant speed a falling object reaches when air resistance balances the force of gravity is the terminal velocity.

Air Resistance

Use Science Words

Word Meaning Ask students to look up the meaning of the adjective *terminal* and use the definition they find to explain the meaning of the term *terminal velocity*. Terminal means "of or relating to an end, extremity, boundary, or terminus." Terminal velocity is the end velocity, or the final velocity with which a particular object falls. It is also the extreme velocity, i.e., the fastest velocity with which the object falls. L2 LS **Linguistic**

Quick Demo

Display a sheet of paper and a dense ball. Ask which will hit the ground first if both are dropped at the same time, and why. Have students observe as both are dropped. Then, crumple up the paper and drop it and the ball. Explain that the paper fell faster this time because its shape caused it to encounter less air resistance. L2 LS **Visual-Spatial**

Make a Model

Have each student use coffee filters to make three different models of parachutes. Ask them to make the first parachute using a single coffee filter. Then, have them add coffee filters to make larger parachutes. Have them attach small objects to the parachutes, drop them, and measure the duration of their fall. L2 LS **Kinesthetic**

Use an Analogy

Increasing the area of an object to increase air resistance in free fall is analogous to spreading a larger sail on a sailboat to increase the force of the wind against the sail.

Skydiving Ask students to draw pictures and write descriptions of what happens from the time a skydiver jumps out of a plane until he or she lands on the ground. Ask students to use the following terms: free fall, terminal velocity, air resistance, gravity, and acceleration due to gravity. Make sure they indicate when the forces on the skydiver are balanced and when they are unbalanced. P

Resource Manager

Chapter Resources Booklet
Enrichment, p. 31
Reinforcement, p. 28
Transparency Activity, pp. 47–48

3 Assess

Reteach

Have students identify the forces acting on them as they sit in a car that is speeding up. Gravity pulls down, the seat pushes up; the back of the seat pushes forward, accelerated by the engine, static friction between the students' bodies and the seat pulls the students back. L2

LS Logical-Mathematical

Challenge

A 0.125-kg baseball is pitched at 45 m/s and is struck by the bat and sent back toward the pitcher at −45 m/s. If the ball is in contact with the bat for 0.0025 s, how hard does the bat hit the ball? What forces act on the ball after the bat hits it? $F = (0.125\ kg)[(45\ m/s) - (-45\ m/s)] \div 0.0025\ s = 4{,}500\ N$. After the bat hits the ball, the only forces acting on the ball are gravity and air resistance.

L3 **Logical-Mathematical**

Process Have students calculate the force of Earth's gravity acting on a person with a mass of 50 kg. $F = ma = 50\ kg \times 9.8\ m/s^2 = 490\ N$ Use **PASC,** p. 101.

Figure 12
Sky divers can change their air resistance by changing the position of their arms and legs.
A In a spread-eagle position, the air resistance of the sky diver is greater. **B** With the legs closed and the arms tucked back against the body, the sky diver's shape is narrower and the air resistance is less.

Air Resistance and Shape

The amount of air resistance depends on the object's shape, as well as its speed. Moving at the same speed, the air resistance on a pointed, narrow object is less than on a broad, flat object, such as a leaf or a piece of paper. A falling sky diver in a spread-eagle position, as shown in **Figure 12A,** might reach a terminal velocity of about 200 km/h. But with the arms tucked backward and the legs closed, air resistance is less, and the skydiver might reach a terminal velocity of over 300 km/h. When the skydiver opens the parachute, the force of air resistance on an open parachute is so large that the skydiver's terminal velocity quickly is reduced to about 20 km/h.

Section  Assessment

1. A human cannonball with a mass of 80 kg is fired out of a cannon with a force of 6,400 N. Find the acceleration.
2. You are riding a bike at 20 km/h when you stop pedaling. Draw a simple picture of you on a bike. Using arrows to represent forces, draw and label all the forces acting on you as you coast along.
3. If your bike is moving at 20 km/h and you come to a stop in 1 min, at what rate did you accelerate?
4. What happens when the air resistance force equals the weight of a falling object?
5. **Think Critically** Explain how you can determine the direction of a force by watching an object's change in motion.

Skill Builder Activities

6. **Drawing Conclusions** Three students are pushing on a box. Two students are pushing on the left side, and one is pushing on the right side. One student on the left pushes with a force of 10 N and the other pushes with a force of 15 N. The student of the right pushes with a force of 20 N. In what direction will the box move? Explain your answer. **For more help, refer to the Science Skill Handbook.**
7. **Solving One-Step Equations** A 1-kg ball is moving at 2 m/s. A force stops the ball in 4 s. Find the acceleration of the ball by dividing the change in speed on the ball by the time needed to stop. Then find the force. **For more help, refer to the Math Skill Handbook.**

Answers to Section Assessment

1. $a = F_{net}/m = 6{,}400\ N/80\ kg = 80\ m/s^2$
2. The force of the bicycle pushes upward and is equal to the force of gravity pulling downward. Air resistance and friction act against the direction of motion.
3. $20\ km/h = 5.55\ m/s$; $a = (5.55\ m/s - 0\ m/s) \div 60\ s = 0.09\ m/s^2$
4. The object no longer accelerates and falls at its terminal velocity.
5. The net force is always in the direction of the acceleration. The net force acts in the direction of the motion as the object speeds up, opposite as the object slows down, and at an angle when the object changes direction.
6. Forces pushing on the left are 10 N + 15 N = 25 N; force pushing on the right is 20 N; net force on the box is 25 N − 20 N = 5 N from the left. The box moves to the right.
7. $a = (2\ m/s - 0\ m/s) \div 4\ s = 0.5\ m/s^2$; $F = ma = 1\ kg \times 0.5\ m/s^2 = 0.5\ N$

SECTION 3

Newton's Third Law

Action and Reaction

Newton's first two laws explain everything about the motion of a single object. If the forces acting on the object are balanced, the object will remain at rest or stay in motion with constant velocity. If the forces are unbalanced, the object will accelerate in the direction of the net force. However, Newton's first two laws do not explain how two or more objects exert forces on each other.

Newton's final law describes the connection between the object supplying the force and the object receiving the force. Suppose you push on a wall. It may surprise you to learn that if you push on a wall, the wall also pushes on you. According to **Newton's third law of motion,** forces always act in equal but opposite pairs. Another way of saying this is for every action, there is an equal but opposite reaction. This means that when you push on a wall, the wall pushes back on you with a force equal in strength to the force you exerted. When one object exerts a force on another object, the second object exerts the same size force on the first object, as shown in **Figure 13.**

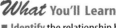

As You Read

***What* You'll Learn**

- **Identify** the relationship between the forces that objects exert on each other.

Vocabulary
Newton's third law of motion

***Why* It's Important**
Newton's third law can help you predict how objects will affect one another.

Figure 13
The car jack is pushing up on the car with the same amount of force with which the car is pushing down on the jack.

SECTION

Newton's Third Law

1 Motivate

Bellringer Transparency

Display the Section Focus Transparency for Section 3. Use the accompanying Transparency Activity Master. L2 ELL

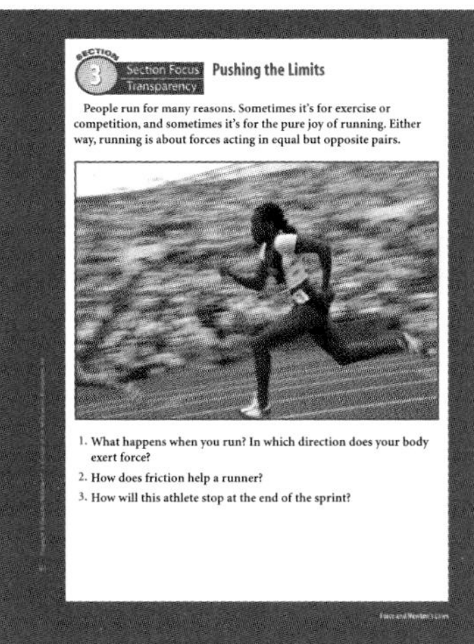
Section Focus Transparency 3 — Pushing the Limits

People run for many reasons. Sometimes it's for exercise or competition, and sometimes it's for the pure joy of running. Either way, running is about forces acting in equal but opposite pairs.

1. What happens when you run? In which direction does your body exert force?
2. How does friction help a runner?
3. How will this athlete stop at the end of the sprint?

Tie to Prior Knowledge

Ask students to describe the force exerted on them by their chairs. The force of the chairs pushes up on them, countering the force of gravity pulling them down. The chair's force is equal to that of gravity, so students don't move. Explain that according to Newton's third law of motion, all forces act in pairs. They will learn more about these pairs of forces in this section.

Resource Manager

Chapter Resources Booklet
Transparency Activity, p. 46
Directed Reading for Content Mastery, pp. 20, 22

Section Assessment Planner

PORTFOLIO
Assessment, p. 211

PERFORMANCE ASSESSMENT
MiniLAB, p. 211
Skill Builder Activities, p. 212
See page 220 for more options.

CONTENT ASSESSMENT
Section, p. 212
Challenge, p. 212
Chapter, pp. 220–221

2 Teach

Action and Reaction

Caption Answer

Figure 14 The car with the smaller mass accelerates more.

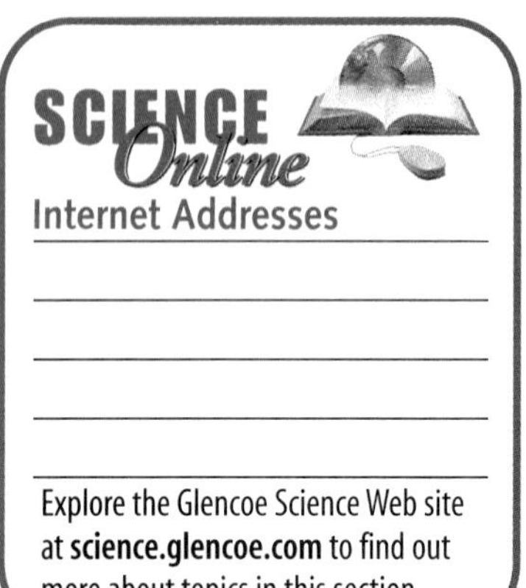

Explore the Glencoe Science Web site at **science.glencoe.com** to find out more about topics in this section.

Activity

Have students perform or act out various activities that demonstrate action and reaction, while other students describe how the activities demonstrate Newton's third law. For example, a student might pretend to be swimming or rowing a boat, and other students would describe how pushing on the water propels a person through the water as the water pushes back. L2 LS **Kinesthetic**

Discussion

What happens when the force that pushes on a surface is greater than the force with which the surface can push back? The surface breaks or is deformed. L2 LS **Logical-Mathematical**

Figure 14
In this collision, the first car exerts a force on the second. The second exerts the same force in the opposite direction on the first car. *Which car do you think accelerates more?*

Research Visit the Glencoe Science Web site at **science.glencoe.com** for more information about how birds and other animals fly. Communicate to your class what you learn.

Action and Reaction Forces Don't Cancel If action and reaction force pairs are equal and opposite, how can anything move? Won't the action and reaction forces cancel? The answer is no, action and reaction force pairs don't cancel because they act on different objects. Forces can cancel only if they act on the same object.

For example, imagine you're driving a bumper car and are about to ram a friend in another car, as shown in **Figure 14.** When the two cars collide, your car pushes on the other car. By Newton's third law, that car pushes on your car with the same force, but in the opposite direction. One force of the action-reaction force pair is exerted on your friend's car, and the other force of the force pair is exerted on your car. Another example of an action-reaction pair is shown in **Figure 15.**

You constantly use action-reaction force pairs as you move about. When you jump, you push down on the ground with your legs. The ground then pushes up on you. It is this upward force that pushes you into the air. Your motion and the motion of all objects around you can be explained by Newton's laws of motion, as summarized in **Figure 16.**

Figure 15
When the child pushes off the wall, the wall pushes against the child.

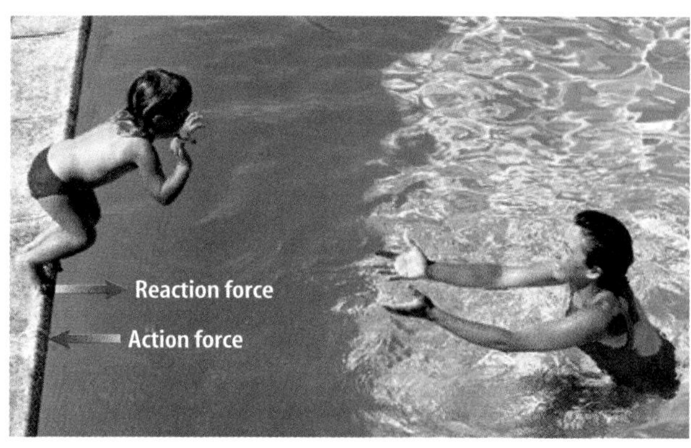

Birds and other flying creatures also use Newton's third law. When a bird flies, its wings push in a downward and a backward direction. This pushes air downward and backward. By Newton's third law, the air pushes back on the bird in the opposite directions—upward and forward. This is the force that keeps a bird in the air and propels it forward.

Resource Manager

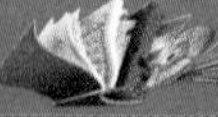

Chapter Resources Booklet
MiniLAB, p. 4

Cultural Diversity, p. 63

208 CHAPTER 7 Force and Newton's Laws

VISUALIZING NEWTON'S LAWS IN SPORTS

Figure 16

Although it is not obvious, Newton's laws of motion are demonstrated in sports activities all the time. According to the first law, if an object is in motion, it moves in a straight line with constant speed unless a net force acts on it. If an object is at rest, it stays at rest unless a net force acts on it. The second law states that a net force acting on an object causes the object to accelerate in the direction of the force. The third law can be understood this way—for every action force, there is an equal and opposite reaction force.

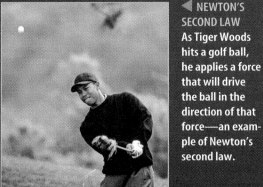

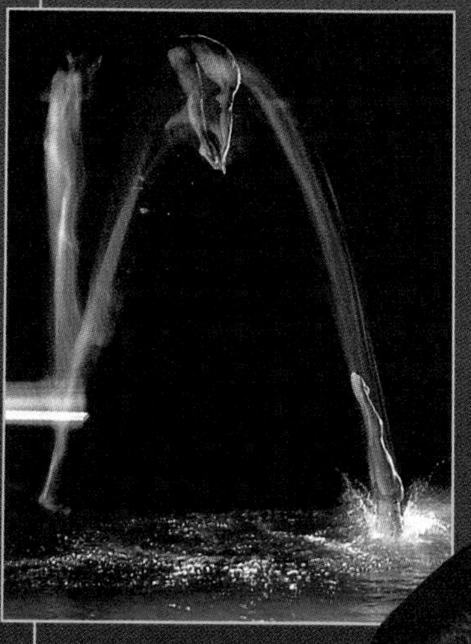

▲ NEWTON'S FIRST LAW According to Newton's first law, the diver does not move in a straight line with constant speed because of the force of gravity.

◀ NEWTON'S SECOND LAW As Tiger Woods hits a golf ball, he applies a force that will drive the ball in the direction of that force—an example of Newton's second law.

▶ NEWTON'S THIRD LAW Newton's third law applies even when objects do not move. Here a gymnast pushes downward on the bars. The bars push back on the gymnast with an equal force.

Resource Manager

Chapter Resources Booklet
- Enrichment, p. 32
- Transparency Activity, pp. 47–48

Performance Assessment in the Science Classroom, p. 36

NATIONAL GEOGRAPHIC

Visualizing Newton's Laws in Sports

Have students examine the pictures and read the captions. Then ask the following questions.

A shot put has a much greater mass than a discus. How does Newton's second law explain why a discus can be thrown about twice as far as a shot put? Because of its greater mass, the shot put must be thrown with much more force than the discus to reach the same acceleration.

How does Newton's third law explain the direction a boat crew must move the oars in order to move the boat forward? The crew applies a backward force to the water through the oars. The water applies an equal and opposite force on the oars. This force propels the oars and thus the boat through the water.

Activity

Have groups of students cut out magazine pictures showing examples of Newton's laws of motion in sports. Have them mount each picture on poster board. Ask each group to present their pictures to the class, explaining the forces at work in each example. LS **Visual-Spatial**

Extension

Ask students to select a sport not shown on this page and write reports on how Newton's laws apply in the sport they have chosen. Encourage them to illustrate their reports with diagrams. LS **Linguistic and Visual-Spatial**

Action and Reaction, continued

Fun Fact

As the space shuttle soars into space, it never accelerates any faster than 4 g's. This is four times the rate at which an object falls, and is about what you feel at the bottom of a loop on a fast roller-coaster. The difference is that the astronauts feel this acceleration for eight minutes. In just nine seconds they are moving faster than the speed of sound.

Discussion

Two minutes after launch of the space shuttle, all the fuel from the large solid rocket boosters is used up, and these boosters drop off the shuttle and fall back to Earth. This makes the shuttle much lighter and easier to accelerate. **What do you think happens at this point to keep the shuttle accelerating smoothly?** The rate of combustion in the engine is decreased.
L3 LS **Logical-Mathematical**

Visual Learning

Figure 18 Review with students the action-reaction forces between the gas molecules and the rocket. Tell students that the force on the rocket, called the thrust, is equal to the mass ejected per second times the velocity of the expelled gases. **How is this equivalent to F = ma?** ma = mv/s
L2 LS **Logical-Mathematical**

Figure 17
The force of the ground on your foot is equal and opposite to the force of your foot on the ground.

How do astronauts live under conditions of weightlessness? To find out more about the effects of weightlessness, see the **Living in Space Field Guide** at the end of the book.

Large and Small Objects Sometimes it's easy not to notice an action-reaction pair is because one of the objects is often much more massive and appears to remain motionless when a force acts on it. It has so much inertia, or tendency to remain at rest, that it hardly accelerates. Walking is a good example. When you walk forward, you push backward on the ground. Your shoe pushes Earth backward, and Earth pushes your shoe forward, as shown in **Figure 16.** Earth has so much mass compared to you that it does not move noticeably when you push it. If you step on something that has less mass than you do, like a skateboard, you can see it being pushed back.

A Rocket Launch The launching of a space shuttle is a spectacular example of Newton's third law. Three rocket engines supply the force, called thrust, that lifts the rocket. When the rocket fuel is ignited, a hot gas is produced. As the gas molecules collide with the inside engine walls, the walls exert a force that pushes them out of the bottom of the engine, as shown in **Figure 18.** This downward push is the action force. The reaction force is the upward push on the rocket engine by the gas molecules. This is the thrust that propels the rocket upward.

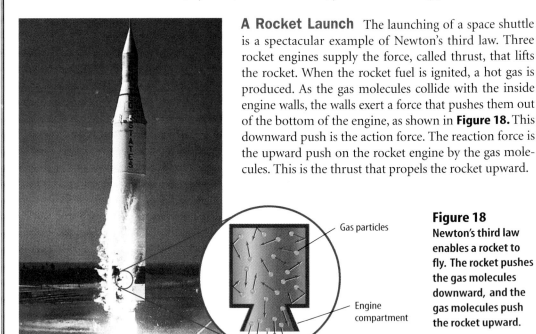

Figure 18
Newton's third law enables a rocket to fly. The rocket pushes the gas molecules downward, and the gas molecules push the rocket upward.

Cultural Diversity

Chinese Rockets The Chinese were the first to fire rockets. Have students find out more about Chinese rockets. By the 1100s, the Chinese were filling sections of bamboo tubing with gunpowder and shooting them off as fireworks and as weapons. They knew how to weight the rockets to make them fly farther. With time, they learned to make multistage rockets, in which one set of rockets lit the next set. L3 LS **Linguistic**

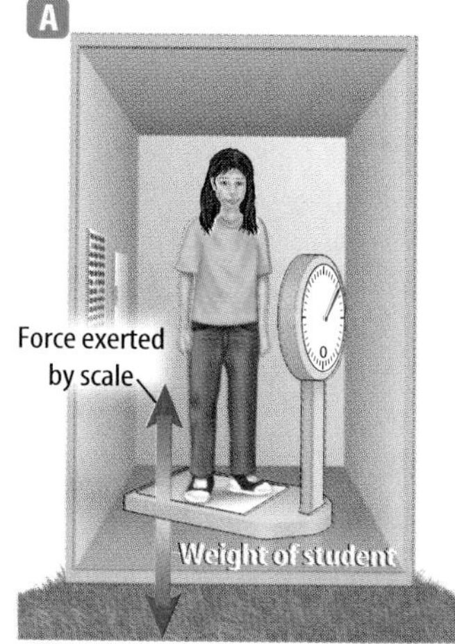

Figure 19
Your weight measured by a scale changes when you are falling.
A When you stand on a scale on Earth, the reading on the scale is your weight. **B** If you were to stand on a scale in a falling elevator, the scale would read zero.

Weightlessness

You may have seen pictures of astronauts floating inside a space shuttle as it orbits Earth. The astronauts are said to be weightless, as if Earth's gravity were no longer pulling on them. Yet the force of gravity on the shuttle is still about 90 percent as large as at Earth's surface. Newton's laws of motion can explain why the astronauts float as if there were no forces acting on them.

Measuring Weight Think about how you measure your weight. When you stand on a scale, your weight pushes down on the scale and causes the springs in the scale to compress. The scale pointer moves from zero and points to your weight. At the same time, by Newton's third law the scale pushes up on you with a force equal to your weight, as shown in **Figure 19A.** This force balances the downward pull of gravity on you.

Free Fall and Weightlessness Now suppose you were standing on a scale in an elevator that is falling, as shown in **Figure 19B.** A falling object is in free fall when the only force acting on the object is gravity. Inside the free-falling elevator, you and the scale are both in free fall. Because the only force acting on you is gravity, the scale no longer is pushing up on you. According to Newton's third law, you no longer push down on the scale. So the scale pointer stays at zero and you seem to be weightless. **Weightlessness** is the condition that occurs in free fall when the weight of an object seems to be zero.

However, you are not really weightless in free fall because Earth is still pulling down on you. With nothing to push up on you, such as your chair, you would have no sensation of weight.

Mini LAB

Measuring Force Pairs

Procedure
1. Work in pairs. Each person needs a **spring scale.**
2. Hook the two scales together. Each person should pull back on a scale. Record the two readings. Pull harder and record the two readings.
3. Continue to pull on both scales, but let the scales move toward one person. Do the readings change?
4. Try to pull in such a way that the two scales have different readings.

Analysis
1. What can you conclude about the pair of forces in each situation?
2. Explain how this experiment demonstrates Newton's third law.

Weightlessness

Purpose Students study the force pairs between two spring scales that are hooked together and pulled by two students. L2 ELL COOP LEARN

LS **Kinesthetic**

Materials two spring scales, string

Teaching Strategies Have students connect the scale hooks with about 30 cm of strong string. Be sure the scales are zeroed, and make sure students pull with the hooks facing each other directly.

Analysis
1. They were always equal to each other.
2. In every case, the forces of the scales pulling on each other were equal and opposite, which follows Newton's third law.

Portfolio Have students make drawings of the spring scales and indicate the forces acting on them in each trial. Use **Performance Assessment in the Science Classroom,** p. 127. P

LAB DEMONSTRATION

Purpose to demonstrate Newton's third law of motion

Materials two identical chairs with wheels, rope, tape, meterstick

Preparation Set the chairs about 3 m apart, and mark their positions with tape.

Procedure Have two students sit in the chairs. Make sure the students are about the same size. Give each student one end of the rope. Have students pull on the rope until the chairs meet. Use tape to mark on the floor the final position of each chair, and measure the distance each chair traveled.

Expected Outcome The chairs will both move about the same distance.

Assessment

How does this show Newton's third law? $F_1 = F_2$. Therefore, $m_1a_1 = m_2a_2$. If the masses of the students plus the chairs are about equal, $a_1 = a_2$; $a = v/t$, so $v_1/t_1 = v_2/t_2$. Time is the same for both, so $v_1 = v_2$; $v = d/t$, so $d_1/t_1 = d_2/t_2$, time is the same, so $d_1 = d_2$.

3 Assess

Reteach

Ask students to cut sports action photos out of magazines or newspapers and paste them into their Science Journals. Then, ask them to identify the action-reaction force pairs that appear in each picture.
L2 LS **Visual-Spatial**

Challenge

Two ice-skaters push off each other. The first skater has a mass of 50 kg and is accelerated 10 m/s² by the push. The second is accelerated 15 m/s² by the push. What is the mass of the second skater? $F_1 = F_2$, so $m_1a_1 = m_2a_2$, and $m_2 = m_1a_1/a_2 = (50\text{ kg} \times 10\text{ m/s}^2) \div 15\text{ m/s}^2 = 33.3\text{ kg}$
L2 LS **Logical-Mathematical**

✔Assessment

Process Suppose a canoe has a mass of 45 kg and a person has a mass of 75 kg. **If the person jumps out of the back end of the canoe into the water, will the canoe or the person have a greater acceleration? Explain.** The canoe; since the forces on the canoe and the person are the same and the canoe has less mass, it will have a greater acceleration. Use **PASC,** p. 101.

Figure 20
These oranges seem to be floating because they are falling around Earth at the same speed as the space shuttle and the astronauts. As a result, they don't seem to be moving relative to the astronauts in the cabin.

Weightlessness in Orbit To understand how objects move in the orbiting space shuttle, imagine you were holding a ball in the free-falling elevator. If you let the ball go, the position of the ball relative to you and the elevator wouldn't change, because you, the ball, and the elevator are moving at the same speed.

However, suppose you give the ball a gentle push downward. While you are pushing the ball, this downward force adds to the downward force of gravity. According to Newton's second law, the acceleration of the ball increases. So while you are pushing, the acceleration of the ball is greater than the acceleration of both you and the elevator. This causes the ball to speed up relative to you and the elevator. After it speeds up, it continues moving faster than you and the elevator, and it drifts downward until it hits the elevator floor.

When the space shuttle orbits Earth, the shuttle and all the objects in it are in free fall. They are falling in a curved path around Earth, instead of falling straight downward. As a result, objects in the shuttle appear to be weightless, as shown in **Figure 20.** A small push causes an object to drift away, just as a small downward push on the ball in the free-falling elevator caused it to drift to the floor.

Section 3 Assessment

1. You push a skateboard with a force of 6 N. If your mass is 60 kg, what is the force that the skateboard exerts on you?
2. A hockey puck is at rest on the ice. What two forces are acting on it?
3. You hit a hockey puck across the ice. When you hit the puck, what forces act on it?
4. Explain how Newton's laws of motion are involved as a player throws a ball and it flies forward and downward across the field.
5. **Think Critically** What would happen if you pushed against a chair that was not bolted to the floor on a space shuttle? What if the chair were bolted down?

Skill Builder Activities

6. **Solving One-Step Equations** A person standing on a canoe throws a cement block over the side. The action force on the cement block is 60 N. The reaction force is on the person and canoe. Their total mass is 100 kg. What is their acceleration? **For more help, refer to the Math Skill Handbook.**
7. **Communicating** Some people have trouble understanding Newton's third law. They reason, "If every action has an equal and opposite reaction, nothing ever will move." Explain why objects still can move. (Consider whether the forces act on the same or different objects.) **For more help, refer to the Science Skill Handbook.**

Answers to Section Assessment

1. 6 N
2. The force of gravity is pulling it down, and the force of the ice is pushing it up.
3. gravity, force of the ice pushing up, your force pushing, friction from the ice
4. A force from the player accelerates the ball (second law); as it moves, gravity pulls it down (second law) while it continues in motion horizontally (first law). The ball pulls Earth toward it with a force equal to that with which Earth pulls it down (third law).
5. The chair would accelerate in the direction of the push and would push you away with an equal but opposite force. If the chair were bolted down, the whole shuttle would move slightly, and you would be pushed back.
6. $a = F/m = 60\text{ N}/100\text{ kg} = 0.6\text{ m/s}^2$
7. Action and reaction forces act on different objects, and unless the objects are somehow held down, each is free to move as a result of the force acting on it.

Activity

Balloon Races

A balloon and a rocket lifting off the launch pad have something in common. Both use Newton's third law. In this experiment, you will compare different balloon rocket designs. The balloon rocket is powered by escaping air, and its motion is determined by Newton's first, second, and third laws.

What You'll Investigate

How do Newton's laws accelerate different balloon rockets?

Materials

balloons of different sizes and shapes
drinking straws
string
tape
meterstick
stopwatch*
**clock*
**Alternate materials*

Safety Precautions

Goals

- **Measure** the speed of a balloon rocket.
- **Describe** how Newton's laws explain a rocket's motion.

Procedure

1. Run a string across the classroom to make a rocket path. Leave one end loose so you can place the rockets on the string easily.
2. Make a balloon rocket according to the diagram. Don't tie the balloon. Let it run down the track. Measure the distance it travels and the time it takes.
3. Repeat step 2 with different balloons.

Conclude and Apply

1. **Compare and contrast** the distances traveled. Which rocket went the greatest distance?
2. **Calculate** the average speed for each rocket. Compare and contrast them. Which rocket has the greatest average speed?
3. **Infer** which aspects of these rockets made them travel far or fast.
4. **Draw** a diagram showing all the forces acting on a balloon rocket.
5. Use Newton's laws of motion to explain the motion of a balloon rocket from launch until it comes to a stop.

Communicating Your Data

Discuss with classmates which balloon rocket traveled the farthest. Why? **For more help, refer to the Science Skill Handbook.**

Resource Manager

Chapter Resources Booklet
Reinforcement, p. 29
Activity Worksheets, pp. 5–6, 7–8
Lab Management and Safety, p. 65

Communicating Your Data

Students should discuss the process of troubleshooting their designs to get them to fly smoothly. The more successful techniques should be highlighted.

Activity

BENCH TESTED

Purpose Students observe Newton's third law of motion acting on rocket balloons. L2 ELL COOP LEARN LS **Kinesthetic**

Process Skills observing, inferring, comparing and contrasting, recognizing cause and effect, controlling variables, measuring, interpreting data

Time 45 minutes

Teaching Strategies Suggest that one student handle the balloon while another measures time.

Answers to Questions

1. Answers will vary.
2. To calculate a balloon's average speed, students will need to note the time and the distance the balloon travels.
3. Answers might include the balloon's size, shape, and air capacity; the thickness of the rubber from which the balloon is made; and the size of the opening.
4. Drawings should include gravity, upward force of the straw, force of the escaping air, and friction.
5. Escaping air pushes the balloon forward (third law). When it runs out of air, it continues a short way (first law) as friction slows it to a stop (second law).

Assessment

Performance Ask students to design nozzles that control the flow of air out the back of the balloon. Test the designs, and award a prize for the best one. Use **PASC,** p. 117.

Activity

BENCH TESTED

Recognize the Problem

Purpose

Students observe how to move an object from any point to another point using only two forces at right angles to each other. L2 ELL LS **Kinesthetic**

Process Skills

observing, forming a hypothesis, designing an experiment, predicting, separating and controlling variables, recognizing cause and effect

Time Required

45 minutes

Materials

Any small ball can be used for the activity, but heavier balls, such as a golf ball, work best.

Form a Hypothesis

Possible Hypotheses

Pull alternately in the two directions, moving along grid lines. Pull in both directions at once to move along diagonals.

Test Your Hypothesis

Possible Procedures

Pull on the skid in each direction, and see how much force you need to apply to make the skid begin to move. Figure out how to make the skid move in the directions necessary to follow the course. Pull the skid through the course.

Activity — Design Your Own Experiment

Modeling Motion in Two Directions

When you move a computer mouse across a mouse pad, how does the rolling ball tell the computer cursor to move in the direction that you push the mouse? Inside the housing for the mouse's ball are two or more rollers that the ball rubs against as you move the mouse. They measure up-and-down and back-and-forth motions. What happens to the rollers when you move diagonally and at different angles?

Recognize the Problem

Can you move a golf ball from one point to another using forces in only two directions?

Form a Hypothesis

How can you combine forces to move in a straight line, along a diagonal, or around corners? Place a golf ball on something that will slide, such as a plastic lid. The plastic lid is called a skid. Lay out a course to follow on the floor. Write a plan for moving your golf ball along the path.

Possible Materials

masking tape
stopwatch*
** watch or clock with a second hand*
meterstick*
**metric tape measure*
spring scales marked in newtons (2)
plastic lid
golf ball*
**tennis ball*
**Alternate materials*

Goals

- **Move** the skid across the ground using two forces.
- **Measure** how fast the skid can be moved.
- **Determine** how smoothly the direction can be changed.

Safety Precautions

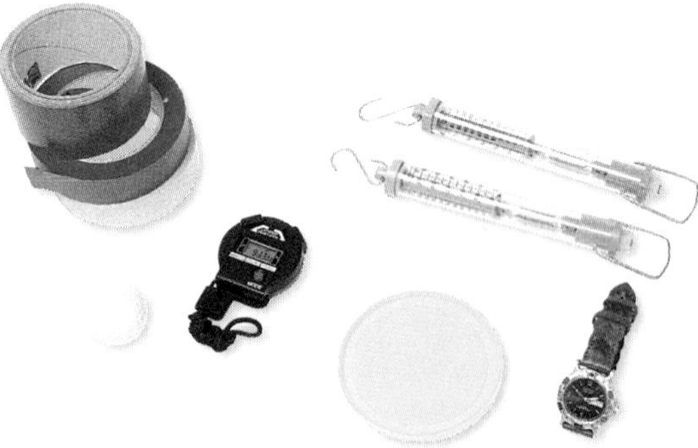

Cultural Diversity

Lacrosse The game of lacrosse is derived from an Iroquois game known as Ga-lahs. This game involves catching and tossing a ball using a thin basket on a stick. Have students learn more about this game and describe it in relation to Newton's laws.

Inclusion Strategies

Learning Disabled Before beginning this activity, have students discuss how it will be performed and what the goal of the activity is. Students should discuss the forces involved in the activity and how Newton's laws apply.

Test Your Hypothesis

Plan

1. Lay out a course that involves two directions, such as always moving forward or left.
2. Attach two spring scales to the skid. One always will pull straight forward. One always will pull to one side. You cannot turn the skid. If one scale is pulling toward the door of your classroom, it always must pull in that direction. (It can pull with zero force if needed, but it can't push.)
3. How will you handle movements along diagonals and turns?
4. How will you measure speed?
5. **Experiment** with your skid. How hard do you have to pull to counteract sliding friction at a given speed? How fast can you accelerate? Can you stop suddenly without spilling the golf ball, or do you need to slow down?
6. **Write** a plan for moving your golf ball along the course by pulling only forward or to one side. Be sure you understand your plan and have considered all the details.

Do

1. Make sure your teacher approves your plan before you start.
2. Move your golf ball along the path.
3. Modify your plan, if needed.
4. **Organize** your data so they can be used to run your course and write them in your Science Journal.
5. **Test** your results with a new route.

Analyze Your Data

1. What was the difference between the two routes? How did this affect the forces you needed to use on the golf ball?
2. How did you separate and control variables in this experiment?
3. Was your hypothesis supported? Explain.

Draw Conclusions

1. What happens when you combine two forces at right angles?
2. If you could pull on all four sides (front, back, left, right) of your skid, could you move anywhere along the floor? Make a hypothesis to explain your answer.

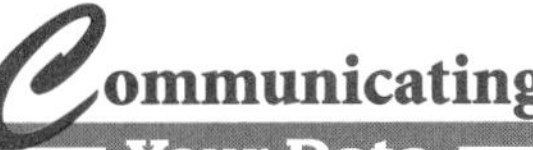

Communicating Your Data

Compare your conclusions with those of other students in your class. **For more help, refer to the Science Skill Handbook.**

Teaching Strategies

Suggest that students try moving the skid by applying forces in one direction followed by the other, and then by applying forces in the two directions at the same time.

Expected Outcome

Students will find it much easier to move the skid by moving one direction at a time. Moving the skid in both directions simultaneously requires them to be more responsive to what they see happening as they pull.

Analyze Your Data

1. Students should find the new route easier than the first if they have learned from their experience.
2. Measuring the forces in each direction separated the variables.
3. Check students' explanations.

Error Analysis

Have students discuss problems they may have had moving the skid through their courses.

Draw Conclusions

1. The object moves on a diagonal between the two forces.
2. Yes; forces in these four directions can be combined to move an object along any line.

Assessment

Performance Ask students to examine a computer mouse and determine how it tells the screen how to move the cursor. Most have one roller for horizontal motion, one for vertical motion, and a third roller for stability. The information from the rollers is combined to move the cursor on the screen in any direction. Use **Performance Assessment in the Science Classroom,** p. 89.

Communicating Your Data

Encourage students to discuss how Newton's three laws affected the results of the activity. Ask them to describe how the activity would have differed if it had been done on an almost frictionless surface such as ice.

Content Background

Air bags have been standard features in automobiles for only a few years, but the first patent for such a device was filed during World War II. The invention was originally designed as an inflatable device for use in crash landings of airplanes. The employment of air bags in cars didn't become an affordable or practical option until the 1970's when new, smaller deployment devices were developed.

Air bags inflate after a chemical reaction, triggered by an impact, releases hot nitrogen gas that expands into the bag. The inflation lasts only a fraction of a second. In that time the inflated bag serves to absorb and dissipate the energy of motion of a passenger in a car that has come to a sudden stop due to a collision. The National Highway Traffic Safety Association reported that air bags prevented over 600 fatalities in 1995. Air bags are designed to supplement, not replace, the use of seat belts and shoulder restraints. These additional safety devices are also designed to slow the movement of a passenger after a collision. Restraints can reduce a passenger's momentum by 80% when worn properly. Air bags absorb much of the rest of the energy. In order to prevent injury these three devices must be used properly. Improper use can result in injuries caused by the safety devices themselves. The NHTSA recorded 170 fatalities caused by air bags between 1990 and 2000. Of these, 63 were adult drivers, 2/3 of whom either did not use, or were improperly using, seat and shoulder restraints.

TIME

SCIENCE ISSUES THAT AFFECT YOU!

Air Bag Safety

After complaints and injuries, air bags in cars are helping all passengers

The car in front of yours stops suddenly. Your mom slams on the brakes, but not fast enough. You hear the crunch of car against car and feel your seat belt grab you. You look up at your mom in the front seat. She's covered with, not blood, thank goodness, but with a big white cloth. You are both okay. Your seat belts and air bags worked perfectly.

Popcorn in the Dash

Air bags have saved more than a thousand lives since 1992. They are like having a giant popcorn kernel in the dashboard, that pops and becomes many times its original size. But unlike popcorn, an air bag is triggered by impact, not heat. When the air bag sensor picks up the vibrations of a crash, a chemical reaction is started. The reaction produces gas that expands in a split second, inflating a balloonlike bag to cushion the driver and possibly the front-seat passenger. The bag deflates just as quickly so it doesn't trap people in the car.

Newton and the Air Bag

When you're traveling in a car, you move with it at whatever speed it is going. According to Newton's first law, you are the object in motion, and you will continue in motion unless acted upon by a force, such as a car crash.

Unfortunately, a crash stops the car, but it doesn't stop you, at least, not right away. You continue moving forward if your car doesn't have air bags or if you haven't buckled your seat belt. You stop when you strike the inside of the car. You hit the dashboard or steering wheel while traveling at the speed of the car. When an air bag inflates, it becomes the force acting on the moving object—you—and it stops you gently.

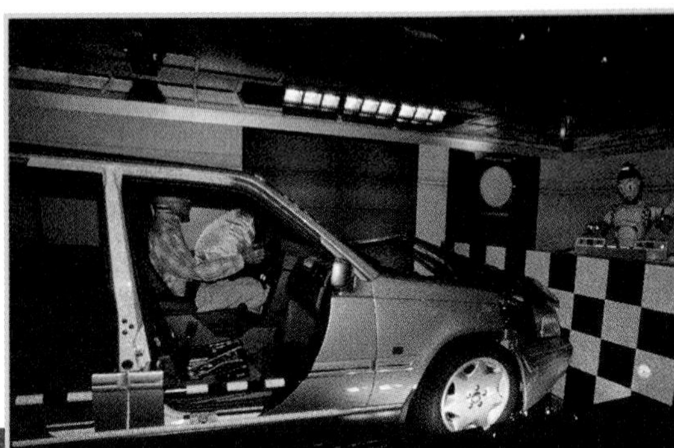

A test measures the speed at which an air bag deploys.

216

Resources for Teachers and Students

Air Bag and Seat Belt Safety Campaign
National Safety Council
1025 Connecticut Ave., NW, Suite 1200
Washington, DC 20036

Local Departments of Motor Vehicles

For information on children and air bags:

Child Safety Seats
National Highway Traffic Safety Administration
400 7th Street, S.W., NTS-13
Washington, DC 20590

National Highway Traffic Safety Administration
Auto Safety Hotline 1-800-424-9393

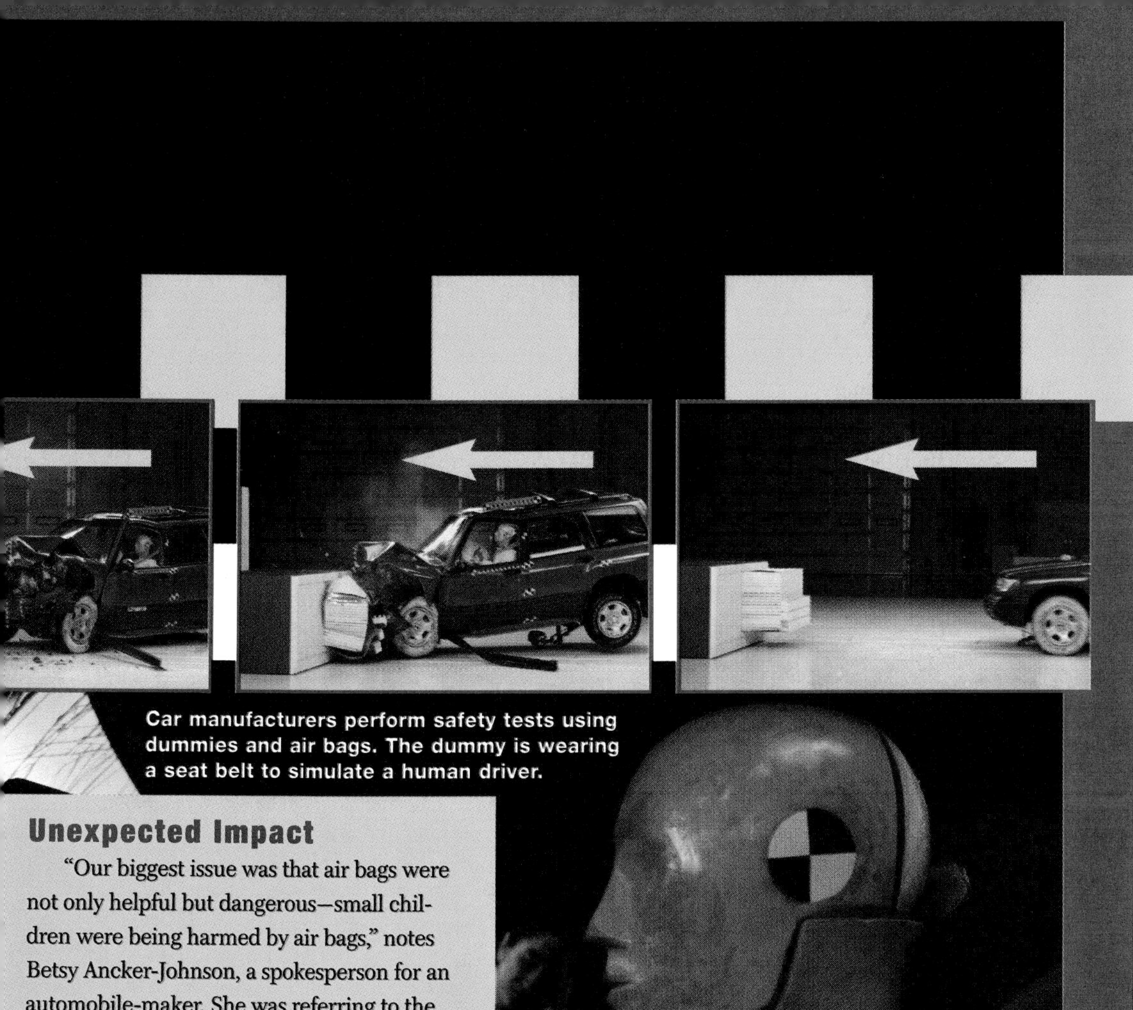

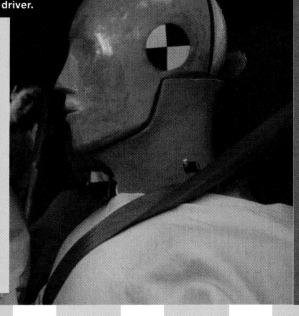

Car manufacturers perform safety tests using dummies and air bags. The dummy is wearing a seat belt to simulate a human driver.

Unexpected Impact

"Our biggest issue was that air bags were not only helpful but dangerous—small children were being harmed by air bags," notes Betsy Ancker-Johnson, a spokesperson for an automobile-maker. She was referring to the fact that air bags pop out with so much force that they have sometimes hurt or killed children and small adults. For this reason, children under the age of 12 should ride in the back seat only, with seat belts buckled. Small adults may have their air bags turned off. Car makers are developing "smart" air bags that will expand just enough to protect a passenger no matter what the size or weight.

CONNECTIONS **Measure** Draw a steering wheel on a paper plate. Ask classmates to hold it 26 cm in front of them. That's the length drivers should have between the chest and the wheel to make air bags safe. Use a tape measure to check. Inform adult drivers in your family about this safety distance.

Online
For more information, visit science.glencoe.com

CONNECTIONS Ask students to investigate the proper use of seat belts and shoulder restraints. Improper placement of seat belts can result in neck injuries caused as a passenger's momentum carries them forward and under a belt. Improper positioning of shoulder restraints can result in chest and upper limb injuries.

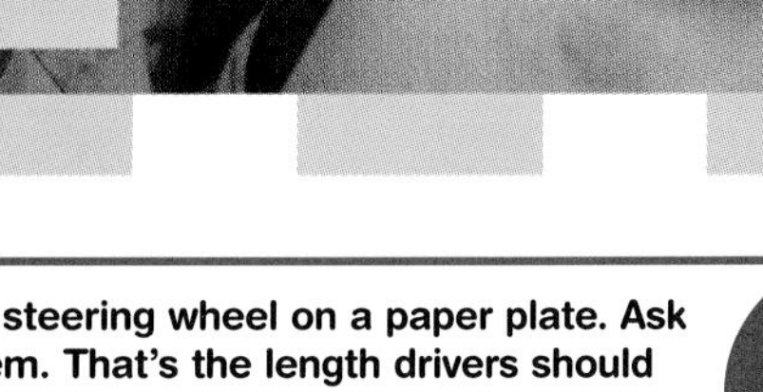

Internet Addresses

Explore the Glencoe Science Web site at **science.glencoe.com** to find out more about topics in this feature.

Discussion

In addition to air bags and seat restraints, how else can injuries be avoided in collisions? Students may suggest improvements in designs of car frames. Much research has gone into the development of crumpling structural frames that will absorb much of the impact of a collision. Also, proper use of children's seats and appropriate placement of children in the passenger compartments are crucial to safety.

Activity

Have students drop eggs from a height of one inch onto a hard floor. Have them increase the height of the drop by half-inch increments until the eggshells bread. Then have them repeat the activity several times with increasingly thick layers of fabric placed on the floor. Direct students to graph their data. Students should see that a yielding material that absorbs energy allows the eggs to withstand falls from greater heights. L2 **Kinesthetic**

Investigate the Issue

Organize the class into small groups. Ask each group to investigate the effects of a different material on energy absorption. They might repeat the experiment in the Activity above with layers of foam padding, balloons inflated to different sizes, or any other material that is available. Have them prepare graphs that summarize their results. **How do these data demonstrate the means by which air bags can prevent serious injuries?**

Chapter 7 Study Guide

Reviewing Main Ideas

Preview

Students can answer the questions in their Science Journals. Discuss the answers as you go through the chapter. **LS Linguistic**

Review

Students can write their answers, then compare them with those of other students. **LS Interpersonal**

Reteach

Students can look at the illustrations and describe details that support the main ideas of the chapter. **LS Visual-Spatial**

Answers to Chapter Review

Section 1

3. Friction stops their motion.

Section 2

2. The bowling ball has more mass.

Section 3

1. The action force is the force of the skater on the left pushing on the skater on the right. The reaction force is the force of the skater on the right pushing back on the skater on the left.

Chapter 7 Study Guide

Reviewing Main Ideas

Section 1 Newton's First Law

1. A force is a push or a pull.
2. The net force is the combination of all the forces acting on an object.
3. Newton's first law states that objects in motion tend to stay in motion and objects at rest tend to stay at rest unless acted upon by a net force. *Why don't objects in motion on Earth, like a soccer ball, stay in motion forever?*

4. Friction is a force that tries to prevent objects from sliding on each other.

Section 2 Newton's Second Law

1. Newton's second law states that an object acted upon by a net force will accelerate in the direction of this force.
2. The acceleration due to a net force is given by the equation $a = F_{net}/m$. *If a baseball bat hits a bowling ball, as seen below, why doesn't the bowling ball accelerate as quickly as a baseball that is hit just as hard?*

3. The normal force is always at a right angle to the surface it is on.
4. When the forces acting on an object are not balanced, the object accelerates in the direction of the net force.

Section 3 Newton's Third Law

1. Newton's third law states that forces always are applied in equal but opposite pairs between two objects. *What are the action and reaction forces acting on the skaters below?*

2. Action and reaction forces don't cancel because they act on different objects.
3. Action-reaction pairs enable you to walk or paddle a canoe. They also enable a rocket to launch and maneuver in space.

FOLDABLES Reading & Study Skills — After You Read

Use the information in your Foldable to help you think of concrete examples for each law of motion. Write them under the tabs.

FOLDABLES Reading & Study Skills — After You Read

After students have read the chapter and completed the Foldable described in Before You Read, have them do the activity on the student page.

Dinah Zike

Fill in the following concept map on Newtons's laws of motion.

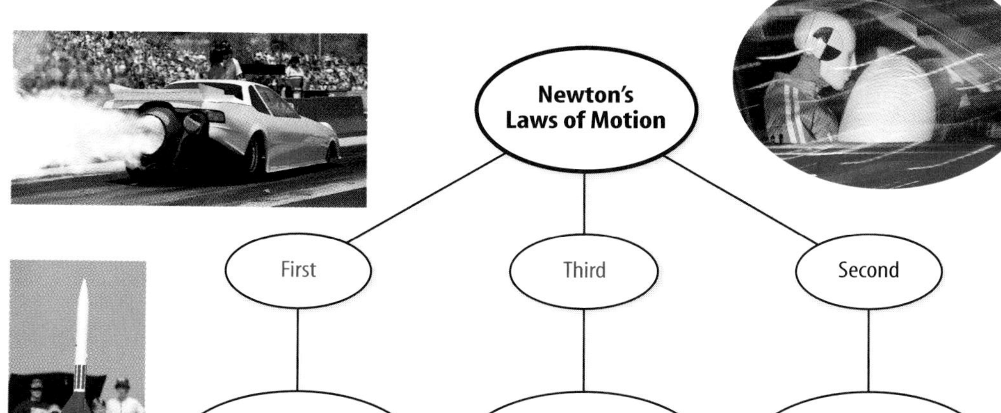

Vocabulary Review

Vocabulary Words

a. balanced forces
b. force
c. friction
d. net force
e. Newton's first law of motion
f. Newton's second law of motion
g. Newton's third law of motion
h. unbalanced forces
i. weight
j. weightlessness

Study Tip

When you read a chapter, make a list of things you find confusing or do not completely understand. Then ask your teacher to explain them.

Using Vocabulary

Explain the differences between the terms in the following sets.

1. force, inertia, weight
2. Newton's first law of motion, Newton's third law of motion
3. friction, force
4. net force, balanced forces
5. weight, weightlessness
6. balanced forces, unbalanced forces
7. friction, weight
8. Newton's first law of motion, Newton's second law of motion
9. friction, unbalanced force
10. net force, Newton's third law of motion

IDENTIFYING Misconceptions

Assess

Use the assessment as follow-up to page 192F after students have completed the chapter.

Procedure Ask students to imagine a bowling ball and a ping-pong bowl in outer space so far from other objects that they experience almost no gravity. The balls are not moving. **Will the force required to move the bowling ball be greater than the force required to move the ping pong ball? Why?** yes, because it has more mass **How do we know friction does not play a part?** In outer space there is no air and thus no friction.

Expected Outcome Students should begin to realize that a larger mass has more inertia, and thus a greater tendency to remain at rest.

Chapter 7 Study Guide

Visualizing Main Ideas

See student page.

Vocabulary Review

Using Vocabulary

1. A force is a push or a pull. Inertia is resistance to changes in motion. Weight is a measure of the force of gravity acting on an object.
2. Newton's first law states that an object will remain at rest or in motion with a constant velocity unless it is acted upon by an outside force. Newton's third law states that if a force acts on the object, the object will react with an equal force.
3. Friction is one type of force.
4. A net force is the total of all forces on an object. If the net force is zero, the forces on an object are balanced forces.
5. Weight is the measure of the gravitational force acting on an object. When an object is in free fall, weight seems to be zero.
6. When balanced forces act on an object, the object does not accelerate. When unbalanced forces act on an object, it does.
7. Friction is a force that acts between two surfaces in contact and opposes motion. Weight is the force of gravity between an object and Earth.
8. Newton's first law says that an unbalanced force will cause an object to accelerate. Newton's second law says how much the object will accelerate: $a = F/m$.
9. The force of friction acts between surfaces to oppose motion caused by an unbalanced force.
10. Net force is the sum of all forces acting on an object. According to Newton's third law, forces always act in equal but opposite pairs.

Chapter 7 Assessment

Checking Concepts

1. A
2. B
3. C
4. A
5. A
6. B
7. A
8. D
9. D
10. C

Thinking Critically

11. Yes; the ball changed direction.
12. Because Earth is so massive, the forces with which people act on it cause very little acceleration.
13. The car is held on the hill by static friction. When the car moves at a constant speed, rolling friction and air resistance balance the force exerted on the wheels by the motor. When the brakes are applied, sliding friction between the brake pads and the wheels slows down the car.
14. There must be, since there is some friction on the ice and the object is moving at constant speed. This means that the sliding friction is balanced by another force.
15. When the foot connects with the ball, the foot accelerates the ball forward (ball has low mass) and the ball accelerates the foot backward, slowing its forward motion somewhat (foot attached to body has high mass).

Chapter 7 Assessment

Checking Concepts

Choose the word or phrase that best answers the question.

1. Which of the following states Newton's third law simply?
   A) action-reaction
   B) balanced-unbalanced
   C) inertia
   D) before-after
2. What is the rubbing called when one surface moves against another surface?
   A) terminal velocity
   B) friction
   C) normal force
   D) inertia
3. What combination of units is equivalent to the newton?
   A) m/s^2
   B) $kg \cdot m/s$
   C) $kg \cdot m/s^2$
   D) kg/m
4. What is a push or pull a definition of?
   A) force
   B) momentum
   C) acceleration
   D) inertia
5. What is the type of friction that is important to walking?
   A) static friction
   B) sliding friction
   C) rolling friction
   D) air resistance
6. An object is accelerated by a net force in which direction?
   A) at an angle to the force
   B) in the direction of the force
   C) in the direction opposite to the force
   D) Any of these is possible.
7. If you exert a net force of 8 N on a 2-kg object, what will its acceleration be?
   A) $4 m/s^2$
   B) $6 m/s^2$
   C) $12 m/s^2$
   D) $16 m/s^2$
8. You are riding on a bike. Which of the following is an example of balanced forces?
   A) You pedal to speed up.
   B) You turn at constant speed.
   C) You coast to slow down.
   D) You pedal at constant speed.
9. Which of the following has no direction?
   A) force
   B) acceleration
   C) velocity
   D) mass
10. You push against a wall with a force of 5 N. What is the force the wall exerts on your hands?
    A) 0 N
    B) 2.5 N
    C) 5 N
    D) 10 N

Thinking Critically

11. A baseball is pitched east at a speed of 40 km/h. The batter hits it west at a speed of 40 km/h. Did the ball accelerate? Explain.
12. Frequently, the pair of forces acting between two objects are not noticed because one of the objects is Earth. Explain why the force acting on Earth isn't noticed.
13. A car is parked on a hill. The driver starts the car, accelerates until the car is driving at constant speed, drives at constant speed, and then brakes to put the brake pads in contact with the spinning wheels. Explain how static friction, sliding friction, rolling friction, and air resistance are acting on the car.
14. You hit a hockey puck and it slides across the ice at constant speed. Is a force keeping it in motion? Explain.
15. Newton's third law describes the forces between two colliding objects. Use this connection to explain the forces acting when you kick a soccer ball.

Developing Skills

16. **Recognizing Cause and Effect** Use Newton's third law to explain how a rocket accelerates upon takeoff.

Chapter Assessment Planner

Portfolio Encourage students to place in their portfolios one or two items of what they consider to be their best work. Examples include:

- Assessment, p. 198
- Science Journal, p. 205
- Assessment, p. 211

Performance Additional performance assessments, Performance Task Assessment Lists, and rubrics for evaluating these activities can be found in Glencoe's **Performance Assessment in the Science Classroom.**

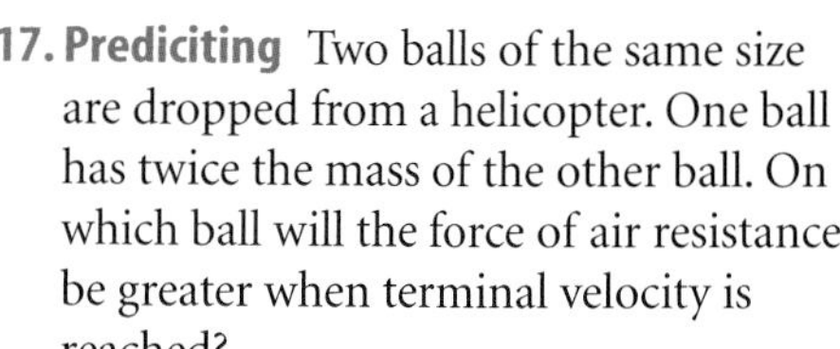

17. Prediciting Two balls of the same size are dropped from a helicopter. One ball has twice the mass of the other ball. On which ball will the force of air resistance be greater when terminal velocity is reached?

18. Interpreting Scientific Illustrations Is the force on the box balanced? Explain.

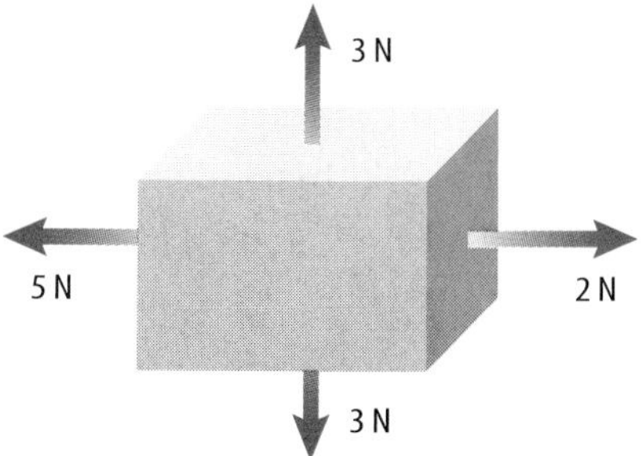

19. Solving One-Step Equations A 0.4-kg object accelerates at 2 m/s^2. Find the force.

Performance Assessment

20. Oral Presentation Research one of Newton's laws of motion and compose an oral presentation. Provide examples of the law. You might want to use a visual aid.

21. Writing in Science Create an experiment that deals with Newton's laws of motion. Document it using the following subject heads: *Title of Experiment, Partners' Names, Hypothesis, Materials, Procedures, Data, Results,* and *Conclusion.*

Technology

Go to the Glencoe Science Web site at **science.glencoe.com** or use the **Glencoe Science CD-ROM** for additional chapter assessment.

THE PRINCETON REVIEW Test Practice

The following diagram shows an experiment in which data were collected about falling objects.

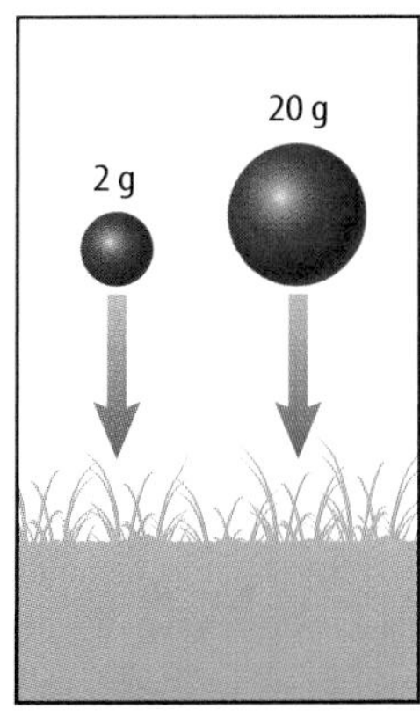

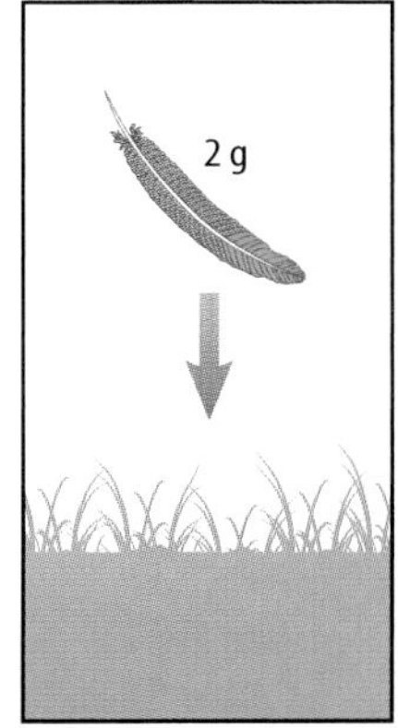

Study the diagram above and then answer the following questions about the experiment.

1. Which of these is the most likely hypothesis for the experiment depicted in the box on the left?
   A) The more an object weighs, the faster it will travel.
   B) The less an object weighs, the faster it will travel.
   C) Lighter objects tend to travel at faster speeds than heavier objects.
   D) Objects of different weights can still travel at the same speed.

2. The feather is traveling at a different speed than the balls because the feather _____.
   F) has more gravity acting upon it
   G) has less gravity acting upon it
   H) has more friction acting upon it
   J) has less friction acting upon it

Chapter 7 Assessment

THE PRINCETON REVIEW Test Practice

The Test-Taking Tip was written by The Princeton Review, the nation's leader in test preparation.

1. D
2. H

Developing Skills

16. The fuel inside the rocket explodes. The gas particles that are formed push against the rocket, and the rocket pushes against them. This pushes the rocket up and the gases out the bottom.
17. the ball with the greater mass
18. No; the net force is pushing to the left with a strength of 3 N
19. $F = ma = 0.4 \text{ kg} \times 2 \text{ m/s}^2 = 0.8 \text{ N}$

Performance Assessment

20. Presentations should focus on one of Newton's laws of motion and should include reasonable examples. Students might include a drawing, a computer display, or a short demonstration of the law. Use **PASC**, p. 143.
21. Students should follow a good scientific method in the design of their experiment. The experiment might focus on an application of the law to various situations. Use **PASC**, p. 159.

✔Assessment Resources

Reproducible Masters

Chapter Resources Booklet
Chapter Review, pp. 37–38
Chapter Tests, pp. 39–42
Assessment Transparency Activity, p. 49

Glencoe Science Web site
Interactive Tutor
Chapter Quizzes

Glencoe Technology

Assessment Transparency
Interactive CD-ROM Chapter Quizzes
ExamView Pro Test Bank
Vocabulary PuzzleMaker Software
MindJogger Videoquiz DVD/VHS

Standardized Test Practice

Reading Comprehension

QUESTION 1: B

Students need to use the information in the passage in order to identify the best supported conclusion.

QUESTION 2: F

Students need to find the underlined word *elastic* in order to locate context clues, such as *rubber* and *bounce*.

Teaching Tip

Remind students that pictures can contain important information. When a picture or diagram appears next to a reading passage, they should both study the picture and read the passage.

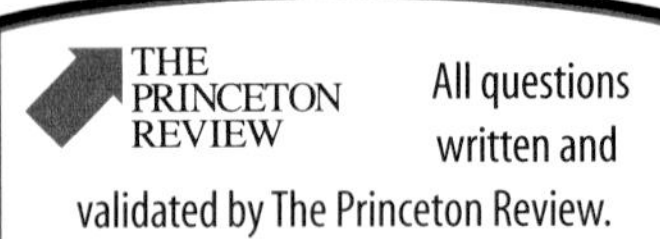

All questions written and validated by The Princeton Review.

Standardized Test Practice

Reading Comprehension

Read the passage. Then read each question that follows the passage. Decide which is the best answer to each question.

Test-Taking Tip Make a list of the important details in the passage.

Bouncing Back

Have you ever noticed that the balls you use for different sports bounce differently? If you played baseball with a tennis ball, the ball would fly into the outfield without much effort when you hit it with your bat. In contrast, if you used a baseball in a tennis match, the ball would not bounce high enough for your opponent to hit it very well. The difference in the way balls bounce depends upon the materials in the balls and the way they are constructed.

A ball drops to the floor as a result of gravity. As the ball drops, it gathers speed. When the ball hits the floor, the energy that it has gained goes into deforming the ball, changing it from its round shape. As the ball changes shape, the molecules within it stretch farther apart in some places and squeeze closer together in other places. The strength of the bonds between molecules, which determines how much they stretch apart and squeeze together, depends on the chemical composition of the materials in the ball.

Most balls are made of rubber. Rubber is <u>elastic</u>, which means that its molecules deform but quickly regain their original shape, making the ball bounce. Rubber is made of long chains of polymer molecules. When these molecules hit a surface, they stretch but then reform. There are different types of rubber polymers—if the polymer chains are tightly linked, they do not deform much and thus they bounce high. Some of the ball's kinetic energy is converted into thermal energy, which is why balls sometimes feel warm after they are dropped.

Sometimes a ball's kinetic energy is converted into thermal energy, making it warm to the touch.

1. According to information in the passage, it is probably accurate to conclude that _____.
   A) all rubber balls bounce the same, no matter what they are made of
   B) rubber polymers help determine a ball's bounce
   C) baseballs are better for playing tennis than tennis balls are for playing baseball
   D) the higher a ball bounces, the more thermal energy that is produced

2. In the context of this passage, the word <u>elastic</u> means _____.
   F) able to bounce
   G) inflexible
   H) tightly linked
   J) warm

222 STANDARDIZED TEST PRACTICE

Reasoning and Skills

Read each question and choose the best answer.

1. Latifah wanted to figure out which race car had the most kinetic energy during a competition. She researched the different race cars to find out their masses. Her experiment could be improved by _____.
   A) writing down a list of observations during the competition
   B) finding out the velocity of each race car during the competition
   C) weighing the cars after the competition
   D) researching motorcycles as well as race cars

Test-Taking Tip Consider the factors that affect an object's kinetic energy.

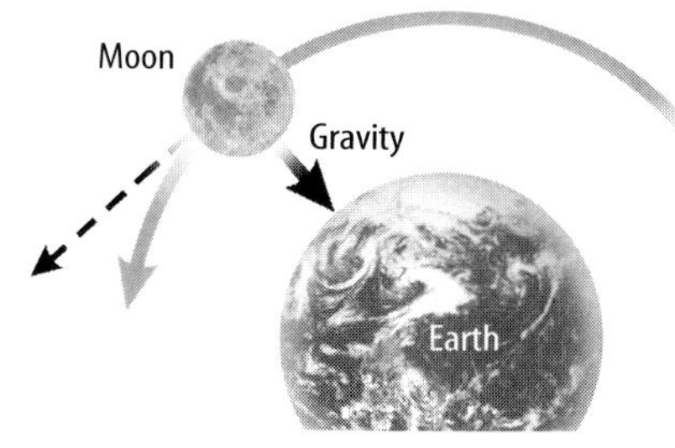

2. Which kind of scientist would most likely use this picture?
   F) geologist
   G) physicist
   H) chemist
   J) zoologist

Test-Taking Tip Review the type of information presented by the picture in column 1.

Training Record

End of Day	Maximum Speed (m/s)
1	10.5
2	11.1
3	11.7
4	12.3

3. These data were collected while an athlete trained for a marathon. If everything remains the same, what will be the maximum speed of the athlete at the end of the sixth month?
   A) 12.9 km/h
   B) 12.6 km/h
   C) 12.0 km/h
   D) 13.5 km/h

Test-Taking Tip Carefully consider the information in both the chart and the question in order to identify the trend.

Consider this question carefully before writing your answer on a separate sheet of paper.

4. As an object's mass increases while its volume stays the same, its density increases. Explain why this statement is true.

Test-Taking Tip Recall the formula for calculating the density of an object.

Standardized Test Practice

Reasoning and Skills

Question 1: B

Students must understand that kinetic energy is determined by mass and velocity.

Question 2: G

Students must understand that gravity and orbital motion are topics in physics.

Question 3: D

Students must analyze the data in the chart to discover a pattern. The chart lists up to the fourth day of training. Students should find the pattern and predict the maximum speed that would most likely be achieved by the runner by the sixth day of training.

Teaching Tip

Explain that when presented with a table or chart, students should always look for a pattern in the data.

Question 4: Answers will vary

Students should mention the formula for density. As the numerator (mass) increases, the value of the fraction increases.

UNIT 4

Unit Contents

✔ Pre-Reading Activity

Have students choose a chapter in this unit and write five things they want to know about the topic. Then have them skim the text for key words to help them locate passages where they think their questions may be answered.

UNIT 4 Energy

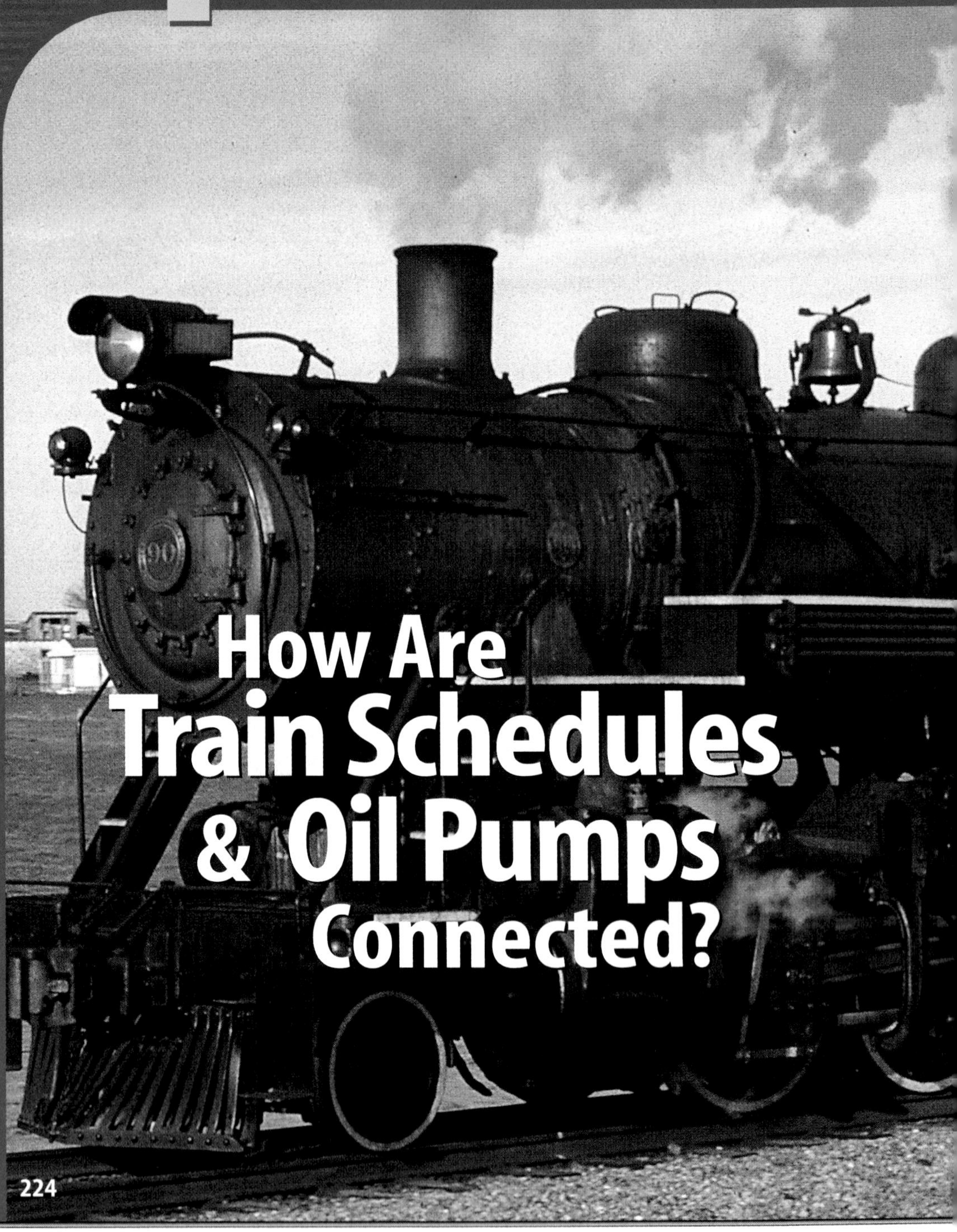

How Are Train Schedules & Oil Pumps Connected?

224

Teacher to Teacher

"When examining compound machines, have students search the classroom, the school, or magazines to identify the compound machine that includes the greatest number of simple machines. Have them identify each simple machine they find."

Kevin Finnegan, Teacher
McCord Middle School
Worthington, OH

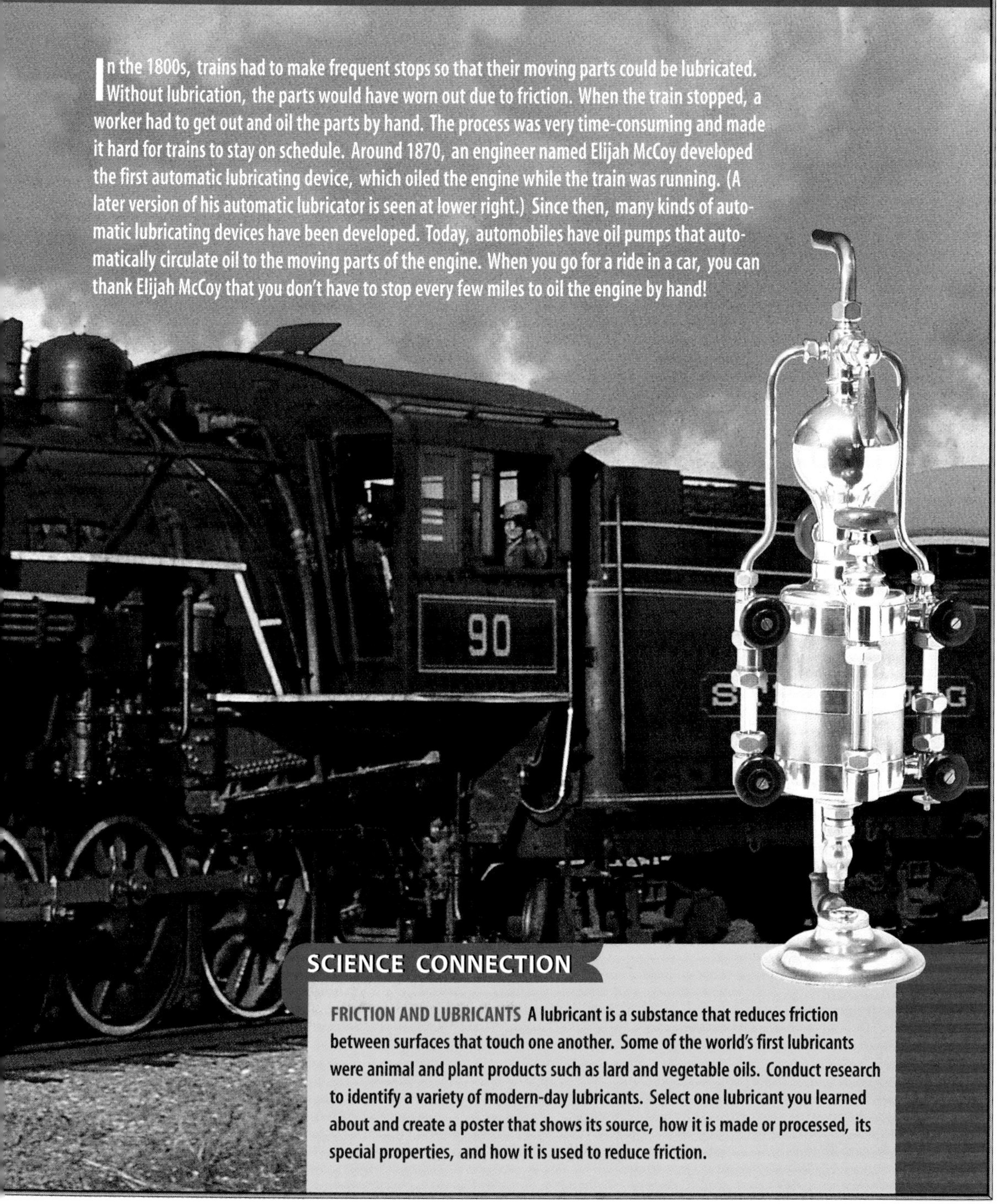

In the 1800s, trains had to make frequent stops so that their moving parts could be lubricated. Without lubrication, the parts would have worn out due to friction. When the train stopped, a worker had to get out and oil the parts by hand. The process was very time-consuming and made it hard for trains to stay on schedule. Around 1870, an engineer named Elijah McCoy developed the first automatic lubricating device, which oiled the engine while the train was running. (A later version of his automatic lubricator is seen at lower right.) Since then, many kinds of automatic lubricating devices have been developed. Today, automobiles have oil pumps that automatically circulate oil to the moving parts of the engine. When you go for a ride in a car, you can thank Elijah McCoy that you don't have to stop every few miles to oil the engine by hand!

SCIENCE CONNECTION

FRICTION AND LUBRICANTS A lubricant is a substance that reduces friction between surfaces that touch one another. Some of the world's first lubricants were animal and plant products such as lard and vegetable oils. Conduct research to identify a variety of modern-day lubricants. Select one lubricant you learned about and create a poster that shows its source, how it is made or processed, its special properties, and how it is used to reduce friction.

Introducing the Unit

How Are Train Schedules & Oil Pumps Connected?

All matter is composed of atoms. Atoms of various kinds are attracted to other atoms. The moving parts of train engines contact one another. The attraction between atoms in these parts produces resistance to motion; this resistance is what we call friction. As the parts move against one another the attractions between atoms are broken. Gradually the matter of the contacting parts is worn away. As the bonds between atoms break, the energy holding them together (potential energy) is released as heat (a form of kinetic energy). The use of lubricants reduces the force of friction between objects by forming a thin layer of frictionless molecules between moving parts. This reduces the damage to the parts and the heat generated by motion. The result is longer-lasting parts and a more efficient use of fuels to produce motion.

Explore the Glencoe Science Web site at **science.glencoe.com** to find out more about topics in this unit.

SCIENCE CONNECTION

Activity

Demonstrate that the energy attracting atoms to one another is released as kinetic energy, or heat, when those bonds are broken. Give each student a rubber band. Instruct them to hold it against their upper lip and to note how warm or cool the material feels. Have the students stretch the rubber band while the bands are in contact with their skin. The rubber band will feel quite warm. As the band resumes its original shape they will feel the material cool down. Explain that stretching the rubber broke some of the forces of attraction between atoms. This energy was released as heat.

Section/Objectives	Standards		Activities/Features
	National	State/Local	
Chapter Opener	See p. 5T for a Key to Standards.		**Explore Activity:** Analyze a marble launch, p. 227 **Before You Read,** p. 227
Section 1 What is energy? 3 sessions 1.5 blocks 1. **Explain** what energy is. 2. **Distinguish** between kinetic energy and potential energy. 3. **Identify** the various forms of energy.	National Content Standards: UCP3, B3		
Section 2 Energy Transformations 3 sessions 1.5 blocks 1. **Apply** the law of conservation of energy to energy transformations. 2. **Identify** how energy changes form. 3. **Describe** how electric power plants produce energy.	National Content Standards: UCP3, A1, B3, F5		**Science Online,** p. 234 **MiniLAB:** Analyzing Energy Transformations, p. 235 **Visualizing Energy Transformations,** p. 236 **Life Science Integration,** p. 237 **Activity:** Hearing with Your Jaw, p. 240
Section 3 Sources of Energy 4 sessions 2 blocks 1. **Explain** what renewable, nonrenewable, and alternative resources are. 2. **Develop** an awareness that the use of any energy source has positive and negative consequences.	National Content Standards: UCP5, A1, B3, F2, F4		**Earth Science Integration,** p. 242 **Science Online,** p. 244 **Problem-Solving Activity:** Is energy outpacing production?, p. 244 **MiniLAB:** Building a Solar Collector, p. 245 **Activity:** Energy to Power Your Life, pp. 250–251

Activity Materials	Reproducible Resources	Section Assessment	Technology
Explore Activity: piece of wood, marble, 1 m piece of molding or pipe	**Chapter Resources Booklet** Foldables Worksheet, p. 15 Directed Reading Overview, p. 17 Note-taking Worksheets, pp. 31–32	GLENCOE'S ASSESSMENT ADVANTAGE	
Need materials? Contact Science Kit at 1-800-828-7777 or www.sciencekit.com on the Internet.	**Chapter Resources Booklet** Transparency Activity, p. 42 Enrichment, p. 28 Reinforcement, p. 25 Directed Reading, p. 18 **Reading and Writing Skill Activities,** p. 35	Portfolio Science Journal, p. 231 Performance Skill Builder Activities, p. 232 Content Section Assessment, p. 232	Section Focus Transparency Interactive CD-ROM/DVD Guided Reading Audio Program
MiniLAB: soft clay, marble, steel ball, rubber ball, table-tennis ball **Activity:** radio or CD player, small electrical motor, headphone jack	**Chapter Resources Booklet** Transparency Activity, p. 43 MiniLAB, p. 3 Enrichment, p. 29 Reinforcement, p. 26 Directed Reading, p. 19 Lab Activity, pp. 9–10 Activity Worksheet, pp. 5–6 **Science Inquiry Labs,** p. 9	Portfolio Curriculum Connection, p. 238 Performance MiniLAB, p. 235 Skill Builder Activities, p. 239 Content Section Assessment, p. 239	Section Focus Transparency Interactive CD-ROM/DVD Guided Reading Audio Program
MiniLAB: large pot lined with black plastic garbage bag and filled with water, clear plastic wrap, thermometer **Activity:** Internet and other resources on energy	**Chapter Resources Booklet** Transparency Activity, p. 44 MiniLAB, p. 4 Enrichment, p. 30 Reinforcement, p. 27 Directed Reading, pp. 19, 20 Lab Activity, pp. 11–13 Activity Worksheet, pp. 7–8 Transparency Activity, pp. 45–46 **Lab Management and Safety,** p. 37	Portfolio Science Journal, p. 242 Performance Problem-Solving Activity, p. 244 MiniLAB, p. 245 Skill Builder Activities, p. 249 Content Section Assessment, p. 249	Section Focus Transparency Teaching Transparency Interactive CD-ROM/DVD Guided Reading Audio Program

End of Chapter Assessment

GLENCOE'S ASSESSMENT ADVANTAGE

Blackline Masters	Technology	Professional Series
Chapter Resources Booklet Chapter Review, pp. 35–36 Chapter Tests, pp. 37–40 **Standardized Test Practice by The Princeton Review,** pp. 35–38	MindJogger Videoquiz CD-ROM Explorations and Quizzes Vocabulary Puzzle Makers ExamView Pro Test Bank Interactive Lesson Planner Interactive Teacher's Edition	Performance Assessment in the Science Classroom (PASC)

Transparencies

Section Focus

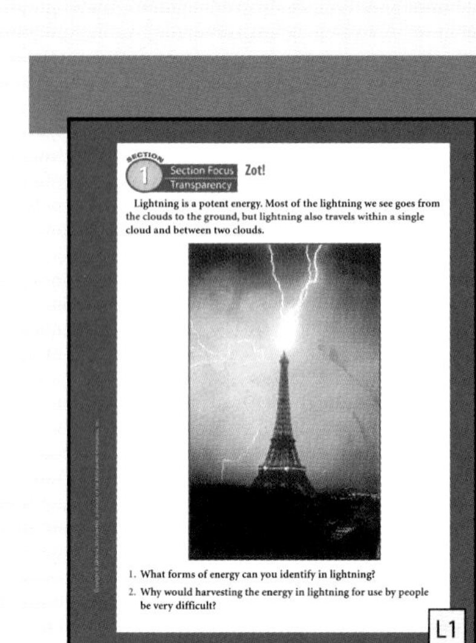
Section 1 Section Focus Transparency **Zot!**

Lightning is a potent energy. Most of the lightning we see goes from the clouds to the ground, but lightning also travels within a single cloud and between two clouds.

1. What forms of energy can you identify in lightning?
2. Why would harvesting the energy in lightning for use by people be very difficult?

L1

Section 2 Section Focus Transparency **Burning Light**

You've probably heard a lot about lasers, but do you know what they really are? The word *laser* stands for light amplification by stimulated emission of radiation. Lasers take incoming energy and transform it into a focused beam of light.

1. How is this laser being used?
2. How is energy changed by a laser? Is there any new energy created?
3. Name some other uses of lasers.

L1

Section 3 Section Focus Transparency **Getting to Know Peat**

Peat is a fuel that is cut from bogs. After the peat is dried, it is burned as an energy source. Peat is formed mostly from plants that fell into bog water and only partly rotted.

1. How do people get energy from peat?
2. Could peat be used to generate electricity? Why or why not?
3. Judging from the paragraph, is it easy to renew peat bogs after the peat is cut?

L1

This is a representation of key blackline masters available in the Teacher Classroom Resources. See Resource Manager boxes within the chapter for additional information.

Assessment

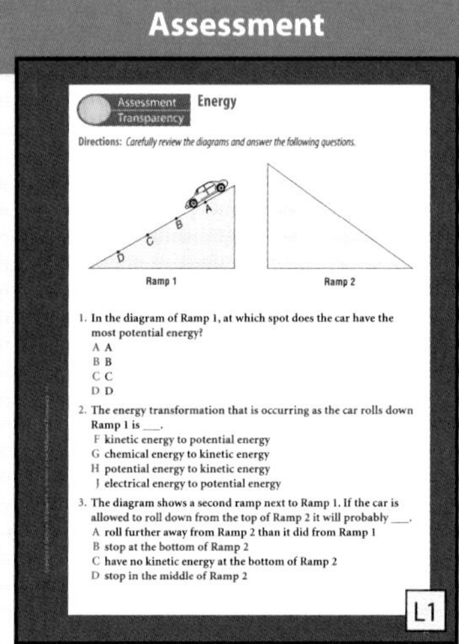
Assessment Transparency **Energy**

Directions: *Carefully review the diagrams and answer the following questions.*

1. In the diagram of Ramp 1, at which spot does the car have the most potential energy?
   A A
   B B
   C C
   D D
2. The energy transformation that is occurring as the car rolls down Ramp 1 is ___.
   F kinetic energy to potential energy
   G chemical energy to kinetic energy
   H potential energy to kinetic energy
   J electrical energy to potential energy
3. The diagram shows a second ramp next to Ramp 1. If the car is allowed to roll down from the top of Ramp 2 it will probably ___.
   A roll further away from Ramp 2 than it did from Ramp 1
   B stop at the bottom of Ramp 2
   C have no kinetic energy at the bottom of Ramp 2
   D stop in the middle of Ramp 2

L1

Teaching

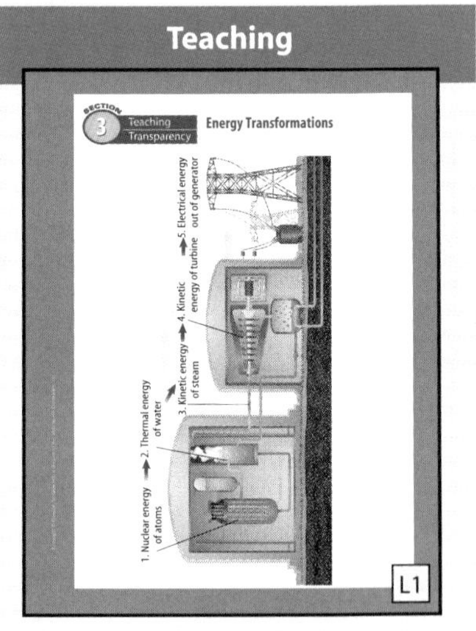
Section 3 Teaching Transparency **Energy Transformations**

L1

Key to Teaching Strategies

The following designations will help you decide which activities are appropriate for your students.

L1 Level 1 activities should be appropriate for students with learning difficulties.

L2 Level 2 activities should be within the ability range of all students.

L3 Level 3 activities are designed for above-average students.

ELL ELL activities should be within the ability range of English Language Learners.

COOP LEARN Cooperative Learning activities are designed for small group work.

LS Multiple Learning Styles logos, as described on page 22T, are used throughout to indicate strategies that address different learning styles.

P These strategies represent student products that can be placed into a best-work portfolio.

Hands-on Activities

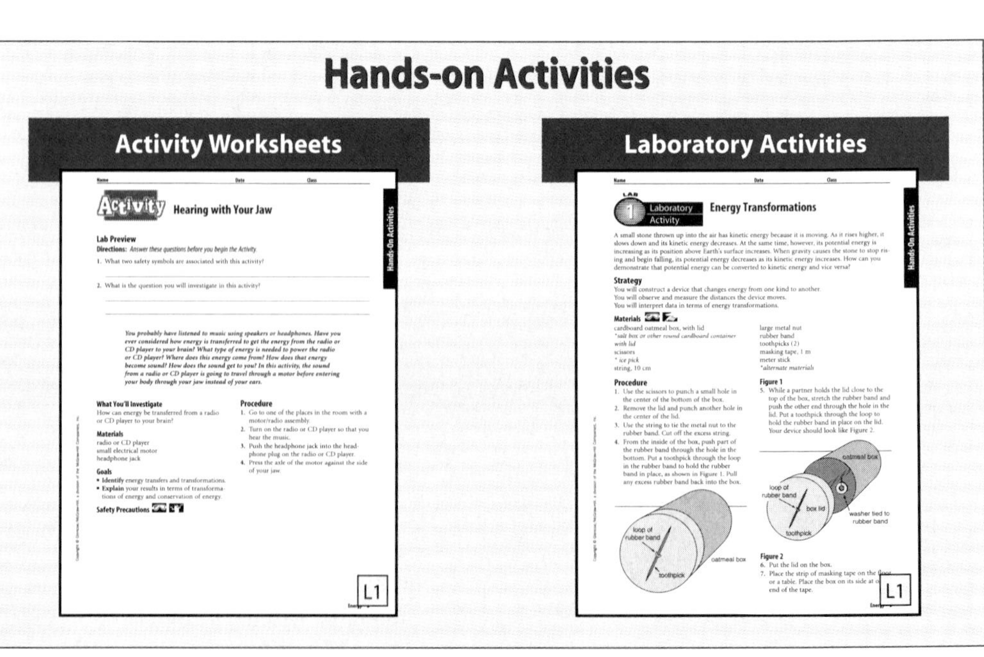

Activity Worksheets

Name Date Class

Activity **Hearing with Your Jaw**

Lab Preview

Directions: *Answer these questions before you begin the Activity.*

1. What two safety symbols are associated with this activity?
2. What is the question you will investigate in this activity?

You probably have listened to music using speakers or headphones. Have you ever considered how energy is transferred to get the energy from the radio or CD player to your brain? What type of energy is needed to power the radio or CD player? Where does this energy come from? How does that energy become sound? How does the sound get to you? In this activity, the sound from a radio or CD player is going to travel through a motor before entering your body through your jaw instead of your ears.

What You'll Investigate

How can energy be transferred from a radio or CD player to your brain?

Materials

radio or CD player
small electrical motor
headphone jack

Goals

- **Identify** energy transfers and transformations.
- **Explain** your results in terms of transformations of energy and conservation of energy.

Safety Precautions

Procedure

1. Go to one of the places in the room with a motor/radio assembly.
2. Turn on the radio or CD player so that you hear the music.
3. Push the headphone jack into the headphone plug on the radio or CD player.
4. Press the axle of the motor against the side of your jaw.

Hands-On Activities

L1

Laboratory Activities

Name Date Class

Lab 1 Laboratory Activity **Energy Transformations**

A small stone thrown up into the air has kinetic energy because it is moving. As it rises higher, it slows down and its kinetic energy decreases. At the same time, however, its potential energy is increasing as its position above Earth's surface increases. When gravity causes the stone to stop rising and begin falling, its potential energy decreases as its kinetic energy increases. How can you demonstrate that potential energy can be converted to kinetic energy and vice versa?

Strategy

You will construct a device that changes energy from one kind to another.
You will observe and measure the distances the device moves.
You will interpret data in terms of energy transformations.

Materials

cardboard oatmeal box, with lid
**salt box or other round cardboard container with lid*
scissors
** ice pick*
string, 10 cm
large metal nut
rubber band
toothpicks (2)
masking tape, 1 m
meter stick
**alternate materials*

Procedure

1. Use the scissors to punch a small hole in the center of the bottom of the box.
2. Remove the lid and punch another hole in the center of the lid.
3. Use the string to tie the metal nut to the rubber band. Cut off the excess string.
4. From the inside of the box, push part of the rubber band through the hole in the bottom. Put a toothpick through the loop in the rubber band to hold the rubber band in place, as shown in Figure 1. Pull any excess rubber band back into the box.

Figure 1

5. While a partner holds the lid close to the top of the box, stretch the rubber band and push the other end through the hole in the lid. Put a toothpick through the loop to hold the rubber band in place on the lid. Your device should look like Figure 2.

Figure 2

6. Put the lid on the box.
7. Place the strip of masking tape on the floor or a table. Place the box on its side at one end of the tape.

Hands-On Activities

L1

Meeting Different Ability Levels

Content Outline

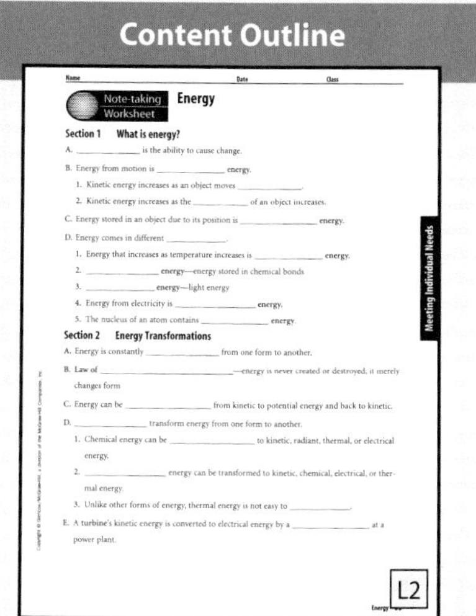
Note-taking Worksheet — Energy

L2

Reinforcement

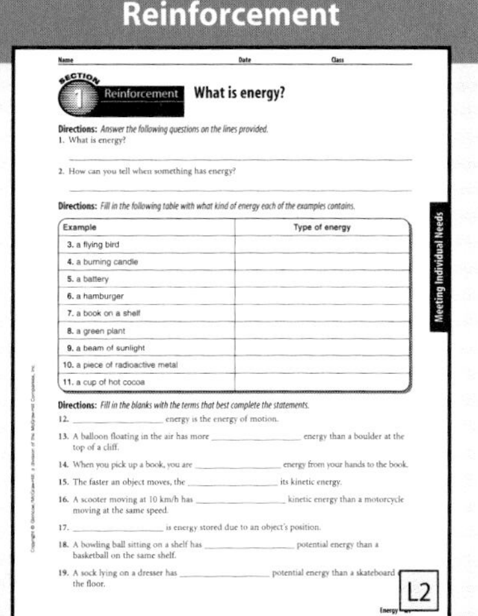
Reinforcement — What is energy?

L2

Directed Reading

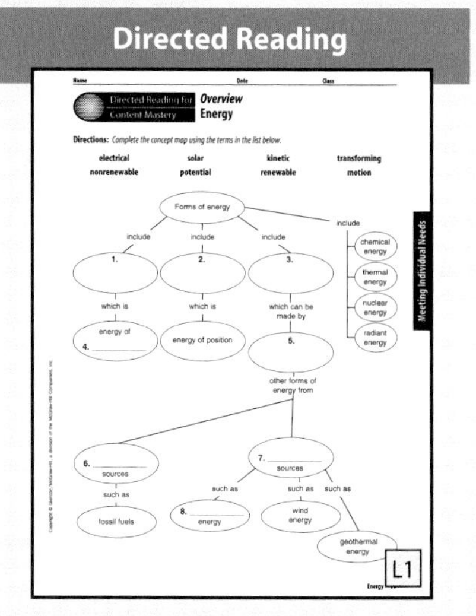
Directed Reading for Content Mastery — Overview: Energy

L1

Assessment

Chapter Tests

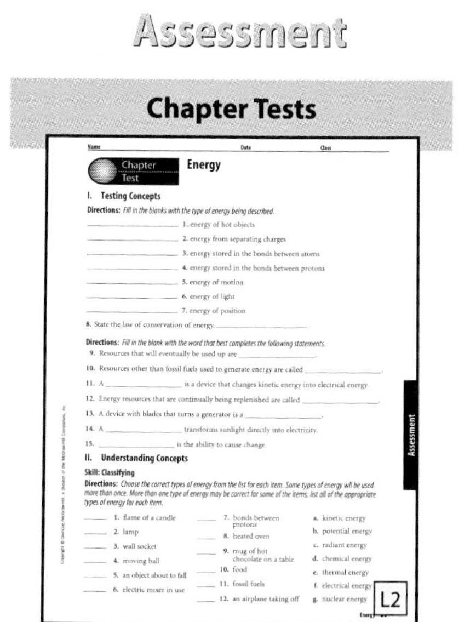
Chapter Test — Energy

L2

Enrichment

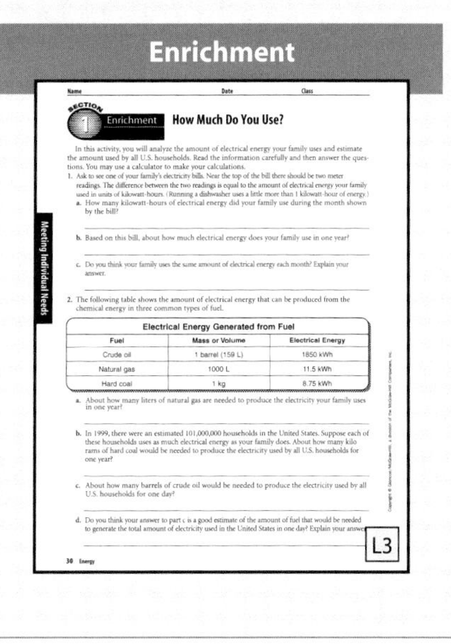
Enrichment — How Much Do You Use?

L3

Spanish Directed Reading

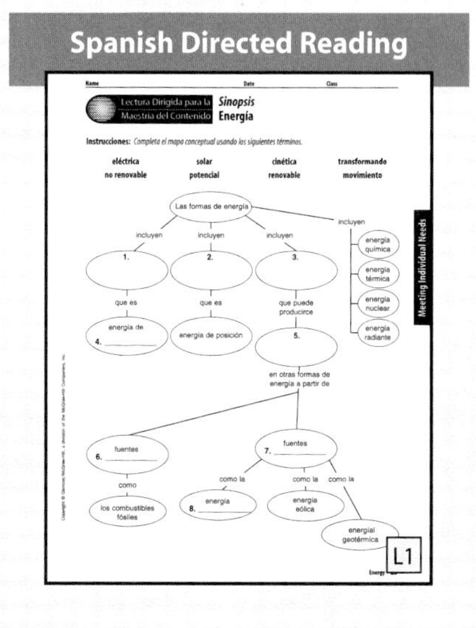
Lectura Dirigida para la Maestría del Contenido — Sinopsis: Energía

L1

Test Practice Workbook

L2

Chapter Review

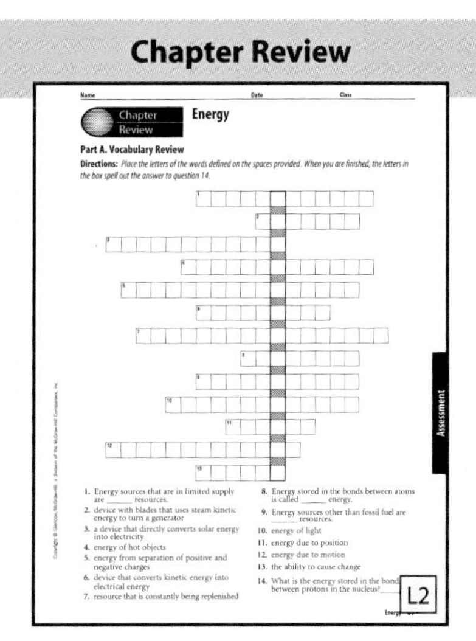
Chapter Review — Energy

L2

Science Content Background

What is energy?

The Nature of Energy

Energy is not matter. Some forms of energy can exist independent of matter such as light. Other forms such as chemical and kinetic energy can only exist with matter.

Student Misconception

Energy is something that is used and then disappears.

Refer to pages 234–235 for content related to this topic.

Energy Transformations

Changing Forms of Energy

In our common experience on Earth, energy is neither created nor destroyed, just transformed from one form into another. Heat is produced from most energy transformations.

The Law of Conservation of Energy

The law of conservation of energy states that energy is neither created nor destroyed, only converted from one form into another. While many things cycle through nature, energy does not; it flows through our world. There may be many energy transformations in its path, but most energy transformations are accompanied by a conversion of some energy into a less useful form of energy: heat.

Keren Su/FPG International

Einstein suggested that mass could be converted to energy and energy into mass. Einstein's famous equation, $E=mc^2$ shows the relationship between mass and energy, and the power unleashed by atomic bombs is evidence that it is true. So the law of conservation of energy isn't completely true, but it works in most situations on our planet.

Sources of Energy

Fossil Fuels

Fossil fuels were once living organisms that obtained energy from the Sun, and could thus be considered a type of solar energy. Unlike more direct forms of solar energy, burning fossil fuels produces carbon dioxide gas and other pollutants.

Geothermal Energy

You don't need to live near a volcano to use geothermal energy. Geothermal heat pumps, in use in 400,000 homes in the United States alone, take advantage of fairly constant below-ground temperatures. The temperature range in the first ten feet of soil is 10° C to 15.5° C (50° F to 60° F). This usually means the soil is warmer than the winter air and cooler than the summer air. In a heat pump, air either gains or loses heat to the ground before entering a heating or cooling unit.

Iceland leads the world in its use of geothermal energy for heating. Almost 90% of its buildings are warmed using water heated by hot magma below Earth's surface. The Philippines is a leader in the use of geothermal energy to produce electricity. Approximately 22% of their electricity is produced with geothermal energy.

For additional content background on this topic, go to the Glencoe Science Web site at science.glencoe.com.

Misconceptions

Find Out What Students Think

Students may think that . . .

- **Energy is something that is used and then disappears.**

Students may have this misconception because people commonly talk about energy as though we use it and then it's gone. An athlete may say, "I ran out of energy." A parent may say, "Turn off the lights. You're wasting energy." An environmentalist may caution that the world is running out of energy. Another problem is that energy can seem abstract. Perhaps it is easy to understand that food contains energy. But energy contained by a book sitting on a desk is more difficult to comprehend.

Demonstration and Discussion

Hold up a windup toy. As you wind it, explain that your actions take energy. Release the toy and allow it to move until it winds down. Ask students to explain what has happened to the energy that you put into the toy. If students say that the toy used it up, ask them to explain what they mean. Did it disappear or become something else? Have students share their ideas.

Promote Understanding

Activity

Use books and tag board to make a U-shaped ramp. Students may have observed similar ramps used in skateboarding and bicycle stunt competitions.

- Hold a marble on top of one side of the ramp. Explain that the marble has potential energy due to its position. Gravity is pulling down on it.
- Release the marble. Explain that as the marble falls, its potential energy is converted to kinetic energy. Then, as the marble rises up the other side of the ramp, the kinetic energy is converted into potential energy.
- Now have students release the marble. Direct them to observe how high the marble rises up on each side of the ramp. Have them mark the heights achieved on each side of the ramp. Have students repeat this process at least five times.
- **How does the maximum height reached by the marble change throughout each trial? Why does the marble go a little less high each time? How do we know the marble will eventually stop rolling?** Help students realize that in this energy transformation between potential energy and kinetic energy, some energy is lost due to friction. This converts some kinetic energy of the marble into heat energy. Have the students rub their hands together to experience friction producing heat energy.

Assess

After completing the chapter, see *Identifying Misconceptions* in the Study Guide.

Energy

Chapter Vocabulary

energy
kinetic energy
potential energy
thermal energy
chemical energy
radiant energy
electrical energy
nuclear energy
law of conservation of energy
generator
turbine
nonrenewable resource
renewable resource
alternative resource
photovoltaic

What do you think?

Science Journal The picture shows panels that collect the Sun's energy. This energy then can be used for heat or converted into electricity.

Energy

Volcanoes, earthquakes, lightning, and hurricanes are some of the most powerful forces in nature. Every one of these phenomena contain a tremendous amount of energy. The river of lava shown in this picture flowing from Mount Etna in Italy has heat energy, light energy, and energy of motion. In this chapter, you will learn about different forms and sources of energy. You will also learn how energy can be transformed from one form into another, and how some forms of energy can be used.

What do you think?

Science Journal Look at the picture below with a classmate. Discuss what is happening. Here's a hint: *Concentrating energy is the key to what is happening here.* Write your answer or best guess in your Science Journal.

226

Theme Connection

Systems and Interactions This chapter explores the various forms of energy, the interactions among them, and how they are harnessed for use in various systems.

A marble and a piece of wood are on a countertop. If nothing disturbs them, they will remain there. However, if you tilt the wood and roll the marble down the slope, the marble acquires a new property—the ability to do something.

Analyze a marble launch

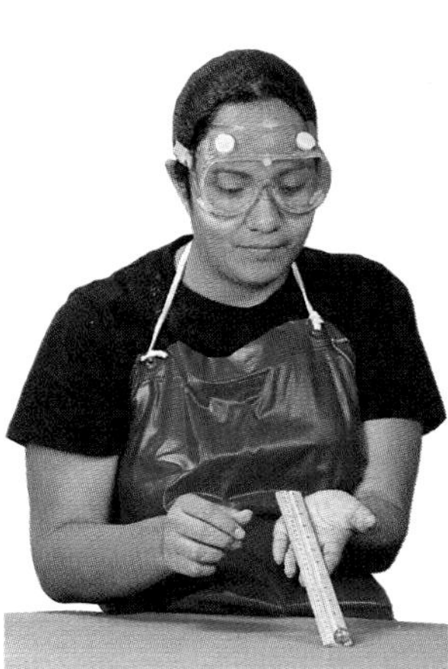

1. Obtain a 1 m piece of molding or pipe to use as a track.
2. On a table, raise one end of the track slightly and measure the height.
3. Roll a marble down the track. Measure the distance from its starting point to where it hits the floor. Repeat. Calculate the average of the two measurements.
4. Repeat steps 2 and 3 for three different heights. Predict what will happen if you use a heavier marble. Test your prediction and record your observations.

Observe

In your Science Journal, describe your experiment and what you discovered. How did the different heights cause the distance to change?

Before You Read

FOLDABLES Reading & Study Skills

Making a Know-Want-Learn Study Fold **Make the following Foldable to help identify what you already know and what you want to know about energy.**

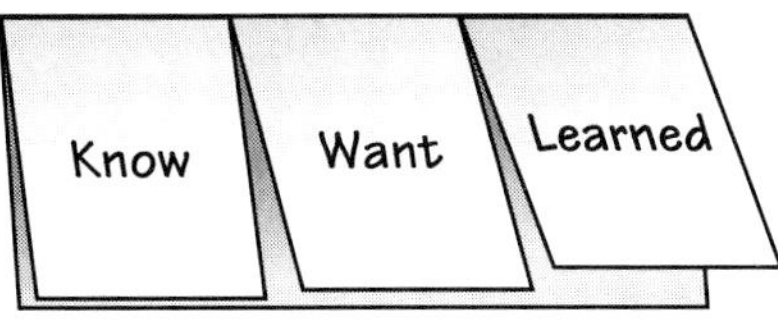

1. Place a sheet of paper in front of you so the long side is at the top. Fold the paper in half from top to bottom.
2. Fold both sides in. Unfold the paper so three sections show.
3. Through the top thickness of paper, cut along each of the fold lines to the topfold, forming three tabs. Label the tabs *Know*, *Want*, and *Learned*.
4. Before you read the chapter, write what you know and what you want to know under the tabs. As you read the chapter, correct what you have written and add more questions.

Before You Read

FOLDABLES Reading & Study Skills

Dinah Zike Study Fold

Purpose This activity provides a Foldable in which students can record what they know and what they would like to know about energy before reading the chapter. The Foldable also helps students determine what they have learned about energy after reading.

For additional help, see Foldable Worksheet p. 15 in **Chapter Resources Booklet,** or go to the Glencoe Science Web site at **science.glencoe.com.** See After You Read in the Study Guide at the end of this chapter.

EXPLORE ACTIVITY

Purpose Use the Explore Activity to help students see how the height from which an object is released on a ramp affects the distance it will roll. L2 ELL COOP LEARN LS **Kinesthetic**

Materials book, piece of molding or pipe 1 m long, glass marble, steel marble, meterstick

Teaching Strategy Make sure students always release the marble at the same point on the ramp, and be sure there isn't a significant bump where the ramp contacts the table. An index card can be used to smooth out the bump.

Observe

The higher the ramp, the farther from the table the marble hits the floor. The more massive marble lands farther from the table because it has more horizontal velocity when it leaves the table than does the less massive marble.

Performance Have students redesign the experiment to explore how changes in the mass of the marble affect an object it strikes. Use **Performance Assessment in the Science Classroom,** p. 105.

SECTION

What is energy?

1 Motivate

Bellringer Transparency

Display the Section Focus Transparency for Section 1. Use the accompanying Transparency Activity Master. L2 ELL

SECTION 1 Section Focus Transparency **Zot!**

Lightning is a potent energy. Most of the lightning we see goes from the clouds to the ground, but lightning also travels within a single cloud and between two clouds.

1. What forms of energy can you identify in lightning?
2. Why would harvesting the energy in lightning for use by people be very difficult?

Tie to Prior Knowledge

Ask students to name changes they have observed going on around them since they got up this morning. Possible answers include lights going on or off, changes in the positions of objects and of themselves, changes in heat, and so on. Tell students that in this section they will learn about some of the causes of these changes.

SECTION

What is energy?

As You Read

***What* You'll Learn**

- **Explain** what energy is.
- **Distinguish** between kinetic energy and potential energy.
- **Identify** the various forms of energy.

Vocabulary

energy
kinetic energy
potential energy
thermal energy
chemical energy
radiant energy
electrical energy
nuclear energy

***Why* It's Important**

Energy is the source of all activity.

The Nature of Energy

What comes to mind when you hear the word *energy?* Do you picture running, leaping, and spinning like a dancer or a gymnast? How would you define energy? When an object has energy, it can make things happen. In other words, **energy** is the ability to cause change. What do the items shown in **Figure 1** have in common?

Look around and notice the changes that are occurring—someone walking by or a ray of sunshine that is streaming through the window and warming your desk. Maybe you can see the wind moving the leaves on a tree. What changes are occurring?

Transferring Energy You might not realize it, but you have a large amount of energy. In fact, everything around you has energy, but you notice it only when a change takes place. Anytime a change occurs, energy is transferred from one object to another. You hear a footstep because energy is transferred from a foot hitting the ground to your ears. Leaves are put into motion when energy in the moving wind is transferred to them. The spot on the desktop becomes warmer when energy is transferred to it from the sunlight. In fact, all objects, including leaves and desktops, have energy.

Figure 1
Energy is the ability to cause change. *How can these objects cause change?*

Section Assessment Planner

PORTFOLIO
Science Journal, p. 231

PERFORMANCE ASSESSMENT
Skill Builder Activities, p. 232
See page 254 for more options.

CONTENT ASSESSMENT
Section, p. 232
Challenge, p. 232
Chapter, pp. 254–255

Energy of Motion

Things that move can cause change. A bowling ball rolls down the alley and knocks down some pins, as in **Figure 2A.** Is energy involved? A change occurs when the pins fall over. The bowling ball causes this change, so the bowling ball has energy. The energy in the motion of the bowling ball causes the pins to fall. As the ball moves, it has a form of energy called kinetic energy. **Kinetic energy** is the energy an object has due to its motion. If an object isn't moving, it doesn't have kinetic energy.

Kinetic Energy and Speed If you roll the bowling ball so it moves faster, what happens when it hits the pins? It might knock down more pins, or it might cause the pins to go flying farther. A faster ball causes more change to occur than a ball that is moving slowly. Look at **Figure 2B.** The professional bowler rolls a fast-moving bowling ball. When her ball hits the pins, more pins go flying than for a slower-moving ball. All that action signals that her ball had a lot of energy. The faster the ball goes, the more kinetic energy it has. This is true for all moving objects. Kinetic energy increases as an object moves faster.

Kinetic Energy and Mass Suppose, as shown in **Figure 2C,** you roll a volleyball down the alley instead of a bowling ball. If the volleyball travels at the same speed as a bowling ball, which do you think will knock over more pins? The number of pins a ball knocks down depends on the energy the ball has. Does the volleyball have less energy than the bowling ball even though they are traveling at the same speed? An important difference between the volleyball and the bowling ball is that the volleyball has less mass. Even though the volleyball is moving at the same speed as the bowling ball, the volleyball has less kinetic energy because it has less mass. Kinetic energy also depends on the mass of a moving object. Kinetic energy increases as the mass of the object increases.

✔ **Reading Check** *Why does a volleyball knock over fewer pins than a bowling ball?*

Figure 2
The kinetic energy of an object depends on two quantities.
What are those quantities?

A **This ball has kinetic energy because it is rolling down the alley.**

B **This ball has more kinetic energy because it has more speed.**

C **This ball has less kinetic energy because it has less mass.**

2 Teach

The Nature of Energy

Text Question Answer

Possible answers: All the items are matter; all have energy.

Caption Answer

Figure 1 The pizza can provide energy to its consumer, the candle flame can warm and burn objects, the car can move itself and everything in it.

Energy of Motion

Caption Answer

Figure 2 mass and motion

Quick Demo

Kinetic energy depends more on speed than mass. Demonstrate this using two pendulum bobs, one having twice the mass of the other. On separate trials, raise each bob to the same vertical height and let it strike a toy car at the bottom of the swing. Measure how far the car moves in each case. Raise the smaller mass to twice the height (which increases its speed). It will cause the car to roll much farther than it did in the first trials. L2

LS **Visual-Spatial**

✔ Reading Check

Answer The volleyball has less energy because it has less mass.

Curriculum Connection

Art Kinetic sculptures move using motors, pendulum action, or slight breezes that act upon sails. Among the most famous are the mobiles of artist Alexander Calder, who invented the art form in the 1920s. Have students research kinetic sculpture and build a sculpture of their own that models this art form. L2 LS **Kinesthetic**

Resource Manager

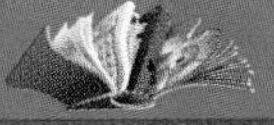

Chapter Resources Booklet

Transparency Activity, p. 42

Directed Reading for Content Mastery, pp. 17, 18

Reading and Writing Skill Activities, p. 35

Energy of Position

Text Question Answer

the object on the higher level with the most mass, unless an object on the lower level has enough mass to make up for the difference in potential energy due to height

Caption Answer

Figure 3 The higher vase has more energy because it has farther to fall. The object with the most mass has the greatest potential energy.

Use Science Words

Word Origin The word *kinetic* comes from the Greek word *kinein*, meaning "to move," while *potential* comes from the Latin root *potens*, meaning "powerful." Have students explain how potential energy and kinetic energy are related to the meanings of their roots. Kinetic energy is the energy an object has because of its motion. Potential energy is energy stored in an object because of its position. An object's potential energy makes it powerful. L2 IN **Linguistic**

Forms of Energy

Activity

Have students measure the temperature of a sample of hot water and of a sample of cold water. Have them mix the samples together and measure the temperature of the mixture every minute for ten minutes. Ask students to make time/temperature graphs of their results. **What happens to the thermal energy of the water?** Thermal energy is transferred from the hot water to the cold water until all the water is at the same temperature. L2 IN **Kinesthetic**

Figure 3
The potential energy of an object depends on its mass and height above the ground.
Which vase has more potential energy, the red one or the blue one?

Energy of Position

An object can have energy even though it is not moving. For example, a glass of water sitting on the kitchen table doesn't have any kinetic energy because it isn't moving. If you accidentally nudge the glass and it falls on the floor, changes occur. Gravity pulls the glass downward, and energy is transferred when the glass hits the floor. Where did this energy come from?

When the glass was sitting on the table, it had potential (puh TEN chul) energy. **Potential energy** is the energy stored in an object because of its position. In this case, the position is the height of the glass above the floor. If the table were higher, the glass would be moving even faster when it hit the floor. The potential energy of the glass is greater if it is higher above the floor. Potential energy also depends on mass. The more massive an object is, the more potential energy it has. Which object in **Figure 3** has the most potential energy?

Forms of Energy

Sound, sunlight, and wind have energy, yet they seem different because they contain different forms of energy. Sound and sunlight contain forms of energy different from the kinetic energy in the motion of the wind. The warmth you feel from sunlight is another type of energy that is different from the energy of motion or position.

Thermal Energy The feeling of warmth from sunlight signals that your body is acquiring more thermal energy. All objects have **thermal energy** that increases as its temperature increases. A cup of hot chocolate has more thermal energy than a cup of cold water, as shown in **Figure 4.** Similarly, the cup of water has more thermal energy than a block of ice of the same mass. Your body continually produces thermal energy. Many chemical reactions that take place inside your cells produce thermal energy. Where does this energy come from? Thermal energy released by chemical reactions comes from another form of energy called chemical energy.

Figure 4
The hotter an object is, the more thermal energy it has. Hot chocolate has more thermal energy than a cup of water, which has more thermal energy than a block of ice.

Teacher FYI

Heat is the flow of energy from a hot system to a cold system. Objects do not contain heat, only thermal energy.

Visual Learning

Figure 4 Point out that if the temperature remains the same, as the mass of a substance increases, the amount of thermal energy it has also increases. **When could a sample of warm water have more thermal energy than a sample of warmer water?** If the cooler sample has more mass than the warmer sample, it might have more thermal energy. L2 IN **Logical-Mathematical**

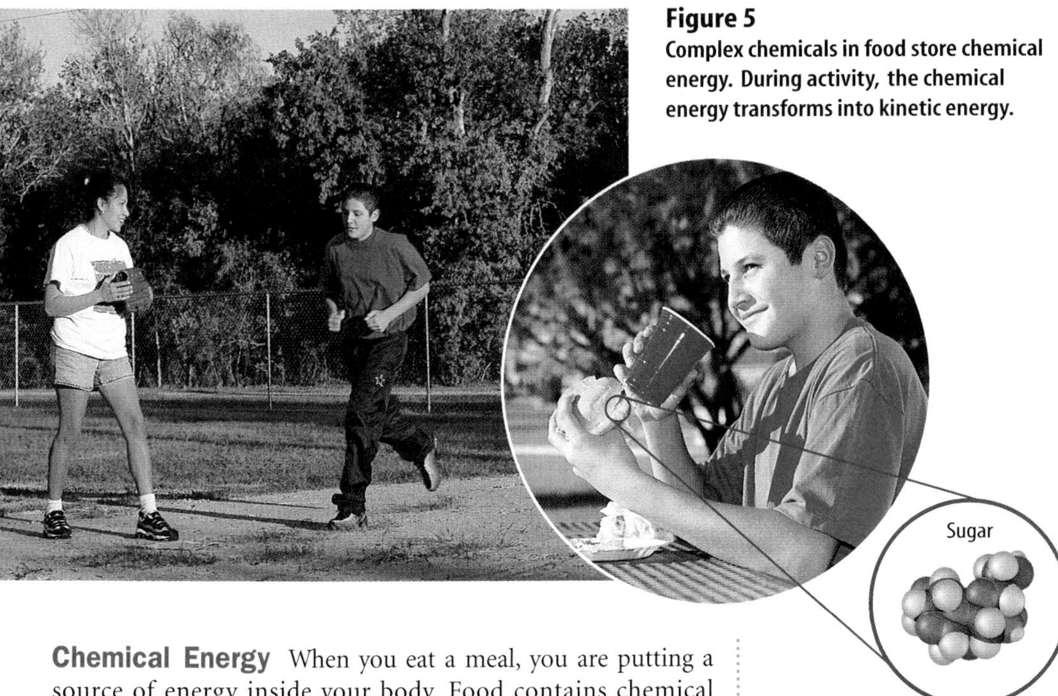

Figure 5
Complex chemicals in food store chemical energy. During activity, the chemical energy transforms into kinetic energy.

Chemical Energy When you eat a meal, you are putting a source of energy inside your body. Food contains chemical energy that your body uses to provide energy for your brain, to power your movements, and to fuel your growth. As in **Figure 5,** food contains chemicals, such as sugar, which can be broken apart in cells. These chemicals are made of atoms that are bonded together, and energy is stored in the bonds between atoms. **Chemical energy** is the energy stored in chemical bonds. When chemicals are broken apart and new chemicals are formed, some of this energy is released. The flame of a candle is the result of chemical energy stored in the wax. When the wax burns, chemical energy is transformed into thermal energy and light energy.

Light Energy Light from the candle flame travels through the air at an incredibly fast speed of 300,000 km/s. This is fast enough to circle Earth seven times in 1 s. When the light strikes something, it either is absorbed, transmitted, or reflected. If the light is absorbed, it will cause the object to warm up a little. In other words, the thermal energy of the object has increased because light transferred energy to it. The type of energy light has is called **radiant energy. Figure 6** shows a coil of wire that produces radiant energy when it is heated. To heat the metal, another type of energy can be used—electrical energy.

Reading Check *How do you know that light has energy?*

Figure 6
In the metal, electrical energy is transformed into thermal energy. As the metal becomes hotter, it emits more radiant energy.

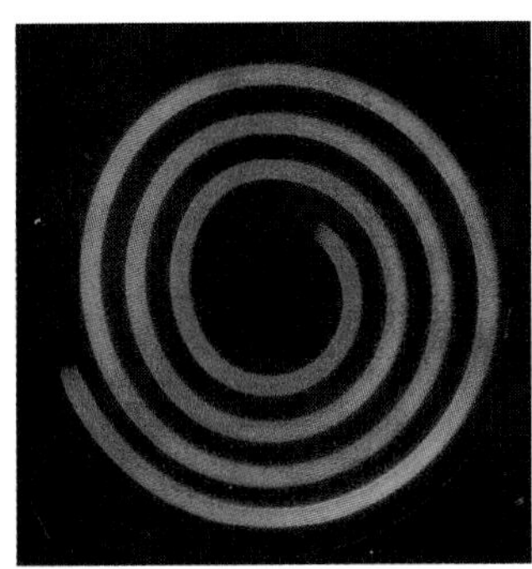

Extension

In living things, the chemical energy in food is released through the process of respiration. Have students research and describe the chemical changes that occur in this process. During respiration, oxygen joins with glucose to release energy that is then used by the cells. Carbon dioxide and water are released as waste products. L3 LS **Linguistic**

Quick Demo

Use a radiometer to show that light has energy. Explain that the black sides absorb the light they receive, while the white sides reflect the light they receive. The absorbed light makes the black sides warmer than the white sides, so they are able to transfer more heat to the air around them. The hotter air molecules exert an unbalanced force on the black sides of the vanes, pushing the vanes around. L2 LS **Visual-Spatial**

Reading Check

Answer Light has energy because it can cause change. For example, absorbed light energy causes things to change temperature.

Science Journal

Chemical Energy Have students list all the chemical energy transformations they encounter in a day. For each item have them list how the chemical energy was transformed or from what it was obtained. Possible answers include combustion of fuel in a car, digestion of food, use of oxygen by the body, photosynthesis in plants, use of battery-powered toys or appliances. L2 LS **Visual-Spatial** P

Resource Manager

Chapter Resources Booklet
Note-taking Worksheets, pp. 31–32
Enrichment, p. 28
Reinforcement, p. 25

3 Assess

Reteach

Have students identify the different types of energy that they rely upon. Discuss the specific tasks each type of energy is used to perform. L1
LS Logical-Mathematical

Challenge

The amount of damage that occurs when vehicles collide depends on the amount of kinetic energy involved in the collision. Remind students that the amount of kinetic energy an object has depends on its speed and its mass. Have students model collisions using toy cars of different masses. Suggest that they use ramps to control the velocity. They could use two ramps for head-on collisions. **Which has a greater effect on damage—velocity or mass?** velocity L2 **LS Kinesthetic**

Oral During the Explore Activity, the more massive marble landed farther from the table than the less massive marble. **What conclusion can you draw about the energy of the two marbles? Explain.** The more massive marble had more kinetic energy than the less massive marble. Use **Performance Assessment in the Science Classroom,** p. 89.

Caption Answer

Figure 7 nuclear energy

Figure 7
Complex power plants are required to obtain useful energy from the nucleus of an atom.
What form of energy is used at this power plant?

Electrical Energy Electrical lighting is one of the many uses of electrical energy. Look around at all the devices that use electrical energy. The electric current that comes out of batteries and wall sockets has **electrical energy.** The amount of electrical energy depends on the voltage. The current out of a 120-V wall socket carries more energy than the current out of a 1.5-V battery. To produce the enormous quantities of electrical energy consumed each day, large power plants are needed. In the United States, about 20 percent of the electrical energy that is generated is from nuclear power plants.

Nuclear Energy Nuclear power plants use energy stored in the nucleus of an atom to generate electricity. Every atomic nucleus contains energy—**nuclear energy**—that can be transformed into other forms of energy. However, releasing the nuclear energy is a complicated process. It involves the construction of complex power plants, as shown in **Figure 7.** In contrast, all that is needed to release chemical energy from wood is a match.

Section 1 Assessment

1. How do you know if an object has energy? Do you have energy? Does a rock?
2. Contrast chemical and nuclear energy.
3. How can chemical energy transform into thermal energy? Into light energy?
4. If two vases are side by side on a high shelf, could one have more potential energy than the other? Explain.
5. **Think Critically** A golf ball and a bowling ball have the same kinetic energy. Which one is moving faster? Explain your answer using what you know about kinetic energy. Suppose the golf ball and the bowling ball have the same speed. Which of the two has more kinetic energy?

Skill Builder Activities

6. **Interpreting Data** Review your results from the Explore Activity. Where did the marble have the most kinetic energy? Where did the marble have the most potential energy? Can you infer a relationship between kinetic energy and potential energy based on your observations? **For more help, refer to the Science Skill Handbook.**
7. **Communicating** The term *energy* is used in everyday language. In your Science Journal, record different expressions and ways of using the word *energy.* Decide which ones match the definition of energy presented in this section. **For more help, refer to the Science Skill Handbook.**

Answers to Section Assessment

1. An object has energy if it is able to cause change. Yes; both you and a rock have energy, because you can both cause change
2. Chemical energy is energy stored in the chemical bonds between atoms. Nuclear energy is stored in the nucleus of an atom.
3. Chemical energy can be transformed into light energy and thermal energy when a chemical reaction occurs. Then some of the energy stored in the chemical bonds is released.
4. Yes, even though the vases are at the same height, one can have more potential energy if it has more mass than the other.
5. The golf ball; in order for the ball with the smaller mass to have the same kinetic energy as the ball with the higher mass, it must be moving faster. When both have the same speed, the bowling ball has greater kinetic energy.
6. It had the most kinetic energy just before it hit the floor. It had the most potential energy at the top of the ramp. Potential energy turns into kinetic energy as an object moves down.
7. Answers will vary.

SECTION

Energy Transformations

Changing Forms of Energy

All forms of energy provide objects with the ability to cause change in their environments. In the world around you, energy is transforming continually between one form and another. You observe these transformations by noticing a change in the environment. Forest fires are a dramatic example of an environmental change that can occur naturally as a result of lightning strikes. Another type of change, shown in **Figure 8,** is a mountain biker pedaling to the top of a hill. What energy transformations occur as he moves up the hill?

Tracking Energy Transformations As the mountain biker pedals, many energy transformations are taking place. In his leg muscles, chemical energy is transforming into kinetic energy. The kinetic energy of his leg muscle transforms into kinetic energy of the bicycle. Some of this energy transforms into potential energy as he moves up the hill. Also, some energy is transformed into thermal energy. His body is warmer because chemical energy is being released. Because of friction, the mechanical parts of the bicycle are warmer, too.

As You Read

***What* You'll Learn**

- **Apply** the law of conservation of energy to energy transformations.
- **Identify** how energy changes form.
- **Describe** how electric power plants produce energy.

Vocabulary

law of conservation of energy
generator
turbine

***Why* It's Important**

Many inventions such as the light bulb, are based upon energy transformations.

Figure 8
The ability to use and transform energy allows the biker to climb the hill. *Identify all the forms of energy that are represented in the photograph.*

Section Assessment Planner

PORTFOLIO
Curriculum Connection, p. 238

PERFORMANCE ASSESSMENT
Try at Home MiniLAB, p. 235
Skill Builder Activities, p. 239
See page 254 for more options.

CONTENT ASSESSMENT
Section, p. 239
Challenge, p. 239
Chapter, pp. 254–255

SECTION

Energy Transformations

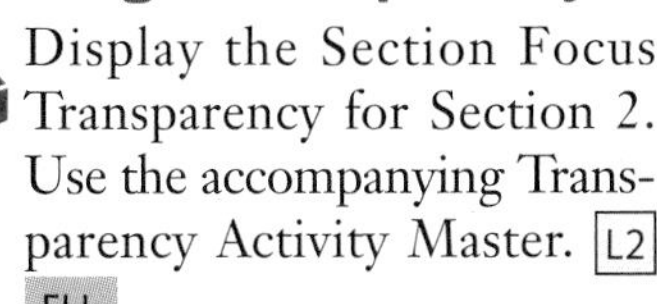

1 Motivate

Bellringer Transparency

Display the Section Focus Transparency for Section 2. Use the accompanying Transparency Activity Master. L2 ELL

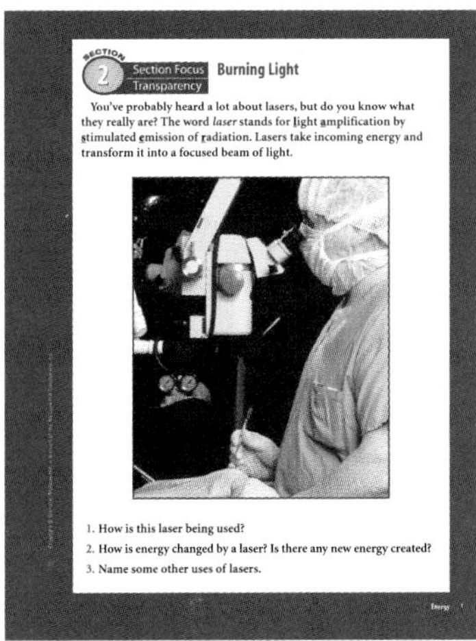

Section Focus Transparency **Burning Light**

You've probably heard a lot about lasers, but do you know what they really are? The word *laser* stands for light amplification by stimulated emission of radiation. Lasers take incoming energy and transform it into a focused beam of light.

1. How is this laser being used?
2. How is energy changed by a laser? Is there any new energy created?
3. Name some other uses of lasers.

Energy

Tie to Prior Knowledge

Have students recall the definition of force. In this section, they will learn that when a force is used to move an object through a distance, work is done and energy is transformed from one form to another. Work is the process in which energy is converted from one form to another.

Resource Manager

Chapter Resources Booklet
Transparency Activity, p. 43
Directed Reading for Content Mastery, p. 19

2 Teach

Changing Forms of Energy

Caption Answer

Figure 8 kinetic energy of the bike, potential energy of the slope, and chemical energy of the rider's exertion

The Law of Conservation of Energy

Answer Energy is never lost. It may be changed into a different form of energy, such as from light into thermal energy.

Changing Kinetic and Potential Energy

Caption Answer

Figure 9 The ball has the most kinetic energy when it leaves and returns to the hand. The ball's total energy is constant.

IDENTIFYING Misconceptions

Students may think that energy is something that is used and then disappears. See page 226F for teacher strategies that address this misconception.

SCIENCE Online

Research Visit the Glencoe Science Web site at **science.glencoe.com** for more information about how energy changes form when it is transformed from one form to another. Use a spreadsheet program to summarize what you've learned.

The Law of Conservation of Energy

It can be a challenge to track energy as it moves from object to object. However, one extremely important principle can serve as a guide as you trace the flow of energy. According to the **law of conservation of energy,** energy is never created or destroyed. The only thing that changes is the form in which energy appears. When the biker is resting at the summit, all his original energy is still around. Some of the energy is in the form of potential energy, which he will use as he coasts down the hill. Some of this energy was changed to thermal energy by friction in the bike. Chemical energy was also changed to thermal energy in the biker's muscles, making him feel hot. As he rests, this thermal energy moves from his body to the air around him. No energy is missing—it can all be accounted for.

Reading Check *Can energy ever be lost? Why or why not?*

Changing Kinetic and Potential Energy

The law of conservation of energy can be used to identify the energy changes in a system, especially if the system is not too complicated. For example, tossing a ball into the air and catching it is a simple system. As shown in **Figure 9,** as the ball leaves your hand, most of its energy is kinetic. As the ball rises, it slows and loses kinetic energy. But, the total energy of the ball hasn't changed. The loss of kinetic energy equals the gain of potential energy as the ball flies higher in the air. The total amount of energy always remains constant. Energy moves from place to place and changes form, but it never is created or destroyed.

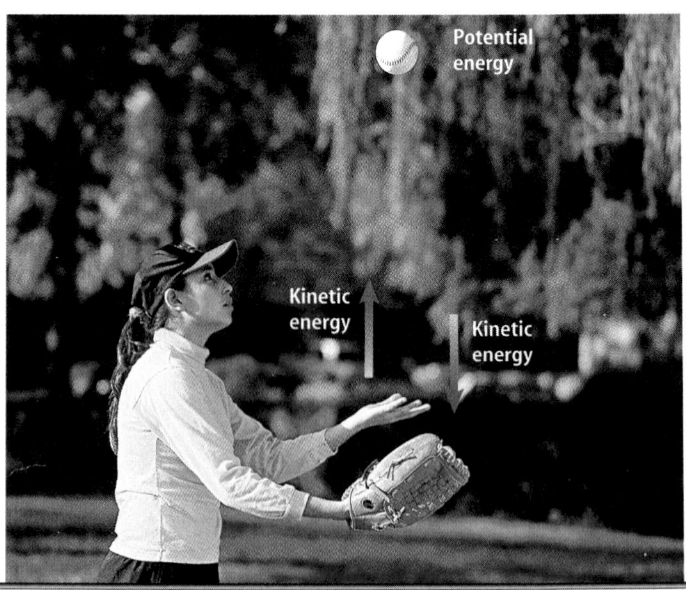

Figure 9
During the flight of the baseball, energy is transforming between kinetic and potential energy.
Where does the ball have the most kinetic energy? Where does the ball have the most total energy?

LAB DEMONSTRATION

Purpose to observe the exchange of potential and kinetic energy

Materials 1.0-kg mass attached to a 2-m string

Procedure Hang the pendulum so the bob just misses the floor at its lowest point. Release the bob at different heights, and measure the height to which it rises at the other end of its swing.

Expected Outcome For small heights, the pendulum will swing to nearly its original height. For higher starting heights, it will swing to a lower height. This is because energy is lost at the point where the pendulum is attached to its pivot.

Assessment

Where does the bob have the greatest potential energy? just before it is released **The greatest kinetic energy?** at the bottom of its swing **How does the height at which the bob is released affect the energy?** Greater height means more total energy.

234 CHAPTER 8 Energy

Figure 10
Hybrid cars that use an electric motor and a gasoline engine for power are now available. These cars get up to 70 mpg. Inventions such as the hybrid car make energy transformations more efficient.

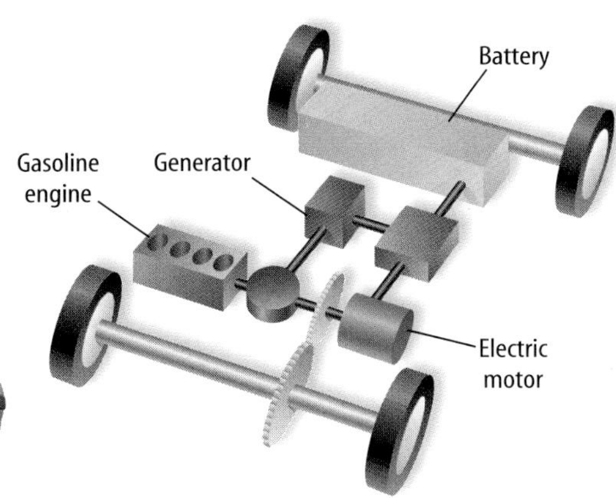

Energy Changes Form

Energy transformations occur constantly all around you. Many machines are devices that transform energy from one form to another. For example, an automobile engine transforms the chemical energy in gasoline into energy of motion. However, not all of the chemical energy is converted into kinetic energy. Instead, some of the chemical energy is converted into thermal energy, and the engine becomes hot. An engine that converts chemical energy into more kinetic energy is a more efficient engine. New types of cars, like the one shown in **Figure 10,** use an electric motor along with a gasoline engine. These engines are more efficient so the car can travel farther on a gallon of gas.

Transforming Chemical Energy Inside your body, chemical energy is also transformed into kinetic energy. Look at **Figure 11.** The transformation of chemical to kinetic energy occurs in muscle cells. There chemical reactions take place that cause certain molecules to bend. Your muscle contracts when many of these molecules bend, and a part of your body moves.

Chemical energy also can be transformed into other forms of energy. For example, burning logs in a fireplace transform the chemical energy in wood into radiant energy and thermal energy. Power plants that burn fuels such as coal transform chemical energy into electrical energy. In this process, some of the chemical energy in coal also is transformed into thermal energy.

In every energy transformation, whether kinetic to potential or chemical to electrical, some thermal energy is released. This thermal energy is said to be lost but it is really only transferred to the environment.

TRY AT HOME Mini LAB

Analyzing Energy Transformations

Procedure

1. Place soft **clay** on the floor and smooth out its surface.
2. Hold a **marble** 1.5 m above the clay and drop it. Measure the depth of the crater made by the marble.
3. Repeat this procedure using a **steel ball,** a **rubber ball,** and a **table-tennis ball.**

Analysis

1. Compare the depths of the craters to determine which ball had the most kinetic energy as it hit the clay. Why did this ball have the most kinetic energy?
2. Explain how potential energy was transformed into kinetic energy during your activity.

Energy Changes Form

Purpose Students observe the difference in kinetic energy of balls of different masses. L2 ELL LS **Kinesthetic**

Materials block of clay, glass marble, steel ball, rubber ball, table tennis ball, metric ruler

Teaching Strategies Suggest students hold a pencil in the crater and mark the depth of the crater on the pencil. Then they can measure the distance marked on the pencil with the metric ruler.

Analysis

1. The ball with the most mass had the greatest kinetic energy. This was probably the steel ball.
2. The balls had potential energy because of the height to which they were raised above the clay. This energy was transformed into kinetic energy as they fell.

Oral Ask students to explain what happened to the kinetic energy of the balls as they landed in the clay. It changed to kinetic energy in the clay and then to thermal energy. Use **PASC,** p. 89.

Internet Addresses

Explore the Glencoe Science Web site at **science.glencoe.com** to find out more about topics in this section.

Resource Manager

Chapter Resources Booklet
MiniLAB, p. 3
Science Inquiry Labs, p. 9

NATIONAL GEOGRAPHIC

Visualizing Energy Transformations

Have students examine the pictures and read the captions. Then ask the following questions.

Why is it necessary for skeletal muscles in the arm to be arranged in pairs? This is necessary so that the muscles can work in opposition to one another. For instance, when the arm is raised by the biceps, as shown in the art drawing, the triceps are needed to lower it.

What is the source of chemical energy for the muscles? Chemical energy is provided by breaking the chemical bonds in the foods we eat.

Activity

Have students research the major muscles in the human leg. Have students make drawings in their Science Journals of their leg muscles. Encourage them to make their drawings similar to those shown for the arm in **Figure 11.** L2 LS **Visual-Spatial**

Extension

Challenge students to research how electrical stimulation is being used to help paraplegics walk again. Encourage students to report their findings to the class.

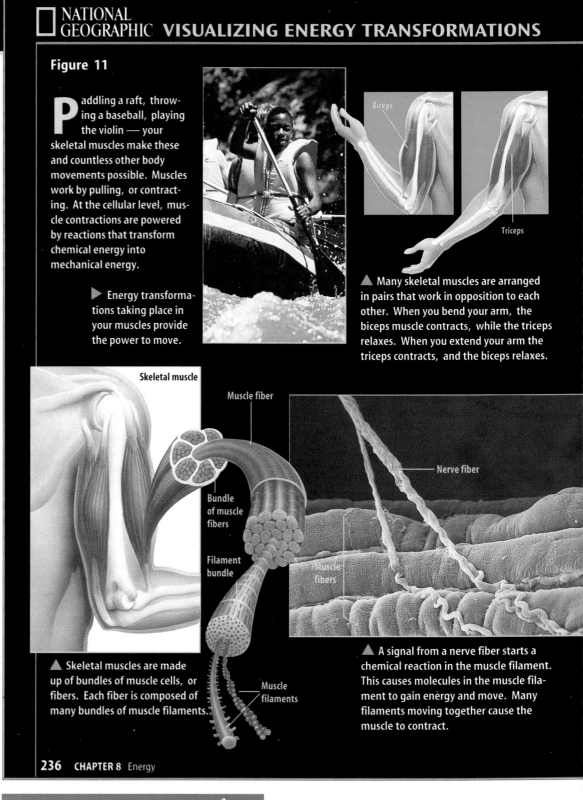

NATIONAL GEOGRAPHIC

VISUALIZING ENERGY TRANSFORMATIONS

Figure 11

Paddling a raft, throwing a baseball, playing the violin — your skeletal muscles make these and countless other body movements possible. Muscles work by pulling, or contracting. At the cellular level, muscle contractions are powered by reactions that transform chemical energy into mechanical energy.

▶ Energy transformations taking place in your muscles provide the power to move.

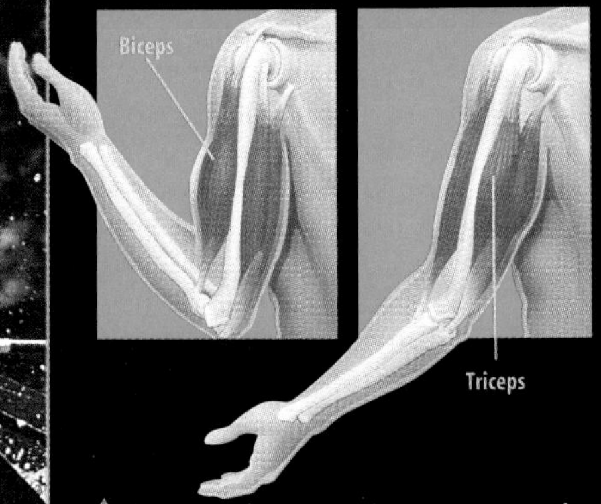

Biceps

Triceps

▲ Many skeletal muscles are arranged in pairs that work in opposition to each other. When you bend your arm, the biceps muscle contracts, while the triceps relaxes. When you extend your arm the triceps contracts, and the biceps relaxes.

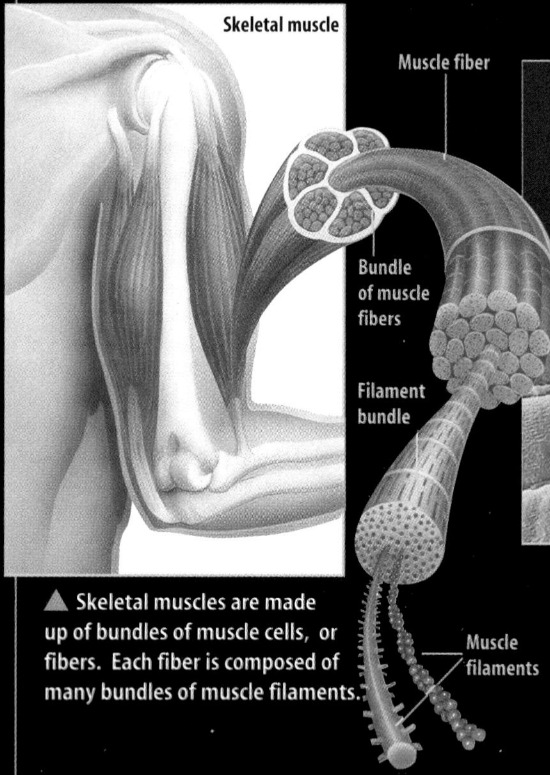

Skeletal muscle

Muscle fiber

Bundle of muscle fibers

Filament bundle

Muscle filaments

Nerve fiber

Muscle fibers

▲ Skeletal muscles are made up of bundles of muscle cells, or fibers. Each fiber is composed of many bundles of muscle filaments.

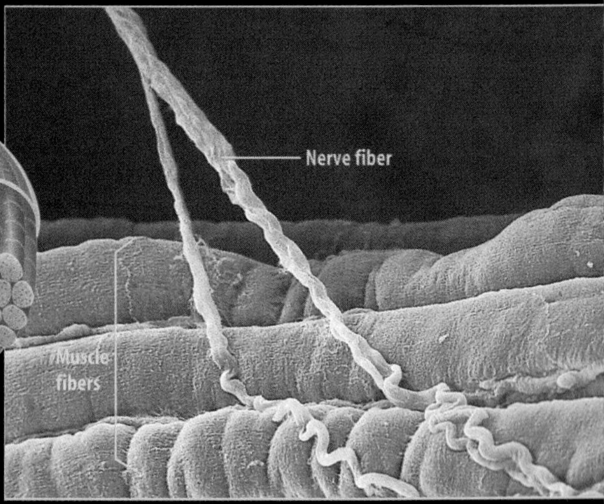

▲ A signal from a nerve fiber starts a chemical reaction in the muscle filament. This causes molecules in the muscle filament to gain energy and move. Many filaments moving together cause the muscle to contract.

Resource Manager

Chapter Resources Booklet
Lab Activity, pp. 9–10

Physical Science Critical Thinking/Problem Solving, p. 17

Figure 12
The simple act of listening to a radio involves many energy transformations. A few are diagrammed here.

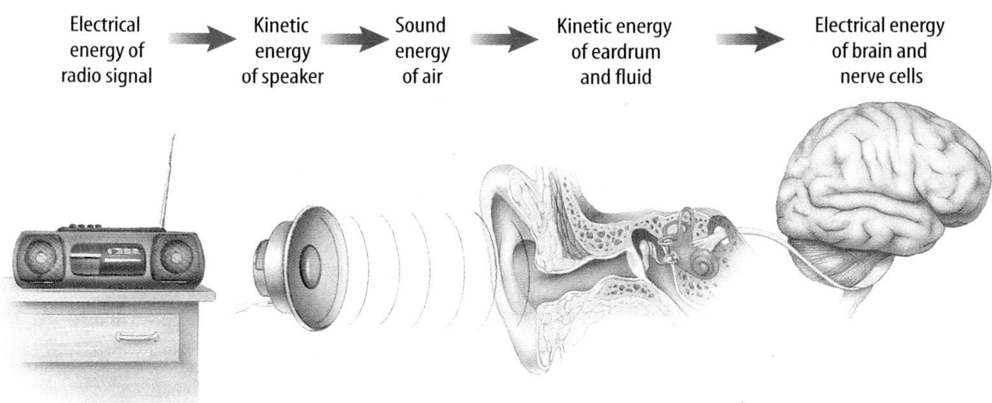

Transforming Electrical Energy Every day you use electrical energy. When you flip a light switch, or turn on a radio or television, or use a hair drier, you are transforming electrical energy to other forms of energy. Every time you plug something into a wall outlet, or use a battery, you are using electrical energy. **Figure 12** shows how electrical energy is transformed into other forms of energy when you listen to a radio. A loudspeaker in the radio converts electrical energy into sound waves that travel to your ear—energy in motion. The energy that is carried by the sound waves causes parts of the ear to move also. This energy of motion is transformed again into chemical and electrical energy in nerve cells, which send the energy to your brain. After you brain interprets this energy as a voice or music, where does the energy go? The energy finally is transformed into thermal energy.

Transforming Thermal Energy Different forms of energy can be transformed into thermal energy. For example, chemical energy changes into thermal energy when something burns. Electrical energy changes into thermal energy when a wire that is carrying an electric current gets hot. Thermal energy can be used to heat buildings and keep you warm. Thermal energy also can be used to heat water. If water is heated to its boiling point, it changes to steam. This steam can be transformed to kinetic energy by steam engines, like the steam locomotives that used to pull trains. Thermal energy also can be transformed into radiant energy. For example, when a bar of metal is heated to a high temperature, it glows and gives off light.

Life Science INTEGRATION

Most organisms have some adaptation for maintaining the correct amount of thermal energy in their bodies. Those living in cooler climates have thick fur coats to keep heat in, and those living in desert regions have skin that reflects the rays of the Sun to keep heat out. Research some of the adaptations different organisms have for controlling the heat in their bodies.

Discussion

How does an incandescent light bulb transform electrical energy into radiant energy? Electrons moving through the filament in the bulb encounter resistance, which heats up the filament so much that it gives off radiant energy. L2
LS **Logical-Mathematical**

IDENTIFYING Misconceptions

Students may believe that unless an object is heated, it has no thermal energy. In fact, all matter has thermal energy. Thermal energy is the energy of motion of the atoms, molecules, and ions that make up matter. These particles are in constant motion in all the matter around us. Scientists believe that these particles stop moving at 0 K, also called absolute zero. Absolute zero is very cold (-273°C). Scientists have not yet succeeded in cooling any matter all the way to absolute zero.

Life Science INTEGRATION

Possible answers: some organisms, such as humans and horses, perspire; some organisms, such as dogs, breath rapidly; some organisms, such as snakes, seek shade or sun. Accept all correct responses.

Teacher FYI

The British scientist James Prescott Joule determined the relationship between thermal energy and mechanical energy, also known as the mechanical equivalent of heat. Today scientists know that 4.186 J of work is necessary to generate 1 cal of thermal energy.

Energy Changes Form, continued

Caption Answer

Figure 13 The only way to store thermal energy is to convert it to some other energy form, such as chemical energy.

Generating Electrical Energy

Caption Answer

Figure 14 coal, oil, natural gas, uranium, the energy from falling water, geothermal energy, and tidal energy

Discussion

Discuss with students the activities in their lives that depend on electrical energy. Possible answers: operating blow-dryers, listening to radios, watching television **Where does the electrical energy for these appliances come from?** Possible answers: from batteries or from power plants that generate electrical energy. L2 IS **Logical-Mathematical**

Activity

Have students turn a hand-held generator when it is not hooked up to a light bulb and then again when it is. Try different wattage light bulbs. **Why was no electrical energy generated when the light bulb was not connected?** There was no circuit in which the current could flow. L2 IS **Kinesthetic**

✔ Reading Check

Answer A generator converts the kinetic energy of a spinning turbine into electrical energy.

Figure 13
Thermal energy quickly leaves hot objects. *What is a way to store thermal energy?*

Storing Energy Unlike other forms of energy, thermal energy is hard to store. As shown in **Figure 13,** thermal energy leaves an object anytime the surrounding environment is colder than the object. In contrast, chemical energy and electrical energy can be stored for future use. Fuels like gasoline and food store chemical energy, and electrical energy is stored in batteries.

Generating Electrical Energy

The enormous amount of electrical energy that is used every day is too large to be stored in batteries. The electrical energy that is available for use at any wall socket must be generated continually by power plants. Every power plant works on the same principle—energy is used to turn a large generator. A **generator** is a machine that transforms kinetic energy into electrical energy. In fossil fuel power plants, coal, oil, or natural gas is burned to boil water. As the hot water boils, the steam rushes through a **turbine,** which is a set of narrowly spaced fan blades. The steam, moving through the blades, turns the turbine, which in turn rotates the generator to produce the electrical energy, as shown in **Figure 14.**

✔ **Reading Check** *What does a generator do?*

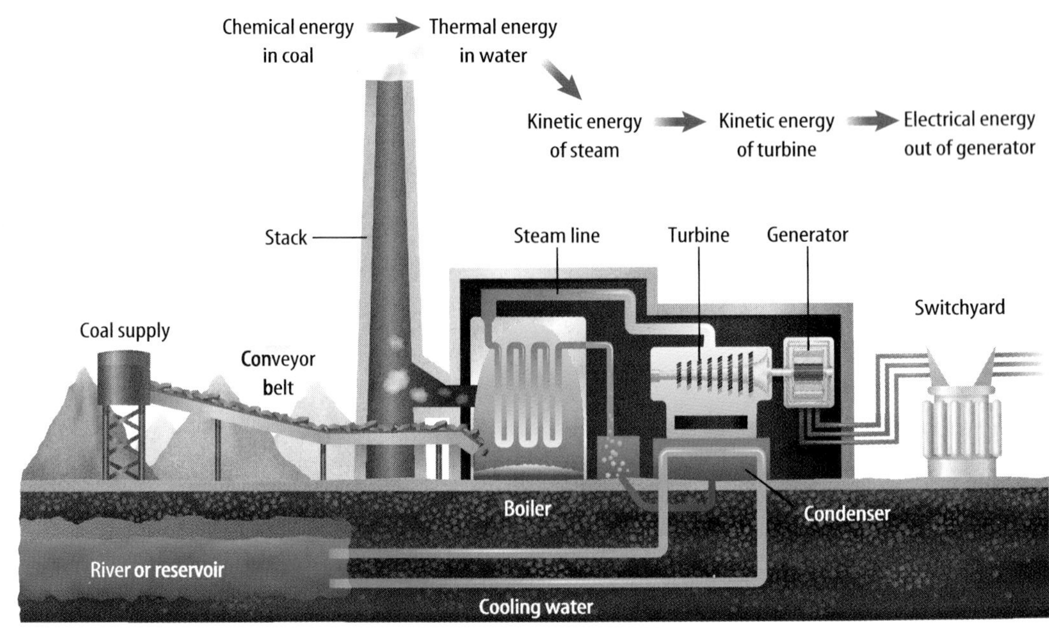

Figure 14
A coal-burning power plant transforms the chemical energy in coal into electrical energy. *What are some of the energy sources that power plants use?*

Resource Manager

Chapter Resources Booklet
Enrichment, p. 29
Reinforcement, p. 26

Curriculum Connection

History The invention of the AC electric generator by Nikola Tesla in 1882 began the second Industrial Revolution. Have students research and write reports about Tesla's life or his research on electricity. Tesla immigrated to the United States from Croatia. Thomas Edison advocated the use of DC electricity, and fought hard to prevent the adoption of Tesla's AC generator. L2 IS **Linguistic** P

Power Plants More than 90 percent of the electrical energy generated in the United States is produced by nuclear and fossil fuel power plants, as shown in **Figure 15.** Other types of power plants include hydroelectric (hi droh ih LEK trihk) and wind. Hydroelectric and wind power plants rely on the same basic principle that all power plants use—they turn a turbine. The turbine is connected to an electric generator. Whether it is falling water or blowing wind supplying the energy, the basic energy transformations are the same.

To analyze the energy transformations in a power plant, you can diagram the energy changes using arrows. A coal-burning power plant generates electrical energy through the following series of energy transformations.

chemical energy of coal → thermal energy of water → kinetic energy of steam → kinetic energy of turbine → electrical energy out of generator

Nuclear power plants use a similar series of transformations. Hydroelectric power plants, however, skip the step of heating the water into steam because the water strikes the turbine directly.

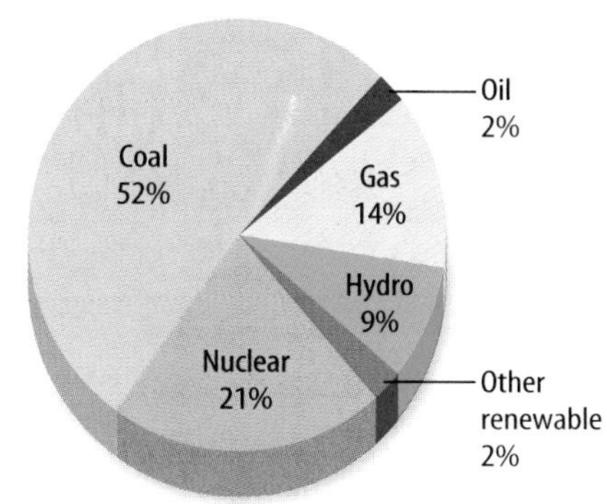

Figure 15
The graph shows sources of electrical energy in the United States. *Think about the lights overhead. Which energy source do you think is being used to provide the electricity for those lights?*

Section 2 Assessment

1. What is the law of conservation of energy?
2. The normal body temperature is 37°C. A house is considered comfortable when the temperature is 25°C. Why is this temperature difference ideal for people?
3. What are the basic steps involved in generating electricity at a power plant?
4. Diagram the energy transformations that take place at a hydroelectric power plant.
5. **Think Critically** You begin pedaling your bicycle, making it move faster and faster. You notice that at first it is easy to speed up, but then it becomes difficult. You pedal with all your strength, yet you cannot go any faster. Use energy concepts to explain what is happening.

Skill Builder Activities

6. **Testing a Hypothesis** If you drop a rubber ball onto a hard surface, the first bounce will be the highest. How much lower will the second bounce be? If you drop the ball on the top of a shoe box, will it bounce as high? Make a hypothesis. Design and conduct an experiment to test your hypothesis. **For more help, refer to the Science Skill Handbook.**
7. **Using Graphics Software** Use graphics software to diagram all the energy transformations that take place during a conversation. What forms of energy are in the sequence from one person making a sound to a second person hearing that sound? **For more help, refer to the Technology Skill Handbook.**

Generating Electrical Energy, continued

Caption Answer

Figure 15 Possible answers: fossil fuels, uranium, falling water A call to the local power plant will yield the type of energy and possibly an invitation for a field trip.

3 Assess

Reteach

Have volunteers explain each type of energy discussed in this section. As each energy type is discussed, challenge students to explain how this form of energy is used in their daily lives. L2

Linguistic

Challenge

A satellite that is orbiting Earth will eventually fall out of its orbit and strike Earth's surface. Have students use energy transformations to help them explain how this happens. The satellite gradually loses energy to friction and loses speed. Eventually it slows down so much that it doesn't have enough speed to keep from falling toward Earth. L3

LS **Logical-Mathematical**

Performance Have students make posters illustrating the energy transformations that occur when oil is used to generate electricity. Chemical energy of oil → thermal energy of water → kinetic energy of steam → kinetic energy of turbine → electrical energy out of generator Use **PASC,** p. 145.

Answers to Section Assessment

1. Energy cannot be created or destroyed.
2. At 25°C, air takes away the same amount of energy that is being produced by the body.
3. Some source provides energy to spin a turbine, which converts kinetic energy to electrical energy.
4. PE of water → KE of falling water → KE of turbine blade and generator coil → electrical energy
5. At the start, most of your energy goes into kinetic energy of the bicycle. As you speed up, less of your energy goes into kinetic energy of the bicycle and more goes into air resistance.
6. Accept all reasonable hypotheses and experiments. Check for control of variables.
7. vocal cords vibrate (kinetic energy), air molecules vibrate (kinetic energy), eardrum vibrates (kinetic energy)

Activity BENCH TESTED

Purpose Students track energy as it moves from electricity to music to vibrations to sound. L2

LS **Auditory-Musical**

Process Skills observing, inferring, predicting

Time Required 20 minutes

Teaching Strategy Have reference books about sound and electricity available.

Troubleshooting Make sure the wiring is securely connected. The motor will not turn even though students will be able to "hear" the music when they press the axle against their jaws.

Answers to Questions

1. Students should hear the sound of the radio or disc.
2. electricity; sound
3. Transformation should start with electrical energy (either from a wall outlet or from a battery), change to mechanical energy, and end with sound energy. If a CD player is used, students might also include light energy.
4. The motor will probably get warmer as it runs. Some of the energy changes to heat because of friction.
5. All of the energy put into the system can be accounted for as motion, heat, light, or sound.

Content Have students work in groups to write a song or poem or make a picture about transfers of energy. Use **PASC**, p. 151.

Activity

Hearing with Your Jaw

You probably have listened to music using speakers or headphones. Have you ever considered how energy is transferred to get the energy from the radio or CD player to your brain? What type of energy is needed to power the radio or CD player? Where does this energy come from? How does that energy become sound? How does the sound get to you? In this activity, the sound from a radio or CD player is going to travel through a motor before entering your body through your jaw instead of your ears.

What You'll Investigate

How can energy be transferred from a radio or CD player to your brain?

Materials

radio or CD player
small electrical motor
headphone jack

Goals

- **Identify** energy transfers and transformations.
- **Explain** your results in terms of transformations of energy and conservation of energy.

Safety Symbols

Procedure

1. Go to one of the places in the room with a motor/radio assembly.
2. Turn on the radio or CD player so that you hear the music.
3. Push the headphone jack into the headphone plug on the radio or CD player.
4. Press the axle of the motor against the side of your jaw.

Conclude and Apply

1. **Describe** what you heard in your Science Journal.
2. What type of energy did you have in the beginning? In the end?
3. **Draw** a diagram to show the all the energy transformations taking place.
4. Did anything get hotter as a result of this activity? Explain.
5. **Explain** your results using the law of conservation of energy.

Compare your conclusions with other students in your class. **For more help, refer to the Science Skill Handbook.**

Communicating Your Data

Students could use an electronic presentation program to present their picture and/or events chain to the rest of the class.

Resource Manager

Chapter Resources Booklet
Activity Worksheet, pp. 5–6

SECTION

Sources of Energy

Using Energy

Press a button on the remote control and your favorite program appears on television. Open your refrigerator and pull out something cold to drink. Ride to the mall in a car. For any of these things to occur, a transfer of energy must take place. Radiant energy is transferred to your television, electrical energy is transferred to your refrigerator, and the chemical energy in gasoline is transferred to the engine of the car.

Every day energy is used to provide light and to heat and cool homes, schools, and workplaces. Energy is used to run cars, buses, trucks, trains, and airplanes that transport people and materials from one place to another. Energy also is used to make clothing and other materials and to cook food.

According to the law of conservation of energy, energy can't be created or destroyed. Energy only can change form. If a car or refrigerator can't create the energy they use, then where does this energy come from?

As You Read

What **You'll Learn**

- **Explain** what renewable, nonrenewable, and alternative resources are.
- **Develop** an awareness that the use of any energy source has positive and negative consequences.

Vocabulary

nonrenewable resource
renewable resource
alternative resource
photovoltaic

Why **It's Important**

Energy is vital for survival and making life comfortable. Developing new energy sources will improve modern standards of living.

Energy Resources

Energy cannot be made, but must come from the natural world. As you can see in **Figure 16,** the surface of Earth receives energy from two sources—the Sun and radioactive atoms in Earth's interior. Of these two energy sources, the energy from the Sun has much more impact on your life. Nearly all the energy you used today can be traced to the Sun, even the gasoline used to power the car or schoolbus you came to school in.

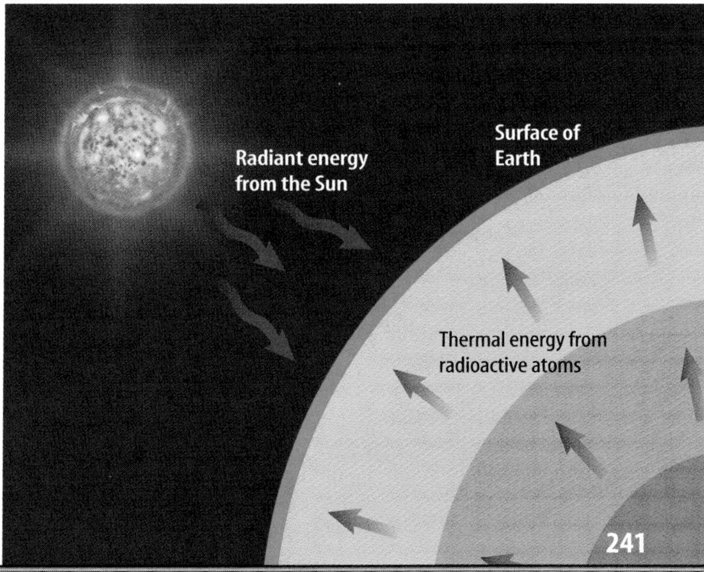

Figure 16
All the energy you use can be traced to one of two sources—the Sun or radioactive atoms in Earth's interior.

Section Assessment Planner

PORTFOLIO
Science Journal, p. 242

PERFORMANCE ASSESSMENT
Problem-Solving Activity, p. 244
MiniLAB, p. 245
Skill Builder Activities, p. 249
See page 254 for more options.

CONTENT ASSESSMENT
Section, p. 249
Challenge, p. 249
Chapter, pp. 254–255

SECTION

Sources of Energy

1 Motivate

Bellringer Transparency

Display the Section Focus Transparency for Section 3. Use the accompanying Transparency Activity Master. L2 ELL

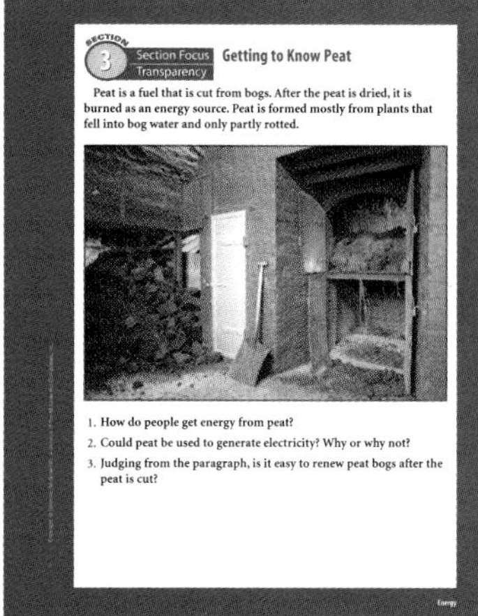

Section Focus Transparency **Getting to Know Peat**

Peat is a fuel that is cut from bogs. After the peat is dried, it is burned as an energy source. Peat is formed mostly from plants that fell into bog water and only partly rotted.

1. How do people get energy from peat?
2. Could peat be used to generate electricity? Why or why not?
3. Judging from the paragraph, is it easy to renew peat bogs after the peat is cut?

Energy

Tie to Prior Knowledge

Remind students that work is force acting through a distance. Explain that all objects with energy have the ability to do work. An object with energy exerts a force on another object. The force pushes the object through a distance, causing the energy of the objects to change. The molecules in fuels have chemical energy that is converted to thermal energy as the fuels are burned. These fast-moving molecules then can do work, such as moving a piston in an engine.

2 Teach

Fossil Fuels

Use an Analogy

In fossil fuels, the chemical energy between the carbon atoms and the other atoms of the original organic matter has been concentrated. Burning fossil fuel yields a high amount of energy for a period of time that is fleeting compared with the time it took to transform the organic material into fossil fuel. In the same way, professional musicians and players of professional sports spend years learning to concentrate their energy and perfecting techniques that may take mere seconds to perform.

Coal was formed from the remains of partially decomposed plants that had accumulated hundreds of millions of years ago. Coal formation gradually occurred after the plant debris had been covered and compressed by rocks, soil, and water and then subjected to great pressure and heat over long periods of time. Oil and natural gas formed from the remains of marine life and plants that had been rapidly buried in fine-grained sediment. This rapid burial prevented these organic debris from completely decomposing; and, along with increases in temperature and pressure, oil and natural gas deposits gradually formed. These fossil fuel deposits all have a link to the past, and reveal important information to geologists about the earth's climate and seas during their formation.

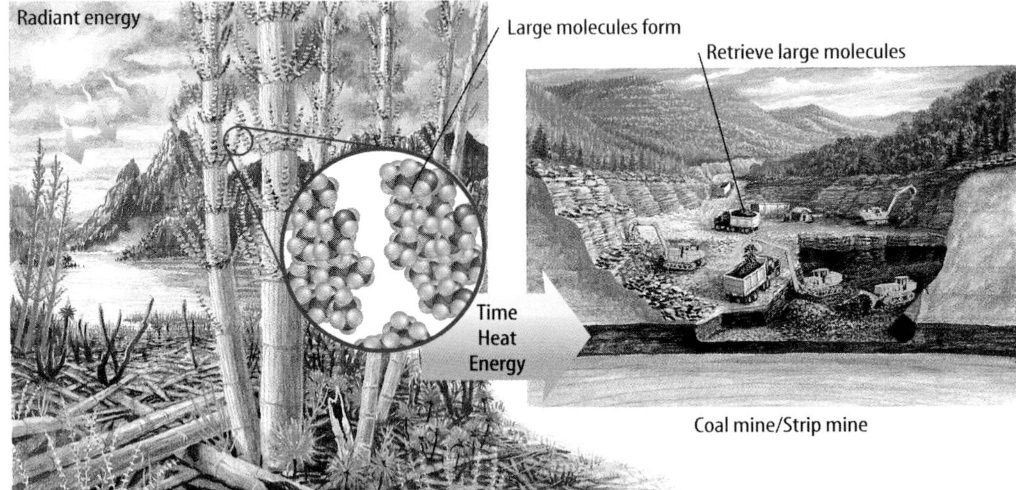

Figure 17
Millions of years ago plants made complex chemicals through the process of photosynthesis. After time, heat, and pressure were applied, the fossil fuels were formed.

The kind of fossil fuels found in the ground depends on the kind of organisms (animal or plant) that died and were buried in that spot. Research coal, oil, and natural gas to find out what type of organisms were primarily responsible for producing each. Could deposits of fossil fuels tell geologists something about Earth's past?

Fossil Fuels

Gasoline is a source of energy that is refined from oil. Oil and natural gas are found underground and were made from the remains of plants and animals that lived in the ocean millions of years ago. Heat and pressure gradually turned these ancient organisms into oil and natural gas. Coal was formed in a similar process. All three fuels are called fossil fuels because they were formed from ancient organisms.

Fossil fuels contain chemical energy. Ancient organisms used radiant energy in sunlight to build complex chemicals through the process of photosynthesis, as shown in **Figure 17.** The chemical energy that was stored in these chemicals is now the energy in fossil fuels.

Using Fossil Fuels The energy used when you ride in a car, turn on a light, or use an electric appliance usually comes from burning fossil fuels. However, it takes millions of years to replace each drop of gasoline and each lump of coal that is burned. At the rate oil is being used, Earth may run out of oil before the end of this century. An energy source that is used up much faster than it can be replaced is a **nonrenewable resource.** Fossil fuels are nonrenewable resources.

Burning fossil fuels to produce energy also generates chemical compounds that cause pollution. Each year billions of kilograms of air pollutants are produced by burning fossil fuels. These pollutants can cause respiratory illnesses and acid rain. Also, the carbon dioxide gas formed when fossil fuels are burned may cause Earth's climate to warm.

Resource Manager

Chapter Resources Booklet
- Transparency Activity, p. 44
- Directed Reading for Content Mastery, pp. 19, 20

Cultural Diversity, p. 45

Science Journal

Energy Matters Some people believe the demand for energy in the world will quadruple in the next fifty years. Have students write paragraphs in their Science Journals speculating how people will meet the demands for more energy. L2 IN **Intrapersonal** P

Nuclear Energy

Can you imagine running an automobile on a 1 kg of fuel that releases 30 million times more energy than 1 L of gas? What could supply so much energy from so little mass? The answer is the nuclei of uranium atoms. Some of these nuclei are unstable and break apart, releasing enormous amounts of energy in the process. This energy can be used to generate electricity by heating water to produce steam that spins an electric generator, as shown in **Figure 18.** Because no fossil fuels are burned, generating electricity using nuclear energy keeps fossil fuels from being used up too quickly. Also, unlike fossil fuel power plants, nuclear power plants produce almost no air pollution. In one year, a typical nuclear power plant generates enough energy to supply 600,000 homes with power, and produces only 1 m^3 of waste.

Nuclear Wastes Like all energy sources, nuclear energy has its advantages and disadvantages. One disadvantage is the amount of nonrenewable uranium in Earth's crust. Another is that the waste produced by nuclear power plants is radioactive and can be dangerous to living things. Some of the materials in the nuclear waste will remain radioactive for many thousands of years. As a result the waste must be stored so no radioactivity is released into the environment for a long time. One method is to seal the waste in a ceramic material, place the ceramic in protective containers, and then bury the containers far underground. However, the burial site would have to carefully chosen so underground water supplies aren't contaminated. Also, the site would have to be safe from earthquakes and other natural disasters that might cause the material to be released.

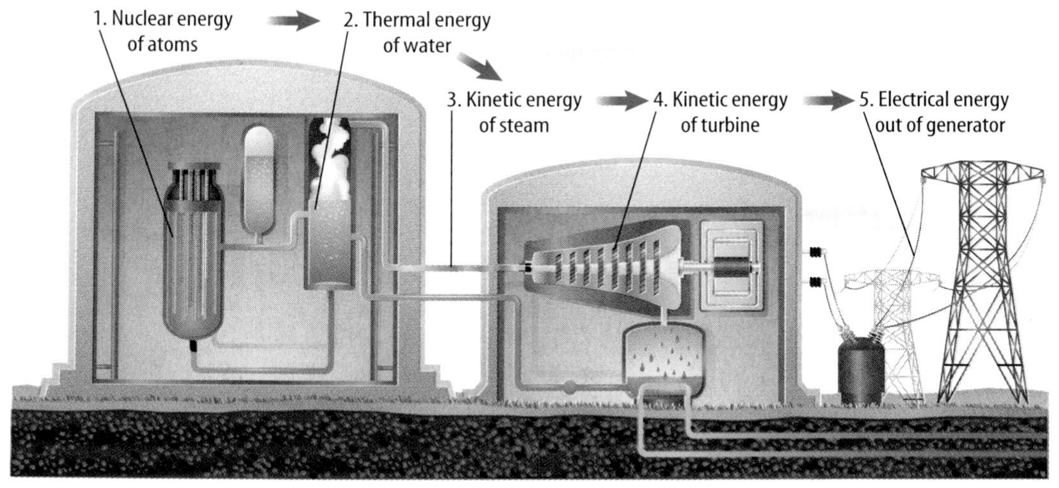

Figure 18
To obtain electrical energy from nuclear energy, a series of energy transformations must occur.

Nuclear Energy

Fun Fact

The nuclear reaction used in nuclear power plants is nuclear fission. In this reaction, a neutron hits the nucleus of a uranium-235 atom and breaks it into two smaller atoms and several neutrons. If enough reactions occur, the neutrons produced by the reaction are enough to keep the reaction going, and it becomes a chain reaction.

Quick Demo

To model the chain reaction that can occur in nuclear fission, place many set mousetraps into a large box with fairly short walls. **Caution:** *Watch your fingers!* The traps should be fairly close together for a good response. Drop a ping pong ball into the box and have students observe what happens. Explain that the ball represents a loose neutron that initiates the fission process while the mousetraps model uranium-235 nuclei. L2 **LS Auditory-Musical**

Extension

The first human use of nuclear fission was in atomic weapons. Have students research the development of these weapons and give speeches describing their findings. During World War II, Albert Einstein twice wrote to President Franklin Delano Roosevelt to warn him that the technology needed to build nuclear weapons existed and that such weapons might be developed by Germany, which could lead to a global disaster. Einstein's warnings led to the formation of the Manhattan Project, which led to development of the world's first atomic weapons and which brought an end to the war in Japan. L2 **LS Linguistic**

Active Reading

Four-Corner Discussion This strategy encourages the class to debate a complex issue. Make four signs: Strongly Agree, Agree, Disagree, and Strongly Disagree. Place one sign in each corner of the room. Write on the chalkboard a statement that will elicit reactions from students. Have the students respond on paper to the statement. After several minutes, direct them to move to the corner with the sign that most closely reflects their opinions. In the corners, students share responses. Each group then selects a spokesperson to report the opinions of the group. After all groups have reported, open the floor for debate. Allow students who have changed their opinions to change corners. Have students conduct a Four-Corner Discussion about the use of nuclear energy.

Hydroelectricity

Visual Learning

Figure 19 Ask students to study the diagram of a hydroelectric generator and then explain why hydroelectric power is more efficient than fossil fuel or nuclear power. Hydroelectric power does not use heat, which is easily lost to the surroundings, to generate electrical energy. In hydroelectric power, the energy of falling water is directly transferred to the turbine blades. L2 LS **Visual-Spatial**

Make a Model

Have students make a pinwheel by folding each corner of a large index card into the center and attaching it to a pencil eraser with a pin. Have students place their pinwheels under a stream of water running from a faucet to observe that the kinetic energy of moving water can be transferred to the blades of a turbine. L1 LS **Kinesthetic**

Problem-Solving Activity

National Math Standards

Correlation to Mathematics Objectives

1, 2, 5, 6, 8–10

Answers

1. 1949=~30; 1999=~70; Consumption has more than doubled.
2. 1949=~30; 1999=~95; Consumption has more than tripled.
3. Additional energy comes from imports.

SCIENCE Online

Data Update Visit the Glencoe Science Web site at **science.glencoe.com** for data about the use of hydroelectricity in various parts of the world. Using a classroom map, present your finds to your class.

Hydroelectricity

Currently, transforming the potential energy of water that is trapped behind dams supplies the world with 15 percent of its electrical energy. Hydroelectricity is the largest renewable source of energy. A **renewable resource** is an energy source that is replenished continually. As long as rain falls in the mountains, water will collect behind dams, and hydroelectric power plants can generate electrical energy, as shown in **Figure 19.**

Although production of hydroelectricity is largely pollution free, it has one major problem. It disrupts the life cycle of aquatic animals, especially fish. This is particularly true in the Northwest where salmon spawn and run. Because salmon return to the spot where they were hatched to lay their eggs, the development of dams has hindered a large fraction of salmon from reproducing. This has greatly reduced the salmon population. Efforts to correct the problem have resulted in the removal of a number of dams and an attempt to help fish bypass the dam using fish ladders. Like most energy sources, hydroelectricity has advantages and disadvantages.

Problem-Solving Activity

Is energy consumption outpacing production?

You use energy every day—to get to school, to watch TV, and to heat or cool your home. The amount of energy consumed by an average person has increased over the last 50 years. Consequently, more energy must be produced.

Energy Overview, 1949–1999

Energy (Quadrillion Btu): 0, 30, 60, 90, 120
Year: 1949, 1954, 1959, 1964, 1969, 1974, 1979, 1984, 1989, 1994, 1999
Consumption
Energy imports
Production

Identifying the Problem

The following graph shows the energy produced and consumed in the United States from 1949 to 1999. How does energy that is consumed by Americans compare with energy that is produced in the United States?

Solving the problem

1. Determine the approximate amount of energy produced in 1949 and in 1999 and how much it has increased in 50 years. Has it doubled or tripled?
2. Do the same for consumption. Has it doubled or tripled?
3. Using what you calculated in step 1 and the graph, where does the additional energy that is needed come from? Give some examples.

Inclusion Strategies

Gifted Have groups of students build solar-powered toy cars. The cars should be built from scratch with parts from other toys. Upon completion, students should make diagrams describing how the cars work. L3 ELL COOP LEARN LS **Kinesthetic**

Cultural Diversity

Three Gorges Dam The largest hydroelectric dam in the world, Three Gorges Dam, is under construction in China. Have students find out more about this dam and present their findings to the class. The dam will produce 18,200 megawatts of electricity and is to be completed in 2009. It will submerge 13 cities, 140 towns, and 1,352 villages, resulting in the loss of countless Chinese antiquities. L2 LS **Linguistic**

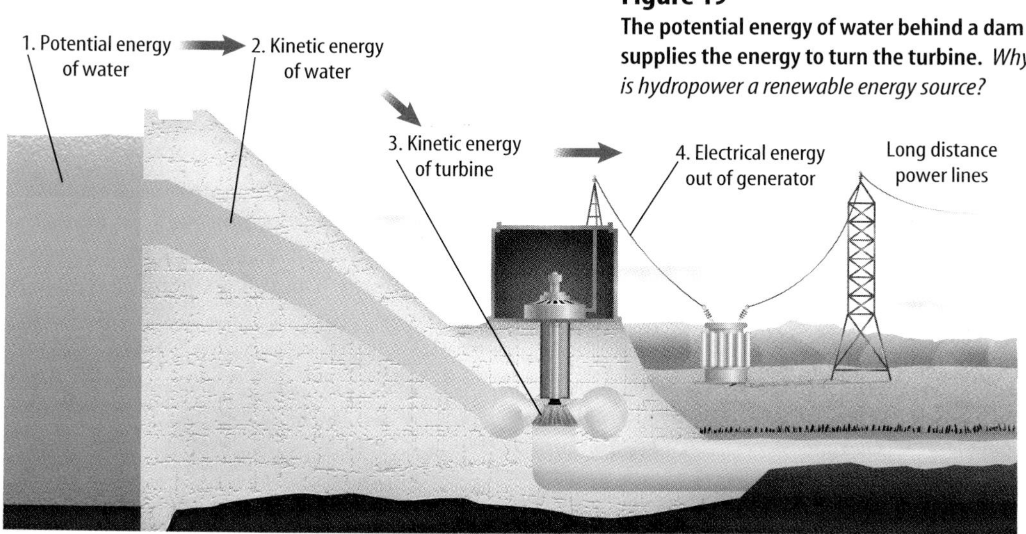

Figure 19
The potential energy of water behind a dam supplies the energy to turn the turbine. *Why is hydropower a renewable energy source?*

Alternative Sources of Energy

Electrical energy can be generated in many ways, unfortunately, each has its problems that affect the environment and the quality of life for humans. Engineers continue to search for new sources of energy that are safer and cause less harm to the environment. These sources often are called **alternative resources.** These alternative resources include solar energy, wind, and geothermal energy.

Solar Energy

The Sun is the origin of almost all the energy that is used on Earth. Because the Sun will go on producing an enormous amount of energy for billions of years, the Sun is an inexhaustible source of energy. This means that the Sun's energy can't be used up by humans.

Each day, the amount of radiant energy that strikes Earth from the Sun is enough to meet human energy needs for 27 years. That's a lot of clean, endless energy. Why isn't this energy used? The most important reason is that it is still less expensive to use fossil and nuclear energy. This advantage will not be the case much longer. As the supply of coal, oil, and natural gas runs out, the cost to find, mine, and refine what's left will make fossil fuel more expensive. At the same time, radiant energy collectors likely will become more efficient.

✔ Reading Check *What is an inexhaustible energy source?*

Mini LAB

Building a Solar Collector

Procedure
1. Line a **large pot** with the black plastic from a **garbage bag** and fill with **water.**
2. Stretch **clear-plastic wrap** over the pot and tape it taut.
3. Make a slit in the top and slide a **thermometer** into the water.
4. Place your solar collector in direct sunlight and monitor the temperature change every 3 min for 15 min.
5. Repeat your experiment without using any plastic.

Analysis
1. Graph the temperature changes in both setups.
2. Explain how your solar collector works.
3. Infer how solar collectors conserve electrical energy.

Caption Answer

Figure 19 because rain keeps falling on the mountains

Alternative Sources of Energy

Discussion

How do renewable and inexhaustible energy sources differ from nonrenewable energy resources? Renewable and inexhaustible energy resources are not likely to be used up by people.

Solar Energy

Purpose Students construct a simple solar collector and analyze how it works. L2
LS Kinesthetic

Materials black plastic garbage bag, scissors, large pot, water, clear plastic wrap, tape, thermometer, watch

Teaching Strategies Explain to students that black materials absorb all the light that reaches them, while shiny metals reflect light.

Analysis
1. The temperature increases faster in the setup with the plastic.
2. The black plastic absorbs heat from the Sun, and the clear plastic traps the heat. This heat is transferred to the water.
3. Solar collectors can be used in place of electricity to heat things.

Process Have students make time/temperature graphs of their data for both collectors. Use **PASC,** p. 111.

Resource Manager

Chapter Resources Booklet
MiniLAB, p. 4
Lab Activity, pp. 11–13
Home and Community Involvement, p. 26

✔ Reading Check

Answer an energy source that can't be used up by humans

Reading Check

Answer converts radiant energy directly into electrical energy

Geothermal Energy

Teacher FYI

Geothermal energy can be used for heating in the winter and cooling in the summer. A loop of pipe with water running through it is inserted below the frost line where the ground stays at a constant temperature of about 10° to 20°C, as in a cave. In summer, when the house air is warmer than this underground temperature, water in the pipe carries underground heat out of the house and underground, where the water is cooled. The water then returns above ground to collect more heat. In the winter, the reverse takes place. This method of heating and cooling is more efficient than many other methods and has recently become cost effective. Also, this method does not depend on thermal vents, which occur in only a few isolated regions of the world, and it can be used nearly everywhere.

Discussion

What advantages does geothermal energy have over burning fossil fuels or using nuclear energy? Possible answers: Geothermal energy is a renewable resource. Using it instead of a nonrenewable resource such as coal or petroleum reserves fossil fuels for other uses, produces little if any air pollution, and eliminates waste disposal problems associated with nuclear power.

Figure 20
Solar energy can be collected and utilized by individuals using **A** thermal collectors or **B** photovoltaic collectors.

Collecting the Sun's Energy Two types of collectors capture the Sun's rays. If you look around your neighborhood, you might see large, rectangular panels attached to the roofs of buildings or houses. If, as in **Figure 20A,** pipes come out of the panel, it is a thermal collector. Using a black surface, a thermal collector heats water by directly absorbing the Sun's radiant energy. Water circulating in this system can be heated to about 70°C. The hot water can be pumped through the house to provide heat. Also, the hot water can be used for washing and bathing. If the panel has no pipes, it is a photovoltaic (foh toh vol TAY ihk) collector, like the one pictured in **Figure 20B.** A **photovoltaic** is a device that transforms radiant energy directly into electrical energy. Photovoltaics are used to power calculators and satellites, including the *International Space Station.*

Reading Check *What does a photovoltaic do?*

Geothermal Energy

Imagine you could take a journey to the center of Earth—down to about 6,400 km below the surface. As you went deeper and deeper, you would find the temperature increasing. In fact, after going only about 3 km, the temperature could have increased enough to boil water. At a depth of 100 km, the temperature could be over 1,000°C. The heat generated inside Earth is called geothermal energy. Some of this heat is produced when unstable radioactive atoms inside Earth decay, converting nuclear energy to thermal energy.

At some places deep within Earth the temperature is hot enough to melt rock. This molten rock, or magma, can rise up close to the surface through cracks in the crust. During a volcanic eruption, magma reaches the surface. In other places, magma gets close to the surface and heats the rock around it.

Geothermal Reservoirs In some regions where magma is close to the surface, rainwater and water from melted snow can seep down to the hot rock through cracks and other openings in Earth's surface. The water then becomes hot and sometimes can form steam. The hot water and steam can be trapped under high pressure in cracks and pockets called geothermal reservoirs. In some places the hot water and steam are close enough to the surface to form hot springs and geysers.

Resource Manager

Chapter Resources Booklet

Enrichment, p. 30

Transparency Activity, pp. 45–46

Cultural Diversity

Geothermal Iceland Iceland gets 50% of its energy from geothermal sources. Fossil fuels are only used to power automobiles, ships, and airplanes. About 86% of all space heating in Iceland is provided by geothermal energy and about 16% of Iceland's electricity is generated using geothermal energy. Geothermal energy is also used to heat outdoor pools, where people swim year round.

Geothermal Power Plants In places where the geothermal reservoirs are less than several kilometers deep, wells can be drilled to reach them. The hot water and steam produced by geothermal energy then can be used by geothermal power plants, like the one in **Figure 21,** to generate electricity.

Most geothermal reservoirs contain hot water under high pressure. **Figure 22** shows how these reservoirs can be used to generate electricity. While geothermal power is an inexhaustible source of energy, geothermal power plants can be built only in regions where geothermal reservoirs are close to the surface, such as in the western United States.

Heat Pumps Geothermal heat helps keep the temperature of the ground at a depth of several meters at a nearly constant temperature of about 10° to 20°C. This constant temperature can be used to cool and heat buildings by using a heat pump.

A heat pump contains a water-filled loop of pipe that is buried to a depth where the temperature is constant. In summer the air is warmer than this underground temperature. Warm water from the building is pumped through the pipe down into the ground. The water cools and then is pumped back to the house where it absorbs more heat, and the cycle is repeated. During the winter, the air is cooler than the ground below. Then, cool water absorbs heat from the ground and releases it into the house.

Figure 21
This geothermal power plant in Nevada produces enough electricity to power about 50,000 homes.

Figure 22
The hot water in a geothermal reservoir is used to generate electricity in a geothermal power plant.

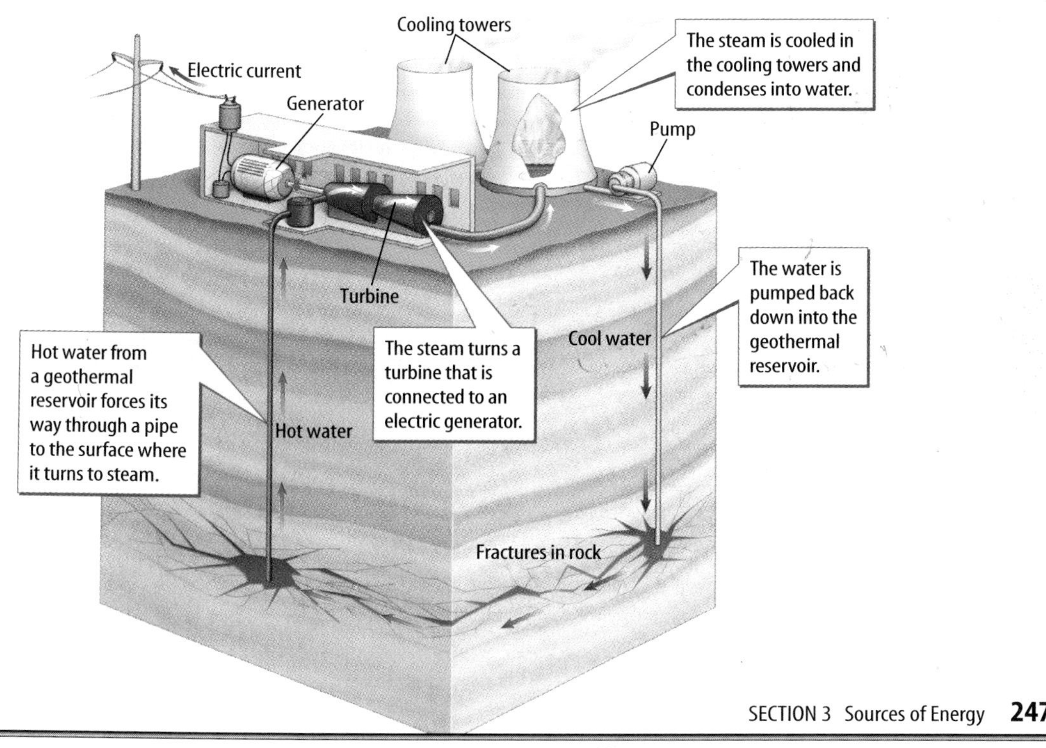
Cooling towers
Electric current
Generator
The steam is cooled in the cooling towers and condenses into water.
Pump
Turbine
Hot water from a geothermal reservoir forces its way through a pipe to the surface where it turns to steam.
The steam turns a turbine that is connected to an electric generator.
Cool water
The water is pumped back down into the geothermal reservoir.
Hot water
Fractures in rock

Use Science Words

Word Origin Have students find the origin of the word *geothermal.* The prefix *geo-* has Greek origins and means "earth." *Thermal* also has Greek origins and means "of or relating to heat."

Extension

In **Figure 22,** the hot water from the geothermal reservoir is pumped to the surface where it changes to steam. Challenge students to find out how the water changes from hot water to steam without additional energy being added. The hot water is under pressure in the underground reservoir and achieves temperatures higher than 100° C. When the pressure begins to drop, the super-hot water changes to steam.

Activity

Have students research how heat pumps are used to heat and cool homes. Students should make a detailed poster showing the process. Have students present their posters to their class or a group of younger students. LS **Visual-Spatial**

Discussion

Why aren't geothermal heat pumps the primary source of heating and cooling in the United States? Possible answers: The cost of initial installation of geothermal heat pump systems is more than conventional equipment. The systems require additional land for the heat-exchanging wells. They work best in moderate climates and are not as effective in colder climates.

Inclusion Strategies

Learning Disabled Have another student use a poster that was made in the activity above to explain each step in the heat pump process. Have learning disabled students define any unfamiliar words in their science journals for future reference. LS **Interpersonal**

Science Journal

Geothermal Heat Pumps Have students make a chart in their Science Journals listing advantages and disadvantages of installing a geothermal heat pump in their home. LS **Logical-Mathematical**

Energy from the Oceans

Discussion

What produces the mechanical energy used in a tidal power plant? The flow of water over a turbine, which causes the turbine to spin; in this way mechanical energy can be changed to electrical energy. **Why is this system available in only a few locations around the world?** There are only a few locations that have a enough difference between the height of high and low tides.

Make a Model

Have groups of students make simple models demonstrating how tidal energy can be used to generate electricity. Instruct students to use their models to explain this process to a group of younger students or another class. LS **Interpersonal**

Activity

Have students make a Venn diagram to compare and contrast hydroelectric and tidal power. LS **Visual-Spatial**

Figure 23
This tidal power plant in Annapolis Royal, Nova Scotia, is the only operating tidal power plant in North America.

Energy from the Oceans

The ocean is in constant motion. If you've been to the seashore you've seen waves roll in. You may have seen the level of the ocean rise and fall over a period of about a half day. This rise and fall in the ocean level is called a tide. The constant movement of the ocean is an inexhaustible source of mechanical energy that can be converted into electric energy. While methods are still being developed to convert the motion in ocean waves to electric energy, several electric power plants using tidal motion have been built.

Using Tidal Energy A high tide and a low tide occur about twice a day. In most places the level of the ocean changes by less than a few meters. However, in some places the change is much greater. In the Bay of Fundy in Eastern Canada, the ocean level changes by 16 m between high tide and low tide. Almost 14 trillion kg of water move into or out of the bay between high and low tide.

Figure 23 shows an electric power plant that has been built along the Bay of Fundy. This power plant generates enough electric energy to power about 12,000 homes. The power plant is constructed so that as the tide rises, water flows through a turbine that causes a electric generator to spin, as shown in **Figure 24A**. The water is then trapped behind a dam. When the tide goes out, the trapped water behind the dam is released through the turbine to generate more electricity, as shown in **Figure 24B.** Each day electric power is generated for about ten hours when the tide is rising and falling.

While tidal energy is a nonpolluting, inexhaustible energy source, its use is limited. Only in a few places is the difference between high and low tide large enough to enable a large electric power plant to be built.

Figure 24
A tidal power plant can generate electricity when the tide is coming in and going out.

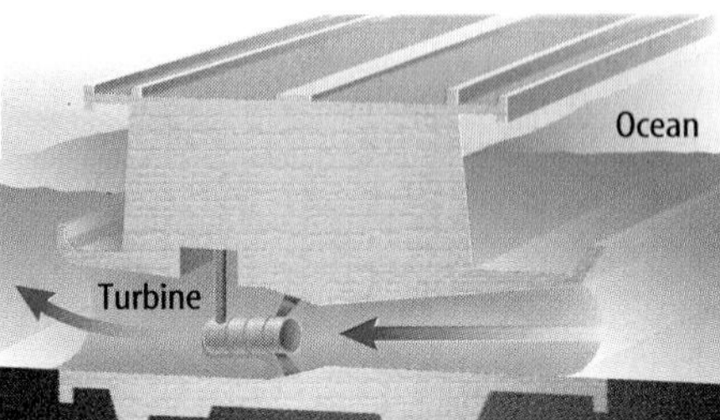

A **As the tide comes in, it turns a turbine connected to a generator. When high tide occurs, gates are closed that trap water behind a dam.**

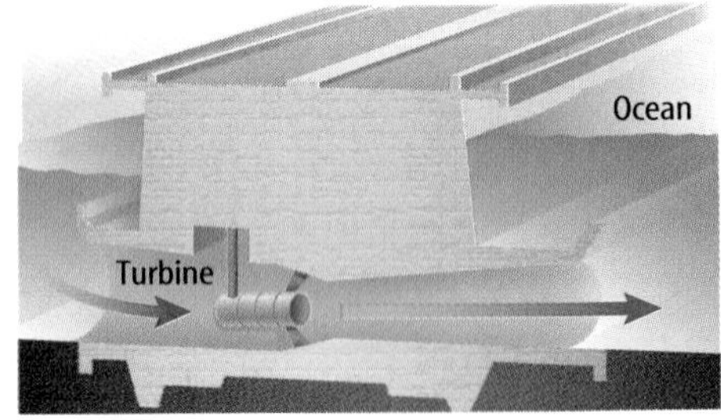

B **As the tide goes out and the ocean level drops, the gates are opened and water from behind the dam flows through the turbine, causing it to spin and turn a generator.**

Curriculum Connection

Geography The first large-scale tidal plant was constructed on the Rance River in Saint-Malo, France. Have students locate this area on a map. LS **Visual-Spatial**

Resource Manager

Chapter Resources Booklet
Reinforcement, p. 27

Wind

Wind is another inexhaustible, clean supply of energy. Modern windmills like the ones in **Figure 25** are twirling monsters that stand 50 m above the ground and have rotors, or propellers, that are 50 m across. The rotors attach directly to the turbine, which turns a generator. One windmill can provide enough energy for nearly 300 homes. Wind farms containing more than 100 windmills can reduce the use of fossil fuels or nuclear energy significantly.

Figure 25
Windmills work on the same basic principles as a power plant. Instead of steam turning a turbine, wind turns the rotors. *What are some of the advantages and disadvantages of using windmills?*

Conserving Energy

As fossil fuels are used up and become more expensive and harder to find, energy shortages may occur. One way to help prevent energy shortages is to make the supply of fossil fuels last longer by using less energy. Reducing the use of energy is called conserving energy.

You can avoid wasting electricity and conserve energy by turning off lights and appliances such as televisions when you are not using them. Also keep doors and windows closed tightly when it's cold or hot to keep heat from leaking out of or into your house. Energy could also be conserved if buildings are properly insulated, especially around windows. The use of oil could be reduced if cars were used less and made more efficient, so they went farther on a liter of gas. Recycling materials such as aluminum cans and glass also helps conserve energy.

Section  Assessment

1. What is the ultimate source of most of the energy stored on Earth?
2. What is a renewable resource? Give an example of a renewable and nonrenewable resource and explain the difference.
3. Give a number of reasons why depending on fossil fuels for energy will lead to trouble in the long run.
4. What are the disadvantages of using hydroelectricity and solar energy?
5. **Think Critically** Even when the surface temperature is hot or cold, the temperature deep inside a cave stays the same. Why?

Skill Builder Activities

6. **Predicting** Why would the amount of solar energy hitting a collector change from day to day throughout the year? Explain your reasoning. If you lived in the far north, how would you ensure that you received the most sunlight every day of the year? **For more help, refer to the Science Skill Handbook.**
7. **Using Proportions** As you go deeper into Earth, it becomes hotter. Using the information from this section, calculate the temperature at the center of Earth if its radius is 6,370 km. **For more help, refer to the Math Skill Handbook.**

Conserving Energy

Caption Answer

Figure 25 Advantages include lack of pollution and the availability of wind. Disadvantages are the potential for killing birds, variability of the wind, towers are unsightly, and a large amount of land is required.

3 Assess

Reteach

Have each student make a list of all of the sources of energy discussed in this section. Ask students to explain how each energy source releases its energy and classify each source as renewable or nonrenewable. L2
LS **Linguistic**

Challenge

Have each student identify the alternative energy source he or she thinks would be most appropriate for use in your area and explain the choice. Ask students why this energy source is a good alternative to fossil fuels. Source selected will depend on where students live. All sources are good alternatives to fossil fuels because they are renewable and likely release fewer pollutants to the environment. L2
LS **Logical-Mathematical**

Oral Where does all the electrical energy produced in power plants end up? It is converted into another type of energy such as thermal, radiant, or sound energy. Use **PASC,** p. 91.

Answers to Section Assessment

1. the Sun's radiation
2. Possible answers: A renewable resource is forever resupplied; water is an example. Fossil fuels are nonrenewable. They exist in fixed amounts in Earth.
3. When they are burned they release pollutants that can cause respiratory diseases and acid rain.
4. The dams used to produce hydroelectricity disrupt the life cycle of aquatic animals, especially salmon. Solar energy is expensive and its technology is not well developed.
5. The soil and rock above it act as an insulator.
6. The position of the Sun in the sky and the number of hours of daylight change during the year. Put the collector on the side of the house facing the Sun during the winter.
7. $(2°C/100\ m) \times (6{,}370{,}000\ m) =$ 127,000°C. The real value is closer to 3,700°C, since the relationship is not proportional.

Activity

BENCH TESTED

Recognize the Problem

Internet Students will use Internet sites that can be accessed through the Glencoe Science Web site at **science.glencoe.com**. They will investigate the types of energy they use in everyday activities. L2

LS **Logical-Mathematical**

Non-Internet Sources Identify different science books to research energy sources.

Time Required

about two days

Preparation

Internet Access the Glencoe Science Web site at **science.glencoe.com** to run through the steps that the students will follow.

Non-Internet Sources Collect books and materials that contain information about energy sources such as gasoline, coal, and solar energy.

Form a Hypothesis

Possible Hypotheses

Direct students to consider activities they do and the tools or equipment they use to do those activities. Those things may require energy to operate. For example, students ride to school on a bus that runs on fuel.

Test Your Hypothesis

Teaching Strategies

Help students understand that different machines and appliances use different forms of energy. They should consider how energy is produced and delivered to them for use.

Activity Use the Internet

Energy to Power Your Life

Over the past 100 years, the amount of energy used in the United States and elsewhere has greatly increased. Today, a number of energy sources are available, such as coal, oil, natural gas, nuclear energy, hydroelectric power, wind, and solar energy. Some of these energy sources are being used up and are nonrenewable, but others are replaced as fast as they are used and, therefore, are renewable. Some energy sources are so vast that human usage has almost no effect on the amount available. These energy sources are inexhaustible.

Think about the types of energy you use at home and school every day. In this activity, you will investigate how and where energy is produced, and how it gets to you. You will also investigate alternative ways energy can be produced, and whether these sources are renewable, nonrenewable, or inexhaustible.

Recognize the Problem

What types of energy do you use every day?

Form a Hypothesis

When you wake up in the morning and turn on a light, you use electrical energy. When you ride to school in a car or bus, its engine consumes chemical energy. What other types of energy do you use? Where is that energy produced? Which energy sources are nonrenewable, which are renewable, and which are inexhaustible? What are other sources of energy that you could use instead?

Local Energy Information	
Energy Type	
Where is that energy produced?	
How is that energy produced?	Answers
How is that energy delivered to you?	will
Is the energy source renewable, nonrenewable, or inexhaustible?	vary
What type of alternative energy source could you use instead?	

Goals

- **Identify** how energy you use is produced and delivered.
- **Investigate** alternative sources for the energy you use.
- **Outline** a plan for how these alternative sources of energy could be used.

Data Source

SCIENCE*Online* Go to the Glencoe Science Web site at **science.glencoe.com** for more information about sources of energy and for data collected by other students.

Resource Manager

Chapter Resources Booklet
Activity Worksheet, pp. 7–8

Lab Management and Safety, p. 73

SCIENCE Online

Internet Addresses

Explore the Glencoe Science Web site at **science.glencoe.com** to find out more about topics in this activity.

Test Your Hypothesis

Plan

1. Think about the activities you do every day and the things you use. When you watch television, listen to the radio, ride in a car, use a hair drier, or turn on the air conditioning, you use energy. Select one activity or appliance that uses energy.
2. **Identify** the type of energy that is used.
3. **Investigate** how that energy is produced and delivered to you.
4. **Determine** if the energy source is renewable, nonrenewable, or inexhaustible.
5. If your energy source is nonrenewable, describe how the energy you use could be produced by renewable sources.

Do

1. Make sure your teacher approves your plan before you start.
2. Organize your findings in a data table, similar to the one that is shown.
3. Go to the Glencoe Science Web site at **science.glencoe.com** to post your data.

Analyze Your Data

1. **Describe** the process for producing and delivering the energy source you researched. How is it created, and how does it get to you?
2. How much of the energy you use every day comes from the energy source you investigated?
3. Is the energy source you researched renewable, nonrenewable, or inexhaustible? Why?
4. Is the production, delivering, and sources of energy the same around the country? Can you see any patterns? Explain.

Draw Conclusions

1. If the energy source you investigated is nonrenewable, describe how you could reduce your use of this energy source.
2. What alternative sources of energy could you use for everyday energy needs? On the computer, create a plan for using renewable or inexhaustible sources wisely.

Communicating Your Data

SCIENCE Online Find this *Use the Internet* activity on the Glencoe Science Web site at **science.glencoe.com**. Post your data in the table that is provided. **Compare** your data to that of other students. **Combine** your data with that of other student and make inferences using the combined data.

Analyze Your Data

1. Answers may vary. One example would be the process for producing gasoline, which involves drilling crude oil from wells, and the process involved in refining the crude oil into the product that we pump at the gas station.
2. If students investigated gasoline, they may discover that it is a small part of their daily energy use.
3. Gasoline is an example of a nonrenewable energy source, because it is a fossil fuel.
4. Answers may vary. When investigating how an energy source is produced and delivered, students may discover that the way the energy source gets to people and its cost varies in different areas of the country.

Draw Conclusions

1. Answers will vary.
2. One strategy may be to replace a calculator that runs on nonrechargeable batteries with one that is powered by solar cells.

Assessment

Process Have students make displays that show their research about an activity or appliance and its energy source. They should include pictures and descriptions of how the energy source used is produced and delivered so it can be used. Use **PASC**, p.135.

Communicating Your Data

Have students make a chart that compares the energy source they investigated with other energy sources that could be used, including alternative or renewable energy sources. Students should also compare costs and environmental impacts.

Chapter 8 Study Guide

Reviewing Main Ideas

Preview

Students can answer the questions in their Science Journals. Discuss the answers as you go through the chapter. **LS Linguistic**

Review

Students can write their answers, then compare them with those of other students. **LS Interpersonal**

Reteach

Students can look at the illustrations and describe details that support the main ideas of the chapter. **LS Visual-Spatial**

Answers to Chapter Review

Section 1

4. The dog and the frisbee both have kinetic and potential energy. The daylight has radiant energy.

Section 3

1. The dammed water is continually replenished but the dam destroys habitat, vegetation, and fish migration.
3. The picture on the left is not as clear because there is a great deal of pollution in the air.

Chapter 8 Study Guide

Reviewing Main Ideas

Section 1 What is energy?

1. Energy is the ability to cause change. Energy is found in many forms.
2. Moving objects have kinetic energy, and all objects have thermal energy.
3. Potential energy is the energy of position. Radiant energy is the energy of light.
4. Electric current carries electrical energy, and atomic nuclei contain nuclear energy. *What are all the forms of energy that are represented in this picture?*

Section 2 Energy Transformations

1. Energy can transform into other types of energy. When energy transforms, a change is observed in the environment.
2. All energy transformations obey the law of conservation of energy, which means no energy is ever created or destroyed.
3. Thermal energy is hard to store and transport, whereas chemical energy is easily stored in such things as wood, gasoline, and food, and is easily transported.
4. Electrical energy is readily transformed into other types of energy. One way it is generated is at power plants when steam rushes through turbines, which spin a generator.

Section 3 Sources of Energy

1. Renewable energy sources include solar, tidal, wind, geothermal, and hydroelectric energy. *Why would the electricity generated from this dam be considered renewable but not necessarily clean?*

2. Fossil fuels are a non-renewable source of energy. As the supply runs out, alternative fuels must be found.
3. Use of each energy source has consequences for humans and for the environment. The benefits of use must be weighed against the harmful side effects. *Look at the two photographs below of the same view of New York*

FOLDABLES Reading & Study Skills — After You Read

Write what you learned about the types, sources and transformation of energy under the Learned tab of your Know-Want-Learn Study Fold.

FOLDABLES Reading & Study Skills — After You Read

After students have read the chapter and completed the Foldable described in Before You Read, have them do the activity on the student page.

Chapter  Study Guide

Visualizing Main Ideas

Use the following terms and phrases to complete the concept map about energy sources: fossil fuels, hydroelectric, solar, wind, oil, coal, photovoltaic, *and* nonrenewable resources.

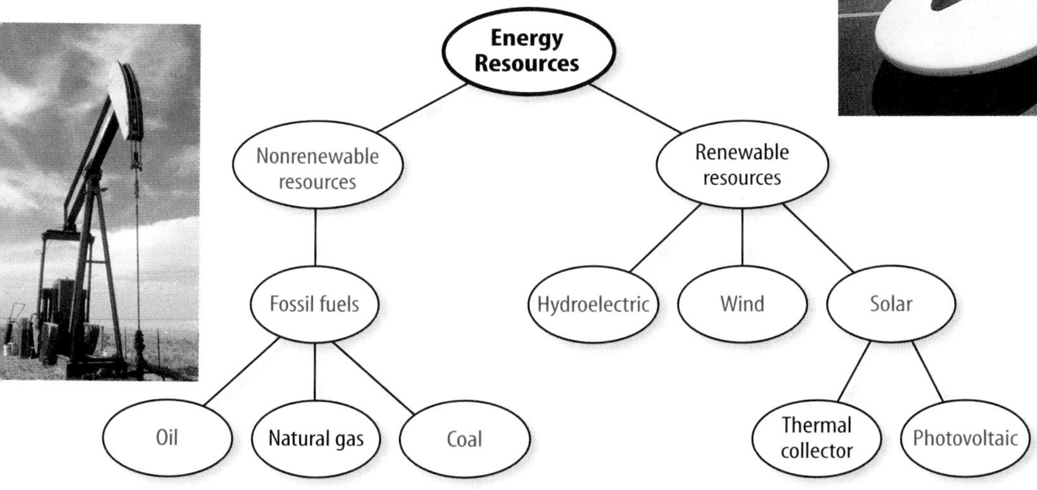

Vocabulary Review

Vocabulary Words

- **a.** alternative resource
- **b.** chemical energy
- **c.** electrical energy
- **d.** energy
- **e.** generator
- **f.** kinetic energy
- **g.** law of conservation of energy
- **h.** nonrenewable resource
- **i.** nuclear energy
- **j.** photovoltaic
- **k.** potential energy
- **l.** radiant energy
- **m.** renewable resource
- **n.** thermal energy
- **o.** turbine

Using Vocabulary

For each set of terms below, explain the relationship that exists.

1. electrical energy, nuclear energy
2. turbine, generator
3. photovoltaic, radiant energy, electrical energy
4. renewable resource, alternative resource
5. potential energy, kinetic energy
6. kinetic energy, electrical energy, generator
7. thermal energy, radiant energy
8. law of conservation of energy, energy transformations
9. nonrenewable resource, chemical energy
10. energy, resource

THE PRINCETON REVIEW **Study Tip**

Practice reading graphs and charts. Make a table that contains the same information as a graph does.

IDENTIFYING Misconceptions

Assess

Use the assessment as follow-up to page 226F after students have completed the chapter.

Activity Display examples of the work of the famous cartoonist Rube Goldberg. Have students draw their own Rube Goldberg style invention that includes four energy transformations. Direct students to draw red arrows to indicate areas where heat loss would occur.

Expected Outcome Students recognize that energy is transferred from one form into another.

Reinforcement Have students exchange drawings and describe the energy transformations depicted.

Chapter 8 Study Guide

Visualizing Main Ideas

See student page.

Vocabulary Review

Using Vocabulary

1. Nuclear energy is sometimes used to generate electrical energy.
2. In an electrical generator, the kinetic energy of a rotating turbine is changed into electrical energy.
3. A photovoltaic collector changes radiant energy from the Sun directly into electrical energy.
4. Alternative resources are renewable resources that are being developed to help replace fossil fuels.
5. Potential energy due to gravity changes to kinetic energy as an object falls.
6. In an electrical generator, the kinetic energy of a rotating turbine is changed into electrical energy.
7. When a piece of material has enough thermal energy, it may emit radiant energy.
8. The law of conservation of energy states that in energy transformations, energy can be neither created nor destroyed. It only can change from one form to another.
9. Some sources of chemical energy, such as fossil fuels, are nonrenewable. Some, such as wood, are renewable.
10. Resources are sources of energy.

Chapter 8 Assessment

Checking Concepts

1. C
2. D
3. D
4. C
5. A
6. A
7. B
8. A
9. D
10. B

Thinking Critically

11. The pendulum is like a swing. At the endpoints of the pendulum's swing, the potential energy is maximum, the speed of the pendulum is zero, and the kinetic energy is zero. As the pendulum moves downward, potential energy is converted to kinetic energy, so that at the midpoint of the swing, the kinetic energy is maximum and the potential energy is minimum. Friction in the pivot will eventually remove all the energy from the pendulum and the pendulum will come to rest.
12. Every object has thermal, chemical, and nuclear energy. Objects sometimes have kinetic, potential energy, and electrical energy. Objects never have radiant energy.
13. In the toaster, electrical energy is converted to radiant energy and thermal energy. The thermal energy causes chemical reactions in the bagel that change chemical energy to thermal energy.
14. noise and danger to birds from the huge rotors
15. Solar energy is for all practical purposes inexhaustible and it is clean. Solar energy is now fairly expensive and inefficient, solar cells are not very attractive, and the amount of energy solar cells collect depends on the time of year. Using solar requires a large amount of land. The manufacture and disposal of solar panels generates pollutants.

Chapter 8 Assessment

Checking Concepts

1. Objects that are able to fall have what type of energy?
   A) kinetic C) potential
   B) radiant D) electrical
2. Which form of energy does light have?
   A) electrical C) kinetic
   B) nuclear D) radiant
3. Muscles perform what type of energy transformation?
   A) kinetic to potential
   B) kinetic to electrical
   C) thermal to radiant
   D) chemical to kinetic
4. Photovoltaics perform what type of energy transformation?
   A) thermal to radiant
   B) kinetic to electrical
   C) radiant to electrical
   D) electrical to thermal
5. Which form of energy does food have?
   A) chemical C) radiant
   B) potential D) electrical
6. Solar energy, wind, and geothermal are what type of energy resource?
   A) renewable C) nonrenewable
   B) inexpensive D) alternative
7. Which of the following is a nonrenewable source of energy?
   A) hydroelectricity C) wind
   B) nuclear D) solar
8. Which of the following resources does not require a turbine to generate electricity?
   A) solar C) hydroelectric
   B) wind D) nuclear
9. Which of the following are fossil fuels?
   A) gas C) oil
   B) coal D) all of these
10. From where does the surface of Earth acquire most of its energy?
    A) radioactivity C) chemicals
    B) Sun D) wind

Thinking Critically

11. Explain how the motion of a pendulum illustrates the exchange between potential and kinetic energy. What will happen if a small amount of friction is in the pivot?
12. Energy riddles: Which forms of energy does every object have? Which forms of energy do objects sometimes have? Which form of energy can an object never have?
13. Describe the energy transformations that occur in the process of toasting a bagel in an electric toaster.
14. What might be a few of the negative consequences of wind power?
15. Explain why the use of solar energy could be superior to fossil fuels. Describe some of the limitations of using solar energy. Does using solar energy have negative consequences? Explain.

Developing Skills

16. **Researching Information** Find out how spacecraft, such as *Galileo*, obtain energy in the outer solar system.

Chapter Assessment Planner

Portfolio Encourage students to place in their portfolios one or two items of what they consider to be their best work. Examples include:

- Science Journal, p. 231
- Curriculum Connection, p. 238
- Science Journal, p. 242

Performance Additional performance assessments, Performance Task Assessment Lists, and rubrics for evaluating these activities can be found in Glencoe's **Performance Assessment in the Science Classroom.**

Chapter 8 Assessment

17. Concept Mapping Complete this concept map about energy.

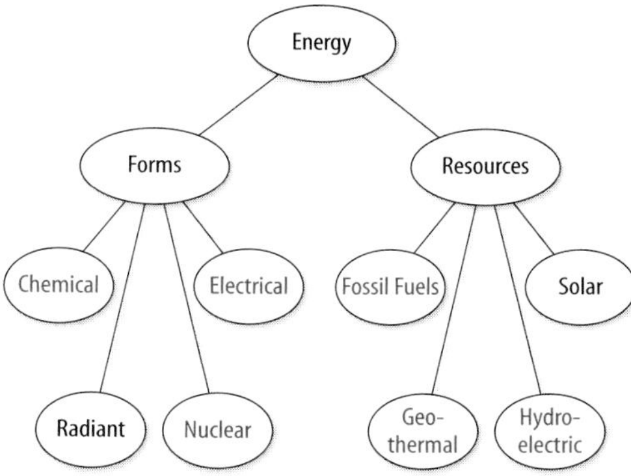

18. Classifying A proposal has been made to use wheat as a source of energy called biomass. It can be made into alcohol, which can be burned in engines. How would you classify this source of energy? Do you see any problems with using this as a source of energy? Explain.

Performance Assessment

19. Multimedia Presentation Alternative sources of energy that weren't discussed include tidal energy, biomass energy, wave energy, and hydrogen fuel cells. Research an alternative energy source and then prepare a digital slide show about the information you found. Use the concepts you learned from this chapter to inform your classmates about the future prospects of such an energy source.

Technology

Go to the Glencoe Science Web site at **science.glencoe.com** or use the **Glencoe Science CD-ROM** for additional chapter assessment.

Test Practice

Throughout the course of one day, you engage in dozens of energy transformations. The table below gives some examples of different energy transformations.

Types of Energy Transformation

Energy Transformation	Example
Potential ⟶ Kinetic	Ball rolling down a hill
Kinetic ⟶ Potential	A pebble tossed upward
Electrical ⟶ Radiant	A desk lamp
Chemical ⟶ Thermal	Burning fossil fuels
	Music from a radio

1. What kind of energy change occurs when coal is burned in a stove?
   A) potential → kinetic
   B) kinetic → potential
   C) electrical → radiant
   D) chemical → thermal

2. Which of these energy transformations will complete the table?
   F) electrical → radiant
   G) sound → electrical
   H) electrical → sound
   J) electrical → chemical

3. An image displayed on a computer screen most closely matches which example in terms of energy transformation?
   A) ball rolling down a hill
   B) a desk lamp
   C) burning fossil fuels
   D) music from a radio

Assessment Resources

Reproducible Masters

Chapter Resources Booklet
Chapter Review, pp. 35–36
Chapter Tests, pp. 37–40
Assessment Transparency Activity, p. 47

Glencoe Science Web site
Interactive Tutor
Chapter Quizzes

Glencoe Technology
Assessment Transparency
Interactive CD-ROM Chapter Quizzes
ExamView Pro Test Bank
Vocabulary PuzzleMaker Software
MindJogger Videoquiz DVD/VHS

Chapter 8 Assessment

Test Practice

The Test-Taking Tip was written by The Princeton Review, the nation's leader in test preparation.

1. D
2. H
3. B

Developing Skills

16. *Galileo* is powered by radioisotope thermoelectric generators (RTG). The RTG fuel is plutonium dioxide, which generates heat as a result of its normal decay. The heat is converted to electrical energy.
17. Check students' work.
18. It is a renewable energy source because more wheat can be grown. Problems include the cost of growing the wheat and converting it to alcohol and whether the wheat is more valuable as food or as fuel. Also, technology would need to be developed for using the alcohol fuel.

Performance Assessment

19. Include hydrogen fusion and encourage students to do more research on the alternative energy sources described in the chapter. Use **PASC**, p. 149.

Section/Objectives	Standards: National	Standards: State/Local	Activities/Features
Chapter Opener	See p. 5T for a Key to Standards.		**Explore Activity:** Compare forces, p. 257 **Before You Read,** p. 257
Section 1 Work and Power 3 sessions 1.5 blocks 1. **Recognize** when work is done. 2. **Calculate** how much work is done. 3. **Explain** the relationship between work and power.	National Content Standards: UCP1, UCP3, UCP4, A1, B2, B3		**Life Science Integration,** p. 258 **Math Skills Activity:** Calculating Work, p. 260 **Science Online,** p. 261 **Math Skills Activity:** Calculating Power, p. 261 **MiniLAB:** Measuring Work and Power, p. 262 **Activity:** Building the Pyramids, p. 263
Section 2 Using Machines 3 sessions 1.5 blocks 1. **Explain** how a machine makes work easier. 2. **Calculate** the mechanical advantages and efficiency of a machine. 3. **Explain** how friction reduces efficiency.	National Content Standards: UCP1, UCP3, UCP4, B2, B3, E1, E2		**Science Online,** p. 265 **Math Skills Activity:** Calculating Mechanical Advantage, p. 265 **Life Science Integration,** p. 267 **Math Skills Activity:** Calculating Efficiency, p. 267
Section 3 Simple Machines 4 sessions 2 blocks 1. **Distinguish** among the different simple machines. 2. **Describe** how to find the mechanical advantage of each simple machine.	National Content Standards: UCP1, UCP3, UCP4, A1, B2, B3, E1, E2, F1		**Visualizing Levers,** p. 273 **MiniLAB:** Observing Pulleys, p. 274 **Activity:** Pulley Power, pp. 276–277 **Science and Society:** Bionic People, pp. 278–279

Activity Materials	Reproducible Resources	Section Assessment	Technology
Explore Activity: ruler, flat eraser, book	**Chapter Resources Booklet** Foldables Worksheet, p. 17 Directed Reading Overview, p. 19 Note-taking Worksheets, pp. 33–35	GLENCOE'S ASSESSMENT ADVANTAGE	
MiniLAB: bathroom scale, meterstick, stopwatch, calculator **Activity:** wood block, tape, spring scale, ruler, thin notebooks, meterstick, several books	**Chapter Resources Booklet** Transparency Activity, p. 44 MiniLAB, p. 3 Lab Activity, pp. 9–12 Enrichment, p. 30 Reinforcement, p. 27 Directed Reading, pp. 19, 20 Activity Worksheet, pp. 5–6 **Cultural Diversity,** p. 63 **Mathematics Skill Activities,** p. 11	Portfolio text, p. 00 Performance Math Skills Activities, pp. 260, 261 MiniLAB, p. 262 Skill Builder Activities, p. 262 Content Section Assessment, p. 262	Section Focus Transparency Interactive CD-ROM/DVD Guided Reading Audio Program
Need materials? Contact Science Kit at 1-800-828-7777 or www.sciencekit.com on the Internet.	**Chapter Resources Booklet** Transparency Activity, p. 45 Enrichment, p. 31 Reinforcement, p. 28 Directed Reading, p. 21 Transparency Activity, pp. 47–48 **Reading and Writing Skill Activities,** p. 35	Portfolio text, p. 00 Performance Math Skills Activities, pp. 265, 267 Skill Builder Activities, p. 268 Content Section Assessment, p. 268	Section Focus Transparency Teaching Transparency Interactive CD-ROM/DVD Guided Reading Audio Program
MiniLAB: 2 broomsticks, rope **Activity:** single- and multiple-pulley systems, nylon rope, steel bar to support the pulley system, meterstick, variety of weights, force spring scale, brick, balance	**Chapter Resources Booklet** Transparency Activity, p. 46 MiniLAB, p. 4 Lab Activity, pp. 13–16 Enrichment, p. 32 Reinforcement, p. 29 Directed Reading, pp. 21, 22 Activity Worksheet, pp. 7–8 **Lab Management and Safety,** p. 39	Portfolio text, p. 00 Performance MiniLAB, p. 274 Skill Builder Activities, p. 275 Content Section Assessment, p. 275	Section Focus Transparency Interactive CD-ROM/DVD Guided Reading Audio Program

End of Chapter Assessment

GLENCOE'S ASSESSMENT ADVANTAGE

Blackline Masters	Technology	Professional Series
Chapter Resources Booklet Chapter Review, pp. 37–38 Chapter Tests, pp. 39–42 **Standardized Test Practice by The Princeton Review,** pp. 39–42	MindJogger Videoquiz CD-ROM Explorations and Quizzes Vocabulary Puzzle Makers ExamView Pro Test Bank Interactive Lesson Planner Interactive Teacher's Edition	Performance Assessment in the Science Classroom (PASC)

Transparencies

Section Focus

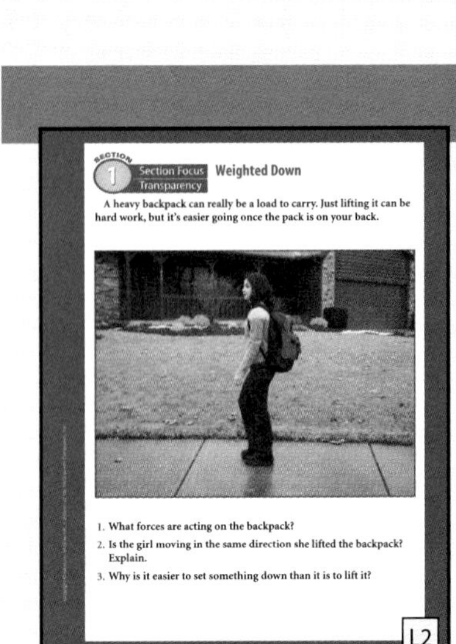
SECTION 1 Section Focus Transparency **Weighted Down**

A heavy backpack can really be a load to carry. Just lifting it can be hard work, but it's easier going once the pack is on your back.

1. What forces are acting on the backpack?
2. Is the girl moving in the same direction she lifted the backpack? Explain.
3. Why is it easier to set something down than it is to lift it?

L2

SECTION 2 Section Focus Transparency **The puck stops here.**

If you've ever tried to walk or skate on ice, you know how difficult it can be. There's a lot less friction on ice than on concrete, making hockey a fast and exciting sport.

1. Why do you sometimes slip when you step onto a patch of ice on the sidewalk?
2. Why does a hockey player move faster than a runner?
3. Why is shooting a puck considered doing work?

L2

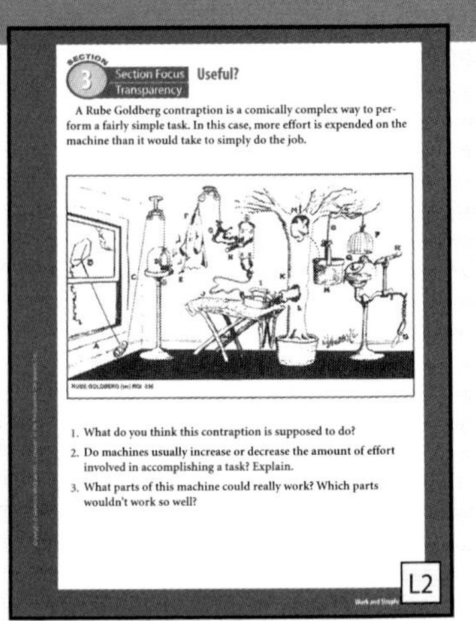
SECTION 3 Section Focus Transparency **Useful?**

A Rube Goldberg contraption is a comically complex way to perform a fairly simple task. In this case, more effort is expended on the machine than it would take to simply do the job.

1. What do you think this contraption is supposed to do?
2. Do machines usually increase or decrease the amount of effort involved in accomplishing a task? Explain.
3. What parts of this machine could really work? Which parts wouldn't work so well?

L2

This is a representation of key blackline masters available in the Teacher Classroom Resources. See Resource Manager boxes within the chapter for additional information.

Assessment

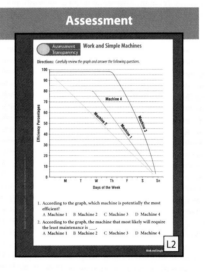

Assessment Transparency **Work and Simple Machines**

Directions: *Carefully review the graph and answer the following questions.*

1. According to the graph, which machine is potentially the most efficient?
   A Machine 1 B Machine 2 C Machine 3 D Machine 4
2. According to the graph, the machine that most likely will require the least maintenance is ___.
   A Machine 1 B Machine 2 C Machine 3 D Machine 4

L2

Teaching

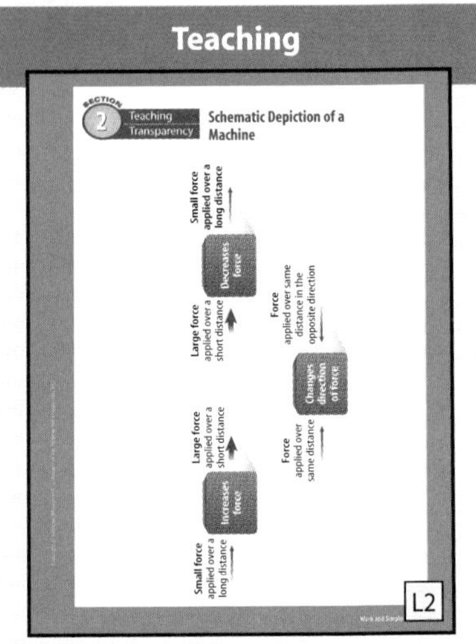
SECTION 2 Teaching Transparency **Schematic Depiction of a Machine**

L2

Key to Teaching Strategies

The following designations will help you decide which activities are appropriate for your students.

- L1 Level 1 activities should be appropriate for students with learning difficulties.
- L2 Level 2 activities should be within the ability range of all students.
- L3 Level 3 activities are designed for above-average students.
- ELL ELL activities should be within the ability range of English Language Learners.
- COOP LEARN Cooperative Learning activities are designed for small group work.
- LS Multiple Learning Styles logos, as described on page 22T, are used throughout to indicate strategies that address different learning styles.
- P These strategies represent student products that can be placed into a best-work portfolio.

Hands-on Activities

Activity Worksheets

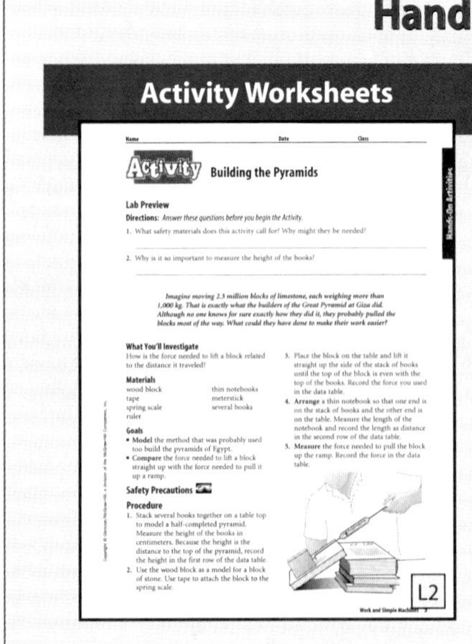
Name Date Class

Activity **Building the Pyramids**

Lab Preview

Directions: *Answer these questions before you begin the Activity.*

1. What safety materials does this activity call for? Why might they be needed?
2. Why is it so important to measure the height of the books?

Imagine moving 2.3 million blocks of limestone, each weighing more than 1,000 kg. That is exactly what the builders of the Great Pyramid at Giza did. Although no one knows for sure exactly how they did it, they probably pulled the blocks most of the way. What could they have done to make their work easier?

What You'll Investigate
How is the force needed to lift a block related to the distance it traveled?

Materials
wood block
tape
spring scale
ruler
thin notebooks
meterstick
several books

Goals
- **Model** the method that was probably used too build the pyramids of Egypt.
- **Compare** the force needed to lift a block straight up with the force needed to pull it up a ramp.

Safety Precautions

Procedure
1. Stack several books together on a table top to model a half-completed pyramid. Measure the height of the books in centimeters. Because the height is the distance to the top of the pyramid, record the height in the first row of the data table.
2. Use the wood block as a model for a block of stone. Use tape to attach the block to the spring scale.
3. Place the block on the table and lift it straight up the side of the stack of books until the top of the block is even with the top of the books. Record the force you used in the data table.
4. **Arrange** a thin notebook so that one end is on the stack of books and the other end is on the table. Measure the length of the notebook and record the length as distance in the second row of the data table.
5. **Measure** the force needed to pull the block up the ramp. Record the force in the data table.

Hands-On Activities

Work and Simple Machines 3

L2

Laboratory Activities

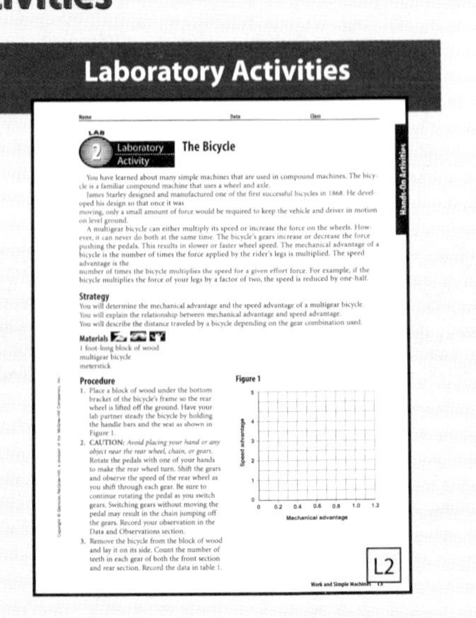
Name Date Class

LAB 2 Laboratory Activity **The Bicycle**

You have learned about many simple machines that are used in compound machines. The bicycle is a familiar compound machine that uses a wheel and axle.

James Starley designed and manufactured one of the first successful bicycles in 1868. He developed his design so that once it was moving, only a small amount of force would be required to keep the vehicle and driver in motion on level ground.

A multigear bicycle can either multiply its speed or increase the force on the wheels. However, it can never do both at the same time. The bicycle's gears increase or decrease the force pushing the pedals. This results in slower or faster wheel speed. The mechanical advantage of a bicycle is the number of times the force applied by the rider's legs is multiplied. The speed advantage is the number of times the bicycle multiplies the speed for a given effort force. For example, if the bicycle multiplies the force of your legs by a factor of two, the speed is reduced by one-half.

Strategy
You will determine the mechanical advantage and the speed advantage of a multigear bicycle.
You will explain the relationship between mechanical advantage and speed advantage.
You will describe the distance traveled by a bicycle depending on the gear combination used.

Materials
1 foot-long block of wood
multigear bicycle
meterstick

Procedure
1. Place a block of wood under the bottom bracket of the bicycle's frame so the rear wheel is lifted off the ground. Have your lab partner steady the bicycle by holding the handle bars and the seat as shown in Figure 1.
2. CAUTION: *Avoid placing your hand or any object near the rear wheel, chain, or gears.* Rotate the pedals with one of your hands to make the rear wheel turn. Shift the gears and observe the speed of the rear wheel as you shift through each gear. Be sure to continue rotating the pedal as you switch gears. Switching gears without moving the pedal may result in the chain jumping off the gears. Record your observation in the Data and Observations section.
3. Remove the bicycle from the block of wood and lay it on its side. Count the number of teeth in each gear of both the front section and rear section. Record the data in table 1.

Figure 1

Hands-On Activities

Work and Simple Machines 13

L2

Meeting Different Ability Levels

Content Outline

Note-taking Worksheet — Work and Simple Machines — Chapter 5

Section 1 Work and Power

A. ___—transfer of energy that occurs when a force makes an object move
1. For work to occur, an object must ___.
2. The motion of the object must be in the ___ as the applied force.

B. Work and energy are related, since energy is always ___ from the object doing the work to the object on which the work is done.

C. Work is done on an object only when ___ is being applied to the object.

D. Calculating work—work equals force (in newtons) times ___

E. ___—amount of work done in a certain amount of time; rate at which work is done
1. ___—power equals work divided by time
2. Power is measured in ___ (W).
3. Since work and energy are ___, power also can be calculated—power equals energy divided by time.

Section 2 Using Machines

A. Device that makes doing work easier is a ___.

B. Machines ___ applied force and/or ___ direction of applied force to make work easier.
1. Same amount of work can be done by applying a small force over a long distance as can be done applying a large force over a short distance, since work equals force times distance.
2. Increasing ___ reduces the amount of force needed to do the work.
3. Some machines change the ___ of the force to do the work.

C. Machines help move things that ___ being moved.
1. Force applied to machine is ___
2. ___—force applied by machine to overcome resistance
3. Amount of energy the machine transfers to the object cannot be ___ than the amount of energy transferred to the machine.
a. Some energy transferred is changed to ___ due to friction.
b. An ideal machine with no ___ would have the same input work as output work.

L2

Reinforcement

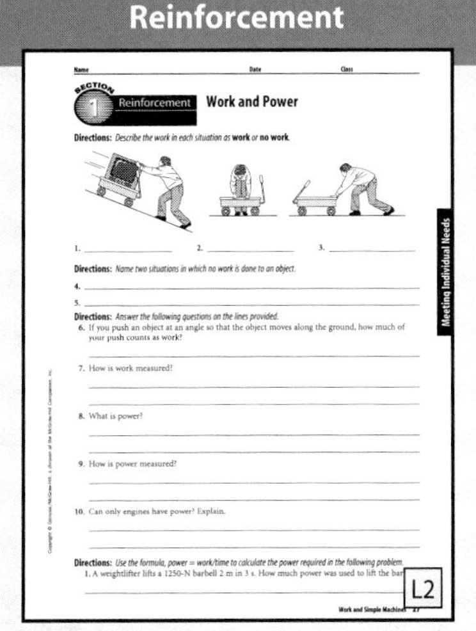

Reinforcement — Work and Power

Directions: Describe the work in each situation as work or no work.

L2

Directed Reading

Directed Reading for Content Mastery — Overview — Work and Simple Machines

Directions: Use the following terms to complete the concept map below.

pivot, pulleys, inclined planes, levers, greater, direction, screws, wedges, lever types

Directions: Answer the following questions on the lines provided.

10. In what three ways are machines useful?

11. You are holding a heavy iron doorstop in front of the class to demonstrate a wedge. Are you doing work? Explain.

L1

Assessment

Chapter Tests

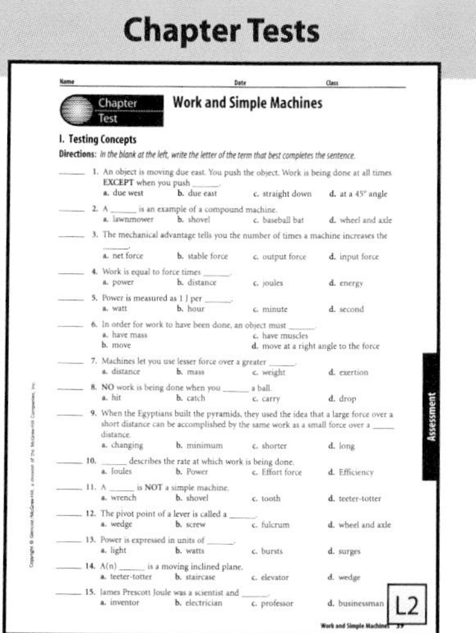

Chapter Test — Work and Simple Machines

L2

Enrichment

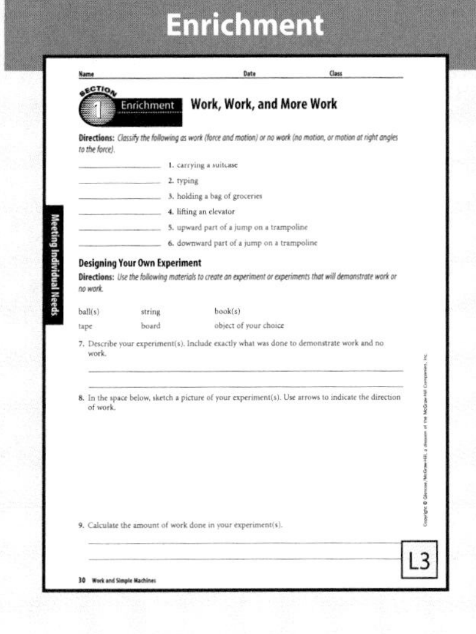

Enrichment — Work, Work, and More Work

L3

Spanish Directed Reading

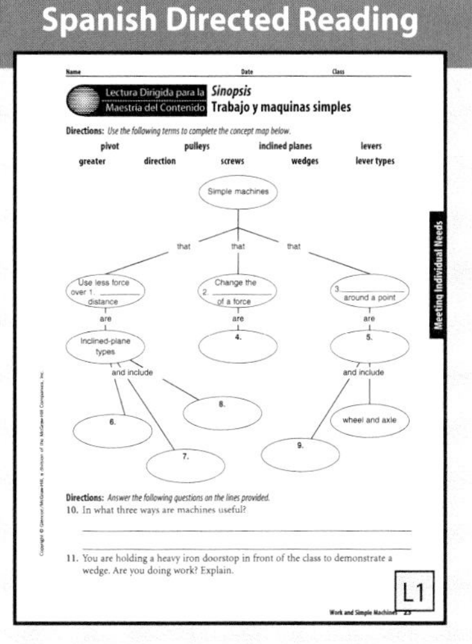

Lectura Dirigida para la Maestría del Contenido — Sinopsis — Trabajo y maquinas simples

L1

Test Practice Workbook

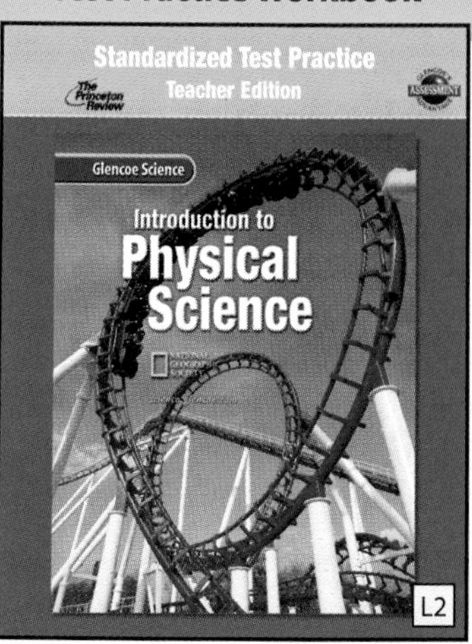

L2

Chapter Review

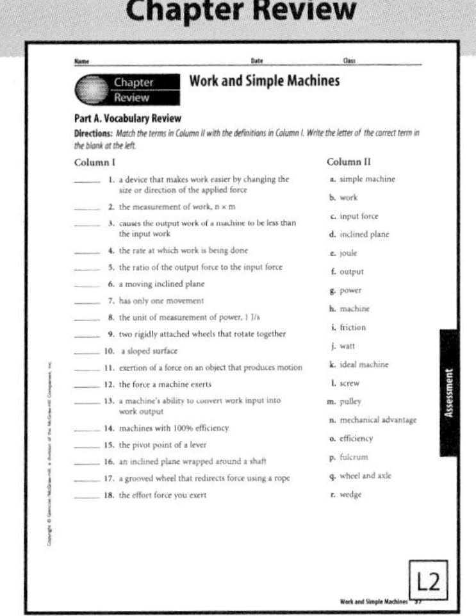

Chapter Review — Work and Simple Machines

L2

Science Content Background

SECTION 1

Work and Power

What is work?

Energy is the ability to produce change. One way to produce change is to do work. Energy is the ability to perform work; work is the process that converts energy from one form to another. The work-energy theorem states that when work is done on an object, the object's kinetic energy changes. The work done is equal to the change in kinetic energy.

Calculating Work

Both energy and work are measured in joules, kg (m^2/s^2). When an object falls, gravity does work equal to (force)(distance) = (mass)(g)(distance) where g is the acceleration due to gravity, 9.8 m/s^2. The kinetic energy changes from 0 to 0.5 mv^2 at the end of the fall. By letting mgd = 0.5 mv^2, you can find the velocity of an object when it hits the ground.

The concept of negative work is somewhat abstract. It is most easily grasped in situations where objects slow down. Here, an object is subjected to a force, usually friction, that reduces the object's kinetic energy. When an object is lifted, Earth's gravitational force does negative work. The lifter does positive work, which is stored as potential energy. When the object is held up, the lifter's muscles move microscopically. The object, however, does not move, so no work is done on it.

Fun Fact

Power companies don't sell you power; they sell you energy. They typically charge for your usage in kilowatt-hours (or some similar units), which is power multiplied by time. Since the units for power are energy divided by time, kilowatt-hours is another way to express units of energy.

SECTION 2

Using Machines

Mechanical Advantage

Mechanical advantage is a measure of a machine's leverage. It relates either the resistance force overcome by the machine to the load force, or the distance through which the effort force acts to the distance the resistance is moved. Together these

Michael Lichter/International Stock

quantities form the equality: $F_e d_e = F_r d_r$. This is the equation of balance of a lever and other simple machines.

Efficiency

When a machine leverages a force, conservation of energy states that the smaller force must act through a greater distance. The work to perform a task is the same no matter how it is done. In reality, with a machine, you must do some extra work because some of the work supplied is lost as heat. The lower the loss, the more efficient the machine.

A perpetual motion machine is a fictitious device that is said to convert all of the input work into an equal or greater amount of output work. An inventor always aspires to make a

Fun Fact

The laws of thermodynamics, which include conservation of energy, describe how energy is transferred under different conditions. Every perpetual motion machine violates at least one of these laws.

machine that is 100 percent efficient, but there is always some energy lost to friction. A carefully designed machine can get close. Getting more out of the machine than is put into it is a clear violation of the law of energy conservation.

The source of energy that allows a machine to work is called the prime mover. Although machines make a job easier, the job may still require a backbreaking effort if you have to supply the energy. The steam engine and the electric motor were invented to ease this burden. They get their energy from coal, oil, electricity, and other sources of energy. An automobile engine has the ability to supply the power of 200 horses, hence the term horsepower for engine capacity.

SECTION 3

Simple Machines

Inclined Plane

Archaeologists believe the ancient Egyptians constructed enormous ramps to move the pyramids' limestone blocks into place. Without the use of wheels or other means of facilitating the move, the ramp needed to drag one of these blocks would require more material than the pyramid itself. Archaeologists discovered the Egyptians had a type of clay called tafla. It becomes slippery when wet. Tests indicate that by using tafla as a lubricant, the Egyptians could have made steeper ramps, requiring much less fill.

Wheel and Axle

The wheel and axle discussed in this chapter is a simple machine. Some wheels and axles, such as those in a car, are more complicated.

You may want to point out to students the two uses of wheels. The wheels on a car or wagon are designed to avoid sliding friction: it's easier to push a grocery cart with wheels than without. Wheels that appear as handles, such as faucets and doorknob, are designed to take advantage of the mechanical advantage of a wheel and axle.

For additional content background on this topic, go to the Glencoe Science Web site at science.glencoe.com.

FPG International

Work and Simple Machines

Chapter Vocabulary

work
power
input force
output force
mechanical advantage
efficiency
simple machine
compound machine
inclined plane
wedge
screw
lever
wheel and axle
pulley

What do you think?

Science Journal This shows a spider mite walking on a micromachine.

CHAPTER 9

Work and Simple Machines

Machines enable people to accomplish many different tasks, from eating a meal to building a skyscraper. In this picture, machines such as cranes and trucks are being used to help construct buildings. In this chapter, you will learn about work and what simple machines are. You also will learn how simple machines make doing work easier.

What do you think?

Science Journal Look at the picture below with a classmate. Discuss what you think this might be or what is happening. Here's a hint: *The other seven legs are just as hairy.* Write down your answer or best guess in your Science Journal.

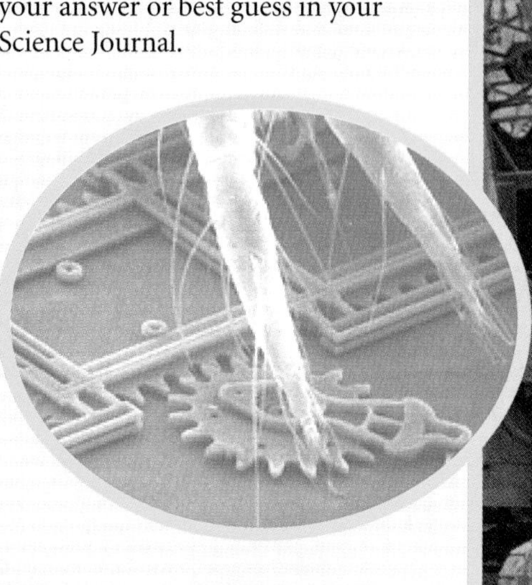

256

Theme Connection

Systems and Interactions Simple machines interact with forces to make work easier. Compound machines are systems in which simple machines work together to do work. The mechanical advantage of a system of machines is determined by the interaction between the system and the force that is put into it.

Two of the world's greatest structures were built using different tools. The Great Pyramid at Giza in Egypt was built nearly 5,000 years ago using blocks of limestone moved into place by hand with ramps and levers. In comparison, the Sears Tower in Chicago was built in 1973 using tons of steel that were hoisted into place by gasoline-powered cranes. How do machines such as ramps, levers, and cranes change the forces needed to do a job?

Compare forces

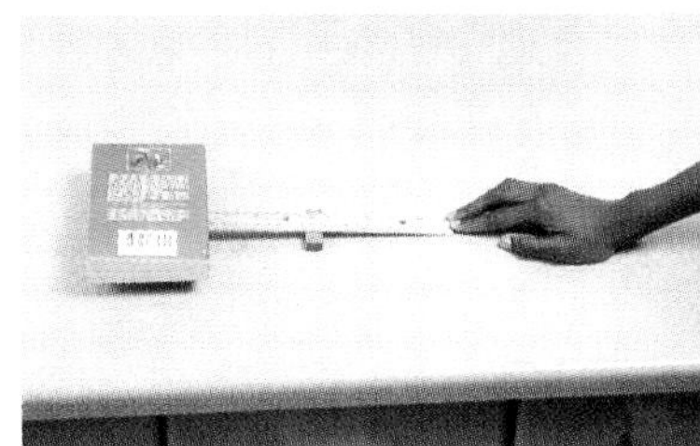

1. Place a ruler on an eraser. Place a book on one end of the ruler.
2. Using one finger, push down on the free end of the ruler to lift the book.
3. Repeat the experiment, placing the eraser in various positions beneath the ruler. Observe how much force is needed in each instance to lift the book.

Observe

In your Science Journal, describe your observations. How did changing the distance between the book and the eraser affect the force needed to lift the book?

Before You Read

FOLDABLES Reading & Study Skills

Making a Main Ideas Study Fold **Make the following Foldable to help you identify the main ideas or major topics of work and simple machines.**

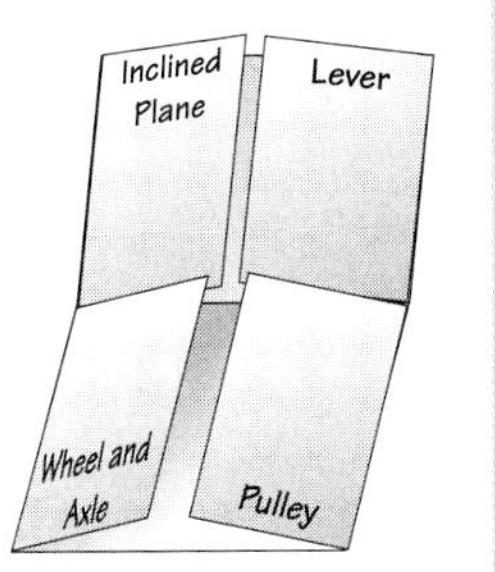

1. Place a sheet of paper in front of you so the long side is at the top. Fold the paper in half from the left side to the right side and then unfold.
2. Fold each side in to the centerfold line to divide the paper into fourths. Fold the paper in half from top to bottom and unfold.
3. Through the top thickness of paper, cut along both of the middle fold lines to form four tabs as shown. Label each tab *Inclined Plane, Wheel and Axle, Lever,* and *Pulley* as shown.
4. Before you read the chapter, fold your Foldable in half to make a book. Title the book *Work* and define work under the title. As you read the chapter, write information under the tabs about the four tools on your Foldable.

257

EXPLORE ACTIVITY

Purpose Use the Explore Activity to introduce students to first-class levers and mechanical advantage. L2 ELL LS **Kinesthetic**

Preparation Before students do the activity, find a book that is not too heavy for the ruler.

Materials ruler, eraser, paperback book

Teaching Strategy Make the activity quantitative by using known weights in place of the book and finger. Expect to find (weight on left) × (distance from fulcrum) = (weight on right) × (distance from fulcrum). Have students measure distance from the center of each object.

Observe

As the book got farther from the eraser, it took more force to balance it.

Process Have students use their results to draw diagrams showing how a small object could be used to balance a heavier object. Use **Performance Assessment in the Science Classroom,** p. 127. L1 LS **Logical-Mathematical**

Before You Read

FOLDABLES Reading & Study Skills

Dinah Zike Study Fold

Purpose Students will demonstrate what they know about the six classes of nutrients available in food by listing examples of foods that provide these nutrients in a Foldable chart.

For additional help, see Foldables Worksheet, p. 17 in **Chapter Resources Booklet,** or go to the Glencoe Science Web site at **science.glencoe.com.** See After You Read in the Study Guide at the end of this chapter.

SECTION

Work and Power

1 Motivate

Bellringer Transparency

Display the Section Focus Transparency for Section 1. Use the accompanying Transparency Activity Master. L2 ELL

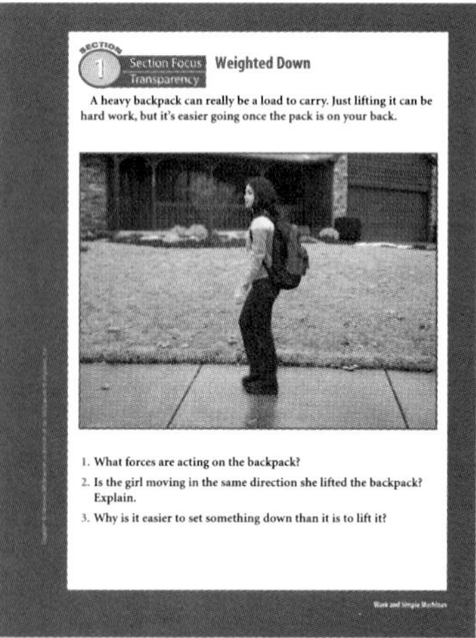

Section Focus Transparency 1 — Weighted Down

A heavy backpack can really be a load to carry. Just lifting it can be hard work, but it's easier going once the pack is on your back.

1. What forces are acting on the backpack?
2. Is the girl moving in the same direction she lifted the backpack? Explain.
3. Why is it easier to set something down than it is to lift it?

Work and Simple Machines

Tie to Prior Knowledge

Have students recall what they know about force and motion. Ask students how the force applied to an object is related to the distance the object travels. For a given object, the greater the force applied, the greater the distance traveled. **What happens if there is resistance to the force, such as friction?** It takes more force to move the object. Tell students that in this section they will be studying forces acting through a distance.

SECTION

Work and Power

As You Read

What You'll Learn

- **Recognize** when work is done.
- **Calculate** how much work is done.
- **Explain** the relation between work and power.

Vocabulary
work
power

Why It's Important
If you understand work, you can make your work easier.

What is work?

What does the term *work* mean to you? You might think of household chores, a job at an office, a factory, a farm, or the homework you do after school. In science, the definition of work is more specific. **Work** is done when a force causes an object to move in the same direction that the force is applied.

Can you think of a way in which you did work today? Maybe it would help to know that you do work when you lift your books, turn a doorknob, raise window blinds, or write with a pen or pencil. You also do work when you walk up a flight of stairs or open and close your school locker. In what other ways do you do work every day?

Work and Motion Your teacher has asked you to move a box of books to the back of the classroom. Try as you might, though, you just can't budge the box because it is too heavy. Although you exerted a force on the box and you feel tired from it, you have not done any work. In order for you to do work, two things must occur. First, you must apply a force to an object. Second, the object must move in the same direction as your applied force. You do work on an object only when the object moves as a result of the force you exert. The girl in **Figure 1** might think she is working by holding the bags of groceries. However, if she is not moving, she is not doing any work because she is not causing something to move.

Reading Check *Why don't you do work when you hold a baby?*

Figure 1
This girl is holding bags of groceries, yet she isn't doing any work. *Why?*

Section Assessment Planner

PORTFOLIO
Life Science Integration, p. 259

PERFORMANCE ASSESSMENT
Math Skills Activity, p. 260
Math Skills Activity, p. 261
Try at Home MiniLAB, p. 262
Skill Builder Activities, p. 262

See page 282 for more options.

CONTENT ASSESSMENT
Section, p. 262
Challenge, p. 262
Chapter, pp. 282–283

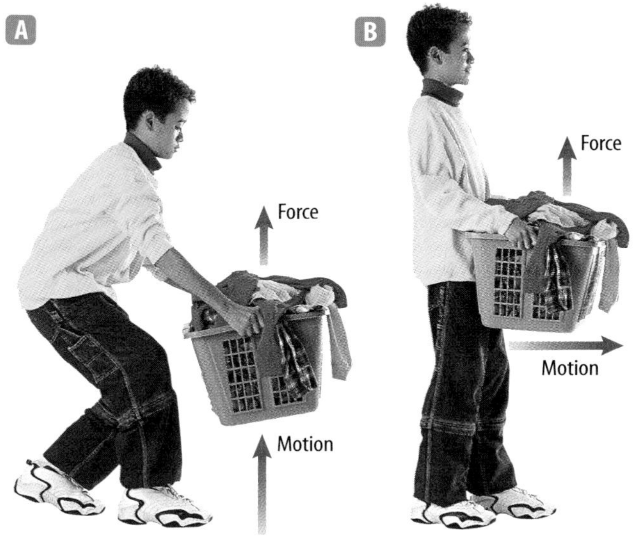

Figure 2
To do work, an object must move in the direction a force is applied. A The boy's arms do work when they exert an upward force on the basket and the basket moves upward. B The boy's arms still exert an upward force on the basket. But when the boy walks forward, no work is done by his arms.

Applying Force and Doing Work Picture yourself lifting the basket of clothes in **Figure 2A.** You can feel your arms exerting a force upward as you lift the basket, and the basket moves upward in the direction of the force your arms applied. Therefore, your arms have done work. Now suppose you carry the basket forward, as in **Figure 2B.** You can still feel your arms applying an upward force on the box to keep it from falling, but now the box is moving forward instead of upward. Because the direction of motion is not in the same direction of the force applied by your arms, no work is done by your arms.

Force in Two Directions Sometimes only part of the force you exert moves an object. Think about what happens when you push a lawn mower. You push at an angle to the ground as shown in **Figure 3.** Part of the force is to the right and part of the force is downward. Only the part of the force that is in the same direction as the motion of the mower—to the right—does work.

Life Science INTEGRATION

You may feel tired after pushing against a wall even though the wall doesn't move. Muscles in your body contract when you push. This contraction is caused by chemical reactions in your muscles that cause molecules to move. As a result, work is done by your body when you push. Research how a muscle contracts and describe what you learned in your Science Journal.

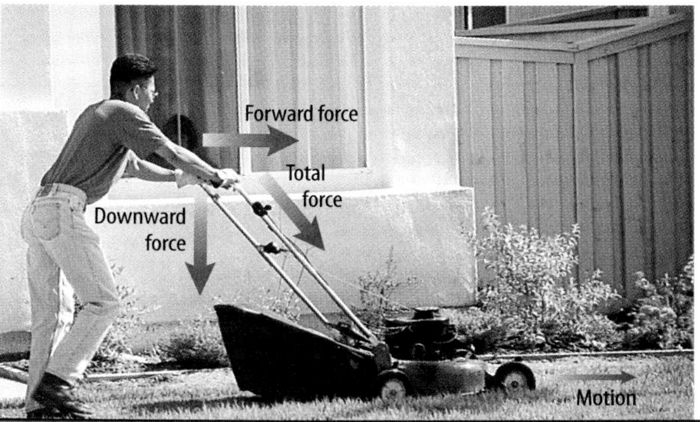

Figure 3
When you exert a force at an angle, only part of your force does work—the part that is in the same direction as the motion of the object.

2 Teach

What is work?

Caption Answer

Figure 1 She isn't moving the groceries.

Answer You are not moving the baby.

Nerves send a message to the muscle causing it to release Ca^{2+} ions. These ions interact with the proteins in the muscle fibers to cause them to contract. When Ca^{2+} ions are no longer being released, the muscle stops contracting. L2 LS **Linguistic** P

Activity

To help students understand how one force can be divided into components in two or more directions, have them push on two sides of a book—for example, left and bottom—using different amounts of force. They will observe how the two forces acting in different directions are added. L2 ELL LS **Kinesthetic**

Fun Fact

Although no work is done while carrying an object at constant speed across a horizontal floor, on start-up (which lasts a very short time) there is a force on the object that accelerates it from rest and starts it moving. Once the object is in motion and up to speed with the person, no work is required to maintain its motion.

Resource Manager

Chapter Resources Booklet

Transparency Activity, p. 44

Directed Reading for Content Mastery, pp. 19, 20

Note-taking Worksheets, pp. 33–35

Visual Learning

Figure 3 Point out to students the angle between the handle of the lawn mower and the ground. Ask students whether more of the force applied by the boy would be down or forward if the angle between the handle and the ground were smaller. More of the force would be forward. L2 LS **Visual-Spatial**

Calculating Work

Reading Check

Answer joule

Quick Demo

Fasten one end of a piece of string to a large toy car, and make a loop in the other end. Hook a spring scale onto the loop, and pull on the spring scale to make the car move. Read the force on the spring scale, and have a student help you measure the distance you moved the car. Calculate the amount of work done. Repeat the demonstration, but this time give a strong pull on the car. Read the spring scale, and then let the string go slack. Unhook the spring scale while the car continues to move. Again have a student help you measure the distance over which the force acted and calculate the amount of work done by you on the car. L2 ELL LS **Visual-Spatial**

Math Skills Activity

National Math Standards

Correlation to Mathematics Objectives

2, 4, 8, 9

Answer to Practice Problem

This is what you know: force = 300 N, distance = 500 m. This is what you need to know: Work. This is the equation you need to use: Work = force × distance. Substitute the known values into the equation: Work = 300 N × 500 m = 1500 J

Calculating Work

Work is done when a force makes an object move. More work is done when the force is increased or the object is moved a greater distance. The work done can be calculated from this equation:

$$\text{Work} = \text{force} \times \text{distance}$$

In SI units, force is measured in newtons and distance is measured in meters. The unit for work is the joule, named in honor of the nineteenth-century scientist James Prescott Joule.

Reading Check ***What is the SI unit for work?***

Work and Distance Suppose you give a book a push and it slides across a table. To calculate the work you did, the distance in the above equation is not the distance the book moved. The distance in the work equation is the distance an object moves while the force is being applied. So the distance in the work equation is the distance the book moved while you were pushing.

Math Skills Activity

Calculating Work

Example Problem

A painter lifts a can of paint that weighs 40 N a distance of 2 m. How much work does she do? Hint: to lift a can weighing 40 N, the painter must exert a force of 40 N.

Solution

1. *This is what you know:* force = 40 N, distance = 2 m
2. *This is what you need to know:* work
3. *This is the equation you need to use:* work = force × distance
4. *Substitute the known values into the equation:* work = 40 N × 2 m = 80 J

Check your answer by dividing it by the distance. Did you calculate the same force that was given?

Practice Problem

As you push a lawn mower, the horizontal force is 300 N. If you push the mower a distance of 500 m, how much work do you do?

For more help, refer to the Math Skill Handbook.

Resource Manager

Chapter Resources Booklet
- Enrichment, p. 30
- Reinforcement, p. 27

Cultural Diversity, p. 63

Mathematics Skill Activities, p. 11

Inclusion Strategies

Physically Challenged Help students who use hand-powered wheelchairs understand how force and distance affect work by having them think about how much effort they must use to move their wheelchairs in various situations, such as starting, moving up a ramp, or moving at a constant rate along a flat surface. L1 LS **Intrapersonal**

260 CHAPTER 9 Work and Simple Machines

What is power?

What does it mean to be powerful? To understand power, imagine two weightlifters lifting the same weight and suppose they lift the weight the same distance. Because they exert the same upward force and move the weight the same distance, each does the same amount of work.

Suppose one weightlifter lifted the weight in 3 s, while the other struggled to lift it in 10 s. You might say that the first weightlifter is stronger, because she lifted the weight in less time. You could also say that she is more powerful. In science, **power** is how quickly work is done. Something has more power or is more powerful if it can do more work in a certain amount of time.

Calculating Power Power can be calculating by dividing the amount of work done by the time needed to do the work. Power can be calculated by this formula:

$$\text{Power} = \frac{\text{work done}}{\text{time needed}}$$

In SI units, the unit of power is the watt, in honor of James Watt, a nineteenth-century British scientist who invented a practical version of the steam engine.

Research Visit the Glencoe Science Web site at **science.glencoe.com** for more information about James Watt and his steam engine. Find out why the unit of power was named after this inventor. Summarize your findings in a brief report.

Math Skills Activity

Calculating Power

Example Problem

You do 200 J of work in 12 s. How much power did you use?

Solution

1. *This is what you know:* work done = 200 J; time needed = 12 s
2. *This is what you need to find:* power
3. *This is the equation you need to use:* power = work done/time needed
4. *Substitute the known values into the equation:* power = 200 J/12 s = 17 watt

Check your answer by dividing it by the work done. Did you calculate the same time that was given?

Practice Problem

In the course of a short race, a car does 500,000 J of work in 7 s. What is the power of the car during the race?

For more help, refer to the Math Skill Handbook.

What is power?

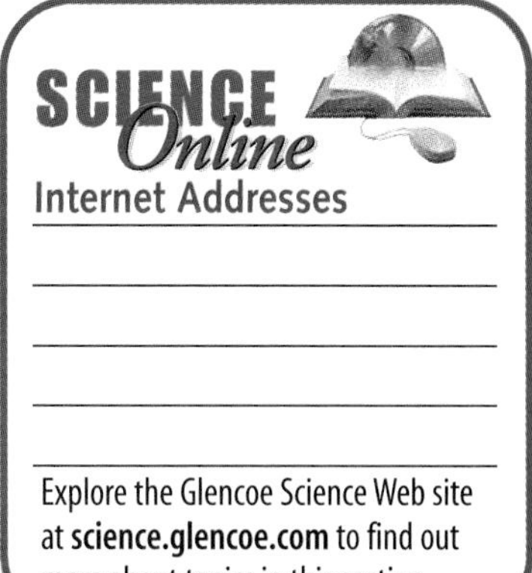

Internet Addresses

Explore the Glencoe Science Web site at **science.glencoe.com** to find out more about topics in this section.

Discussion

To help students understand the relationship between force, work, and power, have them express each in terms of their basic SI units. $F = ma = \text{kg m/s}^2 = \text{N}$; $W = F \times d = mad = \text{kg m/s}^2\ \text{m} = \text{J}$; $P = W/t = (F \times d)/t = mad/t = (\text{kg m/s}^2)\text{m/s} = \text{W}$ L2

LS **Logical-Mathematical**

Math Skills Activity

National Math Standards

Correlation to Mathematics Objectives

2, 4, 8, 9

Answer to Practice Problem

This is what you know: work done = 500,000 J, time needed = 7 s. This is what you need to find: Power. This is the equation you need to use: Power = work done/time needed. 500,000 J/7 s = 71,429 watts

Curriculum Connection

History Explain to students that another unit for measuring work is the calorie. One calorie is equal to 4.19 joules. The kilocalorie, written with a capital C as Calorie, is often used when discussing the energy available from food. One Calorie = 4190 joules. Tell students that walking and running a given distance burn about the same number of Calories. **Under what conditions does running result in a greater number of Calories being burned than walking does?** A greater number of Calories are burned when running for a given period of time rather than walking for the same time period, because a greater distance is covered and therefore more work is done. **Which requires more power, running or walking? Why?** Running; running covers the distance in less time. L2

LS **Logical-Mathematical**

Purpose Students measure and compare work and power. L2
ELL  **Kinesthetic**

Materials scale, meterstick, stairway, stopwatch

Analysis
1. Work will be the same in both cases, but power will be greater when a student runs.
2. Both would double.

Process One dietary calorie is 4,184J. Have students calculate the number of calories used to climb the stairs. Use **PASC,** p. 101.

3 Assess

Reteach

Explain how the same power could be used to lift different weights. The different weights could be lifted different distances or for different amounts of time. L2

Challenge

A 7,500-W engine is used to lift an I beam with a mass of 1,000 kg to a height of 150 m. **How much work must be done to lift this mass at constant speed? How long will it take?** (1,000 kg)(10 m/s^2)(150 m) = 1,500,000 J; t = W/P = 200 s. L3

Content How much power is used when 600 Joules of work are done in 1 min? 10 W Use **PASC,** p. 101.

Measuring Work and Power

Procedure
1. Weigh yourself on a **scale.**
2. Multiply your weight in pounds by 4.45 to convert your weight to newtons.
3. Measure the vertical height of a **ramp or stairway.** **WARNING:** *Make sure the ramp or stairway is clear of all objects.*
4. Time yourself walking slowly and quickly up the ramp or stairway.

Analysis
1. Calculate and compare the work done and power used in each case.
2. How would the work done and power used change if your weight were twice as large?

Work and Energy If you push a chair and make it move, you do work on the chair. You also change the energy of the chair. Recall that when something is moving it has energy of motion, or kinetic energy. By making the chair move, you increase its kinetic energy.

You also change the energy of an object when you do work and lift it higher. An object has potential energy that increases when it is higher above Earth's surface. By lifting an object, you do work and increase its potential energy.

Power and Energy When you do work on an object you increase the energy of the object. Where does this energy come from? Because energy can never be created or destroyed, if the object gains energy then you must lose energy. When you do work on an object you transfer energy to the object, and your energy decreases. The amount of work done is the amount of energy transferred. So power is also equal to the amount of energy transferred in a certain amount of time.

$$\text{Power} = \frac{\text{energy transferred}}{\text{time needed}}$$

Sometimes energy can be transferred even when no work is done, such as when heat flows from a warm to a cold object. In fact, there are many ways energy can be transferred even if no work is done. Power is always the rate at which energy is transferred, or the amount of energy transferred divided by the time needed.

Section  Assessment

1. What conditions must be met for work to be done?
2. How much work was done to lift a 1,000-kg block to the top of the Great Pyramid, 146 m above the ground?
3. How is power related to work?
4. How much power, in watts, is needed to cut a lawn in 50 min if the work involved is 100,000 J?
5. **Think Critically** Suppose you are pulling a wagon at an angle. How can you make your task easier?

Skill Builder Activities

6. **Comparing and Contrasting** Which example involves more power: 200 J of work done in 20 s or 50 J of work done in 4 s? Explain your answer. **For more help, refer to the Science Skill Handbook.**
7. **Solving One-Step Equations** A 7,460-W engine is used to lift a beam weighing 9,800 N up 145 m. How much work must the motor do to lift this beam at constant speed? How much more work must be done to lift it 290 m? **For more help, refer to the Math Skill Handbook.**

Answers to Section Assessment

1. A force must move an object through a distance along the direction of the force.
2. W = mgh = (1,000 kg) × (10 m/s^2) × (146 m) = 1,460,000 J
3. Power is work divided by time.
4. P = 100,000 J/(50 min) × (60 s/min) = 100,000 J/3,000 s = 33 W
5. Pull the wagon without any angle or at a smaller angle.
6. In the first case, 10 W are used; in the second case, 12.5 W are used. Even though less work is done in the second case, it uses more power because it is done at a faster rate.
7. W = mgh = (9,800 N)(145 m) = 1,420,000 J. To lift the beam 290 m, twice as much work, 2,840,000 J, must be done, because it is lifted twice as high.

Building the Pyramids

Imagine moving 2.3 million blocks of limestone, each weighing more than 1,000 kg. That is exactly what the builders of the Great Pyramid at Giza did. Although no one knows for sure exactly how they did it, they probably pulled the blocks most of the way. What could they have done to make their work easier?

What You'll Investigate

How is the force needed to lift a block related to the distance it travels?

Materials

wood block
tape
spring scale
ruler
thin notebooks
meterstick
several books

Goals

- **Compare** the force needed to lift a block with the force needed to pull it up a ramp.

Safety Precautions 

Procedure

1. Stack several books together on a tabletop to model a half-completed pyramid. Measure the height of the books in centimeters. Record the height on the first row of the data table under *Distance.*
2. Use the wood block as a model for a block of stone. Use tape to attach the block to the spring scale.
3. Place the block on the table and lift it straight up the side of the stack of books until the top of the block is even with the top of the books. Record the force shown on the scale in the data table under *Force.*

Work Done Using Different Ramps

Distance (cm)	Force (N)	Work (J)
	Answers will vary	

4. **Arrange** a notebook so that one end is on the stack of books and the other end is on the table. Measure the length of the notebook and record this length as distance in the second row of the data table under *Distance.*
5. **Measure** the force needed to pull the block up the ramp. Record the force in the data table.
6. Repeat steps 4 and 5 using a longer notebook to make the ramp longer.
7. **Calculate** the work done in each row of the data table.

Conclude and Apply

1. How much work did you do in each case?
2. What happened to the force needed as the length of the ramp increased?
3. How could the builders of the pyramids have designed their task to use less force than they would lifting the blocks straight up? Draw a diagram to support your answer.

Communicating Your Data

Add your data to that found by other groups. **For more help, refer to the Science Skill Handbook.**

Activity

BENCH TESTED

Purpose Students investigate the mechanical advantage of a ramp.
L2 ELL COOP LEARN
LS Kinesthetic

Process Skills observing, inferring, comparing and contrasting, making and using tables, interpreting data, making models, separating and controlling variables, working with numbers

Time Required 45 minutes

Teaching Strategy Have students read the force used to pull the block while the block is moving at a constant speed.

Troubleshooting Zero the spring scales before use and secure the ramps so they do not move when a block is pulled along them.

Answers to Questions

1. Work should be similar in each case.
2. It decreased.
3. They could have built ramps along the sides of the pyramids.

Assessment

Content Have each student write a short essay explaining whether he or she thinks the hypothesis that the Egyptians used ramps to build the pyramids is feasible. Use **Performance Assessment in the Science Classroom,** p. 157.

Resource Manager 

Chapter Resources Booklet
MiniLAB, p. 3
Activity Worksheet, pp. 5–6
Lab Activity, pp. 9–12

Communicating Your Data

Encourage students to use a spreadsheet to display their data. If the class pools different ramp lengths, have students plot the results using the graphing routine of the spreadsheet program.

Using Machines

1 Motivate

Bellringer Transparency

Display the Section Focus Transparency for Section 2. Use the accompanying Transparency Activity Master. L2 ELL

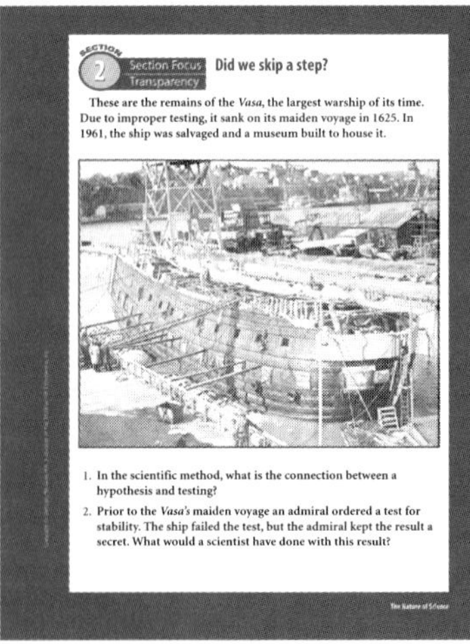

Section 2 Section Focus Transparency **Did we skip a step?**

These are the remains of the *Vasa*, the largest warship of its time. Due to improper testing, it sank on its maiden voyage in 1625. In 1961, the ship was salvaged and a museum built to house it.

1. In the scientific method, what is the connection between a hypothesis and testing?
2. Prior to the *Vasa's* maiden voyage an admiral ordered a test for stability. The ship failed the test, but the admiral kept the result a secret. What would a scientist have done with this result?

Tie to Prior Knowledge

Review with students the law of conservation of energy, which states that energy cannot be created or destroyed but only transformed into different forms. Inform students that in this section they will explore how machines obey this law.

Using Machines

As You Read

***What* You'll Learn**

- **Explain** how a machine makes work easier.
- **Calculate** the mechanical advantages and efficiency of a machine.
- **Explain** how friction reduces efficiency.

Vocabulary
input force
output force
mechanical advantage
efficiency

***Why* It's Important**
Machines can't change the amount of work you need to do, but they can make doing work easier.

What is a machine?

Did you use a machine today? When you think of a machine you might think of a device, such as a car, with many moving parts powered by an engine or an electric motor. But if you used a pair of scissors or a broom, or cut your food with a knife, you used a machine. A machine is simply a device that makes doing work easier. Even a sloping surface can be a machine.

Mechanical Advantage

Even though machines make work easier, they don't decrease the amount of work you need to do. Instead, a machine changes the way in which you do work. When you use a machine, you exert a force over some distance. For example, you exert a force to move a rake or lift the handles of a wheelbarrow. This force is called the effort force, or the **input force.** The work you do on the machine is equal to the input force times the distance over which your force moves the machine. The work that you do on the machine is the input work.

The machine also does work by exerting a force to move an object over some distance. A rake, for example, exerts a force to move leaves. Sometimes this force is called the resistance force because the machine is trying to overcome some resistance. This force also can be called the **output force.** The work that the machine does is the output work. **Figure 4** shows how a machine transforms input work to output work.

When you use a machine, the output work can never be greater than the input work. So what is the advantage of using a machine? A machine makes work easier by changing the amount of force you need to exert, the distance over which the force is exerted, or the direction in which you exert your force.

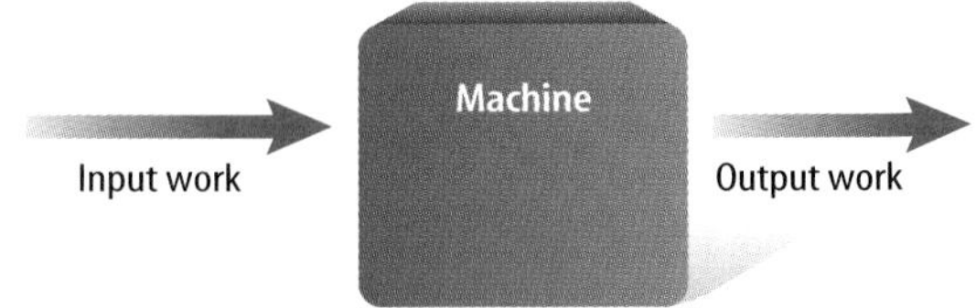

Figure 4
No matter what type of machine is used, the output work is never greater than the input work.

Section Assessment Planner

Portfolio
Active Reading, p. 267

Performance Assessment
Math Skills Activity, p. 265
Math Skills Activity, p. 267
Skill Builder Activities, p. 268
See page 282 for more options.

Content Assessment
Section, p. 268
Challenge, p. 268
Chapter, pp. 282–283

Changing Force Work is equal to force times distance. If work stays the same, what happens to force if you exert a force over a longer distance? You can exert a smaller force. Some machines make work easier by allowing you to exert a smaller force over a longer distance.

The mechanical advantage of a machine compares the input force to the output force. **Mechanical advantage** is the number of times the input force is multiplied by a machine.

$$\text{Mechanical advantage} = \frac{\text{output force}}{\text{input force}}$$

For example, suppose that using a pulley system takes you only 300 N to lift a piano that weighs 1,500 N. To lift the piano, the pulley system exerts an upward force of 1,500 N to overcome the downward pull of gravity. This is the output force. The force you exert on the pulley system in the input force, which is 300 N. So the mechanical advantage of the pulley system is five.

What is the mechanical advantage of a machine?

SCIENCE Online

Research Visit the Glencoe Science Web site at **science.glencoe.com** for more information about early types of tools and how they took advantage of simple machines. Design a poster relating several ancient tools to the simple machines you have studied.

Math Skills Activity

Calculating Mechanical Advantage

Example Problem

To pry the lid off a paint can, you apply a force of 50 N to the handle of a screwdriver. What is the mechanical advantage of the screwdriver if it applies a force of 500 N to the lid?

Solution

1. *This is what you know:* output force = 500 N; input force = 50 N
2. *This is what you need to find:* mechanical advantage
3. *This is the equation you need to use:* mechanical advantage = output force/input force
4. *Substitute the known values:* mechanical advantage = (500 N) / (50 N) = 10.

Check your answer by multiplying it by the input force. Do you calculate the same output force that was given?

Practice Problem

To open a bottle, you apply a force of 50 N to a bottle opener. The bottle opener applies a force of 775 N to the bottle cap. What is the mechanical advantage of the bottle opener?

For more help, refer to the Math Skill Handbook.

2 Teach

Mechanical Advantage

Discussion

How is building skyscrapers today similar to and different from the building of the pyramids? Both are large construction projects in which tools are used. Pyramid construction relied largely on people power, but skyscrapers are built using machines with engines powered by fossil fuels.

SCIENCE Online

Internet Addresses

Explore the Glencoe Science Web site at **science.glencoe.com** to find out more about topics in this section.

Reading Check

Answer the number of times the input force is multiplied by the machine

Math Skills Activity

National Math Standards

Correlation to Mathematics Objectives

2, 4, 8, 9

Answer to Practice Problem

This is what you know: Output Force = 775 N, Input Force = 50 N. This is what you need to know: Mechanical Advantage. This is the equation you need to use: Mechanical Advantage = Output Force/Input Force = 775 N/50 N = 5.5

Teacher FYI

Mechanical advantage (MA) is resistance force divided by effort force. If MA is less than 1, the machine increases either the distance moved by the object or its speed. If MA is equal to 1, the machine changes the direction of the effort force. If MA is greater than 1, the machine increases the effort force.

Resource Manager 

Chapter Resources Booklet

Transparency Activity, p. 45

Directed Reading for Content Mastery, p. 21

Reading and Writing Skill Activities, p. 35

Mechanical Advantage, continued

Visual Learning

Figure 6 Spend a few moments reviewing with students how each machine shown makes work easier. Once students understand the benefits of each machine, have them identify which machines in **Figure 5** work in the same way as those in **Figure 6.** The rake works like the machine in illustration B by multiplying the distance over which the force is applied. The pulley on the flagpole works like the machine in illustration C by changing the direction of the force. L1 LS **Visual-Spatial**

Fun Fact

Mechanical advantage also can be determined by dividing the effort distance (d_e) by the resistance distance (d_r).

Quick Demo

Demonstrate the proper use of a mop and a broom to students. As each machine is used, have students describe how it makes work easier. The mop makes work easier by changing the distance through which a force is applied. A broom changes the direction of the applied force. L1 LS **Visual-Spatial**

Use an Analogy

Ask students whether they have ever used a screwdriver to pry open the lid of a can, such as that on a can of paint. Explain that the movement involved in this process (which actually involves a lever) is the same as that illustrated by the pulley shown in **Figure 5B.** In each case, an effort applied in a downward direction causes the resistance to move upward.

Figure 5
A When you rake leaves, you move your hands a short distance but the end of the rake moves over a longer distance. B Sometimes it is easier to exert your force in a certain direction. This boy would rather pull down on the rope to lift the flag than to climb to the top of the pole and pull up.

Changing Distance Some machines allow you to exert your force over a shorter distance. In these machines, the output force is less than the input force. The rake in **Figure 5A** is this type of machine. You move your hands a small distance at the top of the handle, but the bottom of the rake moves a greater distance as it moves the leaves. The mechanical advantage of this type of machine is less than one because the output force is less than the input force.

Changing Direction Sometimes it is easier to apply a force in a certain direction. For example, it is easier to pull down on the rope in **Figure 5B** than to pull up on it. Some machines enable you to change the direction of the input force. In these machines neither the force nor the distance is changed. The mechanical advantage of this type of machine is equal to one because the output force is equal to the input force. The three ways machines make doing work easier are summarized in **Figure 6.**

Figure 6
Machines are useful because they can A increase force, B increase distance, or C change the direction in which a force is applied.

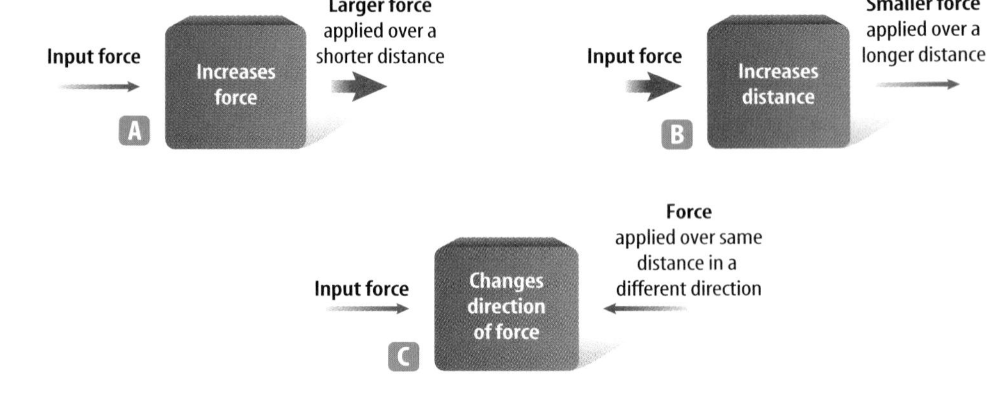

Curriculum Connection

History One type of wheelbarrow was used in Europe during the construction of the cathedrals. It was derived from the barrow, a stretcherlike device carried by two people. Have interested students do research to find out what tools were available for the building of cathedrals or other historic structures. Ask them to find out how existing tools were improved during the projects they research, and have them report their findings to the class in oral presentations. L2 LS **Linguistic**

266 CHAPTER 9 Work and Simple Machines

Efficiency

A machine doesn't increase the input work. For a real machine, the output work done by the machine is always less than the input work that you do on the machine. Remember that anytime two surfaces slide past each other, friction resists their motion. In real machines some input work is always used to overcome friction, so the parts of the machine can move.

The ability of a machine to convert the input work to output work is called the machine's **efficiency.** Efficiency is described as a percent.

$$\text{Efficiency} = \frac{\text{output work}}{\text{input work}} \times 100\%$$

An ideal machine has an efficiency of 100 percent. The efficiency of a real machine is always less than 100 percent, because some work is converted into heat by friction. When friction is reduced, the efficiency of a machine increases.

Reading Check *Why is the efficiency of a real machine less than 100 percent?*

Life Science INTEGRATION

Chemical reactions that enable your muscles to move also produce heat that helps maintain your body temperature. When you shiver, rapid contraction and relaxation of muscle fibers produces a large amount of heat that helps raise your body temperature. This causes the efficiency of your muscles to decrease as more energy is converted into heat.

Math Skills Activity

Calculating Efficiency

Example Problem

Using a pulley system, a crew does 7,500 J of work to load a box that requires 4,500 J of work. What is the efficiency of the pulley system?

Solution

1. *This is what you know:* work output = 4,500 J; work input = 7,500 J
2. *This is what you need to find:* efficiency
3. *This is the equation you need to use:* efficiency = output work/input work × 100%
4. *Substitute the known values:* efficiency = (4,500 J)/(7,500 J) × 100% = 60%

Check your answer by multiplying it by the work input. Do you calculate the same work output that was given?

Practice Problem

You do 100 J of work in pulling out a nail with a claw hammer. If the hammer does 70 J of work, what is the hammer's efficiency?

For more help, refer to the Math Skill Handbook.

Efficiency

Extension

In the late 1800s and early 1900s, many people tried to develop perpetual motion machines. Have interested students use the Internet or library resources to investigate perpetual motion machines and attempts to develop them. Ask students to prepare written reports explaining why these machines are impossible to develop. A perpetual motion machine is a device that can either deliver more work than is put into it or can continue to work with no energy input other than that which was used to start it. L3 IS **Linguistic**

Life Science INTEGRATION

Each time a muscle contracts, millions of molecules of adenosine triphosphate (ATP) react with water to form adenosine diphosphate (ADP) and release energy. Some of this energy is used to run necessary chemical reactions in the body and some is lost as heat.

Reading Check

Answer because some work is converted to heat by friction

Math Skills Activity

National Math Standards

Correlation to Mathematics Objectives

2, 4, 8, 9

Answer to Practice Problem

This is what you know: work input = 100 J, work output = 0 J. This is what you need to find: Efficiency. This is the equation you need to use: Efficiency = work output/work input × 100% = 70 J/100 J × 100% = 70%

Active Reading

Bubble Map In a bubble map, words are clustered to describe a topic or idea. A bubble map can be used for prewriting, to generate ideas before writing, or to review for a test. Have students design a bubble map to help them find the relationship between mechanical advantage and efficiency. L2 IS **Logical-Mathematical** P

Resource Manager

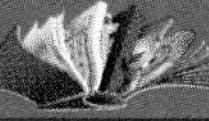

Chapter Resources Booklet

Enrichment, p. 31
Reinforcement, p. 28
Transparency Activity, pp. 47–48

Efficiency, continued

Because friction occurs between surfaces of objects in contact, it would seem reasonable that friction should depend on the size of the area in contact. In fact, friction depends on the force pushing the objects together but not on the size of the area in contact. This is because most of the area that looks on a macroscopic level like it is in contact is actually not microscopically in contact. The best way to increase the number of molecules and atoms in contact is to push the surfaces together.

3 Assess

Reteach

Why is it impossible to have a machine that is perfectly efficient? There is always some amount of friction changing some of the work done by the machine into heat. L1

LS Logical-Mathematical

Challenge

Have students investigate how a car jack works and explain the process in an illustrated drawing. Ask students to estimate the mechanical advantage of a particular jack. L3

LS Logical-Mathematical

Assessment

Performance Have students suggest methods other than using oil for reducing friction in machines. Possible answers: Use another lubricant such as grease; sand surfaces to make them as smooth as possible; use wheels or similar devices to slide one surface over another. Use **PASC,** p. 93.

Figure 7
Lubrication can reduce the friction between two surfaces.

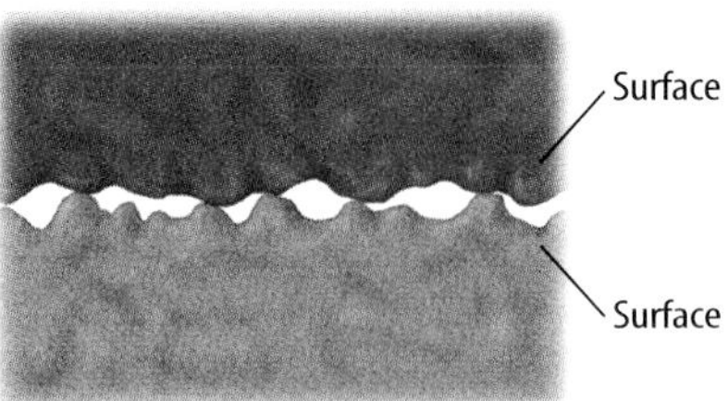

A Two surfaces in contact can stick together where the high spots on each surface come in contact.

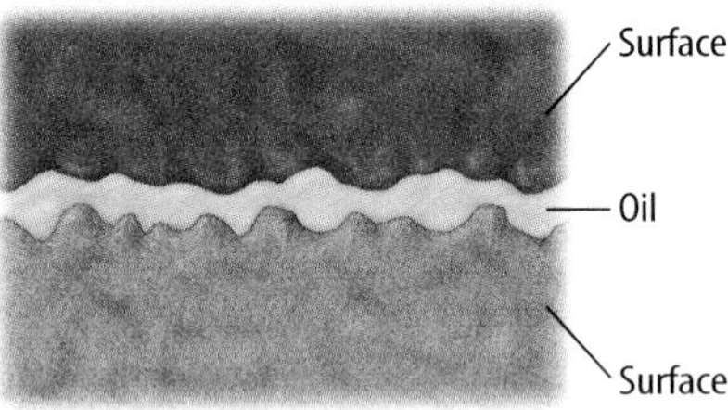

B Adding oil or another lubricant separates the surface so that fewer high spots make contact.

Friction To help understand friction, imagine pushing a heavy box up a ramp. As the box begins to move, the bottom surface of the box slides across the top surface of the ramp. Neither surface is perfectly smooth—each has high spots and low spots, as shown in **Figure 7.**

As the two surfaces slide past each other, high spots on the two surfaces come in contact. At these contact points, shown in **Figure 7A,** atoms and molecules can bond together. This makes the contact points stick together. The attractive forces between all the bonds in the contact points added together is the frictional force that tries to keep the two surfaces from sliding past each other.

To keep the box moving, a force must be applied to break the bonds between the contact points. Even after these bonds are broken and the box moves, new bonds form as different parts of the two surfaces come into contact. So as you keep pushing the box, part of the force that you exert is used to break the bonds that keep forming between the contact points.

Friction and Efficiency One way to reduce friction between two surfaces is to add oil. **Figure 7B** shows how oil fills the gaps between the surfaces, and keeps many of the high spots from making contact. Because there are fewer contact points between the surfaces, the force of friction is reduced. More of the input work then is converted to output work by the machine.

Section  Assessment

1. What are three ways in which machines make work easier?
2. How can you find the mechanical advantage of a machine?
3. You do 150 J of work on a machine and the machine does 90 J of work as a result. What is the efficiency of the machine?
4. Explain how friction reduces the efficiency of machines.
5. **Think Critically** Can a machine be useful even if its mechanical advantage is less than one? Explain and give an example.

Skill Builder Activities

6. **Comparing and Contrasting** How does the efficiency of an ideal machine compare with that of a real machine? **For more help, refer to the Science Skill Handbook.**
7. **Using an Electronic Spreadsheet** On a computer, create a spreadsheet that calculates work from force and distance. Input a value for work and then input several different force values. How does the distance change if the work stays the same and the force decreases? **For more help, refer to the Technology Skill Handbook.**

Answers to Section Assessment

1. increase the force, increase distance, change the direction of the force
2. Divide the output force by the input force.
3. Efficiency = 90 J/150 J × 100 = 60%
4. Friction is a force caused by the attraction of atoms and molecules on one surface for atoms and molecules on another surface. This attraction must be overcome when two objects slide past each other, and it decreases the efficiency of all machines.
5. Yes; this happens when the machine is used to increase distance, as occurs with a rake, baseball bat, or fishing pole.
6. An ideal machine is 100% efficient, since it assumes no friction. All real machines have efficiencies less than 100%.
7. Check students' work.

Simple Machines

What is a simple machine?

What do you think of when you hear the word *machine?* Many people think of machines as complicated devices such as cars, elevators, or computers. However, some machines are as simple as a hammer, shovel, or ramp. A **simple machine** is a machine that does work with only one movement. The six simple machines are the inclined plane, lever, wheel and axle, screw, wedge, and pulley. A machine made up of a combination of simple machines is called a **compound machine.** A can opener is a compound machine. The bicycle in **Figure 8** is a familiar example of another compound machine.

Inclined Plane

Ramps might have enabled the ancient Egyptians to build their pyramids. To move limestone blocks weighing more than 1,000 kg each, archaeologists hypothesize that the Egyptians built enormous ramps. A ramp is a simple machine known as an inclined plane. An **inclined plane** is a flat, sloped surface. Less force is needed to move an object from one height to another using an inclined plane than is needed to lift the object. As the inclined plane becomes longer, the force needed to move the object becomes smaller.

As You Read

***What* You'll Learn**

- **Distinguish** among the different simple machines.
- **Describe** how to find the mechanical advantage of each simple machine.

Vocabulary

simple machine	screw
compound machine	lever
inclined plane	wheel and axle
wedge	pulley

***Why* It's Important**

Simple machines make up all machines.

Figure 8
Devices that use combinations of simple machines, such as this bicycle, are called compound machines.

SECTION

Simple Machines

1 Motivate

Bellringer Transparency

Display the Section Focus Transparency for Section 3. Use the accompanying Transparency Activity Master. L2 ELL

Tie to Prior Knowledge

Remind students of the definition of mechanical advantage and the concept of efficiency as you prepare them to explore the different types of simple machines.

Section Assessment Planner

PORTFOLIO
Science Journal, p. 270

PERFORMANCE ASSESSMENT
MiniLAB, p. 274
Skill Builder Activities, p. 275
See page 282 for more options.

CONTENT ASSESSMENT
Section, p. 275
Challenge, p. 275
Chapter, pp. 282–283

Resource Manager

Chapter Resources Booklet
Transparency Activity, p. 46
Directed Reading for Content Mastery, pp. 21, 22

2 Teach

What is a simple machine?

IDENTIFYING Misconceptions

Many people refer to simple devices such as knives or screwdrivers as tools. Students may think that to be a machine a device must be more complicated, such as an electric drill. In science, however, there is no distinction between machines and tools. A machine is any device that is used to multiply or change the direction of a force. Thus, a hammer or a knife is as much a machine as is a lathe or an electric drill.

Teacher FYI

The materials used to make simple machines must be strong enough to support the weight of the objects they move. For example, a piece of cardboard won't work as an inclined plane to move a refrigerator.

Inclined Plane

Extension

Encourage students with a strong interest in nature to look for examples of the use of simple machines by animals. Examples include the way a parrot uses its powerful bill to crack nuts and the use of sticks by chimpanzees to obtain food that is hard to reach. Ask students to share their findings with the class. L3 LS **Naturalist**

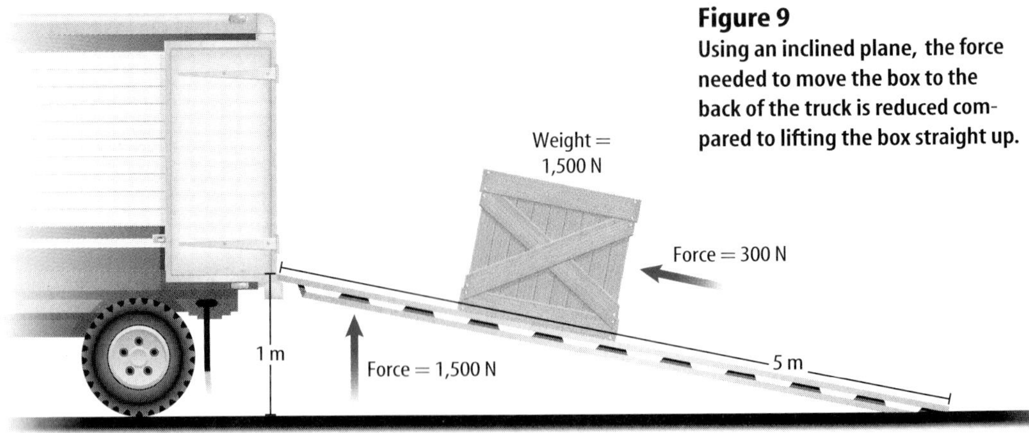

Figure 9
Using an inclined plane, the force needed to move the box to the back of the truck is reduced compared to lifting the box straight up.

Using Inclined Planes Imagine having to lift a box weighing 1,500 N to the back of a truck that is 1 m off the ground. You would have to exert a force of 1,500 N, the weight of the box, over a distance of 1 m, which equals 1,500 J of work. Now suppose that instead you use a 5-m-long ramp, as shown in **Figure 9.** The amount of work you need to do does not change. You still need to do 1,500 J of work. However, the distance over which you exert your force becomes 5 m. You can calculate the force you need to exert by dividing both sides of the equation for work by distance.

$$\text{Force} = \frac{\text{work}}{\text{distance}}$$

If you do 1,500 J of work by exerting a force over 5 m, the force is only 300 N. Because you exert the input force over a distance that is five times as long, you can exert a force that is five times less.

The mechanical advantage of an inclined plane is the length of the inclined plane divided by its height. In this example, the ramp has a mechanical advantage of 5.

Figure 10
This chef's knife is a wedge that slices through food.

Wedge An inclined plane that moves is called a **wedge.** A wedge can have one or two sloping sides. The knife shown in **Figure 10** is an example of a wedge. An axe and certain types of doorstop are also wedges. Just as for an inclined plane, the mechanical advantage of a wedge increases as it becomes longer and thinner.

Science Journal

Inclined Planes Ask students to note all the inclined planes they see in a two-day period. Have them list each one in their Science Journals and describe how it is used. L2 LS **Visual-Spatial** P

Resource Manager 

Physical Science Critical Thinking/Problem Solving, p. 7

Performance Assessment in the Science Classroom, p. 37

Figure 11
Wedge-shaped teeth help tear food.

A Your front teeth help tear an apple apart.

B The wedge-shaped teeth of this Tyrannosaurus Rex show that it was a carnivore.

Wedges in Your Body You have wedges in your body. The bite marks on the apple in **Figure 11A** show how your front teeth are wedge shaped. A wedge changes the direction of the applied effort force. As your push your front teeth into the apple, the downward effort force is changed by the your teeth into a sideways force that pushes the skin of the apple apart.

The teeth of meat eaters, or carnivores, are more wedge shaped than the teeth of plant eaters, or herbivores. The teeth of carnivores are used to cut and rip meat, while herbivores' teeth are used for grinding plant material. By examining the teeth of ancient animals, such as the dinosaur in **Figure 11B,** scientists can determine what the animal ate when it was living.

The Screw Another form of the inclined plane is a screw. A **screw** is an inclined plane wrapped around a cylinder or post. The inclined plane on a screw forms the screw threads. Just like a wedge changes the direction of the effort force applied to it, a screw also changes the direction of the applied force. When you turn a screw, the force applied is changed by the threads to a force that pulls the screw into the material. Friction between the threads and the material holds the screw tightly in place. The mechanical advantage of the screw is the length of the inclined plane wrapped around the screw divided by the length of the screw. The more tightly wrapped the threads are, the easier it is to turn the screw. Examples of screws are shown in **Figure 12.**

Reading Check *How are screws related to the inclined plane?*

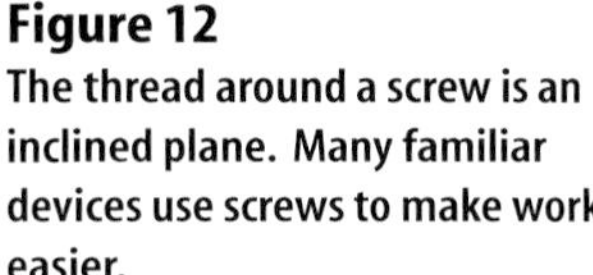

Figure 12
The thread around a screw is an inclined plane. Many familiar devices use screws to make work easier.

Inclined Plane, continued

Life Science INTEGRATION

The saber-toothed tiger, or smilodon (knife-tooth), which became extinct 10,000 years ago, was a ferocious predator that used its 20-cm-long serrated canines for puncturing the thick hides of mastodons and other large animals. It was slightly smaller than today's lion. Its mouth could open to a 120° angle, allowing it to grab and pierce at the same time. **What simple machines are involved in this animal's assault?** wedges in the teeth and lever in the jaw

Reading Check

Answer A wedge is an inclined plane that moves and splits things apart. A screw is an inclined plane wrapped around a shaft.

Activity

Bring in a piece of wood, a screwdriver, and several screws with different numbers of threads. Allow students to experiment to determine how the distance between threads per centimeter of screw length affects the mechanical advantage of the screw. The more threads per centimeter of screw length, the greater its mechanical advantage. L2 ELL LS **Kinesthetic**

Cultural Diversity

Egyptian Construction Until the early part of the twentieth century, the Great Pyramid of Khufu was the world's largest building, covering an area of seven city blocks and weighing 6.5 million tons. In less than 30 years, builders raised more than 2 million blocks to a height of 40 stories. Archaeologists believe the ancient Egyptians constructed enormous ramps to move the pyramid's 1,000-kg limestone blocks into place. A ramp with a length that would enable for about 10 people to drag one of these blocks would require more material than the pyramid itself! Archaeologists discovered that the Egyptians had a type of clay called tafla that is strong and very slippery when wet. Tests indicate that if the Egyptians used *tafla* as a lubricant on the ramps, they could have made steeper ramps, which would have required much less material.

Lever

Use Science Words

Word Origin Have students use a dictionary to find the source of the word *fulcrum* and relate their findings to what a fulcrum does. *Fulcrum* is derived from the Latin *fulcire,* which means "to support." A fulcrum provides the support around which a lever turns. L2 LS **Linguistic**

Make a Model

Have students use a pencil, a ruler, and books to model a first-class lever. Have students experiment to find out how changing the distance between the fulcrum (pencil) and the resistance (books) changes the amount of force that must be exerted to lift the books.

Wheel and Axle

Caption Answer

Figure 15 by making the wheel larger

Teacher FYI

The wheel was invented about the time of the building of the pyramids (3600 B.C.). It was used not for transporting heavy loads but to turn a potter's table. A heavy, round stone was attached to a shaft under the potter's table. With a small kick of the foot, the potter could keep the table turning as the clay was shaped.

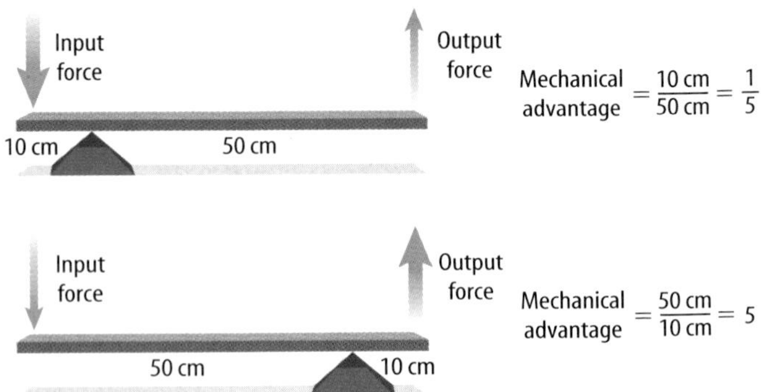

Figure 13
The mechanical advantage of a lever changes as the position of the fulcrum changes. The mechanical advantage increases as the fulcrum is moved closer to the output force.

Lever

You step up to the plate. The pitcher throws the ball and you swing your lever to hit the ball? That's right! A baseball bat is a type of simple machine called a lever. A **lever** is any rigid rod or plank that pivots, or rotates, about a point. The point about which the lever pivots is called a fulcrum.

The mechanical advantage of a lever is found by dividing the distance from the fulcrum to the input force by the distance from the fulcrum to the output force, as shown in **Figure 13.** When the fulcrum is closer to the output force than the input force, the mechanical advantage is greater than one.

Levers are divided into three classes according to the position of the fulcrum with respect to the input force and output force. **Figure 14** shows examples of three classes of levers.

Figure 15
A faucet handle is a wheel and axle. A wheel and axle is similar to a circular lever. The center is the fulcrum, and the wheel and axle turn around it. *How can you increase the mechanical advantage of a wheel and axle?*

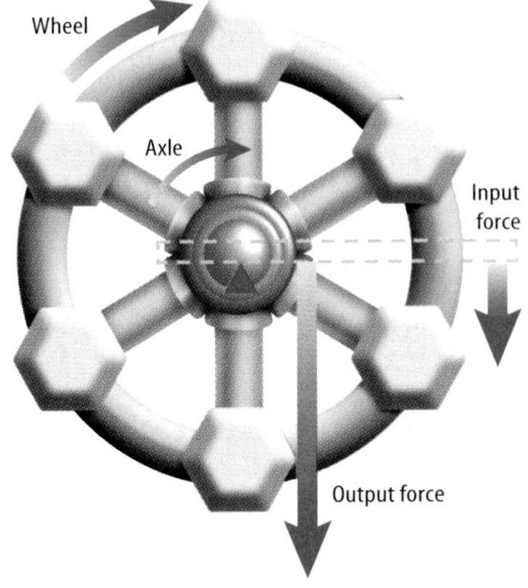

Wheel and Axle

Do you think you could turn a doorknob easily if it were a narrow rod the size of a pencil? It might be possible, but it would be difficult. A doorknob makes it easier for you to open a door because it is a simple machine called a wheel and axle. A **wheel and axle** consists of two circular objects of different sizes that are attached in such a way that they rotate together. As you can see in **Figure 15,** the larger object is the wheel and the smaller object is the axle.

The mechanical advantage of a wheel and axle is usually greater than one. It is found by dividing the radius of the wheel by the radius of the axle. For example, if the radius of the wheel is 12 cm and the radius of the axle is 4 cm, the mechanical advantage is 3.

LAB DEMONSTRATION

Purpose to demonstrate the mechanical advantage of a wheel and axle

Materials wheel and axle, rod, 2 strings, 500-g mass

Preparation Mount the wheel and axle on the support rod.

Procedure Wrap one string clockwise around the axle and the other counterclockwise around the wheel. Hang the 500-g mass from the end of the string on the wheel. Have student volunteers pull down on the string attached to the axle until the mass is lifted about 10 cm.

Expected Outcome The force used to pull is large, and the distance the student's hand moved is small.

✔Assessment

Explain the results, using the concept of mechanical advantage. The mechanical advantage is less than one, because a large input force over a small distance produced a smaller output force over a larger distance.

VISUALIZING LEVERS

Figure 14

Levers are among the simplest of machines, and you probably use them often in everyday life without even realizing it. A lever is a bar that pivots around a fixed point called a fulcrum. As shown here, there are three types of levers—first class, second class, and third class. They differ in where two forces—an input force and an output force—are located in relation to the fulcrum.

▲ Fulcrum
Input force
Output force

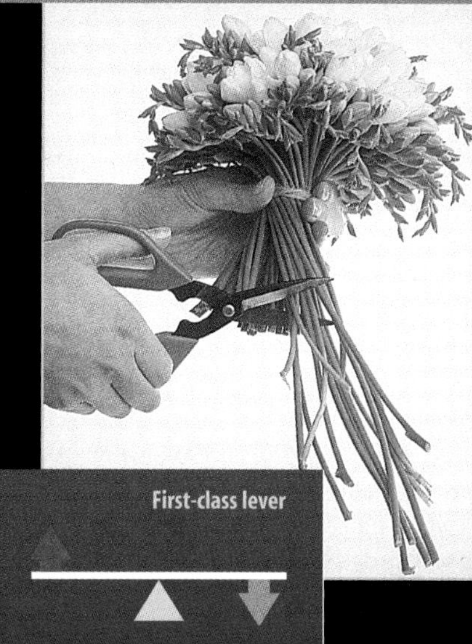

First-class lever

In a first-class lever, the fulcrum is between the input force and the output force. First-class levers, such as scissors and pliers, multiply force or distance depending on where the fulcrum is placed. They always change the direction of the input force, too.

Second-class lever

In a second-class lever, such as a wheelbarrow, the output force is between the input force and the fulcrum. Second-class levers always multiply the input force but don't change its direction.

Third-class lever

In a third-class lever, such as a baseball bat, the input force is between the output force and the fulcrum. Third-class levers multiply the distance of the input force but don't change its direction.

Resource Manager

Chapter Resources Booklet
Enrichment, p. 32
Reinforcement, p. 29

NATIONAL GEOGRAPHIC

Visualizing Levers

Have students examine the pictures and read the captions. Then ask the following questions.

What are the fundamental differences between 1st, 2nd, and 3rd class levers? They differ in the locations of the input force, output force, and fulcrum.

What are other examples of 1st class levers? Answers will vary. Possible answers include crowbar, teeter totter or see-saw, and laboratory balances.

What are other examples of 2nd class levers? Answers will vary. Possible answers include nutcrackers, bottle openers, and doors.

What are other examples of 3rd class levers? Answers will vary. Possible answers include hammers, tweezers, shovels, rakes, and fishing poles.

Activity

Have students assemble collections of the three types of levers. Encourage students to find examples that are not listed in this text. L2 LS **Kinesthetic**

Extension

Encourage students to find large construction or industrial applications of levers. Ask students to share their information with the class. L3 LS **Linguistic**

Fun Fact

The ancient Greek mathematician Archimedes was the first to understand the full potential of the lever. When he announced his discovery to the king, he said, "Give me a place to stand, and I will move the Earth!" He then proceeded to move a grounded ship with an enormous lever.

Wheel and Axle, continued

Caption Answer

Figure 16 Both objects have large wheels and smaller axles. The effort in the ferris wheel is located at the axle, and the effort to run a water wheel is located at the wheel.

Pulley

Purpose Students observe different pulley systems. L2 ELL COOP LEARN LS **Kinesthetic**

Materials 2 broomsticks, 3-m rope

Teaching Strategy Have two students hold the broomsticks in place while the third pulls on the rope for the first trial.

Analysis

1. The rope is harder to pull with two turns than with four turns.
2. It would be easier to pull the sticks together with ten turns of rope.

Oral Ask students to draw diagrams illustrating how a pulley system reduces the amount of effort needed to overcome a resistance force. The pulley multiplies the distance through which the force moves. Use **PASC,** p. 127.

Reading Check

Answer It changes the direction of the force.

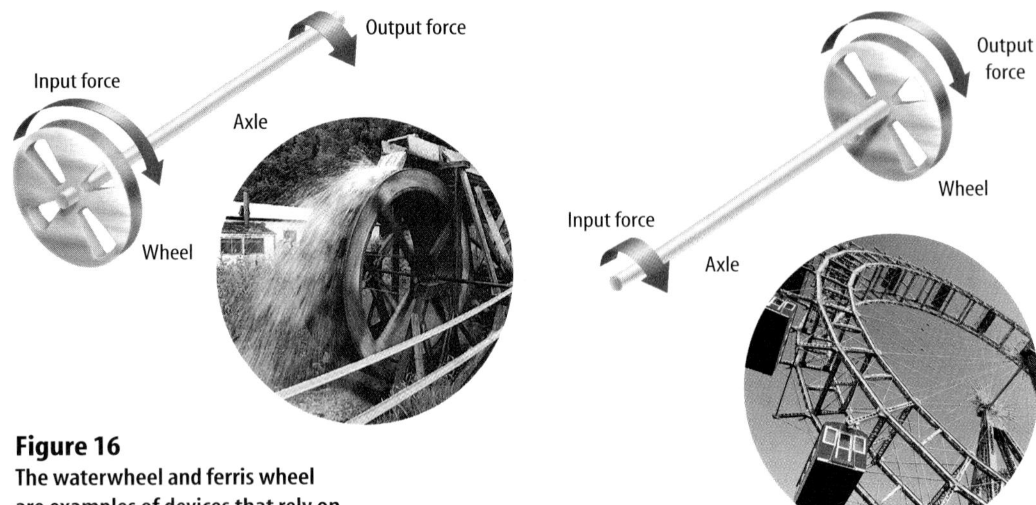

Figure 16
The waterwheel and ferris wheel are examples of devices that rely on a wheel and axle. *How are they alike and how are they different?*

Using Wheels and Axles In some devices, the input force is used to turn the wheel and the output force is exerted by the axle. Because the wheel is larger than the axle, the mechanical advantage is greater than one. So the output force is greater than the input force. A doorknob, a steering wheel, and a screwdriver are examples of this type of wheel and axle.

In other devices, the input force is applied to turn the axle and the output force is exerted by the wheel. Then the mechanical advantage is less than one and the output force is less than the input force. A fan and a ferris wheel are examples of this type of wheel and axle. **Figure 16** shows an example of each type of wheel and axle.

Mini LAB

Observing Pulleys

Procedure

1. Obtain two **broomsticks.** Tie a 3-m-long **rope** to the middle of one stick. Wrap the rope around both sticks four times.
2. Have two students pull the broomsticks apart while a third pulls on the rope.
3. Repeat with two wraps of rope.

Analysis

1. Compare the results.
2. Predict whether it will be easier to pull the broomsticks together with ten wraps of rope.

Pulley

To raise a sail, a sailor pulls down on a rope. The rope uses a simple machine called a pulley to change the direction of the force needed. A **pulley** consists of a grooved wheel with a rope or chain wrapped around it.

Fixed Pulleys Some pulleys, such as the one on a sail, a window blind, or a flagpole, are attached to a structure above your head. When you pull down on the rope, you pull something up. This type of pulley, called a fixed pulley, does not change the force you exert or the distance over which you exert it. Instead, it changes the direction in which you exert your force, as shown in **Figure 17A.** The mechanical advantage of a fixed pulley is 1.

Reading Check *How does a fixed pulley affect the input force?*

Visual Learning

Figure 17 Encourage students to use their fingers to trace the movement of both the effort force and the load in each pulley diagram. Have students use their observations to describe how each pulley works. A single pulley changes the direction of the force; a movable pulley allows a smaller force to be exerted over a longer distance; systems of pulleys both multiply force and change its direction.

Resource Manager

Chapter Resources Booklet
MiniLAB, p. 4
Lab Activity, pp. 13–16

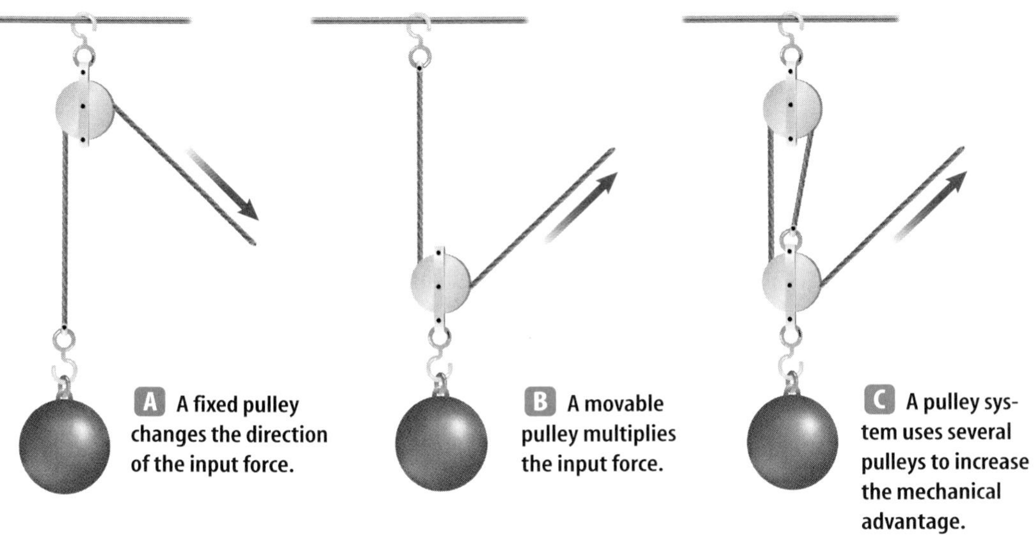

A A fixed pulley changes the direction of the input force.
B A movable pulley multiplies the input force.
C A pulley system uses several pulleys to increase the mechanical advantage.

Figure 17
Pulleys can change force and direction.

Movable Pulleys Another way to use a pulley is to attach it to the object you are lifting, as shown in **Figure 17B.** This type of pulley, called a movable pulley, allows you to exert a smaller force to lift the object. The mechanical advantage of a movable pulley is always 2.

More often you will see combinations of fixed and movable pulleys. Such a combination is called a pulley system. The mechanical advantage of a pulley system is equal to the number of sections of rope pulling up on the object. For the pulley system shown in **Figure 17C** the mechanical advantage is 3.

Section 3 Assessment

1. Define simple and compound machines in your own words.
2. Describe four different simple machines.
3. Explain how the mechanical advantages of a ramp, a wedge, and a screw are similar.
4. How does the mechanical advantage of a wheel and axle change as the size of the wheel increases?
5. **Think Critically** The Great Pyramid is 146 m high. How long would a ramp from the top of the pyramid to the ground need to be to have a mechanical advantage of 4?

Skill Builder Activities

6. **Comparing and Contrasting** How are a lever and a wheel and axle similar? **For more help, refer to the Science Skill Handbook.**
7. **Using Proportions** You are designing a lever to lift an object that weighs 500 N. The lever exerts the output force 1 m from the fulcrum. How far from the fulcrum must an effort force of 250 N be applied to lift the object? Draw a diagram as part of your answer. Label the forces and distances. **For more help, refer to the Math Skill Handbook.**

IDENTIFYING Misconceptions

Pulley systems can be difficult for students to understand. A rule of thumb is that the MA equals the number of pulleys used or the number of sections of rope pulling up on the object.

3 Assess

Reteach

Organize the class into groups, and give each group a machine to present to the class. Group members should describe the features, mechanical advantage, and efficiency of the group's machine and give an example of how it is used. L1 LS **Linguistic**

Challenge

Ask each student to bring in a compound machine or a picture of a compound machine. Have them identify the simple machines that make up the machine they selected and explain how they work together to perform the machine's intended function. L2 ELL LS **Visual-Spatial**

Assessment

Performance Build a pulley system, and ask students to determine the mechanical advantage of the system. Use **Performance Assessment in the Science Classroom,** p. 97.

Answers to Section Assessment

1. A simple machine involves one movement, and a compound machine has two or more linked movements.
2. inclined plane: flat, sloped surface; lever: rigid rod or plank that pivots about a point,; wheel and axle: two circular objects of different sizes that are attached so they rotate together; pulley: grooved wheel with a rope or chain wrapped around it
3. In each, length of the slope divided by rise of the slope is the mechanical advantage.
4. It increases.
5. 4×146 m = 584 m
6. The wheel and axle is like an infinite number of levers fanning around the axle. The axle acts as the fulcrum and the wheel as the lever.
7. output force/effort force = effort distance/output distance; 500 N/250 N = d/1 m; d = 2 m

Activity

BENCH TESTED

Recognize the Problem

Purpose

Students will experiment with multiple pulley systems and use the results to design a pulley system that can lift a heavy load.
L2 ELL LS **Kinesthetic**

Process Skills

observing, inferring, comparing and contrasting, designing an experiment to test a hypothesis, interpreting data, separating and controlling variables, predicting, using numbers

Time Required

90 minutes

Materials

A block and tackle is a good multiple pulley system. The upper set of pulleys is attached to a support, and the lower set is attached to the load.

Safety Precautions

Remind students to be careful when raising the weight.

Form a Hypothesis

Possible Hypothesis

As the number of pulleys increases, the amount of rope needed (distance) increases and the force needed decreases.

Activity Design Your Own Experiment

Pulley Power

Imagine how long it might have taken to build the Sears Tower in Chicago without the aid of a pulley system attached to a crane. Hoisting the 1-ton I beams to a maximum height of 110 stories required large lifting forces and precise control of the beam's movement.

Construction workers also use smaller pulleys that are not attached to cranes to lift supplies to where they are needed. Pulleys are not limited to construction sites. They also are used to lift automobile engines out of cars, to help load and unload heavy objects on ships, and to lift heavy appliances and furniture.

Recognize the Problem

How can you use a pulley system to reduce the force needed to lift a load?

Form a Hypothesis

Write a hypothesis about how pulleys can be combined to make a system of pulleys to lift a heavy load, such as a brick. Consider the efficiency of your system.

Goals

- **Design** a pulley system.
- **Measure** the mechanical advantage and efficiency of the pulley system.

Possible Materials

single- and multiple-pulley systems
nylon rope
steel bar to support the pulley system
meterstick
**metric tape measure*
variety of weights to test pulleys
force spring scale
brick
**heavy book*
balance
**scale*
**Alternate materials*

Safety Precautions

The brick could be dangerous if it falls. Keep your hands and feet clear of it.

276

Test Your Hypothesis

Possible Procedures

Attach several pulleys to the load and an equal number to a support. Weigh the load, and then run a rope through the pulley system, attach a spring scale to the rope, and measure the force needed to pull to lift the load.

Resource Manager 

Chapter Resources Booklet
Activity Worksheet, pp. 7–8

Lab Management and Safety, p. 39

Test Your Hypothesis

Plan

1. Decide how you are going to support your pulley system. What materials will you use?
2. How will you measure the effort force and the resistance force? How will you determine the mechanical advantage? How will you measure efficiency?
3. **Experiment** by lifting small weights with a single pulley, double pulley, and so on. How efficient are the pulleys? In what ways can you increase the efficiency of your setup?
4. Use the results of step 3 to design a pulley system to lift the brick. Draw a diagram of your design. Label the different parts of the pulley system and use arrows to indicate the direction of movement for each section of rope.

Do

1. Make sure your teacher approves your plan before you start.
2. Assemble the pulley system you designed. You might want to test it with a smaller weight before attaching the brick.
3. **Measure** the force needed to lift the brick. How much rope must you pull to raise the brick 10 cm?

Analyze Your Data

1. **Calculate** the ideal mechanical advantage of your design.
2. **Calculate** the actual mechanical advantage of the pulley system you built.
3. **Calculate** the efficiency of your pulley system.
4. How did the mechanical advantage of your pulley system compare with those of your classmates?

Draw Conclusions

1. **Explain** how increasing the number of pulleys increases the mechanical advantage.
2. How could you modify the pulley system to lift a weight twice as heavy with the same effort force used here?
3. **Compare** this real machine with an ideal machine.

Communicating Your Data

Show your design diagram to the class. Review the design and point out good and bad characteristics of your pulley system. **For more help, refer to the Science Skill Handbook.**

Teaching Strategy

Point out that every time a pulley is added to the system, it introduces more weight and friction. This lowers the efficiency and affects the mechanical advantage.

Troubleshooting

You may want to divide the class into groups to tackle different parts of the problem during the design phase.

Expected Outcome

A multiple-pulley system can use a small force to raise a heavy load.

Analyze Your Data

1. (length of rope pulled)/(distance load is raised) = MA
2. (weight of load)/(effort force) = MA
3. $(W_{out}/W_{in})(100\%) = E$, where W_{out} = (weight)(distance raised) and W_{in} = (effort force)(length of rope pulled)
4. Answers will depend on the number of pulleys used and the efficiencies of the pulley systems.

Error Analysis

Have students compare their results and their hypotheses and explain any differences in their results.

Draw Conclusions

1. Each pulley added increases the mechanical advantage by 1.
2. Double the number of pulleys in the system and add an additional pulley or two to compensate for frictional losses.
3. An ideal pulley system would have an efficiency of 100%. The real system has noticeable losses because of friction.

Assessment

Performance How much work would it take for a simple pulley to lift a 910-kg I-beam 450 m? Does the weight of the cable affect the efficiency of the crane as it lifts an I-beam? 4,100,000 J; Yes; the cable is heavy and the crane must lift the cable as well as the I-beam. Use **PASC**, p. 101.

Have each student write a paragraph using information learned in the Activity to explain how to design a pulley system with which one person could lift a building stone into position on a wall.

TIME SCIENCE AND Society

Content Background

In addition to artificial limbs, researchers are developing ears and eyes with electromagnetic devices that will do the work of nerves that have been damaged or are non-existent.

A team of researchers has developed an Artificial Retina Component Chip (ARCC) that is implantable. The ARCC is a silicon microchip embedded with photosensor cells and electrodes. The device can be implanted near the vision center of the retina. Images as well as light passing through the pupil then pass through the ARCC's surface, striking photosensors on the back of the chip. The photosensors convert the image patterns of light and dark into electric impulses, just as a typical eye's rods and cones do. These electric impulses stimulate nerves behind the retina, sending the information to the brain.

A tiny magnetic hearing aid is also being developed. This device captures sounds with a miniature microphone implanted in the ear. The amplified vibrations pass through a small processing unit and an electromagnetic coil, also implanted in the ear. The vibrations are then sent to the inner ear via a tiny magnet attached to the inner ear's round window, a thin membrane at one end of the cochlea. The magnet, about as large as a pencil point, then sends vibrations through the cochlea, stimulating the thousands of hair cells used in normal hearing.

TIME SCIENCE AND Society — SCIENCE ISSUES THAT AFFECT YOU!

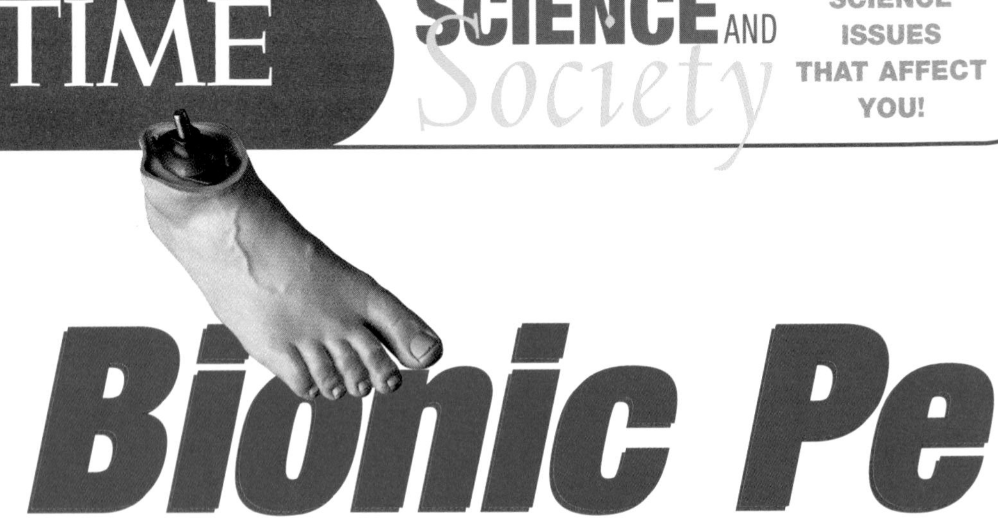

Bionic Pe

People in need of transplants usually receive human organs. But many people's medical problems can only be solved by receiving artificial body parts. These synthetic devices, called prostheses, are used to replace anything from a heart valve to a knee joint. Bionics is the science of creating artificial body parts. A major focus of bionics is the replacement of lost limbs. Through accident, birth defect, or disease, people sometimes lack hands or feet, or even whole arms or legs. For centuries, people have used prostheses to replace limbs. In the past, disabled people used devices like peg legs or artificial arms that ended in a pair of hooks. These protheses didn't do much to replace lost functions of arms and legs.

But today, that's changed, thanks to the work of eighteenth-century scientists Luigi Galvani and Alessandro Volta. Because of their experiments, people began to realize that muscles contract by means of electrical impulses. This knowledge eventually led to an invention called functional neuromuscular stimulation (FNS). Some people are paralyzed because nerves that send electric impulses to certain muscles are destroyed. FNS uses a computer or microprocessor to send electric impulses directly to these muscles. By sending the proper signals, the muscles can be made to move. FNS can allow paralyzed people to walk to a certain extent and to maintain muscle control.

The knowledge that muscles respond to electricity has helped create more effective prostheses. One such prostheses is the myoelectric arm. This battery-powered device connects muscle nerves in an amputated arm to a sensor.

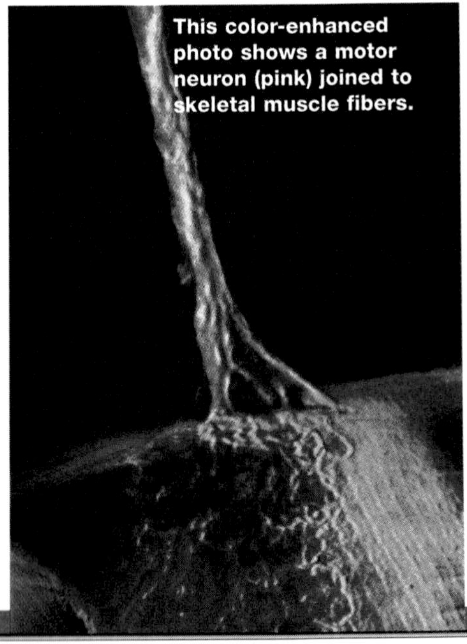
This color-enhanced photo shows a motor neuron (pink) joined to skeletal muscle fibers.

278

Resources for Teachers and Students

Superhumans: A Beginner's Guide to Bionics by Sarah Anless, Ian Thompson (Illustrator), and Stephen Sweet (Illustrator). Millbrook Press. 1998.

Robots and Biological Systems: Towards a New Bionics? by Paolo Dario (Editor), G. Sandini (Editor), and P. Aebischer (Editor). Springer-Verlag, New York Inc. 1993.

Artificial limbs can help people lead normal lives

ople

The sensor detects when the arm tenses, then transmits the signal to an artificial hand, which opens or closes. New prosthetic hands even give a sense of touch, as well as cold and heat.

Today's leg prostheses are also more sophisticated. The latest models are made of strong, lightweight titanium rods built inside a lifelike plastic covering. They allow users to compete in many sports, even tough ones like the triathlon. In addition, new artificial feet let wearers sense when their weight is on their toes, heels, or the sides of their feet. This gives them better balance.

A recent experiment promises even more amazing bionic technologies. Researchers have trained rats to move a robotic arm by using their brain signals that normally control movement—and without using their muscles at all. One day, this research might produce devices that allow paralyzed people to move artificial limbs just by brain power.

People with leg prostheses can participate in sports.

Myoelectric arms make life easier for people who have them.

CONNECTIONS **Research** Use your school's media center to find other aspects of robotics such as walking machines or robots that perform planetary exploration. What are they used for? How do they work? You could take it one step further and learn about cyborgs. Report to the class.

SCIENCE *Online*
For more information, visit science.glencoe.com

Discussion

What are some reasons people need the prosthetic devices discussed in the article? Possible answers include because of loss of the use of limbs due to accidents, birth defects, or disease. L1 LS **Logical-Mathematical**

Extension

Have students use the Internet or other resources available to your school to find out about the uses of bionics in areas such as hearing, vision, and touch. Ask students to investigate the success rates of these new technologies and report their findings to the class. L3 LS **Linguistic**

Investigate the Issue

Take this opportunity to see what students know about robotics already. Where did they get this information? Was it from science fiction movies or magazines? Explore whether any of the students' ideas are feasible or are used currently.

CONNECTIONS Suggest students try the NASA web site for information and illustrations on the use of robots for space exploration. Ask students to include information on the success and failure rates of robotics in space. Encourage them to find out why some designs were used more than once and why some were discarded after one excursion.

SCIENCE *Online*

Internet Addresses

Explore the Glencoe Science Web site at **science.glencoe.com** to find out more about topics in this feature.

Chapter 9 Study Guide

Reviewing Main Ideas

Preview

Students can answer the questions in their Science Journals. Discuss the answers as you go through the chapter. **LS Linguistic**

Review

Students can write their answers, then compare them with those of other students. **LS Interpersonal**

Reteach

Students can look at the illustrations and describe details that support the main ideas of the chapter. **LS Visual-Spatial**

Answers to Chapter Review

Section 1

2. no

Section 2

2. one

Section 3

2. The screwdriver is acting as a first-class lever.

Chapter 9 Study Guide

Reviewing Main Ideas

Section 1 Work and Power

1. Work is done when a force exerted on an object causes the object to move.
2. A force can do work only when it is exerted in the same direction as the object moves. *Is work being done if this car is stuck?*

3. Work is equal to force times distance, and the unit of work is the joule.
4. Power is the rate at which work is done, and the unit of power is the watt.

Section 2 Using Machines

1. A machine changes the size or direction of the input force or the distance over which it is exerted.
2. The mechanical advantage of a machine is its output force divided by its input force. *What is the mechanical advantage of this machine?*

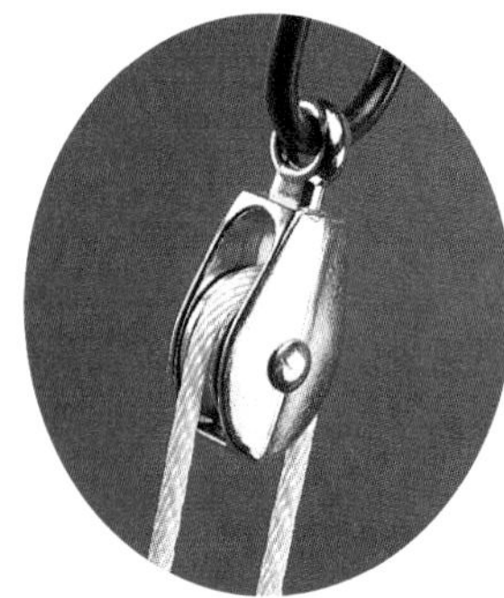

Section 3 Simple Machines

1. A machine that does work with only one movement is a simple machine. A compound machine is a combination of simple machines.
2. Simple machines include the inclined plane, lever, wheel and axle, screw, wedge, and pulley. *What type of simple machine is shown?*

3. Wedges and screws are two types of inclined planes. The mechanical advantage of an inclined plane is its length divided by its height.
4. The mechanical advantage of a lever depends on the location of the fulcrum. The mechanical advantage of a wheel and axle depends on the radius of each circular object.
5. Pulleys can be used to multiply force and change direction. The mechanical advantage of a fixed pulley is one and of a single movable pulley, two.

FOLDABLES Reading & Study Skills

After You Read

To help you review work and simple machines, use the Foldable you made at the beginning of the chapter.

FOLDABLES Reading & Study Skills

After You Read

After students have read the chapter and completed the Foldable described in Before You Read, have them do the activity on the student page.

Dinah Zike

Chapter 9 Study Guide

Visualizing Main Ideas

Complete the following concept map on simple machines.

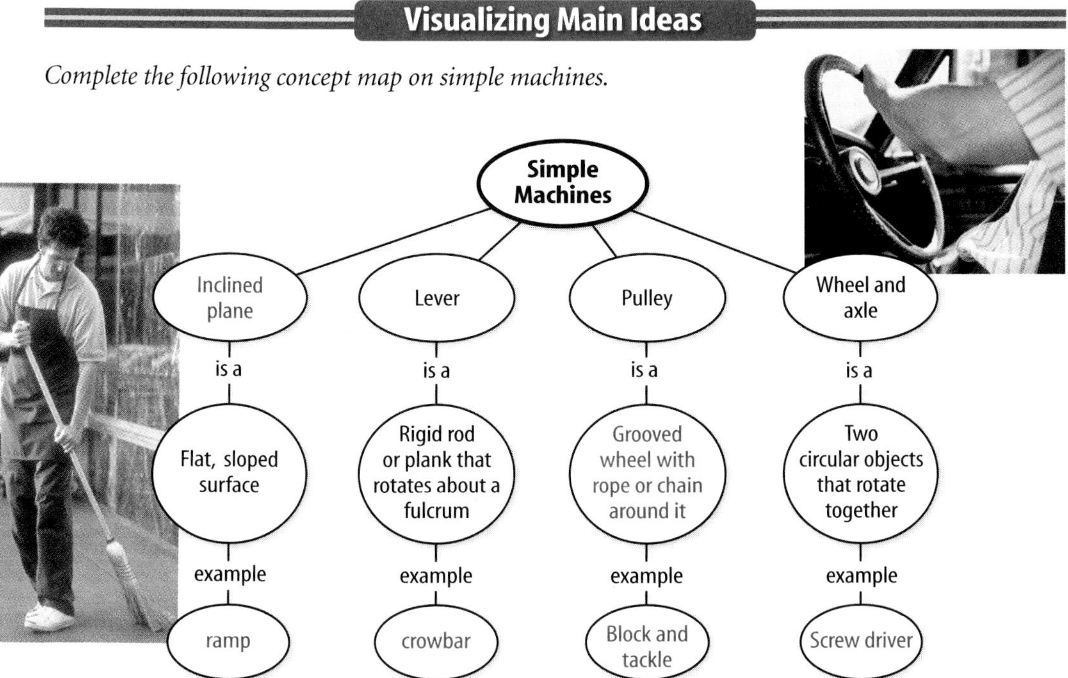

Vocabulary Review

Vocabulary Words

- a. compound machine
- b. efficiency
- c. inclined plane
- d. input force
- e. lever
- f. mechanical advantage
- g. output force
- h. power
- i. pulley
- j. screw
- k. simple machine
- l. wedge
- m. wheel and axle
- n. work

Study Tip

Without looking back at your textbook, write a summary of each section of the chapter after you've read it. If you write it in your own words, you will better remember it.

Using Vocabulary

Each phrase below describes a vocabulary word. Write the vocabulary word that matches the phrase describing it.

1. percentage of work in to work out
2. force put into a machine
3. force exerted on an object by a machine
4. two rigidly attached wheels
5. input force divided by output force
6. a machine with only one movement
7. an inclined plane that moves
8. a rigid rod that rotates about a fulcrum
9. a flat, sloped surface
10. amount of work divided by time

Chapter 9 Study Guide

Visualizing Main Ideas

See student page.

Vocabulary Review

Using Vocabulary

1. efficiency
2. input force
3. output force
4. wheel and axle
5. mechanical advantage
6. simple machine
7. wedge
8. lever
9. inclined plane
10. power

Chapter 9 Assessment

Checking Concepts

1. C
2. D
3. B
4. A
5. B
6. C
7. D
8. B
9. C
10. C

Thinking Critically

11. Earth's gravitational force pulls the object through a distance.
12. The radius of the knob is greater than the radius of the axle. This means that when a force is applied to the knob, the knob moves a greater distance than the axle. The knob and the axle do the same amount of work. Therefore, the axle must multiple the force.
13. $MA = 6/2 = 3$
14. $MA = F_{out}/F_{in}$; $F_{in} = F_{out}/MA = 11{,}000\ N/20 = 550\ N$
15. No; it would need to be at least 3 m from the fulcrum.

Chapter 9 Assessment

Checking Concepts

Choose the word or phrase that best answers the question.

1. Which of the following is a requirement for work to be done?
A) Force is exerted. **C)** Force moves object.
B) Object is carried. **D)** Machine is used.

2. How much work is done when a force of 30 N moves an object a distance of 3 m?
A) 3 J **C)** 30 J
B) 10 J **D)** 90 J

3. How much power is expended when 600 J of work are done in 10 s?
A) 6 W **C)** 600 W
B) 60 W **D)** 610 W

4. Which is an example of a simple machine?
A) baseball bat **C)** can opener
B) bicycle **D)** car

5. What is mechanical advantage?
A) input force/output force
B) output force/input force
C) input work/output work
D) output work/input work

6. What is the mechanical advantage of a machine that changes only the direction of the input force?
A) less than 1 **C)** 1
B) zero **D)** greater than 1

7. A wheel with a radius of 20 cm is attached to an axle with a radius of 1 cm. What is the output force if the input force on the wheel is 100 N?
A) 5 N **C)** 500 N
B) 200 N **D)** 2,000 N

8. Which of the following is a form of the inclined plane?
A) pulley **C)** wheel and axle
B) screw **D)** lever

9. A ramp decreases which of the following?
A) height **C)** input force
B) output force **D)** input distance

10. If a machine takes in 50 J and puts out 45 J, what is its efficiency?
A) 0.9 percent **C)** 90 percent
B) 1.1 percent **D)** 111 percent

Thinking Critically

11. Why could you say that gravity does work on a falling object?

12. A doorknob is an example of a wheel and axle. Explain why turning the knob is easier than turning the axle.

13. What is the mechanical advantage of a 6-m long ramp that extends from a ground-level sidewalk to a 2-m high porch?

14. How much effort force is required to lift an 11,000-N beam using a pulley system with a mechanical advantage of 20?

15. Would a 9 N force applied 2 m from the fulcrum lift the weight? Explain.

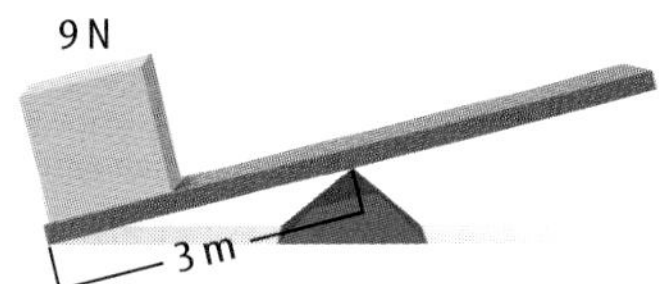

Developing Skills

16. Measuring in SI At the 1976 Olympics, Vasili Aleseev shattered the world record for weight lifting when he lifted 2,500 N from the floor to a point over his head 2 m above the ground. It took him about 5 s to complete the lift. How much work did he do? What was his power?

Chapter Assessment Planner

Portfolio Encourage students to place in their portfolios one or two items of what they consider to be their best work. Examples include:
- Life Science Integration, p. 259
- Active Reading, p. 267
- Science Journal, p. 270

Performance Additional performance assessments, Performance Task Assessment Lists, and rubrics for evaluating these activities can be found in Glencoe's **Performance Assessment in the Science Classroom.**

17. **Predicting** Suppose a lever is in balance. Would this arrangement be in balance on the Moon, where the force of gravity is less? Explain.

18. **Making and Using Graphs** A pulley system has a mechanical advantage of 5. Make a graph of the possible combinations of effort force and resistance force.

19. **Solving One-Step Equations** If you put 8,000 J of work into a machine with an efficiency of 60 percent, what is the work output?

20. **Recognizing Cause and Effect** The diagram below shows a force exerted at an angle to pull a sled. How much work is done if the sled moves 10 m horizontally?

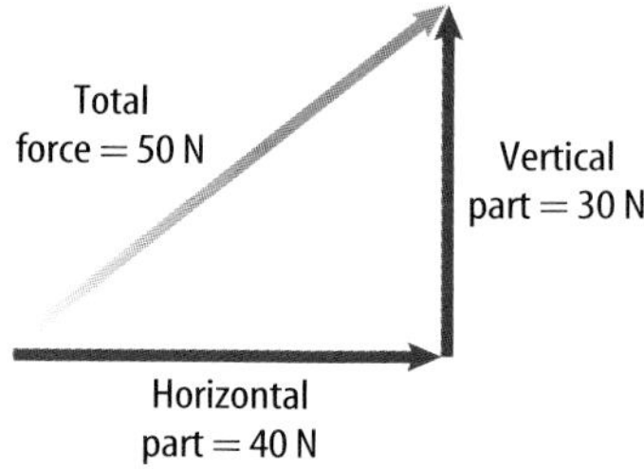

Performance Assessment

21. **Identifying Levers** You have levers in your body. Your muscles and tendons provide the input force. Your joints act as fulcrums. The output force is used to move everything from your head to your hands. Describe and draw any human levers you can identify.

Technology

Go to the Glencoe Science Web site at **science.glencoe.com** or use the **Glencoe Science CD-ROM** for additional chapter assessment.

THE PRINCETON REVIEW Test Practice

At state fairs, participants often compete in pulling a 250-pound rock to a 50-meter height by using a simple pulley system. Each participant gets three tries to reach the 50-meter height.

Top Four Competitors

Participant	Bud	Charley	Maxine	Joey
Attempt 1	35 m	18 m	38 m	43 m
Attempt 2	28 m	23 m	35 m	38 m
Attempt 3	42 m	30 m	36 m	21 m

Study the table and answer the following questions.

1. According to this information, which of the participants pulled the 250-pound rock to the highest average height?
   A) Bud
   B) Charley
   C) Maxine
   D) Joey

2. According to the table, the competitor who did the least amount of total work overall was _____ .
   F) Bud
   G) Charley
   H) Maxine
   J) Joey

3. According to the table, which of the following is true about the amount of work done by Joey over his three attempts, compared to the other top four competitors?
   A) The range is the smallest
   B) The range is the largest
   C) The average is the lowest
   D) The average is the highest

Chapter 9 Assessment

THE PRINCETON REVIEW Test Practice

The Test-Taking Tip was written by The Princeton Review, the nation's leader in test preparation.

1. C
2. G
3. B

Developing Skills

16. work = weight × height = 2,500 N × 2 m = 5,000 J; power = Work/time = 5,000 J/5 s = 1,000 watts.
17. Yes, a lever is in balance when the force times the distance from the fulcrum is the same on both sides of the fulcrum. Since the weights are the forces, the forces will be proportionally smaller.
18. Place input force on the *x*-axis and output forces on the *y*-axis. The graph will be a line with a slope of 5 and will pass through the origin, since there will be no output without an input.
19. $Eff = W_{out}/W_{in} \times 100\%$; rearranging to get W_{out} gives: $W_{out} = Eff/100\% \times W_{in} = 60\%/100\% \times 8{,}000\ J = 4{,}800\ J$.
20. work = force in direction of motion × distance moved by this force = 40 N × 10 m = 400 J

Performance Assessment

21. Arms and legs make great examples of levers. The elbows and knees are the fulcrums.

Assessment Resources

Reproducible Masters

Chapter Resources Booklet
Chapter Review, pp. 37–38
Chapter Tests, pp. 38–42
Assessment Transparency Activity, p. 49

Glencoe Science Web site
Interactive Tutor
Chapter Quizzes

Glencoe Technology
Assessment Transparency
Interactive CD-ROM Chapter Quizzes
ExamView Pro Test Bank
Vocabulary PuzzleMaker Software
MindJogger Videoquiz DVD/VHS

Section/Objectives	Standards		Activities/Features
	National	State/Local	
Chapter Opener	See p. 5T for a Key to Standards.		**Explore Activity:** Compare insulators, p. 285 **Before You Read,** p. 285
Section 1 Temperature and Thermal Energy 3 sessions 1.5 blocks 1. **Explain** how temperature is related to kinetic energy. 2. **Describe** three scales used for measuring temperature. 3. **Define** thermal energy.	National Content Standards: UCP3, B1, B3		**Math Skills Activity:** Converting Fahrenheit to Celsius Temperatures, p. 288
Section 2 Heat 3 sessions 1.5 blocks 1. **Explain** the difference between thermal energy and heat. 2. **Describe** three ways heat is transferred. 3. **Identify** materials that are insulators or conductors.	National Content Standards: UCP3, A1, B1, B3, E2		**MiniLAB:** Comparing Rates of Melting, p. 292 **MiniLAB:** Observing Convection, p. 293 **Life Science Integration,** p. 294 **Activity:** Heating Up and Cooling Down, p. 296
Section 3 Engines and Refrigerators 4 sessions 2 blocks 1. **Identify** what an engine does. 2. **Describe** how an internal combustion engine works. 3. **Explain** how refrigerators and air conditioners create cool environments.	National Content Standards: UCP1, A1, B1, B3, E1, E2, F4, F5		**Science Online,** p. 298 **Visualizing the Four-Stroke Cycle,** p. 299 **Activity:** Comparing Thermal Insulators, pp. 302–303 **Science and Society:** The Heat is On, pp. 304–305

Activity Materials	Reproducible Resources	Section Assessment	Technology
Explore Activity: water, hot plate, beaker, plastic cup, polystyrene cup, graduated cylinder, aluminum foil, 2 thermometers, refrigerator	**Chapter Resources Booklet** Foldables Worksheet, p. 17 Directed Reading Overview, p. 19 Note-taking Worksheets, pp. 33–35	GLENCOE'S ASSESSMENT ADVANTAGE	
Need materials? Contact Science Kit at 1-800-828-7777 or www.sciencekit.com on the Internet.	**Chapter Resources Booklet** Transparency Activity, p. 44 Lab Activity, pp. 9–12 Enrichment, p. 30 Reinforcement, p. 27 Directed Reading, p. 20 **Earth Science Critical Thinking/ Problem Solving,** p. 10	Portfolio Use Science Words, p. 288 Performance Math Skills Activity, p. 288 Skill Builder Activities, p. 289 Content Section Assessment, p. 289	Section Focus Transparency Interactive CD-ROM/DVD Guided Reading Audio Program
MiniLAB: glass, ice, water, 2 coffee cups, clock or watch **MiniLAB:** 250-mL beaker, water, hot plate, 50-mL beaker, penny, metal tongs, dropper, food coloring **Activity:** 5 thermometers, 5 400-mL beakers, stop-watch, refrigerator, stirring rod, hot plate, water	**Chapter Resources Booklet** Transparency Activity, p. 45 MiniLABS, pp. 3, 4 Lab Activity, pp. 13–16 Enrichment, p. 31 Reinforcement, p. 28 Directed Reading, p. 20 Activity Worksheet, pp. 5–6 **Physical Science Critical Thinking/Problem Solving,** p. 5 **Cultural Diversity,** p. 41	Portfolio Active Reading, p. 292 Performance MiniLAB, p. 292 MiniLAB, p. 293 Skill Builder Activities, p. 295 Content Section Assessment, p. 295	Section Focus Transparency Interactive CD-ROM/DVD Guided Reading Audio Program
Activity: hot plate, large beaker, water, graduated cylinder, thermometers, tea, coffee, coffee maker, various beverage containers (each about the same size and shape), covers for the containers, tongs, stopwatch, thermal gloves or mitts	**Chapter Resources Booklet** Transparency Activity, p. 46 Enrichment, p. 32 Reinforcement, p. 29 Directed Reading, pp. 21, 22 Transparency Activity, pp. 47–48 Activity Worksheet, pp. 7–8 **Home and Community Involvement,** p. 49	Portfolio Extension, p. 298 Performance Skill Builder Activities, p. 301 Content Section Assessment, p. 301	Section Focus Transparency Teaching Transparency Interactive CD-ROM/DVD Guided Reading Audio Program

End of Chapter Assessment

GLENCOE'S ASSESSMENT ADVANTAGE

Blackline Masters	Technology	Professional Series
Chapter Resources Booklet Chapter Review, pp. 37–38 Chapter Tests, pp. 39–42 **Standardized Test Practice by The Princeton Review,** pp. 43–46	MindJogger Videoquiz CD-ROM Explorations and Quizzes Vocabulary Puzzle Makers ExamView Pro Test Bank Interactive Lesson Planner Interactive Teacher's Edition	Performance Assessment in the Science Classroom (PASC)

Transparencies

Section Focus

Section 1 Section Focus Transparency **Coping With Winter**

Japanese macaques are one of the few species of primates that can live outside of the tropics. These macaques live on Honshu Island in Japan.

1. What do you think the air temperature is like in this photo? What is the water temperature like? How do you know?
2. What accounts for the water's temperature?
3. If you were told that the temperature of the water was 40 degrees, would that be meaningful? Why or why not?

L2

Section 2 Section Focus Transparency **Hot Times**

The inside and the outside of this building are at different temperatures. In areas that are well insulated, little thermal energy is transferred from the inside to the outside. In other areas, however, a lot of heat escapes.

1. What colors do you think indicate areas where a lot of energy is transferred? Where are these areas?
2. What does insulation do?
3. How do you feel if you sit in the shade on a sunny day? How do you feel in the sun even if the temperature is the same? Why?

L2

Section 3 Section Focus Transparency **Southward Bound**

Icebergs in the North Atlantic are pushed south by the Labrador Current. This is dangerous because the Labrador Current can take icebergs into the shipping lanes, the part of the ocean that ships travel between Europe and North America. Today, the U.S. Coast Guard International Ice Patrol carefully monitors icebergs that may threaten ships in the North Atlantic.

1. Describe the different states of water in the photo above.
2. Icebergs from the North Atlantic usually don't get much south of roughly 40°N latitude (that's about as far south as New Jersey). Why is this?
3. Does the volume of water in the ocean change when a floating iceberg melts?

L2

This is a representation of key blackline masters available in the Teacher Classroom Resources. See Resource Manager boxes within the chapter for additional information.

Assessment

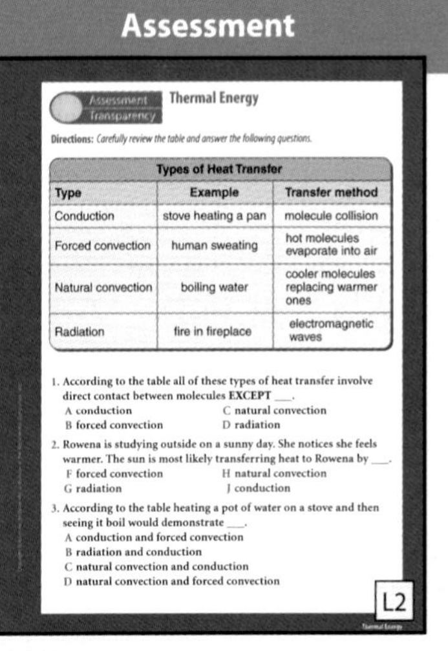
Assessment Transparency **Thermal Energy**

Directions: Carefully review the table and answer the following questions.

Types of Heat Transfer		
Type	Example	Transfer method
Conduction	stove heating a pan	molecule collision
Forced convection	human sweating	hot molecules evaporate into air
Natural convection	boiling water	cooler molecules replacing warmer ones
Radiation	fire in fireplace	electromagnetic waves

1. According to the table all of these types of heat transfer involve direct contact between molecules EXCEPT ___.
   A conduction C natural convection
   B forced convection D radiation
2. Rowena is studying outside on a sunny day. She notices she feels warmer. The sun is most likely transferring heat to Rowena by ___.
   F forced convection H natural convection
   G radiation J conduction
3. According to the table heating a pot of water on a stove and then seeing it boil would demonstrate ___.
   A conduction and forced convection
   B radiation and conduction
   C natural convection and conduction
   D natural convection and forced convection

L2

Teaching

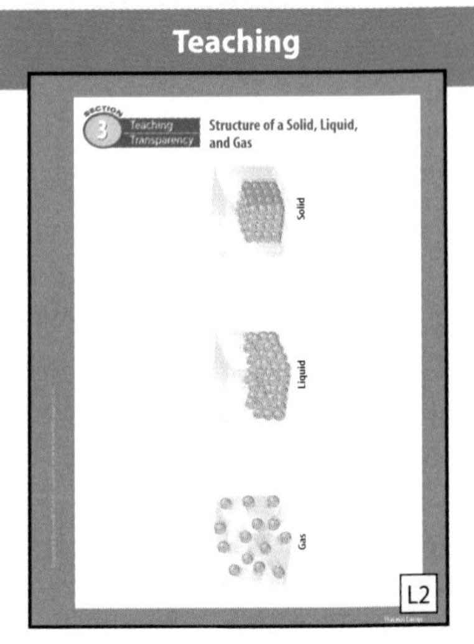
Section 3 Teaching Transparency **Structure of a Solid, Liquid, and Gas**

L2

Key to Teaching Strategies

The following designations will help you decide which activities are appropriate for your students.

- L1 Level 1 activities should be appropriate for students with learning difficulties.
- L2 Level 2 activities should be within the ability range of all students.
- L3 Level 3 activities are designed for above-average students.
- ELL ELL activities should be within the ability range of English Language Learners.
- COOP LEARN Cooperative Learning activities are designed for small group work.
- LS Multiple Learning Styles logos, as described on page 22T, are used throughout to indicate strategies that address different learning styles.
- P These strategies represent student products that can be placed into a best-work portfolio.

Hands-on Activities

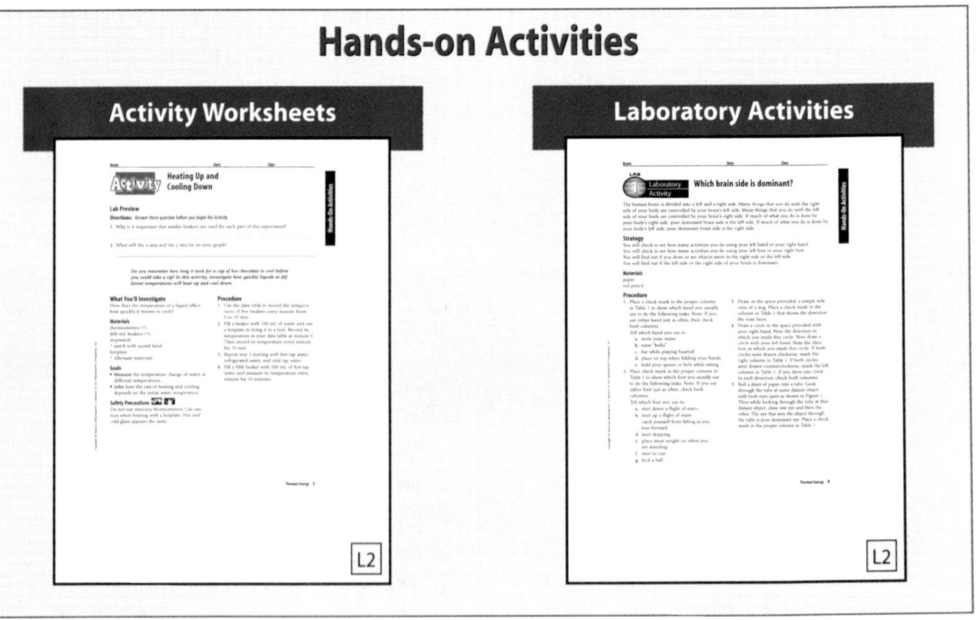
Activity Worksheets

Activity **Heating Up and Cooling Down**

L2

Laboratory Activities

Laboratory Activity **Which brain side is dominant?**

L2

Meeting Different Ability Levels

Content Outline

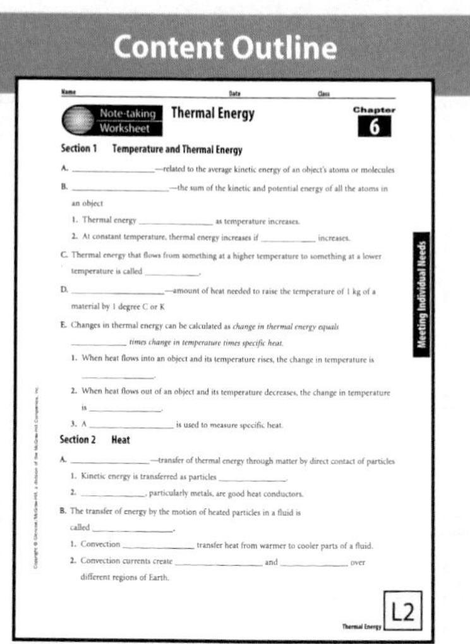

Reinforcement

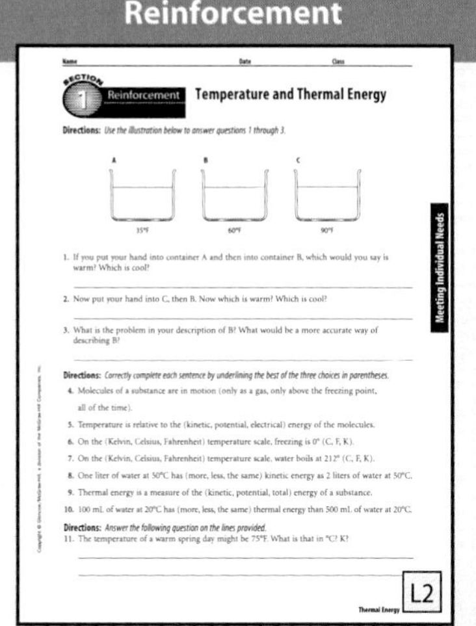

Directed Reading

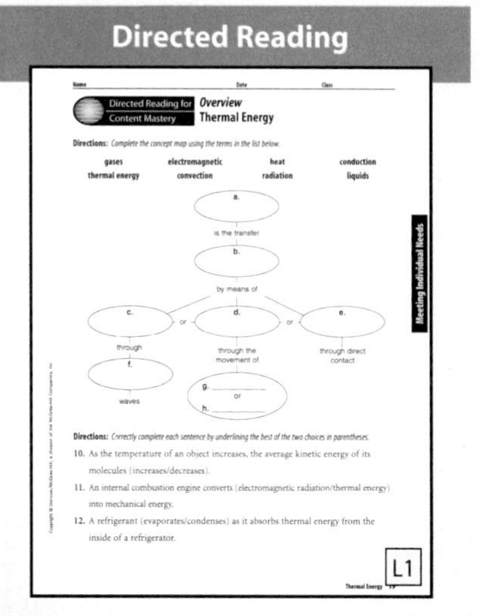

Assessment

Chapter Tests

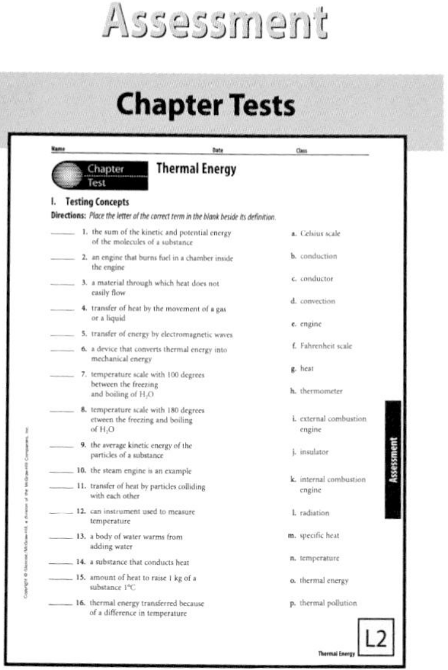

Enrichment

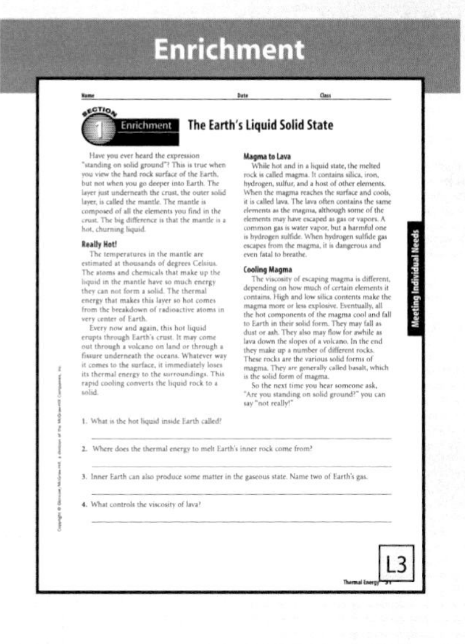

Spanish Directed Reading

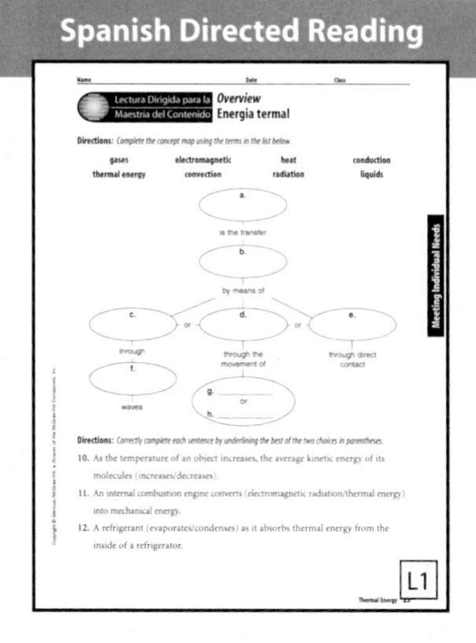

Test Practice Workbook

Chapter Review

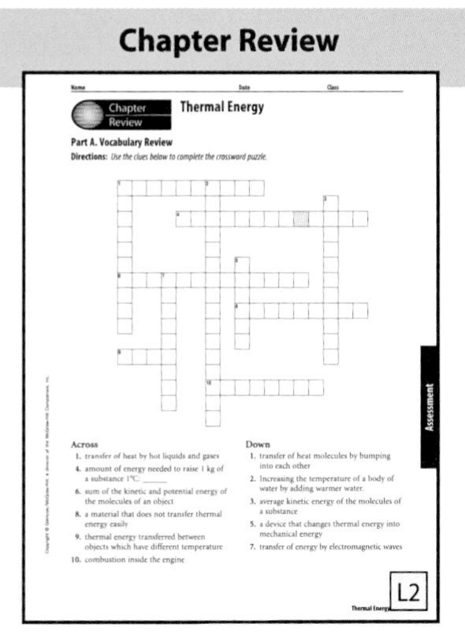

Science Content Background

SECTION 1 Temperature and Thermal Energy

What's Hot? What's Cold?

It's important to differentiate between temperature and thermal energy. A small rock at a temperature of 90°C has less thermal energy than a large boulder at a temperature of 80°C.

The common thermometer is a glass tube filled with a liquid that expands when heated. Digital thermometers, such as those put into children's ears, rely on the increases in electrical resistance with higher temperatures to determine temperature.

Three temperature scales are in common use around the world. Most people use the Celsius scale. People in the United States use the Fahrenheit scale. While U.S. scientists typically use the Celsius or Kelvin scales, the exception is found with many U.S. meteorologists who report weather data in Fahrenheit degrees.

The Kelvin scale is the official SI unit of temperature. Unlike the other two scales, it is impossible to have a negative Kelvin temperature. Kelvin allows for excellent comparisons between objects at different temperatures. With temperatures of 20 and 40° K, we can say that one temperature is twice as hot as the other. When comparing temperatures of 20° and 40° in either C or F, we cannot say that one is twice as hot as the other because these scales were created with arbitrary points of reference.

Fun Fact

Aluminum foil has one side that is shinier than the other. The shiny side reflects radiant heat better. So if you want something to stay cool, wrap it with the shiny side out. If you want something to stay warm, wrap it with the shiny side in.

Thermal Energy

The SI unit of thermal energy is the joule. The calorie is another frequently used unit. One calorie, equal to 4.184 joules, is the amount of heat needed to raise one gram of water one degree Celsius. This amount is so small that with food energy we use units of kilocalories (1,000 calories). We still call these units Calories, but with a capital C. So if a chocolate bar contains 150 Calories, it really has 150,000 calories, or 627,600 joules, of energy.

Superstock

SECTION 2 Heat

Heat and Thermal Energy

The term *thermodynamics* comes from Latin words that mean "heat flow." The First Law of Thermodynamics is simply the Law of Conservation of Energy applied to thermal energy. Thermal energy doesn't magically disappear or appear, it is transferred between objects or it is produced as a result of energy conversions.

Things don't share coldness, they share heat. So ice doesn't "give cold" to your drink, the ice is absorbs heat from your beverage. If you touch a piece of wood and piece of metal, both of which are at the same temperature, the metal feels colder. This is because the metal conducts heat away from your finger faster than does wood, causing a cold sensation.

Heat Absorption

Water has a very high specific heat. For example if you have one gram of water and one gram of aluminum and you add one calorie of heat to each, the water will increase in temperature by only one degree, while the aluminum will increase in temperature by five degrees.

States of Matter

Plasma, the fourth state of matter, is a highly ionized gas. It is rare on Earth but it is the most common state of matter in the universe. It occurs in stars and in interstellar space.

Changing States

Which contains more thermal energy: 100°C liquid water or 100°C steam? Anyone who was ever burned by steam knows the correct answer—steam! Thermal energy is the sum of both kinetic and potential energy. The steam, although at the same temperature as the liquid water, has more potential or latent energy. This is energy it absorbed in the phase change from a liquid to a gas.

Thermal Expansion

Unlike most materials that expand when heated, water that is 1, 2, or 3° C contracts when heated. Water is most dense at 4°C. This property is helpful to pond life because it means that in a pond covered with ice, fish can find a relatively warm spot of 4°C at the bottom.

SECTION 3 Engines and Refrigerators

Heat Engines

The expansion of gases when heated drives heat engines. The hot gases push a cylinder back, which drives a wheel.

Refrigerators

Refrigerators are the reverse of heat engines. In heat engines, heat is produced to do work. In refrigerators work is done to remove heat. In 1851 John Gorrie, a Florida Physician, received the first U.S. Patent for a refrigeration device. He was convinced that malaria could be stopped by making a room cold, so he invented the device to cool patient's hospital rooms.

For additional content background on this topic, go to the Glencoe Science Web site at science.glencoe.com.

Freon (CCl_2F_2) is the most widely used refrigerant in air conditioning and refrigeration units. However, when pipes rupture the liquid turns into a gas and escapes. Freon is a chlorofluorocarbon (CFC) that has been found to cause the depletion of the ozone layer. Presently other, non-CFC materials such as ammonia are being used as refrigerants.

Superstock

Thermal Energy

Chapter Vocabulary

temperature
thermal energy
heat
conduction
radiation
convection
conductor
specific heat
thermal pollution
engine
internal combustion engine

What do you think?

Science Journal The picture shows an old-fashioned version of a refrigerator called an icebox. Food was kept cool because melting ice removed heat from the box.

CHAPTER 10

Thermal Energy

On a sunny day you can feel the energy from the Sun as heat. The dishes shown here collect some of that energy and convert it into other forms of energy. How does heat energy travel through space? And how can heat energy be used to make cars move and refrigerate food? In this chapter you will learn about thermal energy and heat. You also will learn how heat is transferred from place to place and how the flow of heat can be controlled using different materials.

What do you think?

Science Journal Can you guess what this is a picture of? Here's a hint: *The one shown here is old, but you use a modern version of it every day.* In your Science Journal, write what you think it is and how you think it worked.

Theme Connection

Energy The thermal energy of a material is the sum of the kinetic and potential energy of its particles. Thermal energy can be used to do work in engines and refrigerators.

People spend a lot of time and money trapping heat. A substance that traps heat is called an insulator, and people use all kinds of insulators. They install fluffy insulation behind the walls of their homes to trap heat, wear coats with down feathers to trap their body heat, and pour hot drinks into insulated mugs. During this activity, you will compare the insulating properties of three different materials.

Compare insulators

1. Warm 300 mL of water on a hot plate without bringing the water to a boil.
2. Pour 100 mL of warm water into a paper cup, 100 mL into a plastic cup, and 100 mL into a polystyrene cup. The cups should be equal in size.
3. Cover each cup with aluminum foil and punch a thermometer through the foil lid of each cup and into the water.
4. Record the temperature of the water in each cup.
5. Place the cups in a refrigerator for 15 min.
6. Record the temperature of the water in each cup again.

Observe

Write a paragraph in your Science Journal comparing the insulating properties of the three materials.

Before You Read

Making a Main Ideas Study Fold **Make the following Foldable to help you identify the major topics about thermal energy.**

1. Place a sheet of paper in front of you so the short side is at the top. Fold the top third of the paper down and the bottom third up.
2. Open the paper and label the three sections *Temperature, Thermal Energy,* and *Heat.*
3. Before you read the chapter, write what you know about each on your Foldable. As you read the chapter, add to and correct what you have written.

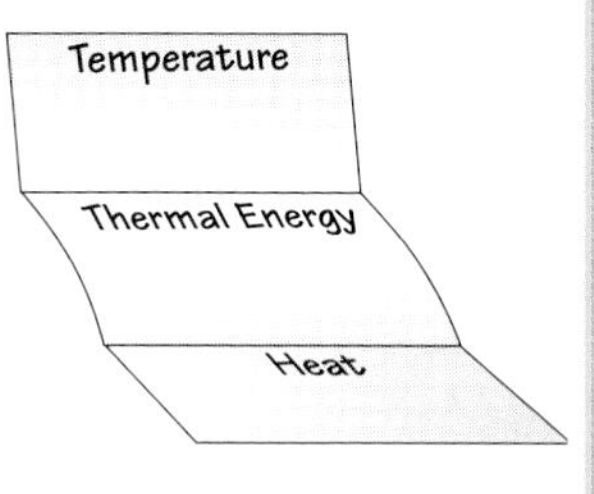

285

Before You Read

FOLDABLES Reading & Study Skills

Dinah Zike Study Fold

Purpose Students make a Foldable and use it to record what they know about temperature, thermal energy, and heat before, as, and after they read the chapter.

For additional help, see Foldables Worksheet, p. 17 in **Chapter Resources Booklet,** or go to the Glencoe Science Web site at **science.glencoe.com.** See After You Read in the Study Guide at the end of this chapter.

EXPLORE ACTIVITY

Purpose Use the Explore Activity to introduce students to the concept that some materials conduct heat better than others. L2 LS **Kinesthetic**

Preparation Purchase paper cups, plastic cups, polystyrene cups, and aluminum foil. Set up a hotplate for each group.

Materials hotplate, water, paper cup, plastic cup, polystyrene cup, sheet of aluminum foil, 3 thermometers, refrigerator

Teaching Strategy Divide the class into groups of three students. In each group, assign each student the task of preparing one of the cups of water.

Observe

The temperature of the water in the polystyrene cup decreases less than that of the water in the plastic or paper cups. This means that polystyrene is a better insulator.

Process Ask students to use materials in their homes to construct an insulator for a cup. Have students test their insulators using procedure of the Explore Activity. Use **Performance Assessment in the Science Classroom,** p. 97.

SECTION

Temperature and Thermal Energy

1 Motivate

Bellringer Transparency

Display the Section Focus Transparency for Section 1. Use the accompanying Transparency Activity Master. L2 ELL

Section Focus Transparency 1 — Coping With Winter

Japanese macaques are one of the few species of primates that can live outside of the tropics. These macaques live on Honshu Island in Japan.

1. What do you think the air temperature is like in this photo? What is the water temperature like? How do you know?
2. What accounts for the water's temperature?
3. If you were told that the temperature of the water was 40 degrees, would that be meaningful? Why or why not?

Thermal Energy

Tie to Prior Knowledge

Ask students what the temperature would be on a warm day. They will probably say about 85°. Explain that 85°F is about 29° on the Celsius scale. In this section students will learn about temperature scales and how temperature is related to energy.

SECTION

Temperature and Thermal Energy

As You Read

What **You'll Learn**

- **Explain** how temperature is related to kinetic energy.
- **Describe** three scales used for measuring temperature.
- **Define** thermal energy.

Vocabulary

temperature
thermal energy

Why **It's Important**

Temperature and thermal energy influence the movement of heat in the environment.

What's Hot? What's Cold?

Imagine it's a hot day and you jump into a swimming pool to cool off. When you first hit the water, you might think it feels cold. Perhaps someone else, who has been swimming for a few minutes, thinks the water feels warm. When you swim in water, touch a hot pan, or swallow a cold drink, your sense of touch tells you whether something is hot or cold. However, the words *cold, warm,* and *hot* can mean different things to different people.

Temperature How hot or cold something feels is related to its temperature. To understand temperature, think of a glass of water sitting on a table. The water might seem perfectly still, but is it? **Figure 1** shows that water is made of molecules that are in constant motion. Because these molecules are always moving, they have energy of motion, or kinetic energy.

However, all water molecules don't move at the same speed. Some are moving faster and some are moving slower. **Temperature** is a measure of the average value of the kinetic energy of the molecules in a substance. The more kinetic energy the molecules have, the higher the temperature. Molecules have more kinetic energy when they are moving faster. So the higher the temperature, the faster the molecules are moving, as shown in **Figure 1.**

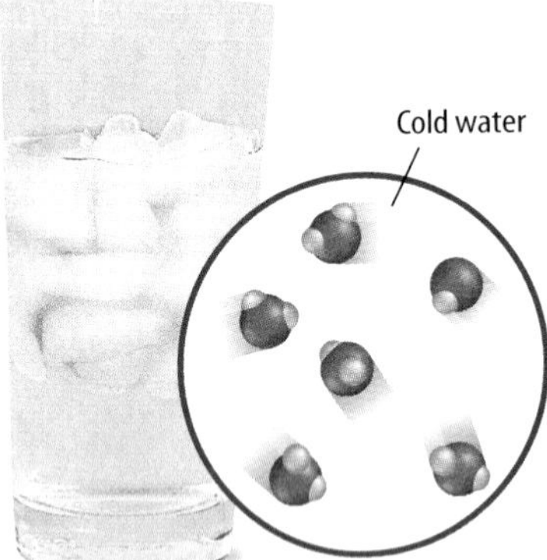

Figure 1
The temperature of a substance depends on how fast its molecules are moving. Water molecules are moving faster in the hot water on the left than in the cold water on the right.

Section Assessment Planner

PORTFOLIO
Use Science Words, p. 288

PERFORMANCE ASSESSMENT
Math Skills Activity, p. 288
Skill Builder Activities, p. 289
See page 308 for more options.

CONTENT ASSESSMENT
Section, p. 289
Challenge, p. 289
Chapter, pp. 308–309

286 CHAPTER 10 Thermal Energy

Thermal Expansion It wasn't an earthquake that caused the road to buckle in **Figure 2.** Hot weather caused the concrete to expand so much that it cracked, and the pieces squeezed each other upward. When the temperature of an object is increased, its molecules speed up and tend to move farther apart. This causes the object to expand. When the object is cooled, its molecules slow down and move closer together. This causes the object to shrink, or contract.

Almost all substances expand when they are heated and contract when they are cooled. The amount of expansion or contraction depends on the type of material and the change in temperature. For example, liquids usually expand more than solids. Also, the greater the change in temperature, the more an object expands or contracts.

Why do materials expand when their temperatures increase?

Figure 2
Most objects expand as their temperatures increase. Pieces of this concrete road forced each other upward when the concrete expanded on a hot day.

Measuring Temperature

The temperature of an object depends on the kinetic energy of all the molecules in an object. However, molecules are so small and objects contain so many of them, that it is impossible to measure the kinetic energy of all the individual molecules.

Instead, a practical way to measure temperature is to use a thermometer. Thermometers usually use the expansion and contraction of materials to measure temperature. One common type of thermometer uses a glass tube containing a liquid. When the temperature of the liquid increases, it expands so that the height of the liquid in the tube depends on the temperature.

Temperature Scales To be able to give a number for the temperature, a thermometer has to have a temperature scale. Two common temperature scales are the Fahrenheit and Celsius scales, shown in **Figure 3.**

On the Fahrenheit scale, the freezing point of water is given the temperature 32°F and the boiling point 212°F. The space between the boiling point and the freezing point is divided into 180 equal degrees. The Fahrenheit scale is used mainly in the United States and Canada.

On the Celsius temperature scale, the freezing point of water is given the temperature 0°C and the boiling point is given the temperature 100°C. Because there are only 100 Celsius degrees between the boiling and freezing point of water, Celsius degrees are bigger than Fahrenheit degrees. Which is warmer, 50°F or 50°C?

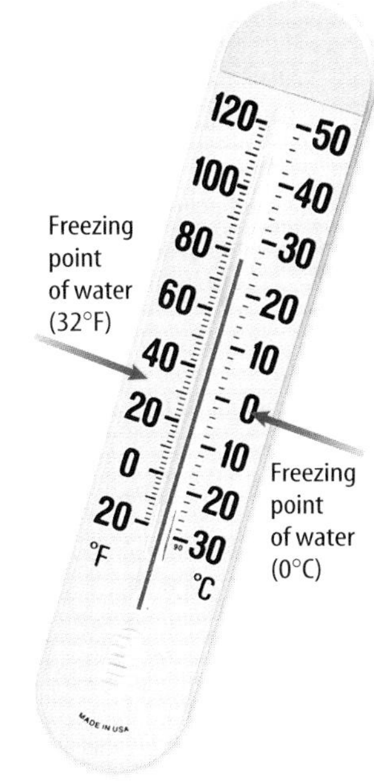

Figure 3
The Fahrenheit and Celsius scales are the most commonly used temperature scales. *Which has the most degrees between the boiling and freezing points of water?*

2 Teach

What's hot? What's cold?

Reading Check

Answer When the temperature of an object is increased, its molecules speed up and tend to move farther apart.

Measuring Temperature

Extension

Many liquid thermometers use mercury or alcohol. Have students investigate why these liquids are used instead of water. The volume of both mercury and alcohol changes uniformly over the measured temperatures, and neither alcohol nor mercury sticks to the glass tube. Water cannot be used because its molecular structure causes its volume to increase as its temperature decreases from 4°C to 0°C. Also, water freezes at 0°C, so thermometers using it would not be able to measure below that point. L2 LS **Linguistic**

Use an Analogy

Use a comparison with a sponge to explain thermal expansion. When dry, the sponge is shriveled, but when you add water, it gets larger. Similarly, when you add thermal energy to a solid material, its volume increases.

Caption Answer

Figure 3 the Fahrenheit scale

Visual Learning

Figure 3 Point out the liquid in the thermometer that indicates the temperature. **What temperature does this thermometer show in °F?** about 78°F **In celsius?** about 26°C
L2 LS **Visual-Spatial**

Text Question Answer

50°C is warmer.

Resource Manager

Chapter Resources Booklet
- Transparency Activity, p. 44
- Directed Reading for Content Mastery, pp. 19, 20
- Note-taking Worksheets, pp. 33–35

Curriculum Connection

Music Like many other objects, musical instruments undergo thermal expansion. Have students find out what problems this causes for musicians. Thermal expansion and contraction cause the vibrating parts of instruments, including the strings of stringed instruments, to change size. This changes the rate at which they vibrate, causing the instruments to go out of tune.
L2 LS **Linguistic**

Fun Fact

A degree on the Kelvin scale is called a kelvin and is designated by the symbol K (not °K). The kelvin is the official SI unit for measuring temperature.

Use Science Words

Word Meaning Have students find out why the three temperature scales discussed in this section are called the Fahrenheit, Celsius, and Kelvin scales. Ask them to write their findings in their Science Journals. The Fahrenheit scale was developed by the German physicist Daniel Gabriel Fahrenheit in 1724. The Celsius scale was developed by Anders Celsius in 1742. The Kelvin scale was proposed by Lord Kelvin (William Thomson) in 1848. L2 ELL LS Linguistic P

Extension

If the temperature of a liquid is 8°C, what is its temperature on the Fahrenheit scale? 46.4°F **On the Kelvin scale?** 281 K

Math Skills Activity

National Math Standards

Correlation to Mathematics Objectives

1, 2, 4, 6, 9, 10

Answer to Practice Problem

98.6 − 32 = 66.6
66.6 × 5 = 333.0
333.0 ÷ 9 = 37.0
98.6 °F = 37.0 °C

Converting Fahrenheit and Celsius Temperatures on the Fahrenheit scale can be converted to Celsius temperatures using this formula.

$$°C = \left(\frac{5}{9}\right)(°F - 32)$$

For example, to convert 68°F to Celsius, first subtract 32, multiply by 5, then divide by 9. The result is 20°C.

The Kelvin Scale Another temperature scale that is sometimes used is the Kelvin Scale. On this scale, 0 K is the lowest temperature an object can have. This temperature is known as absolute zero. The size of a degree on the Kelvin scale is the same as on the Celsius scale. You can change from Kelvin degrees to Celsius degrees by subtracting 273 from the Kelvin temperature.

$$°C = K - 273$$

Math Skills Activity

Converting Fahrenheit to Celsius Temperatures

Example Problem

On the a hot summer day, a Fahrenheit thermometer shows the temperature to be 86°F. What is this temperature on the Celsius scale?

Solution

1. *This is what you know:* Fahrenheit temperature: °F = 86
2. *This is what you need to know:* Celsius temperature: °C
3. *This is the equation you need to use:* $°C = \left(\frac{5}{9}\right)(°F - 32)$
4. *Substitute the known values:* $°C = \left(\frac{5}{9}\right)(86 - 32)$ $= \left(\frac{5}{9}\right)(54) = 30$

Check your answer by multiplying it by $\frac{9}{5}$ and adding 32.

Do you calculate the same temperature that was given?

Practice Problem

A person's body temperature is 98.6°F. What is this temperature on the Celsius scale?

For more help, refer to the Math Skill Handbook.

Resource Manager

Chapter Resources Booklet
- Lab Activity, pp. 9–12
- Enrichment, p. 30
- Reinforcement, p. 27

Mathematics Skill Activities, p. 11

Teacher FYI

Scientists often say that at absolute zero all molecular motion stops. In fact, at absolute zero molecules still have vibrational energy known as zero point energy.

288 CHAPTER 10 Thermal Energy

Thermal Energy

The temperature of an object is related to the average kinetic energy of its molecules. But molecules also have potential energy. Potential energy is energy that the molecules have that can be converted into kinetic energy. The sum of the kinetic and potential energy of all the molecules in an object is the **thermal energy** of the object.

The Potential Energy of Molecules When you hold a ball above the ground, it has potential energy. When you drop the ball, its potential energy is converted into kinetic energy as the ball falls toward Earth. It is the attractive force of gravity between Earth and the ball that gives the ball potential energy.

The molecules in a material also exert attractive forces on each other. As a result, the molecules in a material have potential energy. As the molecules get closer together or farther apart, their potential energy changes.

Increasing Thermal Energy Temperature and thermal energy are different. Suppose you have two glasses with the same amount of milk, and at the same temperature. If you pour both glasses of milk into a pitcher, as shown in **Figure 4,** the temperature of the milk won't change. However, because there are more molecules of milk in the pitcher, the thermal energy of the milk in the pitcher is greater. Because the amount of milk doubled, the thermal energy of the milk doubled.

Figure 4
When two substances of equal temperature are combined, the temperature remains the same, but the thermal energy increases.

Section  Assessment

1. Explain the difference between temperature and thermal energy.
2. Write a formula for converting from Fahrenheit to Kelvin.
3. How are temperature and kinetic energy related?
4. How does a thermometer use the thermal expansion of a material to measure temperature?
5. **Think Critically** You have two identical bottles of soda. One is placed in the Sun, the other in an ice chest. Which has more thermal energy? Explain.

Skill Builder Activities

6. **Making and Using Tables** Make a table showing the Fahrenheit, Celsius, and Kelvin temperature of the following: *normal body temperature, air temperature on a summer day,* and *air temperature on a winter day.* **For more help, refer to the Science Skill Handbook.**
7. **Solving One-Step Equations** The turkey you're cooking for dinner will be ready when it reaches an internal temperature of 180°F. Convert this temperature to °C and K. **For more help, refer to the Math Skill Handbook.**

Thermal Energy

Fun Fact

Thermal energy is frequently called internal energy.

3 Assess

Reteach

Have students work in pairs using the Internet and other reference sources to determine the typical daytime temperature in your community for each season. Ask them to give the temperatures in Fahrenheit, Celsius, and Kelvin. L2 LS **Naturalist**

Challenge

Have students work in small groups to design a temperature scale based on something other than the boiling and freezing points of water. L3 LS **Logical-Mathematical**

✔Assessment

Oral Have small groups of students practice converting between Fahrenheit and Celsius. One student will say a Fahrenheit temperature and see which of the other students can first calculate the temperature in Celsius. Use **PASC,** p. 101.

Answers to Section Assessment

1. Temperature is the average kinetic energy of the particles in matter. Thermal energy is the total kinetic and potential energy of the particles.
2. $K = (5/9) \times (°F - 32) + 273$
3. Temperature is the average kinetic energy of the particles in matter.
4. As the temperature increases, molecules in a material move faster, causing the material to expand and indicate the temperature.
5. The bottle in the Sun has more thermal energy. Radiation from the Sun transfers thermal energy to the bottle of soda in the Sun, while the bottle of soda in the ice chest transfers thermal energy to the ice.
6. Normal body temperature is about 98.6°F, 37°C, and 310 K. A summer day is about 85°F, 29°C, and 302 K. A winter day is about 35°F, 2°C, and 275 K.
7. 82.2°C; 355.2K

SECTION

Heat

1 Motivate

Bellringer Transparency

Display the Section Focus Transparency for Section 2. Use the accompanying Transparency Activity Master. L2 ELL

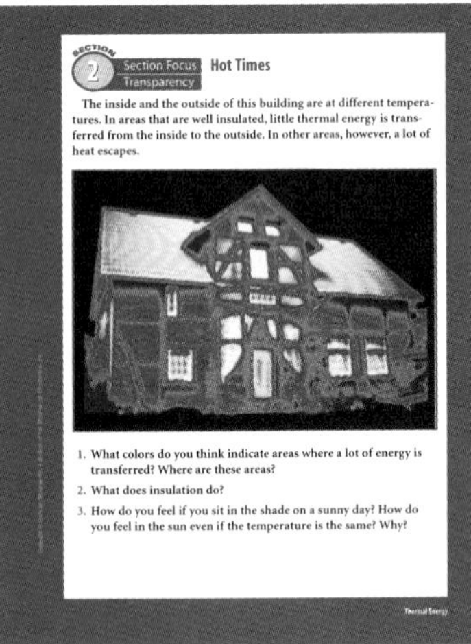

SECTION 2 Section Focus Transparency **Hot Times**

The inside and the outside of this building are at different temperatures. In areas that are well insulated, little thermal energy is transferred from the inside to the outside. In other areas, however, a lot of heat escapes.

1. What colors do you think indicate areas where a lot of energy is transferred? Where are these areas?
2. What does insulation do?
3. How do you feel if you sit in the shade on a sunny day? How do you feel in the sun even if the temperature is the same? Why?

Thermal Energy

Tie to Prior Knowledge

Ask students to name some ways things are heated. They might mention heating food in a microwave, a furnace heating a home, or heat from the Sun on a summer day. This section explores heat and the ways thermal energy is transferred.

SECTION

Heat

As You Read

What You'll Learn

- **Explain** the difference between thermal energy and heat.
- **Describe** three ways heat is transferred.
- **Identify** materials that are insulators or conductors.

Vocabulary

heat
conduction
radiation
convection
conductor
specific heat
thermal pollution

Why It's Important

A knowledge of heat and how it is transferred will help you learn to use energy more efficiently.

Heat and Thermal Energy

It's the heat of the day. Heat the oven to 375°F. A heat wave has hit the Midwest. You've often heard the word *heat,* but what is it? Is it something you can see? Can an object have heat? Is heat anything like thermal energy? **Heat** is thermal energy that is transferred from one object to another when the objects are at different temperatures. The amount of heat that is transferred when two objects are brought into contact depends on the difference in temperature between the objects.

For example, no heat is transferred when two pots of boiling water are touching, because the water in both pots is at the same temperature. However, heat is transferred from a pot of boiling water that touches a pot full of ice water. The boiling water cools down and the ice water gets hotter. **Figure 5** shows how heat is transferred only when the boiling water touches something cooler.

Transfer of Heat When heat is transferred, thermal energy always moves from warmer to cooler objects. Heat never flows from a cooler object to a warmer object. The warmer object loses thermal energy and becomes cooler as the cooler object gains thermal energy and becomes warmer. This process of heat transfer can occur in three ways—by conduction, radiation, or convection.

Figure 5
Heat is transferred only when two objects are at different temperatures. Heat always moves from the warmer object to the cooler object.

Section Assessment Planner

PORTFOLIO
Active Reading, p. 292

PERFORMANCE ASSESSMENT
Try At Home MiniLAB, p. 292
MiniLAB, p. 293
Skill Builder Activities, p. 295
See page 308 for more options.

CONTENT ASSESSMENT
Section, p. 295
Challenge, p. 295
Chapter, pp. 308–309

Conduction When you eat hot pizza, you experience conduction. As the hot pizza touches your mouth, heat moves from the pizza to your mouth. This transfer of heat by direct contact is called **conduction.** Conduction occurs when the particles of one substance collide with the particles of another substance and transfer some kinetic energy.

Imagine holding an ice cube in your hand, as in **Figure 6.** The faster-moving molecules in your warm hand bump against the slower-moving molecules in the cold ice. In these collisions, energy is passed from molecule to molecule. Heat flows from your warmer hand to the colder ice, and the slow-moving molecules in the ice move faster. As a result, the ice becomes warmer and its temperature increases. Molecules in your hand move more slowly as they lose thermal energy, and your hand becomes cooler.

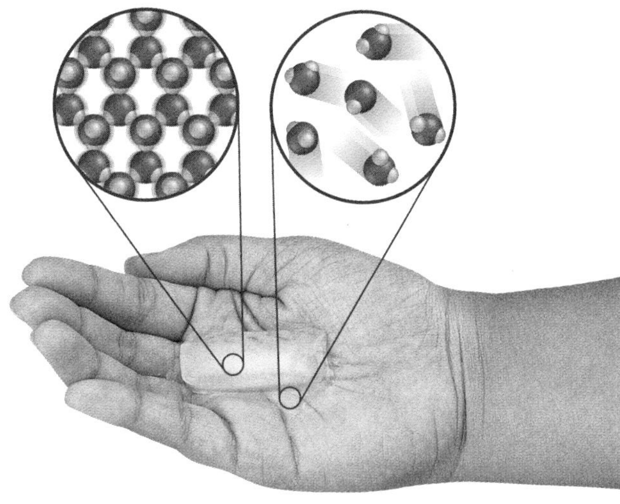

Figure 6
An ice cube in your hand melts because of conduction. *What is being transferred as the ice cube melts?*

Conduction occurs most easily in solids, where the bonds between atoms and molecules keep them close together. Because they are so close together, atoms and molecules in a solid need to move only a short distance before they bump into one another and transfer energy.

✔ Reading Check *Why does conduction occur easily in solids?*

Radiation On a beautiful, clear day, you walk outside and notice the warmth of the Sun. You know that the Sun heats Earth, but how does this transfer of thermal energy occur? The heat transfer does not occur by conduction, because almost no matter exists between the Sun and Earth. Instead, heat is transferred from the Sun to Earth by radiation. Heat transfer by **radiation** occurs when energy is transferred by electromagnetic waves. These invisible waves carry energy through empty space, as well as through matter. The transfer of thermal energy by radiation can occur in empty space, as well as in solids, liquids, and gases.

The Sun is not the only source of radiation. All objects emit electromagnetic radiation, although warm objects emit more radiation than cool objects. The warmth you feel when you sit next to a fireplace is due to heat transferred by radiation from the fire to your skin.

2 Teach

Heat and Thermal Energy

IDENTIFYING Misconceptions

Students may think that an object can have heat. Stress that heat is energy that is transferred from one object to another. Before and after it is transferred, it is thermal energy.

Activity

To demonstrate the difference between thermal energy and heat, cut out several large cardboard circles. On one side of each circle write "thermal energy," and on the other side write "heat." Have two groups of students stand near each other. Have one group hold cards with the "thermal energy" side showing. Then have the group pass the cards to the other group. During the transfer, the "heat" side should be showing. When the other group receives the cards, they should be turned again to show the "thermal energy" side. L2 LS **Kinesthetic**

Caption Answer

Figure 6 Thermal energy moves from your hand to the ice.

✔ Reading Check

Answer The atoms and molecules are close to one another.

Teacher FYI

The wavelength of electromagnetic radiation an object emits is determined in part by its temperature. Objects at higher temperatures emit radiation with shorter wavelengths, and objects at lower temperatures emit radiation with longer wavelengths. Heat radiation is in the range of infrared wavelengths.

Resource Manager

Chapter Resources Booklet
Transparency Activity, p. 45
Directed Reading for Content Mastery, p. 20

Heat and Thermal Energy, continued

Purpose Students observe the effect of ice water on melting ice. L2 IN **Kinesthetic**

Materials glass, ice, water, 2 coffee cups, timer

Teaching Strategy If possible, use clear cups so students can watch the ice melt.

Analysis

1. The ice cube in the ice water melted faster. Ice water is a poor insulator.
2. Air is a better insulator. The molecules in air are farther apart than those in water, so they don't collide as often and therefore they don't transfer thermal energy as fast.

Process Have students write up their results as lab reports. Suggest they include illustrations. Use **Performance Assessment in the Science Classroom,** p. 119.

Discussion

Why do you sometimes think you see a layer of water on a hot road in the summer? The hot road warms the air just above it. What appears to be water is light reflecting off the layer of warm air that is rising because of convection. L3 IN **Logical-Mathematical**

Extension

Have students research to find how convection acts inside Earth. Radioactive decay of materials within Earth produces thermal energy that is transferred by convection through molten rock in Earth's outer core and mantle. L3 IN **Linguistic**

Comparing Rates of Melting

Procedure

1. Prepare ice water by filling a glass with ice, and then adding water. Let the glass sit until all the ice melts.
2. Place an ice cube in a coffee cup.
3. Place a similar-sized ice cube in another coffee cup and add ice water to a depth of about 1 cm.
4. Time how long it takes both ice cubes to melt.

Analysis

1. Which ice cube melted fastest? Why?
2. Is air or water a better insulator? Explain.

Convection When you heat a pot of water on a stove, heat can be transferred through the water by another process besides conduction and radiation. In a gas or liquid, molecules can move much more easily then they can in a solid. As a result, the more energetic molecules can travel from one place to another, and carry their energy along with them. This transfer of thermal energy by the movement of molecules from one part of a material to another is called **convection.**

Transferring Heat by Convection As a pot of water is heated, heat is transferred by convection. First, thermal energy is transferred to the water molecules at the bottom of the pot from the stove. These water molecules move faster as their thermal energy increases. The faster-moving molecules tend to be farther apart than the slower-moving molecules in the cooler water above. Because the molecules are farther apart in the warm water, this water is less dense than the cooler water. As a result, the warm water rises and is replaced at the bottom of the pot by cooler water. The cooler water is heated, rises, and the cycle is repeated until all the water in the pan is at the same temperature.

Natural Convection Convection can occur naturally when hot gas or liquid naturally moves from one place to another. For example, imagine the shore of a lake. During the day, the water is cooler than the land. As shown in **Figure 7,** air above the warm land is heated by conduction. When the air gets hotter, its particles move faster and get farther from each other, making the air less dense. The cooler, denser air from over the lake flows in over the land, pushing the less dense air upward. You feel this movement of incoming cool air as wind. The cooler air then is heated by the land and also begins to rise.

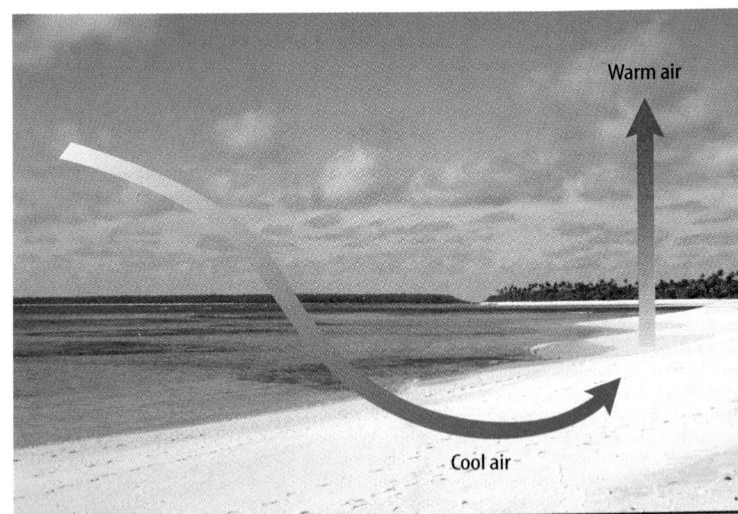

Figure 7
Wind movement near a lake or ocean results from natural convection. Air is heated by the land and becomes less dense. Denser cool air rushes in, pushing the warm air up. The cooler air then is heated by the land and rises and the cycle is repeated.

292 CHAPTER 10 Thermal Energy

Active Reading

Cause-and-Effect Chart This strategy is used to focus on cause-and-effect reasoning. In the center, students write the topic that they are trying to understand. On the left side, they write the apparent causes of the topic. On the right side, they write the apparent effects of the topic. Have students design a Cause-and-Effect chart for convection. 

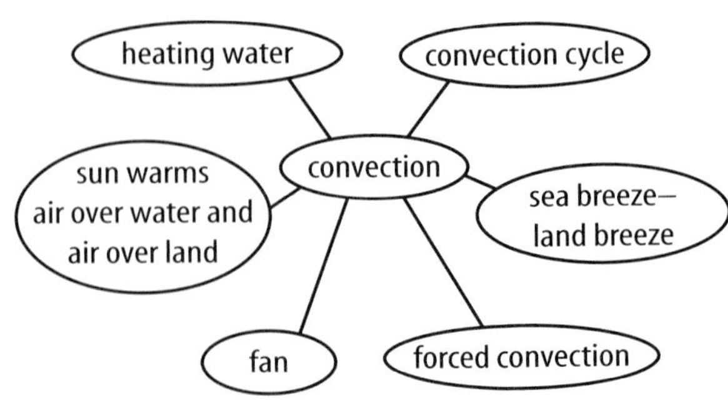

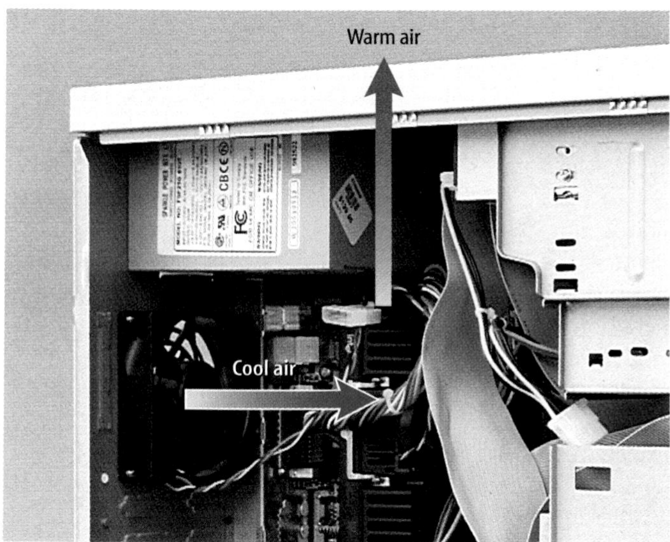

Figure 8
This computer uses forced convection to keep the electronic components surrounded by cooler air.

Forced Convection Sometimes convection can be forced. Forced convection occurs when an outside force pushes the air to make it move and transfer heat. A fan is one type of device that is used to move air. For example, computers use fans to keep their electrical components from getting too hot, which can damage them. The fan blows cool air onto the hot electronic components, as shown in **Figure 8.** Heat from the electronic components is transferred to the air around them by conduction. The warm air is pushed away as cool air rushes in. The hot components then continue to lose heat as the fan blows cool air over them.

Thermal Conductors

Why are cooking pans usually made of metal? Why does the handle of a metal spoon in a bowl of hot soup become warm? The answer to both questions is that metal is a good conductor. A **conductor** is any material that easily transfers heat. Some materials are good conductors because of the types of atoms they contain.

Reading Check *What is a conductor?*

Remember that an atom has a nucleus surrounded by one or more electrons. Certain materials, such as metals, have some electrons that are not held tightly by the nucleus and are freer to move around. These loosely held electrons can bump into other atoms and help transfer thermal energy. The best conductors of heat are metals such as gold and copper.

Mini LAB

Observing Convection

Procedure

1. Fill a **250-mL beaker** with room-temperature **water** and let it stand undisturbed for at least 1 min.
2. Using a **hot plate,** heat a small amount of water in a **50-mL beaker** until it is almost boiling.
WARNING: *Do not touch the heated hot plate.*
3. Carefully drop a **penny** into the hot water and let it stand for about 1 min.
4. Take the penny out of the hot water with **metal tongs** and place it on a table. Immediately place the 250-mL beaker on the penny.
5. Using a **dropper,** gently place one drop of **food coloring** on the bottom of the 250-mL beaker of water.
6. Observe what happens in the beaker for several minutes.

Analysis

1. What happened when you placed the food coloring in the 250-mL beaker? Why?

Purpose Students observe convection. L2 LS **Kinesthetic**

Materials 250-mL beaker, hot plate, water, 50-mL beaker, penny, tweezers, dropper, food coloring

Teaching Strategy Students should observe that the column of water directly above the penny (the heat source) is most affected by the convection currents.

Safety Precautions Remind students not to touch the hot plate.

Troubleshooting Be sure that the water is as still as possible when adding the food coloring.

Analysis

1. A column of colored water rose through the clear water then fell on the sides. The hot water is much less dense than the cool water, so the hot water rose.

Process Ask students to predict what would happen to the water in the beaker if they continued to apply thermal energy only to the center part. The food coloring would be completely mixed in so that all of the water would become colored. Use **PASC,** p. 89.

Thermal Conductors

Reading Check

Answer any material that easily transfers thermal energy

Resource Manager

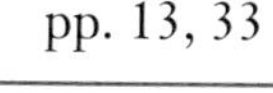

Chapter Resources Booklet
MiniLABs, pp. 3, 4
Lab Activity, pp. 13–16

Reading and Writing Skill Activities, pp. 13, 33

Visual Learning

Figure 8 In order for forced convection to be possible, the computer must be designed to allow sufficient air flow. Have students describe how this is done in this picture. Ask students to suggest an alternate method for dissipating thermal energy in computers. Some computers are designed to use natural, rather than forced, convection. L2 LS **Visual-Spatial**

Thermal Insulators

A polar bear's long, outer "guard hairs" are hollow in order to trap heat from the Sun. A thick undercoat of fur provides insulation, and the bear's black skin absorbs heat from the guard hairs. Blubber is a layer of fat cells and connective tissue that serves as insulation to retain body heat.

Activity

Have students work in small groups to devise ways to keep a beaker of hot water from cooling. Conduct a contest to see which group's method works the best. L2 ELL COOP LEARN

LS **Interpersonal**

Heat Absorption

Make a Model

Have students work in small groups to make models of an energy-efficient room. Ceilings of the rooms should be removable so students can demonstrate and explain the design to the rest of the class. Students should be encouraged to use what they have learned about the transfer of thermal energy, insulators, and conductors in their designs. Models can be tested and compared by heating them with a strong lamp and measuring the loss of thermal energy over a period of time. L3 ELL COOP LEARN LS **Kinesthetic**

Life Science INTEGRATION

To survive in its arctic environment, a polar bear needs good insulation against the cold. Underneath its fur, a polar bear has 10 cm of insulating blubber. Research how blubber helps insulate the polar bear from the cold air and write your findings in your Science Journal.

Thermal Insulators

If you're cooking food, you want the pan to conduct heat easily from the stove to your food, but you do not want the heat to move easily to the handle of the pan. An insulator is a material in which heat doesn't flow easily. Most pans have handles that are made from insulators. Liquids and gases are usually better insulators than solids are. Air is a good insulator, and insulating materials usually are filled with air spaces to reduce heat loss by conduction. Materials that are good conductors, such as metals, are poor insulators, and poor conductors usually are good insulators.

Houses and buildings are made with insulating materials to reduce heat conduction between the inside and outside. Fluffy insulation like that shown in **Figure 9** is put in the walls. Some windows have double layers of glass that sandwich a layer of air or other insulating gas. This reduces the outward flow of heat in the winter and the inward flow of heat in the summer.

Heat Absorption

On a hot day, you can walk barefoot across the lawn, but the asphalt pavement of a street or driveway is too hot to walk on. Why is the pavement hotter than the grass? All objects absorb heat at different rates, depending on the materials they are made of.

Figure 9
The insulation in houses and buildings helps stop the transfer of heat between the air inside and air outside.

Specific Heat The amount of heat needed to change the temperature of a substance is related to its specific heat. The **specific heat** of a substance is the amount of heat needed to raise the temperature of 1 kg of that substance by 1°C.

More heat is needed to change the temperature of a material with a high specific heat than one with a low specific heat. For example, the sand on a beach has a lower specific heat than water has. When you're at the beach during the day, the sand feels much warmer than the water does. Radiation from the Sun warms the sand and the water. Because of its lower specific heat, the sand heats up faster than the water. At night, however, the sand feels cool and the water feels warmer. The temperature of the water changes more slowly than the temperature of the sand as they lose thermal energy to the cooler night air.

LAB DEMONSTRATION

Purpose to observe how water conducts thermal energy away from a container so that it doesn't overheat and burn

Materials balloon; water; candle flame; sheet of paper cut, folded, and taped into a paper box with top open and all edges sealed with tape

Procedure Fill the balloon with water. Place the candle flame directly in contact the with balloon. You may hold it there for some time. Fill the paper box with water and hold the flame in contact with the box.

Expected Outcome The balloon and the box will get warm, but they do not ignite.

The candle flame was very hot. Why didn't it catch the paper or balloon on fire? The water conducted the thermal energy away from the balloon and the paper. Water has a high specific heat, and it absorbed the thermal energy from the flame.

294 CHAPTER 10 Thermal Energy

Thermal Pollution

Some electric power plants and factories often produce hot water as a by-product. If this hot water is released into a nearby ocean, lake, or river, it will raise the temperature of the water nearby. This increase in the temperature of a body of water caused by adding warmer water is called **thermal pollution.** Rainwater that is heated after it falls on warm roads or parking lots also can cause thermal pollution if it runs off into a river or lake.

Effects of Thermal Pollution Increasing the water temperature causes fish and other aquatic organisms to use more oxygen. Because warmer water contains less dissolved oxygen than cooler water, some organisms can die due to a lack of oxygen. Also, in warmer water, many organisms become more sensitive to chemical pollutants, parasites, and diseases.

Reducing Thermal Pollution Thermal pollution can be reduced by cooling the warm water produced by factories, power plants, and runoff before it is released into a body of water. Cooling towers like the ones shown in **Figure 10** are used to cool the water from some power plants and factories. In some places the warm water is held in cooling ponds where it cools before it is released.

Figure 10
This power plant uses cooling towers to cool its waste water before releasing into the lake.

Section 2 Assessment

1. Why isn't it correct to say that an object has heat?
2. Describe the three ways that heat can be transferred.
3. Look around your classroom and name some objects that are good insulators and some that are good conductors.
4. Will an object with a high specific heat or a low specific heat absorb more heat before it changes temperature?
5. **Think Critically** Is it better to have heating vents in your home near the floor or near the ceiling? Why?

Skill Builder Activities

6. **Recognizing Cause and Effect** England and southern Canada are at about the same latitude, and yet they have different climates. Canada has cold winters, but England has only cool winters because of a nearby warm ocean current. Use what you've learned about heat transfer to explain this effect. **For more help, refer to the Science Skill Handbook.**
7. **Communicating** In your Science Journal, describe several examples of heat transfer by conduction in your everyday life. **For more help, refer to the Science Skill Handbook.**

3 Assess

Reteach

Have students identify ways that knowledge about the heat absorption properties of materials can be used in their everyday lives. Possible answers: it can help them choose the best colors of clothing to wear in summer, and whether to sit on a plastic bench or a wooden bench on a hot summer day. L2

LS **Logical-Mathematical**

Challenge

Have students use what they have learned about conductivity to explain why stainless steel pans often have a copper coating on the bottom. Copper has a high conductivity, so it provides even cooking. L3

LS **Logical-Mathematical**

Process Show pictures illustrating the transfer of thermal energy, such as boiling water or people warming themselves near an open fire. Have students explain how thermal energy is transferred in each picture. Use **Performance Assessment in the Science Classroom,** p. 89.

Answers to Section Assessment

1. An object has thermal energy. Heat is thermal energy that is transferred from one object to another.
2. Conduction is the transfer of thermal energy by direct contact of particles. Convection transfers thermal energy by movement of fluids from one place to another. Radiation is the transfer of thermal energy by electromagnetic waves.
3. possible insulators: brick wall, air; possible conductors: anything metal
4. an object with high specific heat
5. Near the floor; if the vents are near the ceiling, the hot air will tend to stay near the ceiling. If the vents are near the floor, the hot air will rise and heat the entire room.
6. The warm ocean current near England warms the nearby air, which flows over England.
7. Students might mention ice melting in a glass of tea, the warmth you feel when you hold a cup of hot cocoa, or the heat you feel when you lean against a car on a hot day.

Resource Manager

Chapter Resources Booklet
Enrichment, p. 31
Reinforcement, p. 28
Activity Worksheet, pp. 5–6

Activity

BENCH TESTED

Purpose Students observe how the initial temperature of a liquid affects how quickly it warms or cools.

Process Skills observing, comparing, measuring in SI, making and using tables, recording data, making and using graphs, inferring

Time Required 45 minutes

Safety Precautions Caution students to use oven mitts when removing hot beakers from the plate.

Teaching Strategies

- Remind students to fill each beaker to exactly the 100-mL line.
- Students should turn on the hotplate and allow it to heat up before placing the first beaker of water on the hotplate. Remind students NOT to change the heat setting on the hotplate.
- Suggest students use different colored pencils to plot each of the five lines on the graph.

Answers to Questions

1. Graphics may vary, but should indicate that the colder the initial temperature of the water, the lower its temperature will be at the end of 10 minutes. The hot tap water will show a decrease in temperature over 10 minutes.
2. The rates of heating and cooling should be greater for the water that has a greater difference between its initial temperature and the room temperature.
3. The greater the difference between room temperature and the initial temperature of the water, the greater the heating or cooling rate.

Activity

Heating Up and Cooling Down

Do you remember how long it took for a cup of hot chocolate to cool before you could take a sip? In this activity, investigate how quickly liquids at different temperatures will heat up and cool down.

What You'll Investigate

How does the temperature of a liquid affect how quickly it warms or cools?

Materials

thermometers (5)
400-mL beakers (5)
stopwatch
**watch with second hand*
hotplate
**Alternate materials*

Goals

- Measure the temperature change of water at different temperatures.
- Infer how the rate of heating or cooling depends on the initial water temperature.

Safety Precautions

Do not use mercury thermometers. Use caution when heating with a hot plate. Hot and cold glass appears the same.

Procedure

1. Make a data table to record the temperatures of five beakers every minute from 0 to 10 min.
2. Fill a beaker with 100 mL of water and use a hotplate to bring it to a boil. Record its temperature in your data table at minute 0. Then record its temperature every minute for 10 min.

3. Repeat step 2 starting with hot tap water, refrigerated water, and cold tap water.
4. Fill a fifth beaker with 100 mL of hot tap water and measure its temperature every minute for 10 minutes.

Conclude and Apply

1. **Graph** your data. Plot the lines for all five beakers on one graph. **Label** the lines of your graph.
2. **Calculate** the rate of heating or cooling for the water in each beaker by subtracting the initial temperature of the water from the final temperature and then dividing this answer by 10 min.
3. **Infer** from your results how the difference between room temperature and the initial temperature of the water affected the rate at which it heated up or cooled down.

Share your data and graphs with other classmates and explain any differences among your data.

Assessment

Process Ask students to hypothesize what the resulting water temperature would be if you mixed 100 mL of water at 70°C with 100 mL of water at 10°C. Since the masses of water are equal, they will heat and cool at the same rate, so the temperature of the mixture should be 40°C. Use **Performance Assessment in the Science Classroom,** p. 93.

Communicating Your Data

Suggest students use a spreadsheet program to graph their results. Students should discuss why their data and graphs did or did not agree.

SECTION 3

Engines and Refrigerators

Heat Engines

Cars have engines. Motorcycles have engines. Lawn mowers have engines. Engines are used everywhere. How do they work? An **engine** is any device that converts thermal energy into mechanical energy. One type of engine burns fuel to produce thermal energy. In an external combustion engine, such as the steam engine shown in **Figure 11,** the fuel is burned outside the engine. The burning fuel converts water into steam that pushes a piston. The moving piston can then do useful work.

Reading Check *What is an engine?*

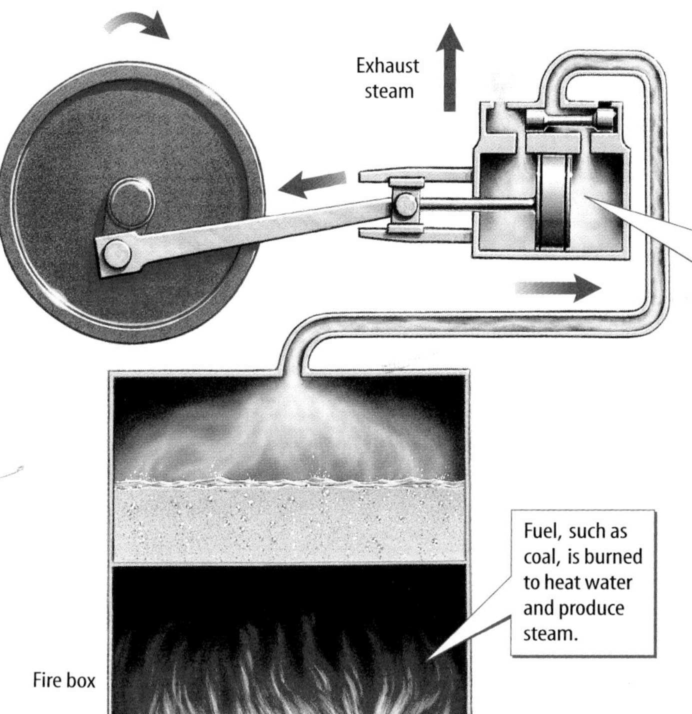
Exhaust steam
The steam pushes a piston inside the engine. The movement of the piston causes the engine's wheels to turn.
Fuel, such as coal, is burned to heat water and produce steam.
Fire box

Figure 11
A steam engine is an external combustion engine. The fuel is burned outside the engine to produce thermal energy.

As You Read

What You'll Learn

- **Identify** what an engine does.
- **Describe** how an internal combustion engine works.
- **Explain** how refrigerators and air conditioners create cool environments.

Vocabulary
engine
internal combustion engine

Why It's Important
Engines help you travel every day, and refrigerators keep your food fresh and cold.

Section Assessment Planner

PORTFOLIO
Extension, p. 298

PERFORMANCE ASSESSMENT
Skill Builder Activities, p. 301
See page 308 for more options.

CONTENT ASSESSMENT
Section, p. 301
Challenge, p. 301
Chapter, pp. 308–309

SECTION 3

Engines and Refrigerators

1 Motivate

Bellringer Transparency

Display the Section Focus Transparency for Section 3. Use the accompanying Transparency Activity Master. L2 ELL

SECTION 3 Section Focus Transparency **Southward Bound**

Icebergs in the North Atlantic are pushed south by the Labrador Current. This is dangerous because the Labrador Current can take icebergs into the shipping lanes, the part of the ocean that ships travel between Europe and North America. Today, the U.S. Coast Guard International Ice Patrol carefully monitors icebergs that may threaten ships in the North Atlantic.

1. Describe the different states of water in the photo above.
2. Icebergs from the North Atlantic usually don't get much south of roughly 40°N latitude (that's about as far south as New Jersey). Why is this?
3. Does the volume of water in the ocean change when a floating iceberg melts?

Thermal Energy

Tie to Prior Knowledge

Ask students to identify one way they have learned in which the transfer of thermal energy makes matter move. Convection makes air and water move. Tell them that in this section they will learn more ways in which the transfer of thermal energy can be used to make something move.

Resource Manager

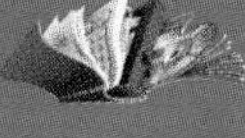

Chapter Resources Booklet
Transparency Activity, p. 46
Reinforcement, p. 29

Heat Engines

Reading Check

Answer any device that converts thermal energy into mechanical energy

Teacher FYI

The internal combustion engine was invented by the German engineer Nikolaus August Otto in 1876.

Extension

Have students research how a jet engine works and prepare a computer presentation about it. A jet engine is a gas turbine engine. As air rushes into the engine, a compressor increases its pressure and temperature. A fine spray of fuel is injected into the high-pressure air and burned. This causes the air to expand, so that it turns a turbine. Part of the energy from the turbine is used to power the compressor. The remainder leaves the system as exhaust to propel the plane forward. L3
LS **Logical-Mathematical** P

Reading Check

Answer When the fuel mixture is ignited, it burns explosively and pushes the piston down.

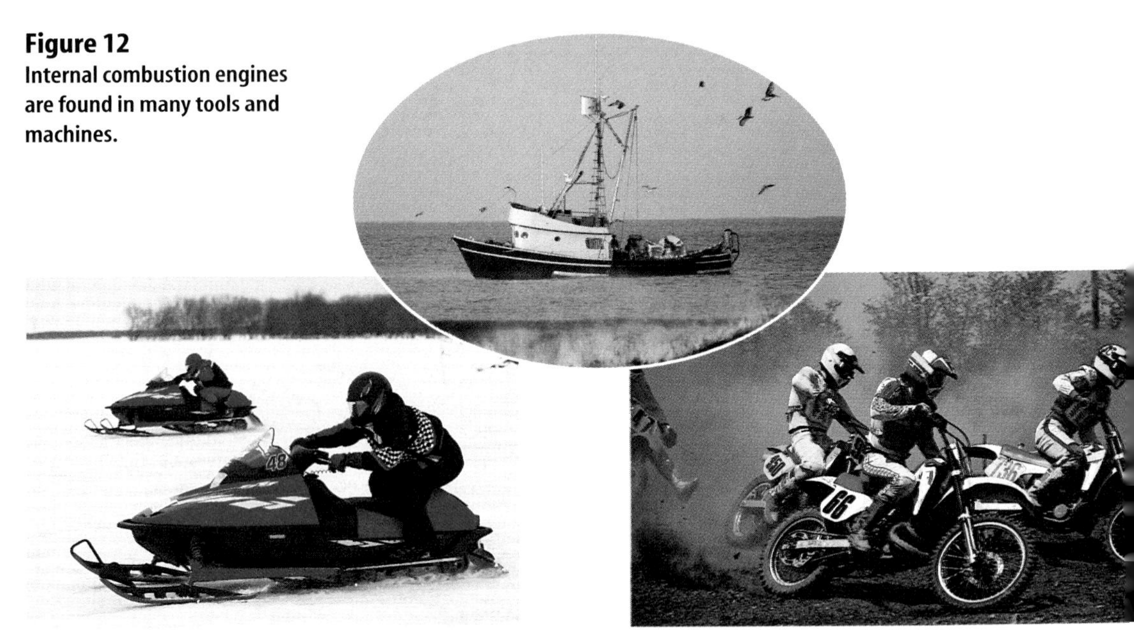

Figure 12
Internal combustion engines are found in many tools and machines.

Internal Combustion Engines The type of engine you are probably most familiar with is the internal combustion engine. In **internal combustion engines,** the fuel burns in a combustion chamber inside the engine. Many machines, including cars, airplanes, buses, boats, trucks, and lawn mowers, use internal combustion engines, as shown in **Figure 12.**

Most cars have an engine with four or more combustion chambers, or cylinders. Usually the more cylinders an engine has, the more power it can produce. Each cylinder contains a piston that can move up and down. A mixture of fuel and air is injected into a combustion chamber and ignited by a spark. When the fuel mixture is ignited, it burns explosively and pushes the piston down. The up-and-down motion of the pistons turns a rod called a crankshaft, which turns the wheels of the car. **Figure 13** shows how an internal combustion engine converts thermal energy to mechanical energy in a process called the four-stroke cycle.

Several kinds of internal combustion engines have been designed. In diesel engines, the air in the cylinder is compressed to such a high pressure that the highly flammable fuel ignites without the need for a spark plug. Many lawn mowers use a two-stroke gasoline engine. The first stroke is a combination of intake and compression. The second stroke is a combination of power and exhaust.

SCIENCE Online

Research Visit the Glencoe Science Web site at **science.glencoe.com** for more information about advancements in the design of internal combustion engines. Evaluate the advantages and disadvantages of these new designs with your classmates.

Reading Check *How does the burning of fuel mixture cause a piston to move?*

SCIENCE Online

Internet Addresses

Explore the Glencoe Science Web site at **science.glencoe.com** to find out more about topics in this section.

Science Journal

Steam Engines The earliest documented steam engine was produced by Heron of Alexandria in ancient Greece. Have students find out more about this engine and draw illustrations of it in their Science Journals. Ask them to include descriptions of how the engine worked. The recoil of steam from inside a ball made the ball rotate. L2 LS **Visual-Spatial**

Figure 13

Most modern cars are powered by fuel-injected internal combustion engines that have a four-stroke combustion cycle. Inside the engine, thermal energy is converted into mechanical energy as gasoline is burned under pressure inside chambers known as cylinders. The steps in the four-stroke cycle are shown here.

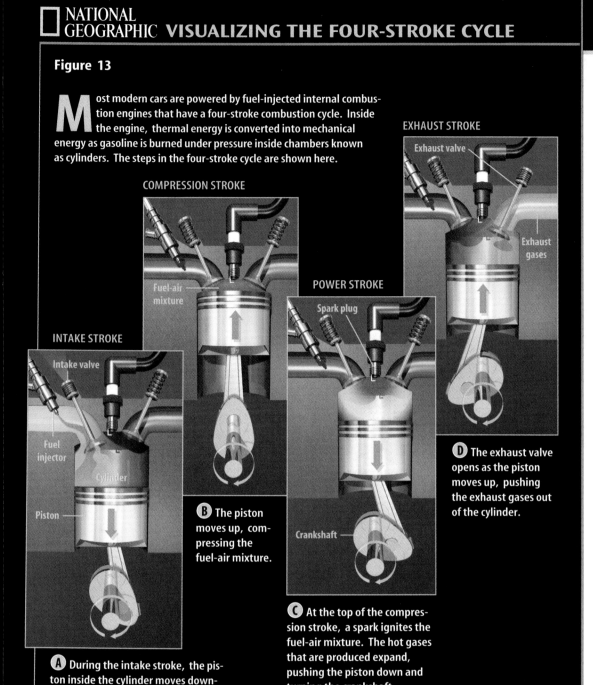

INTAKE STROKE

Intake valve
Fuel injector
Cylinder
Piston

A During the intake stroke, the piston inside the cylinder moves downward. As it does, air fills the cylinder through the intake valve, and a mist of fuel is injected into the cylinder.

COMPRESSION STROKE

Fuel-air mixture

B The piston moves up, compressing the fuel-air mixture.

POWER STROKE

Spark plug
Crankshaft

C At the top of the compression stroke, a spark ignites the fuel-air mixture. The hot gases that are produced expand, pushing the piston down and turning the crankshaft.

EXHAUST STROKE

Exhaust valve
Exhaust gases

D The exhaust valve opens as the piston moves up, pushing the exhaust gases out of the cylinder.

NATIONAL GEOGRAPHIC

Visualizing the Four-Stroke Cycle

Have students examine the pictures and read the captions. Then ask the following questions.

During the compression stroke, the volume of the air/gas mixture is decreased. **How does this affect the pressure of the mixture?** The pressure increases.

How do the thermal energy, density, and temperature of the air/gas mixture change during the compression stroke? They all increase.

Does the thermal energy of the air/gas mixture increase or decrease during the power stroke? It decreases. **What happens to this energy?** The gas exerts a strong force on the piston, so the thermal energy is used to do work on the piston.

Activity

Ask students to work in pairs to make posters similar to this figure, but showing the operation of a typical diesel engine. When presenting their posters to the class, students should explain how the process differs from that of a four-stroke engine.
L3 LS **Visual-Spatial**

Extension

Have students find out how a spark plug works and each write a paragraph explaining what they find. Suggest students include illustrations with their paragraphs.
L3 LS **Logical-Mathematical**

Resource Manager 

Chapter Resources Booklet

Directed Reading for Content Mastery, pp. 21, 22
Enrichment, p. 32
Transparency Activity, pp. 47–48

Refrigerators

Discussion

Is it better to have food in the refrigerator closely packed or spaced out? Why? It is better to have the food spaced out so that air can flow easily and carry heat from the food to the coils inside the refrigerator. L2 LS **Logical-Mathematical**

Extension

Air conditioners in cars typically don't cool unless the car is running. **Why do you think this is the case?** As in a refrigerator, the refrigerant in the air conditioner absorbs heat from the surroundings and then must transfer that heat somehow so it can cool down again in order to absorb more heat from the car. The car engine provides the energy necessary to cool the refrigerant. L3 LS **Logical-Mathematical**

Visual Learning

Figure 14 The arrows on the illustration show the flow of the refrigerant. Point out to students that the refrigerant must be pumped through the system to complete the cycle. Ask students why the refrigerant must go through the compressor. to raise the temperature and evaporate the refrigerant L2 LS **Visual-Spatial**

Caption Answer

Figure 14 Heat is transferred from the refrigerant to the surrounding air through the condensation coil. Heat also moves from the food to the evaporating refrigerant.

Refrigerators

If thermal energy will only flow from something that is warm to something that is cool, how can a refrigerator be cooler inside than the air in the kitchen? Actually a refrigerator is like a heat mover. It absorbs heat from the food and other materials inside the refrigerator. Then it carries the heat to outside the refrigerator, where it is transferred to the surrounding air.

A refrigerator contains a material called a coolant that is pumped through pipes inside and outside the refrigerator. The coolant is the substance that carries heat from the inside to the outside of the refrigerator.

Absorbing Heat **Figure 14** shows how a refrigerator operates. Liquid coolant is forced up a pipe toward the freezer unit. The liquid passes through a device where it changes into a gas. When it changes into a gas, it becomes cold. The cold gas passes through pipes around the inside of the refrigerator. Because the coolant gas is so cold, it absorbs heat from inside the refrigerator, and becomes warmer.

Releasing Heat However, the gas is still colder than the outside air. So, the heat absorbed by the coolant still cannot be transferred to the air. However, the warm coolant gas then passes through a compressor. The compressor compresses the coolant gas, making it warmer than room temperature. The gas then flows through the condenser coils, where it transfer heat to the cooler air in the room. As the coolant gas cools, it changes into a liquid. The liquid is pumped through the device that changes it into a gas, and the cycle is repeated.

Figure 14
As refrigerant moves through the coils inside a refrigerator, it absorbs heat and evaporates. The refrigerant is recycled when it cools and condenses in the outside coils and then is brought back to the inside coils.
Where do the transfers of heat in a refrigerator occur?

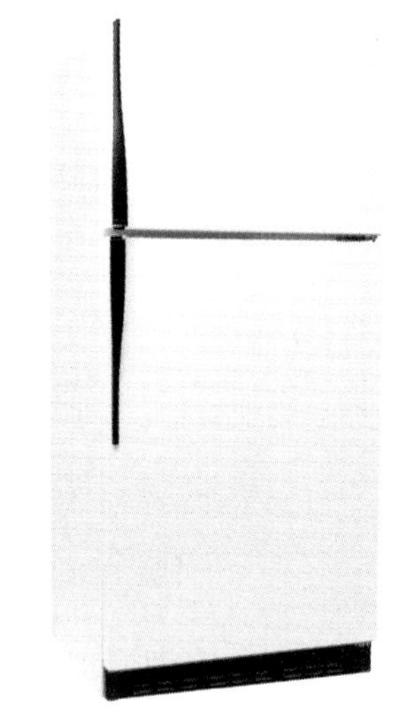

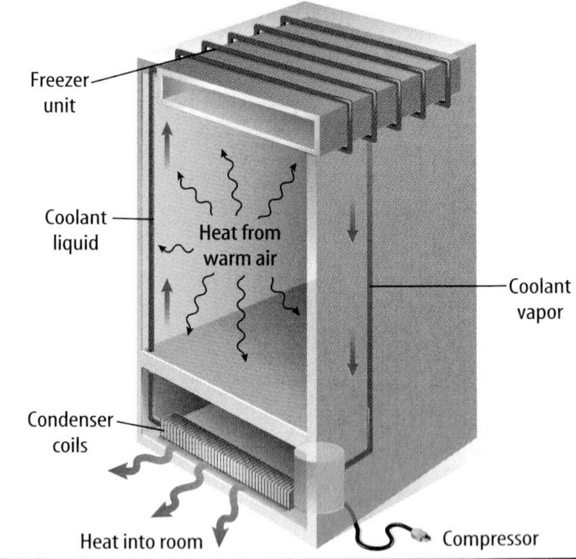

Cultural Diversity

Refrigerated Trucks The first African American member of the American Society of Refrigeration Engineers was Frederick M. Jones. Jones invented a truck refrigeration system in 1939. Have students discuss how this has affected their lives. It made possible such things as the delivery of food from long distances and fresh fruit in winter. L2 LS **Logical-Mathematical**

Resource Manager

Chapter Resources Booklet
Activity Worksheet, pp. 7–8

Air Conditioners Most air conditioners cool in the same way that a refrigerator does. You've probably seen air-conditioning units outside of many houses. As in a refrigerator, heat from inside the house is absorbed by the coolant within pipes inside the air conditioner. The coolant then is compressed by a compressor, and becomes warmer. The warmed coolant travels through pipes that are exposed to the outside air. Here the heat is transferred to the outside air.

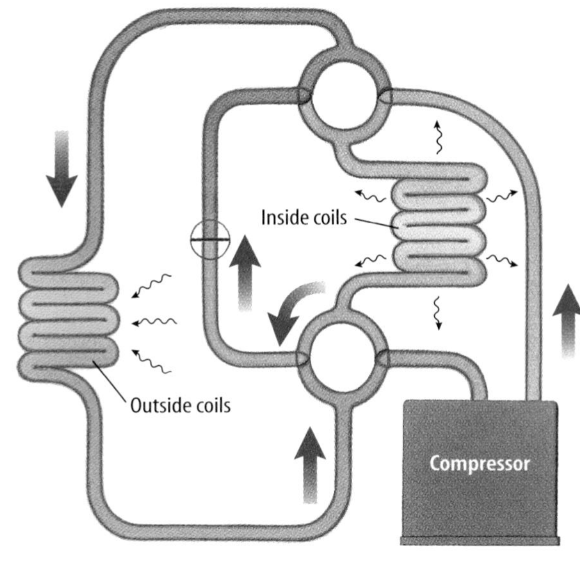

Heat Pumps Some buildings use a heat pump for heating as well as cooling, as shown in **Figure 15.** Like an air conditioner or refrigerator, a heat pump moves heat from one place to another. When a heat pump is used for cooling, it removes heat from the indoor air and transfers it outdoors. When it is used for heating, the heat pump absorbs heat from the outdoor air or some other warm source and transfers this heat inside. The heat pump can reverse itself automatically. It can heat or cool depending on the outside temperature. In summer, the heat pump removes heat from the air inside the building and releases it outside. In winter, it removes heat from cold, outside air and transfers it to the warm house. In areas where the winter temperature is near or below zero, an additional heating coil is added to provide more heat.

Figure 15
A heat pump can be used to heat and cool a building. In heating mode, the coolant absorbs heat through the outside coils. The coolant is warmed when it is compressed, and transfers heat to the room through the inside coils.

Section  Assessment

1. In an engine, thermal energy is converted into what form of energy?
2. What is the source of thermal energy in an internal combustion engine?
3. Why don't diesel engines use spark plugs?
4. Explain how a refrigerator keeps the food compartment cool.
5. **Think Critically** Why do you think a car has four or more cylinders rather than just one cylinder?

Skill Builder Activities

6. **Concept Mapping** Make an events-chain concept map showing the steps in a four-stroke cycle. **For more help, refer to the Science Skill Handbook.**
7. **Using Graphics Software** Using computer graphics or drawing software, make a diagram that shows a typical refrigeration cycle. **For more help, refer to the Technology Skill Handbook.**

3 Assess

Reteach

Have students draw diagrams to help them see that a refrigerator is like an engine working in reverse. L2 **LS Visual-Spatial**

Challenge

The efficiency of an engine is given by the equation Efficiency $= (T_2 - T_1)/T_1 \times 100\%$ where T_1 is the Kelvin temperature of the heat source and T_2 is the Kelvin temperature of the heat output from the engine. Use this equation to show that it is impossible to have 100% efficiency for an engine. The heat output would have to be at 0 K, which is impossible. L3 **LS Logical-Mathematical**

Performance Have students design an engine that uses a heat source other than combustion to perform work. Use **Performance Assessment in the Science Classroom,** p. 117.

Answers to Section Assessment

1. mechanical energy
2. burning fuel
3. In diesel engines, the air/fuel mixture is compressed until the pressure is high enough that the mixture ignites without the need of a spark plug.
4. A refrigerant is forced through a cycle where it repeatedly evaporates and condenses. During evaporation, it absorbs heat from the food compartment, keeping that area cool.
5. Four or more cylinders provide a continual push to the crankshaft. The cylinders are timed so that as the first cylinder exhausts, the second cylinder pushes, and so on.
6. Answers should show the intake, compression, power, and exhaust parts of the cycle.
7. Diagrams should show refrigerant compression, heat transfer through the coils, expansion and evaporation of the refrigerant, and extraction of heat from the food.

Activity

BENCH TESTED

Recognize the Problem

Purpose

Students design an experiment to determine which type of beverage containers best insulate hot drinks. L2

LS Logical-Mathematical

Process Skills

designing an experiment, forming a hypothesis, observing, identifying and controlling variables, making and using tables, measuring in SI, making and using graphs, analyzing results, drawing conclusions

Time Required

two 45-minute periods

Materials

A variety of disposable drink containers (paper, plastic, and polystyrene) can be purchased at supermarkets. Students could also bring in glasses, cups, or mugs from home.

Test Your Hypothesis

Possible Procedures

Heat 500 mL of water to boiling. Measure and pour 100 mL of hot water into each of the five different beverage containers. Cover each container with aluminum foil. Insert a thermometer through the foil into each container. Record the temperature of liquid in each container at the start. Measure and record the temperature of the liquid in each container every minute for 10 minutes.

Activity **Design Your Own Experiment**

Comparing Thermal Insulators

Insulated beverage containers are used to reduce heat transfer. What kinds of containers do you more commonly drink from? Aluminum soda cans? Paper, plastic, or foam cups? Glass containers? In this investigation, compare how well several different containers block heat transfer.

Recognize the Problem

Which types of beverage containers are most effective at blocking heat transfer from a hot drink?

Form a Hypothesis

Predict the temperature change of a hot liquid in several containers made of different materials over a time interval.

Goals

- **Predict** the temperature change of a hot drink in various types of containers over time.
- **Design** an experiment to test the hypothesis and collect data that can be graphed.
- **Interpret** the data.

Possible Materials

hotplate
large beaker
water
graduated cylinder
thermometers
various beverage containers (each about the same size and shape)
material to cover the containers
stopwatch
**watch with a second hand*
tongs
thermal gloves or mitts
tea
coffee
coffee maker

**Alternate materials*

Safety Precautions 

Use caution when heating liquids. Be sure to use tongs or thermal gloves when handling hot materials. Remember that hot and cold glass appears the same. Treat thermometers with care and keep them away from the edges of tables. Avoid using mercury thermometers.

Form a Hypothesis

Possible Hypothesis

Beverage containers made of polystyrene, plastic, and paper will block heat transfer from hot liquids better than containers made of glass, ceramic, or metal.

Data Table Data will vary, but the best insulators will show a slower decrease in temperature of liquid over time.

Temp. (°C)	foam	paper	plastic	glass	metal
Start					
1 min					
2 min					
3 min					
4 min					
5 min					
6 min					
7 min					
8 min					
9 min					
10 min					

Test Your Hypothesis

Plan

1. **Decide** what types of containers you will test. Design an experiment to test your hypothesis. This is a group activity, so make certain that everyone gets to contribute to the discussion.
2. **List** the materials you will use in your experiment. Describe exactly how you will use these materials. Which liquid will you test? What temperature will the liquid begin at? How will you cover the hot liquids in the container? What material will you use as a cover?
3. **Identify** the variables and controls in your experiment.
4. **Design** a data table in your Science Journal to record the observations you make.

Do

1. Ask your teacher to examine the steps of your experiment and your data table before you start.
2. To see the pattern of how well various containers retain heat, you will need to graph your data. What kind of graph will you use? Make certain you take enough measurements during the experiment to make your graph.
3. The time intervals between measurements should be the same. Be sure to keep track of time as the experiment goes along. For how long will you measure the temperature?
4. Carry out your investigation and record your observations.

Analyze Your Data

1. **Graph** your data. Use one graph to show the data collected from all your containers. Label each line on your graph.
2. How can you tell by looking at your graphs which containers retain heat best?
3. Did the water temperature change as you had predicted? Use your data and graph to explain your answers.

Draw Conclusions

1. Why did the rate of temperature change vary among the containers? Did the size of the containers affect the rate of cooling?
2. **Conclude** which containers were the best insulators?

Communicating Your Data

Compare your data and graphs with other classmates and explain any differences in your results or conclusions.

Teaching Strategies

Suggest that students use different colored pencils to graph temperatures of beverages in different containers.

Troubleshooting

Check students' procedures to be sure they have identified and controlled variables.

Expected Outcome

Most results will show that a polystyrene or other insulated container is best at blocking heat transfer.

Analyze Your Data

1. Graphs should be consistent with data in the data table. The containers that are least effective at blocking heat transfer will show the steepest curves.
2. The containers that retain heat best show the least steep curves (the temperature will drop less over the same period of time).
3. Answers will vary depending on students' hypotheses.

Error Analysis

Have students compare their results and their hypotheses and explain why differences occurred.

Draw Conclusions

1. The rate of temperature change varied because some containers are more effective at blocking heat transfer. The size of the containers would not have much effect on the rate of cooling.
2. Answers will vary depending on containers chosen for testing. In general, polystyrene or another insulated container should be the best insulator.

Assessment

Process Show students a picnic cooler. Remind them that people place food in picnic coolers to keep the food cold on a warm day. Ask them if a cooler really cools the food. If not, how does it work? The cooler slows heat transfer between the food and the outside (warm) environment. Use **Performance Assessment in the Science Classroom,** p. 89.

Communicating Your Data

Students can use an electronic database to plot their data and graphs. Printouts of each group's data can be given to the other groups for easier comparison and discussion.

Content Background

Conclusive evidence that cities can be much hotter than surrounding suburban and rural areas was provided in 1998. Scientists at NASA equipped an airplane with heat sensitive cameras and generated images of Salt Lake City, Utah and surrounding areas. Similar images have been obtained from flyovers of Baton Rouge, Louisiana; Atlanta, Georgia; and Sacramento, California.

The images allow precise identification of the hottest and coolest areas, and even of specific buildings, in a city. These studies confirmed that darker colors and certain building materials, such as asphalt, absorb and retain far more heat than do lighter colors and materials like concrete. The images also identify areas that are cooler because of an abundance of foliage.

It is estimated that the additional air-conditioning used to counteract this heat accounts for as much as 10% of electricity used during peak periods. In Los Angeles, this adds up to more than 100 million dollars per year. Additionally, every 1 degree F increases smog production in Los Angeles by 3%. This in turn increases the demand for cooling power by 2%.

Scientists at the Lawrence Berkeley National Laboratory estimate that a decrease in urban areas of just 3 degrees F could result in savings of more than 10 billion dollars nationwide.

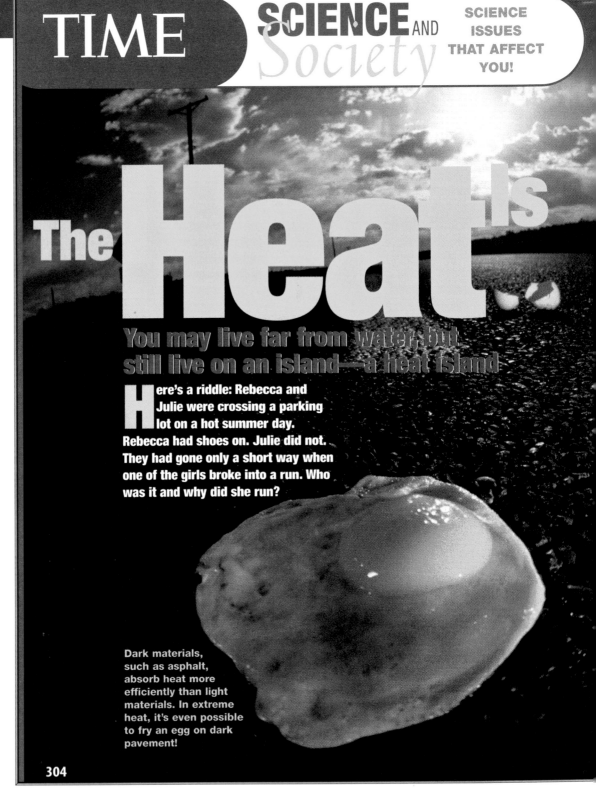

TIME SCIENCE AND Society

SCIENCE ISSUES THAT AFFECT YOU!

The Heat's On

You may live far from water, but still live on an island—a heat island

Here's a riddle: Rebecca and Julie were crossing a parking lot on a hot summer day. Rebecca had shoes on. Julie did not. They had gone only a short way when one of the girls broke into a run. Who was it and why did she run?

Dark materials, such as asphalt, absorb heat more efficiently than light materials. In extreme heat, it's even possible to fry an egg on dark pavement!

304

Resources for Teachers and Students

Heat Islands-And How To Cool Them, Center For Building Science Newsletter, Spring 1994.

"Cities trap heat, make their own weather, study indicates," *Seattle Times*, July 10, 2000.

"Urban Heat," *Architecture*, January 1999.

Learning About Urban Heat Islands, The Heat Island Group Homepage http://eetd.lbl.gov/HeatIsland/

If you guess barefoot Julie, you're right. The hot asphalt of the parking lot scorched her feet, and Julie took off like a shot. Paving and building materials such as asphalt and concrete absorb energy from the Sun and get hotter. Think about all the things that are made of asphalt and concrete in a city.

On

As far as the eye can see, there are buildings and parking lots, sidewalks and streets. The combined effect of these paved surfaces and towering structures can make a city sizzle in the summer. There's even a name for this effect. It's called a heat island.

Hot Times

You can think of a city as an island surrounded by an ocean of green trees. In the midst of those green trees, the air can be up to 8°C cooler than it is downtown. During the day in rural areas, the Sun's energy is absorbed by plants and soil. Some of this energy causes water to evaporate, so less energy is available to heat the surroundings. This keeps the temperature lower.

In cities, where there are fewer trees and plants, the buildings, streets, and sidewalks absorb most of the Sun's energy. And as more energy is absorbed, the temperature increases. As the temperature of the streets and buildings rises, they lose heat to cooler objects in their surroundings. The temperature stops rising when heat energy is released at the same rate that energy from the Sun is absorbed.

Higher temperatures aren't the only problems caused by heat islands. People crank up their air conditioners for relief, so the use of energy skyrockets. Also, the added heat speeds up the rates of chemical reactions in the atmosphere. Smog is due to chemical reactions caused by the interaction of sunlight and vehicle emissions. So hotter air means more smog. And more smog means more health problems.

Cool Cures

Several U.S. cities are working with NASA scientists to come up with a cure for the summertime blues. For instance, dark materials absorb heat more efficiently than light materials. So painting buildings, especially roofs, white can reduce heat and save on cooling bills. In Salt Lake City, Utah, where temperatures on dark rooftops can soar to 65°C, the rooftop of a large warehouse was painted white. "I've been up on it plenty of times," says a worker at the warehouse. "It doesn't come up and just drill you with heat like the black ones do."

Planting even small bushes and trees can help cool a city.

CONNECTIONS Design and Research Go to the Glencoe Science Web site to research NASA's Urban Heat Island Project. What actions are cities taking to reduce the heat-island effect? Design a city area that would help reduce this effect.

Online
For more information, visit science.glencoe.com.

Discussion

What factors should be considered when planning expansion of cities? Possible answers include: use lighter colors and materials that reflect rather than absorb heat. Asphalt should be replaced with cooler materials like concrete. Tracts of trees should be incorporated into urban and suburban design. Strategic planting of shade trees will reduce heat absorption by buildings.

L2 LS **Logical-Mathematical**

Activity

Divide the class into two groups. Have them use simple materials such as shoeboxes or other cardboard materials to make models of buildings. Have the two groups decorate their models with colors that would make them hotter or cooler. Make other components of cities, such as streets, some dark, some light, representing asphalt and concrete. Collect pictures of trees, of people who look comfortable, and of people who appear distressed in heat. Save these for construction of two model cities.

Investigate the Issue

Have students examine the exterior of your school building. Place thermometers near outside walls in direct sun and in shade. Record the differences in temperature. Measure the temperatures near darker and lighter colored walls. Perhaps some walls are made of different materials. Find out how these materials affect the temperatures near them. Work with students to record these data in graphs.

CONNECTIONS Have students use the building models and collected pictures to construct two model cities. One should illustrate a city that absorbs a great deal of heat. The other should illustrate the benefits of a plan that includes the use of color, materials, trees and parks to reduce the heat absorbed in the city. Suggest students incorporate the data collected from your school in the design.

Online

Internet Addresses

Explore the Glencoe Science Web site at **science.glencoe.com** to find out more about topics in this feature.

Chapter 10 Study Guide

Reviewing Main Ideas

Preview

Students can answer the questions in their Science Journals. Discuss the answers as you go through the chapter. **LS Linguistic**

Review

Students can write their answers, then compare them with those of other students. **LS Interpersonal**

Reteach

Students can look at the illustrations and describe details that support the main ideas of the chapter. **LS Visual-Spatial**

Answers to Chapter Review

SECTION 1

3. The thermal energy has increased.

SECTION 2

2. Thermal energy travels from the fire to you by radiation.

SECTION 3

4. to transfer heat to the outside air

Chapter 10 Study Guide

Reviewing Main Ideas

Section 1 Temperature and Thermal Energy

1. Molecules of matter are moving constantly. Temperature is related to the average value of the kinetic energy of the molecules.
2. Thermometers measure temperature. Three common temperature scales are the Celsius, Fahrenheit, and Kelvin scales.
3. Thermal energy is the total kinetic and potential energy of the particles in matter. *How has thermal energy changed when this iron has melted?*

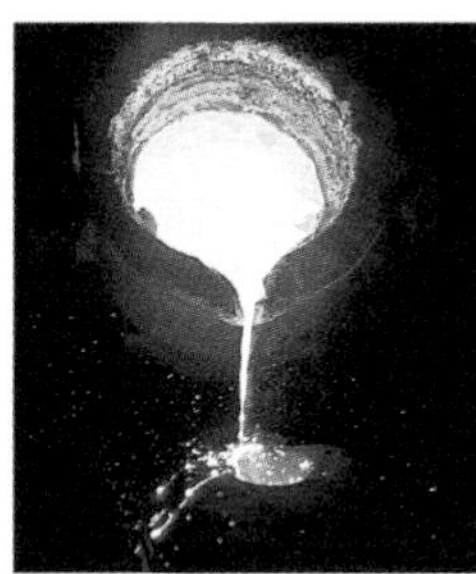

Section 2 Heat

1. Heat is thermal energy that is transferred from a warmer object to a colder object.
2. Heat can be transferred by conduction, convection, and radiation. *Why do you feel warm when you stand in front of a fireplace?*

3. A material that easily transfers heat is called a conductor. A material that resists the flow of heat is an insulator.
4. The specific heat of a substance describes how much heat is needed to change the temperature of the substance.
5. Thermal pollution occurs when warm water is added to a body of water, such as a river or lake.

Section 3 Engines and Refrigerators

1. A device that converts thermal energy into mechanical energy is an engine.
2. In an internal combustion engine, fuel is burned in combustion chambers inside the engine.
3. Internal combustion engines that are used in cars and airplanes burn fuel to do work, using a four-stroke cycle.
4. Refrigerators and air conditioners use a coolant to move heat from one place to another. *Why is one side of this air conditioner placed outdoors?*

FOLDABLES Reading & Study Skills — **After You Read**

Write what you learned about the relationship between heat and thermal energy on the back of your Foldable.

FOLDABLES Reading & Study Skills — **After You Read**

After students have read the chapter and completed the Foldable described in Before You Read, have them do the activity on the student page.

Dinah Zike

Chapter 10 Study Guide

Visualizing Main Ideas

Complete the following cycle map about the four-stroke cycle.

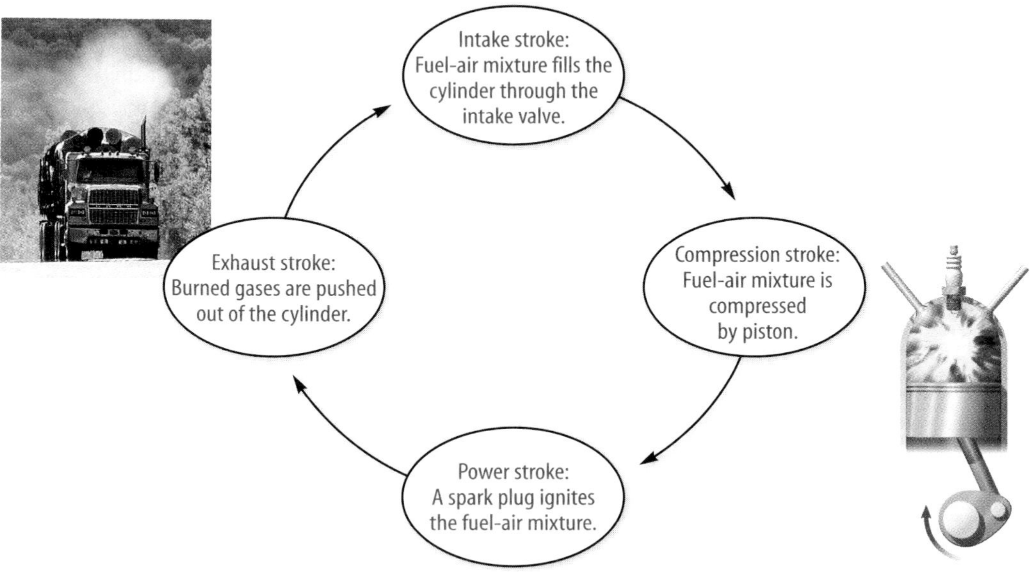
Intake stroke: Fuel-air mixture fills the cylinder through the intake valve.
Compression stroke: Fuel-air mixture is compressed by piston.
Power stroke: A spark plug ignites the fuel-air mixture.
Exhaust stroke: Burned gases are pushed out of the cylinder.

Vocabulary Review

Vocabulary Words

a. conduction
b. conductor
c. convection
d. engine
e. heat
f. internal combustion engine
g. radiation
h. specific heat
i. temperature
j. thermal energy
k. thermal pollution

Study Tip

Practice reading tables. See whether you can devise a graph that shows the same information that a table shows.

Using Vocabulary

Explain the differences in the vocabulary words given below. Then explain how the words are related. Use complete sentences in your answers.

1. internal combustion engine, engine
2. temperature, thermal energy
3. thermal energy, thermal pollution
4. conduction, convection
5. conduction, heat
6. heat, specific heat
7. conduction, radiation
8. convection, radiation
9. conductor, heat

Chapter 10 Study Guide

Visualizing Main Ideas

See student page.

Vocabulary Review

Using Vocabulary

1. An internal combustion engine is a type of engine that is powered by combustion within the engine.
2. Temperature is the average value of the kinetic energy of the molecules in a material. Thermal energy is the sum of all the kinetic and potential energy of the molecules in the material.
3. Thermal energy is the sum of the kinetic and potential energy of the molecules in a material. Thermal pollution is an increase in the temperature of a body of water caused by adding warmer water.
4. Both of these are methods of transferring thermal energy. Conduction transfers thermal energy by direct contact. Convection transfers thermal energy by movement of fluids from one place to another.
5. Conduction is the transfer of thermal energy by direct contact. Heat is thermal energy that is transferred from warmer to cooler objects.
6. Heat is thermal energy transferred from one object to another. Specific heat is a measure of how well a substance absorbs thermal energy.
7. Both of these are methods of transferring thermal energy. Conduction transfers thermal energy by direct contact. Radiation transfers thermal energy by electromagnetic waves.
8. Both of these are methods of transferring thermal energy. Convection transfers thermal energy by movement of fluids from one place to another. Radiation transfers thermal energy by electromagnetic waves.
9. A conductor is any material that easily transfers thermal energy. Heat is thermal energy that is transferred from warmer to cooler objects.

Chapter 10 Assessment

Checking Concepts

1. C
2. D
3. D
4. C
5. C
6. D
7. A
8. A
9. C
10. A

Thinking Critically

11. Convection enables heat to be transferred from the water at the bottom of the pan to the water at the top. As the water at the bottom becomes warm it also becomes less dense and rises. Meanwhile, cooler water takes its place and gets heaterd. As the warm water rises it loses heat to the water around it until it becomes dense enough to sink to the bottom of the pot.
12. 200 K, 50°F, 80°C
13. The layers form pockets of air, which is a good insulator.
14. The phrase would correctly describe heat transfer by convection in fluids. As the lower part of the fluid is heated, it becomes less dense, and is pushed upward by the cooler, denser fluid around it.
15. Liquid coolant is changed to a gas and becomes cold. The cold gas coolant absorbs heat from the material inside the refrigerator and becomes warmer. The gas is then compressed, and becomes even warmer. The warm gas then transfers heat to the room, and cools, becoming a liquid.

Chapter 10 Assessment

Checking Concepts

Choose the word or phrase that best answers the question.

1. What source of thermal energy does an internal combustion engine use?
   A) steam **C)** burning fuel
   B) hot water **D)** refrigerant
2. What happens to most materials when they become warmer?
   A) They contract **C)** They vaporize
   B) They float **D)** They expand
3. Which type of heat transfer occurs when two objects at different temperatures are touching?
   A) convection **C)** condensation
   B) radiation **D)** conduction
4. Which of the following describes the thermal energy of particles in a substance?
   A) average value of all kinetic energy
   B) total value of all kinetic energy
   C) total value of all kinetic and potential energy
   D) average value of all kinetic and potential energy
5. Heat being transferred from the Sun to Earth is an example of which process?
   A) convection **C)** radiation
   B) expansion **D)** conduction
6. Many insulating materials contain spaces filled with air because air is what type of material?
   A) conductor **C)** radiator
   B) coolant **D)** insulator
7. What do thermometers measure?
   A) average kinetic energy of particles
   B) heat of particles
   C) evaporation rate
   D) total energy of particles
8. Which of the following is true?
   A) Warm air is less dense than cool air.
   B) Warm air is as dense as cool air.
   C) Warm air has no density.
   D) Warm air is denser than cool air.
9. Which of these is the name for thermal energy that moves from a warmer object to a cooler one?
   A) kinetic energy **C)** heat
   B) specific heat **D)** temperature
10. If all of the following objects were placed in the sunshine, which would get hottest?
    A) object with low specific heat
    B) object with medium specific heat
    C) object with high specific heat
    D) object with very high specific heat

Thinking Critically

11. Water is a poor conductor of heat. Yet, when you heat water in a pan, the surface gets hot quickly, even though you are applying heat to the bottom of the water. Explain.
12. List the following temperatures from coldest to warmest: 80° C, 200 K, 50° F.
13. Why do several layers of clothing often keep you warmer than a single layer?
14. The phrase "heat rises" is sometimes used to describe the behavior of heat. For what type of materials is this phrase correct? Explain.
15. In a refrigerator, the coolant absorbs heat from inside the refrigerator and then transfers this heat to the air outside. Describe how the temperature of the coolant is changed as it flows through the refrigerator.

Chapter Assessment Planner

Portfolio Encourage students to place in their portfolios one or two items of what they consider to be their best work. Examples include:

- Use Science Words, p. 288
- Active Reading, p. 292
- Extension, p. 298

Performance Additional performance assessments, Performance Task Assessment Lists, and rubrics for evaluating these activities can be found in Glencoe's **Performance Assessment in the Science Classroom.**

Chapter 10 Assessment

Developing Skills

16. Designing an Experiment Some colors of clothing absorb heat better than other colors. Design an experiment that will test various colors by placing them in the hot Sun for a period of time. Explain your results.

17. Drawing Conclusions Would it be possible to cool a kitchen by leaving the refrigerator door open? Explain.

18. Concept Mapping Complete the following concept map on convection in a liquid.

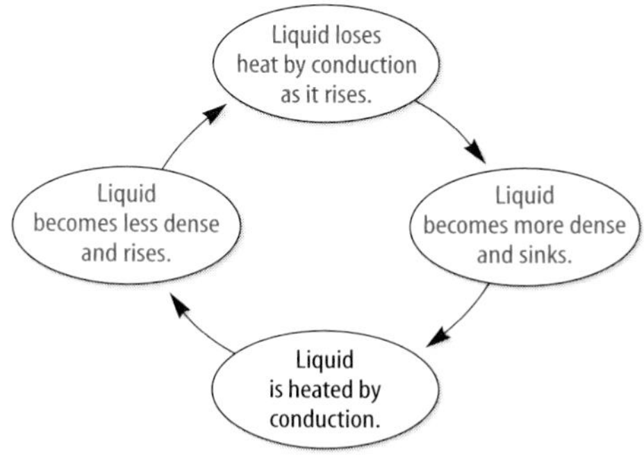

Performance Assessment

19. Poll In the United States, the Fahrenheit temperature scale is used most often. Some people feel that Americans should switch to the Celsius scale. Take a poll of at least 20 people. Find out if they feel the switch to Celsius should be made. Make a list of reasons people give for or against changing.

Technology

Go to the Glencoe Science Web site at **science.glencoe.com** or use the **Glencoe Science CD-ROM** for additional chapter assessment.

THE PRINCETON REVIEW Test Practice

Mrs. Keeley's chemistry class is studying how ice changes to water and then to steam as it is heated. They measured the amount of heat added, and the temperature of the ice, water, and steam. The graph below shows their results.

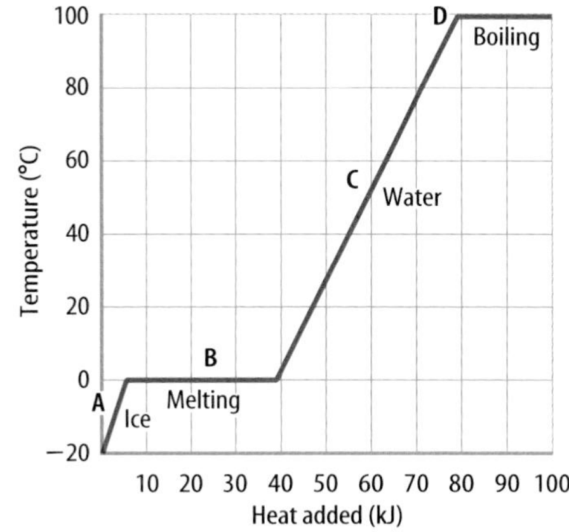

Study the graph and answer the following questions.

1. According to the graph above, at what temperature does ice change to water?

A) 10° C
B) 100° C
C) 0° C
D) −10° C

2. Temperature is a measure of the average kinetic energy of the molecules of a substance. Over what part of the graph does the kinetic energy of the molecules stay the same?

F) A
G) C
H) B
J) Not enough information given

THE PRINCETON REVIEW Test Practice

The Test-Taking Tip was written by The Princeton Review, the nation's leader in test preparation.

1. C
2. H

Developing Skills

16. Results should show that dark colors get warmer than light colors because dark colors absorb heat better.

17. No. The refrigerator transfers heat from the inside of the refrigerator to the air in the room. If the door were left open, the refrigerator would be taking heat from the room and transferring it to the room. For cooling to occur, the heat from the room would have to be transferred outside the room.

18. See student page.

Performance Assessment

19. Some people might say that switching to Celsius is too difficult and unnecessary. Others might say that Celsius is easier to use.

Assessment Resources

 **Reproducible Masters**

Chapter Resources Booklet
Chapter Review, pp. 37–38
Chapter Tests, pp. 39–42
Assessment Transparency Activity, p. 49

Glencoe Science Web site
Interactive Tutor
Chapter Quizzes

Glencoe Technology
Assessment Transparency
Interactive CD-ROM Chapter Quizzes
ExamView Pro Test Bank
Vocabulary PuzzleMaker Software
MindJogger Videoquiz DVD/VHS

Reading Comprehension

Question 1: B

Students must determine the meaning of the underlined word *rechargeable* in the passage by looking for clues in the surrounding context.

Question 2: G

Students must identify the answer choice that is the correct cause in the cause-and-effect relationship.

All questions written and validated by The Princeton Review.

Standardized Test Practice

Reading Comprehension

Read the passage. Then read each question that follows the passage. Decide which is the best answer to each question.

Electric Cars: The Cars of the Future

Have you ever wondered how a car is able to move? As cars burn gasoline, they change chemical energy into heat energy. The engine, in turn, changes heat energy into kinetic energy that rotates the car wheels. Unfortunately, one day we will run out of the fossil fuels that provide gasoline for cars. Hopefully by that time car makers will be manufacturing cars that run on alternative fuels.

In 1991, a group of car and battery manufacturers worked with the Department of Energy in Washington, D.C. Their goal was to design cars that could be mass-manufactured and would run on an electric battery instead of on gasoline.

Batteries store chemical energy. This chemical energy can be changed into electric energy. Eventually, all of the chemical energy in a battery gets used up and the battery doesn't work anymore. Some batteries are rechargeable because the chemical reactions in the battery that produced electric energy can be reversed. Electric cars have rechargeable batteries that can be recharged while the car is parked at home or at work.

Because a car needs a large amount of energy to make it move, the battery in an electric car would have to be very powerful. Some batteries that are now used to start cars are made with lead metal and acid. But these batteries are heavy, expensive, and frequently need to be recharged. So scientists have experimented with other metals such as nickel, iron, and zinc. Already some car manufacturers are producing cars that run almost entirely on batteries.

A hybrid car has an internal combustion engine, a battery, and an electric motor. The internal combustion system provides the power. The electric motor makes the car move. About half of the kinetic energy is recovered during braking and is stored in the battery.

The cost of batteries probably always will make electric cars more expensive to buy. However, fuel for electric vehicles is inexpensive, maintenance is minimal, and electric motors last longer than gasoline engines.

Test-Taking Tip Read the passage slowly to make sure you don't miss any important details.

1. From the story, you can infer that rechargeable means _____.
   A) brand new
   B) reuseable
   C) paid by credit card
   D) disposable

2. Scientists are studying different materials for batteries because lead-acid batteries _____.
   F) break easy
   G) are too expensive
   H) are too small
   J) don't work in cars

310 STANDARDIZED TEST PRACTICE

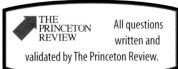

Reasoning and Skills

Read each question and choose the best answer.

1. Why aren't you doing any work when you push against a solid brick wall?
   A) because the wall is much heavier than you are
   B) because you can exert only a very small force
   C) because only machines can do work
   D) because you haven't moved the wall

Test-Taking Tip Recall the definition of work.

2. What would be the best use for this simple machine?
   F) to help get objects onto the back of a truck
   G) to help turn a doorknob
   H) to help lift a piano into a second-story window
   J) as a tool for digging into hard dirt

Test-Taking Tip Consider how the machine works and what you need it to do.

3. Which of the following statements is the best explanation for what likely happened to the sidewalk in the picture above?
   A) An animal that lives underground has tunneled under the sidewalk.
   B) The sidewalk has expanded because of extremely hot weather.
   C) The sidewalk has heaved due to the number of people and other animals that have walked on it.
   D) The sidewalk has contracted because of extremely hot weather.

Test-Taking Tip Consider the kind of force needed to cause such a break. How could this force most likely be produced?

Consider the question carefully before writing your answer on a separate sheet of paper.

4. You have 2 L of water at a temperature of 5°C and 1/4 a L of water at a temperature of 5°C. Which volume has more thermal energy? Why?

Test-Taking Tip Think carefully about the definition of thermal energy.

Standardized Test Practice

Reasoning and Skills

Question 1: D

Students should understand that in order for work to be done, a force must be exerted over a distance.

Question 2: H

Students should understand that a pulley is designed to lift objects by decreasing the force a person exerts and increasing the distance through which the force is exerted. Only answer H requires lifting.

Question 3: B

Students should note that the sidewalk has been pushed up but not separated. Contraction occurs because of cold temperatures and would cause a separation in the sidewalk. Answers A and D are incorrect. People walking on the sidewalk would push the sidewalk down. Answer C is incorrect. Expansion as a result of warm temperatures would cause the sidewalk to be pushed up.

Question 4: Answers will vary.

Students should state that thermal energy is dependent on both volume and temperature. The greater the volume or the higher the temperature, the greater the thermal energy. Because the temperature of both samples of water is the same, the sample with a greater volume has more thermal energy.

UNIT 5

Unit Contents

✔ Pre-Reading Activity

Have students look at illustrations and photographs that depict different types of waves.

UNIT 5 Waves, Sound, and Light

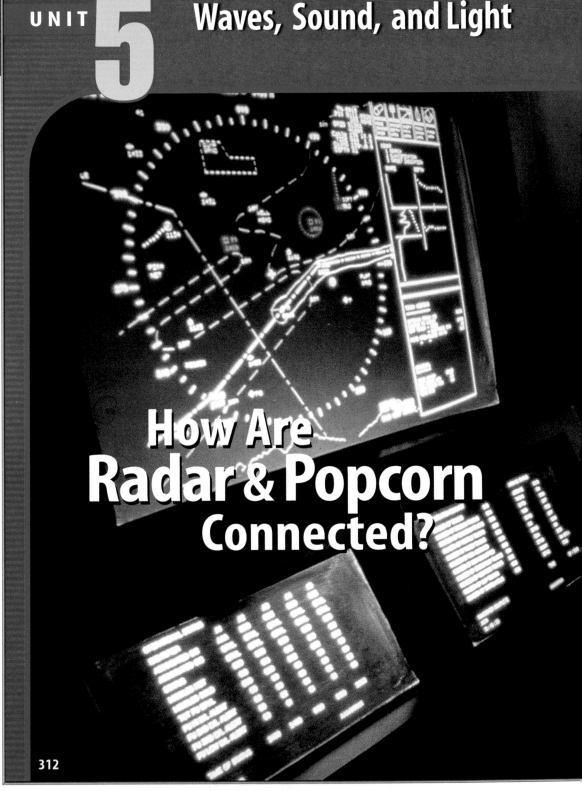

How Are Radar & Popcorn Connected?

312

Teacher to Teacher

"While discussing wave crests, troughs, and wavelengths, place a clear, oblong, heat-resistant baking dish on an overhead projector. Add water. Generate waves with a pencil point, and use pieces of wood as barriers. To reinforce the concepts, have students make waves with a coiled-spring toy and locate the parts of a wave."

Tonya K. Hancock, Teacher
Davis Drive Middle School
Raleigh, NC

NATIONAL GEOGRAPHIC

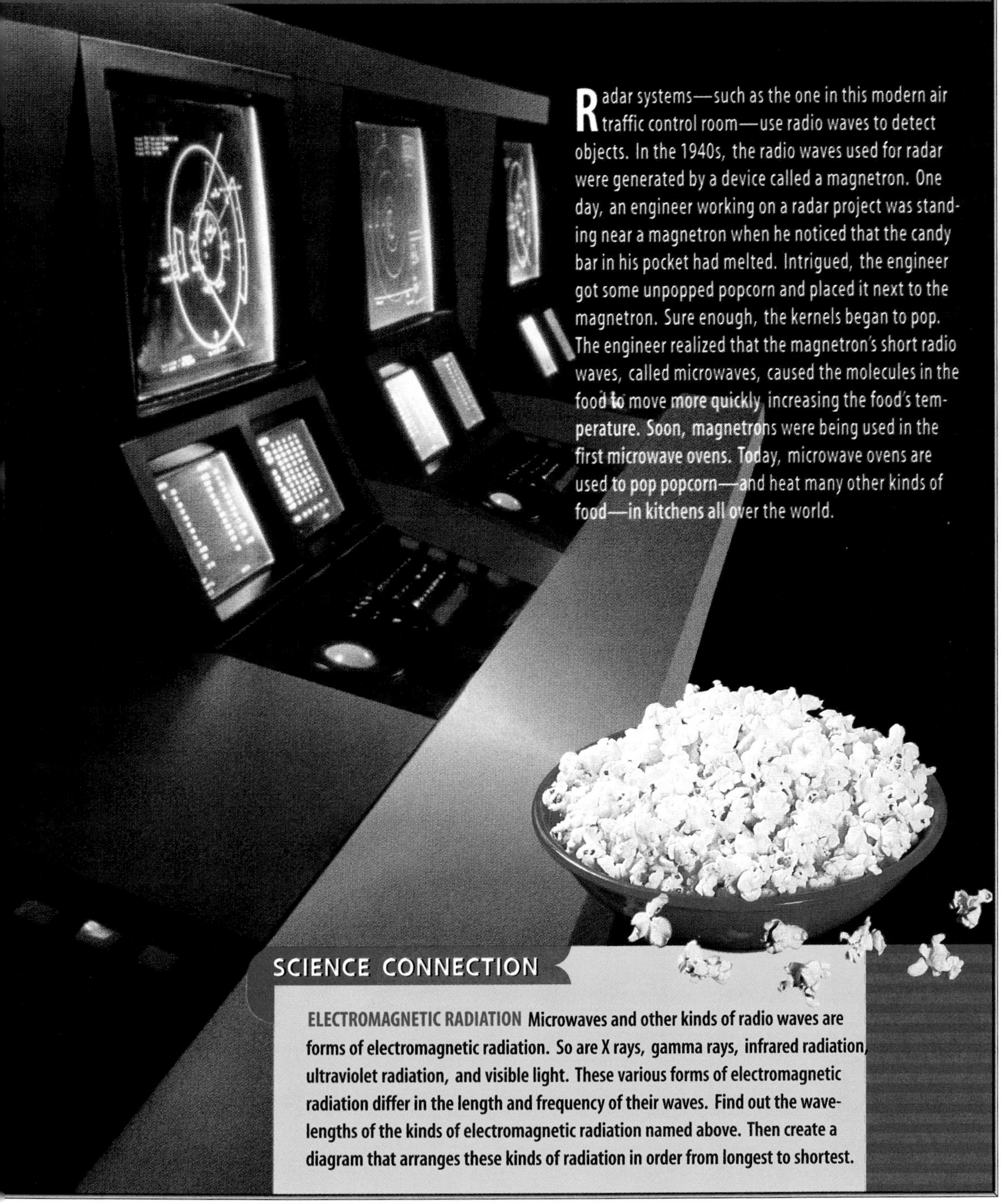

Radar systems—such as the one in this modern air traffic control room—use radio waves to detect objects. In the 1940s, the radio waves used for radar were generated by a device called a magnetron. One day, an engineer working on a radar project was standing near a magnetron when he noticed that the candy bar in his pocket had melted. Intrigued, the engineer got some unpopped popcorn and placed it next to the magnetron. Sure enough, the kernels began to pop. The engineer realized that the magnetron's short radio waves, called microwaves, caused the molecules in the food to move more quickly, increasing the food's temperature. Soon, magnetrons were being used in the first microwave ovens. Today, microwave ovens are used to pop popcorn—and heat many other kinds of food—in kitchens all over the world.

SCIENCE CONNECTION

ELECTROMAGNETIC RADIATION Microwaves and other kinds of radio waves are forms of electromagnetic radiation. So are X rays, gamma rays, infrared radiation, ultraviolet radiation, and visible light. These various forms of electromagnetic radiation differ in the length and frequency of their waves. Find out the wavelengths of the kinds of electromagnetic radiation named above. Then create a diagram that arranges these kinds of radiation in order from longest to shortest.

SCIENCE Online

Internet Addresses

Explore the Glencoe Science Web site at **science.glencoe.com** to find out more about topics in this unit.

Introducing the Unit

How Are Radar & Popcorn Connected?

Popcorn is an example of the forces behind expanding gases. This is because popcorn, like all matter, is composed of atoms in constant motion. To a large extent, the state in which matter exists depends on average kinetic energy or temperature of the particles. Heating a substance is one way to increase an object's temperature. Striking an object with microwaves is another way to increase its temperature.

The waves of energy produced by microwaves are small enough to effectively strike individual atoms. Because all forms of matter obey Newton's laws of motion, energy from the microwave is transferred to the object being heated. As this energy is transferred, the object's temperature rises.

On an atomic level, the particles gain enough energy to change from one state to another. In the case of popcorn, moisture inside the kernel is converted to a gas.

The pressure from this steam builds until the kernel explodes. The kernel is turned inside out. The end result is the familiar looking popcorn.

SCIENCE CONNECTION

Activity

Using index cards, make a deck of cards that show the wavelengths of the various forms of electromagnetic radiation. Have students take turns shuffling and arranging the cards in order of decreasing wavelength.

CHAPTER 11 WAVES

Section/Objectives	Standards		Activities/Features
	National	State/Local	
Chapter Opener	See p. 5T for a Key to Standards.		**Explore Activity:** Observe wave behavior, p. 315 **Before You Read,** p. 315
Section 1 What are Waves 4 sessions 2 blocks 1. **Explain** the relationship among waves, energy, and matter. 2. **Describe** the difference between transverse waves and compressional waves.	National Content Standards: UCP5, A1, B1, B3		**MiniLAB:** Comparing Sounds, p. 319 **Physics Integration,** p. 320
Section 2 Wave Properties 4 sessions 2 blocks 1. **Describe** the relationship between the frequency and wavelength of a wave. 2. **Explain** why waves travel at different speeds.	National Content Standards: UCP3, A1, B3		**Health Integration,** p. 324 **Science Online,** p. 325 **Activity:** Waves on a Spring, p. 326
Section 3 Wave Behavior 5 sessions 2.5 blocks 1. **Explain** how waves can reflect from some surfaces. 2. **Explain** how waves change direction when they move from one material into another. 3. **Describe** how waves are able to bend around barriers.	National Content Standards: UCP2, A1, B1, B3		**MiniLAB:** Observing How Light Refracts, p. 328 **Science Online,** p. 331 **Problem-Solving Activity:** Can you create destructive interference?, p. 331 **Visualizing Interference,** p. 332 **Activity:** Wave Speed, pp. 334–335 **Science Stats:** Waves, Waves, and More Waves, pp. 336–337

Activity Materials	Reproducible Resources	Section Assessment	Technology
Explore Activity: clear plastic plate, a cork or straw, dropper, 1 cm water	**Chapter Resources Booklet** Foldables Worksheet, p. 15 Directed Reading Overview, p. 17 Note-taking Worksheets, pp. 31–32	Glencoe's Assessment Advantage	
MiniLAB: wooden ruler	**Chapter Resources Booklet** Transparency Activity, p. 42 MiniLAB, p. 3 Enrichment, p. 28 Reinforcement, p. 25 Directed Reading, p. 18 Transparency Activity, pp. 45–46	Portfolio Activity, p. 318 Performance MiniLAB, p. 319 Skill Builder Activities, p. 320 Content Section Assessment, p. 320	Section Focus Transparency Teaching Transparency Interactive CD-ROM/DVD Guided Reading Audio Program
Activity: long, coiled spring toy, 5 cm colored yarn, meterstick, stopwatch *Need materials?* Contact Science Kit at 1-800-828-7777 or www.sciencekit.com on the Internet.	**Chapter Resources Booklet** Transparency Activity, p. 43 Enrichment, p. 29 Reinforcement, p. 26 Directed Reading, p. 19 Activity Worksheet, pp. 5–6 Lab Activity, pp. 9–11 **Reading and Writing Skill Activities,** p. 33 **Home and Community Involvement,** p. 42	Portfolio Extension, p. 322 Science Journal, p. 324 Performance Skill Builder Activities, p. 325 Content Section Assessment, p. 325	Section Focus Transparency Interactive CD-ROM/DVD Guided Reading Audio Program
MiniLAB: large, opaque drinking glass or cup, water, white soda straw **Activity:** coiled spring toy, stopwatch, meterstick, tape	**Chapter Resources Booklet** Transparency Activity, p. 44 Enrichment, p. 30 Reinforcement, p. 27 Directed Reading, pp. 19, 20 MiniLAB, p. 4 Lab Activity, pp. 13–14 Activity Worksheet, pp. 7–8 **Lab Management and Safety,** p. 65 **Mathematics Skill Activities,** p. 47	Portfolio Challenge, p. 333 Performance MiniLAB, p. 328 Problem-Solving Activity, p. 331 Skill Builder Activities, p. 333 Content Section Assessment, p. 333	Section Focus Transparency Interactive CD-ROM/DVD Guided Reading Audio Program

End of Chapter Assessment

Glencoe's Assessment Advantage

Blackline Masters	Technology	Professional Series
Chapter Resources Booklet Chapter Review, pp. 35–36 Chapter Tests, pp. 37–40 **Standardized Test Practice by The Princeton Review,** pp. 47–50	MindJogger Videoquiz CD-ROM Explorations and Quizzes Vocabulary Puzzle Makers ExamView Pro Test Bank Interactive Lesson Planner Interactive Teacher's Edition	Performance Assessment in the Science Classroom (PASC)

Transparencies

Section Focus

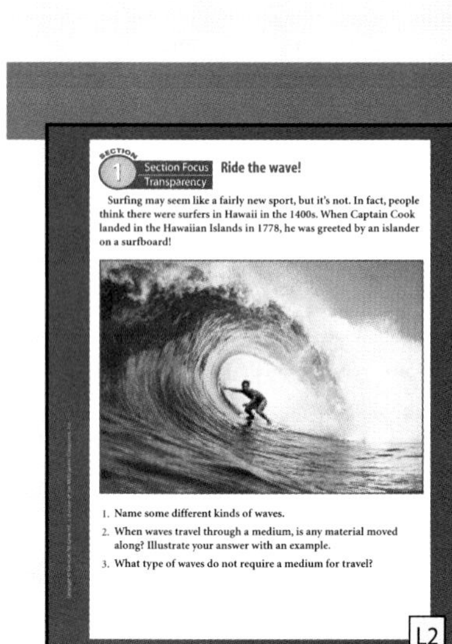
Section 1 Section Focus Transparency **Ride the wave!**

Surfing may seem like a fairly new sport, but it's not. In fact, people think there were surfers in Hawaii in the 1400s. When Captain Cook landed in the Hawaiian Islands in 1778, he was greeted by an islander on a surfboard!

1. Name some different kinds of waves.
2. When waves travel through a medium, is any material moved along? Illustrate your answer with an example.
3. What type of waves do not require a medium for travel?

L2

Section 2 Section Focus Transparency **The Sun's Radiant Energies**

Visible light and ultraviolet (UV) radiation both come from the Sun. UV radiation causes eye damage, skin cancer, and burns skin. Visible light and UV radiation are the same type of wave; the difference between the two is their wavelengths.

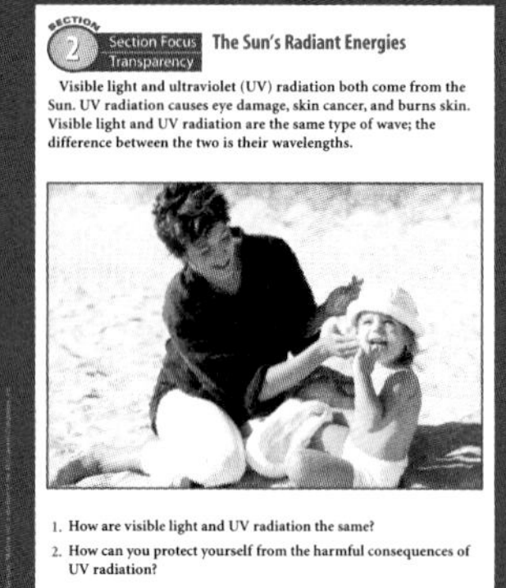

1. How are visible light and UV radiation the same?
2. How can you protect yourself from the harmful consequences of UV radiation?

L2

Section 3 Section Focus Transparency **Wave Art**

Artists work with all kinds of materials, so why not water? This image was made by placing an obstacle in the water and generating waves. As waves reach the obstacle, they move through the holes.

1. Describe what is happening in this picture.
2. What would happen to the wave pattern if both holes were plugged?
3. Do you think sound waves diffract in a similar fashion? Give an example that illustrates your answer.

L2

This is a representation of key blackline masters available in the Teacher Classroom Resources. See Resource Manager boxes within the chapter for additional information.

Assessment

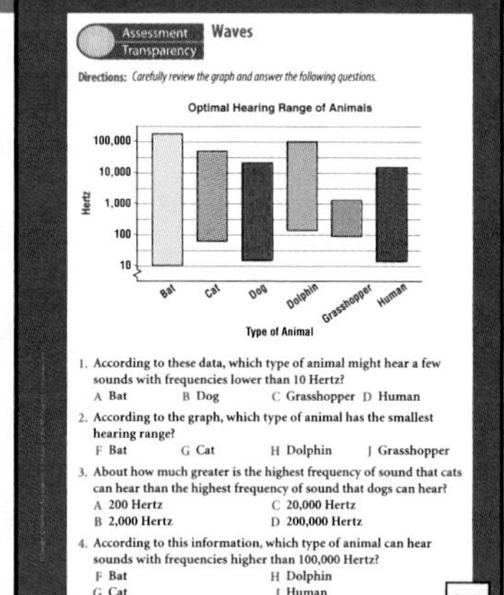
Assessment Transparency **Waves**

Directions: Carefully review the graph and answer the following questions.

1. According to these data, which type of animal might hear a few sounds with frequencies lower than 10 Hertz?
   A Bat B Dog C Grasshopper D Human
2. According to the graph, which type of animal has the smallest hearing range?
   F Bat G Cat H Dolphin J Grasshopper
3. About how much greater is the highest frequency of sound that cats can hear than the highest frequency of sound that dogs can hear?
   A 200 Hertz C 20,000 Hertz
   B 2,000 Hertz D 200,000 Hertz
4. According to this information, which type of animal can hear sounds with frequencies higher than 100,000 Hertz?
   F Bat H Dolphin
   G Cat J Human

L2

Teaching

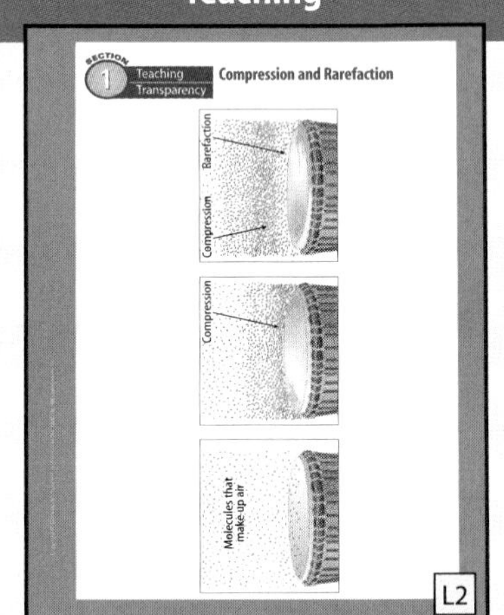
Section 1 Teaching Transparency **Compression and Rarefaction**

L2

Key to Teaching Strategies

The following designations will help you decide which activities are appropriate for your students.

- L1 Level 1 activities should be appropriate for students with learning difficulties.
- L2 Level 2 activities should be within the ability range of all students.
- L3 Level 3 activities are designed for above-average students.
- ELL ELL activities should be within the ability range of English Language Learners.
- COOP LEARN Cooperative Learning activities are designed for small group work.
- LS Multiple Learning Styles logos, as described on page 22T, are used throughout to indicate strategies that address different learning styles.
- P These strategies represent student products that can be placed into a best-work portfolio.

Hands-on Activities

Activity Worksheets

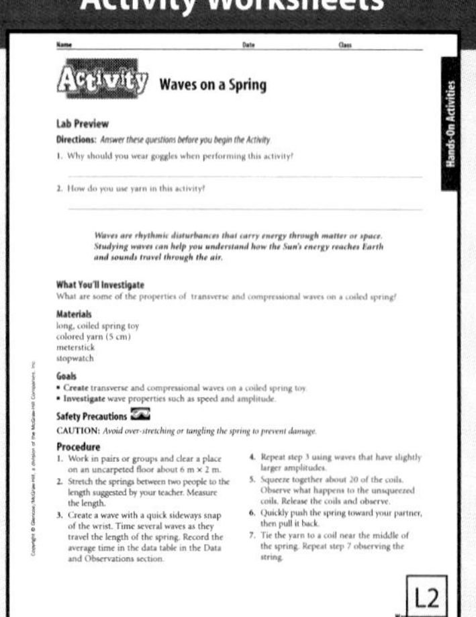
Activity **Waves on a Spring**

Lab Preview

Directions: *Answer these questions before you begin the Activity.*

1. Why should you wear goggles when performing this activity?
2. How do you use yarn in this activity?

Waves are rhythmic disturbances that carry energy through matter or space. Studying waves can help you understand how the Sun's energy reaches Earth and sounds travel through the air.

What You'll Investigate

What are some of the properties of transverse and compressional waves on a coiled spring?

Materials: long, coiled spring toy; colored yarn (5 cm); meterstick; stopwatch

Goals
- Create transverse and compressional waves on a coiled spring toy.
- Investigate wave properties such as speed and amplitude.

L2

Laboratory Activities

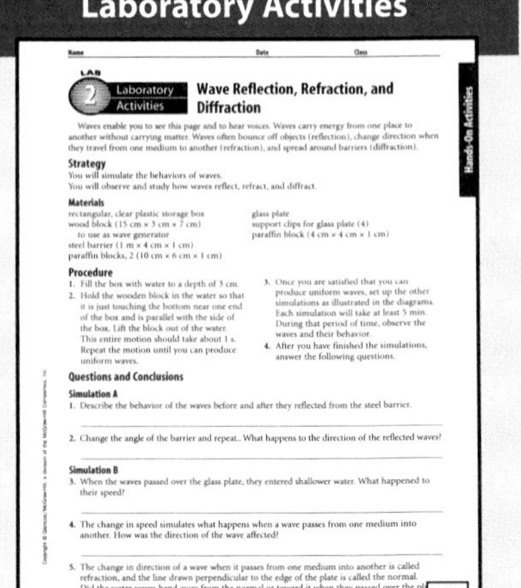
Lab 2 Laboratory Activities **Wave Reflection, Refraction, and Diffraction**

Strategy

You will simulate the behaviors of waves.

You will observe and study how waves reflect, refract, and diffract.

L2

Meeting Different Ability Levels

Content Outline

L2

Reinforcement

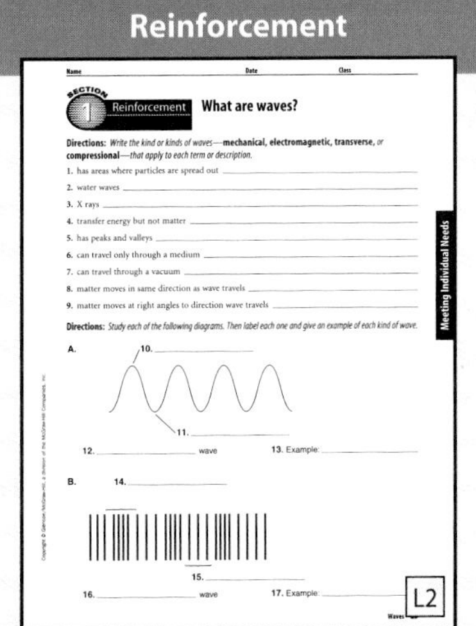

L2

Directed Reading

L1

Assessment

Chapter Tests

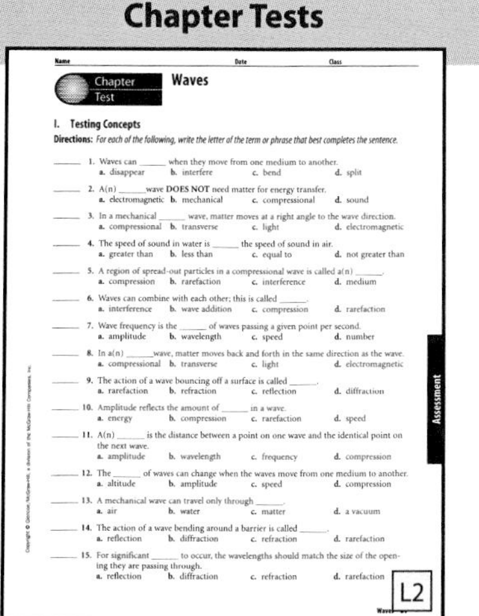

L2

Enrichment

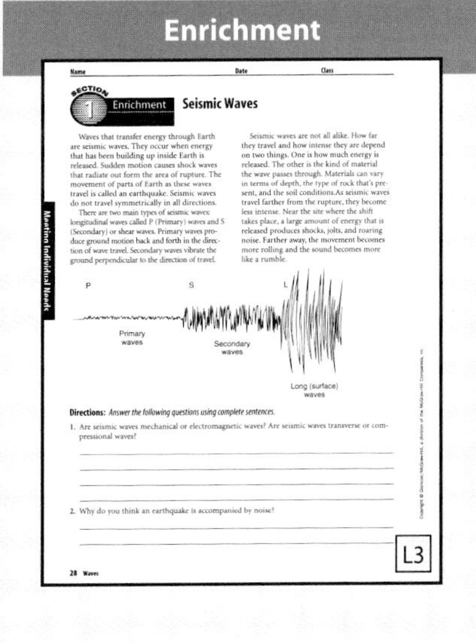

L3

Spanish Directed Reading

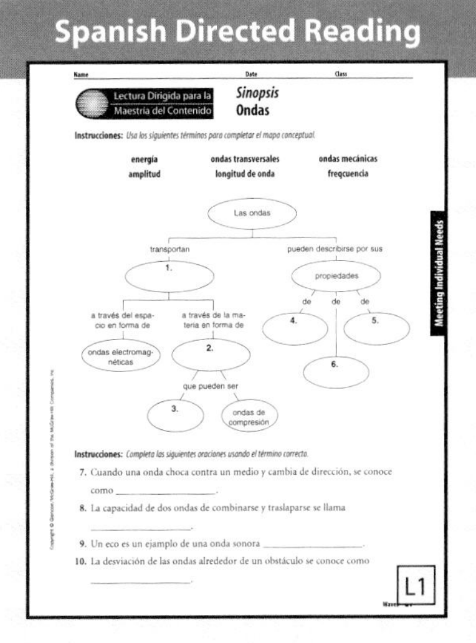

L1

Test Practice Workbook

L2

Chapter Review

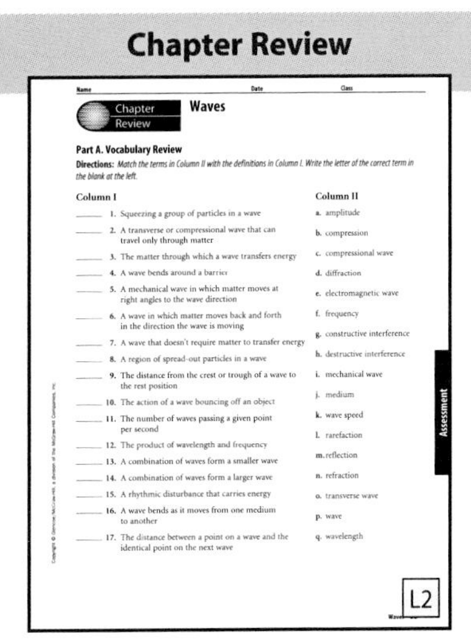

L2

Science Content Background

SECTION 1

What are waves?

What is a wave?

Electromagnetic waves have a dual nature. In describing their emission from matter or absorption by matter, they are best described as particles, usually called photons. During their propagation, they are best described as waves. In electromagnetic waves, which are always transverse, electric and magnetic fields oscillate perpendicular to the direction the waves travel.

SECTION 2

Wave Properties

Wave Movements

Waves travel outward from an energy source. If a rock is thrown into a pond, energy traveling outward from the center is seen as waves, dampening (decreasing in amplitude) as they move through the molecules of water. The wave will move through one complete cycle in one wavelength. The period (T) of a wave is the time it takes one wavelength to pass a fixed point. A wave's period is the reciprocal of its frequency.

Light waves are electromagnetic waves. Visible light has a range of wavelengths between about 400 nm and 700 nm. We know the elements present in stars by the wavelengths of light they emit, which are detected by spectroscopes.

The speed of light in a vacuum is constant at about 3×10^8 m/s. Michelson and Morley accurately measured the speed of light by reflecting light rays from a mountaintop to a rotating mirror.

The amplitude of a sound wave determines its sound intensity, or how loud it is. The more sound energy generated, the louder the sound. Two or more tones produced at the same time produce unpleasant (dissonant) or pleasant (harmonious) sounds, depending on the way the waves interfere. The ratios of the frequencies of the tones determine whether or not they are pleasing.

Fun Fact

Massive bodies have strong gravitational fields. If these bodies undergo some sort of regular motion, oscillations in their gravity fields can, according to theory, be detected. Scientists are currently trying to develop methods of detecting these gravity waves.

SECTION 3

Wave Behavior

Reflection

The angle of incidence (the incoming wave angle) equals the angle of reflection (the outgoing wave angle). This is known as the law of reflection. The angles of incidence and reflection are measured relative to a line drawn perpendicular to the reflecting surface. Diffuse reflection occurs as the light bounces at different angles from uneven surfaces. Diffuse reflection makes the uneven surfaces appear dull.

Refraction

In the case of light waves, a constant called a substance's index of refraction is the speed of light in a vacuum divided by the speed of light in the substance. The index of refraction gives the ratio between the sine of the angle of incidence and the sine of the angle of refraction.

Refraction can be beneficial. For example, eyeglasses and contact lenses correct vision by refracting light rays so that they focus properly on the retina of the eye. Binoculars, microscopes, and telescopes also utilize refraction to produce magnified images of small objects and objects at great distances.

Diffraction

The phenomenon called diffraction occurs as waves bend around barriers or spread through apertures. Diffraction of light can produce fringes (a series of bright and dark lines) as light waves bend around the edges of objects such as razor blades, diffraction gratings, or the teeth of a comb. The fringes, which can be seen on a screen, are a series of constructive and destructive interference patterns. As the light passes through the aperture, each point on the aperture can be considered a new point source of light, a concept known as Huygens' principle. The light reaching a particular point on the screen comes from different points on the aperture, and thus has traveled different distances to the screen. The interference patterns are produced because at different points the phases of the waves add constructively or destructively.

Wave Interference

Sound waves can be made to interfere constructively or destructively as they reflect from a curved wall or a curved backdrop in a concert hall. Much planning and great expense goes into designing the acoustics in a fine performance hall.

Seismic waves are produced by energy traveling through the material medium of Earth. Seismic waves are of three types—S, P, and L. S-waves (secondary waves) are transverse or shear, and cannot travel through fluids. These seismic waves reflect off the fluid outer core of Earth. P-waves, or primary waves, are compressional, or longitudinal, waves. They may pass through all of Earth's materials and are detected first. L-waves are seismic waves that occur along Earth's surface. They cause up-down and rolling motions on the surface, which is why they are so destructive.

Fun Fact

The rainbow pattern seen on the back of compact disks is a diffraction pattern that results from the grooves on the disk and the different wavelengths of visible light.

For additional content background on this topic, go to the Glencoe Science Web site at science.glencoe.com.

Barry L. Runk/Grant Heilman Photography, Inc.

Waves

Chapter Vocabulary

wave
mechanical wave
transverse wave
compressional wave
electromagnetic wave
amplitude
wavelength
frequency
reflection
refraction
diffraction
interference

What do you think?

Science Journal The filters shown are polarizing filters. These filters allow only light waves that vibrate in a specific direction to pass through them. Waves in ordinary light vibrate in all directions.

CHAPTER 11

Waves

On a breezy day in Maui, Hawaii, windsurfers ride the ocean waves. What forces are operating on the windsurfer and his sailboard? The wind catches the sails and helps propel the sailboard, but other forces also are at work—waves. Waves carry energy. You can see the ocean waves in this picture, but there are many kinds of waves you cannot see. Microwaves heat your food, radio waves transmit the music you listen to into your home, and sound waves carry that music from the radio to your ears. In this chapter, you will learn about different types of waves and how they behave.

What do you think?

Science Journal What is this picture about? What causes the light and dark areas? Hint: *Some sunglasses have this kind of lens.* Write your answer or best guess in your Science Journal.

314

Theme Connection

Energy Waves are periodic disturbances that carry energy. The larger the amplitude of the wave, the more energy is transferred.

It's a beautiful autumn day. You are sitting by a pond in a park. Music blares from a school marching band practicing for a big game. The music is carried by waves. A fish jumps, making a splash. Waves spread past a leaf that fell from a tree, causing the leaf to move. In the following activity, you'll observe how waves carry energy that can cause objects to move.

Observe wave behavior

1. Fill a large, clear plastic plate with 1 cm of water.
2. Use a dropper to release a single drop of water onto the water's surface. Repeat.
3. Float a cork or straw on the water.
4. When the water is still, repeat step 2 from a height of 10 cm, then again from 20 cm.

Observe

In your Science Journal, record your observations and describe the movements of the floating object.

Before You Read

Making a Concept Map Study Fold **Make the following Foldable to organize information by diagramming ideas about waves.**

Mechanical Waves
Transverse Waves
Compressional Waves

1. Place a sheet of paper in front of you so the long side is at the top. Fold the bottom of the paper to the top, stopping about four centimeters from the top.
2. Draw an oval above the fold. Write *Mechanical Waves* inside the oval.
3. Fold the paper in half from the left side to the right side and then unfold. Through the top thickness of the paper, cut along the fold line to form two tabs.
4. Draw an oval on each tab. Write *Transverse Waves* in one oval and *Compressional Waves* in the other, as shown. Draw arrows from the large oval to the smaller ovals.
5. As you read the chapter, write information about the two types of mechanical waves under the tabs.

315

EXPLORE ACTIVITY

Purpose Use the Explore Activity to give students an opportunity to observe and describe wave behavior. L2 ELL COOP LEARN

LS **Logical-Mathematical**

Materials large, clear-plastic plate; small cork or piece of a soda straw; dropper; water

Teaching Strategies

- Suggest that students observe closely because the waves will move quickly.
- Tell students to be sure the water is still before adding drops of water. They also should be careful not to disturb the water when adding the cork.

Observe

Circular waves travel outward from the point where the drops hit the water's surface. Drops released from a height of 20 cm cause larger waves and transfer more energy than do drops released from a height of 10 cm. The cork bobs up and down as the waves pass but does not move horizontally.

✔Assessment

Process Provide students with diagrams of transverse waves with different amplitudes. Ask them to identify which diagram shows waves generated by dropping water from a greater height. Use **Performance Assessment in the Science Classroom,** p. 89.

Before You Read

FOLDABLES Reading & Study Skills

Dinah Zike Study Fold

Purpose Have students make and use a Foldable concept map to list examples of and record information on two types of mechanical waves—transverse waves and compressional waves. After reading, students can use the Foldable as a study guide.

For additional help, see Foldables Worksheet p. 15 in **Chapter Resources Booklet,** or go to the Glencoe Science Web site at **science.glencoe.com.** See After You Read in the Study Guide at the end of this chapter.

What are waves?

1 Motivate

Bellringer Transparency

Display the Section Focus Transparency for Section 1. Use the accompanying Transparency Activity Master. L2 ELL

Section 1 Section Focus Transparency **Ride the wave!**

Surfing may seem like a fairly new sport, but it's not. In fact, people think there were surfers in Hawaii in the 1400s. When Captain Cook landed in the Hawaiian Islands in 1778, he was greeted by an islander on a surfboard!

1. Name some different kinds of waves.
2. When waves travel through a medium, is any material moved along? Illustrate your answer with an example.
3. What type of waves do not require a medium for travel?

Tie to Prior Knowledge

Ask students to describe any waves they know of. Discuss with them the form of energy transferred by each wave.

What are waves?

As You Read

What You'll Learn

- **Explain** the relationship among waves, energy, and matter.
- **Describe** the difference between transverse waves and compressional waves.

Vocabulary

wave
mechanical wave
transverse wave
compressional wave
electromagnetic wave

Why It's Important

You can hear music and other sounds because of waves.

What is a wave?

When you are relaxing on an air mattress in a pool and someone does a cannonball off the diving board, you suddenly find yourself bobbing up and down. You can make something move by giving it a push or pull, but the person jumping didn't touch your air mattress. How did the energy from the cannonball dive travel through the water and move your air mattress? The up-and-down motion was caused by the peaks and valleys of the ripples that moved from where the splash occurred. These peaks and valleys make up water waves.

Waves Carry Energy **Waves** are rhythmic disturbances that carry energy without carrying matter, as shown in **Figure 1A.** You can see the energy of the wave from the speedboat traveling outward, but the water only moves up and down. If you've ever felt a clap of thunder, you know that sound waves can carry large amounts of energy. You also transfer energy when you throw something to a friend, as in **Figure 1B.** However, there is a difference between a moving ball and a moving wave. A ball is made of matter, and when it is thrown, the matter moves from one place to another. So, unlike the moving wave, throwing a ball involves the transport of matter as well as energy.

Figure 1
The wave and the thrown ball carry energy.

A **The waves created by a boat move mostly up and down, but the energy travels outward from the boat.**

B **When the ball is thrown, the ball, as well as the energy put into the throw, moves forward.**

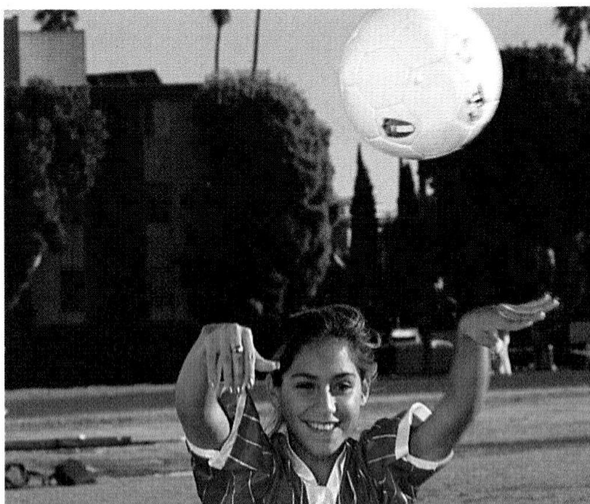

Section Assessment Planner

Portfolio
Activity, p. 318
Performance Assessment
MiniLAB, p. 319
Skill Builder Activities, p. 320
See page 340 for more options.

Content Assessment
Section, p. 320
Challenge, p. 320
Chapter, pp. 340–341

316 CHAPTER 11 Waves

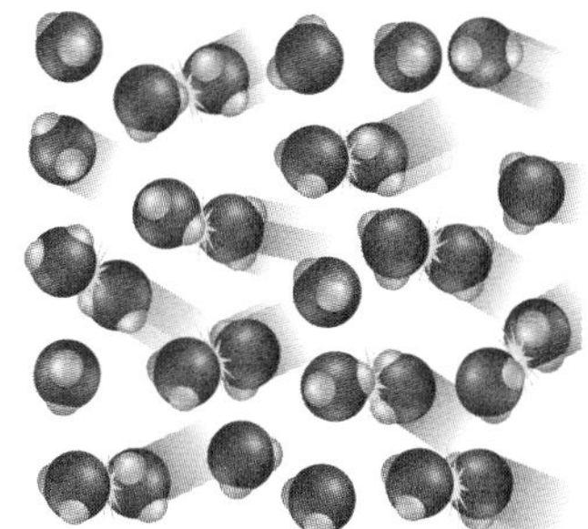

Figure 2
A As the students pass the ball, the students' positions do not change—only the position of the ball changes. **B** The molecules in water bump each other and pass the energy of a wave, even though they don't travel with the wave.

A Model for Waves

How does a wave carry energy without transporting matter? Imagine a line of people, as shown in **Figure 2A.** The first person in line passes a ball to the second person, who passes the ball to the next person, and so on. Passing a ball down a line of people is a model for how waves can transport energy without transporting matter. Even though the ball has traveled, the people in line have not moved. In this model, you can think of the ball as representing energy. What do the people in line represent?

Think about the ripples on the surface of a pond. The energy carried by the ripples travels through the water. The water is made up of water molecules. It is the individual molecules of water that pass the wave energy, just as the people in **Figure 2A** pass the ball. The water molecules transport the energy in a water wave by colliding with the molecules around them, as shown in **Figure 2B.**

Reading Check *What is carried by waves?*

Mechanical Waves

In the wave model, the ball could not be transferred if the line of people didn't exist. The wave energy of a water wave could not be transferred if no water molecules existed. These types of waves, which use matter to transfer energy, are called **mechanical waves.** The matter through which a mechanical wave travels is called a medium. For ripples on a pond, the medium is the water.

A mechanical wave travels as energy is transferred from particle to particle in the medium. For example, a sound wave is a mechanical wave that can travel through air, as well as solids, liquids, and other gases. The sound wave travels through air by transferring energy from gas molecule to gas molecule. Without a medium such as air, you would not hear sounds. In outer space sound waves can't travel because there is no air.

2 Teach

What is a wave?

Discussion

Ask students to describe how being near a source of deep, loud sounds, such as heavy machinery or the subwoofer of a stereo, demonstrates that waves carry energy. You can feel the vibrations as well as hear the sound. L1
IS **Auditory-Musical**

A Model for Waves

Make a Model

Have students duplicate the model described in the text. As they do this, emphasize that they are like the molecules of water through which a wave flows. Point out that the ball is made of matter, but in the model it represents energy. L1
ELL COOP LEARN IS **Kinesthetic**

Answer energy

Mechanical Waves

Students might be surprised that some waves are described as mechanical. The word *mechanical* comes from the Latin word *mechanicus*, meaning "machine." Based on this, have students discuss why mechanical is an appropriate term to use for waves. One definition of *machine* is a device that transmits energy. In a mechanical wave, matter transmits energy. L2
IS **Linguistic**

Resource Manager 

Chapter Resources Booklet
Note-taking Worksheets, pp. 31–32
Transparency Activity, p. 42
Directed Reading for Content Mastery, pp. 17, 18

Visual Learning

Figure 2B Tell students that the water molecules near the surface of a wave actually travel in small circles. The boundary between air and water acts like a solid due to surface tension and pushes on the water molecules. This gives them a combination of transverse and compressional movement. Have students model this movement with a cork in water. L1 ELL IS **Kinesthetic**

Mechanical Waves, continued

Use an Analogy

Ask students to think of people "doing the wave" in a stadium. Point out that this wave is similar to a transverse mechanical wave because the people, like particles, move up and down at right angles to the direction the wave moves. L2 LS **Visual-Spatial**

Quick Demo

Put a clear plate with colored water on an overhead projector. Ask students to predict what will happen to a floating object as waves are generated in the water. Generate waves either by dropping small objects into the water or by moving a finger in the water. The floating object will bob up and down because the water waves are very much like transverse waves. L3 LS **Visual-Spatial**

Reading Check

Answer crests

Activity

Ask students to list on chart paper examples of mechanical waves. Have them draw each type of wave, describe each wave as transverse or compressional, and label the different parts of each wave. L2 COOP LEARN LS **Visual-Spatial** P

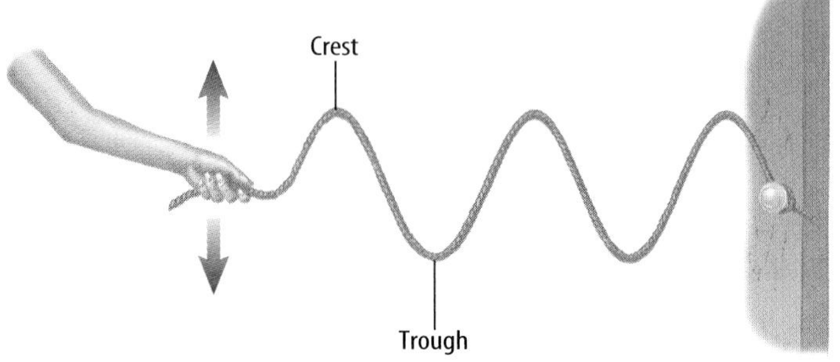

Figure 3
The high points on the wave are called crests and the low points are called troughs.

Transverse Waves In a mechanical **transverse wave,** the wave energy causes the matter in the medium to move up and down or back and forth at right angles to the direction the wave travels. You can make a model of a transverse wave. Stretch a long rope out on the ground. Hold one end in your hand. Now shake the end in your hand back and forth. By adjusting the way you shake the rope, you can create a wave that seems to slide along the rope.

When you first started shaking the rope, it might have appeared that the rope itself was moving away from you. But it was only the wave that was moving away from your hand. The wave energy moves through the rope, but the matter in the rope doesn't travel. You can see that the wave has peaks and valleys at regular intervals. As shown in **Figure 3,** the high points of transverse waves are called crests. The low points are called troughs.

Reading Check *What are the highest points of transverse waves called?*

Figure 4
A compressional wave can travel through a coiled spring toy.

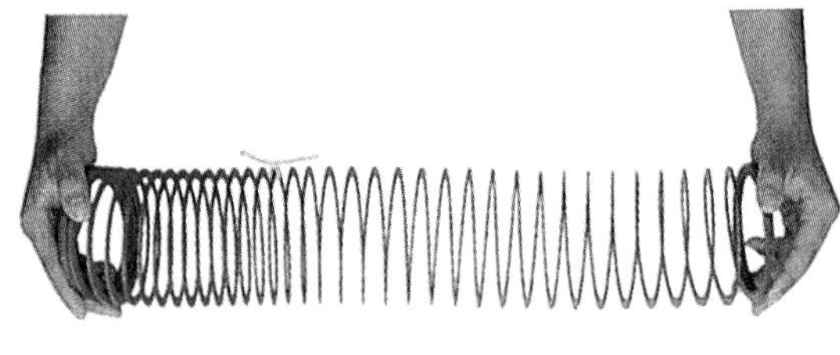

A **As the wave motion begins, the coils near the string are close together and the other coils are far apart.**

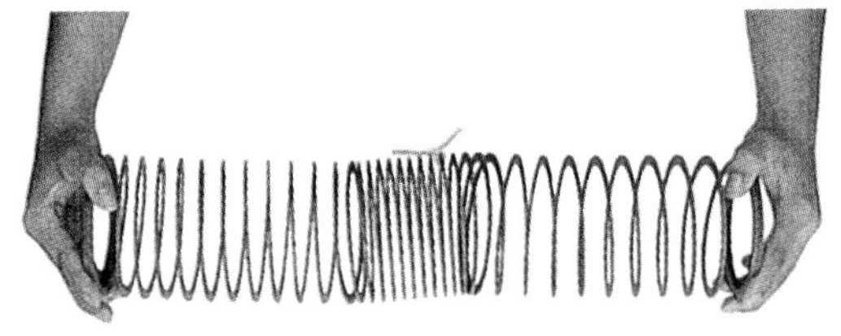

B **The wave, seen in the squeezed and stretched coils, travels along the spring.**

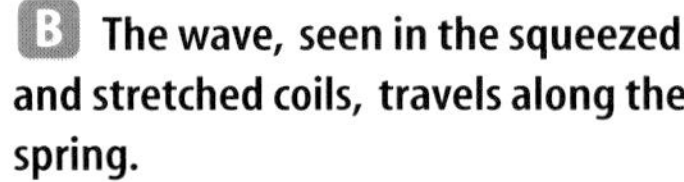

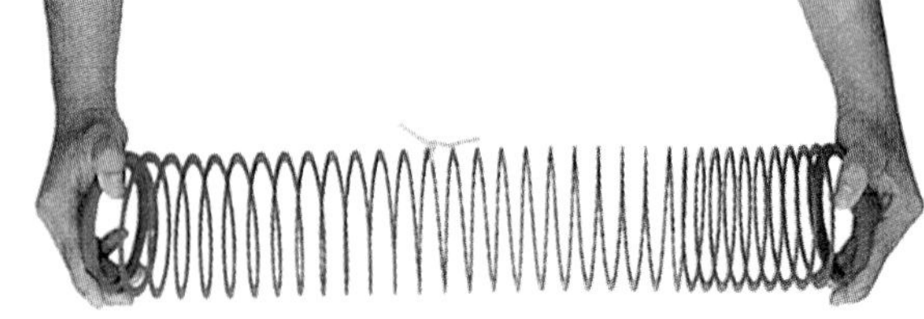

C **The string and coils did not travel with the wave. Each coil moved only slightly forward and then back to its original position.**

Teacher FYI

There are three main types of seismic waves. Primary (P) waves oscillate back and forth along the direction the wave travels. Secondary (S) waves oscillate perpendicular to the direction of wave motion. Surface (L) waves cause horizontal and, sometimes, vertical ground surface movement.

Active Reading

Bubble Map Using a bubble map helps students start ideas flowing about a given topic. Words are clustered to describe a concept. Students can use the bubble map for a prewrite, to generate ideas before writing in their Journals, or to review for a test. Have students design a Bubble Map for the different types of waves described in this section.

Compressional Waves Mechanical waves can be either transverse or compressional. In a **compressional wave,** matter in the medium moves forward and backward in the same direction that the wave travels. You can make a compressional wave by squeezing together and releasing several coils of a coiled spring toy, as shown in **Figure 4.**

You see that the coils move only as the wave passes. They then return to their original position. So, like transverse waves, compressional waves carry only energy forward along the spring. In this example, the spring is the medium the wave moves through, but the spring does not move along with the wave.

Sound Waves Sound waves are compressional waves. How do you make sound waves when you talk or sing? If you hold your fingers against your throat while you hum, you can feel vibrations. These vibrations are the movements of your vocal cords. If you touch a stereo speaker while it's playing, you can feel it vibrating, too. All waves are produced by something that is vibrating.

Making Sound Waves

How do vibrating vocal cords, strings, and other objects make sound waves? To find out, look at the drumhead stretched over the open end of the drum shown in **Figure 5.** When the drumhead moves upward, it touches some of the molecules that make up the air. When everything is quiet, these molecules are spaced about the same distance apart. However, when the drumhead moves upward, it pushes the molecules together. The group of molecules that are squeezed together is called a compression.

When the drumhead moves downward, the molecules have more room and move away from each other. A place where molecules are far apart is called a rarefaction (rar uh FAK shun). These disturbed molecules then collide with the molecules next to them, transferring the energy they are carrying. This causes the compression and the rarefaction to move away from the drumhead.

Mini LAB

Comparing Sounds

Procedure

1. Hold a **wooden ruler** firmly on the edge of your **desk** so that most of it extends off the edge of the desk.
2. Pluck the free end of the ruler so that it vibrates up and down. Use gentle motion at first, then pluck with more energy.
3. Repeat step 2, moving the ruler about 1 cm further onto the desk each time until only about 5 cm extend off the edge.

Analysis

1. Compare the loudness of the sounds that are made using little energy with those made using more energy.
2. Describe the differences in the sound as the ruler was moved.

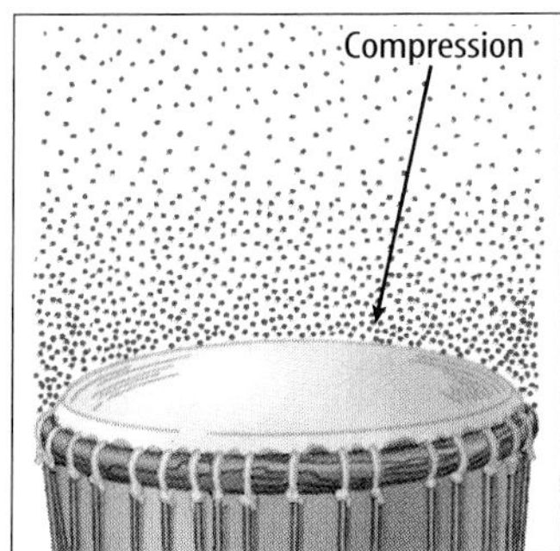

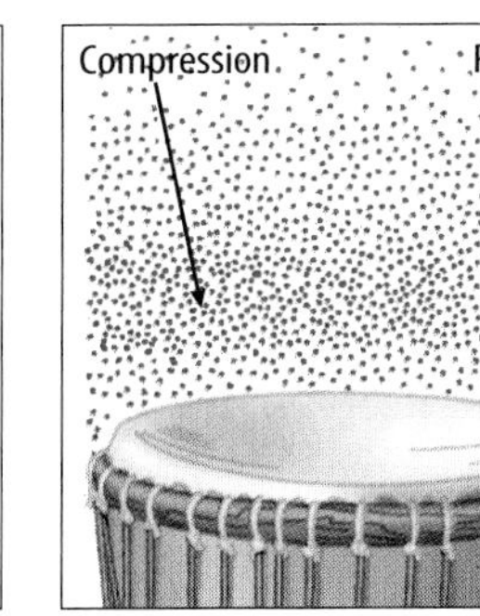
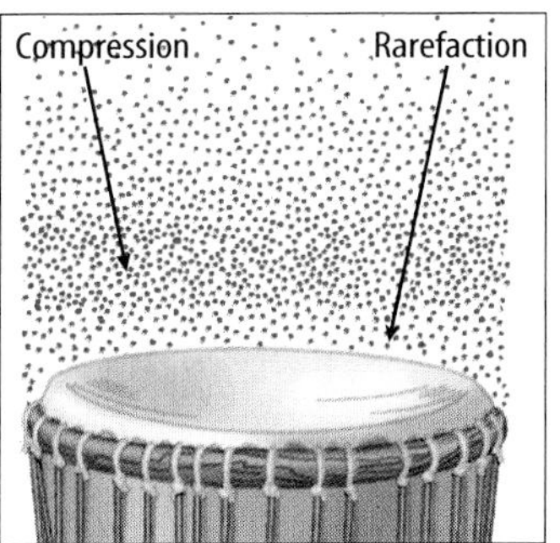

Figure 5
A vibrating drumhead makes compressions and rarefactions in the air. *How do your vocal cords make compressions and rarefactions in air?*

Teacher FYI

Compressional waves are often called longitudinal waves.

Making Sound Waves

Mini LAB

Purpose Students compare and contrast various sounds made by a vibrating object. L2 ELL LS **Auditory-Musical**

Materials wooden ruler

Teaching Strategies Monitor students to ensure their results include information about the length of the ruler hanging over the table.

Troubleshooting Make sure students do not pluck hard enough to break the ruler.

Analysis

1. Using more energy produces louder sounds.
2. The greater the length of the vibrating object, the lower the pitch produced.

Assessment

Performance Give students materials of different lengths and ask them to choose and make sounds with the ones that produce lower-pitched sounds. Use **PASC,** p. 97.

Caption Answer

Figure 5 The vocal cords vibrate, alternately squeezing air particles together and letting them spread apart.

Resource Manager

Chapter Resources Booklet

Transparency Activity, pp. 45–46
Enrichment, p. 28
Reinforcement, p. 25
MiniLAB, p. 3

Inclusion Strategies

Hearing Impaired Some students may not be able to hear the sounds made by the ruler as they do the MiniLAB. Have these students pay attention to feeling the vibrations. They should be able to feel the vibrations with the hand holding the ruler on the desk. Suggest they pluck the ruler several times while paying attention to what they feel. When they are familiar with the feeling, they can finish the lab.

Electromagnetic Waves

Physics INTEGRATION

There are 24 GPS satellites, and they orbit Earth at a height of 17,500 km. Their electromagnetic radio waves can be received all over Earth, regardless of the weather. GPS was designed for and is operated by the U.S. Department of Defense and provides positioning information to military submarines, helicopters, ships, bombers, tanks, and missiles. However, since the signals can be received by an unlimited number of users, they are increasingly important in everyday civilian navigation.

3 Assess

Reteach

Demonstrate compressional and transverse waves using a spring toy. Have students identify each type of wave and the parts of the waves. L2

LS **Visual-Spatial**

Challenge

Ask students to investigate the behavior of surface waves near the seashore and make posters showing what they find. As the waves approach land, water molecules near the surface experience more elliptical movement, causing the waves to form high crests that eventually crash into land. L3 LS **Visual-Spatial**

✔Assessment

Process Have students draw diagrams of transverse and compressional waves, labeling the crests and troughs. Use **PASC**, p. 127.

Physics INTEGRATION

Maybe you've used a global positioning system (GPS) receiver to determine your location while driving, boating, or hiking. Earth-orbiting satellites send electromagnetic radio waves that transmit their exact locations and times of transmission. The GPS receiver uses information from four of these satellites to determine your location to within about 16 m.

Electromagnetic Waves

When you listen to the radio, watch TV, or use a microwave oven to cook, you use a different kind of wave—one that doesn't need matter as a medium.

Waves that do not require matter to carry energy are called **electromagnetic waves.** Electromagnetic waves are transverse waves that are produced by the motion of electrically charged particles. Just like mechanical waves, electromagnetic waves can travel through a medium such as a solid, liquid, or gas. Radio waves are electromagnetic waves that travel through the air from a radio station, and then through the solid walls of your house to reach your radio. However, unlike mechanical waves, electromagnetic waves can travel through outer space or through a vacuum where no matter exists.

Useful Waves In space, which has no air or any other medium, orbiting satellites beam radio waves to TVs, radios, and cellular phones on Earth's surface. However, radio waves are not the only electromagnetic waves traveling in space. You use sunscreen to protect yourself from ultraviolet rays. Infrared and ultraviolet waves travel from the Sun through space before they reach Earth's atmosphere. Infrared waves feel warm when they strike your skin. Other useful electromagnetic waves include X rays and visible light. X rays are useful not only in medical applications, but also for security checks in airports as luggage is scanned. And without visible light you wouldn't see color or be able to read this page.

Section  Assessment

1. Describe the movement of a floating object on a pond when struck by a wave.
2. Why can't a sound wave travel from a satellite to Earth?
3. Give one example of a transverse wave and one example of a compressional wave. How are they similar and different?
4. What is the difference between a mechanical wave and an electromagnetic wave?
5. **Think Critically** How is it possible for a sound wave to transmit energy but not matter?

Skill Builder Activities

6. **Concept Mapping** Create a concept map that shows the relationships among the following: *waves, mechanical waves, electromagnetic waves, compressional waves,* and *transverse waves.* **For more help, refer to the Science Skill Handbook.**
7. **Using a Word Processor** Use word-processing software to write short descriptions of the waves you encounter during a typical day. **For more help, refer to the Technology Skill Handbook.**

Answers to Section Assessment

1. It bobs up and down.
2. It requires a medium through which to travel, and there is no medium in space.
3. Possible answer: Water waves are transverse waves. Sound waves are compressional waves. Compressional waves cause vibration in the direction of wave movement. Transverse waves cause vibration at right angles to the wave's direction. Both involve periodic motion and carry energy.
4. Mechanical waves use matter to transmit energy. Electromagnetic waves do not require matter to carry energy.
5. The wave causes molecules of matter to vibrate and bump neighbor molecules.
6. Answers should show mechanical waves as compressional or transverse; electromagnetic waves are transverse.
7. Answers might include radio waves, sound waves, or waves in a bathtub.

Wave Properties

Amplitude

Can you describe a wave? One way might be to tell how high a water wave rises above, or falls below, the normal level. This distance is called the wave's amplitude. The **amplitude** of a transverse wave is one-half the distance between a crest and a trough, as shown in **Figure 6A.** In a compressional wave, the amplitude is greater when the particles of the medium are squeezed closer together in each compression and spread farther apart in each rarefaction.

Amplitude and Energy A wave's amplitude is related to the energy that the wave carries. For example, the electromagnetic waves that make up bright light have greater amplitudes than the waves that make up dim light. Waves of bright light carry more energy than the waves that make up dim light. In a similar way, loud sound waves have greater amplitudes than soft sound waves. Loud sounds carry more energy than soft sounds. If a sound is loud enough, it can carry enough energy to damage your hearing.

As you can see in **Figure 6B,** when a hurricane strikes a coastal area, the resulting water waves can damage anything that stands in their path. The waves caused by a hurricane carry more energy than the small waves or ripples on a pond.

As You Read

***What* You'll Learn**

- **Describe** the relationship between the frequency and wavelength of a wave.
- **Explain** why waves travel at different speeds.

Vocabulary
amplitude
wavelength
frequency

***Why* It's Important**
The energy carried by a wave depends on its amplitude.

Figure 6
A transverse wave has an amplitude.

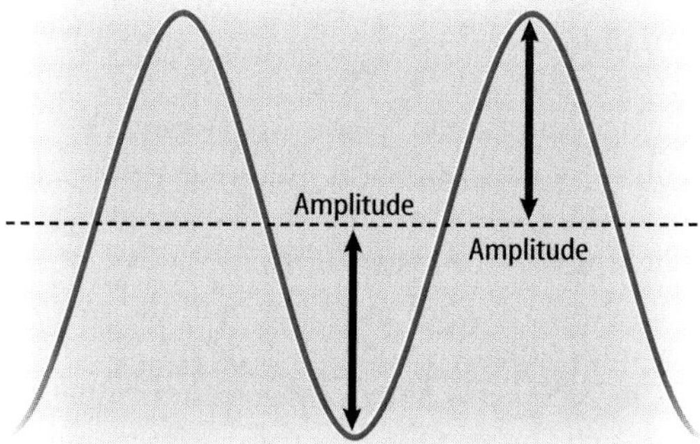

A **The amplitude is a measure of how high the crests are or how deep the troughs are.**

B **A wave of large amplitude is responsible for this damage.**

Wave Properties

1 Motivate

Bellringer Transparency

Display the Section Focus Transparency for Section 2. Use the accompanying Transparency Activity Master. L2 ELL

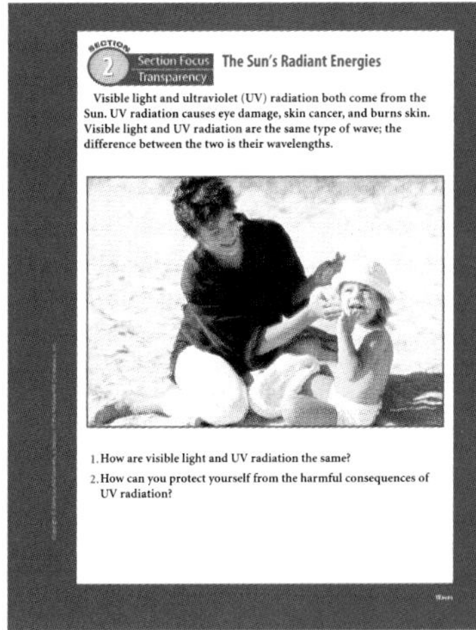

Tie to Prior Knowledge

Ask students whether it takes more or less energy to twirl a jump rope high enough to clear a short person or a tall person. tall Explain that in this section, they will learn how to describe the energy different waves carry.

Section Assessment Planner

PORTFOLIO
Extension, p. 322
Science Journal, p. 324

PERFORMANCE ASSESSMENT
Skill Builder Activities, p. 325
See page 340 for more options.

CONTENT ASSESSMENT
Section, p. 325
Challenge, p. 325
Chapter, pp. 340–341

Resource Manager

Chapter Resources Booklet
Transparency Activity, p. 43
Directed Reading for Content Mastery, p. 19

2 Teach

Amplitude

Fun Fact

Tsunamis can travel thousands of kilometers, in all directions, at speeds of more than 700 km/h. When a tsunami approaches a coastline, the water piles up and forms a wave crest that can tower 30 m high or higher.

Activity

Ask students to bring in magazine and newspaper articles about tidal waves (tsunamis) and earthquakes around the world. Display the articles and discuss with students the relationship between energy, wave amplitude, and the amount of destruction caused. L2 LS **Interpersonal**

Wavelength

Extension

Explain that both compressional and transverse waves are commonly graphed as sine waves with amplitude on the vertical axis and wavelength on the horizontal axis. Have students prepare this type of graph for both waves shown in **Figure 7**. The graph of the transverse wave should closely resemble the wave on the oscilloscope in **Figure 7A**. On the graph of the compressional wave, the height of the graphed wave should reflect the intensity of the compression, while the wavelength should represent the distance between compressions and rarefactions. L3 LS **Visual-Spatial** P

A **For transverse waves, measure crest to crest or trough to trough.**

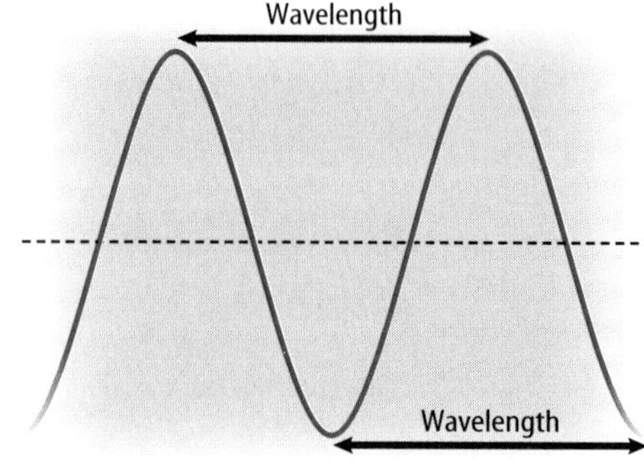

B **For compressional waves, measure from compression to compression or from rarefaction to rarefaction.**

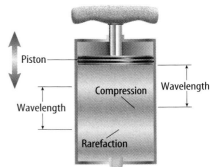

Figure 7
Wavelength is measured differently for transverse and compressional waves.

Figure 8
The wavelengths and frequencies of electromagnetic waves vary.

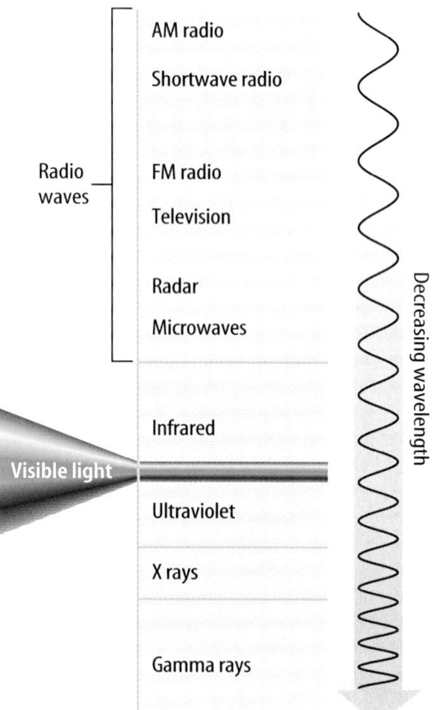

Earth Science INTEGRATION The devastating effect that a wave with large amplitude can have is seen in the aftermath of tsunamis. Tsunamis are huge sea waves that are caused by underwater earthquakes along faults on the seafloor. The movement of the seafloor along the fault produces the wave. As the wave moves toward shallow water and slows down, the amplitude of the wave grows. The tremendous amounts of energy tsunamis carry cause great damage when they move ashore.

Wavelength

Another way to describe a wave is by its wavelength. For a transverse wave, **wavelength** is the distance from the top of one crest to the top of the next crest, or from the bottom of one trough to the bottom of the next trough, as shown in **Figure 7A.** For a compressional wave, the wavelength is the distance between the center of one compression and the center of the next compression, or from the center of one rarefaction to the center of the next rarefaction, as shown in **Figure 7B.**

Wavelength is an important characteristic of a wave. For example, the difference between red light and green light is that they have different wavelengths. The wavelength of red light is longer than the wavelength of green light. It is the wavelength of visible light that determines its color. Some electromagnetic waves, like X rays, have extremely short wavelengths. Others, like microwaves, have longer wavelengths. The range of wavelengths of electromagnetic waves is shown in **Figure 8.**

Visual Learning

Figure 8 This figure shows that shorter wavelength implies higher frequency. We also know that electromagnetic waves are made of particles called photons. Waves with a longer wavelength have lower energy per photon than waves with a shorter wavelength. The amplitude of the waves depends on the energy per unit area (i.e., the number of photons per unit area), not the energy per photon.

Teacher FYI

The threshold of human hearing for sound intensity (loudness) is 0 dB (10^{-12} watts ÷ m^2). Hearing damage commences at sustained levels of about 85 dB. Normal conversation has an intensity of about 60 dB. A jet engine can generate noise levels of about 120 dB to 140 dB.

Frequency

The **frequency** of a wave is the number of wavelengths that pass a given point in 1s. The unit of frequency is the number of wavelengths per second, or hertz (Hz). Recall that waves are produced by something that vibrates. The faster the vibration is, the higher the frequency is of the wave that is produced.

Reading Check *How is the frequency of a wave measured?*

A Sidewalk Model For waves that travel with the same speed, frequency and wavelength are related. To model this relationship, imagine people on two parallel moving sidewalks in an airport, as shown in **Figure 9.** One sidewalk has four travelers spaced 4 m apart. The other sidewalk has 16 travelers spaced 1 m apart.

Now imagine that both sidewalks are moving at the same speed and approaching a pillar between them. On which sidewalk will more people go past the pillar? On the sidewalk with the shorter distance between people, four people will pass the pillar for each one person on the other sidewalk. When four people pass the pillar on the first sidewalk, 16 people pass the pillar on the second sidewalk.

Figure 9
This moving sidewalk illustration shows how wavelength and frequency are related.

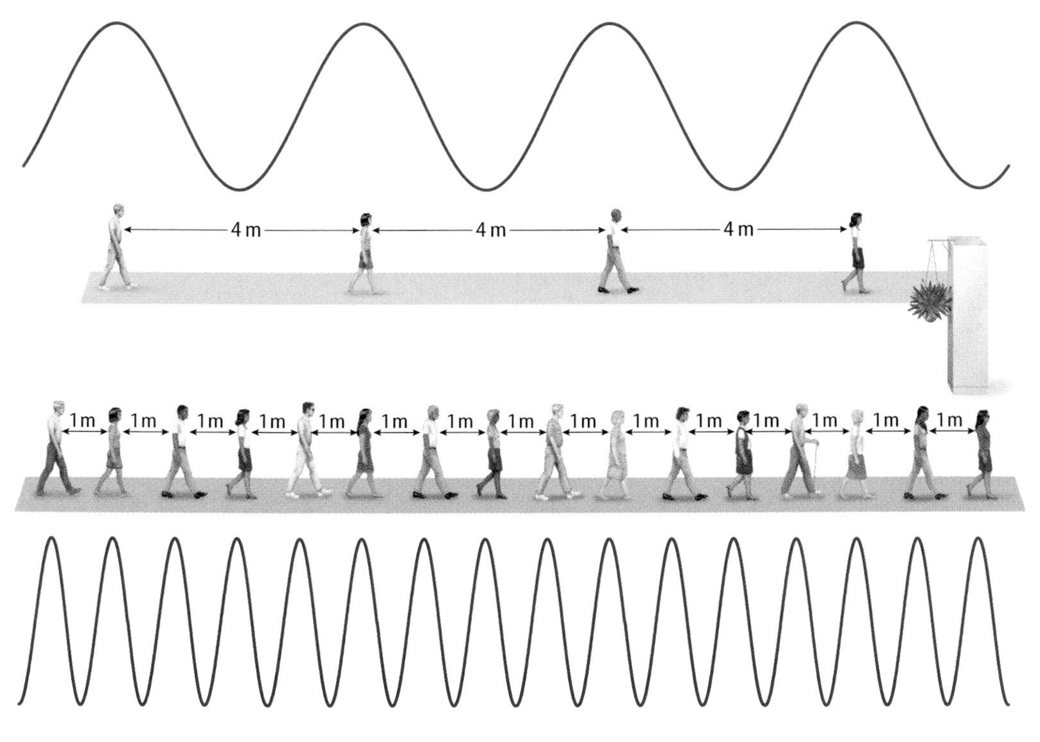

Frequency

Use Science Words

Word Origin Have students investigate the origin of the word *hertz* and why it is used to describe frequency. The unit hertz was named after Heinrich Hertz, a German physicist who studied electromagnetic waves. L2 **Linguistic**

Reading Check

Answer in wavelengths per second

Extension

Many animals communicate using sounds that are inaudible to humans. Have students research animals that do this and prepare reports about the frequencies at which the animals make sounds. Possible animals to study include whales and dolphins, which use ultrasonic frequencies, and elephants and hippos, which use infrasonic frequencies. L3 **Linguistic**

Discussion

How does pressing a string on a guitar affect the frequency of the sound produced? It shortens the string, which increases the frequency of the sound the string produces when it is plucked. **How does this relate to the sounds produced by a harp?** On a harp, the short strings produce high frequency sounds and the long strings produce low frequency sounds. L2 **Auditory-Musical**

Resource Manager

Chapter Resources Booklet
Enrichment, p. 29

Home and Community Involvement, p. 42

Reading and Writing Skill Activities, p. 33

Curriculum Connection

Music Have students find out what quarter tones are and play recordings of music with quarter tones for the class. The difference in frequency between two adjacent pitches in some types of music, including Hindu music, is about half that between adjacent pitches in western music. These pitches are called quarter tones. L3
ELL **Auditory-Musical**

Frequency, continued

Activity

Have each student fill a bowl with water and dip a pencil into and out of the water to form waves. They should notice that dipping the pencil with low frequency produces waves with longer wavelengths (greater distance between crests) than dipping the pencil with high frequency. Have students use a stopwatch to help calibrate the frequencies of their waves. L1 ELL IS **Kinesthetic**

The wavelengths are much shorter that those of the soundwaves we hear.

Quick Demo

Have students who play instruments demonstrate compressional waves of high and low frequency by producing notes of varying pitch. If an oscilloscope is available, connect it to a transducer (microphone) to show students the wavelengths and amplitudes of the notes. L2 ELL IS **Auditory-Musical**

Health INTEGRATION

Sound waves with ultra-high frequencies cannot be heard by the human ear, but are used by medical professionals in several ways. They perform echocardiograms of the heart, produce ultrasound images of internal organs, break up blockages in arteries and kill bacteria and sterilize surgical instruments. *How do the wavelengths of these sound waves compare to sound waves you can hear?*

Frequency and Wavelength Suppose that each person in **Figure 9** represents the crest of a wave. Then the movement of people on the first sidewalk is like a wave with a wavelength of 4 m. For the second sidewalk, the wavelength would be 1 m. On the first sidewalk, where the wavelength is longer, the people pass the pillar *less* frequently. Longer wavelengths result in smaller frequencies. The people pass the pillar *more* frequently on the second sidewalk, where the wavelength is shorter. Larger frequencies result in shorter wavelengths. This is true for all waves that travel at the same speed. As the frequency of a wave increases, its wavelength decreases.

Color and Pitch Because frequency and wavelength are related, either the wavelength or frequency of a light wave determines the color of the light. For example, blue light has a larger frequency and shorter wavelength then red light.

In a sound wave, either the wavelength or frequency determines the pitch. Pitch is how high or low a sound seems to be. A flute makes musical notes with a high pitch and produces sounds of high frequency. A tuba produces notes with a low pitch and a low frequency. When you sing a musical scale, the pitch and frequency increase from note to note. Wavelength and frequency are also related for sound waves. As the frequency of sound waves increase, their wavelength decreases. **Figure 10** shows how the frequency and wavelength change for notes on the musical scale.

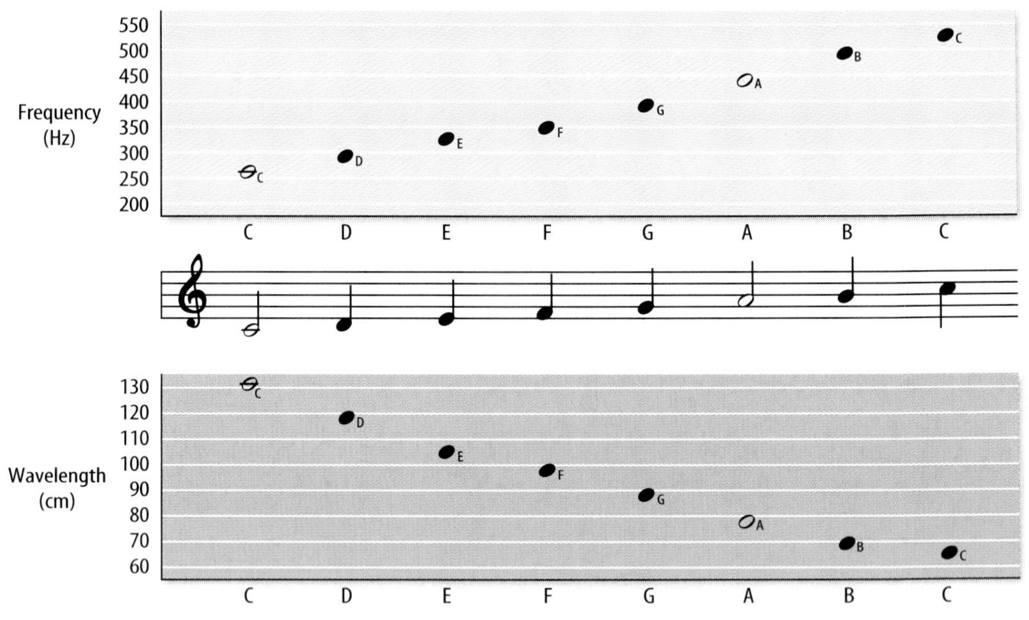

Figure 10
The frequency of the notes on a musical scale increases as the notes get higher in pitch, but the wavelength of the notes decreases.

324 CHAPTER 11 Waves

Science Journal

Musical Instruments Ask students to investigate various musical instruments and write in their Science Journals what vibrates on each instrument to make sound and how this produces certain pitches. Students might mention the reed of a clarinet or the lips of a trumpet player. Air inside the instrument also vibrates. The shape and material of the instrument affect pitch. L3 IS **Linguistic** P

Resource Manager

Chapter Resources Booklet
Reinforcement, p. 26

Cultural Diversity, p. 61

Wave Speed

You've probably watched a distant thunderstorm approach on a hot summer day. You see a bolt of lightning flash between a dark cloud and the ground. Do the sound waves, or thunder, produced by the lightning bolt reach your ears at the same instant you see the lightning? If the thunderstorm is many kilometers away, several seconds will pass between when you see the lightning and when you hear the thunder. This happens because light travels much faster in air than sound does. Light is an electromagnetic wave that travels through air at about 300 million m/s. On the other hand, sound is a mechanical wave that travels through air at about 340 m/s.

Mechanical waves such as sound travel faster in a medium in which the atoms that make up the medium are closer together. Sound travels faster in solids than in liquids and faster in liquids than in gases. This is because atoms are closer to each other in a solid than in a liquid, and closer together in a liquid than in a gas.

Electromagnetic waves such as light behave differently than mechanical waves. Unlike mechanical waves, they travel faster in gases than in solids or liquids. You know that you can get to your next class faster if the hallways are nearly empty than if they are filled with other students. Electromagnetic waves behave the same way. If many atoms are in the medium, electromagnetic waves are slowed down. For example, the speed of light is one and a half times faster in air than it is in glass.

SCIENCE Online

Research Visit the Glencoe Science Web site at **science.glencoe.com** for information about wave speed in different materials. Make a graph to show the differences.

Section  Assessment

1. How does the frequency of a wave change as its wavelength changes?
2. Why is a sound wave with a large amplitude more likely to damage your hearing than one with a small amplitude?
3. What accounts for the time difference in seeing and hearing a fireworks display?
4. Why is the statement "The speed of light is 300 million m/s" not always correct?
5. **Think Critically** Explain the differences between the waves that make up bright, green light and dim, red light.

Skill Builder Activities

6. **Predicting** A biologist studying bison puts her ear next to the ground. By doing this she knows that the herd is coming toward her. Explain. **For more help, refer to the** **Science Skill Handbook.**
7. **Solving One-Step Equations** The product of the wavelength and the frequency of a wave is the speed of the wave. If a sound wave traveling through water has a speed of 1,470 m/s and a frequency of 2,340 Hz, what is its wavelength? **For more help, refer to the** **Math Skill Handbook.**

Answers to Section Assessment

1. The frequency increases as the wavelength decreases.
2. Waves having large amplitudes carry more energy than waves with small amplitudes.
3. Light travels much faster than sound.
4. The speed of light varies, depending on the medium through which it travels. The speed of light is 300 million m/s in air.
5. The waves that make up bright green light have shorter wavelengths, higher frequencies, and larger amplitudes.
6. The biologist can hear the vibrations in the ground caused by the moving herd.
7. wavelength = wave speed ÷ wave frequency = 1,470 m/s ÷ 2,340 Hz = 0.628 m

Wave Speed

Internet Addresses

Explore the Glencoe Science Web site at **science.glencoe.com** to find out more about topics in this section.

3 Assess

Reteach

Have students use a spiral drawing toy to demonstrate the amplitude, wavelength, and frequency of a wave. L1

LS Kinesthetic

Challenge

Compare the sound of a siren moving toward you with the sound of a siren moving away from you. When the siren is moving toward you, the wavelengths of the compressional waves decrease, resulting in higher pitches. As the siren moves away from you, the wavelengths increase and the pitches get lower. This is known as the Doppler effect. L3

LS Logical-Mathematical

✔Assessment

Process Fill test tubes with different amounts of water and tap on them gently with a glass stirring rod. Have students explain the differences between the pitches produced. The more water in a tube, the shorter the wavelength of air that fits in the tube, so the higher the pitch produced when the glass is tapped. Use **PASC,** p. 89.

Activity

BENCH TESTED

Purpose Students make waves with a coiled-spring toy and observe the waves. L2 ELL COOP LEARN IN Kinesthetic

Process Skills observing and inferring, comparing and contrasting, interpreting data, classifying, making and using tables

Time Required 45 minutes

Safety Precautions Space student groups far enough apart that the coiled springs do not interfere with each other.

Teaching Strategies

- Help students compare the two types of waves they generate.
- Help students recognize the parts of a wave.

Troubleshooting Watch students to ensure that they do not tangle or overstretch the coiled springs.

Answers to Questions

1. In steps 4 and 5, transverse waves were produced. In steps 6 to 8, compressional waves were produced.
2. Check students' work.
3. rarefaction
4. The yarn moved back and forth from a fixed position, while the wave moved along the spring from one end to the other.

Process Have students draw and label the parts of each type of wave they generated in the activity. Use **PASC,** p. 127.

Activity

Waves on a Spring

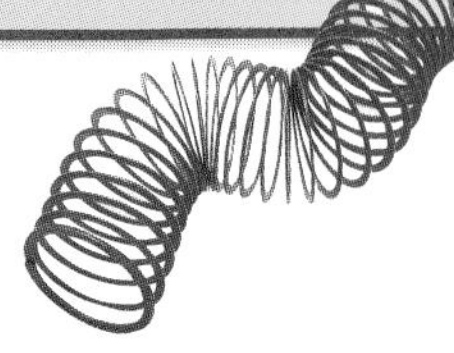

Waves are rhythmic disturbances that carry energy through matter or space. Studying waves can help you understand how the Sun's energy reaches Earth and sounds travel through the air.

What You'll Investigate

What are some of the properties of transverse and compressional waves on a coiled spring?

Materials

long, coiled spring toy
colored yarn (5 cm)
meterstick
stopwatch

Goals

- **Create** transverse and compressional waves on a coiled spring toy.
- **Investigate** wave properties such as speed and amplitude.

Safety Precautions

WARNING: *Avoid overstretching or tangling the spring to prevent injury or damage.*

Procedure

1. **Prepare** a data table such as the one shown.

Wave Data	
Length of stretched spring toy	4.20 m
Average time for a wave to travel from end to end—step 4	1.35 s
Average time for a wave to travel from end to end—step 5	1.25 s

2. Work in pairs or groups and clear a place on an uncarpeted floor about 6 m × 2 m.
3. Stretch the springs between two people to the length suggested by your teacher. Measure the length.
4. Create a wave with a quick, sideways snap of the wrist. Time several waves as they travel the length of the spring. Record the average time in your data table.
5. Repeat step 4 using waves that have slightly larger amplitudes.
6. Squeeze together about 20 of the coils. Observe what happens to the unsqueezed coils. Release the coils and observe.
7. Quickly push the spring toward your partner, then pull it back.
8. Tie the yarn to a coil near the middle of the spring. Repeat step 7, observing the string.

Conclude and Apply

1. **Classify** the wave pulses you created in each step as compressional or transverse.
2. **Calculate** and compare the speeds of the waves in steps 4 and 5.
3. **Classify** the unsqueezed coils in step 6 as a compression or a rarefaction.
4. **Compare and contrast** the motion of the yarn in step 8 with the motion of the wave.

Communicating Your Data

Write a summary paragraph of how this activity demonstrated any of the vocabulary words from the first two sections of the chapter. **For more help,** refer to the Science Skill Handbook.

Communicating Your Data

Have students use a computer graphics program to create a display explaining the results of the activity.

Resource Manager

Chapter Resources Booklet

Lab Activity, pp. 9–11
Activity Worksheet, pp. 5–6

SECTION

Wave Behavior

Reflection

What causes the echo when you yell across an empty gymnasium or down a long, empty hallway? Why can you see your face when you look in a mirror? The echo of your voice and the face you see in the mirror are caused by wave reflection.

Reflection occurs when a wave strikes an object or surface and bounces off. An echo is reflected sound. Sound reflects from all surfaces. Your echo bounces off the walls, floor, ceiling, furniture, and people. You see your face in a mirror or a still pond, as shown in **Figure 11A,** because of reflection. Light waves produced by a source of light such as the Sun or a lightbulb bounce off your face, strike the mirror, and reflect back to your eyes.

A mirror is smooth and even, therefore you see a clearly reflected image. However, when light reflects from an uneven or rough surface, you can't see an image because the reflected light scatters in many different directions, as shown in **Figure 11B.**

Reading Check *What causes reflection?*

As You Read

***What* You'll Learn**

- **Explain** how waves can reflect from some surfaces.
- **Explain** how waves change direction when they move from one material into another.
- **Describe** how waves are able to bend around barriers.

Vocabulary

reflection
refraction
diffraction
interference

***Why* It's Important**

The reflection of waves enables you to see objects around you.

A The smooth surface of a still pond allows light to reflect back to you so you can see your image.

B The rough, uneven surface of the same pond causes the light to reflect in many directions so that no sharp image is visible.

Figure 11
The image formed by reflection depends on the smoothness of the surface.

Section Assessment Planner

PORTFOLIO
Challenge, p. 333

PERFORMANCE ASSESSMENT
Try at Home MiniLAB, p. 328
Skill Builder Activities, p. 333
See page 340 for more options.

CONTENT ASSESSMENT
Section, p. 333
Challenge, p. 333
Chapter, pp. 340–341

SECTION 3

Wave Behavior

1 Motivate

Bellringer Transparency

Display the Section Focus Transparency for Section 3. Use the accompanying Transparency Activity Master. L2 ELL

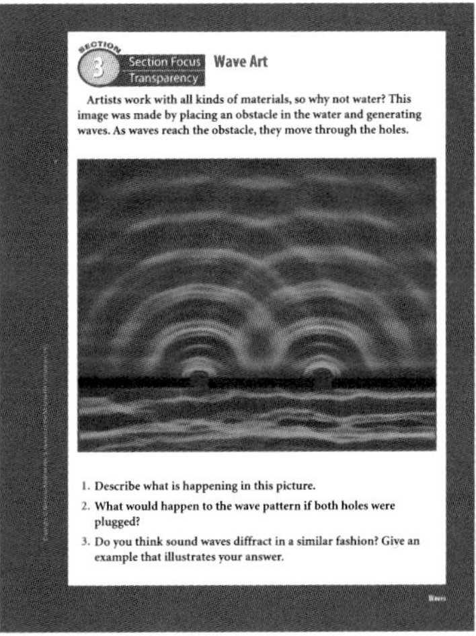

Tie to Prior Knowledge

Remind students that visible light rays are electromagnetic waves. Discuss whether they can see themselves in a mirror without light rays. Explain that in this section, they will learn how waves reflect and refract.

2 Teach

Reflection

Reading Check

Answer the bouncing of a wave off an object

Refraction

Quick Demo

Demonstrate that different colors of white light refract at different angles by shining an intense beam of white light through a prism in a darkened room. L2 ELL LS **Visual-Spatial**

Purpose Students observe how light refracts. L1 ELL LS **Visual-Spatial**

Materials white soda straw, opaque drinking glass or cup; water

Teaching Strategy The larger the diameter of the glass or cup, the easier it will be to see the refraction. Also, tell students to fill the glass or cup almost to the top.

Analysis

1. The straw appears to be straight.
2. The straw appears to bend at the water's surface. Light reflects from the straw and refracts as it passes from the water into the air. The speed of the light waves is also reduced in water.

Performance Have students draw ray diagrams in their Science Journals that show how the light waves refract. Use **PASC**, p. 127.

TRY AT HOME Mini LAB

Observing How Light Refracts

Procedure

1. Fill a **large, opaque drinking glass or cup with water.**
2. Place a **white soda straw** in the water at an angle.
3. Looking directly down into the cup from above, observe the straw where it meets the water.
4. Placing yourself so that the straw angles to your left or right, slowly back away about 1 m. Observe the straw as it appears above, at, and below the surface of the water.

Analysis

1. Describe the straw's appearance from above.
2. Compare the straw's appearance above and below the water's surface in step 4. Draw a diagram and explain the apparent effect.

Refraction

You've already seen that a wave changes direction when it reflects from a surface. Waves also can change direction in another way. Perhaps you have tried to grab a sinking object when you are in a swimming pool, only to come up empty-handed. Yet you were sure you grabbed right where you saw the object. This happens because the light rays from the object change direction as they pass from the water into the air. The bending of a wave as it moves from one medium into another is called **refraction.**

Refraction and Wave Speed Remember that the speed of a wave can be different in different materials. For example, light waves travel faster in air than in water. Refraction occurs when the speed of a wave changes as it passes from one substance to another, as shown in **Figure 12.** A line that is perpendicular to the water's surface is called the normal. When a light ray passes from air into water, it slows down and bends toward the normal. When the ray passes from water into air, it speeds up and bends away from the normal. The larger the change in speed of the light wave is, the larger the change in direction is.

You notice refraction when you look down into a fishbowl. Refraction makes the fish appear to be closer to the surface but farther away from you than it is, as shown in **Figure 13.** Light rays reflected from the fish are bent away from the normal as they pass from water to air. Your brain interprets the light that enters your eyes by assuming that light rays always travel in straight lines. As a result, the light rays seem to be coming from a fish that is in a different location.

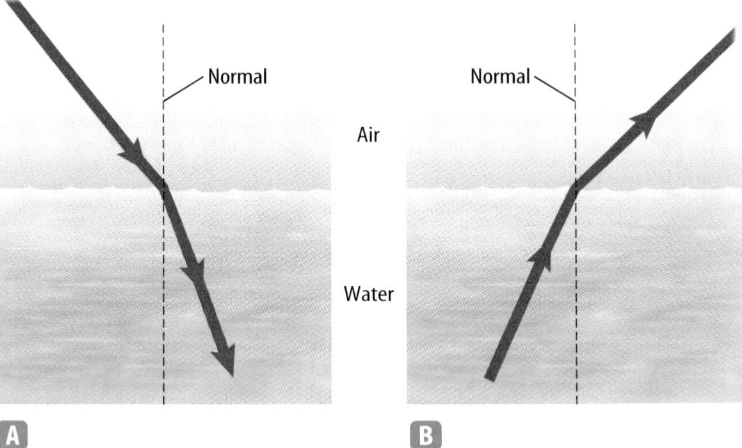

Figure 12
A wave is refracted when it changes speed. A As the light ray passes from air to water, it refracts toward the normal. B As the light ray passes from water to air, it refracts away from the normal.

Cultural Diversity

An Advanced Warning System The Chinese used pottery jars to detect the sounds of an advancing enemy. Leather membranes were stretched over the mouths of empty 80-L pottery jars. The jars were lowered into deep shafts that were dug a few paces apart around the city, and men with good hearing were stationed nearby. Not only could they hear the sounds of an approaching army, but by listening to different sounds from the shafts, the watchers also could judge from which direction the enemy was coming and how far away the enemy was. **Why do you think the jars were put in shafts deep underground?** The thudding footsteps of the approaching army produced low-frequency, long-wavelength vibrations in the ground. The shafts had to be deep enough to receive those sound vibrations and amplify them. L3 LS **Logical-Mathematical**

Color from Refraction Refraction causes prisms to separate sunlight into many colors and produces rainbows too. **Figure 14** illustrates how refraction and reflection produce a rainbow when light waves from the Sun pass into and out of water droplets in the air.

What produces a rainbow?

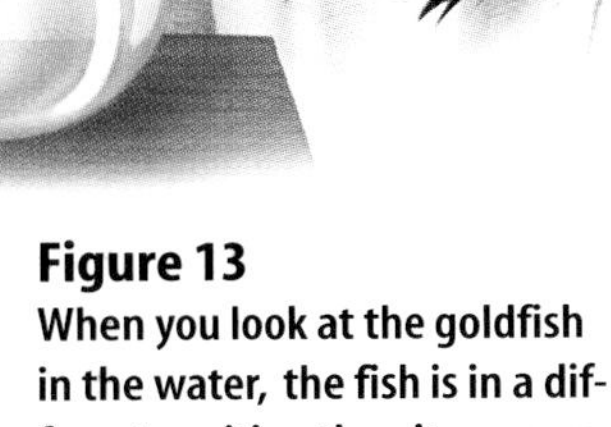

Figure 13
When you look at the goldfish in the water, the fish is in a different position than it appears.

Diffraction

Why can you hear music from the band room when you are down the hall? You can hear the music because the sound waves bend as they pass through an open doorway. This bending isn't caused by refraction. Remember that refraction occurs when waves change speed, but sound waves have the same speed in the band room and in the hallway. Instead the bending is caused by diffraction. **Diffraction** is the bending of waves around a barrier.

Diffraction of Light Waves Can light waves diffract, too? You can hear your friends in the band room but you can't see them until you reach the open door. Therefore, you know the light waves do not diffract as much as sound waves do.

Are light waves able to diffract at all? Light waves do bend around the edges of an open door. However, for an opening as wide as a door, the amount the light bends is extremely small. As a result, the diffraction of light is far too small to allow you to see around a corner.

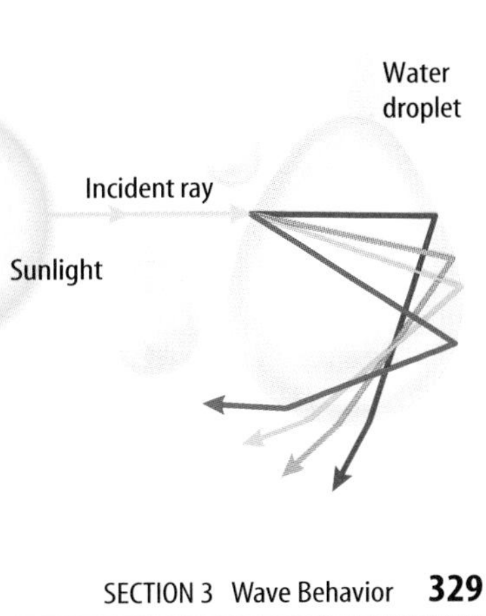

Figure 14
Light rays refract as they enter and leave each water drop. Each color refracts at different angles because of their different wavelengths, so they separate into the colors of the spectrum.

Reading Check

Answer Sunlight refracts as it enters raindrops, reflects from the far inside surfaces of the drops, and refracts as it leaves the drops.

Visual Learning

Figure 14 When you look at a rainbow, you see an arc of colors. The refraction of light from water drops actually produces a circle of light, but we can only see the top of the circle because the ground blocks out the lower part. Red is at the top because, as you see in the sketch of the raindrop, red is bent less. Violet is at the bottom because it is bent more. Have students draw sketches to show how the reflections create a circle with red on the outside. L1 ELL
LS **Visual-Spatial**

Diffraction

Quick Demo

Tell each student to straighten the first two fingers of one hand, spreading the fingers slightly to make a small slit between them. Then have students view a bright light through the slit. They will see fringes, or black lines, between their fingers as a result of diffraction. L1 ELL LS **Kinesthetic**

Teacher FYI

The speed of light in a material depends on the characteristics of the material and the frequency of the incident light. High-frequency, short-wavelength light, such as violet light, travels more slowly in a material than lower-frequency, longer-wavelength light, such as red light. This means the violet light bends more than the red light as it moves from a vacuum (or air) to a denser medium.

Resource Manager

Chapter Resources Booklet
Transparency Activity, p. 44
Enrichment, p. 30
MiniLAB, p. 4

What happens when waves meet?

Quick Demo

Help students understand how to graph the addition of waves by demonstrating it on an overhead projector. Overlap transparencies of drawings of waves as you add them together. L2 LS **Visual-Spatial**

Discussion

Have students consider what happens when three waves overlap. **If three waves interfere at a given point and have amplitudes of +3 units, +2 units, and −5 units, what is the amplitude of the resultant wave at that point?** 0 units L2 LS **Logical-Mathematical**

IDENTIFYING Misconceptions

Students may think that as waves move from one medium to another and are refracted, the wavelength and frequency of the waves change. However, only the speed and direction of the waves change.

Diffraction and Wavelength The reason that light waves don't diffract much when they pass through an open door is that the wavelengths of visible light are much smaller than the width of the door. Light waves have wavelengths between 400 and 700 billionths of a meter, while the width of doorway is about one meter. Sound waves that you can hear have much longer wavelengths. They bend more easily around the corners of an open door. A wave is diffracted more when its wavelength is similar in size to the barrier or opening.

Diffraction of Water Waves Perhaps you have noticed water waves bending around barriers. For example, when water waves strike obstacles such as the islands shown in **Figure 15,** they don't stop moving. Here the size and spacing of the islands is not too different from the wavelength of the water waves. So the water waves bend around the islands, and keep on moving. They also spread out after they pass through openings between the islands. If the islands were much larger than the water wavelength, less diffraction would occur.

What happens when waves meet?

Suppose you throw two pebbles into a still pond. Ripples spread from the impact of each pebble and travel toward each other. What happens when two of these ripples meet? Do they collide like billiard balls and change direction? Waves behave differently from billiard balls when they meet. In fact, after they pass, waves continue moving as though the other waves never existed.

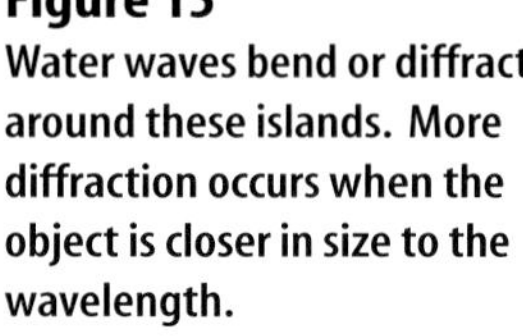

Figure 15
Water waves bend or diffract around these islands. More diffraction occurs when the object is closer in size to the wavelength.

LAB DEMONSTRATION

Purpose to observe wave behavior

Materials 2 pencils; paper; large, rectangular glass baking dish; water

Preparation Fill the dish with water to a depth of 2 cm. Use several books on each side to suspend the pan over a sheet of white paper. Place a strong light about 40 cm above the pan. Dim all other lights.

Procedure To form waves, vibrate a vertical pencil up and down on one side of the pan. Show interference by vibrating two vertical pencils, about 10 cm apart, up and down at one end of the pan. Place an object in the path of the waves to show diffraction.

Expected Outcome Students observe reflection, diffraction, and interference.

What would the waves have looked like if you had held the pencil horizontally instead of vertically when vibrating it? They would have formed a line of waves instead of circles.

Wave Interference When two waves overlap a new wave is formed by adding the two waves together. The ability of two waves to combine and form a new wave when they overlap is called **interference.** After they overlap, the individual waves continue to travel on in their original form.

The different ways waves can interfere are shown in **Figure 16** on the next page. Sometimes when the waves meet, the crest of one wave overlaps the crest of another wave. This is called constructive interference. The amplitudes of these combining waves add together to make a larger wave while they overlap. Destructive interference occurs when the crest of one wave overlaps the trough of another wave. In destructive interference, the amplitudes of the two waves combine to make a wave with a smaller amplitude. If the two waves have equal amplitudes and meet crest to trough, they cancel each other during the overlap.

Waves and Particles Like waves of water, when light travels through a small opening, such as a narrow slit, the light spreads out in all directions on the other side of the slit. If small particles, instead of waves, were sent through the slit, they would continue in a straight line without spreading. The spreading, or diffraction, is only a property of waves. Interference also doesn't occur with particles. If waves meet, they reinforce or cancel each other, then travel on. If particles approach each other, they either collide and scatter or miss each other completely. Interference, like diffraction, is a property of waves, not particles.

Research Visit the Glencoe Science Web site at **science.glencoe.com** for more information about wave interference.

Problem-Solving Activity

Can you create destructive interference?

Your brother is vacuuming and you can't hear the television. Is it possible to diminish the sound of the vacuum so you can hear the TV? Can you eliminate unpleasant sounds and keep the sounds you do want to hear?

Identifying the Problem

It is possible to create a frequency that will destructively interfere with the sound of the vacuum and not the television. The graph shows the waves created by the vacuum and the television.

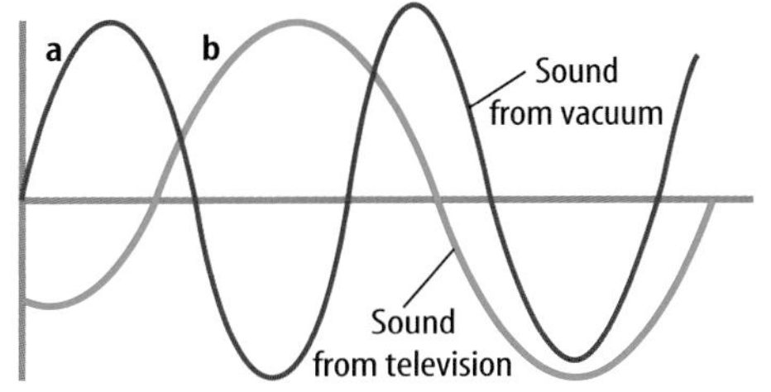

Solving the Problem

1. Can you create the graph of a wave that will eliminate the noise from the vacuum but not the television?
2. Can you create the graph of a wave that would amplify the sound of the television?

Extension

Explain to students that when an incident wave (one moving toward an object) and a reflected wave (one bounced off an object) meet, they sometimes form a standing, or stationary, wave. Because of the interference pattern, the standing wave doesn't appear to be traveling. You can demonstrate a standing wave using a rope. Tie one end of the rope firmly to a doorknob or a laboratory table. Shake the other end to produce various standing wave patterns. L3

LS **Visual-Spatial**

Discussion

How does interference affect the way music sounds in different concert halls? Constructive and destructive interference patterns in a concert hall determine whether sound waves produced by individual voices or instruments combine to form waves that are pleasant or displeasing to listeners' ears. L3

LS **Logical-Mathematical**

Problem-Solving Activity

National Math Standards

Correlation to Mathematics Objectives

2, 5, 6, 8–10

Answers

1. The wave must be the opposite of the vacuum wave. That is, it must trough when the vacuum wave crests, and vice versa.
2. Any wave that crests and troughs in the same place will amplify the wave.

Resource Manager 

Chapter Resources Booklet

Directed Reading for Content Mastery, pp. 19, 20

Mathematics Skill Activities, p. 47

SCIENCE Online

Internet Addresses

Explore the Glencoe Science Web site at **science.glencoe.com** to find out more about topics in this section.

NATIONAL GEOGRAPHIC

Visualizing Interference

Have students examine the pictures and read the captions. Then ask the following questions.

Two waves both with an amplitude of 2 m pass through each other. The maximum amplitude reached is 4 m. Is this constructive or destructive interference? constructive

Two waves both with an amplitude of 2 m approach each other and the peak of the crest of one wave passes through the bottom of the trough of the other wave. What is the amplitude of the resulting wave at that instant? zero L2 LS **Visual-Spatial**

Activity

Have two students hold the ends of a long rope. Ask students to practice making waves with the rope by moving their hands vertically or horizontally in quick strokes. The students should then work together to set up constructive and destructive interference with the waves in their ropes. L3 LS **Kinesthetic**

Extension

Challenge students to find out how radio waves are used in radar and how stealth airplanes are built to evade detection by radar. Have students work in pairs to make posters showing the airplane profiles used and the materials used to enable these planes to avoid detection.

NATIONAL GEOGRAPHIC **VISUALIZING INTERFERENCE**

Figure 16

Whether they are ripples on a pond or huge ocean swells, when water waves meet they can combine to form new waves in a process called interference. As shown below, wave interference can be constructive or destructive.

Constructive Interference

In constructive interference, a wave with greater amplitude is formed.

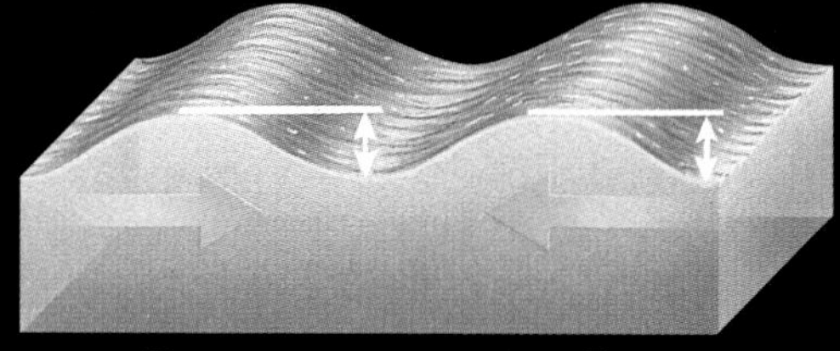

A B The crests of two waves—A and B—approach each other.

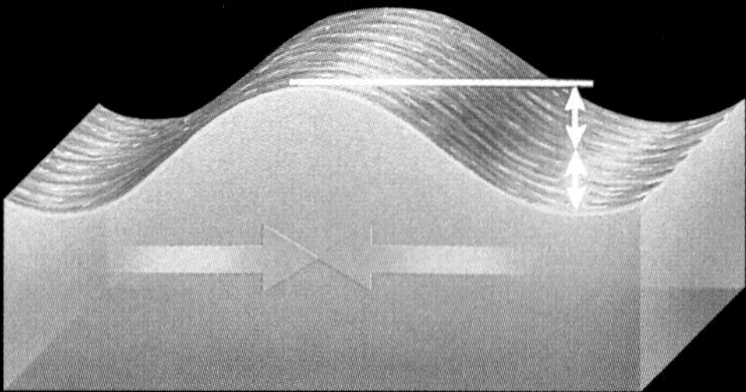

The two waves form a larger wave where the crests of both waves overlap.

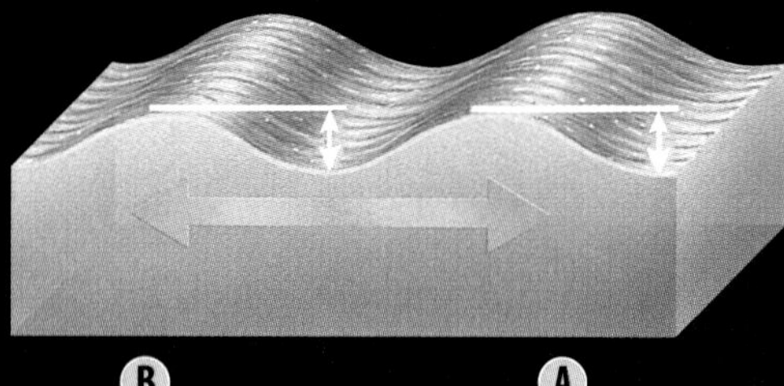

B A The original waves pass through each other and go on as they started.

Destructive Interference

In destructive interference, a wave with a smaller amplitude is formed.

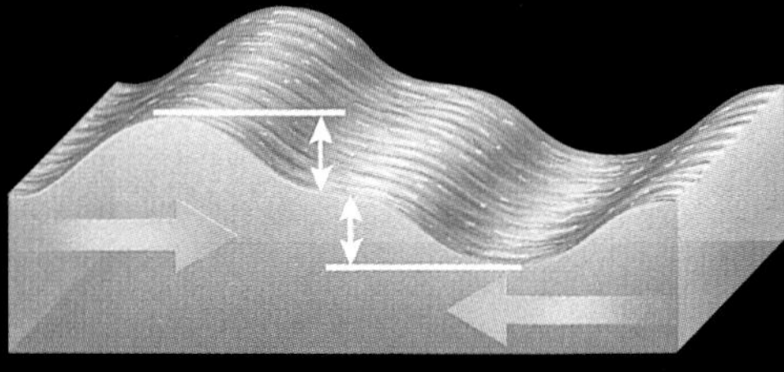

A B The crest of one wave approaches the trough of another.

If the two waves have equal amplitude, they momentarily cancel when they meet.

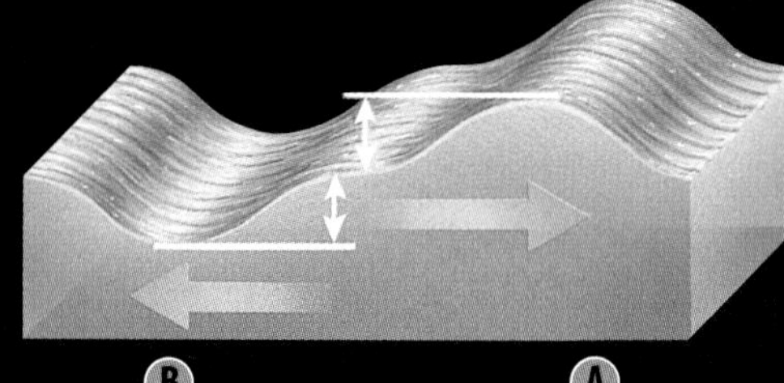

B A The original waves pass through each other and go on as they started.

332 CHAPTER 11

Resource Manager

Chapter Resources Booklet

Lab Activity, pp. 13–14

Reinforcement, p. 27

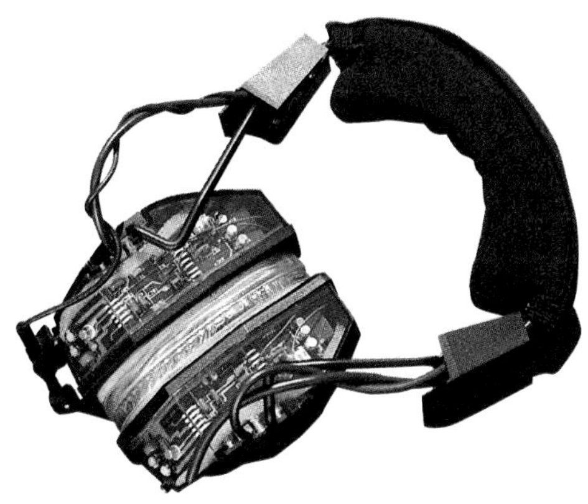

Using Interference You might have seen someone use a power lawn mower or a chain saw. In the past, many people who performed these tasks damaged their hearing because of the loud noises produced by these machines. Today, specially designed ear protectors absorb the sound from lawn mowers and chain saws. The ear protectors lower the amplitudes of the harmful waves. The waves that reach the ears have smaller amplitudes and won't damage eardrums.

Reducing Noise Pilots and passengers of small planes have a more complicated problem. They can't use ear protectors to shut out all the noise of the plane's motor. If they did, the pilots wouldn't be able to hear instructions from air-traffic controllers, and the passengers wouldn't be able to hear each other talk. To solve this problem, engineers invented special devices that contain electronic circuits as shown in **Figure 17.** These circuits detect the vibrations from the aircraft that make noise and produce sound frequencies that destructively interfere with those vibrations. However, the sound frequencies produced do not interfere with human voices, so people can hear and understand normal conversation. In these examples, destructive interference can be a benefit.

Figure 17
Some airplane pilots use special ear protectors that interfere with engine noise but don't block human voices.

Section  Assessment

1. Why don't you see your reflection in a building made of rough, white stone?
2. If you're standing on one side of a building, how are you able to hear the siren of an ambulance on the other side?
3. What behavior of light enables magnifying glasses and contact lenses to bend light rays and help people see more clearly?
4. What is diffraction? How does the amount of diffraction depend on wavelength?
5. **Think Critically** Why don't light rays that stream through an open window into a darkened room spread evenly through the entire room?

Skill Builder Activities

6. **Comparing and Contrasting** When light rays pass from water into a certain type of glass, the rays refract toward the normal. Compare and contrast the speed of light in water and in the glass. **For more help, refer to the** Science Skill Handbook.
7. **Communicating** Watch carefully as you travel home from school or walk down your street. What examples of wave reflection and refraction do you notice? Describe each of these in your Science Journal and explain your reasons. **For more help, refer to the** Science Skill Handbook.

3 Assess

Reteach

Divide the class in half and conduct a baseball game review with words from this chapter. Players match words with meanings and are out when they miss a word. Each team has three outs before the turn shifts to the other team. L2 COOP LEARN

Interpersonal

Challenge

Have pairs of students prepare posters showing the types of waves produced by a combination of (1) two transverse waves in which crests overlap, (2) two transverse waves in which crests and troughs overlap, (3) two compressional waves in which crests overlap, and (4) two compressional waves in which crests and troughs overlap. L3 COOP LEARN **Visual-Spatial** P

Content Have students draw diagrams illustrating the refraction, reflection, diffraction, and interference of waves. Use **Performance Assessment in the Science Classroom,** p. 127.

Answers to Section Assessment

1. The rough surface scatters light in all directions.
2. Sound diffracts easily around objects such as buildings.
3. refraction
4. Diffraction is the bending of waves around a barrier. A wave is diffracted more when its wavelength is similar in size to the barrier or opening.
5. Waves of light travel in straight lines. The waves of light that come through the window travel in straight lines until they reach objects that absorb or reflect them. Also, the light waves have very small wavelengths, so very little diffraction occurs as they move through a wide opening such as a window.
6. Because the light rays refract toward the normal, their speed must be lower in the glass than in water.
7. Answers might include reflection of light off a puddle or window or refraction of light through a prism. Others may mention the reflection of sirens, horns, or traffic noise.

Activity

BENCH TESTED

Recognize the problem

Purpose

Students will model the behavior of seismic waves by creating transverse standing waves on a demonstration spring or coiled toy spring. Factors such as length, type of spring, and frequency will be varied and controlled to determine how the speed of a wave within a coil depends upon such factors. By comparing their results with those of others, students can make generalizations about waves within a spring, and by analogy, seismic waves within the earth.

Process Skills

observing, measuring, calculating, separating and controlling variables, predicting

Time Required

45 minute class

Materials

Demonstration springs sold by science educational supply companies create the best waves. Toy springs can also be used to create waves, and if springs are not available, a length of rope or hose will serve as a substitute wave maker. A metric tape measure can replace a meterstick.

Safety Precautions

Caution students not use or swing the spring anywhere but on the floor.

Form a Hypothesis

Possible Hypothesis

The hypothesis of most students will reflect that the speed of a wave is determined by dividing the distance the wave travels by the time it takes for the wave to travel one wavelength.

Activity Design Your Own Experiment

Wave Speed

When an earthquake occurs, the waves of energy are recorded at points all over the world by instruments called seismographs. By comparing the data that they collected from their seismographs, scientists discovered that the interior of Earth must be made of layers of different materials. How did the seismographs tell them that Earth is not the same material all the way through?

Recognize the Problem

Can the speed of a wave be used to identify the medium through which it travels?

Form a Hypothesis

Think about what you know about the relationship between the frequency, wavelength, and speed of a wave in a medium. Make a hypothesis about how you can measure the speed of a wave within a medium, and use that information to identify an unknown medium.

Goals

- **Measure** the speed of a wave within a coiled spring toy.
- **Predict** whether the speed you measured will be different in other types of coiled spring toys.

Materials

coiled spring toy
stopwatch
*clock with a second hand
meterstick
tape

*Alternate materials

Safety Precautions

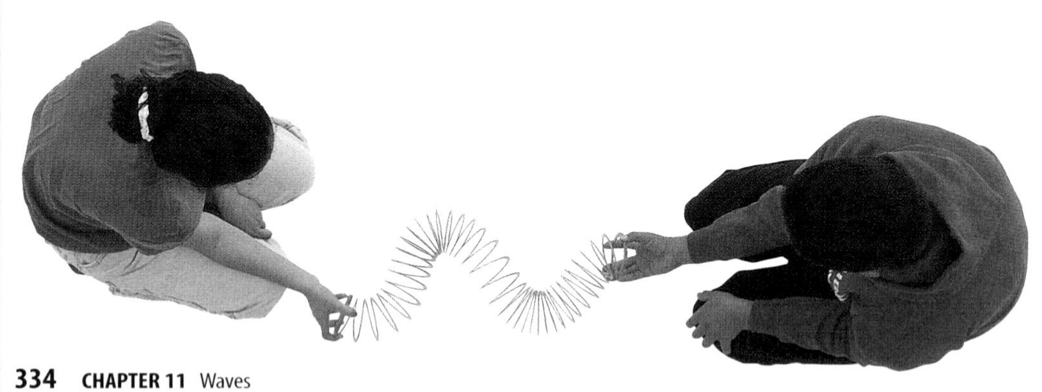

Resource Manager

Chapter Resources Booklet
Activity Worksheet, pp. 7–8

Lab Management and Safety, p. 65

SCIENCE Online

Internet Addresses

Explore the Glencoe Science Web site at **science.glencoe.com** to find out more about topics in this activity.

Test Your Hypothesis

Plan

1. Make a data table in your Science Journal like the one shown.
2. In your Science Journal, write a detailed description of the coiled spring toy you are going to use. Be sure to include its mass and diameter, the width of a coil, and what it is made of.
3. **Decide** as a group how you will measure the frequency and length of waves in the spring toy. What are your variables? Which variables must be controlled? What variable do you want to measure?
4. Repeat your experiment three times.

Wave Data

	Trial 1	Trial 2	Trial 3
Length spring was stretched (m)	3.30	3.30	3.91
Number of crests	2	3	4
Wavelength (m)	3.30	2.20	1.96
# of vibrations timed	10	10	10
# of seconds vibrations were timed	5.49	3.60	6.01
Wave speed (m/s)	6.01	6.12	6.29

Do

1. Make sure your teacher approves your plan before you start.
2. Carry out the experiment.
3. While you are doing the experiment, record your observations and measurements in your data table.

Analyze Your Data

1. **Calculate** the frequency of the waves by dividing the number of vibrations you timed by the number of seconds you timed them. Record your results in your data table.
2. Use the following formula to calculate the speed of a wave in each trial.

$$\text{wavelength} \times \text{wave frequency} = \text{wave speed}$$

3. Average the wave speeds from your trials to determine the average speed of a wave in your coiled spring toy.

Draw Conclusions

1. How do the variables affect the wave speed in spring toys? Was your hypothesis supported?
2. Would it make a difference if an earthquake wave were transmitted through Earth's solid mantle or the molten outer core?

Post a description of your coiled spring toy and the results of your experiment on a bulletin board in your classroom. **Compare and contrast** your results with other students in your class.

Test Your Hypothesis

Possible Procedures

Help your student groups create standing waves. While a student holds one end of the coiled-spring toy stationary, have another student move the other end from side to side with a rhythm that produces a standing wave.

Tie to Prior Knowledge

Most students will have observed waves moving through a medium such as ocean waves or ripples on a pond.

Expected Outcome

Students will create standing transverse waves and measure their frequency, wavelengths, and speeds. From this data, they will predict the speed of waves in other types of coiled springs.

Analyze Your Data

1. Based on the sample data in the table, frequencies were as follows: Trial 1, 1.82 Hz; Trial 2, 2.78 Hz; Trial 3, 1.66 Hz.
2. Based on the sample data in the table, speeds were as follows: Trial 1, 6.01 m/s; Trial 2, 6.12 m/s; Trial 3, 6.29 m/s.
3. Average wave speed is 6.14 m/s.

Error Analysis

Ask student groups to compare data with other groups and explain any significant discrepancies.

Draw Conclusions

1. Answers will vary.
2. Yes, a transverse wave would not be transmitted through Earth's molten core.

Assessment

Oral Ask students how they might determine the speed of water waves that are crashing ashore at a beach. Time the waves coming ashore to determine the frequency. Estimate the distance between wave crests to determine wavelength. The product of these two numbers is the speed of the wave. Use **PASC,** p. 89

Encourage students to record their data in electronically designed spreadsheets.

Science Stats

Content Background

Electromagnetic, ocean, and sound are different types of waves. Each of these waves propagate in a different manner. Electromagnetic waves do not require a media for travel and can carry energy through the vacuum of space. The following names of these waves are familiar to us: radio, microwave, infrared, visible light, ultraviolet, X rays, and gamma rays. Surface ocean waves are a mixture of longitudinal and transverse waves that carry energy through the water. Sound waves are longitudinal waves that can carry energy through solids, liquids, and gases. The velocity of waves can be determined by the equation velocity = wavelength × frequency.

Discussion

Waves are described by their frequency (pulses per second), wavelength (distance from two corresponding points on two successive waves), amplitude (distance from trough or crest to baseline), and speed. **What do the numbers represent in each of the examples?** 34 meters, amplitude; 966 km/h, speed; 800 pulses per second, frequency; 8 km/s and 4.8 km/s, speed

Extension

Have students research the speeds of light and sound. The speed of light is 3.00 × 108 m/s. The speed of sound varies with the type of medium and other conditions such as density, temperature, and pressure.

Science Stats

Waves, Waves, and More Waves

Did you know...

. . . You are constantly surrounded by a sea of waves even when you're on dry land! Electromagnetic waves around us are used to cook our food and transmit signals to our radios and televisions. Light itself is an electromagnetic wave.

. . . The highest recorded ocean wave was 34 meters high, which is comparable to the height of a ten-story building. This super wave was seen in the North Pacific Ocean and recorded by the crew of the naval ship *USS Ramapo* in 1933.

. . . Tsunamis—huge ocean waves—travel at speeds near 966 km/h.

. . . Waves let dolphins see with their ears! A dolphin sends out ultrasonic pulses, or clicks, at speeds of 800 pulses per second. These sound waves echo back to the dolphin after they hit another object. This process—echolocation—allows dolphins to recognize obstacles and meals.

SCIENCE Online

Internet Addresses

Explore the Glencoe Science Web site at **science.glencoe.com** to find out more about topics in this feature.

Connecting To Math

. . . Earthquakes are caused by a variety of seismic waves— waves of energy that ripple through Earth after sub-surface rock breaks suddenly. The fastest are P and S waves. P waves are compressional waves that travel at about 8 km/s. S waves, which move like ocean waves, travel at about 4.8 km/s.

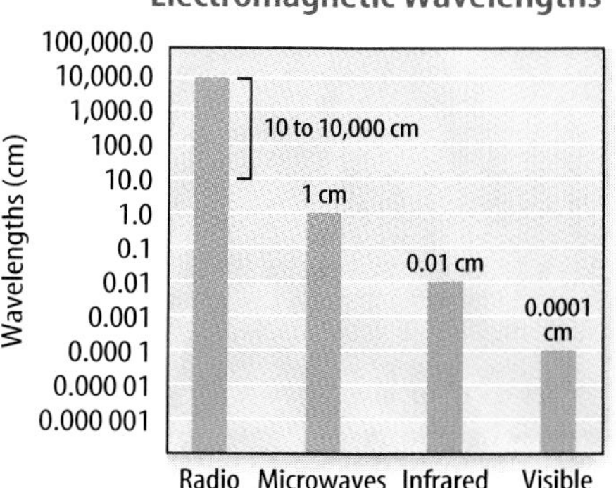

. . . Radio waves from space were discovered in 1932 by Karl G. Jansky, an American engineer. His amazing discovery led to creation of radio astronomy, a field that explores parts of the universe that are hidden by interstellar dust or too distant for optical observation.

Do the Math

1. A museum with a dolphin exhibit plays dolphin clicks for its visitors at a speed 250 times slower than the speed at which the dolphins emit them. How many clicks do the visitors hear in 10 s?
2. Tsunamis form in the ocean when an earthquake occurs on the ocean floor. How long will it take a tsunami to travel 4,500 km?
3. Make a bar graph to show the speeds of P waves, S waves and tsunamis. Use km/h as your unit of speed.

Go Further

Go to **science.glencoe.com** to learn about discoveries by radio astronomers. Graph the distances of these discoveries from Earth.

SCIENCE STATS 337

Connecting To Math

Do the Math

Teaching Strategies

Remind students that distance = velocity × time, and that there are 3,600 seconds in an hour.

Answers

1. 32 pulses
2. 4.7 h at 966 km/h
3. Students should make a bar graph with tsunamis traveling 966 km/h, P waves at 28,800 km/h, and S waves at 17,280 km/h.

Go Further

Have students find the frequency of radio waves. **Are these waves low frequency or high frequency waves in the electromagnetic spectrum?** low

Visual Learning

Electromagnetic Wavelengths **How many times greater is the wavelength of infrared waves than that of visible waves?** 100 times **How many times greater is the wavelength for microwaves compared to infrared waves?** 100 times **How many times greater is the wavelength for microwaves compared to visible waves?** 10,000 times

Chapter 11 Study Guide

Reviewing Main Ideas

Preview

Students can answer the questions in their Science Journals. Discuss the answers as you go through the chapter. LS **Linguistic**

Review

Students can write their answers, then compare them with those of other students. LS **Interpersonal**

Reteach

Students can look at the illustrations and describe details that support the main ideas of the chapter. LS **Visual-Spatial**

Answers to Chapter Review

Section 1

4. The boat moves perpendicular to the direction of motion of the waves.

Section 2

4. amplitude

Section 3

1. The surface is rough, so the light waves bounce off in many directions.

Chapter 11 Study Guide

Reviewing Main Ideas

Section 1 What are waves?

1. Waves are rhythmic disturbances that carry energy but not matter.
2. Mechanical waves can travel only through matter. Electromagnetic waves can travel through matter and space.
3. In a mechanical transverse wave, matter in the medium moves back and forth at right angles to the direction the wave travels.
4. In a compressional wave, matter in the medium moves forward and backward in the same direction as the wave. *How does the boat in the picture move as the water wave goes by?*

Section 2 Wave Properties

1. The amplitude of a transverse wave is one half the distance between a crest and a trough.
2. The energy carried by a wave increases as the amplitude increases.
3. Wavelength is the distance between neighboring crests or neighboring troughs.
4. The frequency of a wave is the number of wavelengths that pass a given point in 1 s. *What characteristic of a wave is indicated in the figure at the top of the next column?*

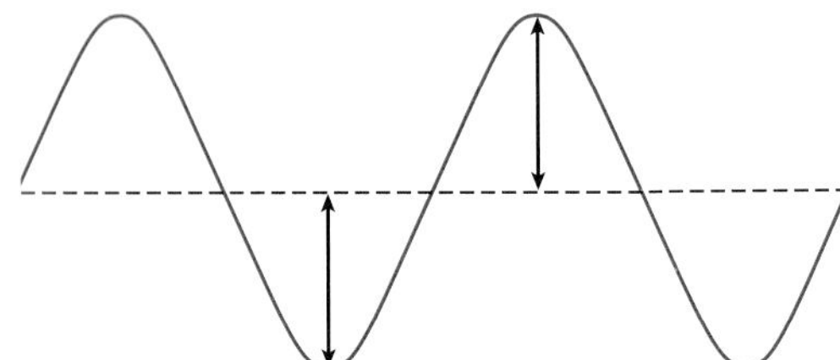

5. Waves travel through different materials at different speeds.

Section 3 Wave Behavior

1. Reflection occurs when a wave strikes an object or surface and bounces off. *Why doesn't the foil show a clear image?*
2. The bending of a wave as it moves from one medium into another is called refraction. A wave changes direction, or refracts, when the speed of the wave changes.
3. The bending of waves around a barrier is called diffraction.
4. Interference occurs when two or more waves combine and form a new wave when they overlap.

FOLDABLES Reading & Study Skills — **After You Read**

Use your Concept Map Study Fold to compare and contrast transverse and compressional mechanical waves.

FOLDABLES Reading & Study Skills — **After You Read**

After students have read the chapter and completed the Foldable described in Before You Read, have them do the activity on the student page.

Dinah Zike

Chapter 11 Study Guide

Visualizing Main Ideas

Complete the following spider map about waves.

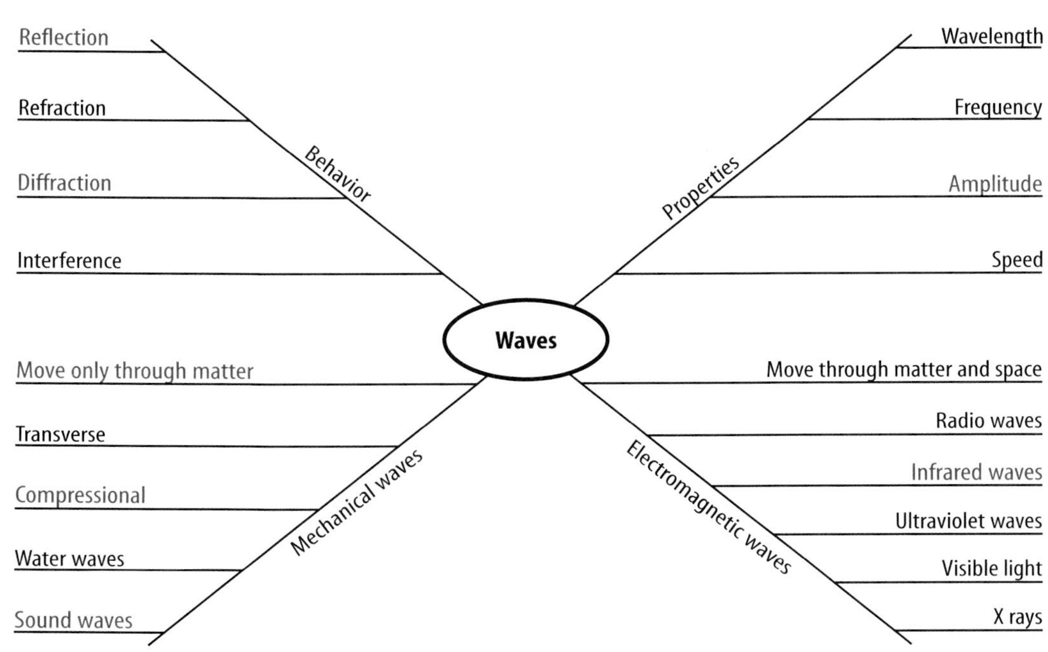

Vocabulary Review

Vocabulary Words

a. amplitude
b. compressional wave
c. diffraction
d. electromagnetic wave
e. frequency
f. interference
g. mechanical wave
h. reflection
i. refraction
j. transverse wave
k. wave
l. wavelength

Study Tip

After you've read a chapter, go back to the beginning and speed-read through what you've just read. This will help your memory.

Using Vocabulary

Using the list, replace the underlined words with the correct vocabulary words.

1. Diffraction is the change in direction of a wave when it strikes a surface.
2. The type of wave that has rarefactions is a transverse wave.
3. The distance between two adjacent crests of a transverse wave is the frequency.
4. The more energy a wave carries, the greater its wavelength is.
5. A mechanical wave can travel through space without a medium.

Chapter 11 Study Guide

Visualizing Main Ideas

See student page.

Vocabulary Review

Using Vocabulary

1. Reflection
2. compressional wave
3. wavelength
4. amplitude
5. electromagnetic wave

Chapter 11 Assessment

Checking Concepts

1. D
2. C
3. B
4. B
5. A
6. D
7. A
8. C
9. D
10. A

Thinking Critically

11. Compressional; each car is pushed into the next. The cars then rebound. This is like a compressional wave.
12. Yes; yes; electromagnetic waves can travel through space and matter.
13. The frequency decreases because fewer waves pass a given point in 1 s.
14. because the rough surface reflects the light rays in many different directions
15. Light travels much faster than sound, so the flash of the cannon will reach you before the sound will.

Chapter 11 Assessment

Checking Concepts

Choose the word or phrase that best answers the question.

1. What is the material through which mechanical waves travel?
   A) charged particles **C)** a vacuum
   B) space **D)** a medium
2. What is carried from particle to particle in a water wave?
   A) speed **C)** energy
   B) amplitude **D)** matter
3. What are the lowest points on a transverse wave called?
   A) crests **C)** compressions
   B) troughs **D)** rarefactions
4. What determines the pitch of a sound wave?
   A) amplitude **C)** speed
   B) frequency **D)** refraction
5. What is the distance between adjacent wave compressions?
   A) one wavelength **C)** 1 m/s
   B) 1 km **D)** 1 Hz
6. What occurs when a wave strikes an object or surface and bounces off?
   A) diffraction
   B) refraction
   C) a change in speed
   D) reflection
7. What is the name for a change in the direction of a wave when it passes from one medium into another?
   A) refraction **C)** reflection
   B) interference **D)** diffraction
8. What type of wave is a sound wave?
   A) transverse **C)** compressional
   B) electromagnetic **D)** refracted
9. When two waves overlap and interfere destructively, what does the resulting wave have?
   A) a greater amplitude
   B) more energy
   C) a change in frequency
   D) a lower amplitude
10. What is the difference between blue light and green light?
    A) They have different wavelengths.
    B) One is a transverse wave and the other is not.
    C) They have different pitch.
    D) One is mechanical and the other is not.

Thinking Critically

11. Explain what kind of wave—transverse or compressional—is produced when an engine bumps into a string of coupled railroad cars on a track.
12. Is it possible for an electromagnetic wave to travel through a vacuum? Through matter? Explain your answers.
13. Why does the frequency of a wave decrease as the wavelength increases?
14. Why don't you see your reflected image when you look at a white, rough surface?
15. If a cannon fires at a great distance from you, why do you see the flash before you hear the sound?

Developing Skills

16. **Solving One-Step Equations** A microwave travels at the speed of light and has a wavelength of 0.022 m. If the wave speed is equal to the wavelength times the frequency, what is the frequency of the microwave?

Chapter Assessment Planner

Portfolio Encourage students to place in their portfolios one or two items of what they consider to be their best work. Examples include:

- Activity, p. 318
- Extension, p. 322
- Science Journal, p. 324
- Challenge, p. 333

Performance Additional performance assessments, Performance Task Assessment Lists, and rubrics for evaluating these activities can be found in Glencoe's **Performance Assessment in the Science Classroom.**

17. Forming Hypotheses Form a hypothesis that can explain this observation. Waves A and B travel away from Earth through Earth's atmosphere. Wave A continues on into space, but wave B does not.

18. Recognizing Cause and Effect Explain how the object shown below causes compressions and rarefactions as it vibrates in air.

1 2 3 4

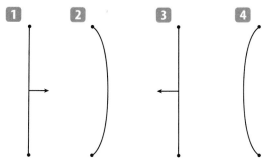

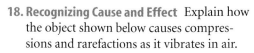

19. Comparing and Contrasting AM radio waves have wavelengths between about 200 m and 600 m, while FM radio waves have wavelengths of about 3 m. Why can AM radio signals often be heard behind buildings and mountains but FM radio signals cannot?

Performance Assessment

20. Making Flashcards Work with a partner to make flashcards for the bold-faced terms in the chapter. Illustrate each term on the front of the cards. Write the term and its definition on the back of the card. Use the cards to review the terms with another team.

Technology

Go to the Glencoe Science Web site at **science.glencoe.com** or use the **Glencoe Science CD-ROM** for additional chapter assessment.

THE PRINCETON REVIEW Test Practice

Kamisha's science teacher told her that her remote control sent signals to the TV and VCR by using infrared waves. She decided to do some research about waves. The information she gathered is shown in the diagram below.

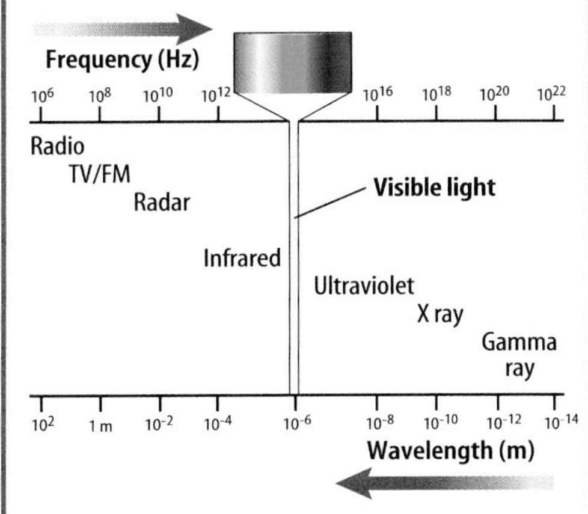

1. According to the diagram, which type of wave has a wavelength greater than 1 m?
   A) radio
   B) infrared
   C) ultraviolet
   D) X ray

2. According to the diagram, which type of wave has the HIGHEST frequency?
   F) radio
   G) ultraviolet
   H) X ray
   J) gamma ray

Assessment Resources

Reproducible Masters

Chapter Resources Booklet
Chapter Review, pp. 35–36
Chapter Tests, pp. 37–40
Assessment Transparency Activity, p. 47

Glencoe Science Web site
Interactive Tutor
Chapter Quizzes

Glencoe Technology
Assessment Transparency
Interactive CD-ROM Chapter Quizzes
ExamView Pro Test Bank
Vocabulary PuzzleMaker Software
MindJogger Videoquiz DVD/VHS

Chapter 11 Assessment

THE PRINCETON REVIEW Test Practice

The Test-Taking Tip was written by The Princeton Review, the nation's leader in test preparation.

1. A
2. J

Developing Skills

16. about 13.6 billion Hz
17. Wave A is an electromagnetic wave and wave B is a mechanical wave.
18. The vibrating object moves back and forth, colliding with the molecules in the air around it. As the object moves forward, it pushes molecules together to form a compression. As the object moves back toward its original position and beyond, it creates a rarefaction—a region in which molecules are spread farther apart.
19. Because their longer wavelengths are closer to the size of buildings and mountains, AM radio waves diffract around them more than FM radio waves do.

Performance Assessment

20. Use **Performance Assessment in the Science Classroom**, p. 127.

CHAPTER ASSESSMENT 341

Section/Objectives	Standards		Activities/Features
	National	State/Local	
Chapter Opener	See p. 5T for a Key to Standards		**Explore Activity:** Observe throat vibrations, p. 343 **Before You Read,** p. 343
Section 1 What is sound? 3 sessions 1.5 blocks 1. **Identify** the characteristics of sound waves. 2. **Explain** how sound travels. 3. **Describe** the Doppler effect.	National Content Standards: UCP2, A1, B3, D3, F5		**MiniLAB:** Comparing and Contrasting Sounds, p. 346 **Science Online,** p. 349 **Astronomy Integration,** p. 350 **Problem-Solving Activity:** How does Doppler radar work?, p. 350 **Visualizing the Doppler Effect,** p. 351 **Activity:** Observe and Measure Reflection of Sound, p. 354
Section 2 Music 4 sessions 2 blocks 1. **Explain** the difference between music and noise. 2. **Describe** how different instruments produce music. 3. **Explain** how you hear.	National Content Standards: UCP2, A1, B3, C1, F1, F5		**Environmental Science Integration,** p. 356 **MiniLAB:** Modeling a Stringed Instrument, p. 358 **Science Online,** p. 361 **Activity:** Music, pp. 364–365 **Science and Society:** It's a Wrap!, pp. 366–367

Activity Materials	Reproducible Resources	Section Assessment	Technology
Explore Activity: no materials needed	**Chapter Resources Booklet** Foldables Worksheet, p. 15 Directed Reading Overview, p. 17 Note-taking Worksheets, pp. 29–30	GLENCOE'S ASSESSMENT ADVANTAGE	
MiniLAB: set of keys; tub or wide, deep bowl; metal spoon; cotton string; towel; water **Activity:** 2 cardboard tubes (20- to 30-cm long), watch with a second hand that ticks audibly, protractor	**Chapter Resources Booklet** Transparency Activity, p. 40 MiniLAB, p. 3 Enrichment, p. 27 Reinforcement, p. 25 Directed Reading, p. 18 Activity Worksheet, pp. 5–6 Lab Activity, pp. 9–10 **Mathematics Skill Activities,** p. 9 **Reading and Writing Skill Activities,** p. 7 **Science Inquiry Labs,** p. 27	Portfolio Assessment, p. 346 Extension, p. 352 Performance MiniLAB, p. 346 Problem-Solving Activity, p. 350 Skill Builder Activities, p. 353 Content Section Assessment, p. 353	Section Focus Transparency Interactive CD-ROM/DVD Guided Reading Audio Program
MiniLAB: rubber band, shoe box **Activity:** musical instruments, measuring tape, tuning forks *Need materials?* Contact Science Kit at 1-800-828-7777 or www.sciencekit.com on the Internet.	**Chapter Resources Booklet** Transparency Activity, p. 41 MiniLAB, p. 4 Enrichment, p. 28 Reinforcement, p. 26 Directed Reading, pp. 19, 20 Activity Worksheet, pp. 7–8 Transparency Activity, pp. 43–44 Lab Activity, pp. 11–14 **Cultural Diversity,** p. 61 **Lab Management and Safety,** p. 64	Portfolio Assessment, p. 363 Performance MiniLAB, p. 358 Skill Builder Activities, p. 363 Content Section Assessment, p. 363	Section Focus Transparency Teaching Transparency Interactive CD-ROM/DVD Guided Reading Audio Program

GLENCOE'S ASSESSMENT ADVANTAGE

End of Chapter Assessment		
Blackline Masters	**Technology**	**Professional Series**
Chapter Resources Booklet Chapter Review, pp. 33–34 Chapter Tests, pp. 35–38 **Standardized Test Practice by The Princeton Review,** pp. 51–54	MindJogger Videoquiz CD-ROM Explorations and Quizzes Vocabulary Puzzle Makers ExamView Pro Test Bank Interactive Lesson Planner Interactive Teacher's Edition	Performance Assessment in the Science Classroom (PASC)

Transparencies

Section Focus

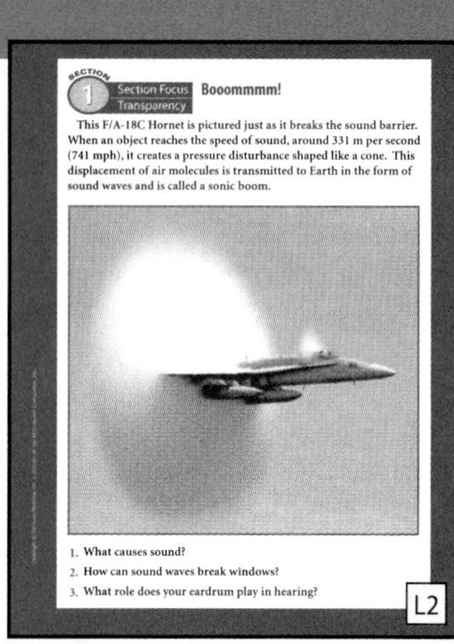
Section 1 Section Focus Transparency **Booommmm!**

This F/A-18C Hornet is pictured just as it breaks the sound barrier. When an object reaches the speed of sound, around 331 m per second (741 mph), it creates a pressure disturbance shaped like a cone. This displacement of air molecules is transmitted to Earth in the form of sound waves and is called a sonic boom.

1. What causes sound?
2. How can sound waves break windows?
3. What role does your eardrum play in hearing?

L2

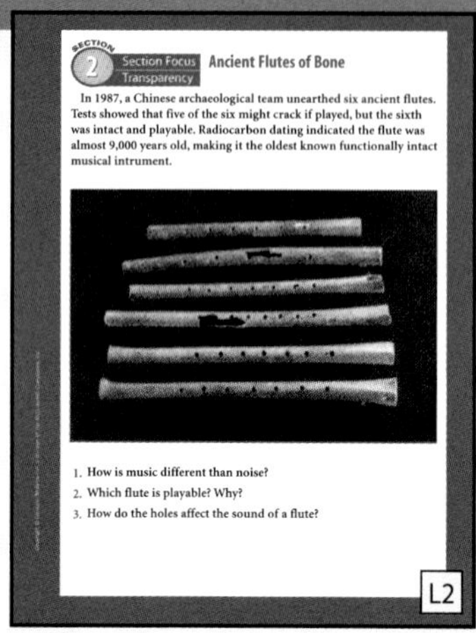
Section 2 Section Focus Transparency **Ancient Flutes of Bone**

In 1987, a Chinese archaeological team unearthed six ancient flutes. Tests showed that five of the six might crack if played, but the sixth was intact and playable. Radiocarbon dating indicated the flute was almost 9,000 years old, making it the oldest known functionally intact musical intrument.

1. How is music different than noise?
2. Which flute is playable? Why?
3. How do the holes affect the sound of a flute?

L2

This is a representation of key blackline masters available in the Teacher Classroom Resources. See Resource Manager boxes within the chapter for additional information.

Assessment

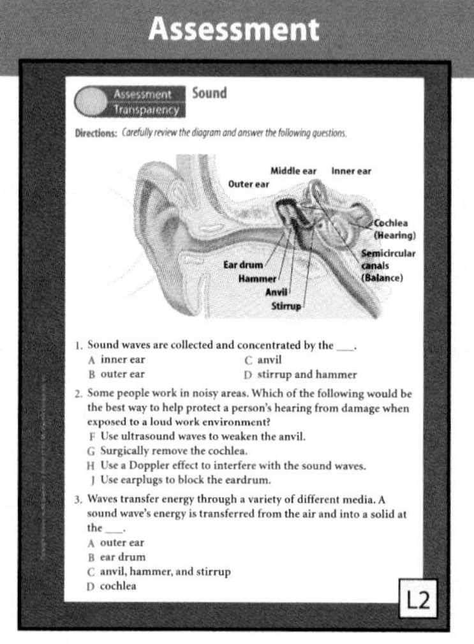
Assessment Transparency **Sound**

Directions: *Carefully review the diagram and answer the following questions.*

1. Sound waves are collected and concentrated by the ___.
   A inner ear
   B outer ear
   C anvil
   D stirrup and hammer
2. Some people work in noisy areas. Which of the following would be the best way to help protect a person's hearing from damage when exposed to a loud work environment?
   F Use ultrasound waves to weaken the anvil.
   G Surgically remove the cochlea.
   H Use a Doppler effect to interfere with the sound waves.
   J Use earplugs to block the eardrum.
3. Waves transfer energy through a variety of different media. A sound wave's energy is transferred from the air and into a solid at the ___.
   A outer ear
   B ear drum
   C anvil, hammer, and stirrup
   D cochlea

L2

Teaching

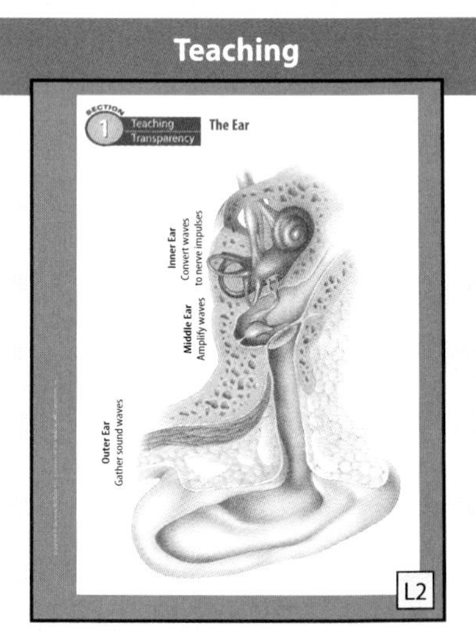
Section 1 Teaching Transparency **The Ear**

L2

Key to Teaching Strategies

The following designations will help you decide which activities are appropriate for your students.

L1 Level 1 activities should be appropriate for students with learning difficulties.

L2 Level 2 activities should be within the ability range of all students.

L3 Level 3 activities are designed for above-average students.

ELL ELL activities should be within the ability range of English Language Learners.

COOP LEARN Cooperative Learning activities are designed for small group work.

LS Multiple Learning Styles logos, as described on page 22T, are used throughout to indicate strategies that address different learning styles.

P These strategies represent student products that can be placed into a best-work portfolio.

Hands-on Activities

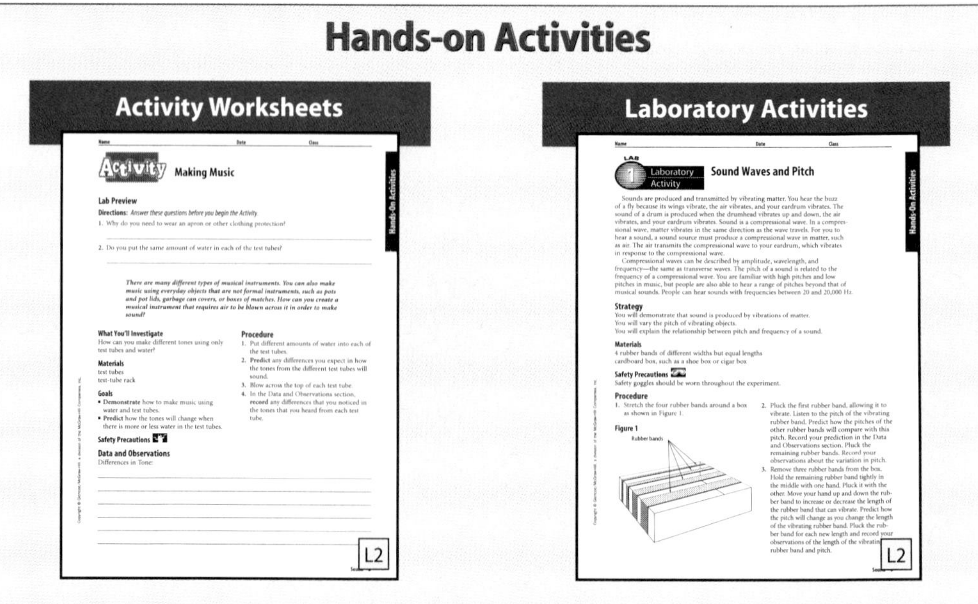

Activity Worksheets

Name Date Class

Activity **Making Music**

Hands-On Activities

Lab Preview

Directions: *Answer these questions before you begin the Activity.*

1. Why do you need to wear an apron or other clothing protection?
2. Do you put the same amount of water in each of the test tubes?

There are many different types of musical instruments. You can also make music using everyday objects that are not formal instruments, such as pots and pot lids, garbage can covers, or boxes of matches. How can you create a musical instrument that requires air to be blown across it in order to make sound?

What You'll Investigate
How can you make different tones using only test tubes and water?

Materials
test tubes
test-tube rack

Goals
- **Demonstrate** how to make music using water and test tubes.
- **Predict** how the tones will change when there is more or less water in the test tubes.

Safety Precautions

Procedure
1. Put different amounts of water into each of the test tubes.
2. **Predict** any differences you expect in how the tones from the different test tubes will sound.
3. Blow across the top of each test tube.
4. In the Data and Observations section, **record** any differences that you noticed in the tones that you heard from each test tube.

Data and Observations
Differences in Tone:

L2

Laboratory Activities

Name Date Class

Lab 1 Laboratory Activity **Sound Waves and Pitch**

Hands-On Activities

Sounds are produced and transmitted by vibrating matter. You hear the buzz of a fly because its wings vibrate, the air vibrates, and your eardrum vibrates. The sound of a drum is produced when the drumhead vibrates up and down, the air vibrates, and your eardrum vibrates. Sound is a compressional wave. In a compressional wave, matter vibrates in the same direction as the wave travels. For you to hear a sound, a sound source must produce a compressional wave in matter, such as air. The air transmits the compressional wave to your eardrum, which vibrates in response to the compressional wave.

Compressional waves can be described by amplitude, wavelength, and frequency—the same as transverse waves. The pitch of a sound is related to the frequency of a compressional wave. You are familiar with high pitches and low pitches in music, but people are also able to hear a range of pitches beyond that of musical sounds. People can hear sounds with frequencies between 20 and 20,000 Hz.

Strategy
You will demonstrate that sound is produced by vibrations of matter.
You will vary the pitch of vibrating objects.
You will explain the relationship between pitch and frequency of a sound.

Materials
4 rubber bands of different widths but equal lengths
cardboard box, such as a shoe box or cigar box

Safety Precautions
Safety goggles should be worn throughout the experiment.

Procedure
1. Stretch the four rubber bands around a box as shown in Figure 1.
2. Pluck the first rubber band, allowing it to vibrate. Listen to the pitch of the vibrating rubber band. Predict how the pitches of the other rubber bands will compare with this pitch. Record your prediction in the Data and Observations section. Pluck the remaining rubber bands. Record your observations about the variation in pitch.
3. Remove three rubber bands from the box. Hold the remaining rubber band tightly in the middle with one hand. Pluck it with the other. Move your hand up and down the rubber band to increase or decrease the length of the rubber band that can vibrate. Predict how the pitch will change as you change the length of the vibrating rubber band. Pluck the rubber band for each new length and record your observations of the length of the vibratin[g] rubber band and pitch.

Figure 1

L2

Meeting Different Ability Levels

Content Outline

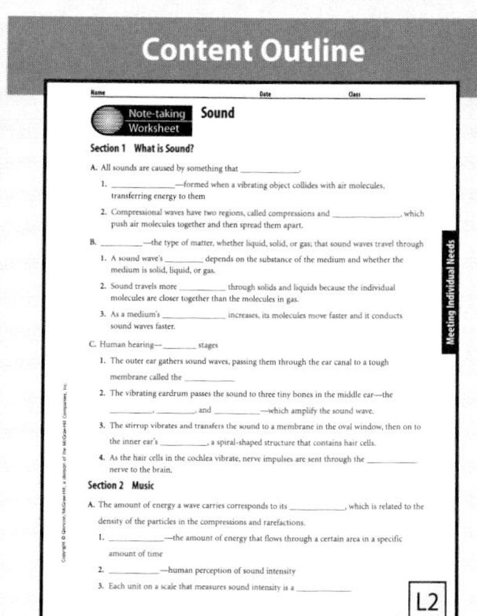

Name Date Class

Note-taking Worksheet — Sound

Section 1 What is Sound?

A. All sounds are caused by something that ______.
1. ______—formed when a vibrating object collides with air molecules, transferring energy to them
2. Compressional waves have two regions, called compressions and ______, which push air molecules together and then spread them apart.

B. ______—the type of matter, whether liquid, solid, or gas, that sound waves travel through
1. A sound wave's ______ depends on the substance of the medium and whether the medium is solid, liquid, or gas.
2. Sound travels more ______ through solids and liquids because the individual molecules are closer together than the molecules in gas.
3. As a medium's ______ increases, its molecules move faster and it conducts sound waves faster.

C. Human hearing—______ stages
1. The outer ear gathers sound waves, passing them through the ear canal to a tough membrane called the ______.
2. The vibrating eardrum passes the sound to three tiny bones in the middle ear—the ______ and ______—which amplify the sound wave.
3. The stirrup vibrates and transfers the sound to a membrane in the oval window, then on to the inner ear's ______, a spiral-shaped structure that contains hair cells.
4. As the hair cells in the cochlea vibrate, nerve impulses are sent through the ______ nerve to the brain.

Section 2 Music

A. The amount of energy a wave carries corresponds to its ______, which is related to the density of the particles in the compressions and rarefactions.
1. ______—the amount of energy that flows through a certain area in a specific amount of time
2. ______—human perception of sound intensity
3. Each unit on a scale that measures sound intensity is a ______.

Meeting Individual Needs

L2

Reinforcement

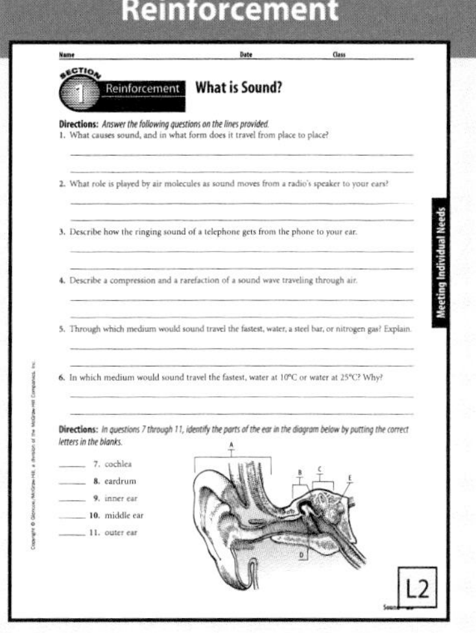

Name Date Class

Section 1 Reinforcement — What is Sound?

Directions: *Answer the following questions on the lines provided.*
1. What causes sound, and in what form does it travel from place to place?
2. What role is played by air molecules as sound moves from a radio's speaker to your ears?
3. Describe how the ringing sound of a telephone gets from the phone to your ear.
4. Describe a compression and a rarefaction of a sound wave traveling through air.
5. Through which medium would sound travel the fastest, water, a steel bar, or nitrogen gas? Explain.
6. In which medium would sound travel the fastest, water at 10°C or water at 25°C? Why?

Directions: *In questions 7 through 11, identify the parts of the ear in the diagram below by putting the correct letters in the blanks.*

____ 7. cochlea
____ 8. eardrum
____ 9. inner ear
____ 10. middle ear
____ 11. outer ear

Meeting Individual Needs

L2

Directed Reading

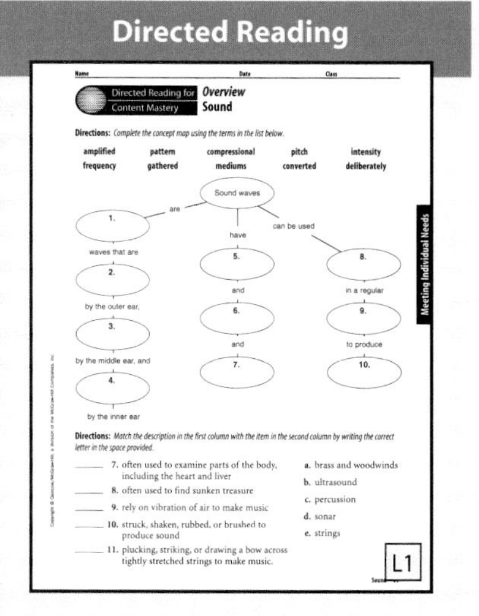

Name Date Class

Directed Reading for Content Mastery — *Overview* Sound

Directions: *Complete the concept map using the terms in the list below.*

amplified	pattern	compressional	pitch	intensity
frequency	gathered	mediums	converted	deliberately

Directions: *Match the description in the first column with the item in the second column by writing the correct letter in the space provided.*

____ 7. often used to examine parts of the body, including the heart and liver — a. brass and woodwinds
____ 8. often used to find sunken treasure — b. ultrasound
____ 9. rely on vibration of air to make music — c. percussion
____ 10. struck, shaken, rubbed, or brushed to produce sound — d. sonar
____ 11. plucking, striking, or drawing a bow across tightly stretched strings to make music. — e. strings

Meeting Individual Needs

L1

Assessment

Chapter Tests

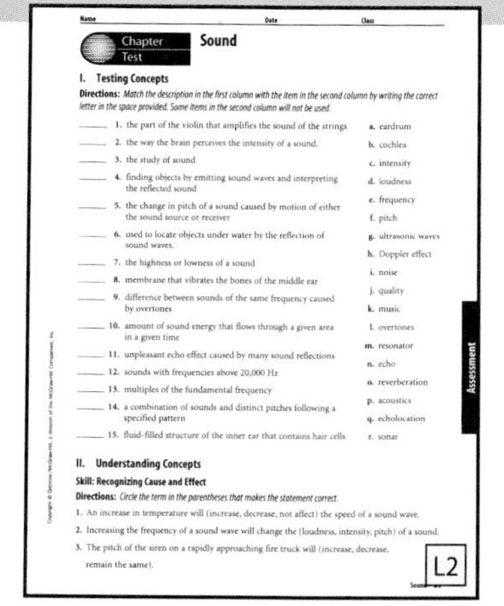

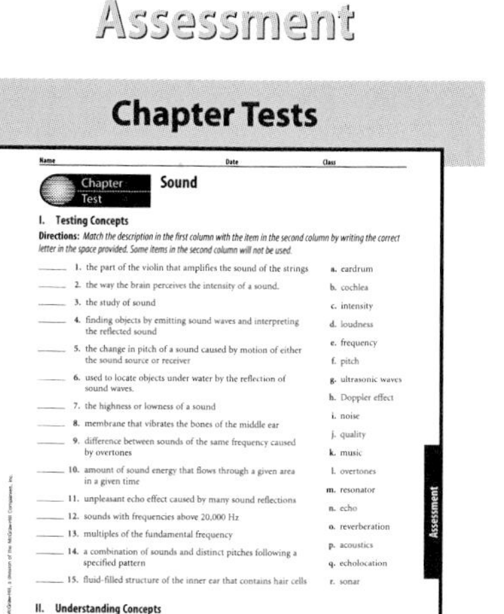

Name Date Class

Chapter Test — Sound

I. Testing Concepts

Directions: *Match the description in the first column with the item in the second column by writing the correct letter in the space provided. Some items in the second column will not be used.*

____ 1. the part of the violin that amplifies the sound of the strings — a. eardrum
____ 2. the way the brain perceives the intensity of a sound. — b. cochlea
____ 3. the study of sound — c. intensity
____ 4. finding objects by emitting sound waves and interpreting the reflected sound — d. loudness
____ 5. the change in pitch of a sound caused by motion of either the sound source or receiver — e. frequency
____ 6. used to locate objects under water by the reflection of sound waves — f. pitch
____ 7. the highness or lowness of a sound — g. ultrasonic waves
____ 8. membrane that vibrates the bones of the middle ear — h. Doppler effect
____ 9. difference between sounds of the same frequency caused by overtones — i. noise
____ 10. amount of sound energy that flows through a given area in a given time — j. quality
____ 11. unpleasant echo effect caused by many sound reflections — k. music
____ 12. sounds with frequencies above 20,000 Hz — l. overtones
____ 13. multiples of the fundamental frequency — m. resonator
____ 14. a combination of sounds and distinct pitches following a specified pattern — n. echo
____ 15. fluid-filled structure of the inner ear that contains hair cells — o. reverberation; p. acoustics; q. echolocation; r. sonar

II. Understanding Concepts

Skill: Recognizing Cause and Effect

Directions: *Circle the term in the parentheses that makes the statement correct.*
1. An increase in temperature will (increase, decrease, not affect) the speed of a sound wave.
2. Increasing the frequency of a sound wave will change the (loudness, intensity, pitch) of a sound.
3. The pitch of the siren on a rapidly approaching fire truck will (increase, decrease, remain the same).

Assessment

L2

Enrichment

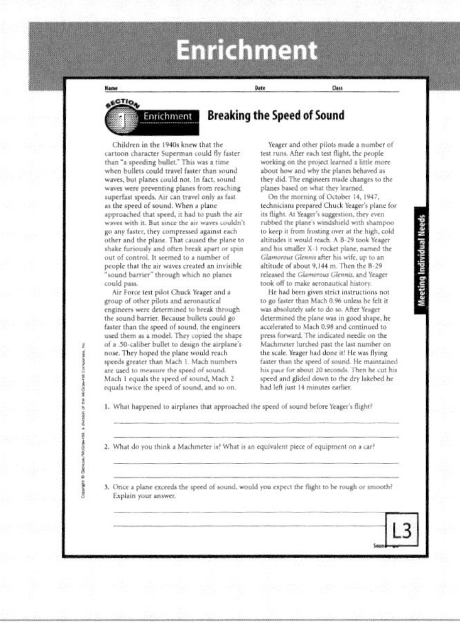

Name Date Class

Section 1 Enrichment — Breaking the Speed of Sound

Children in the 1940s knew that the cartoon character Superman could fly faster than "a speeding bullet." This was a time when bullets could travel faster than sound waves, but planes could not. In fact, sound waves were preventing planes from reaching superfast speeds. Air can travel only as fast as the speed of sound. When a plane approached that speed, it had to push the air waves with it. But since the air waves couldn't go any faster, they compressed against each other and the plane. That caused the plane to shake furiously and often break apart or spin out of control. It seemed to a number of people that the air waves created an invisible "sound barrier" through which no planes could pass.

Air Force test pilot Chuck Yeager and a group of other pilots and aeronautical engineers were determined to break through the sound barrier. Because bullets could go faster than the speed of sound, the engineers used them as a model. They copied the shape of a .50-caliber bullet to design the airplane's nose. They hoped the plane would reach speeds greater than Mach 1. Mach numbers are used to measure the speed of sound. Mach 1 equals the speed of sound, Mach 2 equals twice the speed of sound, and so on.

Yeager and other pilots made a number of test runs. After each test flight, the people working on the project learned a little more about how and why the planes behaved as they did. The engineers made changes to the planes based on what they learned.

On the morning of October 14, 1947, technicians prepared Chuck Yeager's plane for its flight. At Yeager's suggestion, they even rubbed the plane's windshield with shampoo to keep it from frosting over at the high, cold altitudes it would reach. A B-29 took Yeager and his rocket plane, the X-1, named the *Glamorous Glennis* after his wife, up to an altitude of about 9,144 m. Then the B-29 released the *Glamorous Glennis*, and Yeager took off to make aeronautical history.

He had been given strict instructions not to go faster than Mach 0.96 unless he felt it was absolutely safe to do so. After Yeager determined the plane was in good shape, he accelerated to Mach 0.98 and continued to press forward. The indicated needle on the Machmeter lurched past the last number on the scale. Yeager had done it! He was flying faster than the speed of sound. He maintained his pace for about 20 seconds. Then he cut his speed and glided down to the dry lakebed he had left just 14 minutes earlier.

1. What happened to airplanes that approached the speed of sound before Yeager's flight?
2. What do you think a Machmeter is? What is an equivalent piece of equipment on a car?
3. Once a plane exceeds the speed of sound, would you expect the flight to be rough or smooth? Explain your answer.

Meeting Individual Needs

L3

Spanish Directed Reading

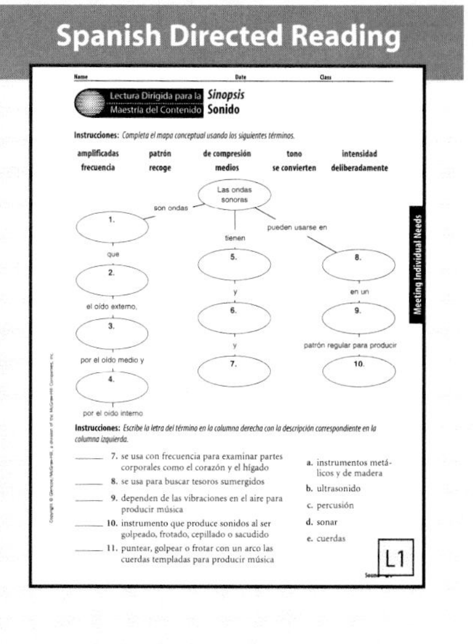

Name Date Class

Lectura Dirigida para la Maestría del Contenido — *Sinopsis* Sonido

Instrucciones: *Completa el mapa conceptual usando los siguientes términos.*

amplificadas	patrón	de compresión	tono	intensidad
frecuencia	recoge	medios	se convierten	deliberadamente

Instrucciones: *Escribe la letra del término en la columna derecha con la descripción correspondiente en la columna izquierda.*

____ 7. se usa con frecuencia para examinar partes corporales como el corazón y el hígado — a. instrumentos metálicos y de madera
____ 8. se usa para buscar tesoros sumergidos — b. ultrasonido
____ 9. dependen de las vibraciones en el aire para producir música — c. percusión
____ 10. instrumento que produce sonidos al ser golpeado, frotado, cepillado o sacudido — d. sonar
____ 11. puntear, golpear o frotar con un arco las cuerdas templadas para producir música — e. cuerdas

Meeting Individual Needs

L1

Test Practice Workbook

Chapter Review

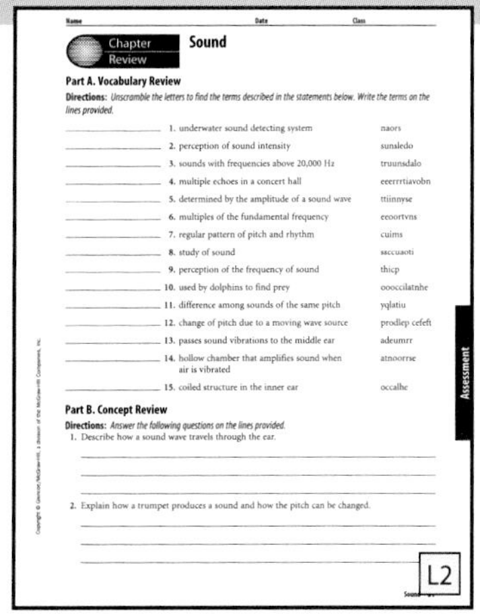

Name Date Class

Chapter Review — Sound

Part A. Vocabulary Review

Directions: *Unscramble the letters to find the terms described in the statements below. Write the terms on the lines provided.*

______	1. underwater sound detecting system	naors
______	2. perception of sound intensity	sunsledo
______	3. sounds with frequencies above 20,000 Hz	trusanlado
______	4. multiple echoes in a concert hall	eeerrrtiaovbn
______	5. determined by the amplitude of a sound wave	ttiinnsse
______	6. multiples of the fundamental frequency	eeoortvns
______	7. regular pattern of pitch and rhythm	cuims
______	8. study of sound	saccuiotti
______	9. perception of the frequency of sound	thicp
______	10. used by dolphins to find prey	ooocciilatnhe
______	11. difference among sounds of the same pitch	yqlatiu
______	12. change of pitch due to a moving wave source	prodiep cefeft
______	13. passes sound vibrations to the middle ear	adeumrr
______	14. hollow chamber that amplifies sound when air is vibrated	atnoorrse
______	15. coiled structure in the inner ear	occalhe

Part B. Concept Review

Directions: *Answer the following questions on the lines provided.*
1. Describe how a sound wave travels through the ear.
2. Explain how a trumpet produces a sound and how the pitch can be changed.

Assessment

L2

Science Content Background

SECTION 1 What is sound?

Sound Waves

Sound waves are mechanical waves, which means they need a medium to travel through and they can't travel through a vacuum. It is important to realize that the sound energy travels through the particles of a medium but the particles return to their original positions.

Sound waves are called compressional or longitudinal waves. The compressions and rarefactions produced cause temporary changes in the pressure of the medium it travels through. Our ears respond to this pressure and interpret it as sound.

The Speed of Sound

Speed is literally how fast the sound travels through particles, as opposed to frequency, which is how often the particles of the medium vibrate back and forth.

The approximate speed of sound through air at room temperature is 343 m/s or 750 miles/hour. While this is fast, light travels about 900,000 times faster. This explains why we see lightning before we hear thunder. To calculate how far away lightning is, multiply the speed of sound by the number of seconds between seeing the lightning and hearing the thunder. If this is three seconds, then the lightning is 3 s × 343 m/s = 1,029 m away. For an approximate distance in miles divide the time by five.

The more dense a gas, the more slowly sound travels through it. This is because dense gases have particles with more mass that resist moving. For example, sound travels about three times faster in helium than it does in air. The squeaky voice produced when talking through helium from a balloon occurs because the sound travels faster from the speaker's vocal chords than it would through normal air. The pitch is not increased, but the different resonance produced results in a different timbre to the voice. (Warning: Breathing helium can be dangerous and it is not recommended.)

Fun Fact

We can use echolocation to estimate the distance of large objects such as the wall of a canyon. Yell and time how long it takes to hear the echo. Since the sound makes a round trip journey, take one half the time and multiply it by the speed of sound. For example, if it takes 2 seconds to hear the echo from the wall, the distance of the canyon is 1 s × 343 m/s = 343 m.

Amplitude and Loudness

Sound intensity can be thought of as how much energy passes through a given area in a given amount of time. Since sound spreads out as it travels, the intensity of the sound decreases as it travels and is proportional to the inverse square of the distance. This means that for every doubling of distance from the source, the intensity of sound is reduced to one-quarter.

Humans can detect very low levels of sound. This threshold is defined as 0 dB. A sound of 0 dB will move our eardrum as little as one-billionth of a centimeter, but we can still hear it.

Frequency and Pitch

The unit of frequency is the Hertz (Hz),which is equal to one cycle per second. The higher the frequency of a wave, the smaller is its wavelength. The velocity of a wave is equal to its frequency multiplied by its wavelength.

For additional content background on this topic, go to the Glencoe Science Web site at science.glencoe.com.

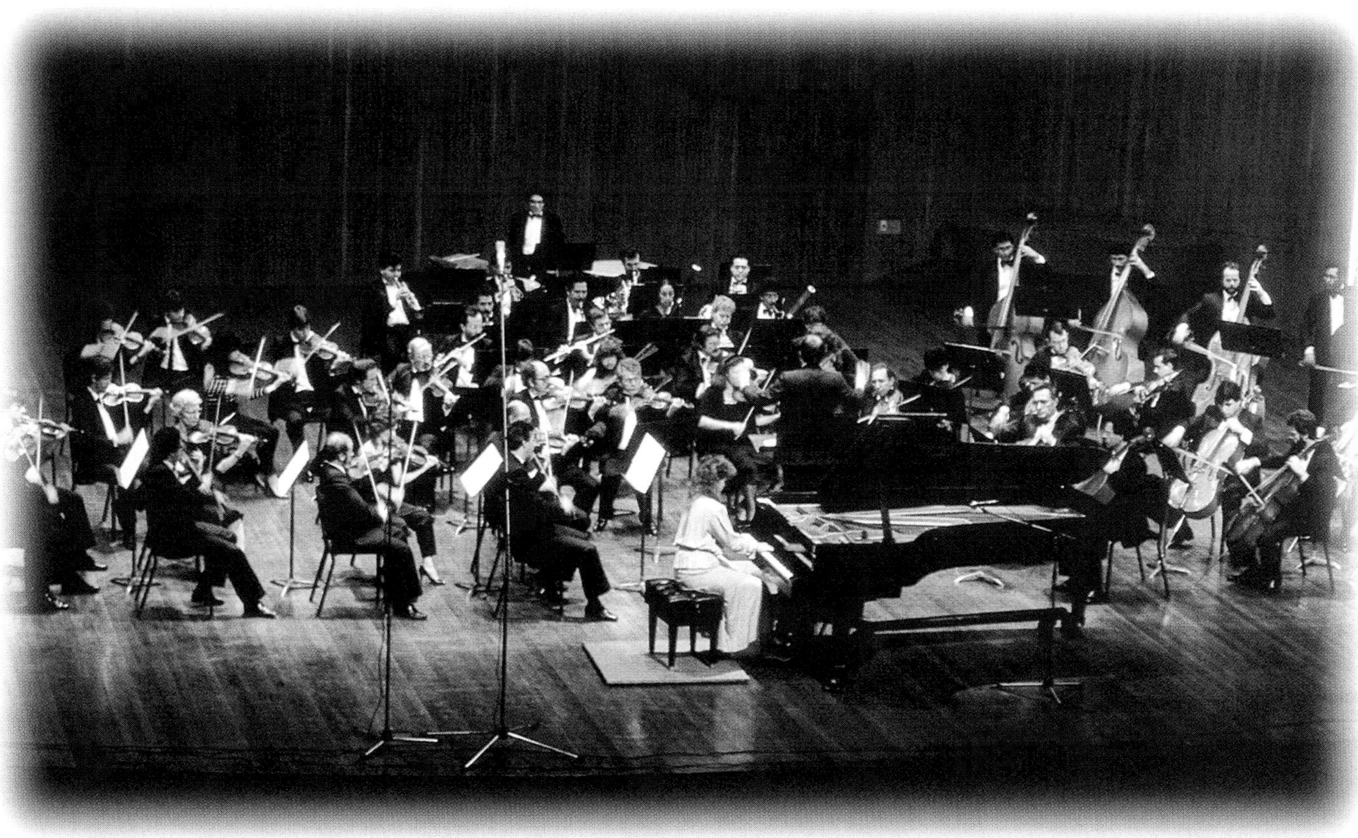

Crandall/The Image Works

SECTION 2 Music

What is music?

The sounds produced by different frequencies are referred to as pitch. People with well-trained ears can detect frequency differences of as little as 3 Hz.

Constructive and destructive interference make some frequencies sound better together than others do. For example, sounds that are separated by a frequency ratio of 2 to 1 are pleasing. In music these sounds are said to be separated by an octave.

A tuning fork sounds louder when it is put on a table. This is because resonance makes the table vibrate with the same frequency. Since the table has a larger surface area, it displaces more air and creates a louder sound. In a similar way the body of a guitar makes a plucked string sound louder. Timbre is the musical term used to describe sounds with the same frequencies but that sound different to our ears.

Fun Fact

Middle C on a piano has a frequency of 261.6 Hz and a wavelength of 132 cm.

The Ear

The ear acts to magnify sound vibrations. The outer ear increases pressure by ten times, the lever system of the middle ear triples the strength of the vibrations, and the inner ear can multiply the strength thirty times. As a result the strength of the vibrations can increase to 8,000 times their initial size.

CHAPTER 12

Sound

Chapter Vocabulary

loudness
pitch
echo
Doppler effect
natural frequency
resonance
fundamental frequency
overtone
reverberation
eardrum

What do you think?

Science Journal The photo shows a guitar string vibrating. The vibration of the string produces the sound.

CHAPTER 12 Sound

Have you ever experienced complete silence? Unless you have stood in a room like this one, you probably have not. This room is lined with materials that absorb sound waves and eliminate sound reflections. The sounds that you hear are created by vibrations. How do vibrations make sounds with different pitches? What makes a sound loud or quiet? In this chapter, you will learn the answers to these questions. You will also learn how musical instruments create sound and how the ear enables you to hear sound.

What do you think?

Science Journal Look at the picture below with a classmate. Discuss what might be happening. Here's a hint: *Sound is caused by vibrations.* Write your answer or best guess in your Science Journal.

342

Theme Connection

Stability and Change Sound waves are produced by periodic changes in the motion of an object. Changes in sound waves bring about changes in sounds.

When you speak or sing, you push air from your lungs past your vocal cords, which are two flaps of tissue inside your throat. When you tighten your vocal cords, you can make the sound have a higher tone. Do this activity to explore how you change the shape of your throat to vary the tone of sound.

Observe throat vibrations

1. Hold your fingers against the front of your throat and say *Aaaah.* Notice the vibration against your fingers.
2. Now vary the tone of this sound from low to high and back again. How do the vibrations in your throat change? Record your observations.
3. Change the sound to an *Ooooh.* What do you notice as you listen? Record your observations.

Observe

In your Science Journal, describe how the shape of your throat changed the tone.

Before You Read

Making a Question Study Fold **Asking yourself questions helps you stay focused so you will better understand sound when you are reading the chapter.**

1. Place a sheet of notebook paper in front of you so the short side is at the top and the holes are on the right side. Fold the paper in half from the left side to the right side.
2. Through the top thickness of paper, cut along every third line from the outside edge to the fold, forming tabs.
3. Before you read the chapter, write a question you have about sound on the front of each tab. As you read the chapter, answer your questions and add more information.

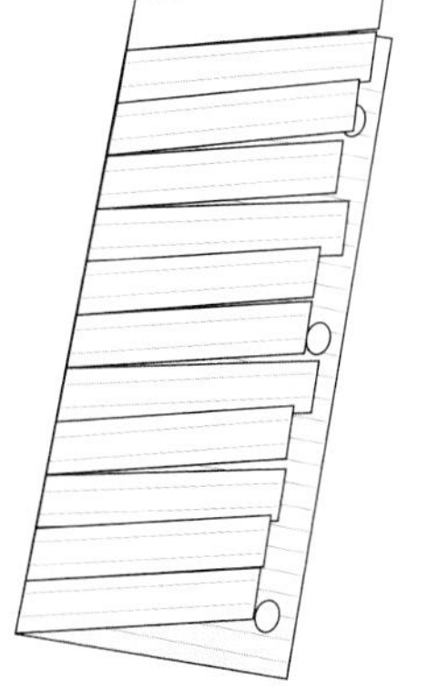

343

Explore Activity

Purpose Use the Explore Activity to demonstrate how the throat changes as the voice changes in pitch. L2 ELL

LS **Auditory-Musical**

Teaching Strategies

- After they observe the tone (really pitch) difference in a single sound, suggest students try holding their hands to their throats while speaking. Pitch varies with the emphasis given to different words. The last word of a question, for example, is at a higher pitch.
- If you have students who speak languages other than English, have them determine how the pitches vary when the same sentence is said in a different language. Some languages use different rules for pitch to indicate a question, statement, or exclamation. Others use changing pitch to alter the meanings of words.

Observe

Possible answer: The muscles in your throat tighten when you produce sounds of a higher pitch.

Assessment

Process Ask students to sing or speak for about 10 seconds while other students sketch a graph of how pitch varies, using dashes at different heights above a line. If students ask a question, the pitch would start on a mid-tone and end on a higher pitch. Use **PASC,** p. 111.

Before You Read

Foldables Reading & Study Skills

Dinah Zike Study Fold

Purpose In this activity, students start thinking about sound before they read the chapter by asking questions to guide their reading. Students record the answers to their questions in a Foldable, which then becomes a study guide.

For additional help, see Foldables Worksheet, p. 13 in **Chapter Resources Booklet,** or go to the Glencoe Science Web site at **science.glencoe.com.** See After You Read in the Study Guide at the end of this chapter.

SECTION 1

What is sound?

1 Motivate

Bellringer Transparency

Display the Section Focus Transparency for Section 1. Use the accompanying Transparency Activity Master. L2 ELL

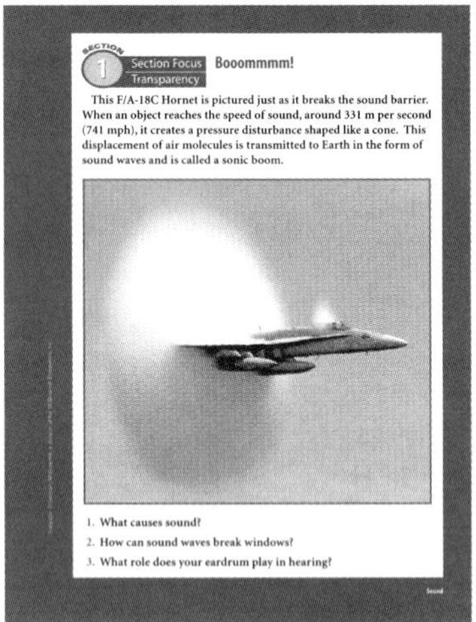

Tie to Prior Knowledge

Ask students what happens when a rock is tossed into a body of water such as a pond or lake. Waves of energy move outward in all directions from the point where the object strikes the water. Explain that sound is a form of energy that also travels in waves. Sound waves, however, are compressional waves, while the waves in water are transverse waves.

Resource Manager

Chapter Resources Booklet
Transparency Activity, p. 40
Directed Reading for Content Mastery, pp. 17, 18

SECTION 1

What is sound?

As You Read

What You'll Learn

- **Identify** the characteristics of sound waves.
- **Explain** how sound travels.
- **Describe** the Doppler effect.

Vocabulary
loudness
pitch
echo
Doppler effect

Why It's Important
Sound gives important information about the world around you.

Sound and Vibration

Think of all the sounds you've heard since you awoke this morning. Did you hear your alarm clock blaring, car horns honking, or locker doors slamming? Every sound has something in common with every other sound. Each is produced by something that vibrates.

Sound Waves

How does an object that is vibrating produce sound? When you speak, the vocal cords in your throat vibrate. These vibrations cause other people to hear your voice. The vibrations produce sound waves that travel to their ears. The other person's ears interpret these sound waves.

A wave carries energy from one place to another without transferring matter. An object that is vibrating in air, such as your vocal cords, produces a sound wave. The vibrating object causes air molecules to move back and forth. As these air molecules collide with those nearby, they cause other air molecules to move back and forth, transferring the energy of the sound wave. A sound wave is a compressional wave, like the wave moving through the coiled spring toy in **Figure 1.** In a compressional wave, particles in the material move back and forth along the direction the wave is moving. In a sound wave, air molecules move back and forth along the direction the sound wave is moving.

Figure 1
When the coils of a coiled spring toy are squeezed together, a compressional wave moves along the spring. The coils move back and forth as the compressional wave moves past them.

Section Assessment Planner

Portfolio
Assessment, p. 346
Extension, p. 352

Performance Assessment
Try at Home MiniLAB, p. 346
Problem-Solving Activity, p. 350
Skill Builder Activities, p. 353
See page 370 for more options.

Content Assessment
Section, p. 353
Challenge, p. 353
Chapter, pp. 370–371

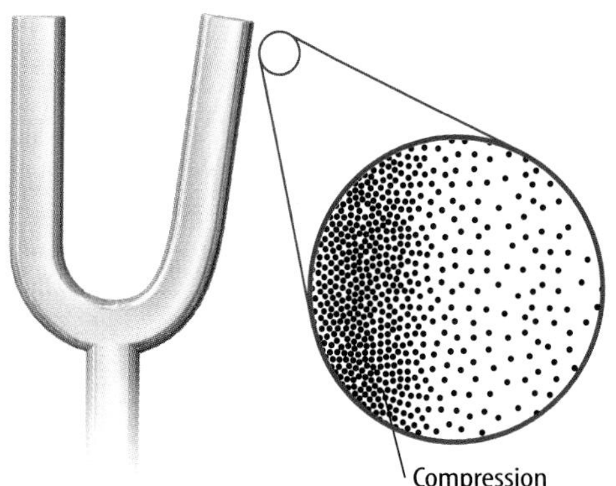

A **When the tuning fork vibrates outward, it forces the air molecules next to it together, creating a region of compression.**

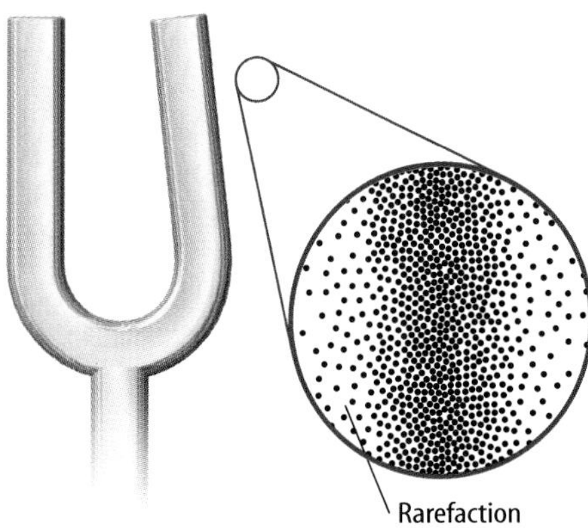

B **When the tuning fork moves back, the air molecules next to it spread apart, creating a region of rarefaction.**

Making Sound Waves When an object vibrates, it exerts a force on the surrounding air. For example, as the end of the tuning fork moves outward into the air, it pushes the air molecules together, as shown in **Figure 2A.** As a result, a region where the air molecules are closer together, or more dense, is created. This region of higher density is called a compression. When the end of the tuning fork moves back, it creates a region of lower density called a rarefaction, as shown in **Figure 2B.** As the tuning fork continues to vibrate, a series of compressions and rarefactions is formed. The compressions and rarefactions move away from the tuning fork as molecules in these regions collide with other nearby molecules.

Like other waves, a sound wave can be described by its wavelength and frequency. The wavelength of a sound wave is shown in **Figure 3.** The frequency of a sound wave is the number of compressions or rarefactions that pass by a given point in one second. An object that vibrates faster forms a sound wave with a higher frequency.

Figure 2
A tuning fork makes a sound wave as the ends of the fork vibrate in the air. *Can a sound wave travel in a vacuum?*

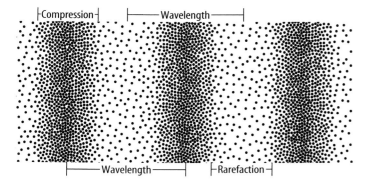

Compression — Wavelength
Wavelength — Rarefaction

Figure 3
Wavelength is the distance from one compression to another or one rarefaction to another. *How does the wavelength of a sound wave relate to its frequency?*

2 Teach

Sound and Vibration

Discussion

Explain to students that people sometimes experience sound as felt vibrations. Ask students to suggest examples of situations in which people might be able to feel the vibrations caused by sound. Possible answers: when a loud stereo vibrates the floor of a room or thunder shakes windows. L2
LS **Logical-Mathematical**

Sound Waves

Caption Answer

Figure 2 no

Students may think that sound travels in space. While this makes space battles simulated in movies more exciting, it is not true. Remind students that particles of matter are spaced very widely in space. The matter particles are too spread out to vibrate against one another and carry sound.

Caption Answer

Figure 3 The greater the wavelength, the lower the frequency.

Active Reading

Jigsaw In this collaborative learning technique, individuals become experts on a portion of a text and share their expertise with a small group, called their home group. Everyone shares responsibility for learning the assigned reading. Assign each person in each home group an expert number (1 through 5, for example). Have students gather into the expert groups that correspond to the number they were assigned. Have them read, discuss, and master chapter concepts and determine how best to teach them to their home groups and share the content they learned in their expert groups. Have students use the Jigsaw strategy with concepts about sound.

The Speed of Sound

Purpose to observe that sound can travel through materials other than air L2

LS Auditory-Musical

Materials ring of keys, tub or wide bowl filled with water, towel, metal spoon, about 2 m of cotton string

Teaching Strategy Students might require an assistant to shake the keys while they submerge an ear in the water.

Analysis

1. Possible answer: Sounds were louder in the water and string than in air. Sounds in water were duller; sounds through string were strong and ringing.
2. Sounds can be distinguished in both water and air, but sound travelling through water was louder and less distinct.

Process Ask students to make an illustration of each part of the experiment, with labels showing how the sound of the metal striking something was transmitted to their ears. Use **PASC,** p. 127. P

TRY AT HOME Mini LAB

Comparing and Contrasting Sounds

Procedure

1. Shake a set of **keys** and listen to the sound they make in air. Then submerge the keys and one ear in **water.** (A **tub** or a wide, deep **bowl** will work.) Again, shake the keys and listen to the sound. Use a **towel** to dry the keys.
2. Tie a **metal spoon** in the middle of a length of **cotton string.** Strike the spoon on something to hear it ring. Now press the ends of the string against your ears and repeat the experiment. What do you hear?

Analysis

1. Did you hear sounds transmitted through water and through string? Describe the sounds.
2. Compare and contrast the sounds in water and in air.

The Speed of Sound

Sound waves can travel through other materials besides air. Even though sound waves travel as compressions and rarefactions through different materials, they might travel at different speeds. As a sound wave travels through a material, the particles in the material it is moving through collide with each other. In a solid, molecules are closer together than in liquids or gases, so collisions between molecules occur more frequently than in liquids or gases. As a result, the speed of sound is usually fastest in solids, where molecules are closest together, and slowest in gases, where molecules are farthest apart. **Table 1** shows the speed of sound through different materials.

The Speed of Sound and Temperature The temperature of the material that sound waves are traveling through also affects the speed of sound. As a substance heats up, its molecules move faster, so they collide more frequently. The more frequent the collisions are, the faster the speed of sound is in the material. For example, the speed of sound in air at 0°C is 331 m/s; at 20°C, it is 343 m/s.

Intensity and Loudness

What's the difference between loud sounds and quiet sounds? Imagine a small, square loop next to your ear. If you could measure the amount of energy a sound wave carries through the loop in 1 s, you would be measuring the intensity of the sound wave. The **loudness** of a sound is the human perception of the intensity of the sound waves that strike the ears.

Sound waves spread out as they travel, so the energy carried by the wave is spread over an ever-increasing area. As a result, the intensity of a sound wave decreases as it travels farther from its source. For example, the loudness of a person's voice decreases as you move farther away.

Table 1 Speed of Sound in Different Materials

Material	Speed (m/s)
Air	343
Water	1,482
Glass	5,640
Steel	5,960

LAB DEMONSTRATION

Purpose to observe the transfer of energy in sound waves

Materials cardboard tube, balloon, rubber bands, candle, matches or lighter, scissors

Procedure Cut pieces from the balloon and stretch them over the two open ends of the cardboard tube. Secure them with the rubber bands, making a drum. Poke a small hole in one end of the drum. Hold this end about 10 cm from a lighted candle, and tap the other end.

Expected Outcome The vibrations made at one end travel through the tube, forcing air through the hole at the other end. This blows out the candle.

Does the strength of the tap on the drum affect the distance from which a candle could be blown out? Explain. Yes; the stronger the tap, the greater the energy in the sound wave. With more energy, the wave can travel farther.

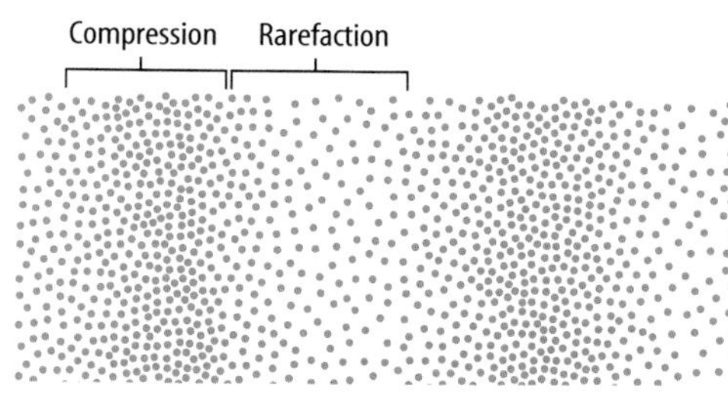

A This sound wave has a lower amplitude.

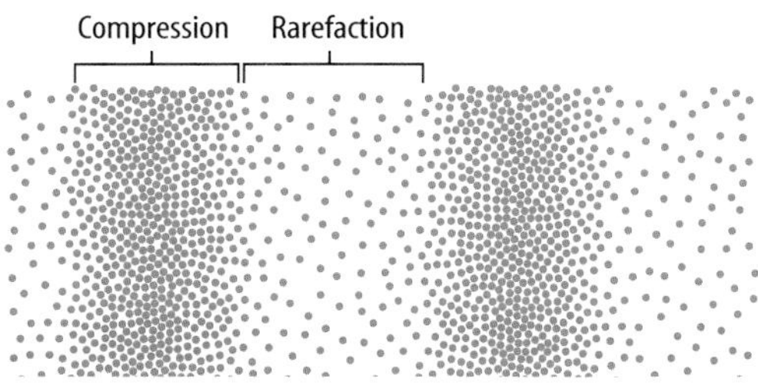

B This sound wave has a higher amplitude. Particles in the material are more compressed in the compressions and more spread out in the rarefactions.

Figure 4
The amplitude of a sound wave depends on how spread out the particles are in the wave.

Amplitude and Energy The loudness of a sound depends on how close you are to the sound's source. It also depends on the amount of energy the sound wave carries. The amount of energy a wave carries depends on its amplitude.

For a compressional wave, such as a sound wave, the amplitude is related to how spread out the molecules are in the compressions and rarefactions, as shown in **Figure 4.** The higher the amplitude of the wave is, the more compressed the particles in the compressions are, and the more spread out they are in the rarefactions. More energy had to be transferred by the vibrating object that created the wave to force the particles closer together or spread them farther apart.

Reading Check *What determines the loudness of different sounds?*

The Decibel Scale Perhaps an adult has said to you, "Turn down your music, it's too loud! You're going to lose your hearing!" Although the perception of loudness varies from person to person, the energy carried by sounds waves can be described by a scale called the decibel (dB) scale. **Figure 5** shows the decibel scale. An increase of 10 dB on the decibel scale means the intensity of a sound has increased by 10 times. However, an increase of 20 dB means the intensity has increased by 100 times.

Hearing damage begins to occur at sound levels of about 85 dB. The amount of damage depends on the frequencies of the sound and the length of time a person is exposed to the sound. Some music concerts produce sound levels as high as 120 dB. The intensity of these sound waves is about 30 billion times greater than the intensity of sound waves that are made by whispering.

Figure 5
The loudness of sound is measured on the decibel scale.

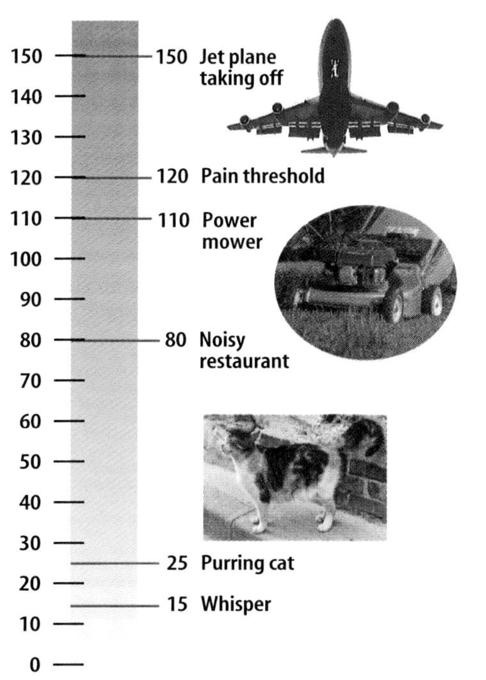

Intensity and Loudness

Teacher FYI

The loudness of sound decreases as it travels away from a source because the waves lose energy to matter and because they radiate out from the source. Sound intensity decreases at $1/r^2$, where r is the distance from the source. For example, the intensity of a sound 100 m from its source is about one-fourth the intensity of the same sound 50 m from its source.

Reading Check

Answer the energy of the sound waves

Activity

Have students bring in various whistles. Have them blow the whistles and rank them from loudest to softest. Afterward, have students examine the whistles to find out what produced the vibration and what feature caused one whistle to be louder than another. L2 ELL
LS **Auditory-Musical**

Visual Learning

Figure 5 Point out the pain threshold, at about 120 dB. **What types of sounds exceed this threshold?** Possible answers: loud music at a concert or a jet taking off
L2 LS **Logical-Mathematical**

Resource Manager

Chapter Resources Booklet
Note-taking Worksheets, pp. 29–30
MiniLAB, p. 3
Home amd Community Involvement, p. 29

Science Journal

Decibels Ask students to find out what the word *decibel* means and how it was coined. Have them write their responses in their Science Journals. A decibel is one-tenth of a bel, named in honor of Alexander Graham Bell. L2 LS **Linguistic**

Frequency and Pitch

Discussion

Have students think of noises that animals make when they fly: the high-pitched whine of a mosquito, the buzz of a fly, and the hum of a hummingbird. Explain that these sounds are caused by the animal's wings vibrating the air and that the pitch corresponds to the speed of vibration. **What change in the movement of the animals' wings causes an increase in pitch?** When pitch rises, the animal is beating its wings more rapidly. L2

LS Logical-Mathematical

Visual Learning

Figure 6 How do the wavelength and frequency of the two waves shown differ? The upper wave has one-half the wavelength and twice the frequency of the other. L2

LS Visual-Spatial

Fun Fact

When you inhale or exhale without making a sound, the vocal cords are separated at the edges of the windpipe. In this position they are not vibrated.

Teacher FYI

When sound is recorded, the frequencies and amplitudes of the sound waves are converted into matching waves of varying voltage. When recorded sound is played back, these voltages are converted into vibrations in the speaker.

Frequency and Pitch

The **pitch** of a sound is how high or low it sounds. For example, a piccolo produces a high-pitched sound or tone, and a tuba makes a low-pitched sound. Pitch corresponds to the frequency of the sound. The higher the pitch is, the higher the frequency is. A sound wave with a frequency of 440 Hz, for example, has a higher pitch than a sound wave with a frequency of 220 Hz.

The human ear can detect sound waves with frequencies between about 20 Hz and 20,000 Hz. However, some animals can detect even higher and lower frequencies. For example, dogs can hear frequencies up to almost 50,000 Hz. Dolphins and bats can hear frequencies as high as 150,000 Hz, and whales can hear frequencies both higher and lower than those heard by humans.

Recall that frequency and wavelength are related. If two sound waves are traveling at the same speed, the wave with the shorter wavelength has a higher frequency. If the wavelength is shorter, then more compressions and rarefactions will go past a given point every second than for a wave with a longer wavelength, as shown in **Figure 6.** Sound waves with a higher pitch have shorter wavelengths than those with a lower pitch.

The Human Voice When you make a sound, you exhale past your vocal cords, causing them to vibrate. The length and thickness of your vocal cords help determine the pitch of your voice. Shorter, thinner vocal cords vibrate at higher frequencies than longer or thicker ones. This explains why children, whose vocal cords are still growing, have higher voices than adults. Muscles in the throat can stretch the vocal cords tighter, letting people vary their pitch within a limited range.

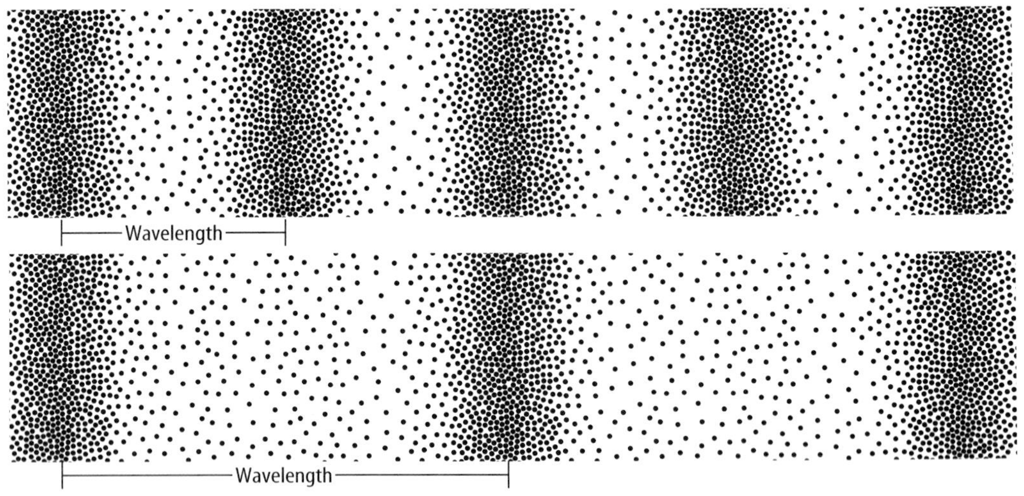

Figure 6 The upper sound wave has a shorter wavelength than the lower wave. If these two sound waves are traveling at the same speed, the upper sound wave has a higher frequency than the lower one. For this wave, more compressions and rarefactions will go past a point every second than for the lower wave.

Cultural Diversity

Measuring Bells More than 2,000 years ago, the Chinese used tuned bells as the basis of their entire system of measurement. They divided the scale into twelve pitches, and had official sets of twelve bells. A stringed tuner about 2.1 m long called a chün was used to standardize the pitches of bells throughout China. The length of a chün would be varied until the pitch of the chün matched the pitch of a standard bell. The chün could then be used to determine the pitch of a bell in a distant city. Pitch pipes later replaced the bells.

Figure 7
Sonar uses reflected sound waves to determine the location and shape of an object.

Echoes

Sound reflects off of hard surfaces, just like other waves do. A reflected sound wave is called an **echo.** If the distance between you and the reflecting surface is great enough—on the edge of a canyon, for example—you can hear the echo of your voice easily. This is because it takes a few seconds for the sound to travel across the canyon and back to your ears.

The delay in the reflection of sound means that the reflection can be used to measure distances. Sonar systems use sound waves to map objects underwater, as shown in **Figure 7.** By measuring the length of time between emitting a pulse of sound and hearing its echo off the ocean floor, the distance to the ocean floor can be measured. Using this method, sonar can map the ocean floor and other undersea features. Sonar also can be used to detect submarines, schools of fish, and other objects.

Research Visit the Glencoe Science Web site at **science.glencoe.com** for more information on how sonar is used to detect objects underwater. Communicate to your class what you learn.

Echolocation Some animals use a method called echolocation to navigate and hunt. Bats, for example, emit high-pitched squeaks and listen for the echoes. The type of echo it hears helps the bat determine exactly where an insect is, as shown in **Figure 8.** Dolphins also use a form of echolocation. Their high-pitched clicks bounce off of objects in the ocean, allowing them to navigate in the same way.

People with visual impairments also have been able to use echolocation. Using their ears, they can interpret echoes to estimate the size and shape of a room, for example.

Figure 8
Bats use echolocation to hunt.
Why is this technique good for hunting at night?

Echoes

Discussion

Have students think about situations in which they have heard echoes. **What characteristics does a room that produces an echo have?** It would be large and have mostly hard surfaces, which are better at reflecting sound waves than are soft surfaces. Point out that soft surfaces such as carpeting and upholstery tend to absorb sounds. Also, the room must be large enough for there to be a delay between the initial sound and the echo. L2
LS **Auditory-Musical**

Explore the Glencoe Science Web site at **science.glencoe.com** to find out more about topics in this section.

Caption Answer

Figure 8 There is little light, so it's difficult to see well at night.

Teacher FYI

Some night-flying moths and butterflies can hear the ultrasonic frequencies used by hunting bats. Tiger moths make ultrasonic clicks when they detect a bat's sonar. This may act to jam the sonar, or it may signal that this insect is a bad-tasting tiger moth.

Curriculum Connection

History Ask students to find out how archaeologists use sonar mapping to learn about history. Archaeologists use sonar to map areas that were once above water level. For example, researchers have mapped the route early Siberian hunter-gatherers may have taken to North America. Using the map and samples collected from the area, they found that forests once grew along the now ice-covered coasts. L2 LS **Linguistic**

Resource Manager

Chapter Resources Booklet

Directed Reading for Content Mastery, pp. 17, 18

Physical Science Critical Thinking/Problem Solving, p. 21

The Doppler Effect

Astronomy INTEGRATION

When stars or galaxies are moving away from us, their light is shifted to lower frequencies, toward the red end of the spectrum. Astronomers call this a red shift. When stars or galaxies are moving toward us, their light is shifted to higher frequencies, toward the blue end of the spectrum. This is called a blue shift. Evidence from the Doppler shifts of stars suggests that almost all of them are moving away from Earth.

Use an Analogy

The change in frequency of sound waves in a Doppler shift is similar to the tossing of a ball between two players who move closer together or farther apart. If the players throw the ball at the same speed each time, the frequency of the tosses will increase as the players approach each other and decrease as the players move apart.

IDENTIFYING Misconceptions

Remind students that the sound waves emitted by the moving object don't change. It is only the frequency at which they reach the listener that changes. The Doppler effect occurs if the source of the sound is moving, if the observer is moving, or if both are moving.

Astronomy INTEGRATION

The frequency of light waves is also changed by the Doppler shift. If a light source is moving away from an observer, the frequencies of the emitted light waves decrease. Research how the Doppler shift is used by astronomers to determine how other objects in the universe are moving relative to Earth.

The Doppler Effect

Perhaps you've heard an ambulance siren as the ambulance speeds toward you, then goes past. You might have noticed that the pitch of the siren gets higher as the ambulance moves toward you. Then as the ambulance moves away, the pitch of the siren gets lower. This change in frequency that is due to the motion of a source of sound is called the **Doppler effect. Figure 9** shows why the Doppler effect occurs.

The Doppler effect occurs whether the sound source or the listener is moving. If you drive past a factory as its whistle blows, the whistle will sound higher pitched as you approach. As you move closer you encounter each sound wave a little earlier than you would if you were sitting still, so the whistle has a higher pitch. When you move away from the whistle, each sound wave takes a little longer to reach you. You hear fewer wavelengths per second, which makes the sound lower in pitch.

Radar guns that are used to measure the speed of cars and baseball pitches also use the Doppler effect. Instead of a sound wave, the radar gun sends out a radar wave. When the radar wave is reflected, its frequency changes depending on the speed of the object, and whether it is moving toward the gun or away from it. The radar gun uses the change in frequency of the reflected wave to determine the object's speed.

Problem-Solving Activity

How does Doppler radar work?

Doppler radar is used by the National Weather Service to detect areas of precipitation and to measure the speed at which a storm moves. Because the wind moves the rain, Doppler radar can "see" into a strong storm and expose the winds. Tornadoes that might be forming in the storm then can be identified.

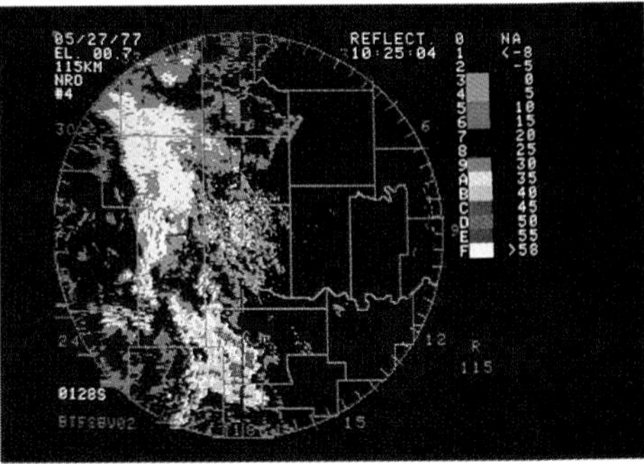

Identify the Problem

An antenna sends out pulses of radio waves as it rotates. The waves bounce off raindrops and return to the antenna at a different frequency, depending on whether the rain is moving toward the antenna or away from it. The change in frequency is due to the Doppler shift.

Solving the Problem

1. If the frequency of the reflected radio waves increases, how is the rain moving relative to the radar station?
2. In a tornado, winds are rotating. How would the radio waves reflected by rotating winds be Doppler-shifted?

Problem-Solving Activity

National Math Standards

Correlation to Mathematics Objectives

6, 8, 9

Answers

1. The rain is moving toward the radar station.
2. The frequency would shift alternately up and down.

Science Journal

Doppler Effect Filmmakers need to put realistic sounds in animated films. Have students write descriptions in their Science Journals of ways to simulate the sounds of cars whizzing by characters standing by the side of the road in an animated film. Possible response: Make sounds that increase in pitch as the cars approach and decrease in pitch as the cars move away. L2 LS **Logical-Mathematical**

NATIONAL GEOGRAPHIC VISUALIZING THE DOPPLER EFFECT

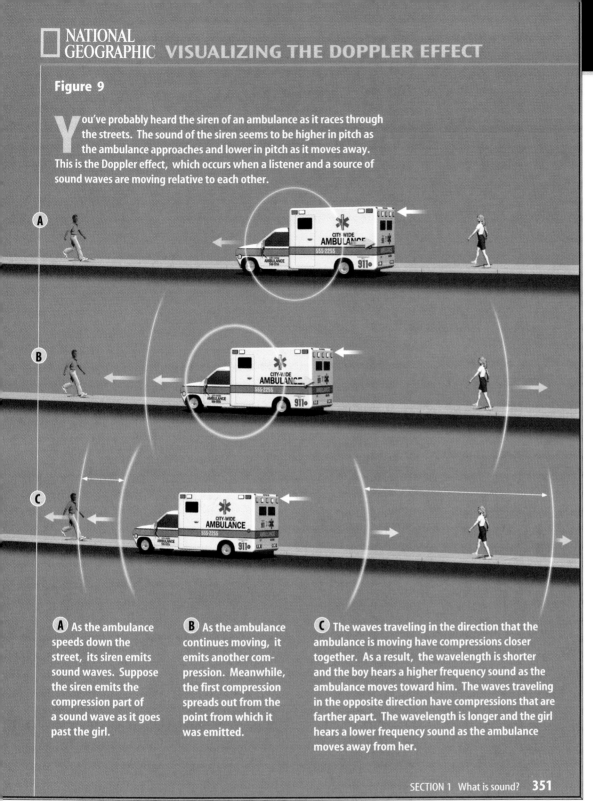

Figure 9

You've probably heard the siren of an ambulance as it races through the streets. The sound of the siren seems to be higher in pitch as the ambulance approaches and lower in pitch as it moves away. This is the Doppler effect, which occurs when a listener and a source of sound waves are moving relative to each other.

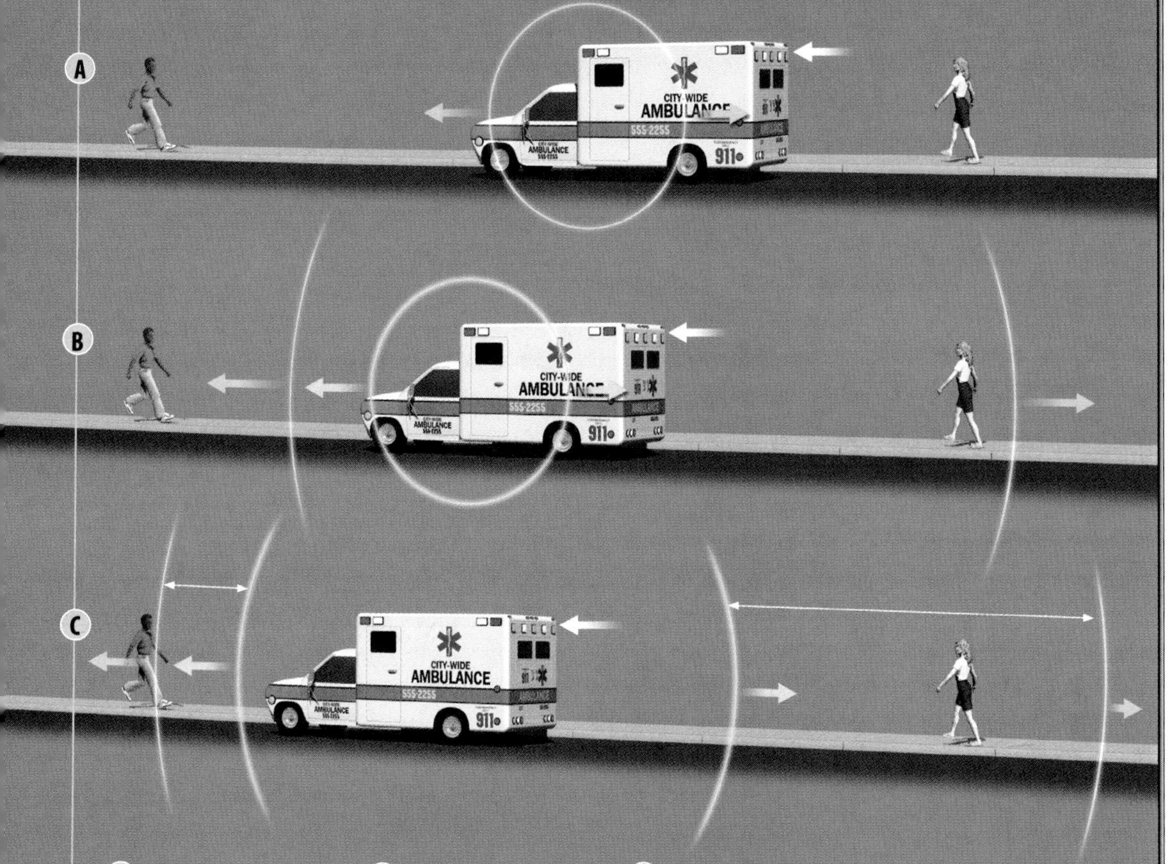

A As the ambulance speeds down the street, its siren emits sound waves. Suppose the siren emits the compression part of a sound wave as it goes past the girl.

B As the ambulance continues moving, it emits another compression. Meanwhile, the first compression spreads out from the point from which it was emitted.

C The waves traveling in the direction that the ambulance is moving have compressions closer together. As a result, the wavelength is shorter and the boy hears a higher frequency sound as the ambulance moves toward him. The waves traveling in the opposite direction have compressions that are farther apart. The wavelength is longer and the girl hears a lower frequency sound as the ambulance moves away from her.

Resource Manager

Chapter Resources Booklet
- Enrichment, p. 27
- Reinforcement, p. 25

Mathematics Skill Activities, p. 9

NATIONAL GEOGRAPHIC

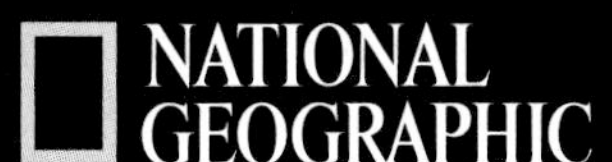

Visualizing the Doppler Effect

Have students examine the pictures and read the captions. Then ask the following questions.

If the source of sound begins to move faster, what will happen to the frequency? The frequency will be shifted even higher in front of the source, and even lower behind the source.

What would happen if the source moved as fast as the sound wave it creates? The waves would bunch up in front of the source. This would intensify the sound, creating a sonic boom like that created by a supersonic airplane.

Activity

Have students work in pairs to demonstrate the Doppler effect in water waves. Have one student in each pair use a finger to make waves in a shallow glass baking dish. Once the waves are moving steadily, have the student move his or her finger toward one side of the dish, while maintaining a steady movement up and down to generate waves. Have the other student observe what happens to the waves. Tell students to switch roles so each will have an opportunity to observe the waves. L2 LS **Kinesthetic**

Extension

Have students research how the Doppler effect is used in medicine. Specifically, they can investigate how doctors use Doppler shifts to analyze blood flow through arteries. L3 LS **Linguistic**

Diffraction of Sound Waves

Discussion

Hearing sound from around a corner is so common you don't think about it. But what would happen if light, which is also a wave, diffracted around the corner of a doorway? You would be able to see what was going on in a room without being in the direct line of sight. The people in the room would also be able to see you. L3 LS **Logical-Mathematical**

Extension

Point out to students that like light waves, sound waves also refract, or change direction, when they pass from one medium to another. Have students research and report on the ways in which sound waves are refracted as they pass through different mediums. When sound waves move to a denser medium in which they travel more quickly, they bend toward the boundary between the two regions. When sound waves move to a region in which they travel more slowly, they are refracted away from the boundary. Sound may be refracted at boundaries between warm and cold air. L3 LS **Linguistic** P

Using Sound Waves

Use Science Words

Word Meaning Have students find the meaning of the prefix *ultra-* and relate this meaning to the meaning of ultrasound. *Ultra-* means "beyond what is ordinary," or "super." Ultrasound is sound that is at high frequencies that are beyond ordinary frequencies. L2 LS **Linguistic**

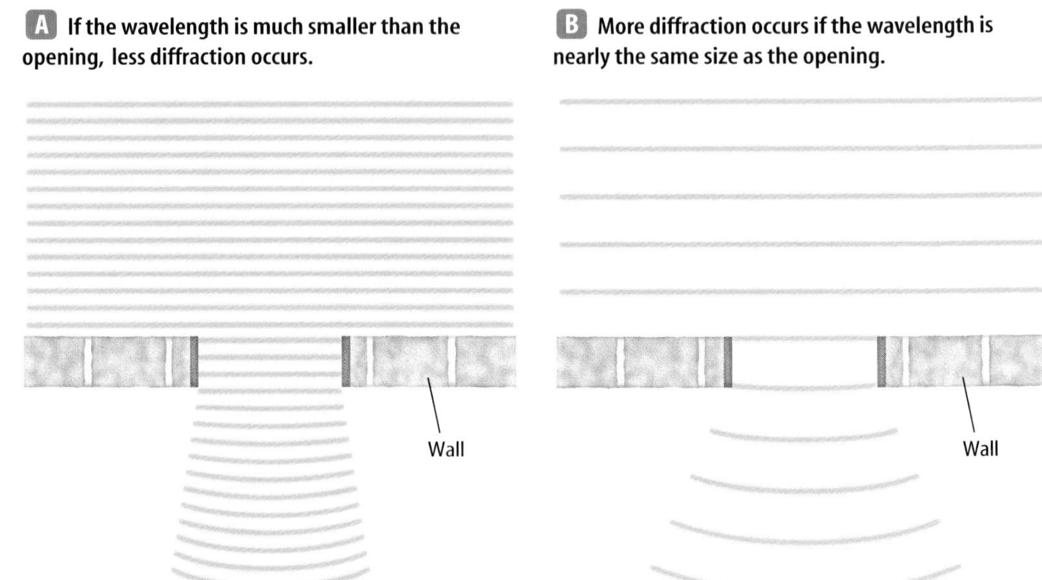
A If the wavelength is much smaller than the opening, less diffraction occurs.
B More diffraction occurs if the wavelength is nearly the same size as the opening.
Wall
Wall

Figure 10
The spreading of a wave by diffraction depends on the wavelength and the size of the opening.

Diffraction of Sound Waves

Like other waves, sound waves diffract. This means they can bend around obstacles or spread out after passing through narrow openings. The amount of diffraction depends on the wavelength of the sound wave compared to the size of the obstacle or opening. More diffraction occurs if the wavelength is nearly the same as the size of the opening or obstacle. If the wavelength is much smaller than the obstacle, almost no diffraction occurs.

You can observe diffraction of sound waves by visiting the school band room during practice. If you stand in the doorway, you will hear the band normally. However, if you stand to one side outside the door or around a corner, you will hear the lower-pitched instruments better. **Figure 10** shows why this happens. The sound waves that are produced by the lower-pitched instruments have lower frequencies and longer wavelengths. These wavelengths are closer to the size of the door opening than the higher-pitched sound waves are. As a result, the longer wavelengths diffract more, and you can hear them even when you're not standing in the doorway.

The diffraction of lower frequencies in the human voice allows you to hear someone talking even when the person is around the corner. This is different from an echo. Echoes occur when sound waves bounce off a hard surface. Diffraction occurs when a wave spreads out after passing through an opening, or when a wave bends around an obstacle.

Teacher FYI

Stereo systems account for differences in the diffraction of sound waves of different frequencies by usually having only one woofer for the low notes, but several tweeters, pointed in different directions, for the high notes.

Resource Manager

Chapter Resources Booklet
Activity Worksheet, pp. 5–6
Lab Activity, pp. 9–10
Reading and Writing Skill Activities, p. 7

Using Sound Waves

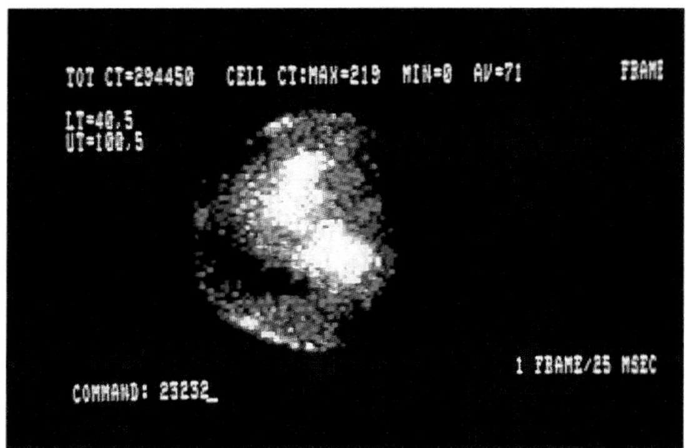

Sound waves can be used to treat certain medical problems. A process called ultrasound uses high-frequency sound waves as an alternative to some surgeries. For example, some people develop small, hard deposits in their kidneys or gall bladders. A doctor can focus ultrasound waves at a patient's kidney or gall bladder. The ultrasound waves cause the deposits to vibrate rapidly until they break apart into small pieces. Then, the body can get rid of them.

Ultrasound can be used to make images of the inside of the body, just as sonar is used to map the seafloor. One common use of ultrasound is to examine a developing fetus. Also, ultrasound along with the Doppler effect can be used to examine the functioning of the heart. An ultrasound image of the heart is shown in **Figure 11.** This technique can help determine if the heart valves and heart muscle are functioning properly, and how blood is flowing through the heart.

The Doppler effect can be also used with sonar to determine the speed and direction of a detected object, such as a submarine or a school of fish.

Figure 11
Ultrasound is used to make this image of the heart. *How else is ultrasound used in medicine?*

Section  Assessment

1. When the amplitude of a sound wave is increased, what happens to the loudness of the sound? The pitch?
2. How does the wavelength of a sound affect the way it moves around corners?
3. How does the temperature of a material affect the speed of sound passing through it? Explain why in terms of the particles within the material.
4. What causes the Doppler effect, and in what ways is it used?
5. **Think Critically** Chemists sometimes use ultrasound machines to clean glassware. How could sound be used to remove particles from glass?

Skill Builder Activities

6. **Using an Electronic Spreadsheet** Think about ten different sounds you've heard today. Make a computer spreadsheet that lists each sound, the vibrating object that made the sound, and how the object was vibrating. **For more help, refer to the Technology Skill Handbook.**
7. **Solving One-Step Equations** If sound travels through water at 1,482 m/s, how far will it travel in 5 s? The speed of sound through air at 20° C is about 340 m/s. How far will sound travel through air in the same amount of time? **For more help, refer to the Math Skill Handbook.**

Caption Answer

Figure 11 Possible answer: to examine a developing fetus

3 Assess

Reteach

Draw a sample sound wave on the board. Ask volunteers to draw waves corresponding to the following: Same pitch, louder: Wave has same frequency, greater amplitude. Same pitch, softer: Wave has same frequency, smaller amplitude. Higher pitch, same volume: Wave has shorter wavelength, same amplitude. Lower pitch, same volume: Wave has longer wavelength, same amplitude. L2
LS Visual-Spatial

Challenge

As a train comes toward you, the Doppler effect causes the sound you hear to start low in pitch and rise. Suppose instead of standing still you were rushing toward the oncoming train. **Would you expect the Doppler shift in the frequency of the train's sound to increase, stay the same, or disappear? Explain.** Increase; because you and the train are coming together more quickly than if you were standing still, the Doppler shift is even greater. L3
LS Logical-Mathematical

Process Ask students to demonstrate that sound is a vibration. Possible answers: Students may show that an object such as a rubber band makes no sound when it is not vibrating, but does make sound when it vibrates. Use **PASC,** p. 143.

Answers to Section Assessment

1. Loudness increases and pitch stays the same.
2. Sounds whose waves are about the same length as the opening are diffracted the most around the corner. Low-pitched sound waves are about the same wavelength as doorways, so they travel more easily around the corners of the doorway.
3. As temperature increases, the speed of sound increases. At higher temperatures the particles move faster and collide more often.
4. The Doppler effect occurs when the source of a wave is moving relative to an observer. It is used in many ways, including by police to measure the speed of cars and trucks on the highway.
5. by vibrating the particles off the glass
6. Check students' work.
7. water: 5 s × 1,482 m/s = 7,410 m; air: 5 s × 340 m/s = 1,700 m.

Activity

BENCH TESTED

Purpose Students observe that sound waves can be reflected and focused. L2 ELL COOP LEARN

LS **Auditory-Musical**

Process Skills observing and inferring, measuring, drawing conclusions

Time Required 30 minutes

Teaching Strategies

- Announce the lab the day before, so enough ticking watches can be located. Check to make sure students can hear the watches ticking.
- Smooth surfaces reflect sound; don't try the experiment on carpeting.

Troubleshooting The two tubes need to be in the same plane. You should be able to hold a piece of poster board up so that the sides of both tubes rest along the poster board. If the tubes are not in the same plane, students will not hear the watch.

Answers to Questions

1. The angles are approximately equal. Sound is reflected so that the angle of incidence equals the angle of reflection.
2. It would be difficult, if not impossible, to hear the ticking of the watch reflected off a soft surface.

Activity

Observe and Measure Reflection of Sound

Like all waves, sound waves can be reflected. When sound waves strike a surface in what direction does the reflected sound wave travel? In this activity you'll focus sound waves using cardboard tubes to help answer this question.

What You'll Investigate

How do the angles made by incoming and reflected sound waves compare?

Materials

cardboard tubes, 20- to 30-cm-long (2)
watch with a second hand that ticks audibly
protractor

Goals

- **Observe** reflection of sound waves.
- **Measure** the angles incoming and reflected sound waves make with a surface.

Safety Precautions

Procedure

1. Work in groups of three. Each person should listen to the watch—first without a tube and then through a tube. The person who hears the watch most easily is the listener.
2. One person should hold one tube at an angle with one end above a table. Hold the watch at the other end of the tube.
3. The listener should hold the second tube at an angle, with one end near their ear and the other end near the end of the first tube that is just above the table. The tubes should be in line with each other.

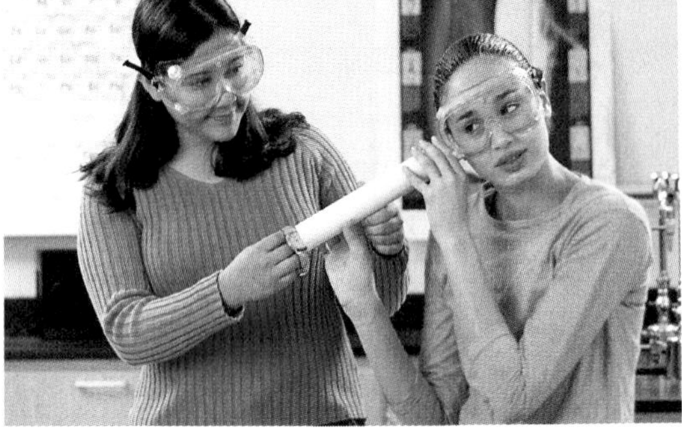

4. Move the first tube until the watch sounds loudest. The listener might need to cover the other ear to block out background noises.
5. With the tubes held steady, the third person should measure the angle that each tube makes with the table.

Conclude and Apply

1. Are the two angles approximately equal or quite different? How does the angle of reflection compare with the angle made by the incoming wave?
2. Predict how your results would change if the waves reflected from a soft surface instead of a hard surface.

Communicating Your Data

Make a scientific illustration to show how the experiment was done. Describe your results using the illustration. **For more help, refer to the Science Skill Handbook.**

Assessment

Process Compare and contrast the reflection of sound with the reflection of light in a mirror. Have two students stand to either side of a mirror. **Can they see themselves in the mirror?** no **Can they see each other?** Yes; both are examples of reflection: the angle between observer and reflecting surface must be the same as the angle between the initial sound or image and that surface. Use **PASC,** p. 89.

Communicating Your Data

Students can view each other's illustrations. As they review the illustrations, they should ask themselves, "If I hadn't done the experiment myself, would I be able to do it based on the illustration?"

354 CHAPTER 12 Sound

SECTION 2

Music

What is music?

What do you like to listen to—rock 'n' roll, country, blues, jazz, rap, or classical? Music and noise are groups of sounds. Why do humans hear some sounds as music and other sounds as noise?

The answer involves sound patterns. Music is a group of sounds that have been deliberately produced to make a regular pattern. Look at **Figure 12.** The sounds that make up music usually have a regular pattern of pitches, or notes. Some natural sounds, such as the patter of rain on a roof, the sound of ocean waves splashing, or the songs of birds can sound musical. On the other hand, noise is usually a group of sounds with no regular pattern. Sounds you hear as noise are irregular and disorganized, such as the sounds of traffic on a city street, or the roar of jet aircraft.

However, the difference between music and noise can vary from person to person. What one person considers to be music, another person might consider noise.

Natural Frequencies Music is created by vibrations. When you sing, your vocal cords vibrate. When you beat a drum, the drumhead vibrates. When you play a guitar, the strings vibrate.

If you tap on a bell with a hard object, the bell produces a sound. When you tap on a bell that is larger or smaller or has a different shape you hear a different sound. The bells sound different because each bell vibrated at different frequencies. A bell vibrates at frequencies that depend on its shape and the material it is made from. Every object will vibrate at certain frequencies called its **natural frequencies.**

As You Read

What You'll Learn

- **Explain** the difference between music and noise.
- **Describe** how different instruments produce music.
- **Explain** how you hear.

Vocabulary

natural frequency
resonance
fundamental frequency
overtone
reverberation
eardrum

Why It's Important

By better understanding how music is produced, you can improve the quality of the sounds you make.

Figure 12
Music and noise have different types of sound patterns.

A Noise has no specific or regular sound wave pattern.

B Music is organized sound. Music has regular sound wave patterns and structures.

SECTION 2

Music

1 Motivate

Bellringer Transparency

Display the Section Focus Transparency for Section 2. Use the accompanying Transparency Activity Master. L2 ELL

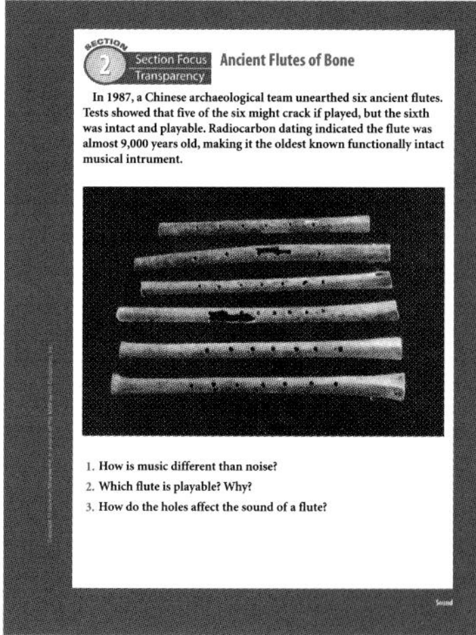
SECTION 2 Section Focus Transparency **Ancient Flutes of Bone**

In 1987, a Chinese archaeological team unearthed six ancient flutes. Tests showed that five of the six might crack if played, but the sixth was intact and playable. Radiocarbon dating indicated the flute was almost 9,000 years old, making it the oldest known functionally intact musical intrument.

1. How is music different than noise?
2. Which flute is playable? Why?
3. How do the holes affect the sound of a flute?

Sound

Tie to Prior Knowledge

Ask students to name any musical instruments they may play. Tell them that this section explains the science of music.

Section Assessment Planner

Portfolio
Assessment, p. 363

Performance Assessment
MiniLAB, p. 358
Skill Builder Activities, p. 363
See page 370 for more options.

Content Assessment
Section, p. 363
Challenge, p. 363
Chapter, pp. 370–371

Resource Manager

Chapter Resources Booklet
Transparency Activity, p. 41
Directed Reading for Content Mastery, pp. 19, 20

2 Teach

What is music?

Discussion

Discuss with students how music differs from noise. **What natural sounds seem and do not seem musical?** Possible answer: Sounds are musical when they make distinguishable pitches and have a regular pattern. L2

LS **Auditory-Musical**

Answer size, shape, and material of the vibrating object

Have students find out about the effect of resonance on the first Tacoma Narrows Bridge, also known as Galloping Gertie. On November 7, 1940, wind started the suspension bridge moving and it collapsed. Some scientists believe the cause of the collapse was resonance, and that the wind caused the bridge to vibrate at its natural frequency. L2 LS **Linguistic**

Quick Demo

Find a container with a plastic lid to use as a drum. Tap the lid while it is off the container. Then fit the lid over the empty container and tap it again. The second sound is louder, because the can and air inside also vibrate. This is an example of resonance. L2

LS **Auditory-Musical**

Resonance is important in fields outside of music. Earthquake-proof buildings, for example, are designed to resonate at frequencies that are different from those encountered in earthquakes.

Musical Instruments and Natural Frequencies Many objects vibrate at one or more natural frequencies when they are struck or disturbed. Like a bell, the natural frequency of any object depends on the size and shape of the object and the material it is made from. Musical instruments use the natural frequencies of strings, drumheads, or columns of air contained in pipes to produce various musical notes.

Reading Check *What determines the natural frequencies?*

Resonance You may have seen the comedy routine in which a loud soprano sings high enough to shatter glass. Sometimes sound waves cause an object to vibrate. When a tuning fork is struck, it vibrates at its natural frequency and produces a sound wave with the same frequency. Suppose you have two tuning forks with the same natural frequency. You strike one tuning fork, and the sound waves it produces strike the other tuning fork. These sound waves would cause the tuning fork that wasn't struck to absorb energy and vibrate. This is an example of resonance. **Resonance** occurs when an object is made to vibrate at its natural frequency by absorbing energy from a sound wave or another object vibrating at this frequency.

Musical instruments use resonance to amplify their sounds. Look at **Figure 13.** The vibrating tuning fork has caused the table to vibrate at the same frequency, or resonate. The combined vibrations of the table and the tuning fork increase the loudness of the sound waves produced.

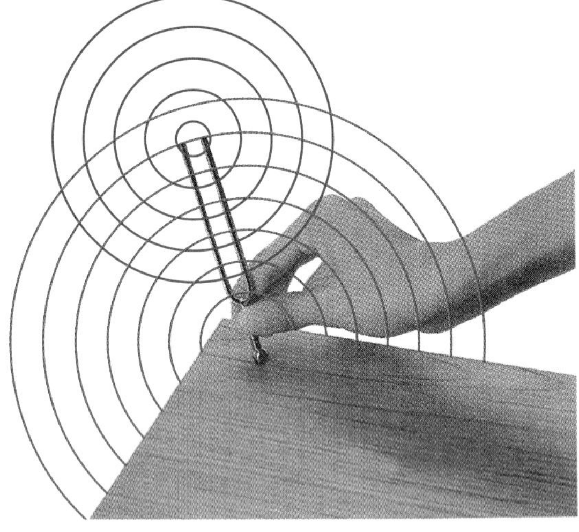

Figure 13
When a vibrating tuning fork is placed against a table, resonance causes the table to vibrate.

Inclusion Strategies

Hearing Impaired Help these students sense the vibrations of sound waves. Have a student hold a balloon while you make a sound. The sound waves will vibrate the balloon, and the vibration will be passed to the student's fingers. Have students use balloons to help them sense sounds during all the sound-producing activities performed in this section.

Visual Learning

Figure 13 Discuss with students the effect touching the vibrating tuning fork to the table has on the sound made by the tuning fork. Vibrations from the tuning fork cause the table to resonate, which makes the sound louder. L2 LS **Visual-Spatial**

Overtones

Before a concert, all orchestra musicians tune their instruments by playing the same note. Even though the note has the same pitch, it sounds different for each instrument. It also sounds different from a tuning fork that vibrates at the same frequency as the note.

A tuning fork produces a single frequency, called a pure tone. However, the notes produced by musical instruments are not pure tones. Most objects have more than one natural frequency at which they can vibrate. As a result, they produce sound waves of more than one frequency.

If you play a single note on a guitar, the pitch that you hear is the lowest frequency produced by the vibrating string. The lowest frequency produced by a vibrating object is the **fundamental frequency.** The vibrating string also produces higher frequencies. These higher frequencies are **overtones,** and have frequencies that are multiples of the fundamental frequency, as shown in **Figure 14.** The number and intensity of the overtones produced by each instrument are different and give instruments their distinctive sound quality.

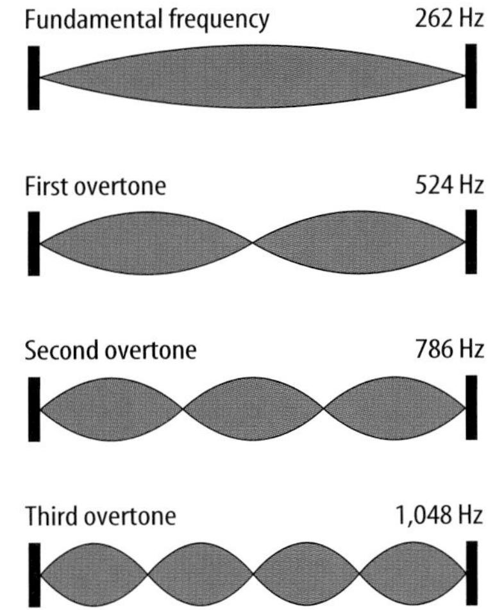

Figure 14
A string vibrates at a fundamental frequency, as well as at overtones. The overtones are multiples of that frequency.

Musical Scales

A musical instrument is a device that produces musical sounds. These sounds are usually part of a musical scale that is a sequence of notes with certain frequencies. For example, **Figure 15** shows the specific sequence of notes that belong to the musical scale of C. Notice that the frequency produced by the instrument doubles after eight successive notes of the scale are played. Other musical scales consist of a different sequence of frequencies.

How many musical instruments can you name? To find out more about musical instruments, see the **Musical Instruments Field Guide** at the back of the book.

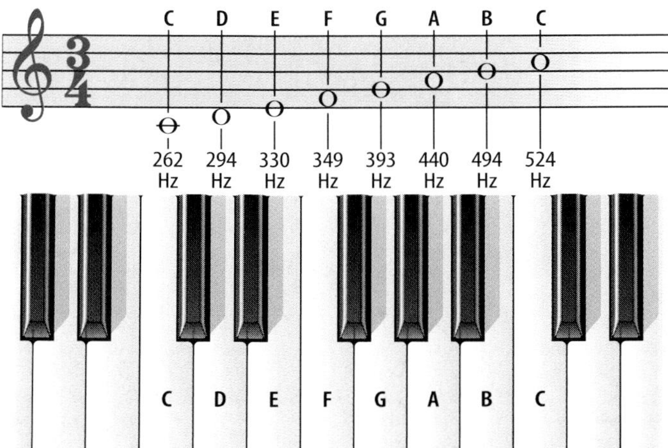

Figure 15
A piano produces a sequence of notes that are a part of a musical scale. *How are the frequencies of the two C notes on this scale related?*

Overtones

Activity

Collect cardboard tubes of different lengths, and turn on music. Have students cover one ear and listen to the sound through different tubes. Ask students what they observe when listening through different tubes. Because the tubes are of different sizes, they resonate at different frequencies, amplifying sounds at those frequencies only. The sound you hear changes depending on the length of the tube you listen through. L2 LS **Auditory-Musical**

Quick Demo

Strike a tuning fork, and then play the same note on a musical instrument. Ask students to compare the sounds. The sounds are different because the number and intensity of the overtones produced by each are different. L2
LS **Auditory-Musical**

Visual Learning

Figure 14 A musician can use knowledge of overtones to control the sound his or her instrument produces. For example, suppose a guitarist presses down at the center of an already vibrating string. The fundamental and the second overtone will both be suppressed, but the first and third overtones will continue to sound. L3
LS **Visual-Spatial**

Musical Scales

Caption Answer

Figure 15 The frequency of the higher C is double that of the lower C.

Resource Manager

Chapter Resources Booklet

Transparency Activity, pp. 43–44

Lab Activity, pp. 11–14

Cultural Diversity

Have interested students research instruments from other countries that are not common in the United States. Have students share their findings in oral reports. Possible instruments include Australia's didgeridoo, Scotland's bagpipes, various instruments that resemble xylophones in Korea, and traditional guitar in parts of Africa and Asia. L2
LS **Linguistic**

Stringed Instruments

Purpose Students observe how changes in a vibrating string change the sound it produces. L2 LS **Auditory-Musical**

Materials rubber band, box

Teaching Strategy Have students use rubber bands of varying lengths and thicknesses.

Troubleshooting Caution students not to let the rubber band snap against their hand.

Analysis

1. When the tension increased, the pitch increased; stretching the rubber band increased the tension and increased the pitch. This matches the predictions for stringed instruments given in the text.
2. The sound became louder when the box was included. This agrees with the text's prediction about using a resonator with a string.

Assessment

Process Have students design a new stringed instrument. They should make a labeled poster explaining how their instrument works. Use **Performance Assessment in the Science Classroom,** p. 123.

Mini LAB

Modeling a Stringed Instrument

Procedure

1. Stretch a **rubber band** between your fingers and pluck it. Listen to the sound and observe the shape of the vibrating band. Record what you hear and see.
2. Stretch the band farther, and repeat step 1.
3. Shorten the amount of the band that can vibrate by holding your finger on one point. Repeat step 1.
4. Stretch the rubber band over an open box, such as a **shoe box.** Repeat step 1.

Analysis

1. How did the sound change when you increased the tension? When you stretched it? Was this what you expected? Explain.
2. How did the sound change when you stretched the band over the box? Did you expect this? Explain.

Stringed Instruments

Stringed instruments, like the cello shown in **Figure 16,** produce music by making strings vibrate. Different methods are used to make the strings vibrate—guitar strings are plucked, piano strings are struck, and a bow is slid across cello strings. The strings often are made of wire. The pitch of the note depends on the length, diameter, and tension of the string—if the string is shorter, narrower, or tighter, the pitch increases. For example, pressing down on a vibrating guitar string shortens its length, and produces a note with a higher pitch. Similarly, the thinner guitar strings produce a higher pitch than the thicker strings.

Amplifying Vibrations The sound produced by a vibrating string is soft. To amplify the sound, stringed instruments usually have a hollow chamber, or box, called a resonator, which contains air. The resonator absorbs energy from the vibrating string and vibrates at its natural frequencies. For example, the body of a guitar is a resonator that amplifies the sound that is produced by the vibrating strings. The vibrating strings cause the guitar's body and the air inside it to resonate. As a result, the vibrating guitar strings sound louder, just as the tuning fork that was placed against the table sounded louder.

The strings can be tightened to produce higher pitched sounds.
Strings vibrate to produce sound.
The resonance in the instrument amplifies the sound with natural frequencies.

Figure 16
A cello is a stringed instrument. When strings vibrate, the natural frequencies of the instrument's body amplify the sound.

Visual Learning

Figure 16 Point out the pegs at the end of the strings, which are used to adjust tension. Individual strings also have different thicknesses, which gives them different natural frequencies and pitches. Note the bridge, supporting the strings. Ask what function the bridge performs. The bridge transfers the vibrations of the strings to the soundboard in the body of the instrument. L2 LS **Visual-Spatial**

Teacher FYI

In stringed instruments, the two ends of the string are held still, and the string vibrates between them. In contrast, the air at the open end of a pipe can vibrate. This changes the shape of the waves in the instrument, giving the sound it produces a different quality.

Percussion

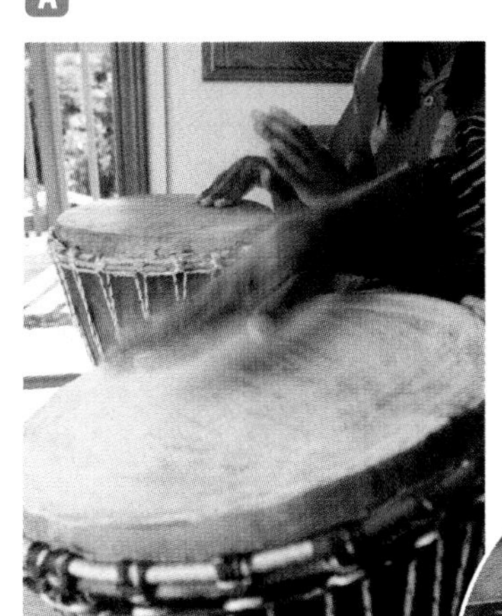

Percussion instruments, such as the drum shown in **Figure 17A,** are struck to make a sound. The surface that is struck vibrates to make the sound you hear. A chamber attached to the vibrating surface resonates to amplify the sound.

Drums and Pitch Some drums have a fixed pitch, but some can be tuned to play different notes. For example, if the drumhead on a kettledrum is tightened, the natural frequency of the drumhead is increased. As a result, the pitches of the sounds that are produced by the kettledrum get higher. A steel drum, shown in **Figure 17B,** plays different notes in the scale when different areas in the drum are struck. In a xylophone, wood or metal bars of different lengths are struck. The longer the bar is, the lower the note that it produces is.

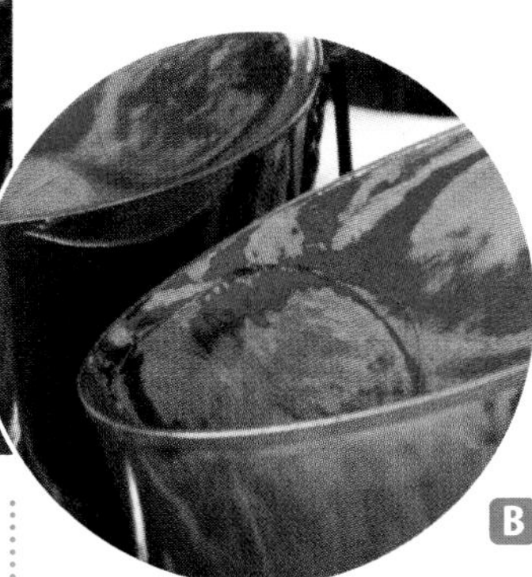

Figure 17
The sounds produced by drums depend on the material that is vibrating. A The vibrating drumhead of this drum is amplified by the resonating air in the body of the drum. B The vibrating steel surface in a steel drum produces loud sounds that don't need to be amplified by an air-filled chamber.

Brass and Woodwinds

Just as the bars of a xylophone have different natural frequencies, so do the air columns in pipes of different lengths. Brass and woodwind instruments, such as those in **Figure 18,** are essentially pipes or tubes of different lengths that sometimes are twisted around to make them easier to hold and carry. To make music from these instruments, the air in the pipes is made to vibrate at various frequencies.

Different methods are used to produce the initial vibration. In a trumpet, a musician's lips vibrate against the mouthpiece. A clarinet player vibrates a reed in a mouthpiece. A flute player blows across a narrow slit. Although the initial vibration produced by these methods contains many frequencies, only the natural frequencies of the column of air are made to vibrate by the instrument.

Figure 18
Brass and woodwind instruments produce sounds in a vibrating column of air. ***What other instruments make sound this way?***

Resource Manager

Chapter Resources Booklet
MiniLAB, p. 4
Cultural Diversity, p. 61

Percussion

Make a Model

Have students make models of drums using oatmeal containers and paper or plastic. Suggest that students cut the cylinders to different heights, such as 10, 20, 30, and 40 cm, and secure a piece of thick paper or plastic to one end of each cylinder. Have students tap on the paper with their fingers to observe the sounds made. Drums of different heights will sound different notes when played. L2 LS **Kinesthetic**

Brass and Woodwinds

Caption Answer

Figure 18 Possible answers: organ, penny whistle, recorder

Visual Learning

Figure 18 With the class, identify the different instruments shown in the photograph. Ask students what all these instruments have in common. They all work by causing air inside pipes to vibrate. L2 LS **Visual-Spatial**

Extension

Just as there are string quartets, there are brass quintets. Ask an interested student to prepare a presentation for the class on the instruments in a brass quintet and the role played by each. Suggest that the student bring in a recording of a brass quintet and play it for the class. A brass quintet includes two trumpets, a trombone, a French horn, and a tuba or bass trombone. L2 LS **Auditory-Musical**

Brass and Woodwinds, continued

Activity

A slide whistle makes a smoothly varying tone rather than a series of notes. To make a slide whistle, you need a metal pipe and a dowel that just fits into the pipe. Attach the end of a party whistle as a mouthpiece. Blow over the top of the pipe or into the mouthpiece while sliding the dowel up and down from the bottom. Have students explain what happens as you slide the dowel. As you vary the length of the vibrating column of air, you vary the pitch. A shorter air column has a higher pitch. L2 LS **Visual-Spatial**

Quick Demo

Have students who play wind or brass instruments demonstrate how the instruments work to the class. As part of their presentations, have students explain how they change the pitch of their instruments. L2 LS **Visual-Spatial**

Beats

Quick Demo

Bring to class a digital tuner, and ask students to bring their musical instruments. Ask pairs of students with the same type of instrument to use the digital tuner to help them tune the 440A on their instruments so that one instrument produces a pitch with a frequency of 440 Hz and the other produces a pitch with a frequency of 435 Hz. Have the students play their A's simultaneously, while the remaining students in the class count the beats produced. They should hear 5 beats per second. L2 LS **Auditory-Musical**

Figure 19
A flute changes pitch as holes are opened and closed.

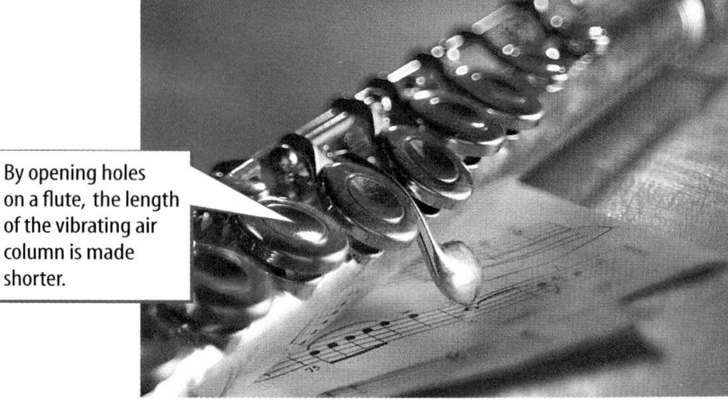

By opening holes on a flute, the length of the vibrating air column is made shorter.

Woodwinds To change the note that is being played, a musician changes the length of the resonating column of air. By making the length of the vibrating air column shorter, the pitch of the sound produced is made higher. In a woodwind such as a flute, saxophone, or clarinet, this is done by closing and opening finger holes along the length of the instrument, as shown in **Figure 19.**

Brass A brass instrument does not have these holes. Musicians vary the pitch in two ways—by blowing harder to make the air resonate at a higher natural frequency or by pressing valves that change the length of the brass tube.

Beats

When two notes are close in frequency, they interfere in a distinctive way. The two waves combine to form a wave that varies slowly in loudness. This slow variation creates beats. **Figure 20** shows the beats that are produced by the interference of two waves with frequencies of 9 Hz and 11 Hz. The frequency of the beat is the difference in the frequencies—in this case 2 Hz. Listening to two tones at the same time with a frequency difference of 2 Hz, you would hear the sound get louder and softer—a beat—two times each second.

Figure 20
Beats are formed when two frequencies that are nearly the same are played together. The sound wave in A has a frequency of 11 Hz and the sound wave in B has a frequency of 9 Hz. When these two sounds are played together, they interfere and form the wave in C that has a frequency of 2 Hz. You would hear 2 beats each second.

A

B

C

Curriculum Connection

History The earliest complete, playable instrument known is a flute from China, dating to about 9,000 years ago. This flute is made from a bird bone and has seven main holes. A tiny extra hole, drilled next to the final hole, appears to adjust a slight defect in the pitch, giving some idea of the practical musical knowledge of the flute's maker. Parts of bone flutes as much as 30,000 years old have been found in parts of Europe. **Why might people have used bones for flutes? What other items would also work?** Bird bones are hollow, and other bones can be hollowed. Hollow plants, such as reeds, can be used, but they would not survive as well in the archaeological record. L2 LS **Logical-Mathematical**

Beats Help Tune Instruments Beats are used to help tune instruments. For example, a piano tuner might hit a tuning fork and then the corresponding key on the piano. Beats are heard when the difference in pitch is small. The piano string is tuned properly when the beats disappear. You might have heard beats while listening to an orchestra tune before a performance. You also can hear beats produced by two engines vibrating at slightly different frequencies.

Reverberation

Sound is reflected by hard surfaces. In an empty gymnasium, the sound of your voice can be reflected back and forth several times by the floor, walls, and ceiling. Repeated echoes of sound are called **reverberation.** In a gym, reverberation makes the sound of your voice linger before it dies out. Some reverberation can make voices or music sound bright and lively. However, reverberation can produce a confusing mess of noise if too many sounds linger for too long. Too little reverberation makes the sound flat and lifeless. Concert halls and theaters, such as the one in **Figure 21,** are designed to produce the appropriate level of reverberation. Acoustical engineers use soft materials to reduce echoes. Special panels that are attached to the walls or suspended from the ceiling are designed to reflect sound toward the audience.

SCIENCE Online

Research Visit the Glencoe Science Web site at **science.glencoe.com** for more information about how concert halls are designed to produce the proper amount of reverberation. Communicate to your class what you learn.

Figure 21
The shape of a concert hall and the materials is contains are designed to control the reflection of sound waves.

SCIENCE Online

Internet Addresses

Explore the Glencoe Science Web site at **science.glencoe.com** to find out more about topics in this section.

Fun Fact

Our ears are capable of hearing beats only if the difference in the frequency of the two notes played is less than 7Hz.

Reverberation

Teacher FYI

Reverberation makes sound confusing because each echo takes a different amount of time to reach your ears. For example, if someone on stage shouts "One-two-three!" you might be hearing "Three!" while simultaneously hearing several slightly offset echoes of "Two!" and a few fainter, offset re-echoes of "One!" It is hard to pick meaning out of this collage of sound.

Use Science Words

Word Meaning Acoustical engineers design buildings and other structures to enhance or reduce sound. Have students find the two meanings of the word *acoustics.* the scientific study of sound; the total effect of sound in a place, especially an enclosed space L2

LS **Linguistic**

Resource Manager

Chapter Resources Booklet

Enrichment, p. 28

Reinforcement, p. 26

Inclusion Strategies

Gifted Have students write reports describing what happens when two sound waves meet. When crests correspond to crests, waves interfere constructively, and the amplitude of the wave increases. If the initial waves are identical, the amplitude of the wave doubles. If the crests in one meet the troughs in the other, the waves interfere destructively. If identical waves interfere exactly destructively, they cancel each other. L3

The Ear

Visual Learning

Figure 22 Have students trace the path of sound as it moves through the ear. Sound moves through the outer ear, ear canal, middle ear, eardrum, hammer, anvil, and stirrup, oval window, and cochlea. Impulses are then carried to the brain where they are interpreted by the auditory nerve. L2 LS **Visual-Spatial**

Quick Demo

Ask students to close their eyes and listen as you speak to them from one point in the room. **Can they point to you? What happens if they cover one ear and listen?** It should be harder to locate you using only one ear. Point out that having an ear on either side of the head makes it easier for someone to pinpoint the place from which a sound comes. L2 LS **Auditory-Musical**

Use an Analogy

Explain that an ear on either side of the head does for hearing what two eyes at the front of the head do for sight. Just as having an ear on either side of the head helps identify the location from which a sound originates, having two eyes on the front of the face provides an individual with depth perception.

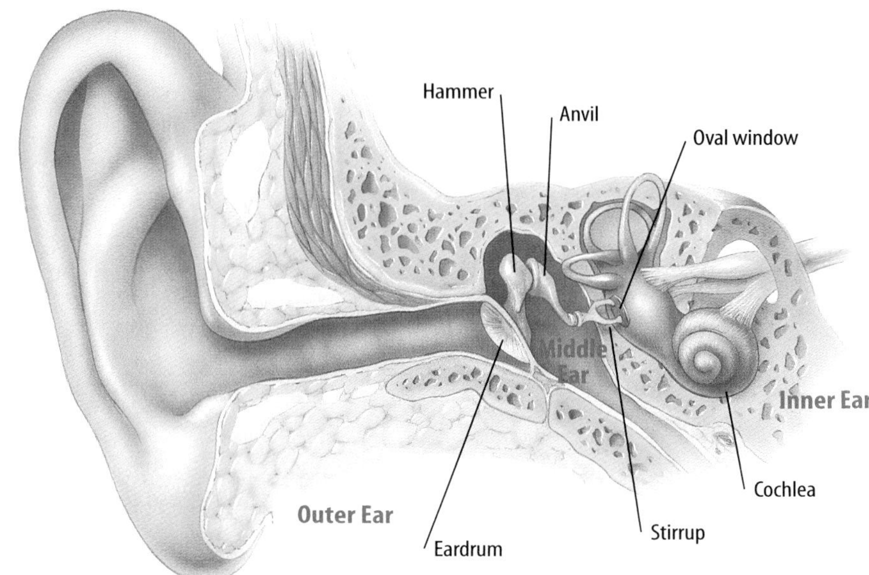

Figure 22
The human ear has three different parts—the outer ear, the middle ear, and the inner ear.

The Ear

Sound is all around you. Sounds are as different as the loud buzz of an alarm clock and the quiet hum of a bee. You hear sounds with your ears. The ear is a complex organ that is able to detect a wide range of sounds. The human ear is illustrated in **Figure 22.** It has three parts—the outer ear, the middle ear, and the inner ear.

The Outer Ear—Sound Collector Your outer ear collects sound waves and directs them into the ear canal. Notice that your outer ear is shaped roughly like a funnel. This shape helps collect sound waves.

Animals that rely on hearing to locate predators or prey often have larger, more adjustable ears than humans, as shown in **Figure 23.** A barn owl, which relies on its excellent hearing for hunting at night, does not have outer ears made of flesh. Instead, the arrangement of its facial feathers helps direct sound to its ears. Sea mammals, on the other hand, have small holes for outer ears, even though their hearing is good.

Figure 23
Animals, such as rabbits and owls, have ears that are adapted to their different needs.

The Middle Ear—Sound Amplifier When sound waves reach the middle ear, they vibrate the **eardrum,** which is a membrane that stretches across the ear canal like a drumhead. When the eardrum vibrates, it passes the vibration to three small connected bones—the hammer, anvil, and stirrup. The bones amplify the vibration of the sound wave, just as a lever can increase a small movement at one end into a larger movement at the other.

Resource Manager

Chapter Resources Booklet
Activity Worksheet, pp. 7–8
Lab Management and Safety, p. 64

Teacher FYI

Why do your ears pop? Your middle ear has an air pocket between the eardrum and oval window membranes. When the pressure of the air on either side of the eardrum is unbalanced, your ears feel blocked. You need to swallow to equalize the pressure. This equalization is felt as a pop of the ears.

The Inner Ear—Sound Interpreter The stirrup vibrates a second membrane called the oval window. This marks the start of the inner ear, which is filled with fluid. Vibrations in the fluid are transmitted to hair-tipped cells lining the cochlea, as shown in **Figure 24.** Different sounds vibrate the cells in different ways. The cells generate signals containing information about the frequency, intensity, and duration of the sound. The nerve impulses travel along the auditory nerve and are transmitted to the part of the brain that is responsible for hearing.

Where are waves detected and interpreted in the ear?

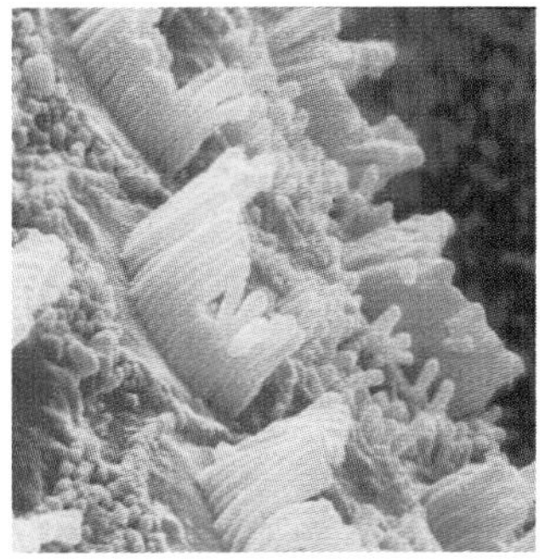

Figure 24
The inner ear contains tiny hair cells that convert vibrations into nerve impulses that travel to the brain.

Hearing Loss

The ear can be damaged by disease, age, and exposure to loud sounds. For example, constant exposure to loud noise can damage hair cells in the cochlea. If these damaged hair cells die, some loss of hearing results because hair cells are not replaced. Hair cells also die as people age. By age 65, most people have lost about 40 percent of these cells and the ability to hear some frequencies is reduced.

The higher frequencies are usually the first to be lost. The loss of the higher frequencies also distorts sound. The soft consonant sounds, such as those made by the letters *s, f, h, sh,* and *ch,* are hard to hear. People with high-frequency hearing loss have trouble distinguishing these sounds in ordinary conversation.

Section  Assessment

1. How are music and noise different?
2. Two bars on a xylophone are 10 cm and 14 cm long. Which bar will produce a lower pitch when struck?
3. Why would the sound of a guitar string sound louder when attached to the body of the guitar than when plucked alone?
4. What are the parts of the human ear, and how do they enable you to hear sound?
5. **Think Critically** As the size of stringed instruments increases from violin to viola, cello, and base, the sound of the instrument becomes lower pitched. Explain.

Skill Builder Activities

6. **Making Models** Illustrate the fundamental and first overtone for a string. **For more help, refer to the Science Skill Handbook.**
7. **Communicating** Imagine that human hearing is much more sensitive than it currently is. Write a story describing a day in the life of your main character. Be sure to describe your setting in detail. For example, does your story take place in a crowded city or a scenic national park? How would life be different? Describe your story in your Science Journal. **For more help, refer to the Science Skill Handbook.**

Reading Check

Answer Sound is detected by the eardrum and interpreted in the cochlea.

3 Assess

Reteach

Ask students to suppose they are stranded on a deserted island. Have them describe some ways they might go about making a drum, a stringed instrument, or a wind instrument. Possible answers: A stringed instrument might be made by stretching a plant fiber between two sticks. A drum might be made by stretching an animal skin over a hollowed out log. L2

LS **Linguistic**

Challenge

Western musical harmony is based on triad chords consisting of the notes *do, mi,* and *sol.* The overtones produced by a piano are called the overtone series and form the basis of western harmony. Have students find out how this works. The first six overtones produced by a note on the piano include *do, do* an octave higher, *sol* an octave and a fifth above *do, do* two octaves higher, and *mi* two octaves and a third above *do.* L3

LS **Logical-Mathematical**

Assessment

Portfolio Have students write descriptions of how closing holes on a woodwind instrument changes the pitch made by the instrument. Closing holes increases the length of the column of air in the instrument, causing the pitch to go down. Use **PASC,** p. 159. P

Answers to Section Assessment

1. Musical sounds have been deliberately produced to make a regular pattern.
2. The 14-cm bar; The larger the vibrating object, the deeper the sound it produces.
3. The body of the guitar acts as a resonator, magnifying the sound.
4. The parts of the ear include the outer ear, the middle ear, and the inner ear. The outer ear collects sound, the middle ear amplifies sound, and the inner ear interprets sound.
5. Larger instruments have longer strings, which produce lower pitches.
6. Drawings should be similar to Figure 14.
7. Possible scenarios: The modern world would be too loud; we would be aware of different parts of nature, such as the sound of an insect or small animal moving; music would change to accommodate our more sensitive hearing; we might be overwhelmed by the sounds of traffic.

Activity

BENCH TESTED

Recognize the Problem

Purpose

Students will investigate what causes different instruments to produce different notes. L2 ELL COOP LEARN **Auditory-Musical**

Process Skills

observing, inferring, comparing and contrasting, measuring, recognizing cause and effect, controlling variables, formulating hypotheses, making and using tables, interpreting data

Time Required

one class period to make measurements, one class period to analyze and check results

Materials

Make sure students are prepared in advance to bring in instruments that they know how to play. String, brass, and woodwind instruments will work best for this activity.

Alternate Materials

If actual band and orchestra instruments are not available, students can make models of instruments.

Safety Precautions

Warn students not to stand in the way of the musicians.

Form a Hypothesis

Possible Hypothesis

Pitch increase if the string or air tube is shortened.

Test Your Hypothesis

Possible Procedure

Choose two notes, such as C and G. Measure the length of the vibrating part of each instrument when the two notes are played. Record your results in a table.

Activity Design Your Own Experiment

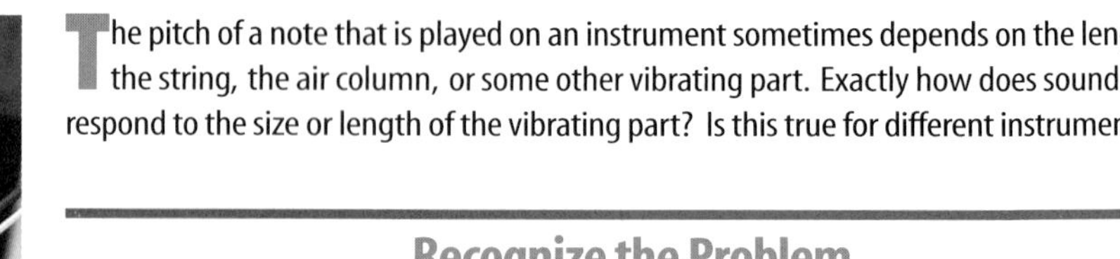

Music

The pitch of a note that is played on an instrument sometimes depends on the length of the string, the air column, or some other vibrating part. Exactly how does sound correspond to the size or length of the vibrating part? Is this true for different instruments?

Recognize the Problem

What causes different instruments to produce different notes?

Form a Hypothesis

Based on your reading and observations, make a hypothesis about what changes in an instrument to produce different notes.

Goals

- **Design** an experiment to compare the changes that are needed in different instruments to produce a variety of different notes.
- **Observe** which changes are made when playing different notes.
- **Measure and record** these changes whenever possible.

Possible Materials

musical instruments
measuring tape
tuning forks

Safety Precautions

Be sure to wash the mouthpiece of any wind instrument before passing it on to another student.

Instrument	What vibrates?	Length of vibrating part	Any other differences?

Test Your Hypothesis

Plan

1. You should do this activity as a class, using as many instruments as possible. You might want to go to the music room or invite friends and relatives who play an instrument to visit the class.
2. As a group, decide how you will measure changes in instruments. Can you measure length in all the instruments you've found? Can you measure thickness or tightness of strings? Two or more should play on each instrument.
3. Refer to the table of wavelengths and frequencies for notes in the scale. Note that no measurements are given—if you measure C to correspond to a string length of 30 cm, for example, the note G will correspond to two thirds of that length.
4. Decide which musical notes you will compare. Prepare a table to collect your data. List the notes you have selected.

Ratios of Wavelengths and Frequencies of Musical Notes

Note	Wavelength	Frequency
C	1	1
D	8/9	9/8
E	4/5	5/4
F	3/4	4/3
G	2/3	3/2
A	3/5	5/3
B	8/15	15/8
C	1/2	2

Do

1. Make sure your teacher approves your plan before you start.
2. Carry out the experiment as planned.
3. While doing the experiment, record your observations and complete the data table.

Analyze Your Data

1. **Compare** the change in each instrument when the two notes are produced.
2. **Compare and contrast** the changes between instruments.
3. What were the controls in this experiment?
4. What were the variables in this experiment?
5. How did you eliminate bias?

Draw Conclusions

1. Did the results support your hypothesis? Explain.
2. **Describe** how you would modify an instrument to increase the pitch of a note that is played.
3. How does tube length relate to pitch?

Communicating Your Data

Demonstrate to another teacher or to family members how the change in the instrument produces a change in sound.

Teaching Strategies

- Make sure that students note differences other than length, such as the different weights of strings.
- Suggest that students first determine how they will measure the distances. Can they determine the path of air in a trumpet? Have they noted where the strings on a violin are fixed?

Expected Outcome

To play a higher note, the vibrating part of the instrument is shortened. If a string, it may also be tighter or thinner. If a brass instrument, the force of air blown may increase to make the air column vibrate in thirds rather than halves, for example.

Analyze Your Data

1. Answers should reflect the relationship between pitch and string or tube length.
2. Answers will depend on instruments used.
3. playing the same notes or using the same instrument
4. playing different notes or using different instruments
5. Answers will vary.

Error Analysis

If students get anomalous results, help them look for possible errors in their measurements.

Draw Conclusions

1. Answers will vary, depending on the students' hypotheses.
2. Reduce the length of the vibrating part of the instrument.
3. In a wind instrument, the shorter the tube, the higher the pitch.

Assessment

Oral Ask students how they would analyze an instrument they'd never seen before. How could they tell what kind of instrument it was? How could they determine how it varied its pitch? Use **Performance Assessment in the Science Classroom,** p. 97.

Communicating Your Data

Have students make illustrated tables of their data that include pictures of the different instruments. Tables should include descriptions of how the instrument changes when the pitch is changed.

Content Background

Explain that sound waves are longitudinal waves that originate when there is a disturbance in the air. Vibrating objects or sudden movement in the air can cause a disturbance. In the case of candy wrappers, the sudden repositioning of the plastic wrapper causes sudden movement in the air molecules near the plastic wrap. This small shock wave causes the air molecules to vibrate at the same frequency as the original movement. As a result, areas where molecules are bunched together (compression) or spread apart (rarefaction) are formed. These longitudinal waves are transmitted right through the middle of things.

A sound wave traveling through air causes very small rapid changes in the air pressure. These changes in pressure, once detected by the ear, are funnelled into the ear canal. At the end of the canal, the energy of the wave is transferred to the eardrum. The eardrum vibrates at the same frequency as the original wave and transfers the energy to the middle ear. The middle ear, which is composed of the hammer, anvil, and stirrup, acts as a safety buffer before transferring the energy of the wave to the inner ear. Once in the inner ear, the energy is sorted and converted to electrical impulses, which are passed on to the brain.

The brain analyzes the sound, and, as a result, we hear the sound inside our head.

TIME SCIENCE AND Society

SCIENCE ISSUES THAT AFFECT YOU!

It's a Wrap!

snap! pop! pop! crackle! snap! snap! crackle!

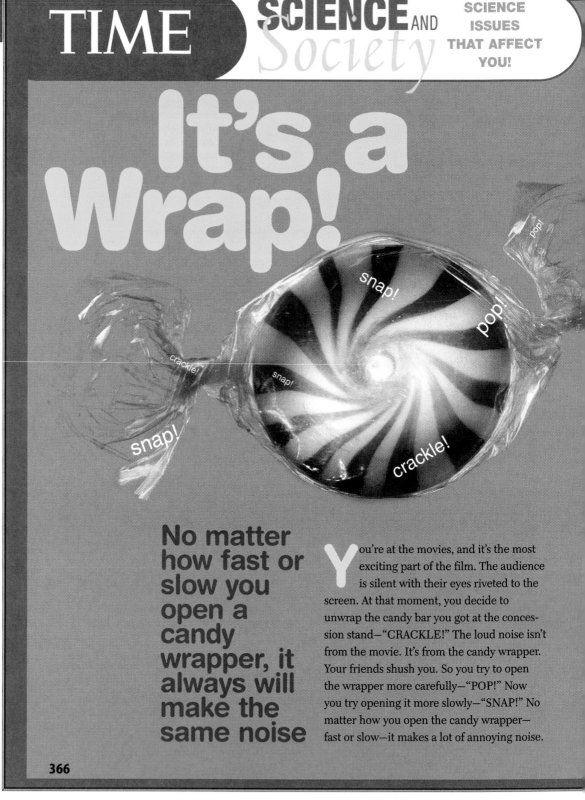

No matter how fast or slow you open a candy wrapper, it always will make the same noise

You're at the movies, and it's the most exciting part of the film. The audience is silent with their eyes riveted to the screen. At that moment, you decide to unwrap the candy bar you got at the concession stand—"CRACKLE!" The loud noise isn't from the movie. It's from the candy wrapper. Your friends shush you. So you try to open the wrapper more carefully—"POP!" Now you try opening it more slowly—"SNAP!" No matter how you open the candy wrapper—fast or slow—it makes a lot of annoying noise.

366

Resources for Teachers and Students

Sound: More Than What You Hear, Christopher F. Lampton, Enslow Publishers Inc., New Jersey, 1992.

Sound Fundamentals Funtastic Science Activities for Kids, Robert W. Wood, McGraw-Hill Companies, Inc, 1997.

The Handy Physics Answer, P. Erik Gundersen, Visible Ink Press, 1999.

Just about everyone has been in that situation at a movie or a concert. And just about everyone has wondered why you can't unwrap candy without making a racket—no matter how hard you try. But now, finally, thanks to the work of a few curious physicists, we know the answer.

To test the plastic problem, researchers took some crinkly wrappers and put them in a silent room. Then the researchers stretched out the wrappers and recorded the sound they made. Next, the crinkling sound was run through a computer. After analyzing the sound, the research team discovered something very interesting—the wrapper didn't make a nonstop, continuous sound. Instead, it made many little separate popping noises. Each of these sound bursts took only a thousandth of a second.

Pop Goes the Wrapper

The researchers found that the loudness of the pops had nothing to do with how fast the plastic was unwrapped. The pops randomly took place. The reason? Little creases in the plastic suddenly snapped into a new position as the wrapper was stretched.

So, if you unwrap candy more slowly, the time between pops will be longer, but the amount of noise made by the pops will be the same. And whether you open the wrapper fast or slow, you'll always hear pops. "And there's nothing you can do about it," said a member of the research team.

Is there another payoff to the candy wrapper research? One scientist said that by understanding what makes a plastic wrapper "snap" when it changes shape, the information can actually help doctors understand molecules in the human body. These molecules, like plastic, can change shape.

But, in the meantime, what are you supposed to do when you absolutely have to open candy in a silent theater? Be considerate of others in the audience. Open the candy as fast as you can, and just get it over with. You can even wait until a noisy part of the movie to hide the crinkle, or open the candy before the film begins.

The pop chart

SOUND LEVEL OVER TIME

The sound that a candy wrapper makes is emitted as a series of pulses or clicks. So, opening a wrapper slowly only increases the length of time in between clicks, but the amount of noise remains the same.

(TALLER SPIKES SIGNIFY LOUDER CLICKS)

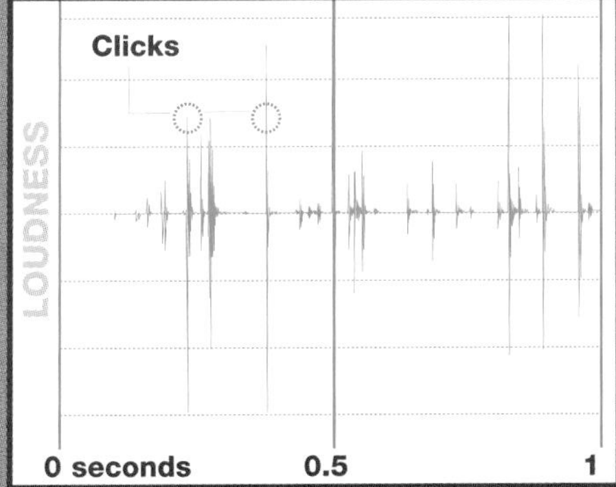

Source: Eric Kramer, Simon's Rock College, 2000

CONNECTIONS Recall and Retell **Have you ever opened a candy wrapper in a quiet place? Did it bother other people? If so, did you try to open it more slowly? What happened?**

Online

For more information, visit science.glencoe.com

Discussion

Suggest students debate this question: **If a tree falls in the forest and no one is there to hear it, is sound formed?** The answer depends on how sound is defined. If sound is characterized as what the human ear perceives, then the answer is no. But if sound is defined as a wave of energy traveling through a medium, then the answer is yes. LS **Interpersonal**

Activity

Divide the class into small groups, and then distribute one piece of wrapped hard candy to each student. Have students take turns trying to unwrap the candy as quietly as possible. Ask students to record the methods used to open the candy and the effectiveness of each. If time permits, have the quietest students from each group compete for quietest in the class. LS **Auditory-Musical**

Investigate the Issue

Ask students to share stories of situations when they may have surprised others with a loud noise or were distracted by a loud noise from someone else. Possible answers should include: a quiet setting like a classroom, and a sudden loud noise such as dropping something, coughing, sneezing, or their stomach growling. Encourage discussion among students about why sudden sounds can be so distracting, using quiet study areas, such as the library, as a basis for the discussion.

CONNECTIONS Have students work in small groups to make lists of different kinds of candies. Next, have students arrange their lists from the noisiest to open to the least noisy. Ask students to describe the outer wrappers of the noisiest and least noisy. Their descriptions should include the type of material used and how easy it is to open. Have students share their conclusions with the class. LS **Interpersonal**

Online

Internet Addresses

Explore the Glencoe Science Web site at **science.glencoe.com** to find out more about topics in this feature.

Chapter 12 Study Guide

Reviewing Main Ideas

Preview

Students can answer the questions in their Science Journals. Discuss the answers as you go through the chapter. LS **Linguistic**

Review

Students can write their answers, then compare them with those of other students. LS **Interpersonal**

Reteach

Students can look at the illustrations and describe details that support the main ideas of the chapter. LS **Visual-Spatial**

Answers to Chapter Review

Section 1

2. through the tracks
5. it goes up

Section 2

4. Resonance causes the body of the violin and the air inside the violin to vibrate.

Chapter 12 Study Guide

Reviewing Main Ideas

Section 1 What is sound?

1. Sound is a compressional wave that travels through matter, such as air. Sound is produced by something that vibrates.
2. The speed of sound is different in different materials. In general, sound travels faster in solids than in liquids, and faster in liquids than in gases. *Will the sound of a train travel faster through the air or through these tracks?*

3. The loudness of a sound depends on the sound's intensity. The intensity increases as the energy carried by the sound wave increases.
4. The pitch of a sound wave corresponds to its frequency. Sound waves can reflect, or bounce, and diffract, or bend around, objects.
5. The Doppler effect occurs when the source of sound and the listener are in motion relative to each other. Sound is shifted up or down in pitch. *What happens to the pitch of the train's horn as it approaches the person?*

Section 2 Music

1. Music is made of sounds that are used in a regular pattern. Noise is made of sounds that are irregular and disorganized.
2. Objects vibrate at their natural frequencies. These depend on the shape of the object and the material it's made of.
3. Resonance occurs when an object is made to vibrate by absorbing energy at one of its natural frequencies.
4. Musical instruments produce notes by vibrating at their natural frequencies. Resonance is used to amplify the sound. *How does resonance make this violin sound louder?*

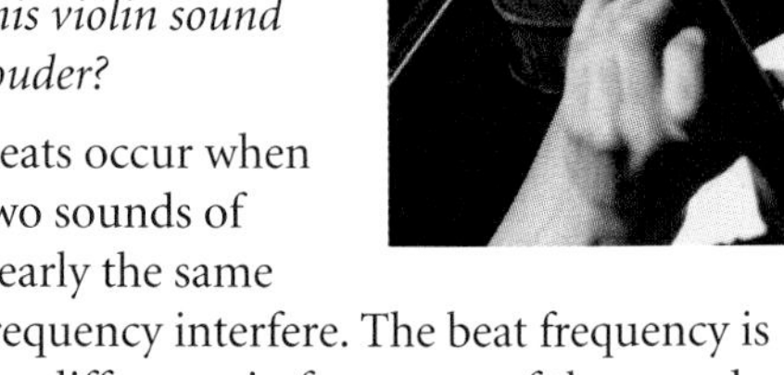

5. Beats occur when two sounds of nearly the same frequency interfere. The beat frequency is the difference in frequency of the sounds.
6. The ear collects sound waves, amplifies the vibrations, and converts the vibrations to nerve impulses.

FOLDABLES Reading & Study Skills — After You Read

Use the library to find answers to any questions remaining on your Question Study Foldable.

FOLDABLES Reading & Study Skills — After You Read

After students have read the chapter and completed the Foldable described in Before You Read, have them do the activity on the student page.

Visualizing Main Ideas

Complete the following concept map on sound.

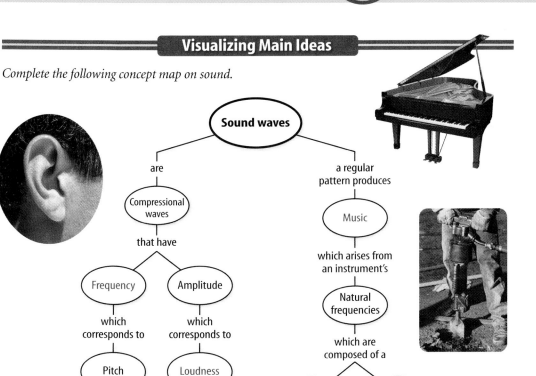

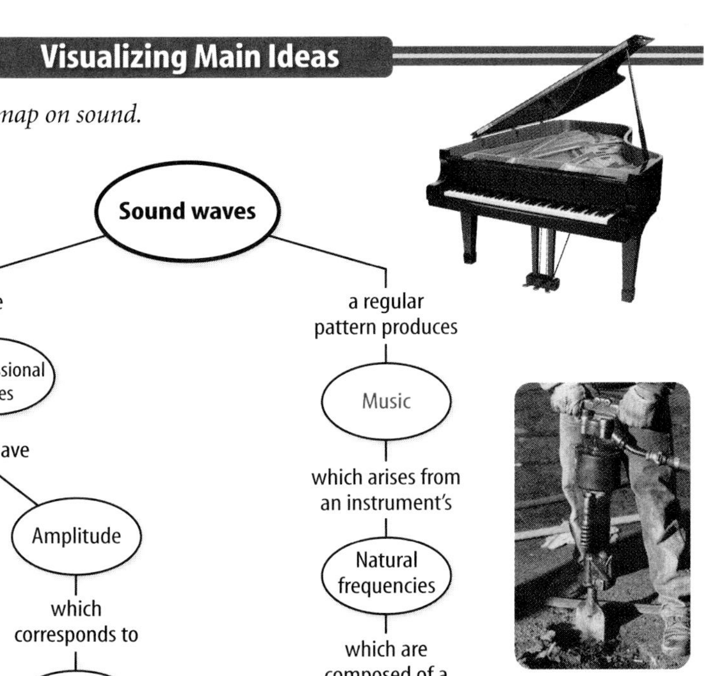

Vocabulary Review

Vocabulary Words

a. Doppler effect
b. eardrum
c. echo
d. fundamental frequency
e. loudness
f. natural frequency
g. overtone
h. pitch
i. resonance
j. reverberation

Study Tip

Recopy your notes from class. As you do, explain each concept in more detail to make sure that you understand it completely.

Using Vocabulary

Distinguish between the terms in each of the following pairs.

1. overtones, fundamental frequency
2. pitch, sound wave
3. pitch, Doppler effect
4. loudness, resonance
5. fundamental, natural frequency
6. loudness, amplitude
7. natural frequency, overtone
8. reverberation, resonance

Chapter 12 Study Guide

Visualizing Main Ideas

See student page.

Vocabulary Review

Using Vocabulary

1. The lowest frequency produced by a vibrating object is the fundamental frequency. The higher frequencies at which it vibrates are overtones.
2. Pitch corresponds to the frequency of a sound wave.
3. The pitch of a sound wave gets higher if the source of the sound and the listener are approaching each other and gets lower if they are moving farther apart. This phenomenon is called the Doppler effect.
4. Loudness corresponds to the energy, or amplitude, of a sound wave. Resonance refers to the tendency of an object to vibrate at its natural frequencies.
5. The fundamental frequency is the lowest natural frequency of an object.
6. The loudness of a sound is indicated by the amplitude of the sound wave.
7. Natural frequencies produced by vibrating objects include the fundamental frequency, which is the lowest natural frequency the object produces, and the overtones, which are multiples of the fundamental frequency.
8. Resonance occurs when an object is made to vibrate at its natural frequency by absorbing energy from a sound wave produced by another vibrating object. Reverberation occurs when sound is reflected many times to produce repeated echoes.

CHAPTER STUDY GUIDE 369

Chapter 12 Assessment

Checking Concepts

1. A
2. B
3. D
4. C
5. A
6. A
7. A
8. C
9. D
10. C

Thinking Critically

11. The pipes act as resonators, each pipe resonating at the pitch produced by the bar above it and amplifying it.
12. The shift in frequency is not large enough to be detected by your ear.
13. Sound vibration would not be amplified as it is in a normal ear. Ability to hear quiet sounds would be affected.
14. Possible frequencies would be 522 Hz and 526 Hz.
15. When you hold the triangle, you keep it from vibrating freely. It cannot vibrate at its natural frequencies, so little sound is produced.

Chapter 12 Assessment

Checking Concepts

Choose the word or phrase that best answers the question.

1. A tone that is lower in pitch is lower in what characteristic?
   A) frequency **C)** loudness
   B) wavelength **D)** resonance
2. If frequency increases, what decreases if speed stays the same?
   A) pitch **C)** loudness
   B) wavelength **D)** resonance
3. What part of the ear is damaged by continued exposure to loud noise?
   A) eardrum **C)** oval window
   B) stirrup **D)** hair cells
4. What is an echo?
   A) diffracted sound
   B) resonating sound
   C) reflected sound
   D) Doppler-shifted sound
5. A trumpeter depresses keys to make the column of air resonating in the trumpet shorter. What happens to the note that is being played?
   A) The pitch is higher. **C)** It is quieter.
   B) The pitch is lower. **D)** It is louder.
6. When tuning a violin, a string is tightened. What happens to the note that is being played on that string?
   A) The pitch is higher. **C)** It is quieter.
   B) The pitch is lower. **D)** It is louder.
7. If air becomes warmer, what happens to the speed of sound in air?
   A) It increases. **C)** It doesn't change.
   B) It decreases. **D)** It varies.
8. Sound is what type of wave?
   A) slow **C)** compressional
   B) transverse **D)** fast
9. What does the middle ear do?
   A) focuses sound
   B) interprets sound
   C) collects sound
   D) transmits and amplifies sound
10. An ambulance siren speeds away from you. What happens to the pitch you hear?
    A) It increases. **C)** It decreases.
    B) It becomes louder. **D)** Nothing happens.

Thinking Critically

11. Some xylophones have open pipes of different lengths hung under each bar. The longer the bar is, the longer the corresponding pipe is. Explain how these pipes amplify the sound of the xylophone.

12. Why don't you notice the Doppler effect for a slow-moving train?
13. Suppose the movement of the bones in the middle ear were reduced. Which would be more affected—the ability is hear quiet sounds, or the ability to hear certain frequencies? Explain your answer.
14. Two flutes are playing at the same time. One flute plays a note with frequency 524 Hz. If two beats are heard per second, what are the possible frequencies the other flute is playing?
15. The triangle is a percussion instrument consisting of an open metal triangle hanging from a string. The triangle is struck by a metal rod, and a chiming sound is heard. If the metal triangle is held in the hand rather than by the string, a quiet, dull sound is made when it is struck. Explain why holding the triangle makes it sound quieter.

Chapter Assessment Planner

Portfolio Encourage students to place in their portfolios one or two items of what they consider to be their best work. Examples include:
- Assessment, p. 346
- Extension, p. 352
- Assessment, p. 363

Performance Additional performance assessments, Performance Task Assessment Lists, and rubrics for evaluating these activities can be found in Glencoe's **Performance Assessment in the Science Classroom.**

Chapter 12 Assessment

Developing Skills

16. **Predicting** If the holes of a flute are all covered while playing, then all uncovered, what happens to the length of the vibrating air column? What happens to the pitch of the note?

17. **Identifying and Manipulating Variables and Controls** Describe an experiment to demonstrate that sound is diffracted.

18. **Making and Using Tables** Make a table to show the first three overtones for a note of G (384 Hz).

19. **Interpreting Scientific Illustrations** The picture shows pan pipes. How are different notes produced on pan pipes?

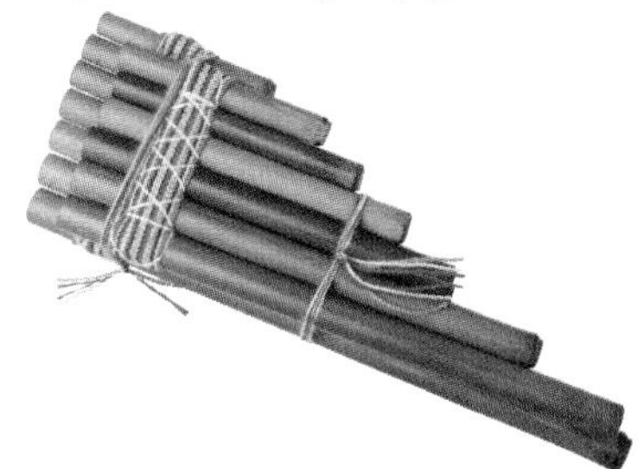

Performance Assessment

20. **Recital** Perform a short musical piece on an instrument. Explain how your actions changed the notes that were produced.

21. **Pamphlet** Create a pamphlet describing how a hearing aid works.

Technology

Go to the Glencoe Science Web site at **science.glencoe.com** or use the **Glencoe Science CD-ROM** for additional chapter assessment.

THE PRINCETON REVIEW Test Practice

Sound travels in waves that change as the pitch and loudness of the sound varies. Here are pictures illustrating four recorded sounds.

Q.

R.

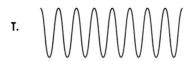

S.

T.

Study the pictures and answer the following questions.

1. Which of the four sounds was getting louder while it was recorded?
   A) Q
   B) R
   C) S
   D) T

2. Which sound had the highest pitch while it was recorded?
   F) Q
   G) R
   H) S
   J) T

Chapter 12 Assessment

THE PRINCETON REVIEW Test Practice

The Test-Taking Tip was written by The Princeton Review, the nation's leader in test preparation.

1. C
2. J

Developing Skills

16. When all holes are covered, the column is longer and the note is lower. When all holes are uncovered, the column is shorter, and the note is higher.

17. Possible answer: set up a radio playing in a room. Leave the room, and stand to one side of the door. If you can hear the music, it must be diffracted around the edge of the door to reach your ears.

18.

Fundamental	384 Hz
First overtone	768 Hz
Second overtone	1,152 Hz
Third overtone	1,536 Hz

19. Air is blown across the top of each individual pipe, resonating the column of air. Each pipe has its own pitch. The longer the pipe, the deeper the note.

Performance Assessment

20. Check students' explanations. Use **PASC**, p. 129.

21. Explanations should include information about how the device collects, transmits, and amplifies sound. Use **PASC**, p. 143.

✔Assessment Resources

Reproducible Masters

Chapter Resources Booklet
Chapter Review, pp. 33–34
Chapter Tests, pp. 35–38
Assessment Transparency Activity, p. 45

Glencoe Science Web site
Interactive Tutor
Chapter Quizzes

Glencoe Technology
Assessment Transparency
Interactive CD-ROM Chapter Quizzes
ExamView Pro Test Bank
Vocabulary PuzzleMaker Software
MindJogger Videoquiz DVD/VHS

Section/Objectives	Standards		Activities/Features
	National	State/Local	
Chapter Opener	See p. 5T for a Key to Standards.		**Explore Activity:** Detecting invisible light, p. 373 **Before You Read,** p. 373
Section 1 The Nature of Electromagnetic Waves 3 sessions 1.5 blocks 1. **Explain** how electromagnetic waves are produced. 2. **Describe** the properties of electromagnetic waves.	National Content Standards: UCP2, A1, B3		**Science Online,** p. 375 **MiniLAB:** Observing Electric Fields, p. 377
Section 2 The Electromagnetic Spectrum 3 sessions 1.5 blocks 1. **Explain** differences among kinds of electromagnetic waves. 2. **Identify** uses for different kinds of electromagnetic waves.	National Content Standards: UCP2, A1, B3, D3, F5		**MiniLAB:** Observing the Focusing of Infrared Rays, p. 381 **Life Science Integration:** p. 384 **Visualizing the Universe,** p. 386 **Activity:** Prisms of Light, p. 388
Section 3 Using Electromagnetic Waves 4 sessions 2 blocks 1. **Explain** different methods of electronic communication. 2. **Compare and contrast** AM and FM signals.	National Content Standards: UCP2, A1, B3, F5, G3		**Astronomy Integration,** p. 390 **Math Skills Activity:** Calculating the Wavelength of Radio Frequencies, p. 391 **Science Online:** p. 392 **Activity:** Spectrum Inspection, pp. 394–395 **Science and History:** Hopping the Frequencies, pp. 396–397

Activity Materials	Reproducible Resources	Section Assessment	Technology
Explore Activity: large sheet of black paper, scissors, metric ruler, glass prism, 2 thermometers, watch or clock, tape	**Chapter Resources Booklet** Foldables Worksheet, p. 15 Directed Reading Overview, p. 17 Note-taking Worksheets, pp. 31–33	Glencoe's Assessment Advantage	
MiniLAB: hard plastic comb, wool sweater or flannel shirt, water faucet	**Chapter Resources Booklet** Transparency Activity, p. 42 MiniLAB, p. 3 Enrichment, p. 28 Reinforcement, p. 25 Directed Reading, p. 18 **Cultural Diversity,** p. 61 **Science Inquiry Labs,** p. 21	Portfolio Science Journal, p. 375 Performance MiniLAB, p. 377 Skill Builder Activities, p. 378 Content Section Assessment, p. 378	Section Focus Transparency Interactive CD-ROM/DVD Guided Reading Audio Program
MiniLAB: concave mirror, metric ruler, electric heater **Activity:** 3 microscope slides, transparent tape, clay, flashlight, water	**Chapter Resources Booklet** Transparency Activity, p. 43 MiniLAB, p. 4 Enrichment, p. 29 Reinforcement, p. 26 Directed Reading, p. 18 Lab Activity, pp. 9–11 Activity Worksheet, pp. 5–6 **Reading and Writing Skill Activities,** p. 25	Portfolio Extension, p. 383 Performance MiniLAB, p. 381 Skill Builder Activities, p. 387 Content Section Assessment, p. 387	Section Focus Transparency Interactive CD-ROM/DVD Guided Reading Audio Program
Activity: diffraction grating, clear incandescent light with dimmer switch, colored pencils	**Chapter Resources Booklet** Transparency Activity, p. 44 Enrichment, p. 30 Reinforcement, p. 27 Directed Reading, pp. 19, 20 Lab Activity, pp. 13–14 Transparency Activity, pp. 45–46 Activity Worksheet, pp. 7–8 **Mathematics Skill Activities,** p. 9 **Lab Management and Safety,** p. 73	Portfolio Curriculum Connection, p. 391 Performance Math Skills Activity, p. 391 Skill Builder Activities, p. 393 Content Section Assessment, p. 393	Section Focus Transparency Teaching Transparency Interactive CD-ROM/DVD Guided Reading Audio Program

Need materials? **Contact Science Kit at 1-800-828-7777 or www.sciencekit.com on the Internet.**

End of Chapter Assessment

Glencoe's Assessment Advantage

Blackline Masters	Technology	Professional Series
Chapter Resources Booklet Chapter Review, pp. 35–36 Chapter Tests, pp. 37–40 **Standardized Test Practice by The Princeton Review,** pp. 55–58	MindJogger Videoquiz CD-ROM Explorations and Quizzes Vocabulary Puzzle Makers ExamView Pro Test Bank Interactive Lesson Planner Interactive Teacher's Edition	Performance Assessment in the Science Classroom (PASC)

Transparencies

Section Focus

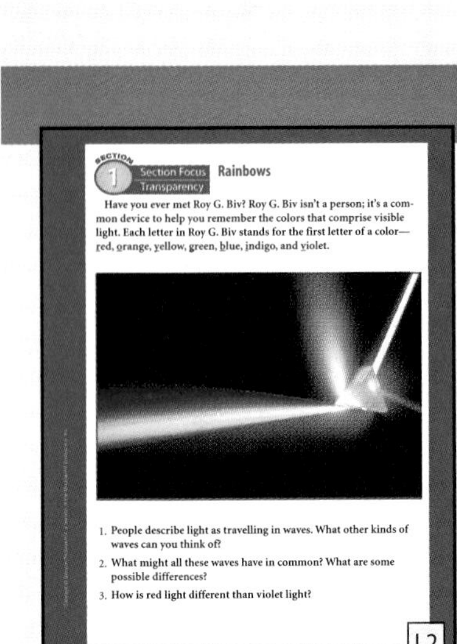
Section 1 Section Focus Transparency **Rainbows**

Have you ever met Roy G. Biv? Roy G. Biv isn't a person; it's a common device to help you remember the colors that comprise visible light. Each letter in Roy G. Biv stands for the first letter of a color—red, orange, yellow, green, blue, indigo, and violet.

1. People describe light as travelling in waves. What other kinds of waves can you think of?
2. What might all these waves have in common? What are some possible differences?
3. How is red light different than violet light?

L2

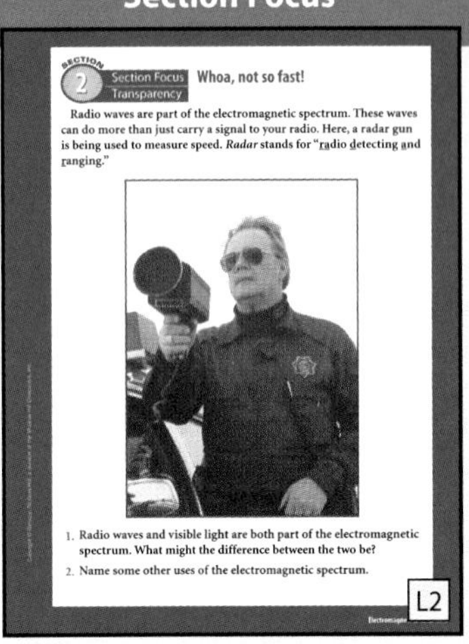
Section 2 Section Focus Transparency **Whoa, not so fast!**

Radio waves are part of the electromagnetic spectrum. These waves can do more than just carry a signal to your radio. Here, a radar gun is being used to measure speed. *Radar* stands for "radio detecting and ranging."

1. Radio waves and visible light are both part of the electromagnetic spectrum. What might the difference between the two be?
2. Name some other uses of the electromagnetic spectrum.

L2

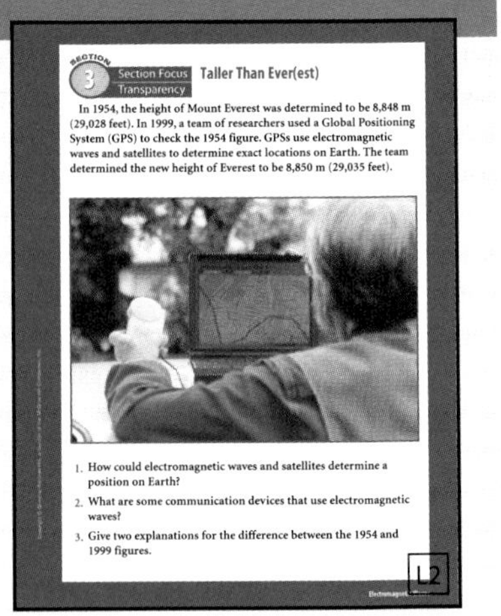
Section 3 Section Focus Transparency **Taller Than Ever(est)**

In 1954, the height of Mount Everest was determined to be 8,848 m (29,028 feet). In 1999, a team of researchers used a Global Positioning System (GPS) to check the 1954 figure. GPSs use electromagnetic waves and satellites to determine exact locations on Earth. The team determined the new height of Everest to be 8,850 m (29,035 feet).

1. How could electromagnetic waves and satellites determine a position on Earth?
2. What are some communication devices that use electromagnetic waves?
3. Give two explanations for the difference between the 1954 and 1999 figures.

L2

This is a representation of key blackline masters available in the Teacher Classroom Resources. See Resource Manager boxes within the chapter for additional information.

Assessment

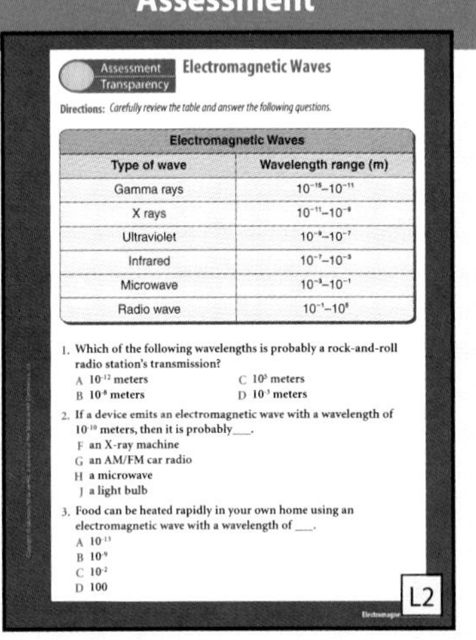
Assessment Transparency **Electromagnetic Waves**

Directions: *Carefully review the table and answer the following questions.*

Electromagnetic Waves	
Type of wave	Wavelength range (m)
Gamma rays	10^{-15}–10^{-11}
X rays	10^{-11}–10^{-8}
Ultraviolet	10^{-8}–10^{-7}
Infrared	10^{-7}–10^{-3}
Microwave	10^{-3}–10^{-1}
Radio wave	10^{-1}–10^{5}

1. Which of the following wavelengths is probably a rock-and-roll radio station's transmission?
   A 10^{-12} meters C 10^{5} meters
   B 10^{-8} meters D 10^{-3} meters
2. If a device emits an electromagnetic wave with a wavelength of 10^{-10} meters, then it is probably ____.
   F an X-ray machine
   G an AM/FM car radio
   H a microwave
   J a light bulb
3. Food can be heated rapidly in your own home using an electromagnetic wave with a wavelength of ____.
   A 10^{-13}
   B 10^{-9}
   C 10^{-2}
   D 100

L2

Teaching

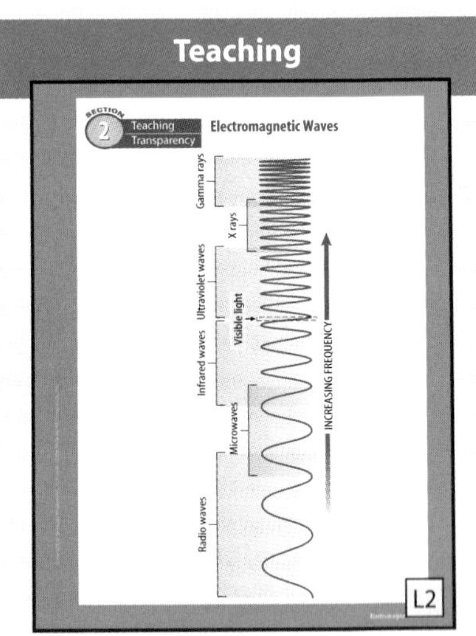
Section 2 Teaching Transparency **Electromagnetic Waves**

L2

Key to Teaching Strategies

The following designations will help you decide which activities are appropriate for your students.

- L1 Level 1 activities should be appropriate for students with learning difficulties.
- L2 Level 2 activities should be within the ability range of all students.
- L3 Level 3 activities are designed for above-average students.
- ELL ELL activities should be within the ability range of English Language Learners.
- COOP LEARN Cooperative Learning activities are designed for small group work.
- LS Multiple Learning Styles logos, as described on page 22T, are used throughout to indicate strategies that address different learning styles.
- P These strategies represent student products that can be placed into a best-work portfolio.

Hands-on Activities

Activity Worksheets

Laboratory Activities

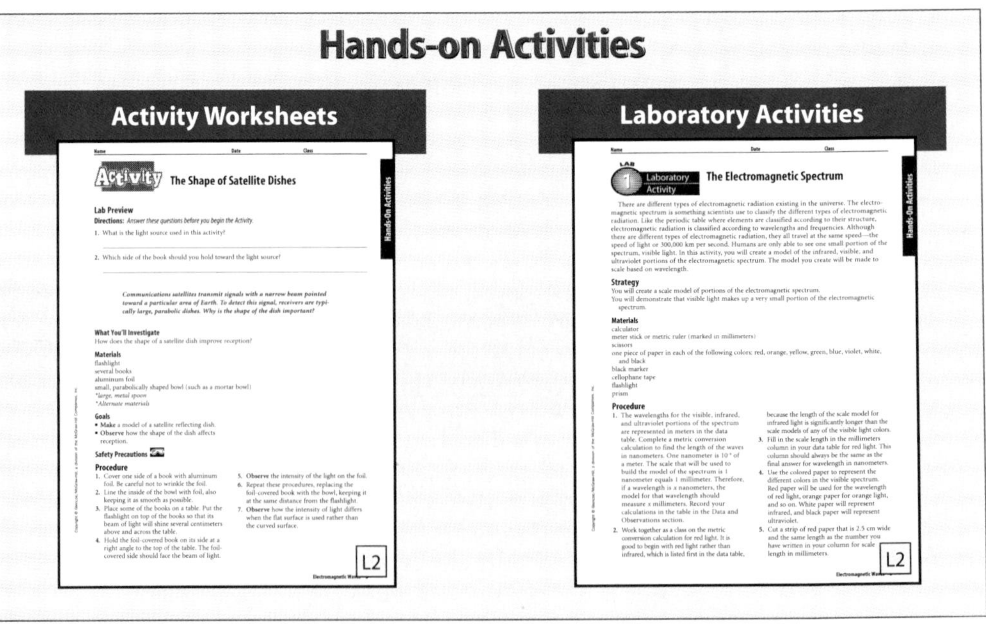
Name Date Class

Activity **The Shape of Satellite Dishes**

Lab Preview

Directions: *Answer these questions before you begin the Activity.*

1. What is the light source used in this activity?
2. Which side of the book should you hold toward the light source?

Communications satellites transmit signals with a narrow beam pointed toward a particular area of Earth. To detect this signal, receivers are typically large, parabolic dishes. Why is the shape of the dish important?

What You'll Investigate

How does the shape of a satellite dish improve reception?

Materials

flashlight
several books
aluminum foil
small, parabolically shaped bowl (such as a mortar bowl)
*large, metal spoon
*Alternate materials

Goals

- **Make** a model of a satellite reflecting dish.
- **Observe** how the shape of the dish affects reception.

Safety Precautions

Procedure

1. Cover one side of a book with aluminum foil. Be careful not to wrinkle the foil.
2. Line the inside of the bowl with foil, also keeping it as smooth as possible.
3. Place some of the books on a table. Put the flashlight on top of the books so that its beam of light will shine several centimeters above and across the table.
4. Hold the foil-covered book on its side at a right angle to the top of the table. The foil-covered side should face the beam of light.
5. **Observe** the intensity of the light on the foil.
6. Repeat these procedures, replacing the foil-covered book with the bowl, keeping it at the same distance from the flashlight.
7. **Observe** how the intensity of light differs when the flat surface is used rather than the curved surface.

Hands-On Activities

L2

Name Date Class

LAB 1 Laboratory Activity **The Electromagnetic Spectrum**

There are different types of electromagnetic radiation existing in the universe. The electromagnetic spectrum is something scientists use to classify the different types of electromagnetic radiation. Like the periodic table where elements are classified according to their structure, electromagnetic radiation is classified according to wavelengths and frequencies. Although there are different types of electromagnetic radiation, they all travel at the same speed—the speed of light or 300,000 km per second. Humans are only able to see one small portion of the spectrum, visible light. In this activity, you will create a model of the infrared, visible, and ultraviolet portions of the electromagnetic spectrum. The model you create will be made to scale based on wavelength.

Strategy

You will create a scale model of portions of the electromagnetic spectrum.
You will demonstrate that visible light makes up a very small portion of the electromagnetic spectrum.

Materials

calculator
meter stick or metric ruler (marked in millimeters)
scissors
one piece of paper in each of the following colors: red, orange, yellow, green, blue, violet, white, and black
black marker
cellophane tape
flashlight
prism

Procedure

1. The wavelengths for the visible, infrared, and ultraviolet portions of the spectrum are represented in meters in the data table. Complete a metric conversion calculation to find the length of the waves in nanometers. One nanometer is 10^{-9} of a meter. The scale that will be used to build the model of the spectrum is 1 nanometer equals 1 millimeter. Therefore, if a wavelength is *x* nanometers, the model for that wavelength should measure *x* millimeters. Record your calculations in the table in the Data and Observations section.
2. Work together as a class on the metric conversion calculation for red light. It is good to begin with red light rather than infrared, which is listed first in the data table, because the length of the scale model for infrared light is significantly longer than the scale models of any of the visible light colors.
3. Fill in the scale length in the millimeters column in your data table for red light. This column should always be the same as the final answer for wavelength in nanometers.
4. Use the colored paper to represent the different colors in the visible spectrum. Red paper will be used for the wavelength of red light, orange paper for orange light, and so on. White paper will represent infrared, and black paper will represent ultraviolet.
5. Cut a strip of red paper that is 2.5 cm wide and the same length as the number you have written in your column for scale length in millimeters.

Hands-On Activities

L2

Meeting Different Ability Levels

Content Outline

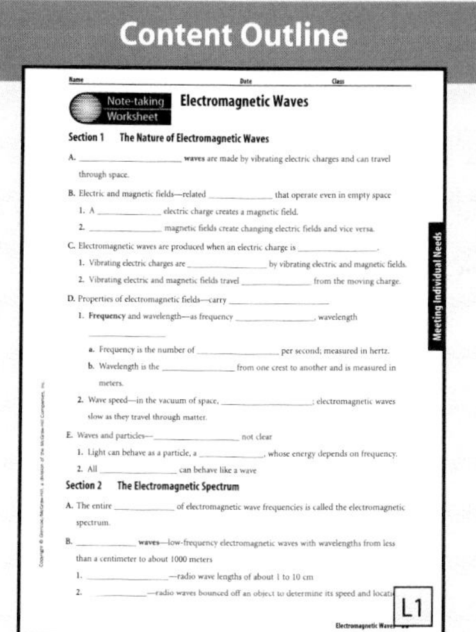

Note-taking Worksheet **Electromagnetic Waves**

Section 1 The Nature of Electromagnetic Waves

L1

Reinforcement

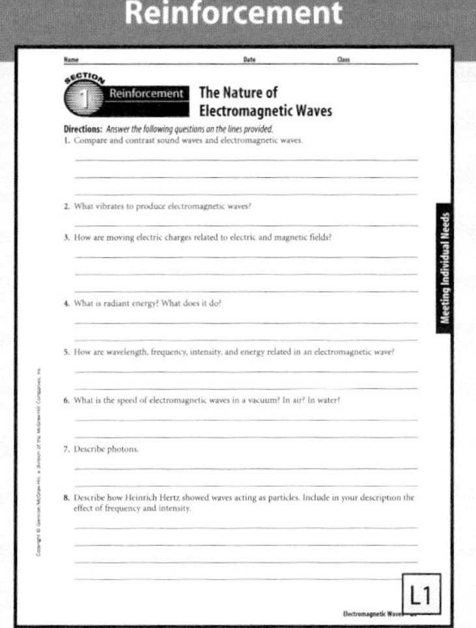

Reinforcement **The Nature of Electromagnetic Waves**

L1

Directed Reading

Directed Reading for Content Mastery *Overview* **Electromagnetic Waves**

L1

Assessment

Chapter Tests

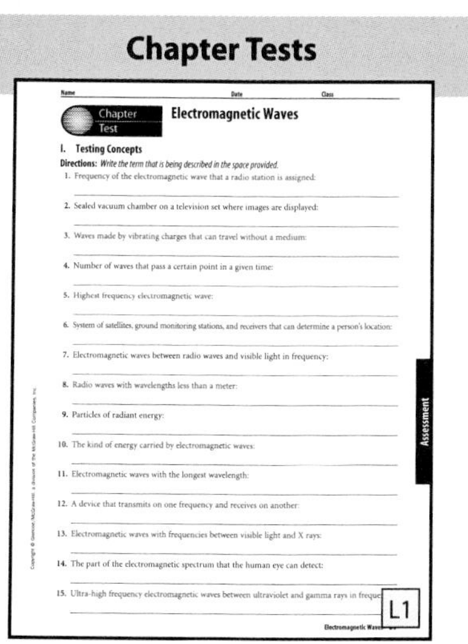

Chapter Test **Electromagnetic Waves**

L1

Enrichment

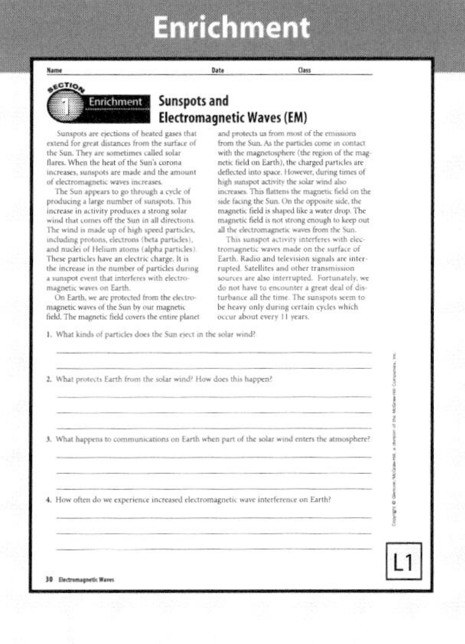

Enrichment **Sunspots and Electromagnetic Waves (EM)**

L1

Spanish Directed Reading

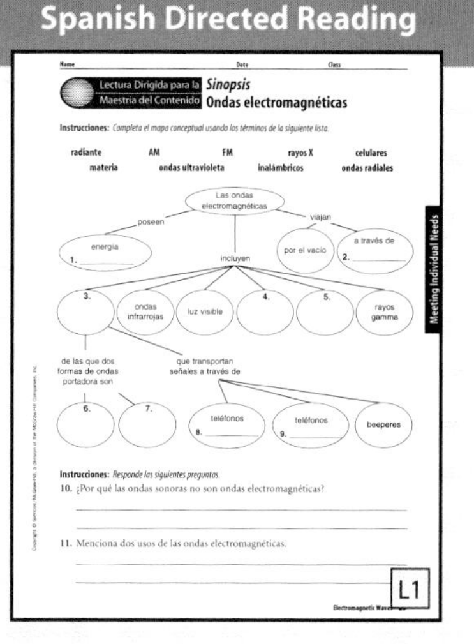

Lectura Dirigida para la Maestría del Contenido *Sinopsis* **Ondas electromagnéticas**

L1

Test Practice Workbook

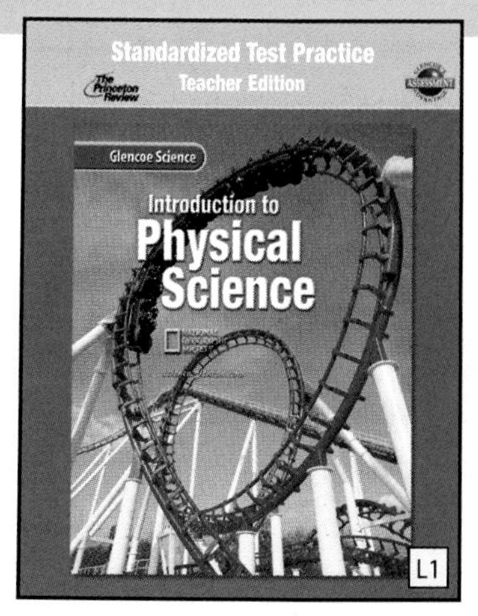

Chapter Review

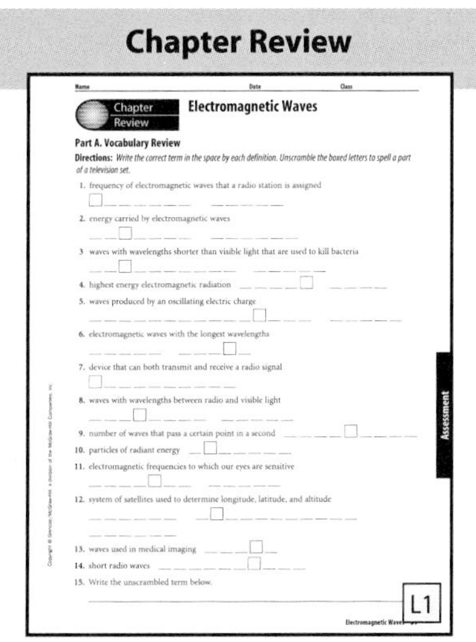

Chapter Review **Electromagnetic Waves**

L1

Science Content Background

SECTION 1 The Nature of Electromagnetic Waves

Waves in Space

From watching TV to heating a cup of cocoa in the microwave, electromagnetic waves are used in many ways in your world. From radio waves to light to X rays they seem so different, but they are a close family sharing their ability to travel through empty space at enormous speeds. In the vast universe, these waves are the only practical travelers. When we seek information about other worlds, we tap the electromagnetic spectrum.

Properties of Electromagnetic Waves

Electromagnetic waves range from short to long wavelengths. Radio waves are the longest and they can be as long as 20 meters. Gamma rays have the shortest wavelengths, which can be as small as 10^{-13} m.

The speed of an electromagnetic wave can be calculated by multiplying its wavelength times its frequency. In free space, this speed is 3×10^8 meters per second.

SECTION 2 The Electromagnetic Spectrum

Radio Waves

In the 1940s Percy Spencer discovered that his candy melted in his pockets when he was working with radar. Then he discovered when the radar was directed on popcorn it caused popping. From these observations, Spencer developed the microwave oven for the Raytheon Corporation, which it called the radar range.

Infrared Waves

All warm objects emit infrared waves. The warmer the object the more radiation it emits.

Infrared waves are used to keep food warm under heat lamps at fast food restaurants. However, not all infrared radiation is hot. One example of infrared rays that are not hot are the infrared rays used in remote controls. These are also called "near infrared" because they are near the wavelengths of visible light.

Student Misconception

Light is very different from other electromagnetic waves such as X rays.

Refer to the facing page for teaching strategies to address this misconception. Refer to pages 379–387 for content related to this topic.

X Rays and Gamma Rays

Radiation detectors detect X rays and gamma rays by the tendency of these rays to ionize atoms. Workers who may be exposed to these types of radiation often wear radiation badges. The badges contain material that is sensitive to these types of radiation. After a period of time the badges are checked to determine the amount of radiation the workers have received.

SECTION 3 Using Electromagnetic Waves

Using Radio Waves

Although Guglielmo Marconi was given credit for inventing radio, a large amount of the credit should have been given to Nikola Tesla. Tesla invented the means to turn electrical energy into radio waves. Electrons accelerating up and down a vertical antenna will produce radio waves.

On some nights you can pick up an AM station a few hundred miles from where it was broadcast. This is because the AM radio waves reflect off of the ionosphere. With FM radio waves, they need to travel in a straight line to reach you and this limits their range.

For additional content background on this topic, go to the Glencoe Science Web site at science.glencoe.com.

Misconceptions

Find Out What Students Think

Students may think that . . .

- **Light is very different from other electromagnetic waves such as X rays.**

Students can see light, but they cannot see other electromagnetic waves. Thus they may think of them as different entities. Additionally, some electromagnetic waves, such as X rays and ultraviolet rays, are perceived as hazardous, while light is perceived as "good."

Activity

Write the following on the board for the class to see. **Which of the following pairs of waves are most similar, "light and sound" or "light and X rays"? Explain your answer.** Ask students to write their answers in their Science Journals. Then have selected students read their answers. Have students try to convince others about their point of view.

Promote Understanding

Demonstration and Activity

Explain that sound waves and water waves need a medium to travel through, while electromagnetic waves can travel through a vacuum. Show students some other similarities among electromagnetic waves.

- Show light reflected by using a mirror and a flashlight.
- Show infrared reflection by using a mirror and a remote control to turn on a television or VCR.
- Show shadow formation by using the flashlight and a board eraser to cast a shadow on the wall.
- Shine an ultraviolet light on a fluorescent rock and then put the eraser in front of it to produce a shadow effect. You can also show developed X-ray film and explain how it shows the shadows of bones.

Explain that visible light, ultraviolet, infrared, and X-ray radiation are all types of electromagnetic radiation.

- Assign student groups one of the following types of waves: radio, microwaves, infrared, visible light, ultraviolet, X rays, and gamma rays. For their type of wave they should use the Internet or library to find the wavelength range, how to detect it, how it is used by people, and if it is harmful to people. If it is harmful to people, they should describe the dangers.
- Have students share their results with other groups until all students have received information about these seven types of electromagnetic waves.

Assess

After completing the chapter, see *Identifying Misconceptions* in the Study Guide.

CHAPTER 

Electromagnetic Waves

Chapter Vocabulary

electromagnetic wave
radiant energy
electromagnetic spectrum
radio wave
infrared wave
visible light
ultraviolet radiation
X ray
gamma ray
carrier wave
Global Positioning System

What do you think?

Science Journal This photograph shows the radio telescope near Aricebo, Puerto Rico. Scientists use telescopes such as these to study electromagnetic waves from space.

CHAPTER 13

Electromagnetic Waves

Wherever you go, you are being bombarded by electromagnetic waves. Some, such as visible light, can be seen. Infrared rays can't be seen but feel warm on your skin. The paint on the tricycle in this picture is being heat cured in an infrared oven. In this chapter, you will learn how electromagnetic waves are formed. You also will learn ways in which electromagnetic waves are used, from cooking to satellite communications.

What do you think?

Science Journal Look at the photograph below with a classmate. Discuss what you think this might be. Here is a hint: *Scientists built this to get a clearer picture.* Write your answer or best guess in your Science Journal.

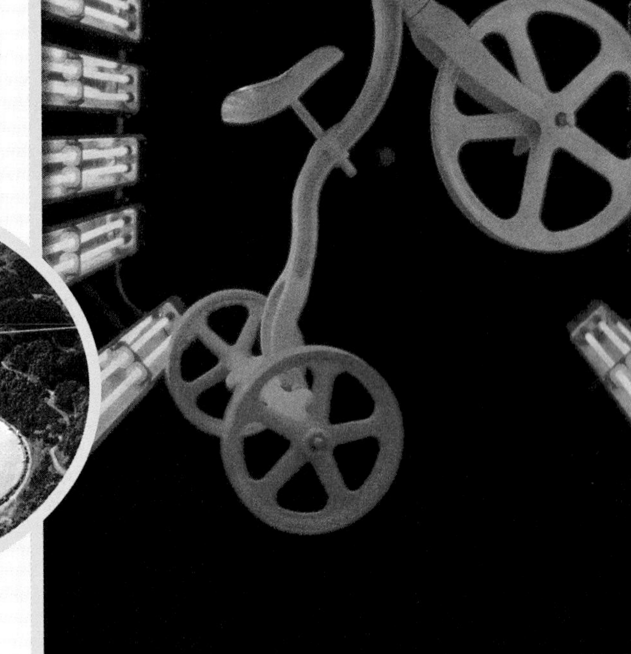

372

Theme Connection

Energy Visible light is only one of the many types of electromagnetic waves. This chapter identifies other types of electromagnetic waves and discusses the types of energy they carry and many of the ways they are used.

Light is a type of wave called an electromagnetic wave. You see light every day, but visible light is only one type of electromagnetic wave. Other electromagnetic waves are all around you, but you cannot see them. How can you detect electromagnetic waves that can't be seen with your eyes?

Detecting invisible light

1. Cut a slit 2 cm long and 0.25 cm wide in the center of a sheet of black paper.
2. Cover a window that is in direct sunlight with the paper.
3. Position a glass prism in front of the light coming through the slit so it makes a visible spectrum on the floor or table.
4. Place one thermometer in the spectrum and a second thermometer just beyond the red light.
5. Measure the temperature in each region after 5 min.

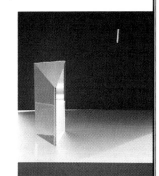

Observe

Write a paragraph in your Science Journal comparing the temperatures of the two regions and offer an explanation for the observed temperatures.

Before You Read

FOLDABLES Reading & Study Skills

Making a Main Ideas Study Fold **Make the following Foldable to help you identify the major topics about electromagnetic waves.**

1. Stack four sheets of paper in front of you so the short sides are at the top.
2. Slide the top sheet up so that about 4 cm of the next sheet show. Slide each sheet up so about 4 cm of the next sheet show.
3. Fold the sheets top to bottom to form eight tabs. Staple along the topfold.
4. Label the tabs *Electromagnetic Spectrum, Radio Waves, Microwaves, Infrared Rays, Visible Light, Ultraviolet Light, X Rays,* and *Gamma Rays.*
5. As you read the chapter, list the things you learn about these electromagnetic waves under the tabs.

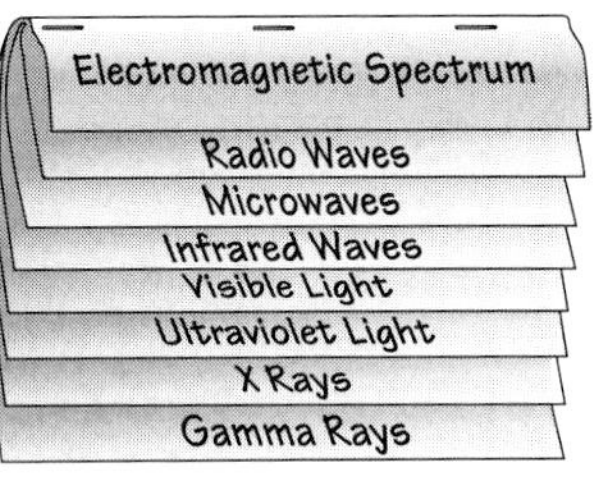

373

Before You Read

FOLDABLES Reading & Study Skills

Dinah Zike Study Fold

Purpose Students make a Foldable to help them determine what they know about electromagnetic waves before they read the chapter. They then use the Foldable to record and organize their notes as they read.

For additional help, see Foldables Worksheet, p. 15 in **Chapter Resources Booklet,** or go to the Glencoe Science Web site at **science.glencoe.com.** See After You Read in the Study Guide at the end of this chapter.

Explore Activity

Purpose Use the Explore Activity to introduce students to the concept that electromagnetic radiation can produce more than light. L2 ELL LS **Kinesthetic**

Preparation Locate a window that gets direct sunlight at the time of day that you wish students to do this activity. Check the weather to make sure the day will be sunny.

Materials black construction paper, tape, metric ruler, scissors, glass prism, two thermometers, watch

Teaching Strategy Explain to students that the visible light from the sun contains many different wavelengths of radiation, and that the prism spreads the wavelengths apart so they can be seen separately.

Observe

The temperature of the visible spectrum and ultraviolet region should be about the same as room temperature, but the infrared region should be significantly warmer. Infrared radiation transfers heat.

Assessment

Oral Ask students what they think the temperature would be of a thermometer placed just beyond the violet end of the spectrum. It would be higher than the other two. Use **Performance Assessment in the Science Classroom,** p. 89.

SECTION

The Nature of Electromagnetic Waves

1 Motivate

Bellringer Transparency

Display the Section Focus Transparency for Section 1. Use the accompanying Transparency Activity Master. L2 ELL

SECTION 1 Section Focus Transparency **Rainbows**

Have you ever met Roy G. Biv? Roy G. Biv isn't a person; it's a common device to help you remember the colors that comprise visible light. Each letter in Roy G. Biv stands for the first letter of a color—red, orange, yellow, green, blue, indigo, and violet.

1. People describe light as travelling in waves. What other kinds of waves can you think of?
2. What might all these waves have in common? What are some possible differences?
3. How is red light different than violet light?

Electromagnetic Waves

Tie to Prior Knowledge

Ask students to name types of waves or rays that they know exist but that they cannot see. Explain that these waves, which share many of the features of visible light but are also different in some ways, are the subject of this chapter.

SECTION

The Nature of Electromagnetic Waves

As You Read

What **You'll Learn**

- **Explain** how electromagnetic waves are produced.
- **Describe** the properties of electromagnetic waves.

Vocabulary

electromagnetic wave
radiant energy

Why **It's Important**

Electromagnetic waves provide energy in many useful forms.

Waves in Space

On a clear day you feel the warmth in the Sun's rays, and you see the brightness of its light. Energy is being transferred from the Sun to your skin and eyes. Who would guess that the way in which this energy is transferred has anything to do with radios, televisions, microwave ovens, or the X-ray pictures that are taken by a doctor or dentist? Yet the Sun and the objects shown in **Figure 1** use the same type of wave to move energy from place to place.

Transferring Energy A wave transfers energy from one place to another without transferring matter. How do waves transfer energy? Waves, such as water waves and sound waves, transfer energy by making particles of matter move. The energy is passed along from particle to particle as they collide with their neighbors. Mechanical waves are the types of waves that use matter to transfer energy.

How can a wave transfer energy from the Sun to Earth? Mechanical waves, for example, can't travel in the space between Earth and the Sun where no matter exists. Instead, this energy is carried by a different type of wave called an electromagnetic wave. An **electromagnetic wave** is a wave that can travel through empty space and is produced by charged particles that are in motion.

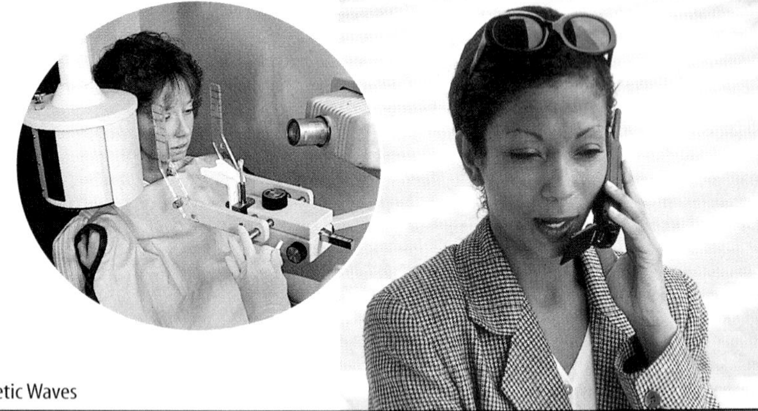

Figure 1
Getting an X ray at the dentist's office and talking on a cell phone are possible because energy is carried through space by electromagnetic waves.

Section Assessment Planner

Portfolio	Content Assessment
Science Journal, p. 375	Section, p. 378
Performance Assessment	Challenge, p. 378
Try At Home MiniLAB, p. 377	Chapter, pp. 400–401
Skill Builder Activities, p. 378	
See page 400 for more options.	

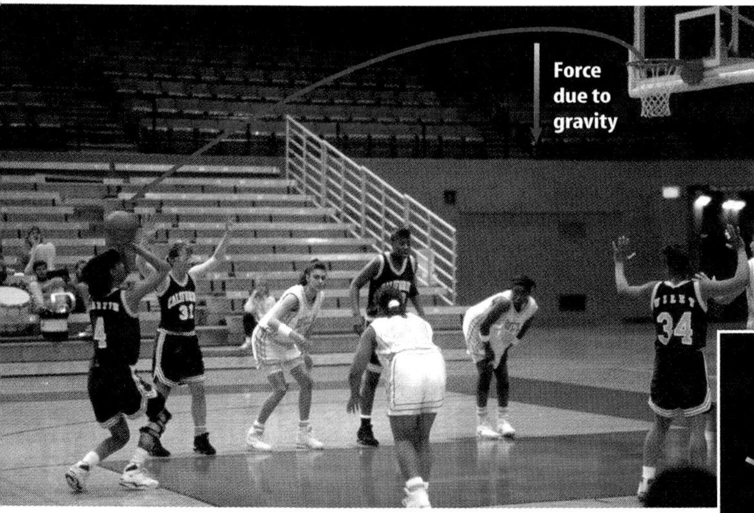

Figure 2
A gravity field surrounds all objects, such as Earth.

A When a ball is thrown, Earth's gravity field exerts a downward force on the ball at every point along the ball's path.

B Earth's gravity field extends out through space, exerting a force on all nearby masses.

Forces and Fields

An electromagnetic wave is made of two parts—an electric field and a magnetic field. These fields are force fields. Although you might wonder what a force field is, you already are familiar with one. Earth is surrounded by a force field—gravity. The gravity field surrounding Earth exerts a force on all objects.

Reading Check *What force field surrounds Earth?*

How does Earth's force field work? If you throw a ball in the air as high as you can, it always falls back to Earth. At every point along the ball's path, the force of gravity pulls down on the ball, as shown in **Figure 2A.** In fact, at every point in space above or at Earth's surface, a ball is acted on by a downward force exerted by Earth's gravity field. The force exerted by this field on a ball could be represented by a downward arrow at any point in space. **Figure 2B** shows this force field that surrounds Earth and extends out into space. In fact, it is Earth's gravity field that causes the Moon to orbit Earth.

Magnetic Fields You know that magnets repel and attract each other even when they aren't touching. Two magnets exert a force on each other when they are some distance apart because each magnet is surrounded by a force field called a magnetic field. Just as a gravity field exerts a force on a mass, a magnetic field exerts a force on another magnet. Magnetic fields cause other magnets to line up along the direction of the magnetic field.

SCIENCE Online

Research In addition to a gravity field, Earth also is surrounded by a magnetic field. Visit the Glencoe Science Web site at **science.glencoe.com** for more information about Earth's gravitational and magnetic force fields. Place the information you gather on a poster to share with your class.

2 Teach

Waves in Space

Quick Demo

Obtain at least two doughnut-shaped magnets. Arrange the magnets so that like poles face each other. Then place a pencil or other object through the holes in the magnets and hold them vertically. Have students observe and then explain the behavior of the magnets. The upper magnet seems to float in the air because of its repulsion for the magnet below it. Push the magnets together, and have students observe that when you release pressure, the magnets automatically spring apart again. L2 LS **Visual-Spatial**

Forces and Fields

Reading Check

Answer a gravity field

SCIENCE Online

Internet Addresses

Explore the Glencoe Science Web site at **science.glencoe.com** to find out more about topics in this section.

Science Journal

Aurorae Have students write paragraphs describing how Earth's magnetic field contributes to the aurora borealis and the aurora australis. Earth's magnetic field is strongest near the poles, so when charged particles from space strike the atmosphere, they are deflected toward the poles. There they cause electrical currents that excite atoms in the atmosphere, causing them to form the aurorae. L2 LS **Linguistic** P

Resource Manager

Chapter Resources Booklet
- Transparency Activity, p. 42
- Directed Reading for Content Mastery, pp. 17, 18
- Note-Taking Worksheets, pp. 31–33

Making Electromagnetic Waves

Make a Model

To help students visualize electromagnetic waves, have them make a model of one. Each student should draw or trace a sine wave on a piece of cardboard, and then draw or trace an identical sine wave on a second piece of cardboard. Have students cut the cardboard, following the outlines of the sine waves. Students should then cut one of the waves in half lengthwise and glue or tape the two halves to either side of the other wave at right angles to it. Make sure students position the waves so that the crest of a vertical wave corresponds to the crest of a horizontal wave. L2

LS **Kinesthetic**

IDENTIFYING Misconceptions

Make sure students understand that as an electromagnetic wave travels, the moving charged particle does not go with it. Only the electric field and its associated magnetic field travel through space.

Figure 3
Force fields surround all magnets and charges.

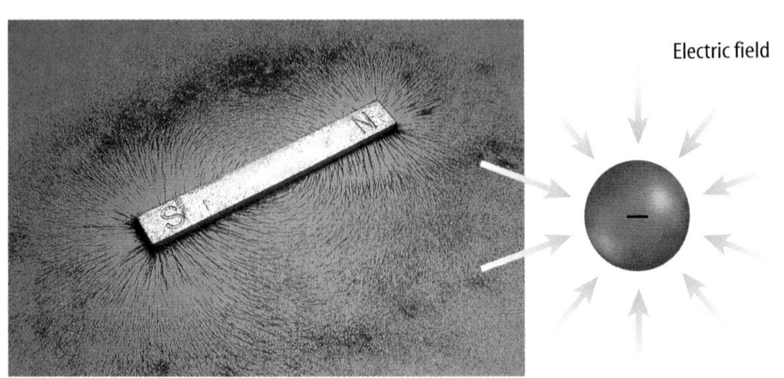

A **A magnetic field surrounds all magnets. The magnetic field exerts a force on iron filings, causing them to line up with the field.**

B **The electric field around an electric charge extends out through space, exerting forces on all nearby charged particles.**

Electric Fields Recall that atoms contain protons, neutrons, and electrons. Protons and electrons have a property called electric charge. The two types of electric charge are positive and negative. Protons have positive charge and electrons have negative charge.

Just as a magnet is surrounded by a magnetic field, a particle that has electric charge, such as a proton or an electron, is surrounded by an electric field, as shown in **Figure 3.** The electric field is a force field that exerts a force on all other charged particles that are in the field.

Making Electromagnetic Waves

An electromagnetic wave is made of electric and magnetic fields. How is such a wave produced? Think about a wave on a rope. You can make a wave on a rope by shaking one end of the rope up and down. Electromagnetic waves are produced by making charged particles, such as electrons, move back and forth, or vibrate.

A charged particle always is surrounded by an electric field. But a charged particle that is moving also is surrounded by a magnetic field. For example, when an electric current flows in a wire, electrons are moving in the wire. As a result, the wire is surrounded by a magnetic field, as shown in **Figure 4.** So a moving charged particle is surrounded by an electric field and a magnetic field.

Figure 4
Electrons moving in a wire produce a magnetic field in the surrounding space.

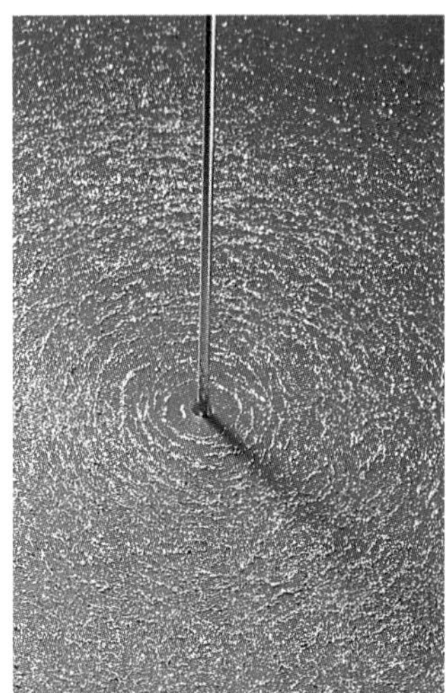

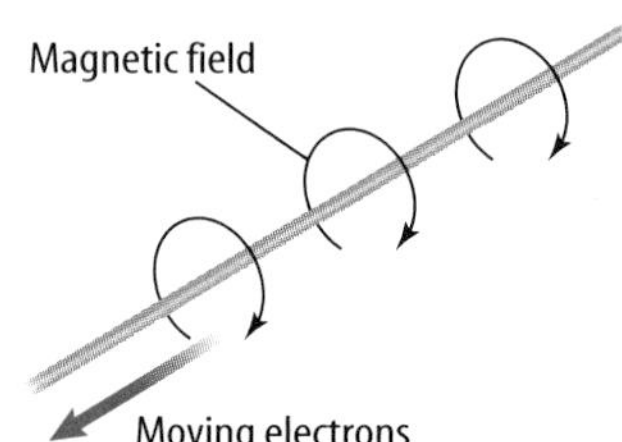

LAB DEMONSTRATION

Purpose to help students visualize the concept of a field

Materials magnet, glass or clear plastic plate, iron filings

Procedure Sprinkle iron filings on the plate. Hold the magnet beneath the plate. Gently shake the plate and have students observe what happens.

Expected Outcome The iron filings align themselves with the magnetic field to produce a map of the field.

Assessment

Why do some of the filings point straight upward? The field is pointing directly upward, or out of the plane of the plate.

Producing Waves When you shake a rope up and down, you produce a wave that moves away from your hand. Likewise, as a charged particle moves up and down, it produces electric and magnetic fields that move away from the vibrating charge. **Figure 5A** shows how these electric and magnetic fields form an electromagnetic wave.

Properties of Electromagnetic Waves

Like all waves, an electromagnetic wave has a frequency and a wavelength. When you create a wave on a rope, you move your hand up and down while holding the rope. Look at **Figure 5B.** Frequency is how many times you move the rope through one complete up and down cycle in 1 s. Wavelength is the distance from one crest to the next or from one trough to the next.

Wavelength and Frequency An electromagnetic wave is produced by a charged particle moving up and down. When the charge makes one complete vibration, one wavelength is created, as shown in **Figure 5A.** Like a wave on a rope, the frequency of an electromagnetic wave is the number of wavelengths that pass by a point in 1 s. This is the same as the number of times in 1 s that the charged particle makes one complete vibration.

TRY AT HOME Mini LAB

Observing Electric Fields

Procedure

1. Rub a **hard, plastic comb** vigorously with a **wool sweater or flannel shirt.**
2. Turn on a **water faucet** to create the smallest possible continuous stream of water.
3. Hold the comb near the stream of water and observe.

Analysis

1. What happened to the stream of water when you held the comb near it?
2. Explain why the stream of water behaved this way.
3. What part of an electromagnetic wave did you create during this activity?

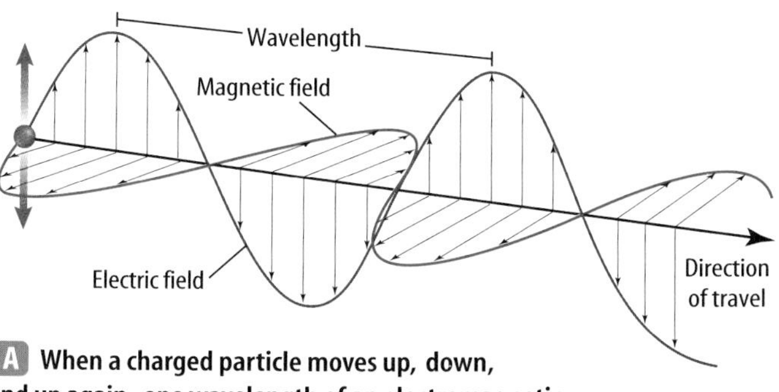

A When a charged particle moves up, down, and up again, one wavelength of an electromagnetic wave is produced.

Figure 5
Vibrations produce waves, whether they are the result of an electron moving back and forth or a hand shaking a rope up and down.

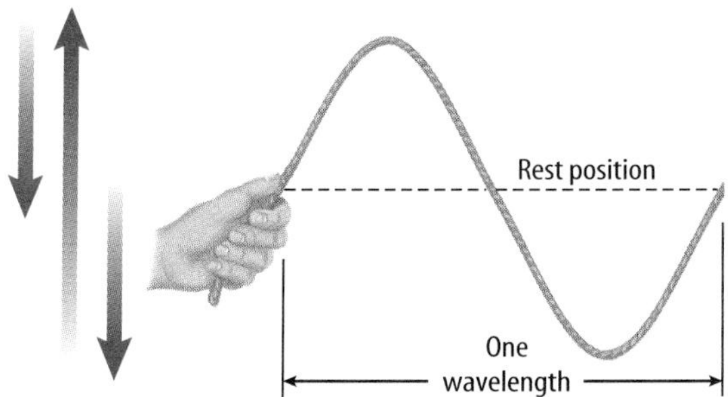

B By shaking the end of a rope down, up, and down again, you make one wavelength.

Properties of Electromagnetic Waves

TRY AT HOME Mini LAB

Purpose Students observe an electric field. L2 LS **Kinesthetic**

Materials hard plastic comb, wool sweater or flannel shirt, water faucet

Teaching Strategies

- Instruct students not to touch the stream of water with their combs.
- Instruct them to hold the comb near the water stream immediately after rubbing it with the wool or flannel.

Analysis

1. The stream of water bent toward the comb.
2. Rubbing the comb with the clothing gave it a charge and produced an electric field. The electric field of the comb attracted the water molecules, which also have a slight charge.
3. the electric field

Assessment

Oral Ask students to explain the difference between the electric field they created and the electric field of an electromagnetic wave. The electric field of an electromagnetic wave is moving, but the electric field they generated was stationary. Use **PASC,** p. 89.

Inclusion Strategies

Learning Disabled Help students visualize wave properties by asking them to use chenille stems to make models of waves. Ask them to make a high-frequency wave and a low-frequency wave. **What is the difference between the two waves?** The crests and troughs of high-frequency waves are closer to each other than those of low-frequency waves. L1 LS **Kinesthetic**

Resource Manager

Chapter Resources Booklet

Enrichment, p. 28
Reinforcement, p. 25
MiniLAB, p. 3
Directed Reading for Content Mastery, p. 18

Visual Learning

Figure 5 Review with students the locations of crests and troughs of a wave. Clarify that one wavelength is a complete vibration of one wave and can be measured from crest to crest, from trough to trough, or between any two corresponding points on a wave.

Properties of Electromagnetic Waves, continued

✔ Reading Check

Answer the energy carried by an electromagnetic wave

IDENTIFYING Misconceptions

Stress that the term *speed of light* refers to the speed at which all electromagnetic waves travel. At this speed, light given off by the Sun reaches Earth in eight minutes. An X ray traveling from the Sun to Earth also would take eight minutes.

3 Assess

Reteach

Ask volunteers to draw waves having large and small frequencies. Use the diagrams to review the parts of a wave, wavelength, and frequency. L1
LS Visual-Spatial

Challenge

Light from the Sun takes eight minutes to reach Earth. Use the speed of light to calculate the distance between Earth and the Sun. $D = t \times v = (300{,}000 \text{ km/s}) \times (480 \text{ s}) = 144{,}000{,}000 \text{ km}$. L3
LS Logical-Mathematical

✔ Assessment

Content Ask students to write paragraphs describing what a force field is. Ask them to give an example of a force field they have seen or experienced. Possible answer: a magnetic field such as that observed in the Lab Demonstration Use **PASC,** p. 159.

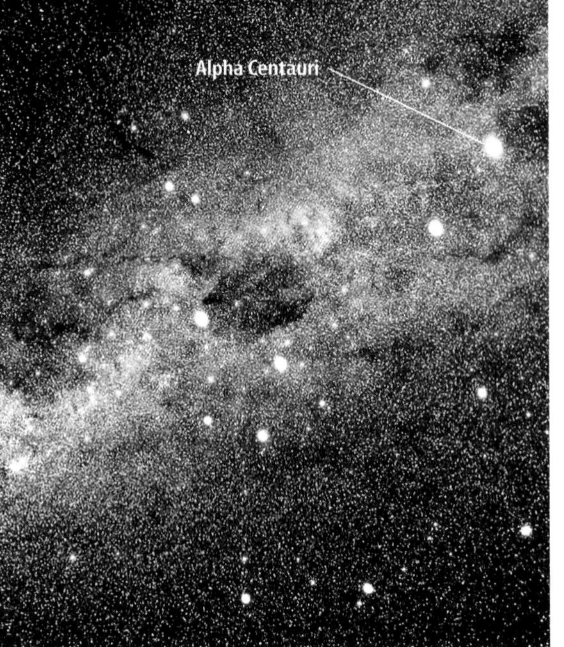

Figure 6
The light you see today from Alpha Centauri left the star more than four years ago.

Radiant Energy The energy carried by an electromagnetic wave is called **radiant energy.** What happens if an electromagnetic wave strikes another charged particle? The electric field part of the wave exerts a force on this particle and causes it to move. Some of the radiant energy carried by the wave is transferred into the energy of motion of the particle.

✔ Reading Check *What is radiant energy?*

The amount of energy that electromagnetic waves carry is determined by the wave's frequency. The higher the frequency of the electromagnetic wave is, the more energy it has.

The Speed of Light All electromagnetic waves, such as light, microwaves, and X rays, travel through space at the same speed. This speed has been measured as 300,000 km/s in space. Because light is an electromagnetic wave, this speed sometimes is called the speed of light. Electromagnetic waves travel so fast that they could travel around the world more than seven times in 1 s. Even though light travels incredibly fast, it still takes years for light from the stars, other than the sun, to reach Earth. **Figure 6** shows the closest star to the solar system, Alpha Centauri. This star is so far away that the light it emits takes more than four years to reach Earth.

Section  Assessment

1. What is an electromagnetic wave?
2. How are electromagnetic waves produced?
3. What two fields surround a moving charged particle?
4. How does the amount of energy carried by a low-frequency wave compare to the amount carried by a high-frequency wave?
5. **Think Critically** Unlike sound waves, electromagnetic waves can travel through a vacuum. What observations can you make to support this statement?

Skill Builder Activities

6. **Comparing and Contrasting** How are electromagnetic waves similar to mechanical waves? How are they different? **For more help, refer to the Science Skill Handbook.**
7. **Calculating Ratios** To go from Earth to Mars, light takes 4 min whereas a spacecraft takes four months. To go to the nearest star, light takes four years. How long would the same spacecraft take to travel to the nearest star? **For more help, refer to the Math Skill Handbook.**

Answers to Section Assessment

1. a wave that can travel through empty space and that is produced by charged particles in motion
2. by charged particles in motion
3. electric fields and magnetic fields
4. A high-frequency wave carries more energy than a low-frequency wave.
5. Possible answers include that light reaches Earth from the Sun.
6. Both mechanical waves and electromagnetic waves carry energy. Mechanical waves require matter through which to travel, but electromagnetic waves don't.
7. The spaceship travels in one month as far as light travels in one minute. There are approximately 43,200 minutes in one month, so it takes the spaceship 43,200 times as long to travel a given distance as it takes light. It would take the ship 172,800 years to reach the nearest star.

378 CHAPTER 13 Electromagnetic Waves

SECTION 2

The Electromagnetic Spectrum

Electromagnetic Waves

The room you are sitting in is bathed in a sea of electromagnetic waves. These electromagnetic waves have a wide range of wavelengths and frequencies. For example, waves with wavelengths from 1 m to 500 m—called radio waves—pass through the walls and windows from distant radio and television broadcast antennas. Other electromagnetic waves—called visible light—have wavelengths more than a million times shorter than radio waves. They are streaming from every object you see.

Classifying Electromagnetic Waves The wide range of electromagnetic waves with different frequencies and wavelengths is called the **electromagnetic spectrum. Figure 7** shows the electromagnetic spectrum. Though many different types of electromagnetic waves exist, they are produced by electric charges that are moving or vibrating. The faster the charge moves or vibrates, the higher the energy of the resulting electromagnetic waves is. Each electromagnetic wave carries radiant energy that increases as the frequency increases. For waves that travel with the same speed, the wavelength increases as frequency decreases. So the energy carried by an electromagnetic wave decreases as the wavelength increases.

As You Read

***What* You'll Learn**

- **Explain** differences among kinds of electromagnetic waves.
- **Identify** uses for different kinds of electromagnetic waves.

Vocabulary

electromagnetic spectrum, radio wave, infrared wave, visible light, ultraviolet radiation, X ray, gamma ray

***Why* It's Important**

Electromagnetic waves are used to cook food, to send and receive information, and to diagnose medical problems.

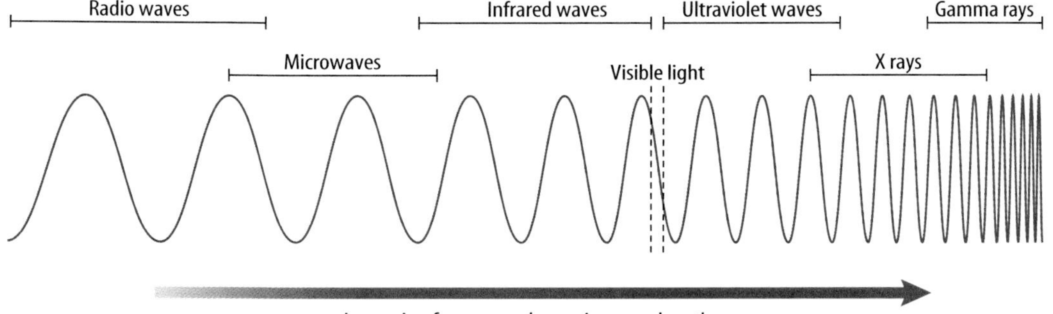

Figure 7
Electromagnetic waves have a spectrum of different frequencies.

Section Assessment Planner

PORTFOLIO
Extension, p. 383

PERFORMANCE ASSESSMENT
MiniLAB, p. 381
Skill Builder Activities, p. 387
See page 400 for more options.

CONTENT ASSESSMENT
Section, p. 387
Challenge, p. 387
Chapter, pp. 400–401

SECTION 2

The Electromagnetic Spectrum

1 Motivate

Bellringer Transparency

Display the Section Focus Transparency for Section 2. Use the accompanying Transparency Activity Master. L2 ELL

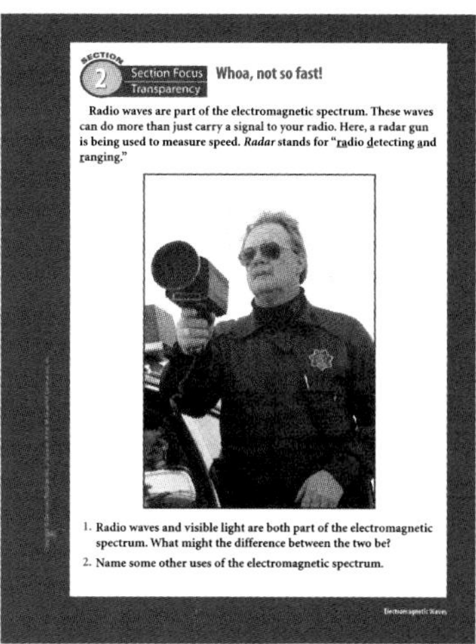

Section 2 Section Focus Transparency **Whoa, not so fast!**

Radio waves are part of the electromagnetic spectrum. These waves can do more than just carry a signal to your radio. Here, a radar gun is being used to measure speed. *Radar* stands for "radio detecting and ranging."

1. **Radio waves and visible light are both part of the electromagnetic spectrum. What might the difference between the two be?**
2. **Name some other uses of the electromagnetic spectrum.**

Electromagnetic Waves

Tie to Prior Knowledge

Ask students whether they have microwave ovens in their homes. Discuss what a microwave is. Then challenge students to explain what the prefix *micro-* refers to. It refers to the fact that the wavelengths of microwaves are smaller than those of radio or TV waves.

Resource Manager

Chapter Resources Booklet
Transparency Activity, p. 43
Directed Reading for Content Mastery, p.18

2 Teach

Electromagnetic Waves

Visual Learning

Figure 7 Point out the wide range of the electromagnetic spectrum. Explain that although humans are able to naturally perceive only the small sliver of the spectrum known as visible light, many instruments are able to observe the other areas. Ask a volunteer to read the names of the parts of the electromagnetic spectrum, from lowest frequency to highest. L1 LS **Visual-Spatial**

Radio Waves

Extension

Ask students whether they ever have lost the signal of a radio station while traveling in a car. Have them find out whether AM or FM signals travel farther and why. FM waves are shorter than AM waves, so are easily blocked by the horizon and by objects. AM waves ricochet off the atmosphere and bounce back to Earth, and thus reach a larger distance. L2

Use Science Words

Word Origins The word *radio* is short for *radiotelegraph*. Ask students to break *radiotelegraph* into its parts, find the meaning of each part, and explain what the parts combine to mean. The prefix *radi-* means "radiant energy "or" radiation," and comes from the Latin word *radius,* meaning "ray." *Tele-* is from the Greek word *tele,* meaning "far away." The suffix *-graph* is from the Greek *graphein,* meaning "to write." A radiotelegraph is a device that transmits or receives communication over a distance by means of radiation. L3 LS **Linguistic**

Figure 8
Antennas are useful in generating and detecting radio waves.

A Vibrating electrons in an antenna produce radio waves.

B Radio waves can vibrate electrons in an antenna.

Radio Waves

Electromagnetic waves with wavelengths longer than about 0.1 m are called radio waves. **Radio waves** have the lowest frequencies of all the electromagnetic waves and carry the least energy. Television signals, as well as AM and FM radio signals, are types of radio waves. Like all electromagnetic waves, radio waves are produced by moving charged particles. One way to make radio waves is to make electrons vibrate up and down in a piece of metal, as shown in **Figure 8A.** This piece of metal is called a transmitting antenna. By changing the rate at which the electrons vibrate, radio waves of different frequencies can be produced that travel outward from the antenna.

Detecting Radio Waves These radio waves can cause electrons in another piece of metal, such as another antenna, to move up and down, as shown in **Figure 8B.** As the electrons in the receiving antenna move up and down, they form an alternating current. This alternating current can be used to produce sound from a loudspeaker. Music, television shows, and telephone signals can be sent with radio waves using a transmitting antenna and a receiving antenna.

Microwaves Radio waves with wavelengths between about 0.1 m and 0.001 m (one tenth and one thousandth of a meter) are called microwaves. They have a higher frequency and a shorter wavelength than the waves that are used in your home radio. Microwaves are used to transmit some phone calls, especially from cellular and portable phones. **Figure 9** shows a microwave tower.

Microwave ovens use microwaves to heat food. The radiant energy streaming through a microwave oven causes water molecules in your food to vibrate faster, which heats the food.

Figure 9
Towers such as the one shown here are used to send and receive microwaves.

Resource Manager

Chapter Resources Booklet
MiniLAB, p. 4
Lab Activity, pp. 9–11

Earth Science Critical Thinking/Problem Solving, pp. 8, 13

Radio Frequencies Have students examine radios they have at home and record the range of frequencies spanned by AM and FM bands. Ask students to determine if AM and FM overlap anywhere, and have them record their findings in their Science Journals. AM stations broadcast in kilohertz (KHz) and FM stations broadcast in megahertz (MHz). The bands do not overlap. L2 LS **Linguistic**

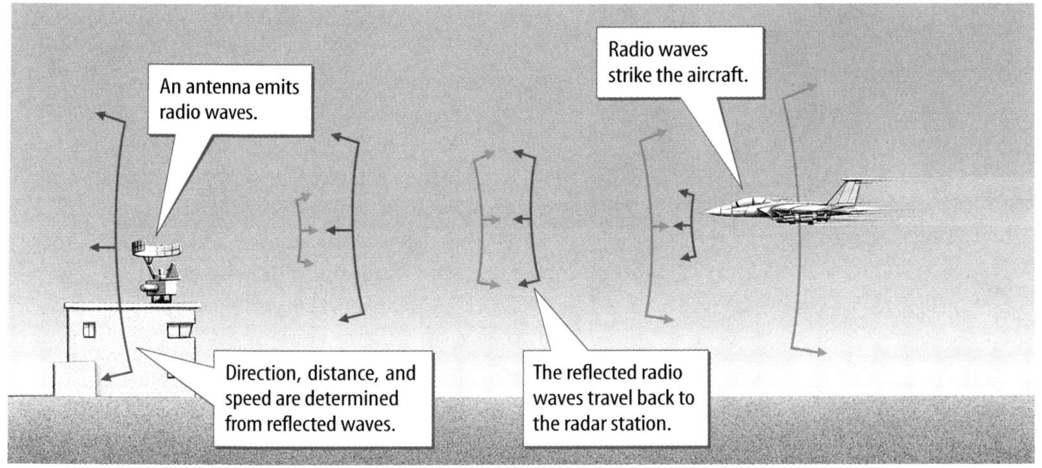
An antenna emits radio waves.
Radio waves strike the aircraft.
Direction, distance, and speed are determined from reflected waves.
The reflected radio waves travel back to the radar station.

Figure 10
Radar stations determine direction, distance, and speed of aircraft.

Radar You might be familiar with echolocation, in which sound waves are reflected off an object to determine its size and location. Some bats and dolphins use echolocation to navigate and hunt. Radar, an acronym for RAdio Detection And Ranging, uses electromagnetic waves to detect objects in the same way. Radar was developed during World War II to detect and warn of incoming enemy aircraft.

Reading Check *What does radar do?*

A radar station sends out radio waves that bounce off an object such as an airplane. Electronic equipment measures the time it takes for the radio waves to travel to the plane, be reflected, and return. Because the speed of the radio waves is known, the distance to the airplane can be calculated from the following formula.

$$\text{distance} = \text{speed} \times \text{time}$$

An example of radar being used is shown in **Figure 10.** Because electromagnetic waves travel so quickly, the entire process takes only a fraction of a second.

Infrared Waves

You might know from experience that when you stand near the glowing coals of a barbecue or the red embers of a campfire, your skin senses the heat and becomes warm. Your skin may also feel warm near a hot object that is not glowing. The heat you are sensing with your skin is from electromagnetic waves. These electromagnetic waves are called **infrared waves** and have wavelengths between one thousandth and 0.7 millionths of a meter.

Mini LAB

Observing the Focusing of Infrared Rays

Procedure
1. Place a **concave mirror** 2 m to 3 m away from an **electric heater.** Turn on the heater.
2. Place the palm of your hand in front of the mirror and move it back until you feel heat on your palm. Note the location of the warm area.
3. Move the heater to a new location. Where does the warm area move? Where does the visual image move?

Analysis
1. Did you observe the warm area? Where?
2. Compare the location of the warm area to the location of the visual image.

Teacher FYI

Ice is transparent to radar waves, but rock is not. Thus the thickness of the Antarctic ice sheet can be measured by reflecting radar waves from the bedrock below the ice sheet. By measuring the time it takes for a wave to travel through the ice and return to the surface, the ice's thickness can be calculated.

Reading Check

Answer Radar sends out radio waves that reflect off objects and return to the sender, who uses them to determine the size and location of the objects they hit.

Extension

Have interested students find out what Doppler radar is and how it differs from conventional radar. Doppler radar processes the shift in the frequency of a wave as it moves toward or away from the observer. L3 **LS Linguistic**

Infrared Waves

Purpose Students observe the effects of electromagnetic waves. L2 ELL **LS Kinesthetic**

Materials concave mirror, electric heater, metric ruler

Teaching Strategy Suggest students work in pairs, so as one moves the heater the other can find the hot spot.

Safety Precautions Caution students not to leave the heater on and unattended.

Analysis
1. The location of the hot spot will depend on the focal length of the mirror.
2. The visual image appears to be on the surface of the mirror, and the hot spot is above the mirror.

Process Ask each student to draw a diagram showing what happens to the infrared rays after they hit the mirror. Use **PASC,** p. 127.

Infrared Waves, continued

Activity

Provide students with a remote control that uses infrared radiation and a working television or other appliance that can be operated with the remote. Have students try to use the remote to operate the appliance when a solid object is between the remote and the appliance. Then have students bounce the beam off a mirror to operate the appliance. L2 ELL

LS **Visual-Spatial**

Fun Fact

Cameras with auto-focus capabilities typically use infrared beams that are reflected off the intended photographic target. These data provide the camera with a distance so that it can accurately focus the image.

Visible Light

Identifying Misconceptions

Students may think that visible light is very different from other electromagnetic waves such as X rays. See page 372F for teaching strategies that address this misconception.

Figure 11
A pit viper hunting in the dark can detect the infrared waves that the warm body of its prey emits.

Detecting Infrared Waves Infrared rays are emitted by almost every object. In any material the atoms and molecules are in constant motion. Electrons in the atoms and molecules also move and vibrate. As a result, they give off electromagnetic waves. Most of the electromagnetic waves given off by an object at room temperature are infrared waves and have a wavelength of about 0.000 01 m, or one hundred thousandth of a meter.

Infrared detectors detect objects that are warmer or colder than their environment. They can be used to map wildfires obscured by smoke or to survey underground volcanic activity. Infrared waves also are used to carry signals in some electronics devices, just as radio waves do. Remote controls for TVs and VCRs use infrared rays.

Animals and Infrared Waves Because they are warm, all living things emit infrared radiation. Some animals can detect infrared radiation directly. Piranhas, for example, can see into the infrared, which helps them find prey in the murky Amazon River. Pit vipers, such as rattlesnakes, have special organs just under their eyes that detect changes in infrared waves, as shown in **Figure 11.** If warm prey, such as a mouse, is nearby, the snake can sense and track it, even in the dark.

Visible Light

As the temperature of an object increases, the atoms and molecules move faster. The electrons also move and vibrate faster, and give off electromagnetic waves of higher frequency and shorter wavelength. If the temperature is high enough, the object might glow, as in **Figure 12.** The electromagnetic waves the hot object is emitting are now detectable with your eyes and are called **visible light.** Visible light has wavelengths between about 0.7 and 0.4 millionths of a meter. What you see as different colors are electromagnetic waves of different wavelengths. Red light has the longest wavelength (lowest frequency), and blue light has the shortest wavelength (highest frequency).

Most objects that you see do not give off visible light. They simply reflect the visible light that is emitted by a source of light, such as the Sun or a lightbulb. Some light sources give off visible light because they are at a high temperature.

Figure 12
When objects are heated, their electrons vibrate faster. With enough energy, the vibrating electrons will emit visible light.

Teacher FYI

Sir Isaac Newton suggested that light is composed of many colors mixed together. Newton separated white light into colors with a prism to support his hypothesis. His ideas were later published in his work *Opticks.*

Resource Manager

Chapter Resources Booklet
Reinforcement, p. 26
Cultural Diversity, p. 51

Inclusion Strategies

Gifted Have students find out how different kinds of night vision systems work and present their findings to the class. Most night vision systems amplify the small amount of light that already exists. However, some systems make it possible to see infrared even when there is no visible light at all. Infrared light also can be used as an illuminator or flashlight to see objects in total darkness. L3 LS **Linguistic**

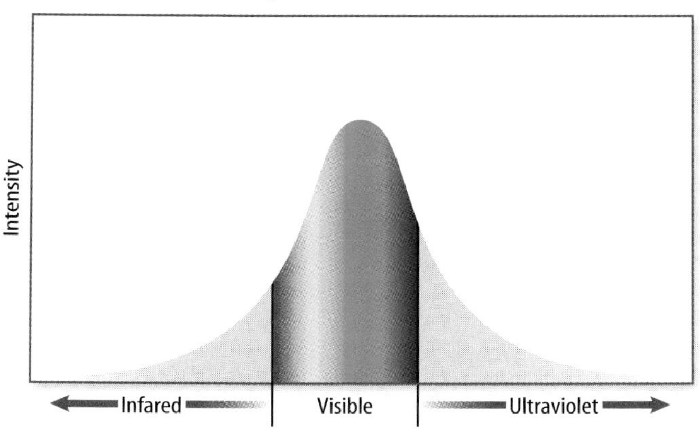

Figure 13
Electromagnetic waves from the Sun have a range of frequencies centered about the visible region. *Which frequencies of light is the Sun brightest in?*

Ultraviolet Radiation

Ultraviolet radiation is higher in frequency than visible light and has even shorter wavelengths—between 0.4 millionths of a meter and one billionth of a meter. Ultraviolet radiation has higher frequencies than visible light and carries more energy. The radiant energy carried by an ultraviolet wave can be enough to damage the large, fragile molecules that make up living cells. Too much ultraviolet radiation can damage or kill healthy cells.

Figure 13 shows the electromagnetic waves emitted by the Sun, some of which are in the ultraviolet region. Too much exposure to those ultraviolet waves can cause sunburn. Exposure to these waves over a long period of time can lead to early aging of the skin and possibly skin cancer. You can protect yourself from receiving too much ultraviolet radiation by wearing sunglasses and sunscreen, and staying out of the Sun when it is most intense.

Figure 14
Sterilizing devices, such as this goggle sterilizer, use ultraviolet waves to kill organisms on the equipment.

Beneficial Uses of UV Radiation A few minutes of exposure each day to ultraviolet radiation from the Sun enables your body to produce the vitamin D it needs. Most people receive that amount during normal activity. The body's natural defense against too much ultraviolet radiation is to tan. However, a tan can be a sign that overexposure to ultraviolet radiation has occurred.

Ultraviolet radiation's cell-killing effect has led to its use as a disinfectant for surgical equipment in hospitals. In some high school chemistry labs, ultraviolet rays are used to sterilize goggles, as shown in **Figure 14.**

Science Journal

SPF Have students investigate different types of sunscreens and report on what SPF numbers mean. Ask students to determine which sunscreen is best for their individual skin types and write their findings in their Science Journals. SPF means sun protection factor. It is an indication of how much longer you can stay in the sun without burning than you could without a sunscreen with that SPF. L2 LS **Intrapersonal**

Ultraviolet Radiation

Caption Answer

Figure 13 visible

Extension

Ultraviolet radiation is made up of two types, UVA and UVB. Both types can contribute to skin cancer and sunburn. Ask students to find out what UVA and UVB are and what each type of UV radiation does. Have them make miniposters illustrating their findings. UVA is UV radiation with wavelengths of 320–400 nanometers. UVA penetrates the skin more deeply than UVB does and is mostly responsible for wrinkling and leathering of the skin. UVA also may directly cause some skin cancers. UVB is UV radiation with wavelengths of 290–320 nanometers. UVB produces sunburn and is considered the main cause of skin cancer. L2 LS **Visual-Spatial** P

Teacher FYI

Sunscreens chemically absorb UV rays, and sunblocks physically deflect them. Sunscreen blocks higher frequency UVB radiation effectively but provides less UVA protection. The Skin Cancer Foundation recommends that people use sunscreen with an SPF of at least 15, which blocks 93 percent of UVB.

Use Science Words

Word Meaning Ask students to look in a dictionary to find the meanings of the prefixes *infra-* and *ultra-*. Have them then explain why these prefixes are used in the terms infrared and ultraviolet. The prefix *infra-* means "below," and the prefix *ultra-* means "situated beyond." Infrared means "below red," and ultraviolet means "situated beyond violet." L2 LS **Linguistic**

Ultraviolet Radiation, continued

Life Science INTEGRATION

Since warm-blooded animals make their own body heat, they don't have to rely on their environment to maintain their temperature and can inhabit a wide range of climates. However, warm-blooded animals spend a large amount of energy maintaining their body temperatures, so they need to eat a large amount of food. Cold-blooded animals don't expend energy to heat their bodies, so they need to eat less food. Pit vipers would have an easier time detecting warm-blooded animals.

X Rays and Gamma Rays

Use an Analogy

Compare the role of sunscreen to that of the ozone layer. Point out that just as sunscreen blocks some ultraviolet radiation from the skin and prevents burning, the ozone layer blocks some ultraviolet radiation from reaching Earth's surface, where it could be harmful to the cells of living things. Without the ozone shield, there probably would be very little life on Earth.

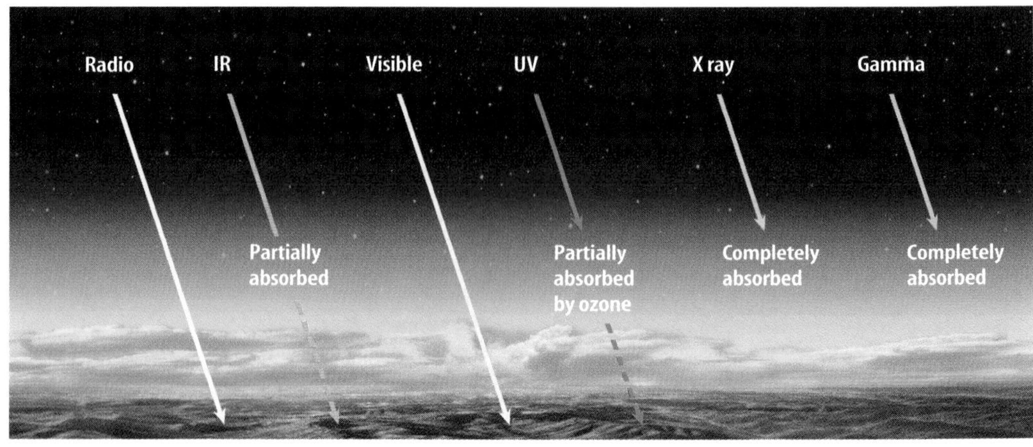

Figure 15
Earth's atmosphere serves as a shield to block certain types of electromagnetic waves from reaching the surface.

Life Science INTEGRATION

Warm-blooded animals, such as mammals, produce their own body heat. Cold-blooded animals, such as reptiles, absorb heat from the environment. Brainstorm the possible advantages of being either warm-blooded or cold-blooded. Which animals would be easier for a pit viper to detect?

The Ozone Layer Much of the ultraviolet radiation arriving at Earth is absorbed in the upper atmosphere by the ozone layer, as shown in **Figure 15.** Ozone is a molecule that has three oxygen atoms and is formed high in Earth's atmosphere.

However, chemical compounds called CFCs, which are used in air conditioners and refrigerators, can react chemically with ozone. This reaction causes ozone to break down and increases the amount of ultraviolet radiation that penetrates the atmosphere. To prevent this, the use of CFCs is being phased out.

Ultraviolet radiation is not the only type of electromagnetic wave absorbed by Earth's atmosphere. Higher energy waves of X rays and gamma rays also are absorbed. The atmosphere is transparent to radio waves and visible light and partially transparent to infrared waves.

X Rays and Gamma Rays

Ultraviolet rays can penetrate the top layer of your skin. **X rays,** with an even higher frequency than ultraviolet rays, have enough energy to go right through skin and muscle. Heavy lead metal is required to stop the penetrating power of X rays.

Gamma rays have the highest frequency and, therefore, the most penetrating power. They are produced by changes in the nuclei of atoms. When protons and neutrons bond together in nuclear fusion or break apart from each other in nuclear fission, enormous quantities of energy are released. Some of this energy is released as gamma rays.

Just as too much ultraviolet radiation can hurt or kill cells, too much X ray or gamma radiation can have the same effect. Because the energy of the waves is so much higher, the exposure that is needed to cause damage is much less.

Resource Manager

Reading and Writing Skill Activities, p. 25

Curriculum Connection

Math X rays were discovered accidentally by Wilhelm Roentgen in 1895. Because they were a mystery and x is the usual symbol for an unknown in mathematics, they were named X rays. Have students find out what the unit named for Roentgen measures and what other units are used to make similar measurements. Radioactivity is measured in roentgens. The curie and the gray also measure radioactivity.

384 CHAPTER 13 Electromagnetic Waves

Using High-Energy Electromagnetic Radiation The fact that X rays can pass through the human body makes them good for medical diagnosis, as shown in **Figure 16.** X rays pass through the less dense tissues in skin and other organs. These X rays strike a film, creating a shadow image of the denser tissues.

Although the radiation received from getting one medical or dental X ray is not harmful, the cumulative effect of numerous X rays can be dangerous. Doctors therefore try to avoid giving too many X rays. Lead shields or aprons, which protect the internal organs in your body, are used by anyone in the room who is not receiving the X ray. Lead is dense enough to absorb X rays, so they do not pass through the apron into the body. The patient also wears an apron if it will not interfere with the X ray such as when getting a dental X ray.

Using Gamma Rays X rays can harm, but gamma rays can kill. However, gamma rays have beneficial uses, just as X rays do. A beam of gamma rays focused on a cancerous tumor can kill the tumor. Gamma radiation also can cleanse food of disease-causing bacteria. More than 1,500 Americans die each year from *Salmonella* bacteria in poultry and *E. coli* bacteria in meat. Although gamma radiation has been used since 1963 to kill bacteria in food, this method is not widely used in the food insustry.

Figure 16
Dense tissues such as bone absorb more X rays than do softer tissues. Consequently, dense tissues leave a shadow on film that can be use to diagnose medical and dental conditions.

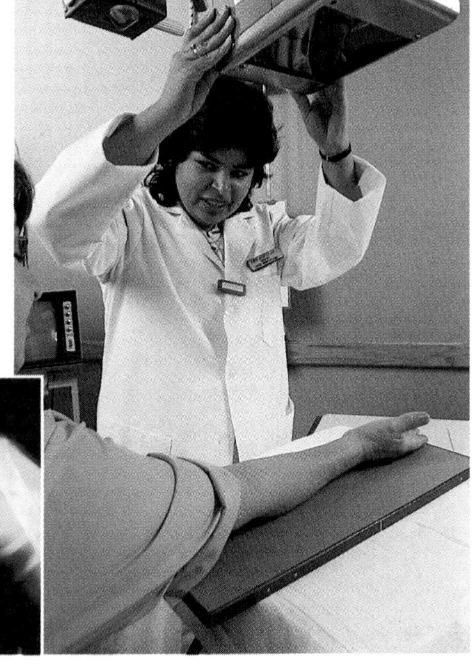

Astronomy Across the Spectrum

Some astronomical objects produce no visible light and are known only through infrared and radio images. Some galaxies emit X rays from regions that do not emit visible light. Studying astronomy using only visible light would be like looking at only one color in a picture. **Figure 17** shows how different electromagnetic waves can be used to study the universe.

IDENTIFYING Misconceptions

Students often will associate any use of the word *radiation* incorrectly with nuclear connotations. Point out that gamma rays can result from nuclear changes. However, none of the other types of electromagnetic radiation studied in this chapter are associated with nuclear decay.

Visual Learning

Figure 16 After students have examined the images and read the caption, have them identify which of the following tissues would show up most clearly on an X-ray photograph—the teeth or the tongue. Why? The teeth would show up more clearly because they are more dense than the tongue. L2 **Logical-Mathematical**

Astronomy Across the Spectrum

Extension

Have students find out what spectroscopy is and some of its uses. Ask them to make multimedia presentations of their findings to the class. Spectroscopy is the study of how electromagnetic radiation interacts with matter. Spectroscopic studies can be used to identify the substances that make up objects, including stars and other bodies in space. L3 **Linguistic**

Active Reading

Jigsaw In this collaborative learning technique, individuals become experts on a portion of a text and share their expertise with a small group, called their home group. Everyone shares the responsibility for learning the assigned reading. Assign each person in each group an expert number (1 through 5, for example). Have students gather into the expert groups that correspond to the number they were assigned. Have them read, discuss, and master chapter concepts and determine how best to teach these concepts to their home groups. Have students return to their home groups and share the content they learned in their expert groups. Have students use the Jigsaw strategy as they learn about different types of electromagnetic waves.

Visualizing the Universe

Have students examine the pictures and read the captions. Then ask the following questions.

Why have astronomers only recently studied wavelengths other than visible light? Possible answer: Detecting these different types of waves requires advanced technologies that were not always available.

Why might the sun or other celestial objects look different when various types of waves are being detected? Possible answer: While an object may be a strong emitter of one type of wave, it may not emit another type. Dust, atmosphere, or other objects may block out certain wavelengths too.

Activity

Have students look at photographs of various celestial objects from a variety of different types of telescopes. Have students locate the type of wavelength used for each photograph on the electromagnetic spectrum. L2 LS **Visual-Spatial**

Extension

Have students search for astronomical pictures that are made from wavelengths other than visible light. Students should prepare a presentation for their class using their photographs. L2 LS **Visual-Spatial**

Figure 17

For centuries, astronomers studied the universe using only the visible light coming from planets, moons, and stars. But many objects in space also emit X rays, ultraviolet and infrared radiation, and radio waves. Scientists now use telescopes that can "see" these different types of electromagnetic waves. As these images of the Sun reveal, the new tools are providing remarkable views of objects in the universe.

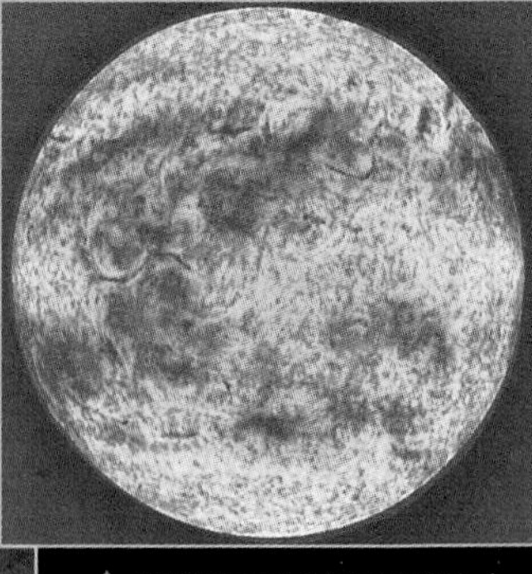

▲ INFRARED RADIATION **An infrared telescope reveals that the Sun's surface temperature is not uniform. Some areas are hotter than others.**

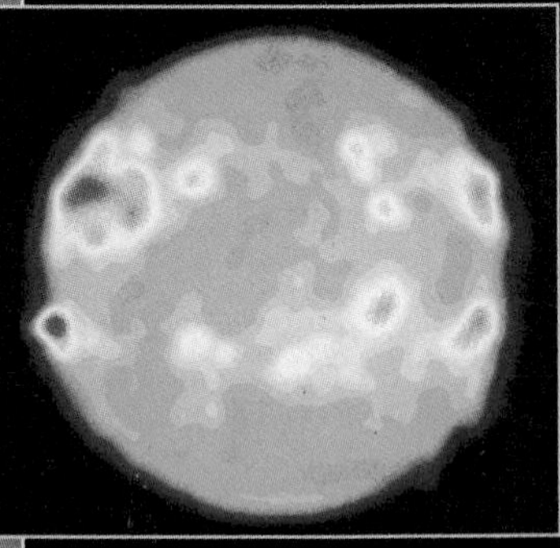

▲ RADIO WAVES **Radio telescopes detect radio waves given off by the Sun, which have much longer wavelengths than visible light.**

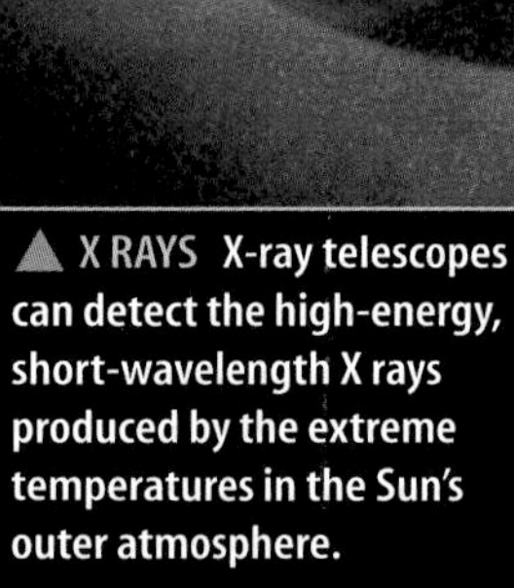

▲ X RAYS **X-ray telescopes can detect the high-energy, short-wavelength X rays produced by the extreme temperatures in the Sun's outer atmosphere.**

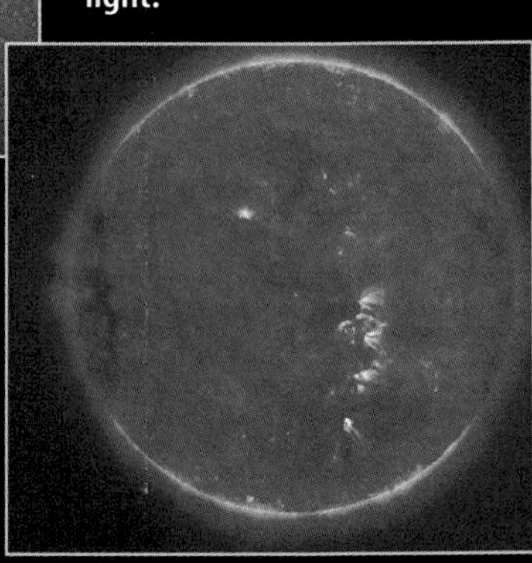

▶ ULTRAVIOLET RADIATION **Telescopes sensitive to ultraviolet radiation—electromagnetic waves with shorter wavelengths than visible light—can "see" the Sun's outer atmosphere.**

Resource Manager

Chapter Resources Booklet
Enrichment, p. 29

Figure 18
Launching satellite observatories above Earth's atmosphere is the only way to see the universe at electromagnetic wavelengths that are absorbed by Earth's atmosphere.

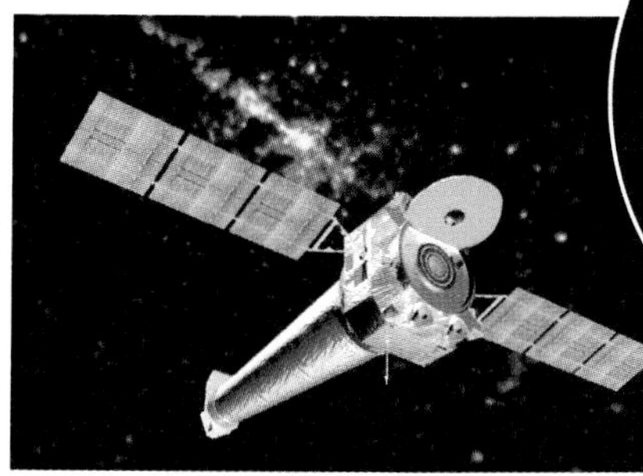

Satellite Observations Recall from **Figure 15** that Earth's atmosphere blocks many parts of the electromagnetic spectrum. For example, X rays, gamma rays, most ultraviolet rays, and some infrared rays cannot pass through. This is one reason for placing telescopes on satellites. An X-ray image of the galaxy taken from space collects much more information than one taken from Earth's surface. **Figure 18** shows three such satellites—the Extreme Ultraviolet Explorer (EUVE), the Chandra X-Ray Observatory, and the Infrared Space Observatory (ISO).

Why are telescopes sent into space on artificial satellites?

Section  2 Assessment

1. List three types of electromagnetic waves produced by the Sun.
2. Why is ultraviolet light more damaging to cells than infrared light is?
3. Give an application of infrared waves.
4. Describe the difference between X rays and gamma rays.
5. **Think Critically** How is the atmosphere absorbing electromagnetic waves like the process that occurs in a microwave oven?

Skill Builder Activities

6. **Recognizing Cause and Effect** If visible light is the effect, what is the cause? Do the different colors of light have different causes? **For more help, refer to the Science Skill Handbook.**
7. **Using a Database** What do images of the same object look like in different wavelengths? Use a database to research this topic and present a report to your class. **For more help, refer to the Technology Skill Handbook.**

Astronomy Across the Spectrum, continued

Reading Check

Answer to detect wavelengths of electromagnetic radiation that are blocked by the atmosphere

3 Assess

Reteach

Ask students to draw diagrams of the electromagnetic spectrum, labeling the electromagnetic waves studied in this section. In order of increasing frequency, the waves studied are AM radio waves, FM radio waves, microwaves, infrared waves, visible light waves, ultraviolet waves, X rays, and gamma waves. L2
LS **Visual-Spatial**

Challenge

Why couldn't radio waves, infrared waves, or visible light be used to kill a cancerous tumor? These low-frequency waves don't carry enough energy to kill living cells. L2 LS **Logical-Mathematical**

Assessment

Content Organize the class into groups, and have each group make a four-page pamphlet describing the basic characteristics and uses of one of the types of waves studied. Use **Performance Assessment in the Science Classroom,** p. 169.

Answers to Section Assessment

1. ultraviolet radiation, visible light, radio waves
2. It has a higher frequency and more energy, so it can penetrate the skin.
3. Possible answer: Pit vipers use infrared waves to sense their prey in the dark.
4. Gamma rays have a higher frequency and more energy than X rays.
5. In a microwave oven molecules of water absorb energy from microwaves, which makes the molecules move faster and heat up. In the atmosphere molecules absorb energy from electromagnetic waves, which makes the molecules move faster and heat up.
6. Charges moving and radiating energy cause light. Yes; each color is caused by charges moving at a different frequency.
7. Students should find that objects appear to be different colors in different-colored light.

Activity

BENCH TESTED

Purpose Students observe that light is composed of various colors or frequencies. L2

LS **Visual-Spatial**

Process Skills observing, inferring, recognizing cause and effect, formulating models

Time Required 40 minutes

Safety Precautions Caution students to be careful not to break the glass slides.

Teaching Strategy The prism may need to be moved around to produce a spectrum.

Answers to Questions

1. red, orange, yellow, green, blue, indigo, violet
2. The water in the air acts like a prism.
3. droplets of water
4. refraction, or the bending of light as it passes from one medium to another
5. Infrared light is just beyond red, and ultraviolet is just past violet.

Process Have students hypothesize about the role of the water in the prism. Then have them test their hypotheses by removing the water and seeing the effect this has on the spectrum. The water makes the different colors separate more. Without the water, the spectrum is harder to see. Use **Performance Assessment in the Science Classroom,** p. 97.

Activity

Prisms of Light

Do you know what light is? Many would answer that light is what you turn on to see at night. However, visible light is made of many different frequencies of the electromagnetic spectrum. A prism can separate visible light into its different frequencies. You see different frequencies of light as different colors. What colors do you see when light passes through a prism?

What You'll Investigate

What happens to visible light as it passes through a prism?

Goals

- **Construct** a prism and observe the different colors that are produced.
- **Infer** how the order of the colors corresponds to the electromagnetic spectrum.

Materials

microscope slides (3)
transparent tape
clay
flashlight
water

Safety Precautions

Procedure

1. Carefully tape the three slides together on their long sides so they form a long prism.
2. Place one end of the prism into a softened piece of clay so the prism is standing upright.
3. Fill the prism with water and put it on a table that is against a dark wall.
4. Shine a flashlight beam through the prism so the light becomes visible on the wall.

Conclude and Apply

1. What was the order of the colors you saw on the wall?
2. **Infer** how a rainbow is created in nature without the use of a prism.
3. What in nature acts similar to a prism to separate visible light?
4. The range of colors, called the spectrum, that you see through the prism is a result of what property of light?
5. The human eye responds best to the green and yellow hues that are found in the middle of the spectrum. Based on the spectrum that is emitted from your prism, infer where infrared light and ultraviolet light are positioned on the electromagnetic spectrum.

Communicating Your Data

Compare your conclusions with those of other students in your class. **For more help, refer to the Science Skill Handbook.**

Communicating Your Data

Have each student make a labeled diagram that illustrates the procedure and results of the experiment.

Resource Manager

Chapter Resources Booklet
Activity Worksheet, pp. 5–6

388 CHAPTER 13 Electromagnetic Waves

SECTION

Using Electromagnetic Waves

Telecommunications

In the past week, have you spoken on the phone, watched television, done research on the Internet, or listened to the radio? Today you can talk to someone far away or transmit and receive information over long distances almost instantly. Thanks to telecommunication the world is becoming increasingly connected through the use of electrical impulses and radio waves.

Using Radio Waves

For sending information, the most versatile type of electromagnetic wave to use is radio. Using radio waves to communicate has several advantages. For example, radio waves pass through walls and windows easily. Radio waves do not interact with humans, so they are not harmful to people like ultraviolet rays or X rays are. So for most telecommunication technology, such as TVs, radios, and telephones, radio waves are the electromagnetic wave of choice. **Figure 19** shows the basic method for using radio waves to transmit information—in this case, taking sound from one location and reproducing the sound in a second location.

As You Read

What **You'll Learn**

- **Explain** different methods of electronic communication.
- **Compare and contrast** AM and FM signals.

Vocabulary

Carrier wave
Global Positioning System

Why **It's Important**

Telecommunication enables people to contact others and collect information worldwide.

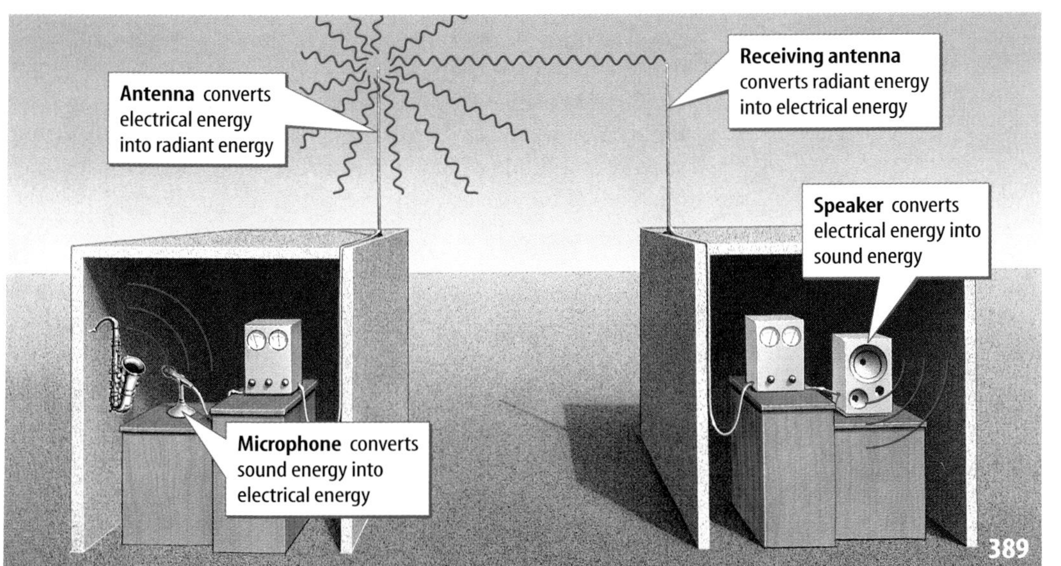

Antenna converts electrical energy into radiant energy
Receiving antenna converts radiant energy into electrical energy
Speaker converts electrical energy into sound energy
Microphone converts sound energy into electrical energy

Figure 19
Radio transmission relies on conversions among sound, electrical, and radiant energies.

389

Section Assessment Planner

PORTFOLIO
Curriculum Connection, p. 391

PERFORMANCE ASSESSMENT
Math Skills Activity, p. 391
Skill Builder Activities, p. 393
See page 400 for more options.

CONTENT ASSESSMENT
Section, p. 393
Challenge, p. 393
Chapter, pp. 400–401

SECTION

Using Electromagnetic Waves

1 Motivate

Bellringer Transparency

Display the Section Focus Transparency for Section 3. Use the accompanying Transparency Activity Master. L2 ELL

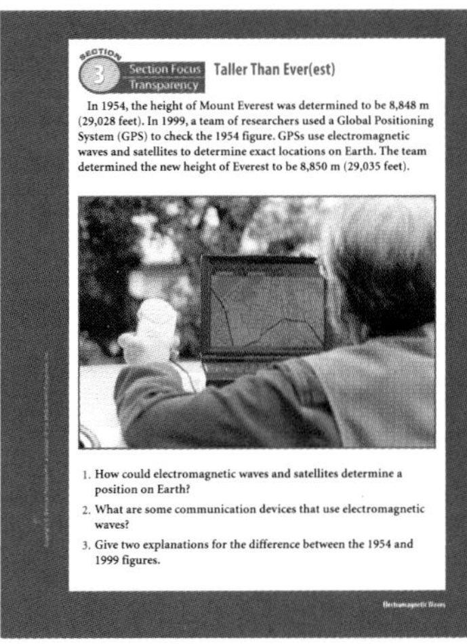
Section 3 Section Focus Transparency **Taller Than Ever(est)**

In 1954, the height of Mount Everest was determined to be 8,848 m (29,028 feet). In 1999, a team of researchers used a Global Positioning System (GPS) to check the 1954 figure. GPSs use electromagnetic waves and satellites to determine exact locations on Earth. The team determined the new height of Everest to be 8,850 m (29,035 feet).

1. How could electromagnetic waves and satellites determine a position on Earth?
2. What are some communication devices that use electromagnetic waves?
3. Give two explanations for the difference between the 1954 and 1999 figures.

Tie to Prior Knowledge

Ask students whether they have ever used a cordless, cellular, or digital phone. Point out that all of these communication devices work using electromagnetic waves.

2 Teach

Using Radio Waves

Visual Learning

Figure 19 Review with students the generation of an electromagnetic wave in an antenna shown in this figure. **What determines the amplitude of the wave?** the distance the charge moves up and down in the antenna **What determines the frequency of the wave?** how fast the charge moves up and down in the antenna **What determines the wavelength of the wave?** The wavelength is determined by the frequency. L2 LS **Visual-Spatial**

Astronomy INTEGRATION

Pulsars are small, heavy, collapsed stars called neutron stars that rotate about once per second. They have enormous magnetic fields.They emit beams of radio waves once per rotation. If Earth happens to be on the path of the beam, we detect a regular periodic radio signal. Because it is so regular, it is easy to understand how it may have been interpreted as a signal from an alien civilization.

Fun Fact

Because they were originally believed to be communications from an alien civilization, pulsars were almost named LGMs, which stood for "Little Green Men."

Figure 20
An information signal can be stored on a carrier wave in two ways—amplitude modulation or frequency modulation.

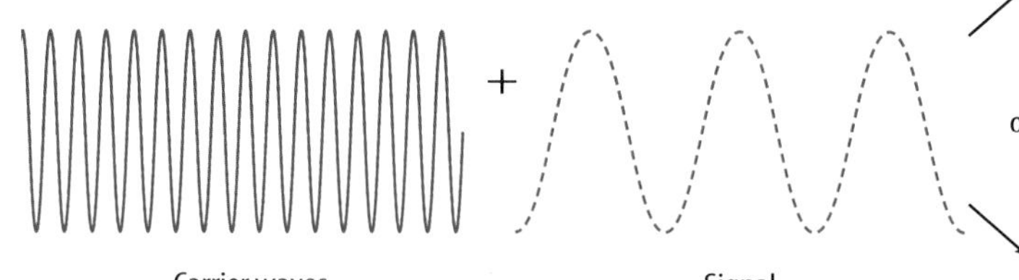

or

Amplitude modulated wave

Frequency modulated wave

Radio Transmission The simplest way to transmit a signal is to start and stop it. Morse code uses such an on/off signal. Modern telecommunications use altered waves. Each radio station is assigned one particular frequency at which to transmit, such as 105.1 MHz. The assigned frequency is the **carrier wave** for that station. A carrier wave's frequency is where you tune your radio to receive a particular station's broadcast. To carry information on the carrier wave, either the amplitude or the frequency of the carrier wave is changed, or modulated.

Amplitude Modulation The letters *AM* in AM radio stands for amplitude modulation, which means that the amplitude of the carrier wave is changed to transmit information. The original sound is transformed into an electrical signal that is used to vary the amplitude of the carrier wave, as shown in **Figure 20.** Note that the frequency of the carrier wave doesn't change—only the amplitude changes. An AM receiver tunes to the frequency of the carrier wave. Then the information that is stored in the varying amplitude of the carrier wave creates an electrical signal that goes to the speaker, reproducing the original sound.

Astronomy INTEGRATION

Pulsars are astronomical objects that emit periodic bursts of radio waves. The pattern of pulses is regular. Investigate how pulsars originate and communicate to your class what you learn. Why might pulsars have seemed to be signals from intelligent life?

Frequency Modulation FM radio works in much the same way as AM radio, but the frequency instead of the amplitude is modulated, as shown in **Figure 20.** In this case, the receiver uses the information stored in the varying frequency of the carrier wave to create an electrical signal. When the electrical signal reaches the speakers, the original sound is reproduced.

Reading Check *What is frequency modulation?*

Reading Check

Answer in radio transmission, the variation of the frequency of a carrier wave to carry information

Science Journal

Early Communication Have students write about how they think information was spread before any type of electronic communication existed. Challenge them to describe the speed and accuracy of such communication and compare it with ways they communicate today. L1 LS **Linguistic**

Cultural Diversity

Early Observations in Astronomy In 1054, Chinese astronomers observed a massive supernova explosion where the Crab Nebula now exists. A pulsar now can be detected at the heart of this nebula. Have students calculate how many years ago the supernova exploded and how many times their age this is. The formula (this year − 1054) ÷ student's age will give the answer. L2 LS **Logical-Mathematical**

Telephones

A telephone contains a microphone in the mouthpiece that converts a sound wave into an electric signal. The electric signal is carried through a wire to the telephone network. There, the signal might remain electric or be converted into a radio or microwave signal for transmission through the air. The electric signal also can be converted into a light wave for transmission through fiber-optic cables.

At the receiving end, the signal is converted back to an electric signal. A speaker in the earpiece of the phone changes the electric signal into a sound wave.

Reading Check *What device converts sound into an electric signal?*

Math Skills Activity

Calculating the Wavelength of Radio Frequencies

Example Problem

You are listening to an FM station with a frequency of 94.9 MHz or 94,900,000 Hz. How long are the wavelengths that strike the antenna? For any wave, the wavelength equals the wave speed divided by the frequency. The speed of radio waves is 300,000,000 m/s. The SI unit of frequency, Hz, is equal to l/s.

Solution

1. *This is what you know:* frequency = 94,900,000 Hz; wave speed = 300,000,000 ms
2. *This is what you need to find:* wavelength
3. *This is the equation you need to use:* wavelength = wave speed/frequency
4. *Substitute the known values:* wavelength = 300,000,000 m/s / 94,900,000 Hz = 3.16 m

Check your answer by multiplying the units. Do you calculate a unit of distance for your answer?

Practice Problems

1. Your friend prefers an AM radio station at 1,520 kHz (1,520 thousand vibrations each second). What is the wavelength of this frequency? Which has a longer wavelength, AM or FM radio waves?
2. An AM radio station operates at 580 kHz (580 thousand vibrations each second). What is the wavelength of this frequency? What is the relationship between frequency and wavelength?

For more help, refer to the Math Skill Handbook.

Telephones

Activity

Encourage students to make flowcharts detailing the transmission of a signal from one telephone to another, using the text description as a guide. L1
LS **Visual-Spatial**

Reading Check

Answer a microphone

Teacher FYI

Fiber-optic cables have several advantages over copper wires. They are much smaller, will never rust or corrode, and aren't susceptible to electronic interference. A single pair of fiber-optic cables can carry more than 1,000 conversations simultaneously. Several of these cables could fit through the eye of a needle.

Math Skills Activity

National Math Standards

Correlation to Mathematics Objectives

1,2,8,9

Answers to Practice Problems

1. 197.4 m; AM radio waves
2. 517.2 m; wavelength = speed of light ÷ frequency

Curriculum Connection

History Have students investigate the invention of the telephone and prepare posters showing some aspect of this historic event. The telephone was invented by Alexander Graham Bell in 1876. L2
LS **Visual-Spatial** P

Resource Manager

Chapter Resources Booklet

Transparency Activity, p. 44
Directed Reading for Content Mastery, pp. 19, 20
Enrichment, p. 30
Reinforcement, p. 27

Telephones, continued

Use Science Words

Word Meaning Ask students to find the origin of the term *cell phone*. The term *cell phone* refers to the cell, or the area that one tower can serve. A cell tower can cover a range with as much as up to a 35-mile radius. Tower cells overlap so that coverage isn't lost. L2 IS **Linguistic**

Discussion

Why is there a limit to the number of people who can talk on cell phones in a particular cell at the same time? Each phone uses a different frequency. If all of the assigned frequencies are being used, no other phones can be used at that time. L3 IS **Logical-Mathematical**

Communications Satellites

Make a Model

Have students find the locations of two or three geosynchronous communications satellites above Earth and make models showing their positions. Geosynchronous satellites orbit Earth directly above the equator once every 24 hours, so that each is always above the same point on the equator. They maintain an altitude of about 35,800 km. L2 IS **Visual-Spatial**

Figure 21 Electromagnetic waves make using telephones easier.

A Cordless phones use radio waves to allow users to talk from anywhere in the house.

B Radio waves enable cell phone users to send or receive calls without using wires.

Remote Phones A telephone does not have to transmit its signal through wires. In a cordless phone, the electrical signal produced by the microphone is transmitted through an antenna in the handset to the base. **Figure 21A** shows how incoming signals are transmitted from the base to the handset. A cellular phone uses an antenna to broadcast and receive information between the phone and a base station, as shown in **Figure 21B.** The base station uses radio waves to communicate with other stations in a network.

Research Visit the Glencoe Science Web site at **science.glencoe.com** for more information about how satellites are used in around-the-world communications. Summarize what you learn in an informational handout.

Pagers The base station also is used in a pager system. When you dial a pager, the signal is sent to a base station. From there, an electromagnetic signal is sent to the pager. The pager beeps or vibrates to indicate that someone has called. With a touch-tone phone, you can transmit numeric information, such as your phone number, which the pager will receive and display.

Communications Satellites

How do you send information to the other side of the world? Radio waves can't be sent directly through Earth. Instead, radio signals are sent to satellites. The satellites can communicate with other satellites or with ground stations. Some communications satellites are in geosynchronous orbit, meaning each satellite remains above the same point on the ground.

Resource Manager

Chapter Resources Booklet
- Lab Activity, pp. 13–14
- Transparency Activity, pp. 45–46
- Activity Worksheet, pp. 7–8

Lab Management and Safety, p. 73

SCIENCE Online
Internet Addresses

Explore the Glencoe Science Web site at **science.glencoe.com** to find out more about topics in this section.

The Global Positioning System

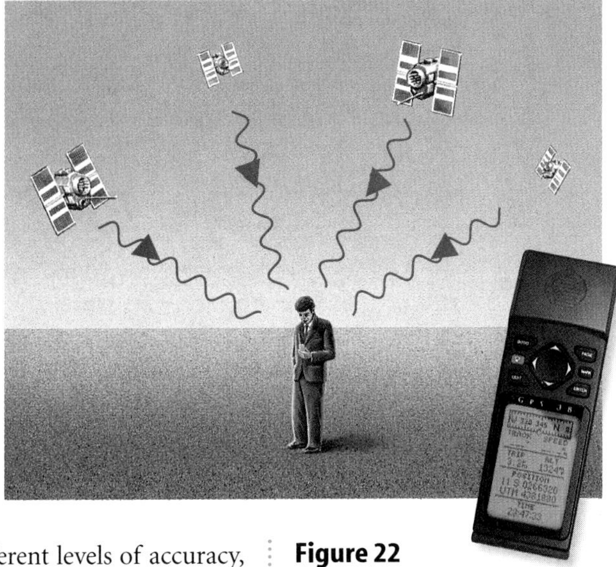

Satellites also are used as part of the **Global Positioning System,** or GPS. GPS is used to locate objects on Earth. The system consists of satellites, ground-based stations, and portable units with receivers, as illustrated in **Figure 22.**

GPS measures the time it takes for a user's portable unit to receive radio waves from several satellites. The time shows how far the receiver is from each satellite. By communicating with several satellites, a user's longitude, latitude, and elevation can be determined. Different receivers have different levels of accuracy, giving location to within a few hundred meters for sailors or within centimeters for surveyors working on topographic maps.

Figure 22
The Global Positioning System (GPS) works by using a series of satellites, ground-based stations, and portable units with receivers.

Reading Check *What is GPS used for?*

Many of these forms of communication have been developed over the past few decades. For example, an Internet connection transfers images and sound using the telephone network, just as a television signal transfers images and sound using radio waves. What forms of telecommunications do you think you'll be using a few decades from now?

Section  Assessment

1. What is a modulated radio signal?
2. What does a microphone do? What does a speaker do?
3. What types of information does a GPS receiver provide for its user?
4. What is a communications satellite?
5. **Think Critically** Electromagnetic waves travel more slowly in materials such as glass than through air. What might be the benefit of sending information in glass wires be?

Skill Builder Activities

6. **Researching Information** Find out more about a form of telecommunications, such as email or shortwave radio. **For more help, refer to the Science Skill Handbook.**
7. **Communicating** Think of a story you have enjoyed about a time before telecommunications or one in which telecommunication was not possible. How would telecommunications have changed the story? **For more help, refer to the Science Skill Handbook.**

Answers to Section Assessment

1. a radio signal in which either the amplitude or frequency has been varied to carry information
2. A microphone transforms sound waves into electrical signals, and a speaker transforms electrical signals into sound waves.
3. longitude, latitude, and elevation
4. a satellite that relays electromagnetic waves used to communicate
5. The glass may be cheaper, lighter, or capable of carrying more signals.
6. Check students' work for accuracy.
7. Accept all reasonable responses. In some situations, telecommunication might have improved things; in others it might have made things worse.

The Global Positioning System

Reading Check

Answer Possible answers: vehicle navigation, surveying, hiking navigation, farming, spying

Visual Learning

Figure 22 Point out the variety of components used in the Global Positioning System. Explain that several satellites must cooperate to get complete coverage of the planet. Three or four satellites must compare times to determine the position of an object.

3 Assess

Reteach

Explain the energy transformations that occur as sound is transported via a normal telephone. Help students make diagrams to outline the steps. L2 **LS Visual-Spatial**

Challenge

Ask students to find the difference between a digital signal and analog signal. A digital signal is composed of combinations of 1's and 0's that produce discrete digits that carry information. An analog signal uses waves to carry information. L3 **LS Linguistic**

Assessment

Process Have students write short explanations of how a normal telephone, a cordless phone, and a cell phone send information. A normal telephone sends information as electrical signals that travel through telephone wire. A cordless phone sends information as radio waves from the phone to the receiver, then through phone lines as electrical signals. A cell phone sends signals all the way from one customer to another as radio waves. Use **PASC,** p. 159.

Activity

BENCH TESTED

Recognize the Problem

Purpose

Students identify the color spectrum of a light source and relate the wavelength of the colors to the temperature of the light source. L2

LS **Logical-Mathematical**

Process Skills

observing, interpreting data, inferring, communicating, making and using tables, comparing and contrasting, recognizing cause and effect, forming operational definitions, forming a hypothesis, designing an experiment, using numbers

Time Required

40 minutes

Materials

Dimmer switches can be obtained at local hardware stores.

Alternate Materials

Use clear 4-, 15-, 25-, 60-, and 100-watt lightbulbs if a dimmer is not available.

Safety Precautions

Caution students that current from a 120-V AC wall socket can be lethal. Remind students that lightbulbs can become hot.

Form a Hypothesis

Possible Hypothesis Students may hypothesize that the spectra remain the same regardless of the brightness of the light source.

Activity — *Design Your Own Experiment*

Spectrum Inspection

You've heard the term "red-hot" used to describe something that is unusually hot. When a piece of metal is heated it may give off a red glow or even a yellow glow. All objects emit electromagnetic waves. How do the wavelengths of these waves depend on the temperature of the object?

Recognize the Problem

How do the wavelengths of light produced by a lightbulb depend on the temperature of the lightbulb?

Form a Hypothesis

The brightness of a lightbulb increases as its temperature increases. Form a hypothesis describing how the wavelengths emitted by a lightbulb will change as the brightness of a lightbulb changes.

Goals

- **Design** an experiment that determines the relationship between brightness and the wavelengths emitted by a lightbulb.
- **Observe** the wavelengths of light emitted by a lightbulb as its brightness changes.

Safety Precautions

WARNING: Be sure all electrical cords and connections are intact and that you have a dry working area. Do not touch the bulbs as they may be hot.

Possible Materials

diffraction grating
power supply with variable resister switch
clear, tubular lightbulb and socket
red, yellow, and blue colored pencils

Inclusion Strategies

Learning Disabled Before beginning the activity, have students discuss the relationship between color, frequency, and energy. Ask questions that help students realize that colors near the red end of the spectrum have lower frequencies, longer wavelengths, and lower energy. They should also realize that hotter objects emit more blue light. LS **Interpersonal**

Curriculum Connection

Astronomy The color of a star is an indication of its temperature. The coolest stars are reddish, and the hottest stars are slightly blue. Encourage students to look outside at night and attempt to identify different colors of stars. L2 LS **Naturalist**

Test Your Hypothesis

Plan

1. **Decide** how you will determine the effect of lightbulb brightness on the colors of light that are emitted.
2. As shown in the photo at the right, you will look toward the light through the diffraction grating to detect the colors of light emitted by the bulb. The color spectrum will appear to the right and to the left of the bulb.
3. **List** the specific steps you will need to take to test your hypothesis. Describe precisely what you will do in each step. Will you first test the bulb at a bright or dim setting? How many settings will you test? (Try at least three.) How will you record your observations in an organized way?
4. **List** the materials you will need for your experiment. Describe exactly how and in which order you will use these materials.
5. **Identify** any constants and variables in your experiment.

Do

1. Make sure your teacher approves your plan before you start.
2. **Perform** your experiment as planned.
3. While doing your experiment, write down any observations you make in your Science Journal.

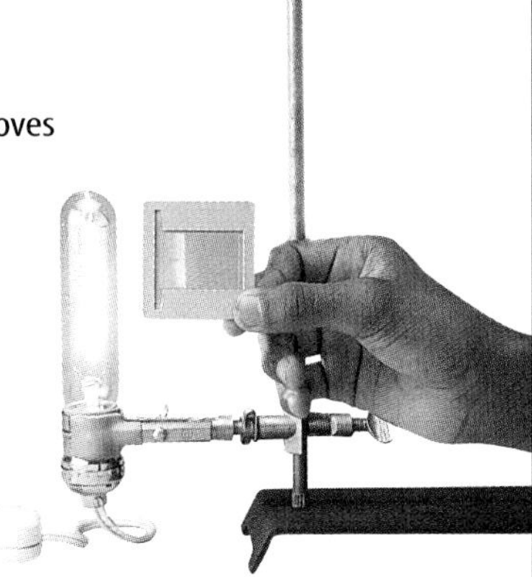

Analyze Your Data

1. Use the colored pencils to draw the color spectrum emitted by each brightness.
2. Which colors appeared as the bulb became brighter? Did any colors disappear?
3. How did the wavelengths emitted by the bulb change as the bulb became brighter?
4. Infer how the wavelengths emitted by the lightbulb changed as it became hotter.

Draw Conclusions

1. If an object becomes hotter, what happens to the wavelengths it emits?
2. How do the wavelengths that the bulb emits change if it is turned off?
3. From your results, infer whether red stars or yellow stars are hotter.

Communicating Your Data

Compare your results with others in your class. How many different colors were seen?

Test Your Hypothesis

Possible Procedures

Align the grating with the filament and observe the spectrum. Vary power to the lamp and observe the spectrum again.

Teaching Strategy

Students should hold the diffraction grating near their eyes for best observations.

Expected Outcome

Students should observe all colors from bright light but decreased blue from dimmer light.

Analyze Your Data

1. Drawings should show all colors present from bright lights, but less blue as the brightness decreases.
2. All colors are visible when the bulb is bright. Bluish colors fade in dimmer light.
3. Short wavelengths are visible from brighter light.
4. Short wavelengths are visible from a hotter bulb.

Error Analysis

What would you see if the diffraction grating were not aligned with the axis of the filament?

Draw Conclusions

1. It emits shorter wavelengths.
2. The bulb cools off, so the wavelengths increase beyond the red end of the spectrum.
3. yellow stars

Assessment

Process Predict how the spectrum you see in the diffraction grating would differ if you looked at different types of bulbs, such as a colored lightbulb, neon light, or fluorescent bulb. Test your predictions. The spectrum will vary with the nature of the light source and its temperature. Use **PASC,** p. 97.

Communicating Your Data

Have students compare the drawings they made of the spectrum for the different settings of the dimmer switch.

Content Background

Today there are three main types of wireless networking technology.

Radio operates in the public portion of the radio spectrum. It uses spread-spectrum technology. Spread-spectrum technology has two major methods of operation: direct sequence and frequency hopping, the type Ms. Lamarr was instrumental in developing.

Microwave technology is typically used in long-range setups and satellite communications.

Finally, there is infrared laser communication, which uses coherent beams of infrared light to transmit data.

Frequency-hopping spread-spectrum technology (FHSS) was developed by the military for secure communications. Every few milliseconds, a FHSS signal bounces between different specific points in a designated area of the electromagnetic spectrum, reducing interference from other signals and making it very difficult to listen in on the transmission. The drawback is that FHSS is relatively slow, and in congested cities with a lot of radio traffic, range can be reduced. Under those circumstances, FHSS is roughly the equivalent of being a lane hopper in rush-hour traffic.

TIME SCIENCE AND HISTORY

SCIENCE CAN CHANGE THE COURSE OF HISTORY!

Hedy Lamarr, actor and inventor

Hopping the

Ringgggg. There it is—that familiar beep! Out come the cellular phones—from purses, pockets, book bags, belt clips, and briefcases. At any given moment, a million wireless signals are flying through the air—and not just cell phone signals. With radio and television signals, Internet data, and even Global Positioning System information coming at us, the air seems like a pretty crowded place. How do all of these signals get to the right place? How does a cellular phone pick out its own signal from among the clutter? The answer lies in a concept developed in 1940 by Hedy Lamarr.

Lamarr was born in Vienna, Austria. In 1937, she left Austria to escape Hitler's invading Nazi army. Lamarr left for another reason, as well. She was determined to pursue a career as an actor. And she became a famous movie star.

In 1940, Lamarr came up with an idea to keep radio signals that guided torpedoes from being jammed. Her idea, called frequency hopping, involved breaking the radio signal that was guiding the torpedo into tiny parts and rapidly changing their frequency. The enemy would not be able to keep up with the changes and thus would not be able to divert the torpedo from its target. Lamarr worked with a partner who helped her figure out how to make the idea work. They were awarded a patent for their idea in 1942.

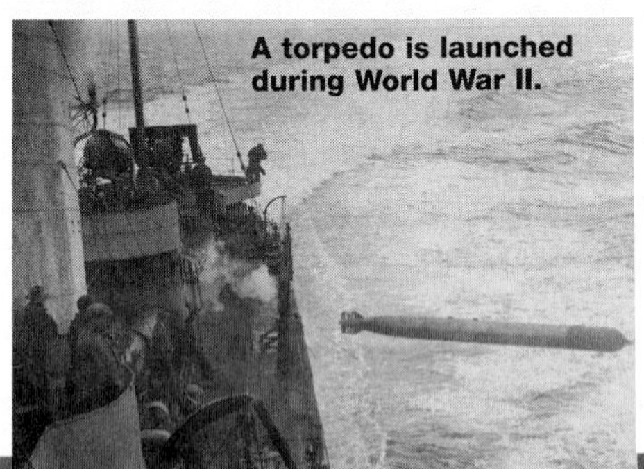

A torpedo is launched during World War II.

396

Resources for Teachers and Students

Practical Spread Spectrum: Frequency Hopping, Vol. 2, by Charles O. Phillips, Aegean Park Press, 1996.

Wireless Radio: A Brief History, by Lewis Coe, McFarland and Company, 1996.

Spread Spectrum

Lamarr's idea was ahead of its time. The digital technology that allowed efficient operation of her system wasn't invented until decades later. However, after 1962, frequency hopping was adopted and used in U.S. military communications. It was the development of cellular phones, however, that benefited the most from Lamarr's concept. Cellular phones and other wireless technologies operate by breaking their signals into smaller parts, called packets. The packets are encoded in a certain way for particular receivers and are spread across bands of the electromagnetic spectrum. In this way, millions of users can use the same frequencies at the same time.

Frequencies

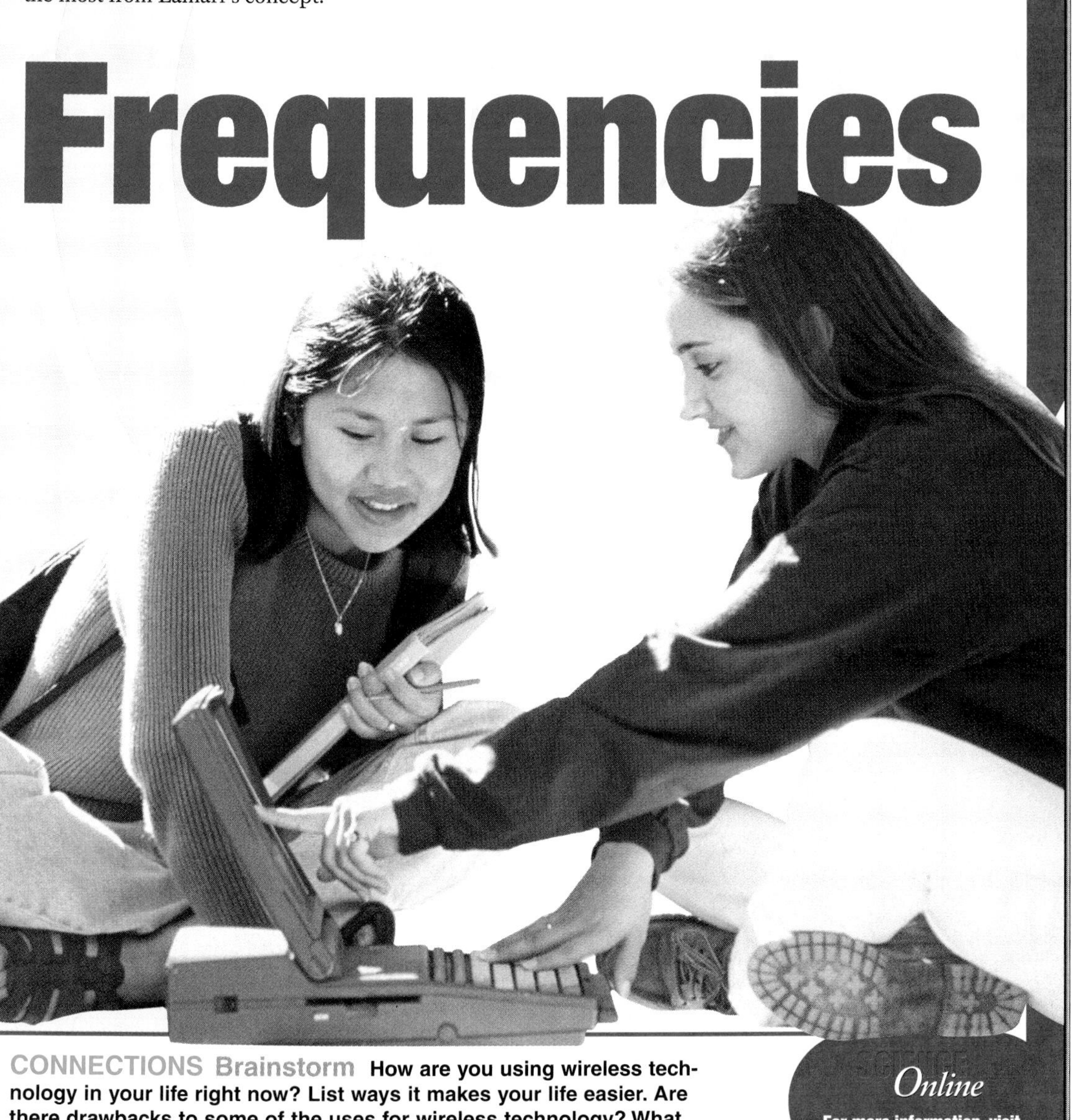

CONNECTIONS Brainstorm **How are you using wireless technology in your life right now? List ways it makes your life easier. Are there drawbacks to some of the uses for wireless technology? What are they?**

Online
For more information, visit science.glencoe.com

Discussion

Why was Ms. Lamarr's idea ahead of its time? When she introduced the idea, the technology wasn't available to make it work well. L2

LS Logical-Mathematical

Historical Significance

To make students better aware of the significance of the history of radio in our technologically advanced age, have them find out about the history of radio through a research project. As a class, make a timeline to illustrate the history of radio. Break the class into groups and give each group a ten or twenty year span of history to study, starting with the turn of the twentieth century. Have each group find the discoveries and inventions that occurred during its assigned period of time that significantly advanced the wireless communication industry and present their findings to the class.

CONNECTIONS Discuss with students how the Internet has made life easier and if it has caused any problems. If students have access to cell phones, ask what the good and bad points of this technology has been. Even students who do not have access to this technology should be able to deduce such information.

Online

Internet Addresses

Explore the Glencoe Science Web site at **science.glencoe.com** to find out more about topics in this feature.

Chapter 13 Study Guide

Reviewing Main Ideas

Preview

Students can answer the questions in their Science Journals. Discuss the answers as you go through the chapter. **LS Linguistic**

Review

Students can write their answers, then compare them with those of other students. **LS Interpersonal**

Reteach

Students can look at the illustrations and describe details that support the main ideas of the chapter. **LS Visual-Spatial**

Answers to Chapter Review

Section 1

2. Both waves have a frequency and wavelength. Both carry energy.

Section 2

2. The infrared camera detects the infrared radiation given off by the person's body.

Section 3

3. Possible answer: After your voice is transformed into an electronic signal, that signal may be sent by radio or microwaves to another location.

Chapter 13 Study Guide

Reviewing Main Ideas

Section 1 The Nature of Electromagnetic Waves

1. Moving charges generate vibrating electric and magnetic fields. These vibrating fields travel through space and are called electromagnetic waves.
2. Electromagnetic waves, like all waves, have wavelenth, frequency, and energy. *How are ocean waves similar to electromagnetic waves?*

Section 2 The Electromagnetic Spectrum

1. Radio waves have the longest wavelength and lowest energy. Microwaves and radar are subsets of radio waves.
2. All objects emit infrared waves. If you see an object, visible light must be coming from it. *At night, how can a person be detected by an infrared camera?*

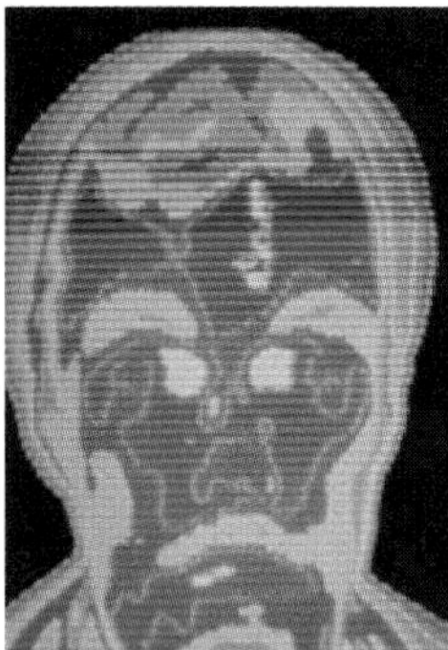

3. Ultraviolet waves have a higher frequency and more energy than visible light.
4. X rays and gamma rays are highly penetrating and can be dangerous to living organisms.

Section 3 Using Electromagnetic Waves

1. Communications systems use visible light, radio waves, or electrical signals to transmit information.
2. Radios use modulated carrier waves to transmit information.
3. Electromagnetic waves are used in telephone technologies to make communication easier and faster. *What is one way an electromagnetic wave is used in telephone communication?*

4. Communications satellites relay information from different points on Earth so a transmission can go around the globe. The Global Positioning System is one application of satellites.

FOLDABLES Reading & Study Skills — **After You Read**

Using the information on your Foldable, compare and contrast visible and invisible waves that form the electromagnetic spectrum.

FOLDABLES Reading & Study Skills — **After You Read**

After students have read the chapter and completed the Foldable described in Before You Read, have them do the activity on the student page.

Dinah Zike

Visualizing Main Ideas

Complete the following spider map about electromagnetic waves.

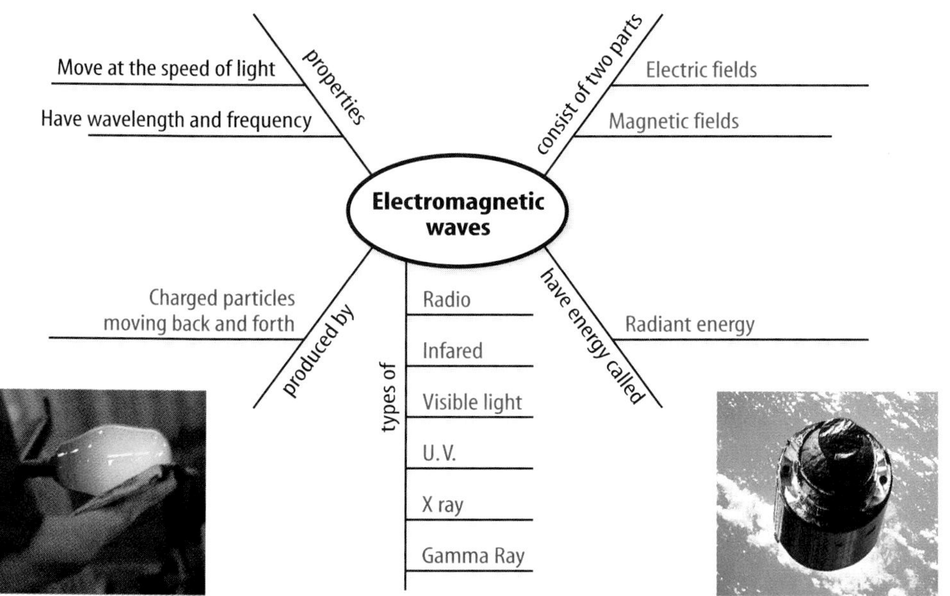

Vocabulary Review

Vocabulary Words

a. carrier wave
b. electromagnetic spectrum
c. electromagnetic wave
d. gamma ray
e. Global Positioning System
f. infrared wave
g. radiant energy
h. radio wave
i. ultraviolet radiation
j. visible light
k. X ray

Using Vocabulary

Explain the difference between the terms in each of the following pairs.

1. infrared wave, radio wave
2. radio wave, carrier wave
3. communications satellite, GPS
4. visible light, ultraviolet radiation
5. X ray, gamma ray
6. electromagnetic spectrum, rainbow
7. X ray, photograph
8. television wave, AM radio wave
9. electromagnetic wave, light
10. infrared wave, ultraviolet wave

Study Tip

After you read a chapter, write ten questions that it answers. Wait one day and then try to recall the answers. Look up what you can't remember.

IDENTIFYING Misconceptions

Assess

Use the assessment as follow-up to page 372F after students have completed the chapter.

Procedure Provide this list of electromagnetic waves: radio, microwaves, infrared, visible light, ultraviolet, X rays, and gamma rays. Have students compare and contrast visible light with any two other types of electromagnetic waves by completing charts giving the wavelength range, means of detection, uses, and dangers of the three types of electromagnetic waves.

Expected Outcome Students should realize that light is similar to electromagnetic radiation of other wavelengths.

Chapter 13 Study Guide

Visualizing Main Ideas

See student page.

Vocabulary Review

Using Vocabulary

1. Infrared waves have higher frequencies and more energy than radio waves.
2. In radio communication, a carrier wave is a radio wave of a particular frequency and amplitude that is modulated in either amplitude or frequency to carry information.
3. A communications satellite is a geosynchronous satellite used to transfer communication signals. GPS is a system of satellites and receivers used to determine locations on Earth.
4. Visible light is the section of the electromagnetic spectrum that we see with our eyes. Ultraviolet radiation is electromagnetic radiation at a slightly higher frequency than visible light.
5. Gamma rays have a higher frequency and more energy than X rays, and can cause more harm to living things.
6. The electromagnetic spectrum is the entire range of electromagnetic waves. A rainbow is the spectrum of visible light.
7. Photographs register a chemical reaction to light, and X rays register a chemical reaction to X radiation.
8. An AM radio wave is a type of television wave.
9. Electromagnetic waves with wavelengths between 0.4 and 0.7 millionths of a meter are light.
10. An infrared wave has a slightly lower frequency than red light, and an ultraviolet wave has a slightly higher frequency than violet light.

Chapter 13 Assessment

Checking Concepts

1. D
2. D
3. C
4. A
5. B
6. B
7. D
8. D
9. D
10. A

Thinking Critically

11. Infrared light has a lower frequency than visible light, so it possesses less energy. This means that the area beyond red would have been cooler than the room.
12. They can receive electromagnetic radiation that the atmosphere absorbs.
13. The fact that the light it gives off has higher frequencies and therefore more energy than red light indicates that it is hotter than the object glowing red.
14. If the tissue in the tumor is dense enough, X rays will not pass through it and it will show up as a dark shadow on X-ray film.
15. Possible answer: There are many frequencies of radio waves, and radio waves can travel through air and through empty space.

Chapter 13 Assessment

Checking Concepts

Choose the word or phrase that best answers the question.

1. Which type of force field surrounds a moving electron?
   A) gravity **B)** electric **C)** magnetic **D)** all of these
2. What does a microphone transform?
   A) light waves to sound waves
   B) radio waves to an electrical signal
   C) sound waves to electromagnetic waves
   D) sound waves to an electrical signal
3. Which of the following electromagnetic waves have the lowest frequency?
   A) visible light **B)** infrared waves **C)** radio waves **D)** X rays
4. What happens to the energy of an electromagnetic wave as its frequency increases?
   A) It increases.
   B) It decreases.
   C) It stays the same.
   D) It oscillates up and down.
5. What type of wave do all hot objects emit?
   A) radio **B)** infrared **C)** visible **D)** ultraviolet
6. What can detect radio waves?
   A) film **B)** antenna **C)** eyes **D)** skin
7. What type of wave passes through people?
   A) infrared **B)** visible **C)** ultraviolet **D)** gamma
8. Which color has the lowest frequency?
   A) green **B)** violet **C)** yellow **D)** red
9. What is the key device that allows remote phones to function?
   A) X ray **B)** satellite **C)** GPS **D)** antenna
10. What does *A* in AM stand for?
   A) amplitude **B)** antenna **C)** astronomical **D)** Alpha centauri

Thinking Critically

11. Infrared light was discovered when a scientist placed a thermometer in each band of the light spectrum produced by a prism. Would the area just beyond red have been warmer or cooler than the room? Explain.
12. Astronomers have built telescopes on Earth that have flexible mirrors that can eliminate the distortions due to the atmosphere. What advantages would a space-based telescope have over these?
13. Heated objects often give off visible light of a particular color. Explain why an object that glows bluish-white is hotter than one that glows red.
14. How can an X ray be used to determine the location of a cancerous tumor?
15. Why are many communications systems based on radio waves?

Developing Skills

16. **Calculating Ratios** How far does light travel in 1 min? How does this compare with the distance to the Moon?
17. **Recognizing Cause and Effect** As you ride in the car, the radio alternates between two different stations. How can the antenna pick up two stations at once?
18. **Classifying** List the colors of the visible spectrum in order of increasing frequency.

Chapter Assessment Planner

Portfolio Encourage students to place in their portfolios one or two items of what they consider to be their best work. Examples include:

- Science Journal, p. 375
- Extension, p. 383
- Curriculum Connection, p. 391

Performance Additional performance assessments, Performance Task Assessment Lists, and rubrics for evaluating these activities can be found in Glencoe's **Performance Assessment in the Science Classroom.**

Chapter 13 Assessment

19. **Comparing and Contrasting** Compare and contrast ultraviolet and infrared light.

20. **Concept Mapping** Electromagnetic waves are grouped according to their frequencies. In the following concept map, write each frequency group and one way humans make use of the electromagnetic waves in that group. For example, in the second set of ovals, you might write "X rays" and "to see inside humans."

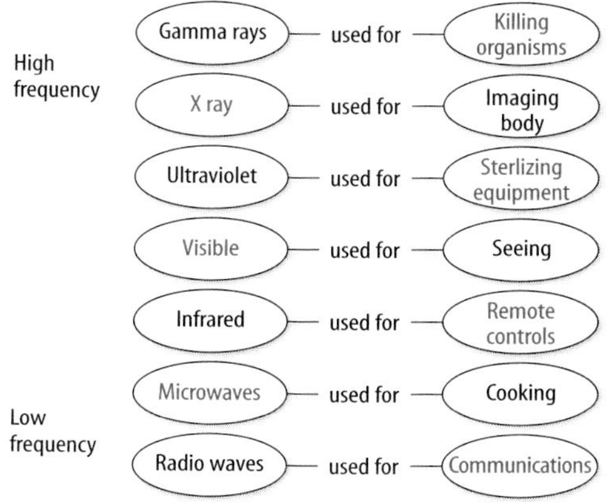

Performance Assessment

21. **Oral Presentation** Explain to the class how a radio signal is generated, transmitted, and received.

22. **Poster** Make a poster showing the parts of the electromagnetic spectrum. Show how frequency, wavelength, and energy change throughout the spectrum. How is each wave generated? What are some uses of each?

Technology

Go to the Glencoe Science Web site at **science.glencoe.com** or use the **Glencoe Science CD-ROM** for additional chapter assessment.

Test Practice

Mr. Rubama's class was studying how radio waves are transmitted. An experimental setup involving radio waves and glass is shown below.

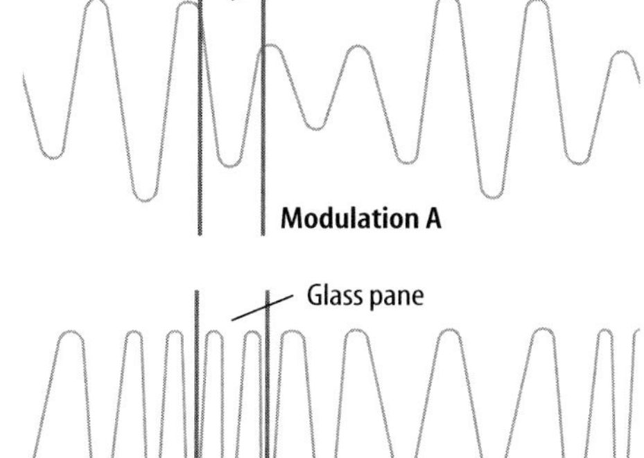

Study the illustrations and answer the following questions.

1. Which of these questions would most likely be answered by this experiment?
   A) How fast do radio waves travel through the air?
   B) Why do some waves travel more quickly than other waves?
   C) Where do radio waves come from?
   D) Can radio waves travel through glass?

2. Which of the following describes how the wave in Modulation A is different from the wave in Modulation B?
   F) It is a radio wave.
   G) It is frequency modulated.
   H) It is amplitude modulated.
   J) It is a a carrier wave.

Chapter 13 Assessment

THE PRINCETON REVIEW

Test Practice

The Test-Taking Tip was written by The Princeton Review, the nation's leader in test preparation.

1. D
2. H

Developing Skills

16. d = tv = 60 sec/min × 300,000 km/sec = 18,000,000 km/min; This is about 50 times the distance to the Moon, which is 378,000, km.
17. You are at the point where the areas covered by the two radio stations overlap.
18. red, orange, yellow, green, blue, indigo, violet
19. Infrared has a lower frequency, lower energy, and longer wavelength than ultraviolet light.
20. See student page.

Performance Assessment

21. Students should show or explain sound being converted into electrical signals and these signals being transmitted as electromagnetic waves, received, and reconverted into sound waves. Use **PASC**, p. 143.
22. The spectrum should cover electromagnetic waves from radio to gamma rays. Many uses are listed in this chapter. Use **PASC**, p. 145.

Assessment Resources

Reproducible Masters

Chapter Resources Booklet
Chapter Review, pp. 35–36
Chapter Tests, pp. 37–40
Assessment Transparency Activity, p. 47

Glencoe Science Web site
Interactive Tutor
Chapter Quizzes

Glencoe Technology

Assessment Transparency
Interactive CD-ROM Chapter Quizzes
ExamView Pro Test Bank
Vocabulary PuzzleMaker Software
MindJogger Videoquiz DVD/VHS

<table>
<tr><th rowspan="2">Section/Objectives</th><th colspan="2">Standards</th><th rowspan="2">Activities/Features</th></tr>
<tr><th>National</th><th>State/Local</th></tr>
<tr><td>Chapter Opener</td><td>See p. 5T for a Key to Standards.</td><td></td><td>Explore Activity: Observe the bending of light, p. 403
Before You Read, p. 403</td></tr>
<tr><td>Section 1 Properties of Light
4 sessions
2 blocks
1. Describe the wave nature of light.
2. Explain how light interacts with materials.
3. Determine why objects appear to have color</td><td>National Content Standards: UCP2, A1, B3</td><td></td><td>MiniLAB: Observing Colors in the Dark, p. 405</td></tr>
<tr><td>Section 2 Reflection and Mirrors
5 sessions
2.5 blocks
1. Explain how light is reflected from rough and smooth surfaces.
2. Determine how mirrors form an image.
3. Describe how concave and convex mirrors form an image</td><td>National Content Standards: UCP2, A1, B3, E1</td><td></td><td>Physics Integration, p. 411
Visualizing Reflections in Concave Mirrors, p. 413
Activity: Reflection from a Plane Mirror, p. 415</td></tr>
<tr><td>Section 3 Refraction and Lenses
3 sessions
1.5 blocks
1. Determine why light rays refract.
2. Explain how convex and concave lenses form images.</td><td>National Content Standards: UCP2, B3, E1, F1</td><td></td><td>Science Online, p. 418</td></tr>
<tr><td>Section 4 Using Mirrors and Lenses
6 sessions
3 blocks
1. Explain how microscopes magnify objects.
2. Explain how telescopes make distant objects visible.
3. Describe how a camera works.</td><td>National Content Standards: UCP2, A1, B3, E1, E2, F1, G1, G3</td><td></td><td>MiniLAB: Forming an Image with a Lens, p. 422
Activity: Image Formation by a Convex Lens, p. 426
Oops! Accidents in Science: Eyeglasses: Inventor Unknown, p. 428</td></tr>
</table>

Activity Materials	Reproducible Resources	Section Assessment	Technology
Explore Activity: 2 paper cups, 2 pennies, water	**Chapter Resources Booklet** Foldables Worksheet, p. 17 Directed Reading Overview, p.19 Note-taking Worksheets, pp. 35–38	Glencoe's Assessment Advantage	
MiniLAB: 6 pieces of paper of different colors (10 cm x 10 cm each), pencil, darkened room	**Chapter Resources Booklet** Transparency Activity, p. 48 MiniLAB, p. 3 Lab Activities, pp. 9–12, 13–16 Enrichment, p. 31 Reinforcement, p. 27 Directed Reading, p. 20	Portfolio Make a Model, p. 406 Performance MiniLAB, p. 405 Skill Builder Activities, p. 408 Content Section Assessment, p. 408	Section Focus Transparency Interactive CD-ROM/DVD Guided Reading Audio Program
Activity: flashlight, protractor, metric ruler, scissors, tape, small plane mirror (at least 10 cm per side), black construction paper, modeling clay, white unlined paper	**Chapter Resources Booklet** Transparency Activity, p. 49 Enrichment, p. 32 Reinforcement, p. 28 Directed Reading, p. 20 Activity Worksheet, pp. 5–6 **Mathematics Skill Activities,** p. 47	Portfolio Visual Learning, p. 410 Performance Skill Builder Activities, p. 414 Content Section Assessment, p. 414	Section Focus Transparency Interactive CD-ROM/DVD Guided Reading Audio Program
Need materials? Contact Science Kit at 1-800-828-7777 or www.sciencekit.com on the Internet.	**Chapter Resources Booklet** Transparency Activity, p. 20 Enrichment, p. 33 Reinforcement, p. 29 Directed Reading, p. 21 Transparency Activity, pp. 53–54	Portfolio Cultural Diversity, p. 417 Performance Skill Builder Activities, p. 420 Content Section Assessment, p. 420	Section Focus Transparency Teaching Transparency Interactive CD-ROM/DVD Guided Reading Audio Program
MiniLAB: glass test tube filled with water and sealed with stopper, card (10 cm x 10 cm, pencil **Activity:** convex lens, modeling clay, meterstick, flashlight, masking tape, cardboard with a white surface (20 cm square)	**Chapter Resources Booklet** Transparency Activity, p. 51 MiniLAB, p. 4 Enrichment, p. 34 Reinforcement, p. 30 Directed Reading, pp. 21, 22 Activity Worksheet, pp. 7–8 **Lab Management and Safety,** p. 64	Portfolio Assessment, p. 425 Performance MiniLAB, p. 422 Skill Builder Activities, p. 425 Content Section Assessment, p. 425	Section Focus Transparency Interactive CD-ROM/DVD Guided Reading Audio Program

End of Chapter Assessment

Glencoe's Assessment Advantage

Blackline Masters	Technology	Professional Series
Chapter Resources Booklet Chapter Review, pp. 41–42 Chapter Tests, pp. 43–46 **Standardized Test Practice by The Princeton Review,** pp. 59–62	MindJogger Videoquiz CD-ROM Explorations and Quizzes Vocabulary Puzzle Makers ExamView Pro Test Bank Interactive Lesson Planner Interactive Teacher's Edition	Performance Assessment in the Science Classroom (PASC)

Transparencies

Section Focus

Section 1 Section Focus Transparency Knight Light

The colors of stained glass are metallic oxides (combinations of different metals and oxygen), but the beautiful colors you see aren't due solely to the coloring in the glass. It's the light passing through the glass that reaches your eyes. The quality of light changes from morning to night, even from moment to moment. Our perception of stained glass changes with the light.

1. Where can you see totally through this window?
2. Where can you see light but not what's on the other side of the window? What do you think causes these differences?

L2

Section 2 Section Focus Transparency Fun-House Mirrors

If you've ever been to an amusement park or fair, you may have seen mirrors like this one. These full-length mirrors provide distorted images of the viewer. They're often found in the fun-house along with other amusing exhibits.

1. Why does a fun-house mirror provide such a different image from an ordinary mirror?
2. How does the surface of the mirror affect how we see the reflecti[on]

L2

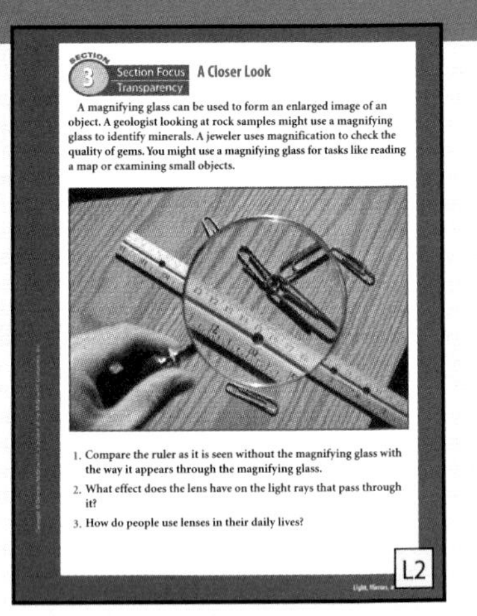
Section 3 Section Focus Transparency A Closer Look

A magnifying glass can be used to form an enlarged image of an object. A geologist looking at rock samples might use a magnifying glass to identify minerals. A jeweler uses magnification to check the quality of gems. You might use a magnifying glass for tasks like reading a map or examining small objects.

1. Compare the ruler as it is seen without the magnifying glass with the way it appears through the magnifying glass.
2. What effect does the lens have on the light rays that pass through it?
3. How do people use lenses in their daily lives?

L2

This is a representation of key blackline masters available in the Teacher Classroom Resources. See Resource Manager boxes within the chapter for additional information.

Assessment

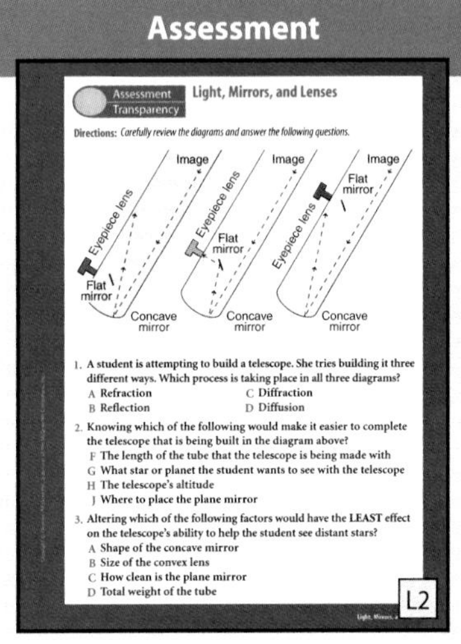
Assessment Transparency Light, Mirrors, and Lenses

Directions: Carefully review the diagrams and answer the following questions.

1. A student is attempting to build a telescope. She tries building it three different ways. Which process is taking place in all three diagrams?
   A Refraction C Diffraction
   B Reflection D Diffusion
2. Knowing which of the following would make it easier to complete the telescope that is being built in the diagram above?
   F The length of the tube that the telescope is being made with
   G What star or planet the student wants to see with the telescope
   H The telescope's altitude
   J Where to place the plane mirror
3. Altering which of the following factors would have the LEAST effect on the telescope's ability to help the student see distant stars?
   A Shape of the concave mirror
   B Size of the convex lens
   C How clean is the plane mirror
   D Total weight of the tube

L2

Teaching

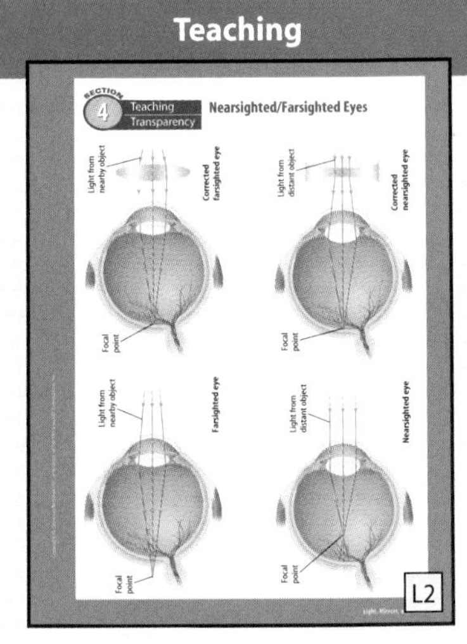
Section 4 Teaching Transparency Nearsighted/Farsighted Eyes

L2

Key to Teaching Strategies

The following designations will help you decide which activities are appropriate for your students.

L1 Level 1 activities should be appropriate for students with learning difficulties.

L2 Level 2 activities should be within the ability range of all students.

L3 Level 3 activities are designed for above-average students.

ELL ELL activities should be within the ability range of English Language Learners.

COOP LEARN Cooperative Learning activities are designed for small group work.

LS Multiple Learning Styles logos, as described on page 22T, are used throughout to indicate strategies that address different learning styles.

P These strategies represent student products that can be placed into a best-work portfolio.

Hands-on Activities

Activity Worksheets

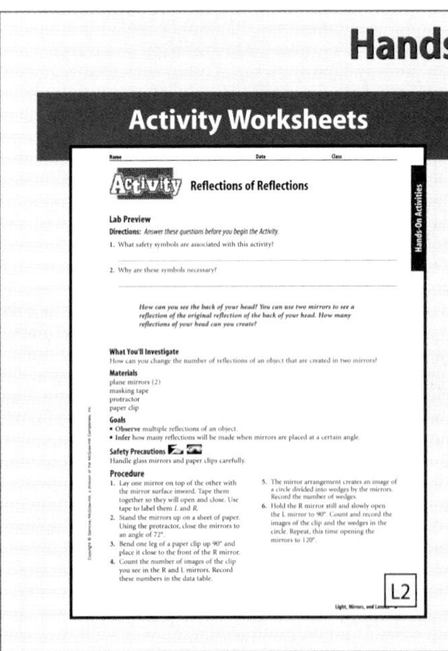
Activity Reflections of Reflections

Lab Preview

Directions: *Answer these questions before you begin the Activity.*

1. What safety symbols are associated with this activity?
2. Why are these symbols necessary?

How can you see the back of your head? You can use two mirrors to see a reflection of the original reflection of the back of your head. How many reflections of your head can you create?

What You'll Investigate

How can you change the number of reflections of an object that are created in two mirrors?

Materials

plane mirrors (2)
masking tape
protractor
paper clip

Goals

- Observe multiple reflections of an object.
- Infer how many reflections will be made when mirrors are placed at a certain angle.

Safety Precautions

Handle glass mirrors and paper clips carefully.

Procedure

1. Lay one mirror on top of the other with the mirror surface inward. Tape them together so they will open and close. Use tape to label them *L* and *R*.
2. Stand the mirrors up on a sheet of paper. Using the protractor, close the mirrors to an angle of 72°.
3. Bend one leg of a paper clip up 90° and place it close to the front of the R mirror.
4. Count the number of images of the clip you see in the R and L mirrors. Record these numbers in the data table.
5. The mirror arrangement creates an image of a circle divided into wedges by the mirrors. Record the number of wedges.
6. Hold the R mirror still and slowly open the L mirror to 90°. Count and record the images of the clip and the wedges in the circle. Repeat, this time opening the mirrors to 120°.

L2

Laboratory Activities

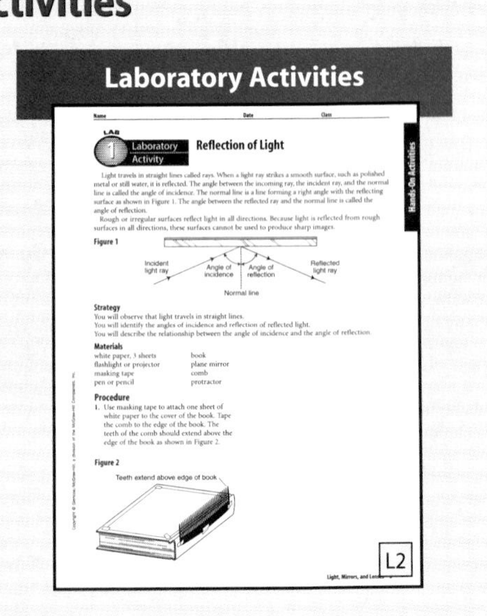
Lab 1 Laboratory Activity Reflection of Light

Light travels in straight lines called rays. When a light ray strikes a smooth surface, such as polished metal or still water, it is reflected. The angle between the incoming ray, the incident ray, and the normal line is called the angle of incidence. The normal line is a line forming a right angle with the reflecting surface as shown in Figure 1. The angle between the reflected ray and the normal line is called the angle of reflection.

Rough or irregular surfaces reflect light in all directions. Because light is reflected from rough surfaces in all directions, these surfaces cannot be used to produce sharp images.

Figure 1

Strategy

You will observe that light travels in straight lines.
You will identify the angles of incidence and reflection of reflected light.
You will describe the relationship between the angle of incidence and the angle of reflection.

Materials

white paper, 3 sheets
flashlight or projector
masking tape
pen or pencil
book
plane mirror
comb
protractor

Procedure

1. Use masking tape to attach one sheet of white paper to the cover of the book. Tape the comb to the edge of the book. The teeth of the comb should extend above the edge of the book as shown in Figure 2.

Figure 2

L2

Meeting Different Ability Levels

Content Outline

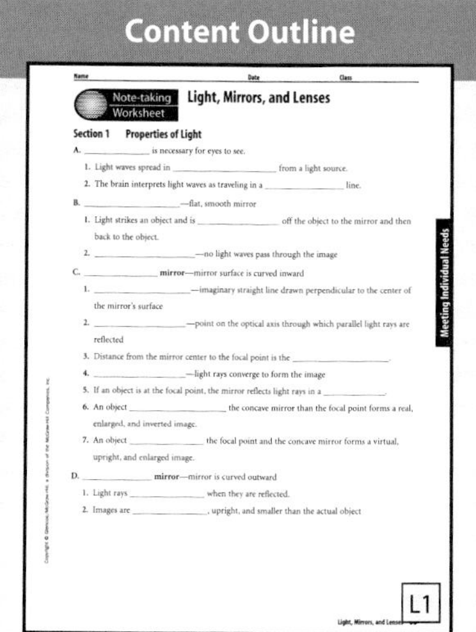
Note-taking Worksheet — Light, Mirrors, and Lenses

Section 1 Properties of Light

A. ________ is necessary for eyes to see.
1. Light waves spread in ________ from a light source.
2. The brain interprets light waves as traveling in a ________ line.

B. ________—flat, smooth mirror
1. Light strikes an object and is ________ off the object to the mirror and then back to the object.
2. ________—no light waves pass through the image

C. ________ mirror—mirror surface is curved inward
1. ________—imaginary straight line drawn perpendicular to the center of the mirror's surface
2. ________—point on the optical axis through which parallel light rays are reflected
3. Distance from the mirror center to the focal point is the ________
4. ________—light rays converge to form the image
5. If an object is at the focal point, the mirror reflects light rays in a ________
6. An object ________ the concave mirror than the focal point forms a real, enlarged, and inverted image.
7. An object ________ the focal point and the concave mirror forms a virtual, upright, and enlarged image.

D. ________ mirror—mirror is curved outward
1. Light rays ________ when they are reflected.
2. Images are ________, upright, and smaller than the actual object

Meeting Individual Needs

L1

Reinforcement

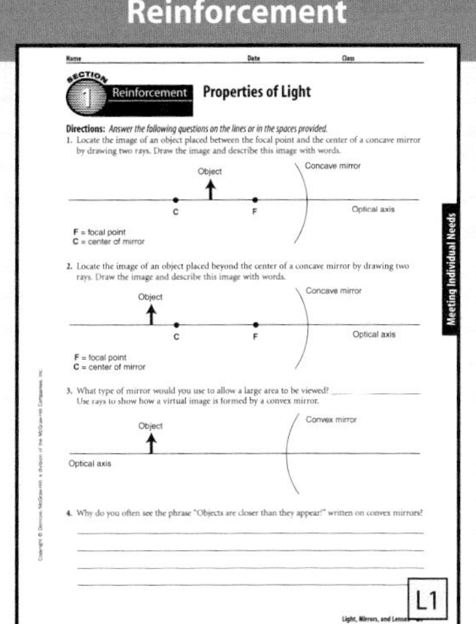
Reinforcement — Properties of Light

Directions: Answer the following questions on the lines or in the spaces provided.

1. Locate the image of an object placed between the focal point and the center of a concave mirror by drawing two rays. Draw the image and describe this image with words.

2. Locate the image of an object placed beyond the center of a concave mirror by drawing two rays. Draw the image and describe this image with words.

3. What type of mirror would you use to allow a large area to be viewed? ________ Use rays to show how a virtual image is formed by a convex mirror.

4. Why do you often see the phrase "Objects are closer than they appear" written on convex mirrors?

Meeting Individual Needs

L1

Directed Reading

Directed Reading for Content Mastery — Overview — Light, Mirrors, and Lenses

Directions: Unscramble the terms in italics to complete the sentences below. Write the terms on the lines provided.

1. When a concave mirror is used to reflect light from an object that is placed farther from the mirror than the focal point, the image formed will be a *lare* image
2. An image that appears to be behind a mirror and cannot be projected onto a screen is called a *trivalu* image.
3. All light rays traveling *lerpalla* to the optical axis are refracted so they pass through the focal point of the lens.
4. Behind the pupil is a flexible convex lens that bends the light rays to form an inverted image on your *tainer*.
5. Most large telescopes today are *gretclenf*.
6. Our view of outer space from the surface of Earth is blurred by Earth's *teersmoaph*.
7. A *leanp* mirror is flat and smooth.
8. All lenses refract *thilg* that passes through them.
9. Light reflected off a subject enters a *macare* through the aperture.
10. When an object is at the *coalf notip* of a concave mirror, the mirror reflects all light rays parallel to the optical axis, creating a beam.
11. The image formed by a *novacec* mirror changes depending on where the object is located.
12. Light rays that hit a convex mirror *deraps trapa* as they are reflected.
13. Light enters your eye through a transparent covering on your eyeball called the *nacrne*.
14. A *comprocise* uses two convex lenses with a relatively short focal length.

Meeting Individual Needs

L1

Assessment

Chapter Tests

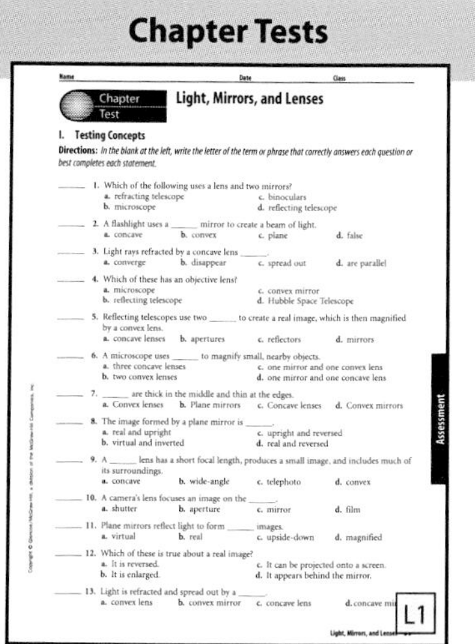
Chapter Test — Light, Mirrors, and Lenses

I. Testing Concepts

Directions: In the blank at the left, write the letter of the term or phrase that correctly answers each question or best completes each statement.

1. Which of the following uses a lens and two mirrors? a. refracting telescope b. microscope c. binoculars d. reflecting telescope
2. A flashlight uses a ____ mirror to create a beam of light. a. concave b. convex c. plane d. false
3. Light rays refracted by a concave lens ____. a. converge b. disappear c. spread out d. are parallel
4. Which of these has an objective lens? a. microscope b. reflecting telescope c. convex mirror d. Hubble Space Telescope
5. Reflecting telescopes use two ____ to create a real image, which is then magnified by a convex lens. a. concave lenses b. apertures c. reflectors d. mirrors
6. A microscope uses ____ to magnify small, nearby objects. a. three concave lenses b. two convex lenses c. one mirror and one convex lens d. one mirror and one concave lens
7. ____ are thick in the middle and thin at the edges. a. Convex lenses b. Plane mirrors c. Concave lenses d. Convex mirrors
8. The image formed by a plane mirror is ____. a. real and upright b. virtual and inverted c. upright and reversed d. real and reversed
9. A ____ lens has a short focal length, produces a small image, and includes much of its surroundings. a. concave b. wide-angle c. telephoto d. convex
10. A camera's lens focuses an image on the ____. a. shutter b. aperture c. mirror d. film
11. Plane mirrors reflect light to form ____ images. a. virtual b. real c. upside-down d. magnified
12. Which of these is true about a real image? a. It is reversed. b. It is enlarged. c. It can be projected onto a screen. d. It appears behind the mirror.
13. Light is refracted and spread out by a ____. a. convex lens b. convex mirror c. concave lens d. concave mi...

Assessment

L1

Enrichment

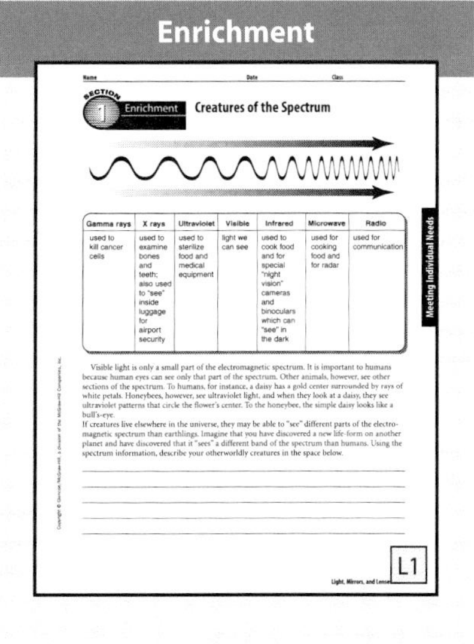
Enrichment — Creatures of the Spectrum

Gamma rays	X rays	Ultraviolet	Visible	Infrared	Microwave	Radio
used to kill cancer cells	used to examine bones and teeth; also used to "see" inside luggage for airport security	used to sterilize food and medical equipment	light we can see	used to cook food and for special "night vision" cameras and binoculars which can "see" in the dark	used for cooking food and for radar	used for communication

Visible light is only a small part of the electromagnetic spectrum. It is important to humans because human eyes can see only that part of the spectrum. Other animals, however, see other sections of the spectrum. To humans, for instance, a daisy has a gold center surrounded by rays of white petals. Honeybees, however, see ultraviolet light, and when they look at a daisy, they see ultraviolet patterns that circle the flower's center. To the honeybee, the simple daisy looks like a bull's-eye.

If creatures live elsewhere in the universe, they may be able to "see" different parts of the electromagnetic spectrum than earthlings. Imagine that you have discovered a new life-form on another planet and have discovered that it "sees" a different band of the spectrum than humans. Using the spectrum information, describe your otherworldly creatures in the space below.

Meeting Individual Needs

L1

Spanish Directed Reading

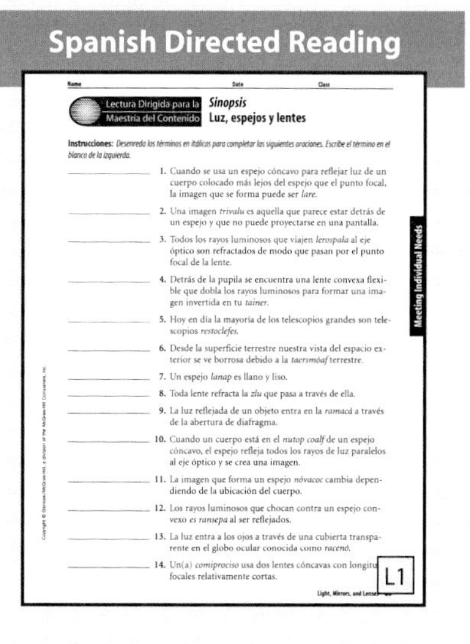
Lectura Dirigida para la Maestría del Contenido — Sinopsis — Luz, espejos y lentes

Instrucciones: Desenreda los términos en itálicas para completar las siguientes oraciones. Escribe el término en el blanco de la izquierda.

1. Cuando se usa un espejo cóncavo para reflejar luz de un cuerpo colocado más lejos del espejo que el punto focal, la imagen que se forma puede ser *lare*.
2. Una imagen *trivalu* es aquella que parece estar detrás de un espejo y que no puede proyectarse en una pantalla.
3. Todos los rayos luminosos que viajen *lerospala* al eje óptico son refractados de modo que pasan por el punto focal de la lente.
4. Detrás de la pupila se encuentra una lente convexa flexible que dobla los rayos luminosos para formar una imagen invertida en tu *tainer*.
5. Hoy en día la mayoría de los telescopios grandes son telescopios *restoclefes*.
6. Desde la superficie terrestre nuestra vista del espacio exterior se ve borrosa debido a la *tuersmiaf* terrestre.
7. Un espejo *lanap* es llano y liso.
8. Toda lente refracta la *zlu* que pasa a través de ella.
9. La luz reflejada de un objeto entra en la *ramacá* a través de la abertura de diafragma.
10. Cuando un cuerpo está en el *nutop coalf* de un espejo cóncavo, el espejo refleja todos los rayos de luz paralelos al eje óptico y se crea una imagen.
11. La imagen que forma un espejo *nóvacoc* cambia dependiendo de la ubicación del cuerpo.
12. Los rayos luminosos que chocan contra un espejo convexo *es ransepa* al ser reflejados.
13. La luz entra a los ojos a través de una cubierta transparente en el globo ocular conocida como *racená*.
14. Un(a) *comiprociso* usa dos lentes cóncavas con longitudes focales relativamente cortas.

Meeting Individual Needs

L1

Test Practice Workbook

Chapter Review

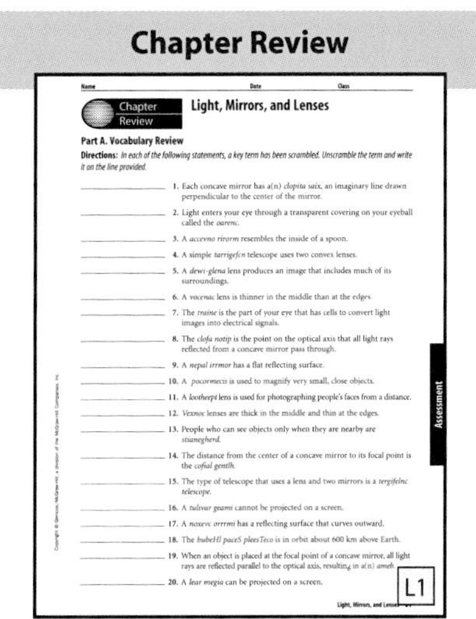
Chapter Review — Light, Mirrors, and Lenses

Part A. Vocabulary Review

Directions: In each of the following statements, a key term has been scrambled. Unscramble the term and write it on the line provided.

1. Each concave mirror has a(n) *clopita sxia*, an imaginary line drawn perpendicular to the center of the mirror.
2. Light enters your eye through a transparent covering on your eyeball called the *aerenc*.
3. A *accevno rirorm* resembles the inside of a spoon.
4. A simple *tarrigefcn* telescope uses two convex lenses.
5. A *dewi-glena* lens produces an image that includes much of its surroundings.
6. A *vocenac* lens is thinner in the middle than at the edges.
7. The *traine* is the part of your eye that has cells to convert light images into electrical signals.
8. The *clofa notip* is the point on the optical axis that all light rays reflected from a concave mirror pass through.
9. A *nepal irrmor* has a flat reflecting surface.
10. A *pocormecis* is used to magnify very small, close objects.
11. A *leothept* lens is used for photographing people's faces from a distance.
12. *Vexnoc* lenses are thick in the middle and thin at the edges.
13. People who can see objects only when they are nearby are *stiuneghred*.
14. The distance from the center of a concave mirror to its focal point is the *cofial gentlh*.
15. The type of telescope that uses a lens and two mirrors is a *terpilcnc* telescope.
16. A *tuliuvr geami* cannot be projected on a screen.
17. A *noxevc orrrmi* has a reflecting surface that curves outward.
18. The *bubelH paceS plessTeco* is in orbit about 600 km above Earth.
19. When an object is placed at the focal point of a concave mirror, all light rays are reflected parallel to the optical axis, resulting in a(n) *amelb*.
20. A *leur megia* can be projected on a screen.

Assessment

L1

Science Content Background

Properties of Light

Light and Matter

When light strikes an object, some of the energy carried by the light wave is absorbed, and some is re-emitted. The frequencies of the re-emitted light waves depend on the types of atoms involved and the bonding between them.

Some objects that are opaque become translucent or transparent if they are made thin enough. Similarly, some objects that are transparent become translucent or opaque if they are made thick enough.

Student Misconception

Light produces an effect but does not travel through matter or space.

Refer to the facing page for teaching strategies to address this misconception. Refer to pages 404–405 for content related to this topic.

A candle burns and illuminates objects on a table. Shadows of cups dance on the walls. The candle is obvious as a source of light. The light's effects of illumination and shadow formation are perceived. The traveling rays of light, however, are not directly observed. Explanations in the science of optics involve traveling light, in the form of rays. Failure to recognize light as traveling rays will interfere with understanding optics.

Reflection and Mirrors

Reflection and Surfaces

Mirrors form two types of images. The image formed by a plane mirror, a convex mirror, or a concave mirror with the object inside the focal point is called a virtual image. A virtual image forms because no light waves emanate from where the image seems to be. A concave mirror forms a real image when the object is outside the focal point. In this case, light waves from the object are brought to focus at the location of the image, and the image can be projected onto a surface placed at this location.

Refraction and Lenses

Concave and Convex Lenses

Lenses also from real and virtual images. Images formed when a lensor mirror causes light waves to diverge are virtual images. Images formed by converging light waves are real images.

SECTION 4

Using Mirrors and Lenses

Microscopes

As an image is magnified, the light from the image is spread over a much larger area, causing the image to appear dim. A high-powered microscope usually illuminates the object with bright light so that the magnified image is as bright as possible.

Telescopes

The large size of a telescope's objective lens or mirror enables it to gather much more light than the human eye alone. If an object is far away, only a small portion of the light from the object strikes an observer's eye. A bright, more detailed image can be formed if more of the light from the object is collected, and this image further magnified.

For additional content background on this topic, go to the Glencoe Science Web site at science.glencoe.com.

IDENTIFYING Misconceptions

Find Out What Students Think

Students may think that . . .

- **Light comes from a source and produces an effect, but light does not travel through matter or vacuums as rays having a finite speed.**

Language and perception play a large role in people's conceptions about the world. People often use the term light to refer to illuminating electrical devices. Phrases such as "turn on the light" and "the light is broken" confirm these uses. The effects of light are constantly and directly observed. For example some things are lit up and others are in shadows. Further, when a light bulb has been turned on it seems to light up the room immediately thus masking the fact that the light took time to travel. Thinking of light as a source or an effect may interfere with an important foundation for optics—learning the concept of light as a traveling entity that moves at finite speeds.

Demonstration

Set up a flashlight on a stack of books. Have the flashlight point to a screen. Turn off the room lights and turn on the flashlight. Have students write down where there is light. They may initially only say there is light (a) at the bulb and (b) at the screen and not realize that light exists between the bulb and the screen as it travels.

Telegraph Colour Library/FPG International

Promote Understanding

Activity

Divide the class into groups.

- Give each group of students a flashlight and a paper screen.
- Have students in each group set its flashlight on books so it shines directly on the paper screen.
- Turn off the classroom lights.
- Ask students to observe the light from the flashlight.
- Ask students if there is light between the flashlight bulb and the paper screen. Have students in each group discuss the question and agree on an answer.
- Turn on the lights and have groups share their thoughts.
- Turn off the lights and then clap chalk erasers above each group's light beams so students can see the dust particles illuminated in the beam.
- Have students discuss again where there is light. Make sure they understand that light exists everywhere along the path from the bulb to the screen.

Assess

After completing the chapter, see *Identifying Misconceptions* in the Study Guide.

CHAPTER 14

Light, Mirrors, and Lenses

Chapter Vocabulary

light ray
medium
reflection
law of reflection
focal point
focal length
refraction
lens
convex lens
concave lens
refracting telescope
reflecting telescope

What do you think?

Science Journal The picture shows optical fibers. The fibers are constructed so that light can leave only through the ends.

CHAPTER 14

Light, Mirrors, and Lenses

You walk through a door of the fun house and are bombarded by images of yourself. In one mirror, your face seems smashed. You turn around and face another mirror—your chin and neck are gigantic. How do mirrors in a fun house make you look so strange? In this chapter, you'll learn how mirrors and lenses create images. You'll also learn why objects have the colors they have, and how you see.

What do you think?

Science Journal Look at the picture below with a classmate. Discuss what you think this might be or what is happening. Here's a hint: *It helps you keep in touch.* Write down your answer or your best guess in your Science Journal.

402

Theme Connection

Energy Light waves carry energy. This energy can pass through materials, be absorbed by materials, and be reflected by materials.

Everything you see results from light waves entering your eyes. These light waves are either given off by objects, such as the Sun and lightbulbs, or reflected by objects, such as trees, books, and people. Lenses and mirrors can cause light to change direction and make objects seem larger or smaller. What happens to light as it passes from one material to another?

Observe the bending of light

1. Place two paper cups next to each other and put a penny in the bottom of each cup.
2. Fill one of the cups with water and observe how the penny looks.
3. Looking straight down at the cups, slide the cup with no water away from you just until you can no longer see the penny.
4. Pour water into this cup and observe what seems to happen to the penny.

Observe

In your Science Journal, record your observations. Did adding water make the cup look deeper or shallower?

Before You Read

FOLDABLES Reading & Study Skills

Making a Question Study Fold **Asking yourself questions helps you stay focused so you will better understand light, mirrors, and lenses when you are reading the chapter.**

1. Stack two sheets of paper in front of you so the short side of both sheets is at the top.
2. Slide the top sheet up so about 4 cm of the bottom sheet show.
3. Fold both sheets top to bottom to form four tabs and staple along the fold as shown.
4. Title the Foldable *Light, Mirrors, and Lenses* as shown. Write these questions on the flaps: *What are the properties of light? What is reflection? What is refraction?*

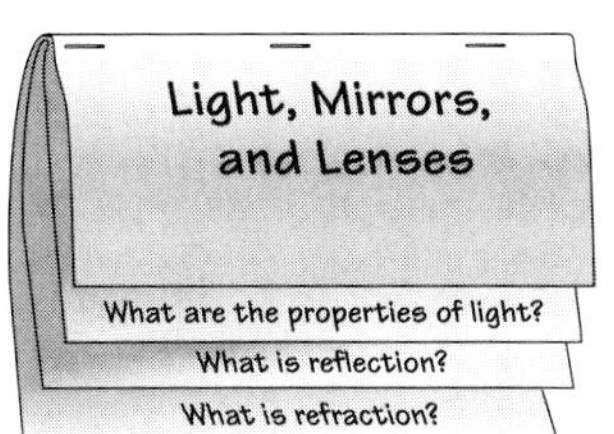

5. Before you read the chapter, try to answer the questions with what you already know. As you read the chapter, add to or correct your answers under the flaps.

EXPLORE ACTIVITY

Purpose Use the Explore Activity to introduce students to the idea that light changes direction when it passes from one material to another. L2 ELL

LS **Visual-Spatial**

Materials two paper cups, two pennies, water

Alternate Materials Any small opaque cups may be used provided they are not too tall.

Troubleshooting In step 4, the penny needs to remain in place so students can observe how the water affects what they see. Suggest that students place the penny near one side of the cup and pour the water near the other side.

Observe

Possible answer: Adding water made the cup seem shallower. When the cup was pushed away so that the penny was not visible, adding water made it possible to see the penny.

Process Ask students to infer why adding water enabled them to see the penny that had been out of their sight. The water bent the light rays. Use **Performance Assessment in the Science Classroom**, p. 89.

Before You Read

FOLDABLES Reading & Study Skills

Dinah Zike Study Fold

Purpose Use this activity to determine what students know about light, reflection, and refraction before they read the chapter. The activity results in a Foldable with three focus questions in which students can record notes and information as they read.

For additional help, see Foldables Worksheet, p. 17 in **Chapter Resources Booklet,** or go to the Glencoe Science Web site at **science.glencoe.com.** See After You Read in the Study Guide at the end of this chapter.

SECTION 1

Properties of Light

1 Motivate

Bellringer Transparency

Display the Section Focus Transparency for Section 1. Use the accompanying Transparency Activity Master. L2 ELL

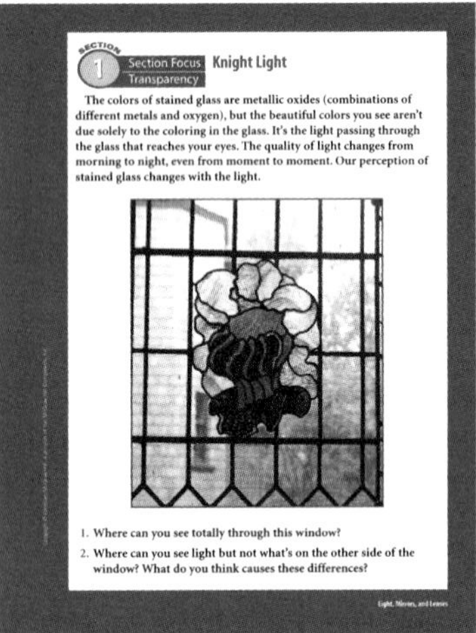

SECTION 1 Section Focus Transparency **Knight Light**

The colors of stained glass are metallic oxides (combinations of different metals and oxygen), but the beautiful colors you see aren't due solely to the coloring in the glass. It's the light passing through the glass that reaches your eyes. The quality of light changes from morning to night, even from moment to moment. Our perception of stained glass changes with the light.

1. Where can you see totally through this window?
2. Where can you see light but not what's on the other side of the window? What do you think causes these differences?

Light, Mirrors, and Lenses

Tie to Prior Knowledge

Have students list types of waves with which they are familiar, such as ocean waves or sound waves. Discuss how these waves are similar to one another and how they are different. Explain that in this section they will learn about light waves.

SECTION 1

Properties of Light

As You Read

***What* You'll Learn**

- **Describe** the wave nature of light.
- **Explain** how light interacts with materials.
- **Determine** why objects appear to have color.

Vocabulary

light ray
medium
reflection

***Why* It's Important**

Most of what you know about your surroundings comes from information carried by light waves.

What is light?

Drop a rock on the smooth surface of a pond, and you'll see ripples spread outward from the spot where the rock struck. The rock produced a wave much like the one in **Figure 1A.** A wave is a rhythmic disturbance that carries energy through matter or space. The matter in this case is the water, and the energy comes from the impact of the rock. As the ripples spread out, they carry some of that energy.

Light is a type of wave that carries energy. A source of light such as the Sun or a lightbulb gives off light waves into space, just as the rock hitting the pond causes waves to form in the water. But while the water waves spread out only on the surface of the pond, light waves spread out in all directions from the light source. **Figure 1B** shows how light waves travel.

Sometimes, however, it is easier to think of light in a different way. A **light ray** is a narrow beam of light that travels in a straight line. You can think of a source of light as giving off, or emitting, a countless number of light rays that are traveling away from the source in all directions.

Figure 1
Waves spread in all directions and carry energy.

A Ripples on the surface of a pond are produced by an object hitting the water. As the ripples spread out from the point of impact, they carry energy.

B A source of light, such as a lightbulb, gives off light rays that travel away from the light source in all directions.

Section Assessment Planner

PORTFOLIO
Make a Model, p. 406

PERFORMANCE ASSESSMENT
Try At Home MiniLAB, p. 405
Skill Builder Activities, p. 408
See page 432 for more options.

CONTENT ASSESSMENT
Section, 408
Challenge, p. 408
Chapter, pp. 432–433

Light Travels Through Space There is, however, one important difference between light waves and the water wave ripples on a pond. If the pond dried up and had no water, ripples could not form. Waves on a pond need a material—water—in which to travel. The material through which a wave travels is called a **medium.** Light is an electromagnetic wave and doesn't need a medium in which to travel. Electromagnetic waves can travel in a vacuum, as well as through materials such as air, water, and glass.

Light and Matter

What can you see when you are in a closed room with no windows and the lights are out? You can see nothing until you turn on a light or open a door to let in light from outside the room. Most objects do not give off light on their own. They can be seen only if light waves from another source bounce off them and into your eyes, as shown in **Figure 2.** The process of light striking an object and bouncing off is called **reflection.** Right now, you can see these words because light emitted by a source of light is reflecting from the page and into your eyes. Not all the light rays reflected from the page strike your eyes. Light rays striking the page are reflected in many directions, and only some of these rays enter your eyes.

Reading Check *What must happen for you to see most objects?*

TRY AT HOME Mini LAB

Observing Colors in the Dark

Procedure

1. Get six pieces of **paper** that are different colors and about 10 cm × 10 cm.
2. Darken a room and wait 10 min for your eyes to adjust to the darkness.
3. Write on each paper what color you think the paper is.
4. Turn on the lights and see if your night vision detected the colors.

Analysis

1. If the room were perfectly dark, what would you see? Explain.
2. Your eyes contain structures called rods and cones. Rods don't detect color, but need only a little light. Cones detect color, but need more light. Which structure was working in the dark room? Explain.

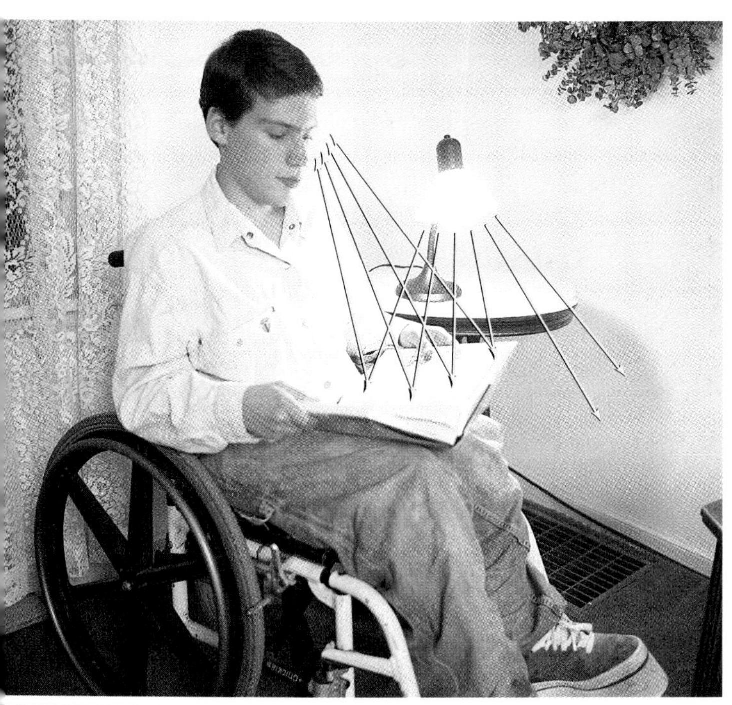

Figure 2
Light waves are given off by the lightbulb. Some of these light waves hit the page and are reflected. The student sees the page when some of these reflected waves enter the student's eyes.

2 Teach

What is light?

Students may think that light produces an effect but does not travel through matter or space. See page 402F for teaching strategies related to this misconception.

Light and Matter

TRY AT HOME Mini LAB

Purpose Students will investigate how their eyes depend on light. L2 ELL LS **Visual-Spatial**

Materials six pieces of paper, each a different color

Teaching Strategy Suggest students try the experiment in rooms with different levels of darkness.

Analysis

1. Nothing; seeing depends on light bouncing off an object.
2. Since some color could be seen, both rods and cones were working.

Process Have students work in small groups to design an experiment to test which colors are easiest to distinguish in dim light. Use **PASC**, p. 95.

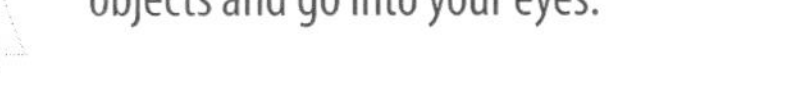

Answer Light must reflect off the objects and go into your eyes.

Resource Manager

Chapter Resources Booklet
Transparency Activity, p. 48
MiniLAB, p. 3
Lab Activity, pp. 9–12, 13–16

Teacher FYI

Visible light is part of the electromagnetic spectrum—waves generated by oscillating electric and magnetic fields. The electromagnetic spectrum also includes radio waves, microwaves, X rays, infrared waves, and ultraviolet waves. The frequency and wavelength of an electromagnetic wave determines which type of wave it is.

Light and Matter, continued

Caption Answer

Figure 3 transparent materials

Make a Model

Glass is transparent to visible light, but is opaque to infrared waves. Objects in a greenhouse absorb the visible light and reemit infrared waves, which can't escape. This causes the temperature in the greenhouse to increase. Have students build a small model of a greenhouse and set the model in the Sun. Have them measure and record the temperature of the air outside and inside this model. Have students compare temperatures and explain the reasons for any differences. L2 ELL COOP LEARN LS **Kinesthetic** P

Color

Use Science Words

Word Meaning Have students define *wavelength* from the meanings of the parts of the word. Wavelength is the distance between two corresponding points on a wave. L2 LS **Linguistic**

Caption Answer

Figure 4 red, orange, yellow, green, blue, indigo, and violet

Extension

Tell students that fluorescent lights and incandescent lights don't produce white light. They produce slightly different colors, depending on the type of bulb used. Have students find out what colors these lights produce. Incandescent bulbs produce light that has more red than white light has, while fluorescent bulbs can vary considerably. L3 LS **Logical-Mathematical**

A An opaque object allows no light to pass through it.

B A translucent object allows some light to pass through it.

C A transparent object allows almost all light to pass through it.

Figure 3
Materials are opaque, translucent, or transparent depending on how much light passes through them. *Which type of material reflects the least amount of light?*

Opaque, Translucent, and Transparent When light waves strike an object, some of the waves are absorbed by it, some of the waves are reflected by it, and some of the light waves might pass straight through it. What happens to light when it strikes the object depends on the material that the object is made of.

All objects reflect and absorb some light waves. Materials that let no light pass through them are opaque (oh PAYK). You cannot see other objects through opaque materials. On the other hand, you clearly can see other objects through materials such as glass and clear plastic that allow nearly all the light that strikes them to pass through. These materials are transparent. A third type of material allows only some light to pass through. Although objects behind these materials are visible, they are not clear. These materials, such as waxed paper or frosted glass, are translucent (trans LEW sent). Examples of opaque, translucent, and transparent objects are shown in **Figure 3.**

Figure 4
A beam of white light passing through a prism is separated into many colors. *What colors can you see emerging from the prism?*

Color

The light from the Sun might look white, but it is a mixture of colors. Each different color of light is a different wavelength. You sometimes can see the different colors of the Sun's light when it passes through raindrops to make a rainbow. As shown in **Figure 4,** white light is separated into different colors when it passes through a prism. The colors in white light range from red to violet. When light waves from all these colors enter the eye at the same time, the brain interprets the mixture as being white.

Curriculum Connection

Math The intensity of light striking a surface decreases as the surface gets farther from the source. This decrease is given by the formula $I = P/d^2$, where I is the light intensity , d is the distance to the source, and P is related to the power emitted by the light source. **If P remains constant, what will be the difference in the intensity of light striking a card 1 m from a lightbulb and light striking a card 4 m from the bulb?** The light striking the card 4 m from the lightbulb will have 1/16 less intensity than will the light striking the card 1 m from the lightbulb. L3 LS **Logical-Mathematical**

Why do Objects Have Color? Why does grass look green or a rose look red? When a mixture of light waves strikes an object that is not transparent, the object absorbs some of the light waves. Some of the light waves that are not absorbed are reflected. If an object reflects red waves and absorbs all the other waves, it looks red. Similarly, if an object looks blue, it reflects only blue light waves and absorbs all the others. An object that reflects all the light waves that strike it looks white, while one that reflects none of the light waves that strike it looks black. **Figure 5** shows gym shoes and socks as seen under white light and as seen when viewed through a red filter that allows only red light to pass through it.

Figure 5
A Examine the pair of gym shoes and socks as they are seen under white light. *Why do the socks look blue under white light?*
B The same shoes and socks were photographed through a red filter. *Why do the blue socks look black when viewed under red light?*

Primary Light Colors How many colors exist? People often say white light is made up of red, orange, yellow, green, blue, and violet light. This isn't completely true, though. Many more colors than this exist. In reality, humans can distinguish thousands of colors, including some such as brown, pink, and purple, that are not found among the colors of the rainbow.

Light of almost any color can be made by mixing different amounts of red, green, and blue light. Red, green, and blue are known as the primary colors. Look at **Figure 6.** White light is produced where beams of red, green, and blue light overlap. Yellow light is produced where red and green light overlap. You see the color yellow because of the way your brain interprets the combination of the red and green light striking your eye. This combination of light waves looks the same as yellow light produced by a prism, even though these light waves have only a single wavelength.

Figure 6
By mixing light from the three primary colors—red, blue, and green—all of the visible colors can be made.

Caption Answers

Figure 5A The socks reflect only blue light.

Figure 5B The red filter allows through only red light. None of the blue light reflected by the socks passes through, so they look black.

Quick Demo

Pass a beam of white light through a prism or hold the prism in front of an overhead projector. Ask students whether the colors that are visible are the only colors of light. Have them justify their answers. No; humans can distinguish thousands of colors. L2 LS **Visual-Spatial**

Extension

Ask students how they know that light has been absorbed or reflected. Have them list the evidence for each, and compare their lists with those made by other students in the class. The darker an object, the more light it absorbs. Absorbing light also raises the temperature of an object. Therefore, objects that reflect light are cooler and lighter in color than those that absorb light. LS **Interpersonal**

Visual Learning

Figure 6 Explain that each of the three primary colors is a range of wavelengths. Red is a range of long wavelengths peaking in the red region. Green is a range of medium-length wavelengths peaking in the green region. Blue is a range of short wavelengths peaking in the blue region. Ask students to use this description to explain the yellow overlap region in the figure. Mixing the longer wavelengths that form red and the medium-length wavelengths that form green produces a range of wavelengths that peaks in the middle of these in the orange region. L3 LS **Visual-Spatial**

Resource Manager

Chapter Resources Booklet
Directed Reading for Content Mastery, pp. 19, 20
Note-taking Worksheets, pp. 35–38

Life Science Critical Thinking/Problem Solving, p. 8

Active Reading

Think-Pair-Share This strategy encourages students to think first before discussing their ideas or thoughts about a topic. Students are asked to respond to a question by writing a response. After thinking for a few minutes, partners share responses to the question. Finally, the teacher asks the students to share responses with the class. Have students become involved in a Think-Pair-Share about color.

Color, continued

Answer yellow, magenta, cyan

3 Assess

Reteach

Quiz students on combining colors. **What are the primary colors of light?** red, green, and blue **What are the primary pigment colors?** yellow, cyan, and magenta **What color is formed when red light and blue light combine?** magenta **What color is formed when yellow pigment and cyan pigment combine?** green L2 **LS Visual-Spatial**

Challenge

How is the rainbow produced when light passes through a prism similar to the rainbow of colors seen on a mud puddle with oil in it? Possible answer: The thin layer of oil separates light into colors just as the glass prism does. L3

LS Logical-Mathematical

Content Ask students to draw diagrams illustrating the difference between light waves and a light ray. A light ray is one of the countless rays emitted by a light source that move away from the source in all directions as light waves. Use **Performance Assessment in the Science Classroom**, p. 127.

Figure 7
The three primary color pigments—yellow, magenta, and cyan—can form all the visible colors when mixed together in various amounts.

Primary Pigment Colors If you like to paint, you might mix two or more different colors to make a new color. Materials like paint that are used to change the color of other objects, such as the walls of a room or an artist's canvas, are called pigments. Mixing pigments together forms colors in a different way than mixing colored lights does.

Like all materials that appear to be colored, pigments absorb some light waves and reflect others. The color of the pigment you see is the color of the light waves that are reflected from it. However, the primary pigment colors are not red, blue, and green—they are yellow, magenta, and cyan. You can make any color of pigment by mixing different amounts of these primary pigment colors, as shown in **Figure 7.**

Reading Check *What are the primary pigment colors?*

Although primary pigment colors are not the same as the primary light colors, they are related. Each primary pigment color results when a pigment absorbs a primary light color. For example, a yellow pigment absorbs blue light and it reflects red and green light, which combine to form yellow. A magenta pigment, on the other hand, absorbs green light and reflects red and blue light, which combine to form magenta. Each of the primary pigment colors is the same color as white light with one primary color removed.

Section  Assessment

1. At night in your room, you are reading a magazine. Describe the path light takes that enables you to see the page.
2. What is the difference between an opaque object and a transparent object?
3. What colors are reflected by an object that appears black? Explain.
4. What is the difference between primary light colors and primary pigment colors?
5. **Think Critically** When you're in direct sunlight, why do you feel cooler if you're wearing light-colored clothes than if you're wearing darker-colored clothes?

Skill Builder Activities

6. **Drawing Conclusions** A white plastic bowl and a black plastic bowl have been sitting in the sunlight. You observe that the black bowl feels warmer than the white bowl. From this information, conclude which of the bowls absorbs and which reflects more sunlight. **For more help, refer to the Science Skill Handbook.**
7. **Communicating** Read an article about the greenhouse effect and draw a diagram in your Science Journal explaining how the greenhouse effect involves absorption. **For more help, refer to the Science Skill Handbook.**

Resource Manager

Chapter Resources Booklet
Enrichment, p. 31
Reinforcement, p. 27

Answers to Section Assessment

1. Light from a lamp reflects off the magazine to your eyes.
2. An opaque object does not let light pass through, and a transparent object does.
3. No colors are reflected by an object that appears black.
4. Primary light colors can be mixed to produce any other color of light. Primary pigment colors result when a pigment absorbs a primary light color.
5. The light-colored clothes reflect light, while the dark-colored clothes absorb light, which raises their temperature.
6. The black bowl absorbs more sunlight, and the white bowl reflects more sunlight.
7. Light passes through the atmosphere and is absorbed by Earth. It is reemitted as infrared radiation that can't escape through the atmosphere, so it warms Earth.

408 CHAPTER 14 Light, Mirrors, and Lenses

SECTION

Reflection and Mirrors

The Law of Reflection

You've probably noticed your image on the surface of a pool or lake. If the surface of the water was smooth, you could see your face clearly. If the surface of the water was wavy, however, your face might have seemed distorted. The image you saw was the result of light reflecting from the surface and traveling to your eyes. How the light was reflected determined the sharpness of the image you saw.

When a light ray strikes a surface and is reflected as in **Figure 8,** the reflected ray obeys the law of reflection. Imagine a line that is drawn perpendicular to the surface where the light ray strikes. This line is called the normal to the surface. The incoming ray and the normal form an angle called the angle of incidence. The reflected light ray forms an angle with the normal called the angle of reflection. According to the **law of reflection,** the angle of incidence is equal to the angle of reflection. This is true for any surface, no matter what material it is made of.

Reflection from Surfaces

Why can you see your reflection in some surfaces and not others? Why does a piece of shiny metal make a good mirror, but a piece of paper does not? The answers have to do with the smoothness of each surface.

As You Read

What You'll Learn

- **Explain** how light is reflected from rough and smooth surfaces.
- **Determine** how mirrors form an image.
- **Describe** how concave and convex mirrors form an image.

Vocabulary

law of reflection
focal point
focal length

Why It's Important

Mirrors can change the direction of light waves and enable you to see images, such as your own face, that normally would not be in view.

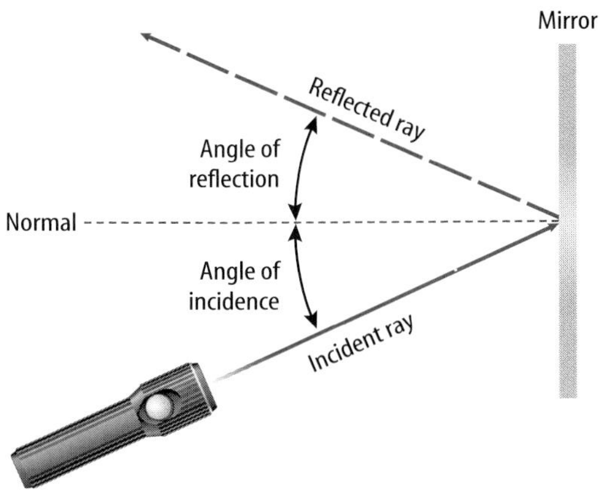

Figure 8
A light ray strikes a surface and is reflected. The angle of incidence is always equal to the angle of reflection. This is the law of reflection.

Section Assessment Planner

Portfolio
Visual Learning, p. 410
Performance Assessment
Skill Builder Activities, p. 414
See page 432 for more options.

Content Assessment
Section, p. 414
Challenge, p. 414
Chapter, pp. 432–433

SECTION

Reflection and Mirrors

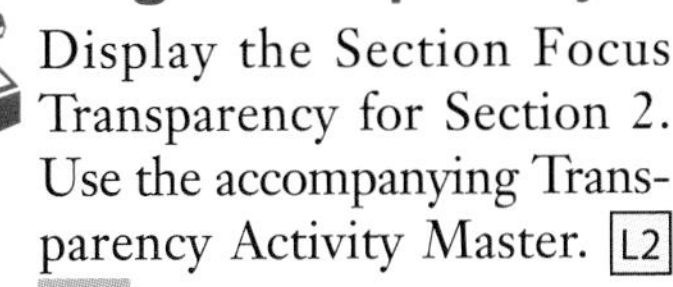

Bellringer Transparency

Display the Section Focus Transparency for Section 2. Use the accompanying Transparency Activity Master. L2 ELL

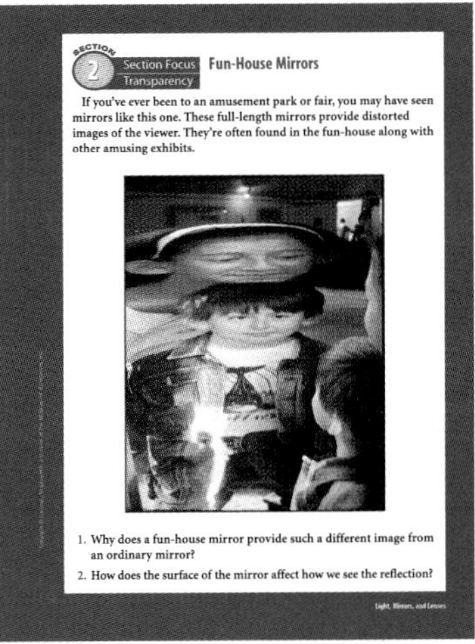

SECTION 2 Section Focus Transparency **Fun-House Mirrors**

If you've ever been to an amusement park or fair, you may have seen mirrors like this one. These full-length mirrors provide distorted images of the viewer. They're often found in the fun-house along with other amusing exhibits.

1. Why does a fun-house mirror provide such a different image from an ordinary mirror?
2. How does the surface of the mirror affect how we see the reflection?

Light, Mirrors, and Lenses

Tie to Prior Knowledge

Ask students to describe how a ball bounces off a flat surface. Compare the angles the ball makes with the surface before and after the bounce. The angles are the same. Tell students that when light is reflected off flat surfaces, the angle it makes with the surface before it reflects is the same as the angle it makes after it reflects.

2 Teach

The Law of Reflection

Quick Demo

Draw on the board a diagram showing a surface, a line normal to that surface, and a light ray striking the surface and being reflected. Point out to students the angle of incidence and the angle of reflection. Make sure these two angles are the same. L2 LS **Visual-Spatial**

Make a Model

Have students work in small groups to model the law of reflection. First, students should use chalk to draw a line normal to a wall. One student should then roll a ball toward the wall at a pre-determined angle to the normal. Another student will determine the angle of reflection that the ball makes as it bounces off the wall. Students should be able to relate this to the way light reflects off a flat surface. L2 LS **Kinesthetic**

Reflection from Surfaces

Teacher FYI

In order to give a mirror the ability to reflect, the hills and valleys on the surface must be smaller than the wavelengths of visible light, or smaller than about 40 millionths of a centimeter.

Figure 9
A highly magnified view of the surface of a paper towel shows that the surface is made of many cellulose wood fibers that make it rough and uneven.

Regular and Diffuse Reflection Even though the surface of the paper might seem smooth, it's not as smooth as the surface of a mirror. **Figure 9** shows how rough the surface of a piece of paper looks when it is viewed under a microscope. The rough surface causes light rays to be reflected from it in many directions, as shown in **Figure 10A.** This uneven reflection of light waves from a rough surface is diffuse reflection. The smoother surfaces of mirrors, as shown in **Figure 10B,** reflect light waves in a much more regular way. For example, parallel rays remain parallel after they are reflected from a mirror. Reflection from mirrors is known as regular reflection. Light waves that are regularly reflected from a surface form the image you see in a mirror or any other smooth surface. Whether a surface is smooth or rough, every light ray that strikes it obeys the law of reflection.

Reading Check *Why does a rough surface cause a diffuse reflection?*

Scattering of Light When diffuse reflection occurs, light waves that were traveling in a single direction are reflected, and then travel in many different directions. Scattering occurs when light waves traveling in one direction are made to travel in many different directions. Scattering also can occur when light waves strike small particles, such as dust. You may have seen dust particles floating in a beam of sunlight. When the light waves in the sunbeam strike a dust particle, they are scattered in all directions. You see the dust particle as bright specks of light when some of these scattered light waves enter your eye.

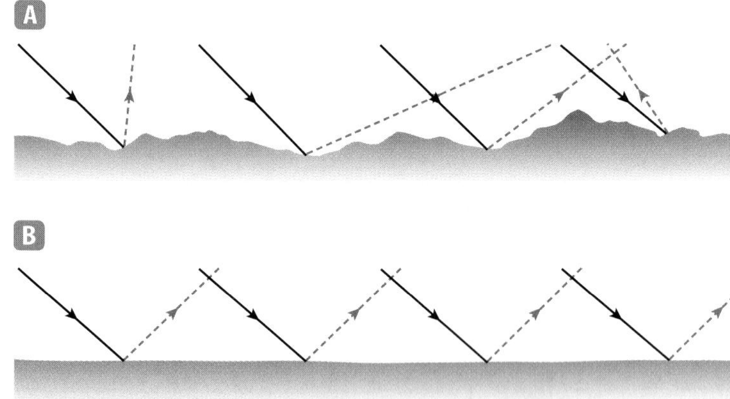

Figure 10
A A rough surface causes parallel light rays to be reflected in many different directions.
B A smooth surface causes parallel light rays to be reflected in a single direction.

Visual Learning

Figure 10 Review with students the reflection of light from a rough surface shown in **Figure 10A** and the reflection of light from a smooth surface shown in **Figure 10B.** Ask students to draw diagrams showing how light is reflected from a piece of crumpled aluminum foil. The surface of the crumpled foil is rougher than a mirror but less rough than the surface shown in **Figure 10A.** Therefore the light would be reflected to form many different little images as from many little mirrors. L2 LS **Visual-Spatial** P

Reading Check

Answer The rough surface causes light to be reflected in many different directions.

A

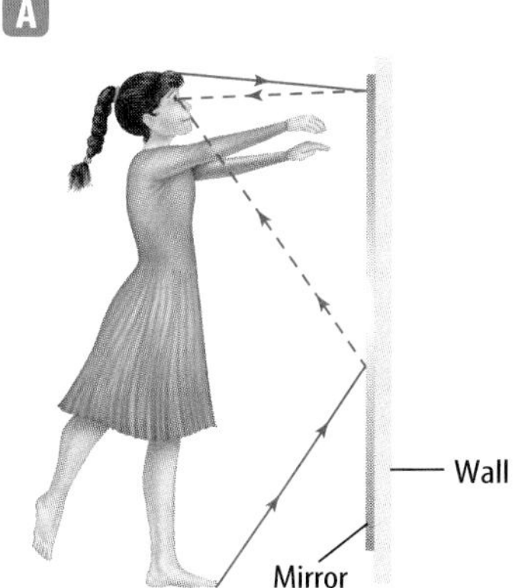

B

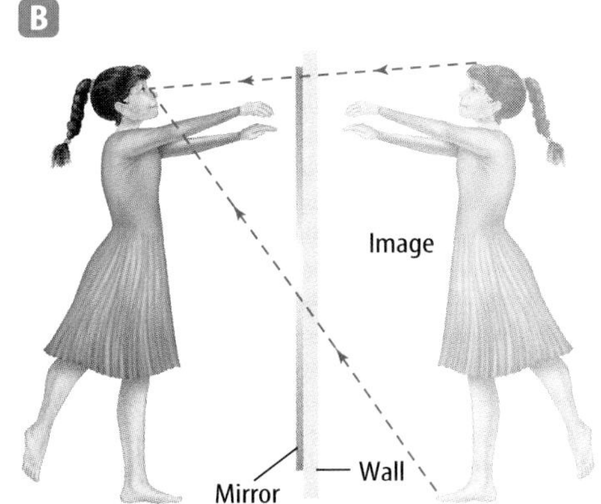

Figure 11
A plane mirror forms an image by changing the direction of light rays. A Light rays that bounce off of a person strike the mirror. Some of these light rays are reflected into the person's eye. B The light rays that are shown entering the person's eye seem to be coming from a person behind the mirror.

Reflection by Plane Mirrors Did you glance in the mirror before leaving for school this morning? If you did, you probably looked at your reflection in a plane mirror. A plane mirror is a mirror with a flat reflecting surface. In a plane mirror, your image looks much the same as it would in a photograph except that your left side is on the right side of your image and your right side is on the left side of your image. Also, your image seems to be coming from behind the mirror. How does a plane mirror form an image?

✔ Reading Check *What is a plane mirror?*

Figure 11 shows a person looking into a plane mirror. Light waves from the Sun or another source of light strike each part of the person. These light rays bounce off of the person according to the law of reflection, and some of them strike the mirror. The rays that strike the mirror also are reflected according to the law of reflection. **Figure 11A** shows the path traveled by a few of the rays that have been reflected off the person and reflected back to the person's eye by the mirror.

The Image in a Plane Mirror Why does the image you see in a plane mirror seem to be behind the mirror? This is a result of how your brain processes the light rays that enter your eyes. Although the light rays bounced off the mirror's surface, your brain interprets them as having followed the path shown by the dashed lines in **Figure 11B.** In other words, your brain always assumes that light rays travel in straight lines without changing direction. This makes the reflected light rays look as if they are coming from behind the mirror, even though no source of light is there. The image also seems to be the same distance behind the mirror as the person is in front of the mirror.

Physics INTEGRATION

When a particle like a marble or a basketball bounces off a surface, it obeys the law of reflection. Because light also obeys the law of reflection, people once thought that light must be a stream of particles. Today, experiments have shown that light can behave as though it were both a wave and a stream of energy bundles called photons. Read an article about photons and write a description in your Science Journal.

Resource Manager

Chapter Resources Booklet
Transparency Activity p. 49
Directed Reading for Content Mastery, p. 20
Mathematics Skill Activities, p. 47

Inclusion Strategies

Visually Impaired For these students, make ray diagrams using yarn wrapped around pushpins pushed into cardboard, polystyrene, or plastic foam board. Pushpins should mark the locations of the mirror and the reflection. For convex and concave mirrors, include pushpins that mark the focal point and focal length of the mirrors. L2 LS **Kinesthetic**

Activity

Provide students with pieces of new aluminum foil. Have them first look at their reflections in the smooth foil, then crumple the foil and observe their reflections again. L2
LS **Visual-Spatial**

✔ Reading Check

Answer a mirror with a flat reflecting surface

Physics INTEGRATION

Many properties of light, such as diffraction and interference, are explained most easily by thinking of light as a wave. However, other properties, such as the ability of light to produce a current by ejecting electrons from a metal (the photoelectric effect), seem to indicate that light has a particulate nature. The packets of light energy that behave as particles are called photons. A photon is the particle that transfers electromagnetic force between particles.

Quick Demo

Pass a hand mirror around the classroom. Ask students to look at their textbooks in the mirror. They will see that left and right are reversed in the mirror. L2
ELL LS **Visual-Spatial**

Activity

Students will be better able to interpret light ray diagrams if they actually draw them. On the board, draw a simple sketch of an object such as a house. Next, draw rays of light bouncing off the top, middle, and bottom part of the object and striking a plane mirror. Let student volunteers draw in the reflected rays. This will show them how the left to right reversal occurs. Have students then draw similar diagrams of their own. L2 ELL
LS **Visual-Spatial**

Concave and Convex Mirrors

✔ Reading Check

Answer A concave mirror is curved inward; a convex mirror is curved outward.

Quick Demo

Have students bring in mirrors of all shapes and curvatures, such as metal bowls and spoons. Show how light reflects differently from each of these mirrors by dimming the lights and reflecting the light from a laser pointer off each surface. If you have a concave mirror, you can demonstrate the focal point by slowly walking up to students, one at a time, with the mirror facing them. Students can watch their images disappear and then turn right side up in the mirror when they are between the mirror and its focal point. L2

LS **Visual-Spatial**

Extension

For mirrors and lenses, the focal length f, the image distance i, and the object distance o are related by the equation $1/f = 1/o + 1/i$. Have students find i of a concave mirror if $f = 3$ cm and $o = 5$ cm. $i = 7.5$ cm **What is the image distance if f remains 3 cm and $o = 2$ cm?** -6 cm Explain that the negative image distance means that the image is formed behind the mirror. This type of image is not a real image, since the light rays do not actually go through the mirror to form an image. This type of image is called a virtual image. L3 LS **Logical-Mathematical**

Concave and Convex Mirrors

Some mirrors are not flat. A concave mirror has a surface that is curved inward, like the inside of a spoon. Unlike plane mirrors, concave mirrors cause light rays to come together, or converge. A convex mirror, on the other hand, has a surface that curves outward, like the outside of a spoon. Convex mirrors cause light waves to spread out, or diverge. These two types of mirrors form images that are different from the images that are formed by plane mirrors. Examples of a concave and a convex mirror are shown in **Figure 12.**

✔ Reading Check *What's the difference between a concave and convex mirror?*

Concave Mirrors The way in which a concave mirror forms an image is shown in **Figure 13.** A straight line drawn perpendicular to the center of a concave or convex mirror is called the optical axis. Light rays that travel parallel to the optical axis and strike the mirror are reflected so that they pass through a single point on the optical axis called the **focal point.** The distance along the optical axis from the center of the mirror to the focal point is called the **focal length.**

The image formed by a concave mirror depends on the position of the object relative to its focal point. If the object is farther from the mirror than the focal point, the image appears to be upside down, or inverted. The size of the image decreases as the object is moved farther away from the mirror. If the object is closer to the mirror than one focal length, the image is upright and gets larger as the object moves closer to the mirror.

A concave mirror can produce a focused beam of light if a source of light is placed at the mirror's focal point, as shown in **Figure 13.** Flashlights and automobile headlights use concave mirrors to produce directed beams of light.

A

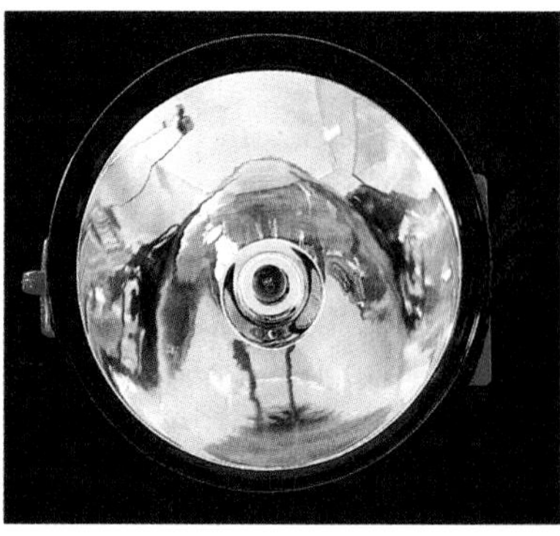

B

Figure 12
Not all mirrors are flat. A A concave mirror has a surface that's curved inward. B A convex mirror has a surface that's curved outward.

Curriculum Connection

Art The artist M.C. Escher is well known for his ability to use shadows and lighting to make the impossible look real. In his painting *Convex and Concave*, he uses curved surfaces to create an optical illusion. Show students a copy of this painting and have them discuss Escher's use of lighting on the convex and concave surfaces.

Inclusion Strategies

Learning Disabled If students have trouble remembering which type of curved surface is concave and which is convex, tell them to remember that a concave surface is curved inward like a cave. To practice using this mnemonic, have them name some curved surfaces and identify them as concave or convex.

VISUALIZING REFLECTIONS IN CONCAVE MIRRORS

Figure 13

Glance into a flat plane mirror and you'll see an upright, same-size image of yourself. But look into a concave mirror, and you'll see yourself larger than life, right side up, or upside down—or not at all! This is because the way a concave mirror forms an image depends on the position of an object in front of the mirror, as shown here.

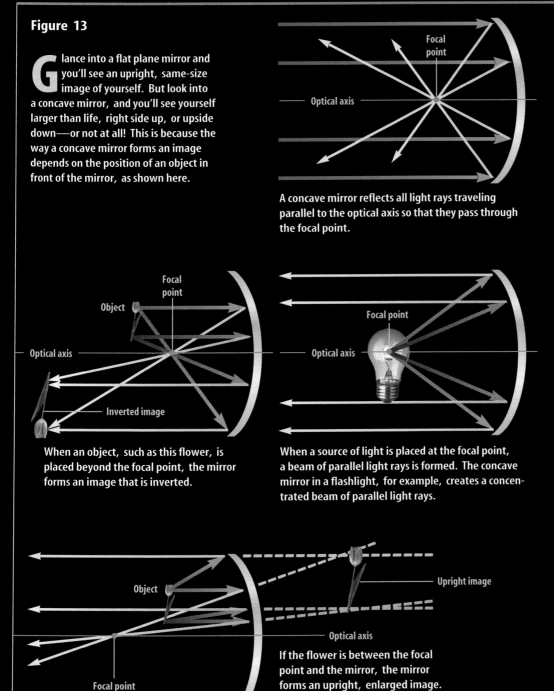

A concave mirror reflects all light rays traveling parallel to the optical axis so that they pass through the focal point.

When an object, such as this flower, is placed beyond the focal point, the mirror forms an image that is inverted.

When a source of light is placed at the focal point, a beam of parallel light rays is formed. The concave mirror in a flashlight, for example, creates a concentrated beam of parallel light rays.

If the flower is between the focal point and the mirror, the mirror forms an upright, enlarged image.

Resource Manager

Chapter Resources Booklet

Enrichment, p. 32
Reinforcement, p. 28
Activity Worksheet, pp. 5–6

Visualizing Reflections in Concave Mirrors

Have students examine the pictures and read the captions. Then ask the following questions.

How could the focal point of a concave mirror be used? Possible answer: since it concentrates all the light that comes in parallel to the optical axis, it could be used to heat something, start a fire, or cook food.

Where might you find a concave mirror? Possible answers: flash light, car headlight, spotlight, spoon, telescope

Activity

Pass out to students shiny metal spoons. Have students look into the concave side of the spoons. Point out how the image is inverted as shown in the diagrams. Since the curvature of the spoon puts the focal point very near the spoon, it is usually impossible to put your eye inside the focal length and get an enlarged upright image. L2 LS **Visual-Spatial**

Extension

Have students investigate the difference between a spherical concave mirror and a parabolic mirror. Ask them to draw diagrams or make posters illustrating the difference between these two types of mirrors. Make sure students realize that a spherical mirror does not focus rays to a single point, but a parabolic mirror does.

Concave and Convex Mirrors, continued

Discussion

If the light rays reflected from a convex mirror spread apart, why is the image formed smaller than the reflected object? The image is formed as if the light rays met behind the mirror. Because the mirror is convex, if the light rays went through it, they would be bent toward the mirror's optical axis, making the image smaller. L3 **Logical-Mathematical**

3 Assess

Reteach

The directions of light rays given by the law of reflection are reversible. Students may think that if they can see someone in a mirror, that person cannot see them. Use a large plane mirror to show students that this is not true. L2 **Visual-Spatial**

Challenge

Ask students whether a satellite dish is a spherical reflector or a parabolic reflector. Why? Satellite dishes are parabolic reflectors so they can focue the incoming signals to a single point. L2 **Visual-Spatial**

✓Assessment

Performance Have students examine their images in both sides of shiny spoons while they move the spoons closer and then farther away. Ask them to form hypotheses about which side of the spoon would serve best as a rearview mirror. the back side Use **PASC**, p. 93.

Figure 14
A convex mirror forms an image that is smaller than the object.

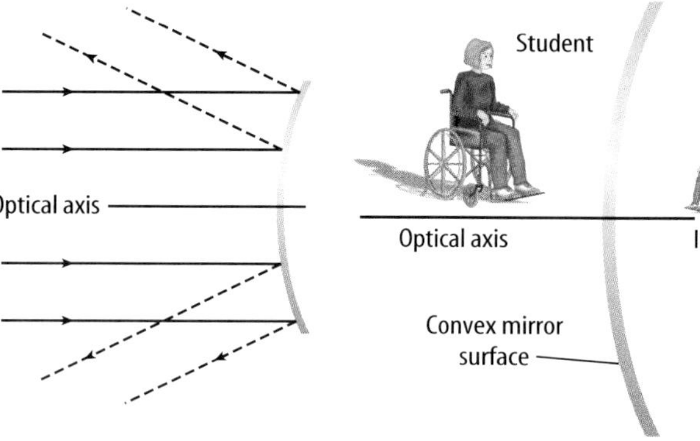

A **A convex mirror causes incoming light rays that are traveling parallel to the optical axis to spread apart after they are reflected.**

B **No matter how far the object is from a convex mirror, the image is always upright and smaller than the object.**

Convex Mirrors A convex mirror has a reflecting surface that curves ourtward. Because the reflecting surface curves outward, a convex mirror causes light rays to spread apart, or diverge, as shown in **Figure 14A.** Like the image formed by a plane mirror, the image formed by a convex mirror seems to be behind the mirror, as shown in **Figure 14B.** Also like a plane mirror, the image formed by a convex mirror is always upright. Unlike a plane mirror or a concave mirror, however, the image formed by a convex mirror is always smaller than the object.

Convex mirrors are used as security mirrors mounted above the aisles in stores and as outside rearview mirrors on cars, trucks and other vehicles. When used in this way, objects in the mirror seem smaller and farther away than they actually are. As a result, you can see a larger area reflected in a convex mirror. A convex mirror is said to have a larger angle of view than a plane mirror.

Section 2 Assessment

1. Describe how light reflects from rough and smooth surfaces.
2. Why are concave mirrors used in flashlights and automobile headlights?
3. What happens to the image in a concave mirror when an object is set closer than its focal point?
4. Why do side mirrors on cars carry the warning that objects are closer than they appear to be?
5. **Think Critically** The surface of a car is covered with dust and looks dull. After the car is washed and waxed, you can see your image reflected in the car's surface. Explain.

Skill Builder Activities

6. **Forming Hypotheses** When you look at a window at night, you sometimes can see two images of yourself reflected from the window. Make a hypothesis to explain why two images are seen. **For more help, refer to the Science Skill Handbook.**
7. **Using an Electronic Spreadsheet** Design a table using spreadsheet software to compare the images formed by plane, concave, and convex mirrors. Include in your table how the images depend on the distance of the object from the mirror. **For more help, refer to the Technology Skill Handbook.**

Answers to Section Assessment

1. Light is reflected from a rough surface to form a diffuse image. Light is reflected from a smooth surface to form a clear image.
2. They focus the light into a narrow beam.
3. The image is upright and is magnified.
4. The mirrors are convex and make objects appear smaller than they are. The brain interprets this to mean that objects are farther away than they are.
5. With the dust removed and the wax filling in the dents, the surface is smoother.
6. One image is caused by reflection from the inside surface of the glass, and one is caused by reflection from the outside surface of the glass.
7. Check students' work.

Activity

Reflection from a Plane Mirror

A light ray strikes the surface of a plane mirror and is reflected. Does a relationship exist between the direction of the incoming light ray and the direction of the reflected light ray?

What You'll Investigate

How does the angle of incidence compare with the angle of reflection for a plane mirror?

Materials

flashlight	small plane mirror, at least 10 cm on a side
protractor	black construction paper
metric ruler	modeling clay
scissors	white unlined paper
tape	

Goals

- **Measure** the angle of incidence and the angle of reflection for a light ray reflected from a plane mirror.

Safety Precautions

Procedure

1. With the scissors, cut a slit in the construction paper and tape it over the flashlight lens.
2. Place the mirror at one end of the unlined paper. Push the mirror into the lump of clay so it stands vertically, and tilt the mirror so it leans slightly toward the table.
3. **Measure** with the ruler to find the center of the bottom edge of the mirror and mark it. Then use the protractor and the ruler to draw a line on the paper perpendicular to the mirror from the mark. Label this line *P*.
4. Using the protractor and the ruler, draw lines on the paper outward from the mark at the center of the mirror at angles of 30°, 45°, and 60° to line *P*.
5. Turn on the flashlight and place it so the beam is along the 60° line. This is the angle of incidence. Locate the reflected beam on the paper, and measure the angle that the reflected beam makes with line *P*. Record this angle in your data table. This is the angle of reflection. If you cannot see the reflected beam, slightly increase the tilt of the mirror.
6. Repeat step 5 for the 30°, 45°, and *P* lines.

Conclude and Apply

1. What happened to the beam of light when it was shined along line *P?*
2. What can you infer about the relationship between the angle of incidence and the angle of reflection?

Communicating Your Data

Make a poster that shows your measured angles of reflection for angles of incidence of 30°, 45°, and 60°. Write the relationship between the angles of incidence and reflection at the bottom.

Assessment

Performance Have students work in small groups to examine what happens if a second mirror is placed in the path of the light reflected from the first mirror. Use **Performance Assessment in the Science Classroom**, p. 97.

Communicating Your Data

Students can prepare a computer presentation of their data by using graphics software to make the posters.

Activity

BENCH TESTED

Purpose Students investigate light reflection from a plane mirror by comparing the angle of incidence to the angle of reflection. L2 ELL COOP LEARN LS **Kinesthetic**

Process Skills observing and inferring, comparing and contrasting, recognizing cause and effect, measuring, communicating

Time Required 50 minutes

Alternate Materials A laser pointer can be used instead of a flashlight.

Safety Precautions Caution students that the edge of the mirror may be sharp. If using a laser pointer, warn students not to look directly into the beam or point the beam toward another person.

Teaching Strategies

- The protractor should be held against the mirror when measuring the angles.
- The slit in the construction paper should be very thin and the construction paper should be held against the face of the flashlight.

Troubleshooting Students may have trouble seeing the beam before and after it reflects off the mirror. Suggest that they experiment with holding the flashlight closer to or farther from the mirror until the beam is clear.

Answers to Questions

1. It was reflected straight back along the same line.
2. The angle of incidence equals the angle of reflection.

SECTION 3

Refraction and Lenses

1 Motivate

Bellringer Transparency

Display the Section Focus Transparency for Section 3. Use the accompanying Transparency Activity Master. L2 ELL

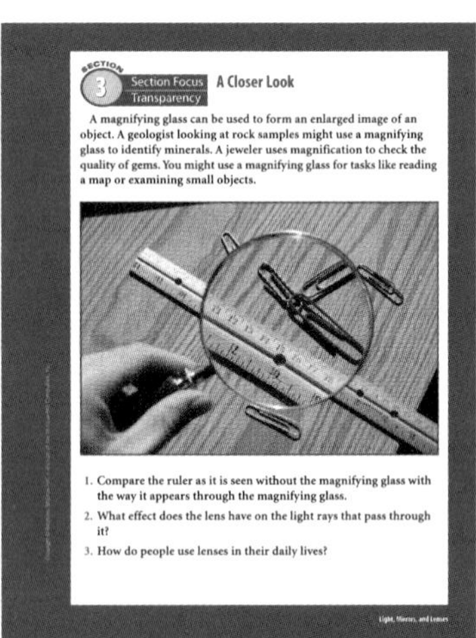

Section 3 Section Focus Transparency A Closer Look

A magnifying glass can be used to form an enlarged image of an object. A geologist looking at rock samples might use a magnifying glass to identify minerals. A jeweler uses magnification to check the quality of gems. You might use a magnifying glass for tasks like reading a map or examining small objects.

1. Compare the ruler as it is seen without the magnifying glass with the way it appears through the magnifying glass.
2. What effect does the lens have on the light rays that pass through it?
3. How do people use lenses in their daily lives?

Light, Mirrors, and Lenses

Tie to Prior Knowledge

Students may have noticed that a friend standing in a swimming pool seems shorter than he or she actually is. This illusion occurs because light bends as it passes from water to air.

SECTION 3

Refraction and Lenses

As You Read

What You'll Learn

- **Determine** why light rays refract.
- **Explain** how convex and concave lenses form images.

Vocabulary

refraction
lens
convex lens
concave lens

Why It's Important

Many of the images you see every day in photographs, on TV, and in movies are made using lenses.

Refraction

Objects that are in water can sometimes look strange. A pencil in a glass of water sometimes looks as if it's bent, or as if the part of the pencil in air is shifted compared to the part in water. If you place a penny in the bottom of the cup, and watch it as you add water, the penny may seem to disappear. Illusions such as these are due to the bending of light rays as they pass from one material to another. What causes light rays to change direction?

The Speeds of Light

The speed of light in empty space is about 300 million m/s. Light passing through a material such as air, water, or glass, however, travels more slowly than this. This is because the atoms that make up the material interact with the light waves and slow them down. **Figure 15** compares the speed of light in some different materials.

Figure 15
Light travels at different speeds in different materials.

Air

A **The speed of light through air is 300 million m/s.**

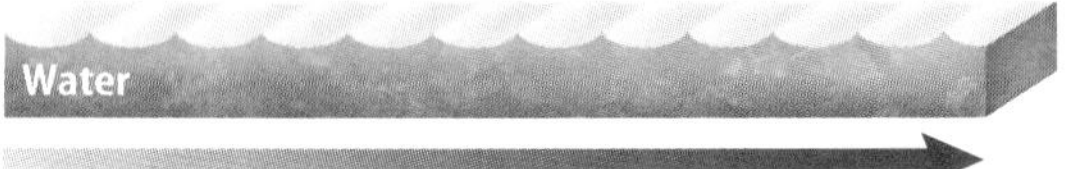

B **Speed of light through water is 227 million m/s.**

Glass

C **The speed of light through glass is 197 million m/s.**

Diamond

D **The speed of light through diamond is 125 million m/s.**

Section Assessment Planner

Portfolio
Cultural Diversity, p. 417

Performance Assessment
Skill Builder Activities, p. 420
See page 432 for more options.

Content Assessment
Section, p. 420
Challenge, p. 420
Chapter, pp. 432–433

The Refraction of Light Waves

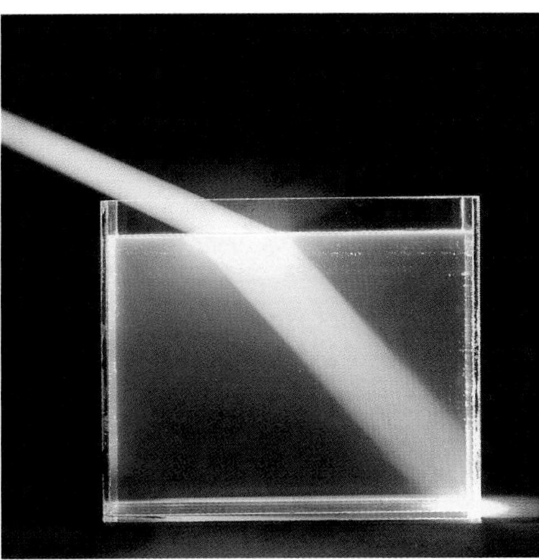

Light rays from the part of a pencil that is underwater travel through water, glass, and then air before they reach your eye. The speed of light is different in each of these mediums. What happens when a light wave travels from one medium into another in which its speed is different? If the wave is traveling at an angle to the boundary between the two media, it changes direction, or bends. This bending is due to the change in speed the wave undergoes as it moves from one medium into the other. The bending of light waves due to a change in speed is called **refraction.** **Figure 16** shows an example of refraction. The greater the change in speed is, the more the light wave bends, or refracts.

What causes light to bend?

Figure 16
A light ray is bent as it travels from air into glass. *In which medium does light travel more slowly?*

Why does a change in speed cause the light wave to bend? Think about what happens to the wheels of a car as they move from pavement to mud at an angle, as in **Figure 17.** The wheels slip a little in the mud and don't move forward as fast as they do on the pavement. The wheel that enters the mud first gets slowed down a little, but the other wheel on that axle continues at the original speed. The difference in speed between the two wheels then causes the wheel axle to turn, so the car turns a little. Light waves behave in the same way.

Imagine again a light wave traveling at an angle from air into water. The first part of the wave to enter the water is slowed, just as the car wheel that first hit the mud was slowed. The rest of the wave keeps slowing down as it moves from the air into the water. As long as one part of the light wave is moving faster than the rest of the wave, the wave continues to bend.

Figure 17
An axle turns as the wheels cross the boundary between pavement and mud. *How would the axle turn if the wheels were going from mud to pavement?*

Convex and Concave Lenses

Do you like photographing your friends and family? Have you ever watched a bird through binoculars or peered at something tiny through a magnifying glass? All of these activities involve the use of lenses. A **lens** is a transparent object with at least one curved side that causes light to bend. The amount of bending can be controlled by making the sides of the lenses more or less curved. The more curved the sides of a lens are, the more light will be bent after it enters the lens.

Resource Manager

Chapter Resources Booklet
Transparency Activity, p. 50
Directed Reading for Content Mastery, p. 21
Home and Community Involvement, p. 31

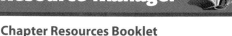

Cultural Diversity

Ibn al-Haytham The Arab scientist Ibn al-Haytham (born A.D. 965) was the first to recognize that refraction occurs because light travels at different speeds through different substances. Have students present reports on other things al-Haytham learned about light. He was the first to use the term ray of light, and he developed the idea that vision occurs in response to light hitting the eye. L2 P

2 Teach

Refraction

Quick Demo

Use a toy car to model how light bends when it moves from one medium to another. Place a thin pamphlet on a desk or table. Roll the toy car toward the pamphlet at a 90° angle, and then at a 45° angle. Ask students to observe what happens as the car encounters the pamphlet. L2 LS **Visual-Spatial**

The Speeds of Light

Teacher FYI

The speed of light in air was measured accurately by Albert Michelson, who won the Nobel prize in 1907 for his work. Using a rotating eight-sided mirror, he measured the time light took to make a round-trip between mountain tops that were a known distance apart.

Fun Fact

Rainbows are formed when sunlight is refracted by water droplets in the air. If light traveled at the same speed in water and air, there would be no rainbows.

The Refraction of Light Waves

Reading Check

Answer a change of speed when the wave moves from one medium to another

Caption Answers

Figure 16 glass
Figure 17 the opposite way

Convex and Concave Lenses

Use Science Words

Word Origins Have students find the origin of the word *lens*. It comes from the Latin word *lens* meaning "lentil." Draw a lentil on the board. **What type of lens does a lentil resemble?** a convex/convex lens

IDENTIFYING Misconceptions

Students believe that holding a magnifying glass closer to their eyes will magnify the object more. Make sure they understand that the closer the convex lens of a magnifying glass is to the object, the larger the image it produces.

Reading Check

Answer Hold the lens more than two focal lengths from the object.

Internet Addresses

Explore the Glencoe Science Web site at **science.glencoe.com** to find out more about topics in this section.

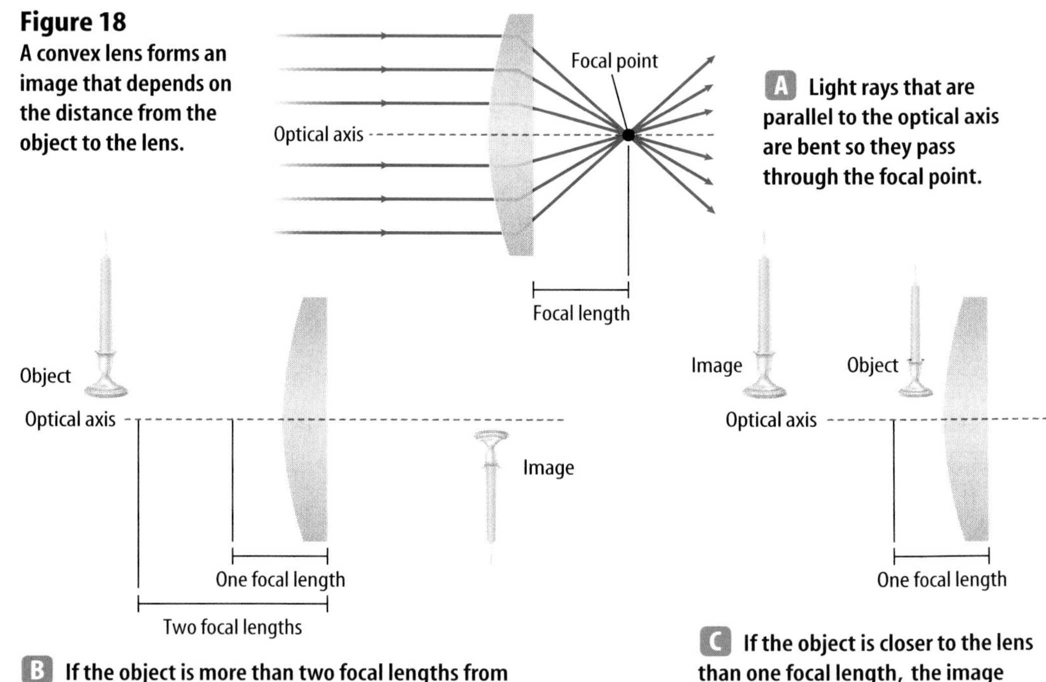

Figure 18
A convex lens forms an image that depends on the distance from the object to the lens.

A Light rays that are parallel to the optical axis are bent so they pass through the focal point.

B If the object is more than two focal lengths from the lens, the image formed is smaller than the object and inverted.

C If the object is closer to the lens than one focal length, the image formed is enlarged and upright.

Convex Lenses A lens that is thicker in the center than at the edges is a **convex lens.** The more curved the lens is, the closer the focal point is to the lens, and so the shorter the focal length of the lens is. Light rays traveling parallel to the optical axis of a convex lens are bent so they meet at the focal point, as shown in **Figure 18A.** Because convex lenses cause light waves to meet, they also are called converging lenses.

The image formed by a convex lens is similar to the image formed by a concave mirror. For both, the type of image depends on how far the object is from the focal point. Look at **Figure 18B.** If the object is farther than two focal lengths from the lens, the image seen through the lens is inverted and smaller than the object.

Reading Check ***How can a convex lens be used to make objects appear upside down?***

If the object is closer to the lens than one focal length, then the image formed is right-side up and larger than the object, as shown in **Figure 18C.** A magnifying glass forms an image in this way. The image in a magnifying glass is right-side up and larger than the object. The image continues to get larger as the magnifying glass is brought closer to the object.

SCIENCE Online

Research Visit the Glencoe Science web site at **science.glencoe.com** for information about the optical devices that use convex lenses. Prepare a poster or other presentation for your class describing some of these devices.

LAB DEMONSTRATION

Purpose to show how different materials refract light

Materials dropper, bottle, microscope immersion oil

Preparation Make certain that you use an ordinary glass dropper.

Procedure Fill the bottle almost to the top with immersion oil. Put the dropper into the oil. Show the bottle to the students. Squeeze the dropper top and release. Show the bottle again.

Expected Outcome When the dropper filled with air is first put into the bottle, it is visible. When it is filled with immersion oil, it becomes invisible.

Assessment

Why did the dropper disappear after the oil was added? The glass of the dropper bends light in the same way (it has the same refractive index) as the immersion oil does.

Concave Lenses A lens that is thicker at the edges than in the middle is a **concave lens.** A concave lens also is called a diverging lens. **Figure 19** shows how light rays traveling parallel to the optical axis are bent after passing through a concave lens.

A concave lens causes light rays to diverge, so light rays are not brought to a focus. The type of image that is formed by a concave lens is similar to one that is formed by a convex mirror. The image is upright and smaller than the object.

Optical axis

Figure 19
A concave lens causes light rays traveling parallel to the optical axis to diverge.

Total Internal Reflection

When you look at a glass window, you sometimes can see your reflection in the window. You see a reflection because some of the light waves reflected from you are reflected back to your eyes when they strike the window. This is an example of a partial reflection—only some of the light waves striking the window are reflected. However, sometimes all the light waves that strike the boundary between two transparent materials can be reflected. This process is called total internal reflection.

The Critical Angle To see how total internal reflection occurs, look at **Figure 20.** Light travels faster in air than in water, so the refracted beam is bent away from the normal. As the angle between the incident beam and the normal increases, the refracted beam bends closer to the air-water boundary. At the same time, more of the light waves striking the boundary are reflected and fewer are refracted.

If a light beam in water strikes the boundary so that the angle with the normal is greater than the critical angle, total internal reflection occurs. Then all the light waves are reflected at the air-water boundary, just as if a mirror were there. The size of the critical angle depends on the two materials involved. For light passing from water to air the critical angle is about 48 degrees.

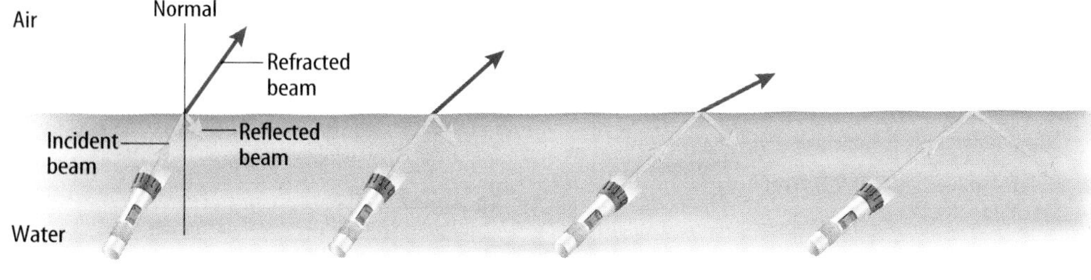

Figure 20
When a light beam passes from one medium to another, some of its energy is reflected (red) and some is refracted (blue). As the incident beam makes a larger angle with the normal, less light energy is refracted, and more is reflected. At the critical angle, all the light is reflected.

Visual Learning

Figure 19 Point out to students that a ray traveling along the optical axis of either type of lens is not refracted at all. Ask students why this is true. The ray encounters no curved surface as it strikes the lens so it passes through with no change in direction. L2

LS **Visual-Spatial**

Activity

Have students hold concave and convex lenses close to some printing and then move the lenses away from the printing to see how the images obtained with the two lenses are different. L2 LS **Visual-Spatial**

Total Internal Reflection

Quick Demo

In a darkened room, demonstrate total internal reflection using a laser pointer and a 45°–45°–90° glass prism. Point the beam toward the largest face of the prism. Slowly vary the incident angle until it is perpendicular to the face and pointing toward the middle of one of the other faces. The beam should emerge back through the large face. Next, point the beam directly toward one of the small faces. The reflected beam should emerge from the other small face. LS **Visual-Spatial**

Fun Fact

Total internal reflection is the reason that diamonds sparkle. Diamonds have a critical angle of only about 25°. When they are precisely cut, light can reflect several times before leaving the diamond.

Teacher FYI

Light waves of different colors refract by different amounts. Since white light is composed of all colors, these colors refract differently when they pass through a lens. Instead of a sharp converged image, various blurry colors may be seen. This effect is called chromatic aberration. It is an effect that opticians try to minimize.

Resource Manager

Chapter Resources Booklet

Enrichment, p. 33

Reinforcement, p. 29

Transparency Activity, pp. 53–54

Optical Fibers

Quick Demo

Inexpensive optical fibers can be obtained from many science supply companies. Shine light through some so students can see how the light emerges through the other end. LS **Visual-Spatial**

3 Assess

Reteach

Have students make ray diagrams of convex and concave lenses in which the object is two focal lengths from the lens. Tell them to choose objects that don't have vertical or horizontal symmetry so that the orientation after the light passes through the lens is clear. **Which type of lens always produces an upright image?** concave L2

LS **Visual-Spatial**

Challenge

Have students describe what happens to light as it passes through air masses or air pockets of different temperatures. As light passes from a pocket of air at one temperature to a pocket of air at another temperature, it changes speed and is refracted. This refraction leads to the formation of mirages. L3

LS **Logical-Mathematical**

Performance Draw on the board a ray diagram of light from an object moving to a lens. Have students predict the location, orientation, and size of the image produced. Use **PASC,** p. 89.

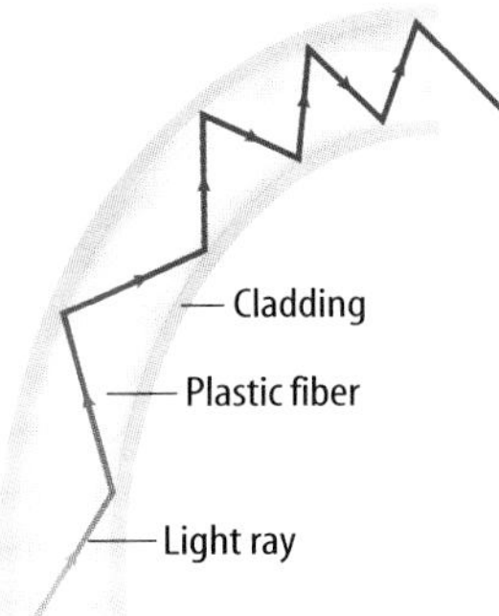

Figure 21
An optical fiber is made of materials that cause total internal reflection to occur. As a result, a light beam can travel for many kilometers through an optical fiber and lose almost no energy.

Optical Fibers

A device called an optical fiber can make a light beam travel in a path that is curved or even twisted. Optical fibers are thin, flexible, transparent fibers. An optical fiber is like a light pipe. Even if the fiber is bent, light that enters one end of the fiber comes out the other end.

Total internal reflection makes light transmission in optical fibers possible. A thin fiber of glass or plastic is covered with another material called cladding in which light travels faster. When light strikes the boundary between the fiber and the cladding, total internal reflection occurs. In this way, the beam bounces along inside the fiber as shown in **Figure 21.**

Using Optical Fibers Optical fibers are used most commonly in communications. Telephone conversations, television programs, and computer information can be coded in light beams. These beams then can be sent from one place to another using optical fibers. Because of total internal reflection, signals can't leak from one fiber to another and interfere with other messages. As a result, the signal is transmitted clearly. Phone conversations also can be changed into light and sent along optical fibers. One optical fiber the thickness of a human hair can carry thousands of phone conversations.

Section 3 Assessment

1. How is the image that is formed by a concave lens similar to the image that is formed by a convex mirror?
2. To magnify an object, would you use a convex lens or a concave lens?
3. Describe two ways, using convex and concave lenses, to form an image that is smaller than the object.
4. What are some uses for convex and concave lenses?
5. **Think Critically** A light wave is bent more when it travels from air to glass than when it travels from air to water. Is the speed of light greater in water or glass? Explain.

Skill Builder Activities

6. **Predicting** Air that is cool is more dense than air that is warm. Look at **Figure 15** and predict whether the speed of light is faster in warm air or cool air. **For more help, refer to the Science Skill Handbook.**
7. **Solving One-Step Equations** Earth is about 150 million km from the Sun. Use the formula

$$\text{Distance} = \text{speed} \times \text{time}$$

to calculate how many seconds it takes a beam of light to travel from Earth to the Sun. About how many minutes does it take? About how many hours does it take? **For more help, refer to the Math Skill Handbook.**

Answers to Section Assessment

1. They are both upright and smaller than the object.
2. convex lens
3. A person could use a concave lens or a person could hold a convex lens more than two focal lengths from the object.
4. Convex lenses are used in microscopes, telescopes, hand lenses, and cameras to magnify and focus objects. Concave lenses are used to correct nearsightedness.
5. The speed of light is greater in water. The greater the change in speed, the more the wave is bent. Since the wave is bent less as it travels from air to water, light must slow down less as it moves from air to water.
6. Light travels faster in warm air.
7. time = distance ÷ speed = 150,000,000 km ÷ 300,000 km/s = 500 s = 8.3 min = 0.14 hr

SECTION 4

Using Mirrors and Lenses

Microscopes

For almost 500 years, lenses have been used to observe objects that are too small to be seen with the unaided eye. The first microscopes were simple and magnified less than 100 times. Today a compound microscope like the one in **Figure 22A** uses a combination of lenses to magnify objects by as much as 2,500 times.

Figure 22B shows how a microscope forms an image. An object, such as an insect or a drop of water from a pond, is placed close to a convex lens called the objective lens. This lens produces an enlarged image inside the microscope tube. The light rays from that image then pass through a second convex lens called the eyepiece lens. This lens further magnifies the image formed by the objective lens. By using two lenses, a much larger image is formed than a single lens can produce.

As You Read

***What* You'll Learn**

- **Explain** how microscopes magnify objects.
- **Explain** how telescopes make distant objects visible.
- **Describe** how a camera works.

Vocabulary

refracting telescope
reflecting telescope

***Why* It's Important**

Microscopes and telescopes are used to view parts of the universe that can't be seen with the unaided eye.

Figure 22
A compound microscope uses lenses to magnify objects.

A A compound microscope often has more than one objective lens—each providing a different magnification. A light underneath the objective lens makes the image bright enough to see clearly.

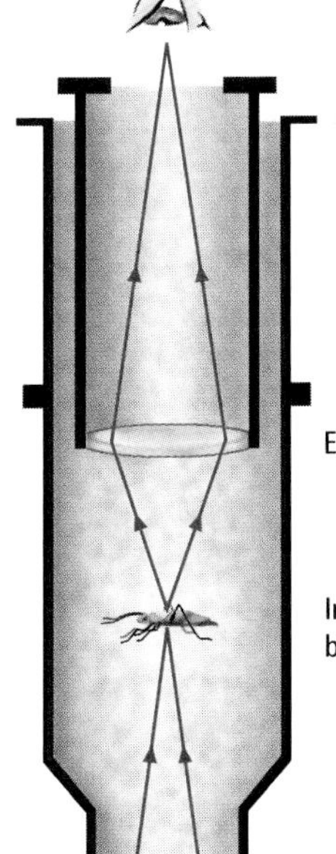

B The objective lens in a compound microscope forms an enlarged image, which is then magnified by the eyepiece.

Section Assessment Planner

PORTFOLIO
Assessment, p. 425

PERFORMANCE ASSESSMENT
MiniLAB, p. 422
Skill Builder Activities, p. 425
See page 432 for more options.

CONTENT ASSESSMENT
Section, p. 425
Challenge, p. 425
Chapter, pp. 432–433

SECTION 4

Using Mirrors and Lenses

1 Motivate

Bellringer Transparency

Display the Section Focus Transparency for Section 4. Use the accompanying Transparency Activity Master. L2 ELL

Section 4 Section Focus Transparency **I Spy**

Originally created in 1608 by a Dutch optician named Hans Lippershey, the telescope was put to use by Galileo to observe the Moon and planets. It was soon put to other uses, hence it became known as a "spyglass."

1. Suggest some practical uses to which the instrument was first applied. Why did it earn the name "spyglass"?
2. What modern equivalent of the spyglass can be used at sporting events? How is it an improvement?

Tie to Prior Knowledge

Discuss with students situations in which they may have seen objects reduced or enlarged by lenses. Ask them how they think the image on a movie screen becomes so large. The image on the film is enlarged using convex lenses.

Resource Manager

Chapter Resources Booklet
Transparency Activity, p. 51
Directed Reading for Content Mastery, pp. 21, 22

2 Teach

Microscopes

Visual Learning

Figure 22 Point out the eyepiece lens and the objective lens on the microscope. Explain that any microscope with at least two lenses is called a compound microscope. A simple microscope is a magnifier such as a hand lens that has only one lens. L2 LS **Visual-Spatial**

Telescopes

Use an Analogy

Ask students how they might collect as much rainwater as possible. One way would be to use large containers that collect many raindrops. Explain that using a large container to collect raindrops is similar to using a large objective lens in a telescope to collect light.

Reading Check

Answer It gathers light from objects to form images that are enlarged by the eyepiece.

Purpose Students investigate how a water lens affects images. LS **Visual-Spatial**

Materials test tube with stopper, index card, water

Troubleshooting If an air bubble enters the test tube as students fill it, have them hold the tube slightly slanted so the bubble stays at one end.

Analysis

1. double-convex along one axis
2. Close to the card the image was magnified; far from the card the image was reduced and inverted.

Mini LAB

Forming an Image with a Lens

Procedure

1. Fill a **glass test tube** with **water** and seal it with a **stopper.**
2. Write your name on a **10-cm × 10-cm card.** Lay the test tube on the card and observe the appearance of your name.
3. Hold the test tube about 1 cm above the card and observe the appearance of your name. Record your observations.
4. Observe what happens to your name as you slowly move the test tube away from the card. Record your observations.

Analysis

1. Is the water-filled test tube a concave lens or a convex lens?
2. Compare the image that formed when the test tube was close to the card with the image that formed when the test tube was far from the card.

Telescopes

Just as microscopes are used to magnify very small objects, telescopes are used to examine objects that are very far away. The first telescopes were made at about the same time as the first microscopes. Much of what we know about the Moon, the solar system, and the distant universe has come from images and other information gathered by telescopes.

Refracting Telescopes The simplest **refracting telescopes** use two convex lenses to form an image of a distant object. Just as in a compound microscope, light passes through an objective lens that forms an image. That image is then magnified by an eyepiece, as shown in **Figure 23A.**

An important difference between a telescope and a microscope is the size of the objective lens. The main purpose of a telescope is not to magnify an image. A telescope's main purpose is to gather as much light as possible from distant objects. The larger an objective lens is, the more light that can enter it. This makes images of faraway objects look brighter and more detailed when they are magnified by the eyepiece. With a large enough objective lens, it's possible to see stars and galaxies that are many trillions of kilometers away. **Figure 23B** shows the largest refracting telescope ever made.

Reading Check *How does a telescope's objective lens enable distant objects to be seen?*

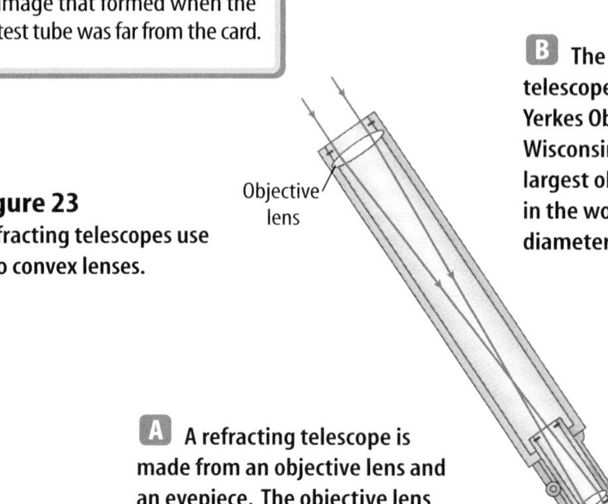

Figure 23
Refracting telescopes use two convex lenses.

A A refracting telescope is made from an objective lens and an eyepiece. The objective lens forms an image that is magnified by the eyepiece.

B The refracting telescope at the Yerkes Observatory in Wisconsin has the largest objective lens in the world. It has a diameter of 1 m.

Process Ask students to predict how the image would be affected if the test tube was held so that its axis was perpendicular to the line along which the name is written. Have them test their predictions. Use **PASC,** p. 103.

Resource Manager

Chapter Resources Booklet
MiniLAB, p. 4

Physical Science Critical Thinking/Problem Solving, p. 22

422 CHAPTER 14 Light, Mirrors, and Lenses

Figure 24
Reflecting telescopes gather light by using a concave mirror.

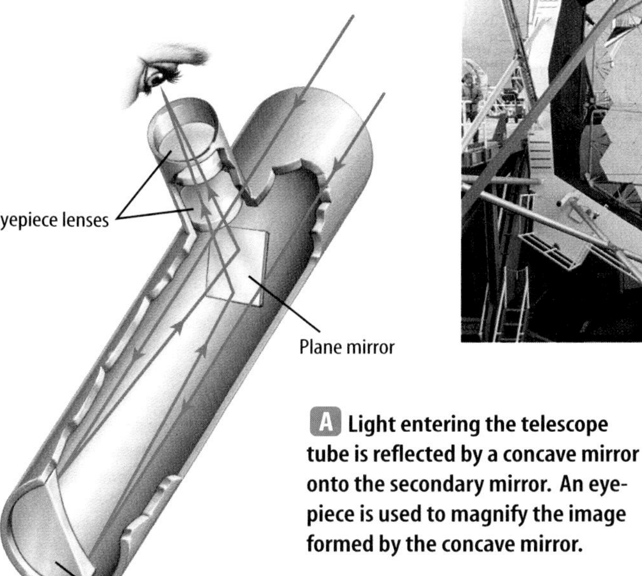

A **Light entering the telescope tube is reflected by a concave mirror onto the secondary mirror. An eyepiece is used to magnify the image formed by the concave mirror.**

B **The concave mirror of the Keck telescope in Mauna Kea, Hawaii, is made of six-sided segments that are 1.8 m across.**

Reflecting Telescopes Refracting telescopes have size limitations. One problem is that the objective lens can be supported only around its edges. If the lens is extremely large, it cannot be supported enough to keep the glass from sagging slightly under its own weight. This causes the image that the lens forms to become distorted.

Reflecting telescopes can be made much larger than refracting telescopes. **Reflecting telescopes** have a concave mirror instead of a concave objective lens to gather the light from distant objects. As shown in **Figure 24A,** the large concave mirror focuses light onto a secondary mirror that directs it to the eyepiece, which magnifies the image.

Because only the one reflecting surface on the mirror needs to be made carefully and kept clean, telescope mirrors are less expensive to make and maintain than lenses of a similar size. Also, mirrors can be supported not only at their edges but also on their back sides. They can be made much larger without sagging under their own weight. The Keck telescope in Hawaii, shown in **Figure 24B,** is the largest reflecting telescope in the world. Its large concave mirror is 10 m in diameter, and is made of 36 six-sided segments. Each segment is 1.8 m in size and the segments are pieced together to form the mirror.

Discussion

The largest telescopes are located on high mountaintops in isolated areas of places such as Chile and Hawaii. **Why are these good places for telescopes?** They have little light from the environment, and at the tops of mountains there is less atmosphere to distort the telescope's images. **Why is the *Hubble Space Telescope* located in orbit around Earth?** to avoid light and air pollution, to avoid vibrations from highways, and mostly to avoid distortion by Earth's atmosphere L2

LS **Logical-Mathematical**

Make a Model

Have students work in small groups to make models of the two different types of telescopes and label the various parts on each. They do not have to use actual optics but merely represent them. They should also describe major differences and similarities between the two types of telescopes. L2

COOP LEARN LS **Kinesthetic** P

Teacher FYI

At a cost of $1.5 billion, the *Hubble Space Telescope* provides sharper images of astronomical objects than do Earthbound telescopes with mirrors several times larger. However, when it was first deployed, it produced images that were somewhat blurry. The problem was traced to a small error in shaping the curvature of the telescope's mirror. Astronauts on a later space shuttle mission installed corrective optics that canceled the effects of the mirror's misshapen surface.

Visual Learning

Figure 24 With students, trace the path of light through a reflecting telescope. Explain that when the light is reflected through a hole in the concave mirror instead of through the side of the tube, the secondary mirror is convex instead of planar. **Why?** to focus the light rays on the hole in the mirror L3 LS **Visual-Spatial**

Science Journal

Edwin Hubble Ask students to write or present short reports on Edwin Hubble and his accomplishments. Hubble lived from 1889 to 1953. He classified galaxies and formulated Hubble's law, which states that the distances between galaxies are increasing and that the universe is expanding. L3 LS **Linguistic**

Cameras

✔ Reading Check

Answer a convex lens

Extension

Ask students if they have ever seen a photograph in which the eyes of everyone in the picture are red. Have students research to find out what causes this problem and how it can be avoided. The red eyes occur when light from the camera's flash reflects off blood vessels in the back of a person's eyes. It can be avoided in various ways, such as by turning on enough lights to cause the person's pupils to contract. L2 LS **Linguistic**

Make a Model

A pinhole camera produces an inverted image without a lens. The simplest form of a pinhole camera is just a box with a tiny hole at one end covered by a simple shutter. Light entering the hole is focused onto film in the box to produce an image. Have students work in pairs to research and make their own pinhole cameras. Ask students to explain why a small hole is necessary. A small hole allows in only a narrow beam of light, so the image is sharp. L2 LS **Kinesthetic**

Lasers

Use Science Words

Word Meaning Explain to students that the word *laser* is an acronym for *L*ight *A*mplification by *S*timulated *E*mission of *R*adiation. In a laser, atoms are excited to a higher level of energy. They are then stimulated to emit their excess energy as light of one wavelength. This process occurs repeatedly to achieve an intense, monochromatic beam of light.

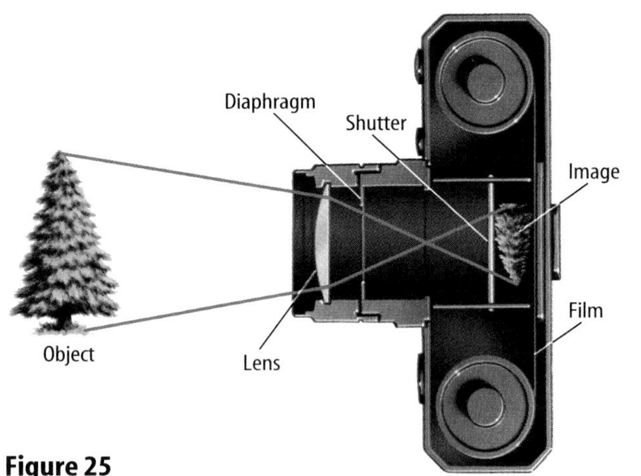

Figure 25
A camera uses a convex lens to form an image on a piece of light-sensitive film. The image formed by a camera lens is smaller than the object.

Cameras

You probably see photographs taken by cameras almost every day. A typical camera uses a convex lens to form an image on a section of film, just as your eye's lens focuses an image on your retina. The convex lens has a short focal length so that it forms an image that is smaller than the object and inverted on the film. Look at the camera shown in **Figure 25.** When the shutter is open, the convex lens focuses an image on a piece of film that is sensitive to light. Light-sensitive film contains chemicals that undergo chemical reactions when light hits it. The brighter parts of the image affect the film more than the darker parts do.

✔ Reading Check ***What type of lens does a camera use?***

An image that is too bright can overexpose the film by causing too much of the light-sensitive material to react. On the other hand, if too little light reaches the film, the image might be too dark. To control how much light reaches the film, many cameras have a device called a diaphragm. The diaphragm is opened to let more light onto the film and closed to reduce the amount of light that strikes the film.

Lasers

Perhaps you've seen the narrow, intense beams of laser light used in a laser light show. Intense laser beams are also used for different kinds of surgery. Why can laser beams be so intense? One reason is that, unlike ordinary light, a laser beam doesn't spread out as it travels.

Spreading Light Beams Suppose you shine a flashlight on a wall in a darkened room. The size of the spot of light on the wall depends on the distance between the flashlight and the wall. As the flashlight moves farther from the wall, the spot of light gets larger. This is because the beam of light produced by the flashlight spreads out as it travels. As a result, the energy carried by the light waves in the beam is spread over an increasingly larger area as the light beam travels. As the energy is spread over a larger area, the energy becomes less concentrated and the intensity of the beam decreases.

Resource Manager 

Chapter Resources Booklet
Enrichment, p. 34
Reinforcement, p. 30
Cultural Diversity, pp. 51, 57

Teacher FYI

Miniature semiconductor diode lasers are used to produce the light that transmits information in optical fibers.

Figure 26
Laser light is different from the light produced by a lightbulb.

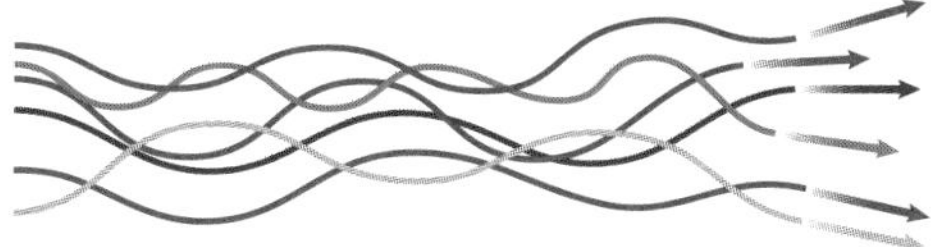

A **The light from a bulb contains waves with many different wavelengths that are out of phase and traveling in different directions.**

B **The light from a laser contains waves with only one wavelength that are in phase and traveling in the same direction.**

Using Laser Light Laser light is different from the light produced by the flashlight in several ways, as shown in **Figure 26.** One difference is that in a beam of laser light, the crests and troughs of the light waves overlap, so the waves are in phase.

Because a laser beam doesn't spread out, a large amount of energy can be applied to a very small area. This property enables lasers to be used for cutting and welding materials and as a replacement for scalpels in surgery. Less intense laser light is used for such applications as reading and writing to CDs or in grocery store bar-code readers. Surveyors and builders use lasers to measure distances, angles, and heights. Laser beams also are used to transmit information through space or through optical fibers.

Section  Assessment

1. How is a compound microscope different from a magnifying lens?
2. Compare and contrast reflecting and refracting telescope. Why aren't refracting telescopes bigger than reflecting telescopes?
3. Why is the objective lens of a refracting telescope bigger than the objective lens of a microscope?
4. Describe how laser light is different from the light produced by a light bulb.
5. **Think Critically** Could a camera with a concave lens instead of a convex lens still take pictures? Explain.

Skill Builder Activities

6. **Communicating** Using words, pictures, or other media, think of a way to explain to a friend how convex and concave lenses work. **For more help, refer to the Science Skill Handbook.**
7. **Solving One-Step Equations** The size of an image is related to the magnification of an optical instrument by the following formula:

$$\text{Image size} = \text{magnification} \times \text{object size}$$

A blood cell has a diameter of about 0.001 cm. How large is the image formed by a microscope with a magnification of 1,000? **For more help, refer to the Math Skill Handbook.**

Answers to Section Assessment

1. A magnifying lens has one lens. Compound microscopes use two or more lenses.
2. The objective lens of a refracting telescope can be supported only around its edges, and the lens's weight can cause it to bend slightly if it is too large. In place of this lens, a reflecting telescope uses a mirror that can be supported in back and be made larger.
3. The lens is made large so it can collect a large amount of light.
4. Laser light is a narrow, intense beam that doesn't spread out. Light from a light bulb spreads out as it travels.
5. No; a concave lens would cause the light coming into the camera to diverge so that it could not be brought to a focus on the film.
6. Possible answers: Demonstrate the use of lenses, or show how lenses work, using pictures or diagrams.
7. image size = 0.001 cm × 1,000 = 1 cm

Quick Demo

Point an intense beam of light from a flashlight through a prism so that students can see it split into colors. Next, point a beam of light from a laser pointer through the prism. Students will see that it remains one color. LS **Visual-Spatial**

3 Assess

Reteach

Have students hypothesize why photographs may not come out as perfectly as they expect. **Why would a photograph be too dark?** Possible answer: The diaphragm let in too little light. **Why would a photograph be out of focus?** Possible answer: The lens was in the wrong position and didn't focus the image exactly on the film. L2 LS **Logical-Mathematical**

Challenge

Obtain a disposable camera. Be sure the capacitor is discharged by taking a picture. Remove the battery to disable the capacitor circuit inside. Take the camera apart and remove the plastic lens assembly. Point out to students that there is more than one lens in the camera. Ask students why this is necessary. The second convex lens pulls the light rays in, effectively shortening the focal length of the first lens. This makes it possible to have a lens with a longer focal length in a shorter space. L3 LS **Logical-Mathematical**

✔Assessment

Portfolio Have each student make a drawing that shows how a radio telescope collects radio waves. Use **PASC**, p. 127. P

Activity

BENCH TESTED

What You'll Investigate

Purpose

Students investigate the images formed by a convex lens and observe how the image is affected when the distance between the lens and the light source is altered. L2

LS **Kinesthetic**

Process Skills

observing and inferring, recognizing cause and effect, measuring in SI, predicting, communicating, making and using tables

Time Required

1 hour

Materials

The flashlight should have a narrow, intense beam to produce a clear image. If possible, you should be able to adjust the collimation of the beam. To help students clearly see how the image size has changed, you may wish to have them mark off a centimeter or millimeter scale on the cardboard ahead of time. You could also print these out on cardstock using a computer.

Alternate Materials

Inexpensive lens supports are available from science supply companies. These can be attached to a meter stick to provide a clean, secure support. Similar supports are available for holding the cards.

Activity

Image Formation by a Convex Lens

The type of image formed by a convex lens, also called a converging lens, is related to the distance of the object from the lens. This distance is called the object distance. The location of the image also is related to the distance of the object from the lens. The distance from the lens to the image is called the image distance. What happens to the position of the image as the object gets nearer or farther from the lens?

What You'll Investigate

How are the image distance and object distance related for a convex lens?

Materials

convex lens
modeling clay
meterstick
flashlight
masking tape
20-cm square piece of cardboard with a white surface

Goals

- **Measure** the image distance as the object distance changes.
- **Observe** the type of image formed as the object distance changes.

Safety Precautions

Resource Manager

Chapter Resources Booklet
Activity Worksheet, pp. 7–8

Lab Management and Safety, p. 64

Inclusion Strategies

Learning Disabled Before beginning the activity, have student volunteers draw diagrams on the board showing a beam of light as it reflects off a convex lens. Different diagrams should be drawn showing the object distance shorter than and longer than the focal length of the lens.

Curriculum Connection

Art Artists must have a basic understanding of optics when painting a picture that shows light reflected by surfaces or transmitted through objects. Have students use what they have learned about light shining through convex lenses to make paintings or drawings showing sunlight shining through a glass of water.

Procedure

1. **Design** a data table to record your data in. Make three columns in your table—one column for the object distance, another for the image distance, and the third for the type of image.
2. Use the modeling clay to make the lens stand upright on the lab table.
3. Form the letter *F* on the glass surface of the flashlight with masking tape.
4. Turn on the flashlight and place it 1 m from the lens. Position the flashlight so the flashlight beam is shining through the lens.
5. **Record** the distance from the flashlight to the lens in the object distance column in your data table.
6. Hold the cardboard vertically upright on the other side of the lens, and move it back and forth until a sharp image of the letter *F* is obtained.
7. **Measure** the distance of the card from the lens using the meterstick, and record this distance in the image distance column in your data table.
8. **Record** in the third column of your data table whether the image is upright or inverted, and smaller or larger.
9. Repeat steps 4 through 8 for object distances of 0.50 m and 0.25 m and record your data in your data table.

Convex Lens Data

Object Distance (m)	Image Distance (m)	Image Type
1.00	0.43	inverted, smaller
0.50	0.75	inverted, larger
0.25	1.50	upright, larger

Conclude and Apply

1. How did the image distance change as the object distance decreased?
2. How did the image change as the object distance decreased?
3. What would happen to the size of the image if the flashlight were much farther away than 1 m?

Communicating Your Data

Demonstrate this activity to a third-grade class and explain how it works. **For more help, refer to the** Science Skill Handbook.

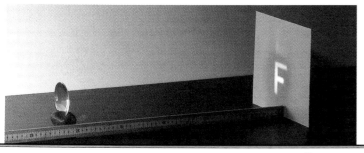

Procedure

Teaching Strategies

- Slightly darkening the room will make the images easier to observe.
- The data obtained by students will depend on the type of lens and the focal length of the lens.

Tie to Prior Knowledge

Students may have noticed that looking through a clear glass of water produces a magnified image of an object.

Expected Outcome

Decreasing the object distance increases the image distance and increases the size of the image. If the object distance is less than the focal length of the lens, the image will appear upright.

Conclude and Apply

1. It increased.
2. It became larger. When the object distance was less than the focal length of the lens, the image was upright.
3. It would be too small to see.

Error Analysis

Discuss with students how the image is affected if the flashlight beam is too spread out.

Assessment

Oral How would the data obtained for the image distance and the image type differ if a double convex lens were used instead of a plano-convex lens? The lens would bend the light more so the image distance and the image would be smaller. Use **PASC**, p. 89.

Communicating Your Data

When demonstrating the activity to the third-grade class, have students make simple drawings that show how the curve of the lens redirects the light to cause the image inversion and the increase or decrease in size.

Oops! Accidents in SCIENCE

SOMETIMES GREAT DISCOVERIES HAPPEN BY ACCIDENT!

Content Background

Nearsighted people actually have stronger eyes than farsighted people do. The lens of a nearsighted eye is so curved that it brings far off images into sharp focus at a spot in front of the retina. Many older people are farsighted because, as people age, the muscle behind the eye's lens becomes less flexible. This muscle cannot, therefore, bend the lens sufficiently to enable it to focus nearby objects. This condition is called presbyopia.

Discussion

Eyeglasses developed when methods people had been using to help themselves see more clearly were combined with technology that allowed lenses to be worn. **Describe some other inventions that resulted when people put together old methods with new technology.** Possible answer: An electrical toaster combines using heat to toast bread with the use of electrical resistance to produce heat. L2

LS **Logical-Mathematical**

Eyeglasses

"It is not yet twenty years since the art of making spectacles, one of the most useful arts on Earth, was discovered. I myself have seen and conversed with the man who made them first."

This quote from an Italian monk dates back to 1306 and is one of the first historical records to refer to eyeglasses. Unfortunately, the monk, Giordano, never actually named the man he met. Thus, the inventor of eyeglasses—one of the most widely used forms of technology today—remains unknown.

The mystery exists, in part, because different cultures in different places used some type of magnifying tool to improve their vision. These tools eventually merged into what today is recognized as a pair of glasses. For example, a rock-crystal lens made by early Assyrians who lived 3,500 years ago in what is now Iraq, may have been used to improve vision. About 2,000 years ago, the Roman writer Seneca looked through a glass globe of water to make the letters appear bigger in the books he read. By the 10th century, glasses were invented in China, but they were used to keep away bad luck, not to improve vision. Trade between China and Europe, however, likely led some unknown inventor to come up with an idea.

The inventor fused two metal-ringed magnifying lenses together so they could perch on the nose.

In 1456, the printing press was invented. Suddenly, there was more to read, which, in turn, made the ability to see clearly more important. In Europe, eyeglasses began to appear in paintings of scholars, clergy, and the upper classes—the only people who knew how to read at the time. Although the ability to read spread fairly quickly, eyeglasses were so expensive only the rich could afford them. In the early 1700s, for example, glasses cost roughly $200, which is comparable to thousands of dollars today. By the mid-1800s, improvements in manufacturing techniques made eyeglasses much less expensive to make, and thus this important invention became widely available to people of all walks of life.

428

Resources for Teachers and Students

Samuele Mazza, "Spectacles," 1996.

Margery Nichelason, "What's New in Old Eyeware," *Cricket*, May 1995, pp. 42–44.

Anne Harding, "A Closer Look at Eye Surgery," in *Harvard Health Letter*, June 1996, Vol. 21 Issue 8, p. 4

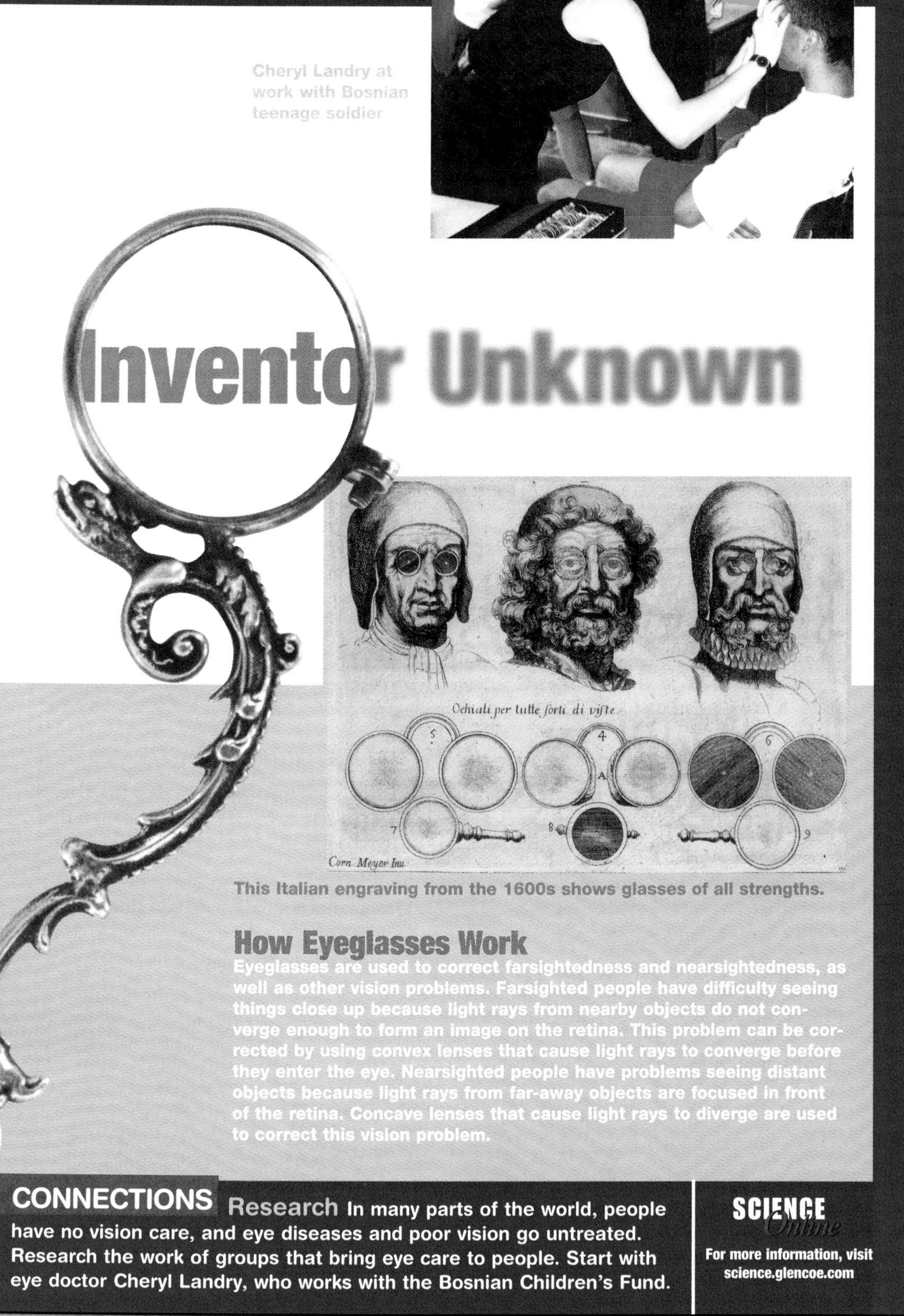

This Italian engraving from the 1600s shows glasses of all strengths.

How Eyeglasses Work

Eyeglasses are used to correct farsightedness and nearsightedness, as well as other vision problems. Farsighted people have difficulty seeing things close up because light rays from nearby objects do not converge enough to form an image on the retina. This problem can be corrected by using convex lenses that cause light rays to converge before they enter the eye. Nearsighted people have problems seeing distant objects because light rays from far-away objects are focused in front of the retina. Concave lenses that cause light rays to diverge are used to correct this vision problem.

CONNECTIONS Research In many parts of the world, people have no vision care, and eye diseases and poor vision go untreated. Research the work of groups that bring eye care to people. Start with eye doctor Cheryl Landry, who works with the Bosnian Children's Fund.

SCIENCE Online For more information, visit science.glencoe.com

Activity

Eyeglasses are made up of lenses and the frames that keep them in place. In order for eyeglasses to be widely available, cheap ways to make effective frames had to be developed. Divide the class into groups and have each group design a cheap and effective way to keep lenses on a person's face. The lenses must stay positioned so the person can see through them, and the designs must not use metal. Have students make models of their designs to display for the class. L2 **Kinesthetic**

Analyze the Event

Have students consider the daily activities of most people during the time before eyeglasses came into common use. **Does this provide any clues about why glasses were slow to come into common use?** Many people probably didn't need to see clearly in order to do the tasks they had to do. L2 **Logical-Mathematical**

CONNECTIONS Optometrist Cheryl Landry has made several trips to Bosnia to provide eyecare to refugees. She began her crusade at her own expense. Crucial to her mission is collecting used eyeglasses that she can fit to the people there. Encourage students to do research on organizations in their local area which help provide eyecare to people.

SCIENCE Online

Internet Addresses

Explore the Glencoe Science Web site at **science.glencoe.com** to find out more about topics in this feature.

Chapter 14 Study Guide

Reviewing Main Ideas

Preview

Students can answer the questions in their Science Journals. Discuss the answers as you go through the chapter. LS **Linguistic**

Review

Students can write their answers, then compare them with those of other students. LS **Interpersonal**

Reteach

Students can look at the illustrations and describe details that support the main ideas of the chapter. LS **Visual-Spatial**

Answers to Chapter Review

Section 1

3. It reflects wavelengths of light that correspond to red on the visible spectrum.

Section 2

2. The reflecting surface is not smooth.

Section 3

2. It would become smaller.

Chapter 14 Study Guide

Reviewing Main Ideas

Section 1 Properties of Light

1. Light is a wave that can travel through different materials, including a vacuum.
2. When a light wave strikes an object, some of the light wave's energy is reflected, some is absorbed, and some might be transmitted through the object.
3. The color of a light wave depends on its wavelength. The color of an object depends on which wavelengths of light are reflected by the object. *Why does this flower look red?*

4. Almost any color can be made by mixing the primary light colors or the primary pigment colors.

Section 2 Reflection and Mirrors

1. Light reflected from the surface of an object obeys the law of reflection: the angle of incidence equals the angle of reflection.
2. Diffuse reflection occurs when a surface is rough, while regular reflection occurs from very smooth surfaces and produces a clear, mirrorlike image. *Why can't the girl in the photo see her face clearly?*

3. Concave mirrors cause light waves to converge, or meet. Convex mirrors cause light waves to diverge, or spread apart.

Section 3 Refraction and Lenses

1. Light waves change speed when they travel from one medium to another. The waves bend, or refract, at the boundary between the two media.
2. A convex lens causes light waves to converge, and a concave lens causes light waves to diverge. *What would happen to the image of the insect if the magnifying glass in the photo were moved farther away?*

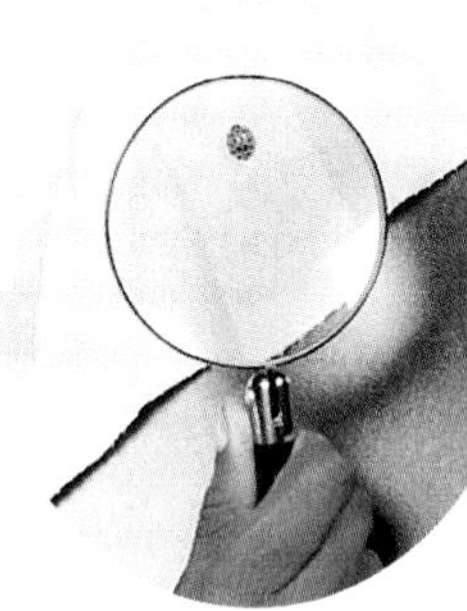

Section 4 Using Mirrors and Lenses

1. A compound microscope is used to enlarge small objects. A convex objective lens forms an enlarged image that is further enlarged by an eyepiece.
2. Most telescopes today are reflecting telescopes, which use a concave mirror to form a real image that is enlarged by an eyepiece.
3. Cameras use a convex lens to form an image on light-sensitive film.

After You Read

On the back of the top flap of your Making a Question Study Fold, explain why most telescopes are reflecting telescopes.

FOLDABLES Reading & Study Skills

After You Read

After students have read the chapter and completed the Foldable described in Before You Read, have them do the activity on the student page.

Dinah Zike

Visualizing Main Ideas

Complete the following concept map.

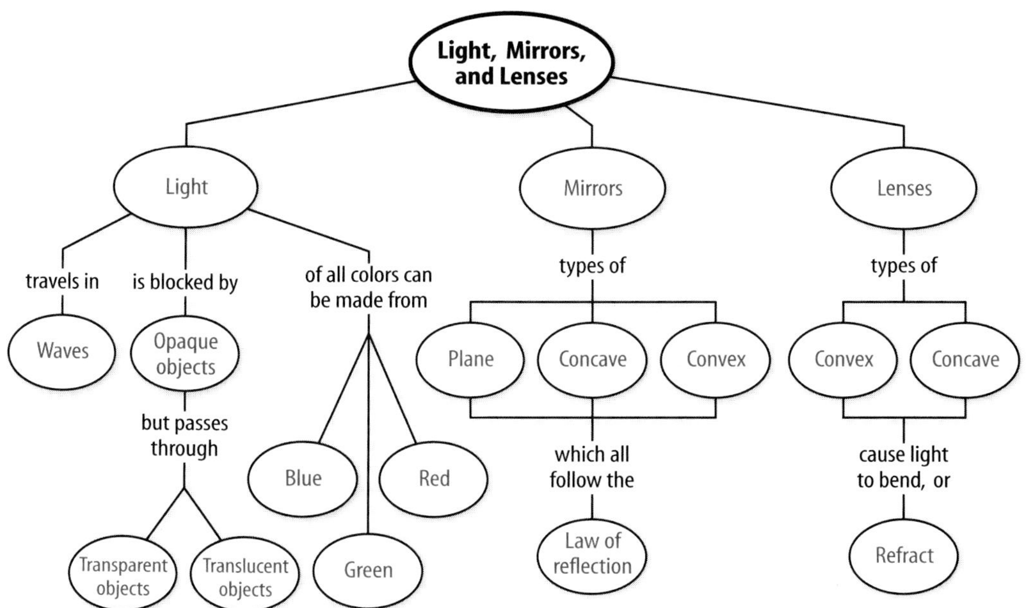

Vocabulary Review

Vocabulary Words

a. concave lens
b. convex lens
c. focal length
d. focal point
e. law of reflection
f. lens
g. light ray
h. medium
i. reflecting telescope
j. reflection
k. refracting telescope
l. refraction

Using Vocabulary

Explain the differences between the terms in the following sets.

1. reflection, refraction
2. concave lens, convex lens
3. light ray, medium
4. focal length, focal point
5. lens, medium
6. law of reflection, refraction
7. reflecting telescope, refracting telescope
8. focal point, light ray
9. lens, focal length

THE PRINCETON REVIEW

Study Tip

If you're not sure of the relationships between terms in a question, make a concept map of the terms to see how they fit together. Ask your teacher if the relationships you drew are correct.

IDENTIFYING Misconceptions

Assess

Use the assessment as follow-up to page 402F after students have completed the chapter.

Procedure Ask students to imagine that at exactly 1:15 PM our Sun was magically turned off. At what time would darkness fall upon Earth? When the Sun is turned off will Pluto remain in the Sun's light the same amount of time as Earth, longer than Earth, or a shorter time than Earth? Have students write their answers to these questions individually, then discuss them as a class.

Expected Outcome Light from the Sun takes approximately 8 minutes to reach Earth, so darkness would fall at 1:23 PM. Since Pluto is farther from the Sun than Earth, it will remain in sunlight longer than Earth.

Chapter 14 Study Guide

Visualizing Main Ideas

See student page.

Vocabulary Review

Using Vocabulary

1. Reflection occurs when light bounces off objects. Refraction occurs when light bends as it changes speed while moving from one medium to another.
2. A concave lens is thicker at the edges than in the middle and it diverges light rays. A convex lens is thicker in the middle than at the edges and it converges rays.
3. A medium is any material through which a wave travels. A light ray is a beam of light traveling from a light source or from a material that has reflected it.
4. Focal length is the distance between a lens or a mirror and its focal point. The focal point is the point at which light rays converge after traveling through a lens or being reflected by a mirror.
5. A medium is any material through which a wave travels. A lens is an object with at least one side curved through which a light wave may travel.
6. The law of reflection describes the relationship between incident and reflected light. Refraction is the relationship between incident and transmitted light.
7. A refracting telescope primarily uses convex lenses to collect light. A reflecting telescope primarily uses a mirror to collect light.
8. A light ray is a beam of light traveling from a light source or from a material that has reflected it. The focal point is the point at which light rays converge after traveling through a lens or being reflected by a mirror.
9. A lens is a transparent, curved object that causes light to bend. Focal length is the distance between a lens or a mirror and its focal point.

Chapter 14 Assessment

Checking Concepts

1. B
2. C
3. A
4. C
5. A
6. C
7. B
8. C
9. D
10. A

Thinking Critically

11. no, only the rays that are traveling parallel to the optical axis
12. No; light rays that are parallel when they strike the surface of a plane mirror remain parallel after they are reflected and do not converge.
13. The water fills in irregularities in the surface, making it smooth.
14. No; refraction must occur for a lens to magnify an object. If the speed of light were the same in all materials, refraction would not occur.
15. Red or green spotlights would make the outfit appear black. These spotlights do not contain any blue light that the outfit could reflect. The outfit would absorb the red and green light from the spotlights and appear black.

Chapter 14 Assessment

Checking Concepts

Choose the word or phrase that completes the sentence or answers the question.

1. Light waves CANNOT travel completely through which of the following?
   A) air **C)** water
   B) rock **D)** a vacuum
2. What determines the color of light?
   A) a prism **C)** its wavelength
   B) its refraction **D)** its incidence
3. If an object reflects red and green light, what color does the object appear to be?
   A) yellow **C)** green
   B) red **D)** purple
4. If an object absorbs all the light that hits it, what color would it be?
   A) white **C)** black
   B) blue **D)** green
5. What type of image is formed by a plane mirror?
   A) upright **C)** magnified
   B) inverted **D)** all of the above
6. How is the angle of incidence related to the angle of reflection?
   A) It's greater. **C)** It's the same.
   B) It's smaller. **D)** It's not focused.
7. Which of the following can be used to magnify objects?
   A) a concave lens **C)** a convex mirror
   B) a convex lens **D)** all of the above
8. Which of the following controls the amount of light striking the film in a camera?
   A) lungs **C)** diaphragm
   B) shutter **D)** lens
9. What is an object that reflects some light and transmits some light called?
   A) colored **C)** opaque
   B) diffuse **D)** translucent
10. Which of the following can help someone who is nearsighted?
    A) a convex lens **C)** a concave lens
    B) a plane mirror **D)** a telephoto lens

Thinking Critically

11. Do all light rays that strike a convex lens pass through the focal point?
12. Does a plane mirror focus light rays? Why or why not?
13. Explain why a rough surface, such as the road in this photo, is a better reflector when it is wet.

14. If the speed of light were the same in all materials, could lenses be used to magnify objects? Why or why not?
15. A singer is wearing a blue outfit. What color spotlights would make the outfit appear to be black? Explain.

Developing Skills

16. **Comparing and Contrasting** Compare and contrast plane and convex mirrors.
17. **Drawing Conclusions** You notice a rainbow of color in a drop of water. Conclude why.
18. **Predicting** Predict what types of camera lenses you would use to take a close-up of a flower and a picture of the Grand Canyon. Explain your choices.
19. **Classifying** Classify the following objects as opaque, translucent, or transparent: a pane of glass, a brick wall, and frosted windows.

Chapter Assessment Planner

Portfolio Encourage students to place in their portfolios one or two items of what they consider to be their best work. Examples include:

- Make a Model, p. 406
- Visual Learning, p. 410
- Cultural Diversity, p. 417
- Assessment, p. 425

Performance Additional performance assessments, Performance Task Assessment Lists, and rubrics for evaluating these activities can be found in Glencoe's **Performance Assessment in the Science Classroom.**

20. Using Graphs The graph below shows how the distance of an image from a convex lens is related to the distance of the object from the lens.

Image Distance (cm): 10, 20, 30, 40, 50
Object Distance (cm): 10, 20, 30, 40, 50

A) How does the image move as the object gets closer to the lens?

B) You can find the magnification of the image with the equation

$$\text{Magnification} = \frac{\text{image distance}}{\text{object distance}}$$

At which object distance is the magnification greatest?

Performance Assessment

21. Poster Make a poster describing the difference between the primary colors of light and the primary colors of pigment.

22. Reverse Writing In a plane mirror, images are reversed. With this in mind, write a "backwards" note to a friend and have him or her read it in a mirror.

TECHNOLOGY

Go to the Glencoe Science Web site at **science.glencoe.com** or use the **Glencoe Science CD-ROM** for additional chapter assessment.

THE PRINCETON REVIEW Test Practice

Nelson learned that the speed of light is 300,000 km/s. Since he knew that the fastest passenger jet, the SST, flies faster than the speed of sound, he did some research to compare the speeds of sound and light.

The Speed of Sound and Light in Different Media

Medium	Speed of Sound (m/s)	Speed of Light (10^8 m/s)
Glass	5,971	1.6
Water	1,486	2.2
Air	335	3.0
Vacuum	0	3.0

Study the table above and answer the following questions.

1. According to the table, in which medium is the speed of sound the fastest and the speed of light the slowest?
   A) glass
   B) water
   C) air
   D) vacuum

2. According to the table, which medium is able to transmit only light?
   F) glass
   G) water
   H) air
   J) vacuum

THE PRINCETON REVIEW Test Practice

The Test-Taking Tip was written by The Princeton Review, the nation's leader in test preparation.

1. A
2. J

Developing Skills

16. Images formed by both are always upright and appear to originate from behind the mirror. Images from a plane mirror are the same size as the object; images from a convex mirror are smaller than the object.

17. Light refracts into the drop, reflects off the inner surface, and refracts out of the drop. The two refractions separate the light into the colors of the rainbow.

18. Possible answers: You might use a telephoto lens to take a close-up of a flower because it would increase the image size. You might use a wide-angle lens to take a picture of the Grand Canyon because it would allow a wide view of the scenery.

19. The glass is transparent, the wall is opaque, and the frosted windows are translucent.

20. **A)** As the object gets closer to the lens, the image gets farther from the lens. **B)** The magnification increases as the object gets closer to the lens; 10 cm.

Performance Assessment

21. Posters should show that primary light colors can be mixed to produce any other color of light. Primary pigment colors result when a pigment absorbs a primary light color. Use **PASC**, p. 145.

22. When writing the notes, students should understand that the image reflected by a plane mirror is upright with left and right sides reversed. Use **PASC**, p. 139.

Assessment Resources

Reproducible Masters

Chapter Resources Booklet
Chapter Review, pp. 41–42
Chapter Tests, pp. 43–46
Assessment Transparency Activity, p. 55

Glencoe Science Web site
Interactive Tutor
Chapter Quizzes

Glencoe Technology
Assessment Transparency
Interactive CD-ROM Chapter Quizzes
ExamView Pro Test Bank
Vocabulary PuzzleMaker Software
MindJogger Videoquiz DVD/VHS

Standardized Test Practice

Reading Comprehension

QUESTION 1: C

Students must identify the answer choice that is the correct cause in the cause-and-effect relationship.

- **Choice A** No; the spyglass was not originally used to view the Moon. Galileo adapted the spyglass for that purpose.
- **Choice B** No; Roger Bacon developed basic ideas about the telescope.
- **Choice C** Yes; the spyglass was originally used to watch other people, such as enemy armies.
- **Choice D** No; although the spyglass was a Dutch invention, that is not the reason for its name.

QUESTION 2: F

Students must use information from the passage to identify the answer choice that is the best supported conclusion.

QUESTION 3: C

Students must use the key word *American* to locate important information in the passage and identify the correct answer choice.

All questions written and validated by The Princeton Review.

Standardized Test Practice

Reading Comprehension

Read the passage. Then read each question that follows the passage. Decide which is the best answer to each question.

The History of the Telescope: An International Story

Roger Bacon, an English scientist, first wrote about the basic ideas behind the operation of a telescope in the 1200s. It was not until the early 1600s, however that Han Lippershey, a Dutchman who made spectacles for people with poor vision, made the first telescope. Lippershey noticed that objects appeared closer if he viewed them through a combination of a concave and a convex lens. He placed the lenses in a tube to hold them more easily. This was the world's first refracting telescope.

A few years later, an Italian scientist, Galileo, was the first to point a telescope toward the stars. Galileo learned of the Dutch invention in 1609. At the time, it was mainly used to see objects on Earth, such as distant ships and enemy armies. This is why the telescope was first called a "spyglass." Galileo made his own telescope and began using it to view the sky. Before this, Galileo had not been particularly interested in astronomy. That quickly changed as he recorded observations of the Moon's surface, spots on the Sun, and four moons circling Jupiter.

Another advance in telescope technology occurred in 1663 when James Gregory, a Scottish scientist, designed the first reflecting telescope. Isaac Newton built the first reflecting telescope 25 years later. The earliest, most valuable contribution to astronomy made by an American was the construction of the Hooker telescope, a reflecting telescope on Mount Wilson. Completed in 1917, its 254 cm reflecting concave mirror allowed astronomers to see other galaxies clearly for the first time.

Since then, scientists have continued to design and build larger and more powerful telescopes. The development of the modern telescope is the result of many years of work by many scientists across the world.

Test-Taking Tip As you read the passage, make a time line of the history of the telescope.

1. The telescope was first called a "spyglass" because it _____.
   A) was helpful in observing the Moon and stars
   B) was designed by Roger Bacon
   C) could be used to watch other people
   D) was first made by a Dutchman

2. According to the passage, scientists often _____.
   F) build upon one other's work
   G) are slow workers
   H) aren't interested in many things
   J) never read the work of other scientists

3. The earliest, most valuable contribution to astronomy made by an American was _____.
   A) the first refracting telescope built in the 1600s
   B) Roger Bacon's basic ideas about the operation of a telescope in the 1200s
   C) the construction of the Hooker telescope on Mount Wilson which allowed astronomers to see other galaxies clearly for the first time
   D) using a telescope to view the Moon's surface, spots on the Sun, and four moons circling Jupiter

Reasoning and Skills

Power of a Lens

Lens	Diopter	Focal length (m)
1	1/4	4
2	1/5	5
3	1/6	6
4	1/7	7
5	1/9	?

1. Diopters are one way to measure the strength of a lens. What is the focal length of lens 5?

A) 5
B) 8
C) 9
D) 10

Test-Taking Tip Study the values for the first three lenses and consider how the diopter value is related to the focal length.

Wavelengths of Electromagnetic Waves

Type of Wave	Wavelength
radio wave	>0.1 m
microwave	0.001m – 0.1 m
infrared wave	0.000 000 7 – 0.001 m
visible light wave	0.000 000 4 – 0.000 000 7 m

2. A wave with a wavelength of 0.03 m would be what type of wave?

F) radio wave
G) microwave
H) infrared wave
J) visible light wave

Test-Taking Tip Read the table's column headings carefully and then reread the question.

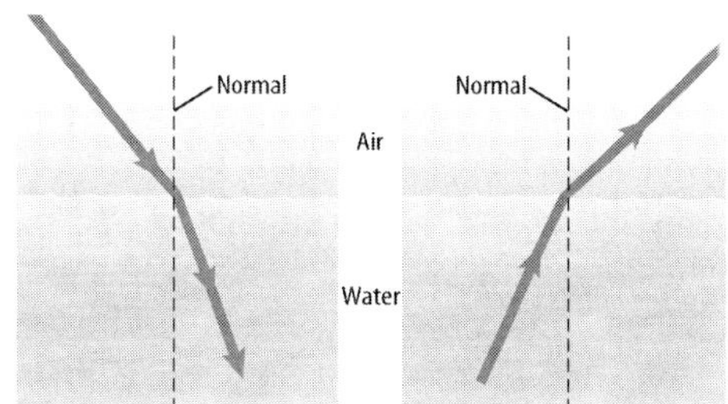

3. What is happening to the wave in this figure?

A) it is being diffracted
B) it is being refracted
C) it is experiencing constructive interference
D) it is experiencing destructive interference

Test-Taking Tip Review the difference between diffraction, refraction, constructive interference, and destructive interference.

4. Explain the relationship between the amplitude of a sound wave and the loudness of a sound. How is the amplitude of the sound wave related to the amount of energy it carries?

Test-Taking Tip Recall the definition of the terms *amplitude* and *loudness*.

Standardized Test Practice

Reasoning and Skills

Question 1: C

Students must study the chart carefully in order to recognize a pattern in the data.

Question 2: G

Students must study the chart carefully in order to decide where 0.03 fits in with the data.

- **Choice F** No; radio waves are greater than 0.1 meters and are much larger than 0.03 m.
- **Choice G** Yes; microwaves range from 0.001 m to 0.1 m. This range includes 0.03 m.
- **Choice H** No; infrared waves are smaller than 0.001 meters and are much smaller than 0.03 m.
- **Choice J** No; visible light waves are smaller than 0.0000007 meters and are much smaller than 0.03 m.

Question 3: B

Students must understand that the bending of waves is called refraction.

Question 4: Answers will vary.

Students should mention that amplitude is wave height, and is a measure of the energy the wave carries. The higher the amplitude, the louder the sound.

UNIT 6

Unit Contents

✔ Pre-Reading Activity

Have students list electrical appliances and devices and tell their major function, such as heating, cooling, lighting, motion, and so forth. They can conduct a scavenger hunt and try to find pictures of these items in this unit.

UNIT 6 Electricity and Magnetism

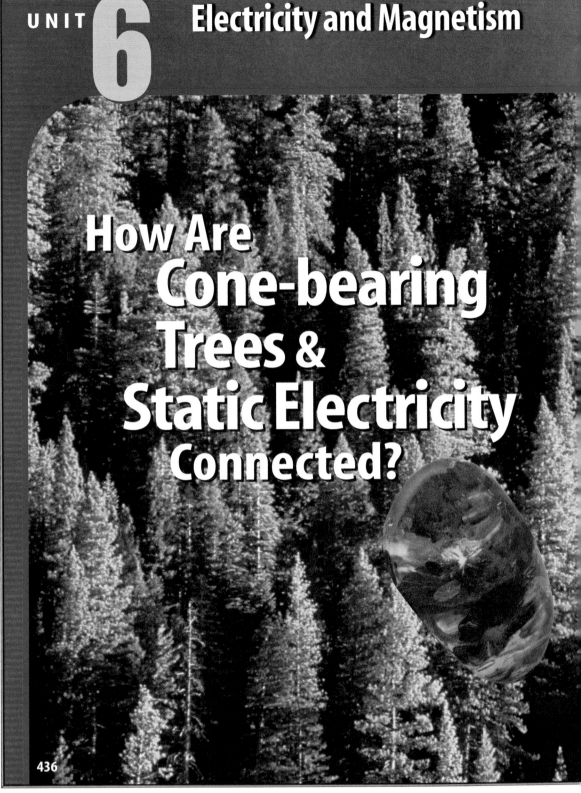

How Are Cone-bearing Trees & Static Electricity Connected?

436

Teacher to Teacher

"I have groups of six to eight students create a human circuit by hooking themselves up. The class identifies the circuit as a series or parallel and predicts whether it will work. Using a set of electrical equipment, have another group create the demonstrated circuit."

Deborah Peters Huffine, Teacher
Noblesville Intermediate School
Noblesville, IN

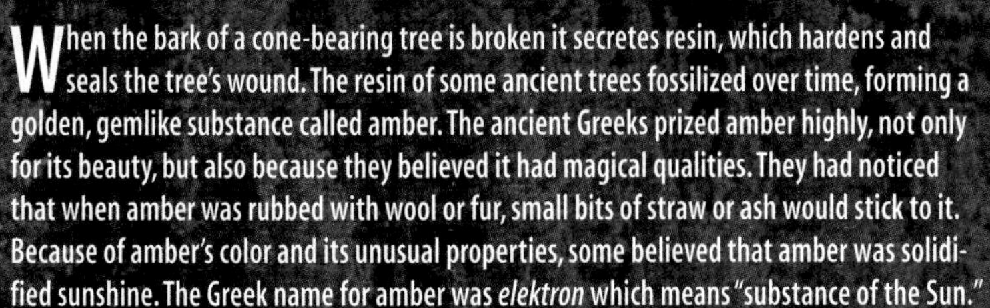

When the bark of a cone-bearing tree is broken it secretes resin, which hardens and seals the tree's wound. The resin of some ancient trees fossilized over time, forming a golden, gemlike substance called amber. The ancient Greeks prized amber highly, not only for its beauty, but also because they believed it had magical qualities. They had noticed that when amber was rubbed with wool or fur, small bits of straw or ash would stick to it. Because of amber's color and its unusual properties, some believed that amber was solidified sunshine. The Greek name for amber was *elektron* which means "substance of the Sun."

By the seventeenth century, the behavior of amber had sparked the curiosity of a number of scientists, and an explanation of amber's behavior finally emerged. When amber is rubbed by wool or fur, static electricity is produced. Today, a device called a Van de Graaff generator, like the one shown below, can produce static electricity involving millions of volts, and has been used to explore the nature of matter in atom-smashing experiments.

SCIENCE CONNECTION

STATIC ELECTRICITY When you dry clothes in a gas or electric dryer, the fabrics often stick together. This "clinging" is due to static electricity. Using the Glencoe Science Web site at **science.glencoe.com** or library resources, find out how clothing becomes charged in a dryer, and how anti-static products work. Write a paragraph in your Science Journal about what you find.

Introducing the Unit

How Are Cone-Bearing Trees & Static Electricity Connected?

It was the working of Baltic amber, the fossilized sap of conifers, that led to the discovery of its electrostatic properties. Thales of Miletus thought its ability to attract feathers and other light objects when rubbed was evidence of a soul.

Post-Renaissance investigation of the electrical properties of amber led to modern electrical science. In 1600, William Gilbert invented the term *Electrica*, from the Latin name for amber, *electrum*, for any material that could be made to act like amber. The electrica would build up and hold a static charge. Metals like steel and copper were called *non-electrics* because they conducted the charge away.

In 1660 Otto Von Guericke built the first static generator from a glass sphere turned by a handle against woolen cloth. By placing a little mercury in the sphere and evacuating the air, Francis Hauksbee was able to make the sphere glow brightly enough to read by.

SCIENCE CONNECTION

Activity

When an insulator acquires a charge, it stays in place until connected to the ground or an object with an opposite charge. Rubbing a balloon on fur or wool will strip electrons from the wool. This negatively charges the balloon and positively charges the wool, causing them to attract. Have students try this with different materials and discuss the results. Suggest that advanced students try to construct a static generator. LS Kinesthetic

SCIENCE Online

Internet Addresses

Explore the Glencoe Science Web site at **science.glencoe.com** to find out more about topics in this unit.

Section/Objectives	Standards		Activities/Features
	National	State/Local	
Chapter Opener	See p. 5T for a Key to Standards.		**Explore Activity:** Investigate electric forces, p. 439 **Before You Read,** p. 439
Section 1 Electric Charge 4 sessions 2 blocks 1. **Describe** how objects can become electrically charged. 2. **Explain** how electric charges affect other electric charges. 3. **Distinguish** between insulators and conductors. 4. **Describe** how electric discharges such as lightning occur.	National Content Standards: UCP2, B3, C1, D1, F3		**Visualizing Nerve Impulses,** p. 442 **Science Online,** p. 444
Section 2 Electric Current 4 sessions 2 blocks 1. **Relate** voltage to the electrical energy carried by an electric current. 2. **Describe** a battery and how it produces an electric current. 3. **Explain** electrical resistance.	National Content Standards: UCP2, A1, B3, E2		**MiniLAB:** Investigating the Electric Force, p. 448 **Chemistry Integration,** p. 449
Section 3 Electric Circuits 5 sessions 2.5 blocks 1. **Explain** how voltage, current, and resistance are related in an electric circuit. 2. **Investigate** the difference between series and parallel circuits. 3. **Determine** the electrical power used in a circuit. 4. **Describe** how to avoid dangerous electric shock.	National Content Standards: UCP2, A1, B3, E2, F1, F5, G2		**Math Skills Activity:** Calculating the Current Used by Lightbulbs, p. 453 **MiniLAB:** Identifying Simple Circuits, p. 454 **Math Skills Activity:** Calculating the Wattage of Lightbulbs, p. 456 **Science Online,** p. 457 **Life Science Integration,** p. 458 **Activity:** Current in a Parallel Circuit, p. 459 **Activity:** A Model for Voltage and Current, pp. 460–461 **Science and Society:** Fire in the Forest, pp. 462–463

Activity Materials	Reproducible Resources	Section Assessment	Technology
Explore Activity: 2 rubber balloons, small bits of paper, piece of wool cloth	**Chapter Resources Booklet** Foldables Worksheet, p. 17 Directed Reading Overview, p. 19 Note-taking Worksheets, pp. 33–35	Glencoe's Assessment Advantage	
Need materials? Contact Science Kit at 1-800-828-7777 or www.sciencekit.com on the Internet.	**Chapter Resources Booklet** Transparency Activity, p. 44 Enrichment, p. 30 Reinforcement, p. 27 Directed Reading, p. 20 Lab Activity, pp. 9–12 **Life Science Critical Thinking/ Problem Solving,** p. 2	Portfolio Assessment, p. 446 Performance Skill Builder Activities, p. 446 Content Section Assessment, p. 446	Section Focus Transparency Interactive CD-ROM/DVD Guided Reading Audio Program
MiniLAB: salt, plate, pepper, rubber or plastic comb, wool cloth	**Chapter Resources Booklet** Transparency Activity, p. 45 MiniLAB, p. 3 Enrichment, p. 31 Reinforcement, p. 28 Directed Reading, p. 21 Transparency Activity, pp. 47–48 Lab Activity, pp. 13–15 **Science Inquiry Labs,** p. 9	Portfolio Assessment, p. 451 Performance MiniLAB, p. 448 Skill Builder Activities, p. 451 Content Section Assessment, p. 451	Section Focus Transparency Teaching Transparency Interactive CD-ROM/DVD Guided Reading Audio Program
MiniLAB: flashlight bulb, wire, battery **Activity:** 1.5-V lightbulbs (4), 1.5-V batteries (2), 10-cm-long pieces of insulated wire (8), 2 battery holders, 4 mini-bulb sockets **Activity:** plastic funnel, 1-m lengths of rubber or plastic tubing of different diameters, meterstick, ring stand with ring, stopwatch, hose clamp, 500-mL beakers (2)	**Chapter Resources Booklet** Transparency Activity, p. 46 MiniLAB, p. 4 Enrichment, p. 32 Reinforcement, p. 29 Directed Reading, pp. 21, 22 Activity Worksheets, pp. 5–6, 7–8 **Mathematics Skill Activities,** p. 11 **Physical Science Critical Thinking/Problem Solving,** p. 8 **Lab Management and Safety,** p. 71	Portfolio Visual Learning, p. 454 Performance Math Skills Activity, p. 453 MiniLAB, p. 454 Math Skill Activity, p. 456 Skill Builder Activities, p. 458 Content Section Assessment, p. 458	Section Focus Transparency Interactive CD-ROM/DVD Guided Reading Audio Program

End of Chapter Assessment

Glencoe's Assessment Advantage

Blackline Masters	Technology	Professional Series
Chapter Resources Booklet Chapter Review, pp. 37–38 Chapter Tests, pp. 39–42 **Standardized Test Practice by The Princeton Review,** pp. 63–66	MindJogger Videoquiz CD-ROM Explorations and Quizzes Vocabulary Puzzle Makers ExamView Pro Test Bank Interactive Lesson Planner Interactive Teacher's Edition	Performance Assessment in the Science Classroom (PASC)

Transparencies

Section Focus

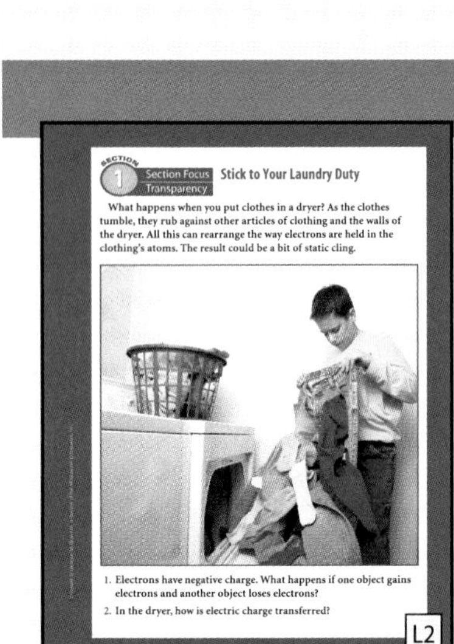

Section 1 Section Focus Transparency **Stick to Your Laundry Duty**

What happens when you put clothes in a dryer? As the clothes tumble, they rub against other articles of clothing and the walls of the dryer. All this can rearrange the way electrons are held in the clothing's atoms. The result could be a bit of static cling.

1. Electrons have negative charge. What happens if one object gains electrons and another object loses electrons?
2. In the dryer, how is electric charge transferred?

L2

Section 2 Section Focus Transparency **Go with the Flow**

In some ways, this waterfall is similar to an electric current. Do you see how the water flows down the cliff? Water takes the path of least resistance—it flows where it's easiest for water to go. Electric currents flow and experience resistance, too.

1. Which has more energy, the waterfall in the picture or Niagara Falls? Explain your answer.
2. How do people use the energy in water currents?
3. How are dams and batteries similar?

L2

Section 3 Section Focus Transparency **One Big Electric Bill**

How profoundly pervasive is electric power? Look at the image below. It shows Earth at night. You can pick out areas like Europe and the east and west coasts of the United States because of all the electric lights.

1. What is the relationship between light density and energy use?
2. If electric lights are an accurate gauge, what areas use the most electricity?
3. What areas use the least electricity?

L2

This is a representation of key blackline masters available in the Teacher Classroom Resources. See Resource Manager boxes within the chapter for additional information.

Assessment

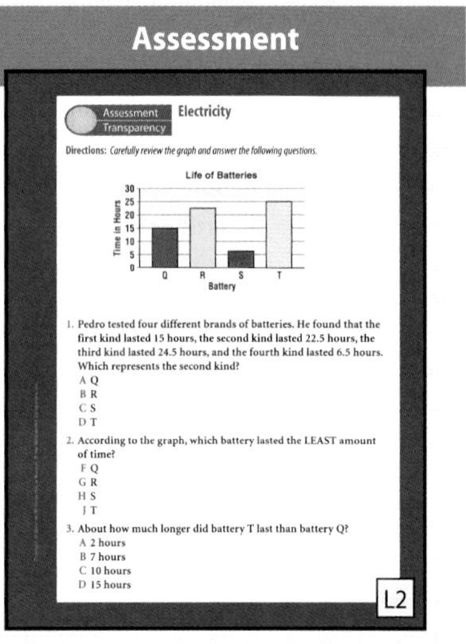

Assessment Transparency **Electricity**

Directions: *Carefully review the graph and answer the following questions.*

1. Pedro tested four different brands of batteries. He found that the first kind lasted 15 hours, the second kind lasted 22.5 hours, the third kind lasted 24.5 hours, and the fourth kind lasted 6.5 hours. Which represents the second kind?
   A Q
   B R
   C S
   D T
2. According to the graph, which battery lasted the LEAST amount of time?
   F Q
   G R
   H S
   J T
3. About how much longer did battery T last than battery Q?
   A 2 hours
   B 7 hours
   C 10 hours
   D 15 hours

L2

Teaching

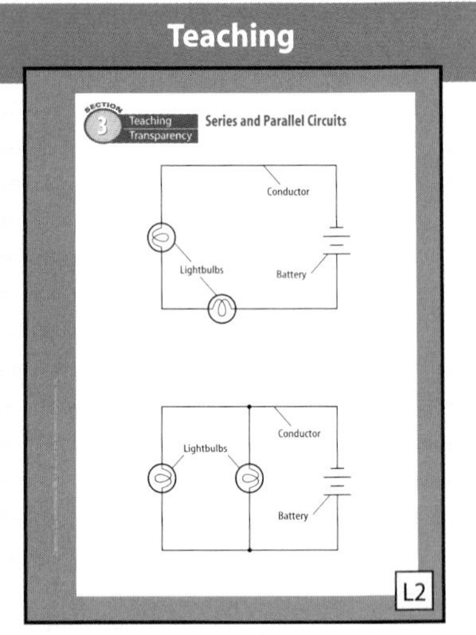

Section 3 Teaching Transparency **Series and Parallel Circuits**

L2

Key to Teaching Strategies

The following designations will help you decide which activities are appropriate for your students.

- L1 Level 1 activities should be appropriate for students with learning difficulties.
- L2 Level 2 activities should be within the ability range of all students.
- L3 Level 3 activities are designed for above-average students.
- ELL ELL activities should be within the ability range of English Language Learners.
- COOP LEARN Cooperative Learning activities are designed for small group work.
- LS Multiple Learning Styles logos, as described on page 22T, are used throughout to indicate strategies that address different learning styles.
- P These strategies represent student products that can be placed into a best-work portfolio.

Hands-on Activities

Activity Worksheets

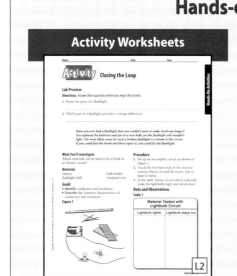

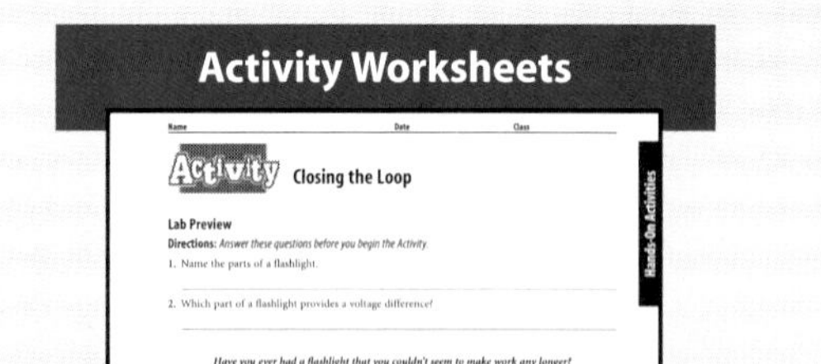

Name Date Class

Activity **Closing the Loop**

Lab Preview

Directions: *Answer these questions before you begin the Activity.*

1. Name the parts of a flashlight.
2. Which part of a flashlight provides a voltage difference?

Have you ever had a flashlight that you couldn't seem to make work any longer? You replaced the batteries and put in a new bulb, yet the flashlight still wouldn't light. The most likely cause for such a broken flashlight is a break in the circuit. If you could find the break and then repair it, you could fix the flashlight.

What You'll Investigate

Which materials can be used to fix a break in an electric circuit?

Materials

battery, flashlight bulb, bulb holder, insulated wire

Goals

- **Identify** conductors and insulators.
- **Describe** the common characteristics of conductors and insulators.

Figure 1

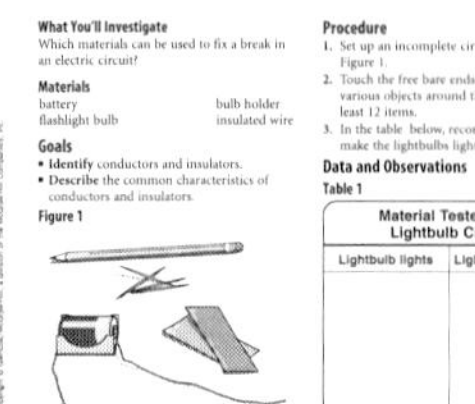

Procedure

1. Set up an incomplete circuit as shown in Figure 1.
2. Touch the free bare ends of the wires to various objects around the room. Test at least 12 items.
3. In the table below, record which materials make the lightbulbs light and which don't.

Data and Observations

Table 1

Material Tested with Lightbulb Circuit	
Lightbulb lights	Lightbulb stays out

L2

Laboratory Activities

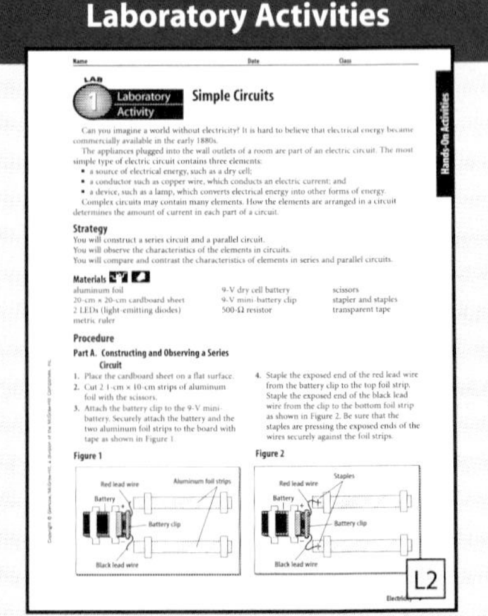

Name Date Class

Lab 1 Laboratory Activity **Simple Circuits**

Can you imagine a world without electricity? It is hard to believe that electrical energy became commercially available in the early 1880s.

The appliances plugged into the wall outlets of a room are part of an electric circuit. The most simple type of electric circuit contains three elements:

- a source of electrical energy, such as a dry cell;
- a conductor such as copper wire, which conducts an electric current; and
- a device, such as a lamp, which converts electrical energy into other forms of energy.

Complex circuits may contain many elements. How the elements are arranged in a circuit determines the amount of current in each part of a circuit.

Strategy

You will construct a series circuit and a parallel circuit.
You will observe the characteristics of the elements in circuits.
You will compare and contrast the characteristics of elements in series and parallel circuits.

Materials

aluminum foil; 20-cm × 20-cm cardboard sheet; 2 LEDs (light-emitting diodes); metric ruler; 9-V dry cell battery; 9-V mini-battery clip; 500-Ω resistor; scissors; stapler and staples; transparent tape

Procedure

Part A. Constructing and Observing a Series Circuit

1. Place the cardboard sheet on a flat surface.
2. Cut 2 1-cm × 10-cm strips of aluminum foil with the scissors.
3. Attach the battery clip to the 9-V mini-battery. Securely attach the battery and the two aluminum foil strips to the board with tape as shown in Figure 1.
4. Staple the exposed end of the red lead wire from the battery clip to the top foil strip. Staple the exposed end of the black lead wire from the clip to the bottom foil strip as shown in Figure 2. Be sure that the staples are pressing the exposed ends of the wires securely against the foil strips.

Figure 1

Figure 2

L2

Meeting Different Ability Levels

Content Outline

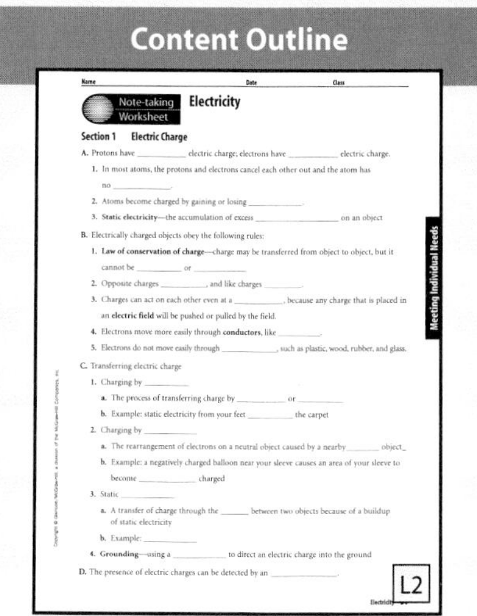

Reinforcement

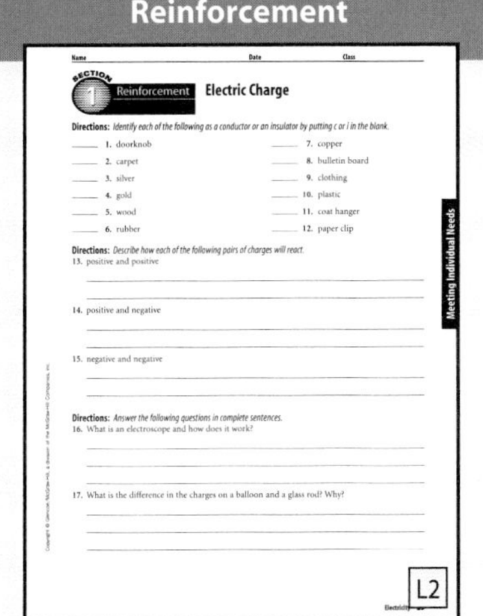

Directed Reading

Name Date Class

Directed Reading for Content Mastery — *Overview* Electricity

Directions: *Complete the sentences crossing out the incorrect words.*

Electricity is **1.** (static, parallel) when electric **2.** (charges, circuits) accumulate on an object by gaining or losing **3.** (branches, electrons) that move more easily in a(n) **4.** (conductor, insulator) than they do in a(n) **5.** (conductor, insulator).

Electricity in the form of a **6.** (current, series) flows from object to object from **7.** (low, high) voltage to **8.** (low, high) voltage. This voltage **9.** (parallel, difference) can be produced by a **10.** (battery, generator) or by a **11.** (battery, generator) at a power plant. Electrical **12.** (charges, circuits) can be **13.** (series, branches) with one **14.** (loop, current) to flow through or they can be **15.** (static, parallel) with two or more **16.** (series, branches) for the electricity.

Directions: *Use the following terms to fill in the blank spaces below.*

Series | Parallel

17. This is a ______ circuit. **18.** This is a ______ circuit.

19. In which circuit will the brightness of the bulbs be diminished as more bulbs are added?

20. In which circuit will both lights go out if one light is turned off?

21. Which circuit is used to provide electricity to houses?

L1

Assessment

Chapter Tests

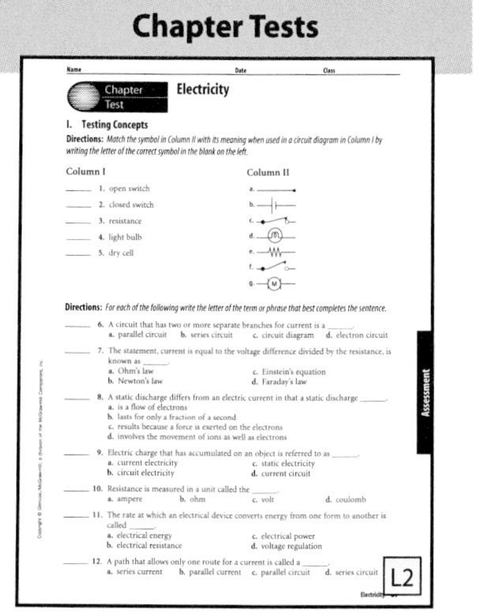

Enrichment

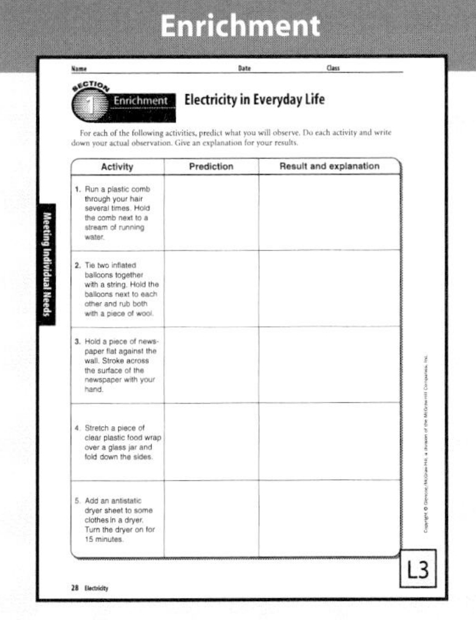

Spanish Directed Reading

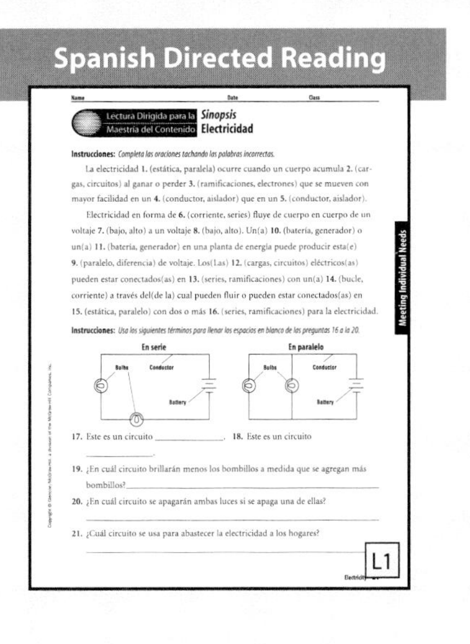

Test Practice Workbook

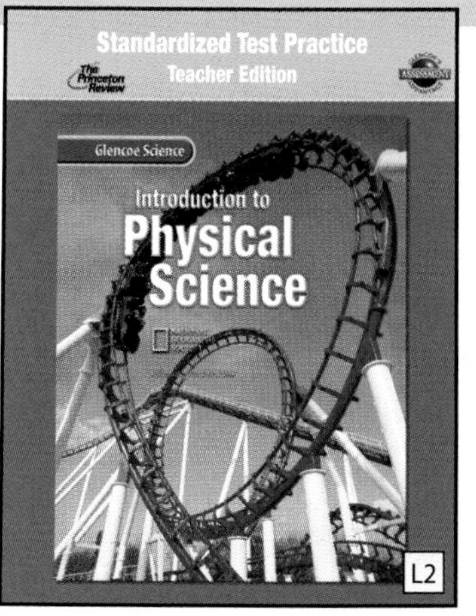

Chapter Review

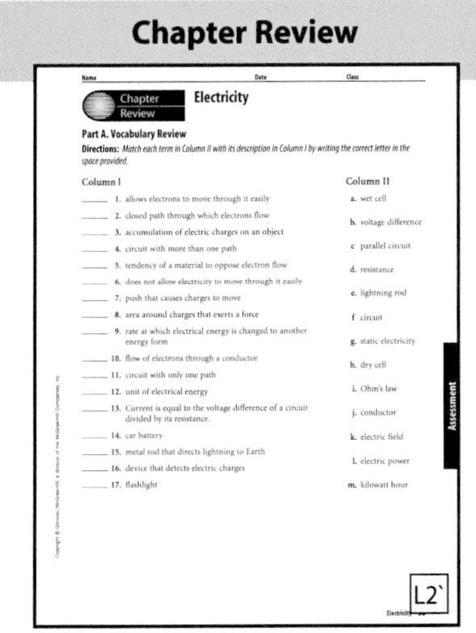

Science Content Background

SECTION 1 Electric Charge

Electricity

Charge is an abstract idea and is not a substance. Charge is the name given to a property acquired by objects, a property that seems to leak away, can be restored by rubbing, can move between objects, is highly mobile on metals, and so on. From observing the interactions between objects, we can infer the existence of a property called charge, but we cannot observe the charge itself, only the interactions it produces. In all of science, the appropriate starting point is not the model but the observation. The concept of charge was invented to provide a plausible explanation for scientists' observations.

SECTION 2 Electric Current

Flow of Charge

Benjamin Franklin's charge model of positive and negative, with conventional current going from positive to negative, is still used today. Electrons were discovered one hundred years later and exhibit the characteristics of negative charge. Franklin defined objects repelled by rubber rods stroked with rabbit fur as negative. They could have easily have been defined as positive. Because rubber rods that have been stroked with rabbit fur repel them, we consider electrons to be negative. When a wire is used as the conductor, the electrons from the metal carry negative charges through the wire. In a fluid conductor, such as the electrolyte inside a battery, positive and negative charges (ions) are free to flow.

Students may wonder about the names of batteries. There are AA, AAA, C, and D; why are there no A or B batteries? In the 1920s, there were A and B batteries, which were used to power crank telephones and early radios. They are no longer produced today.

Pekka Parviainen/ Photo Researchers, Inc.

Student Misconception

Electricity travels from a battery to a light bulb and stops there.

Refer to the facing page for teaching strategies to address this misconception. Refer to pages 447–450 for content related to this topic.

SECTION 3 Electric Circuits

Electrical Safety

In electrical shock, the amount and duration of electrical current moving through the body determines the extent of the damage it does. Low voltage does not imply low hazard. A wall voltage of 120 V is not a particularly high voltage, yet it can be lethal because of the large current that can flow out of the wall socket. An illustrative example of the importance of current is to consider the balloon experiment in the opening Explore Activity. Rubbing a balloon on your hair will charge the balloon to several thousand volts. Even if you touch a 5000-V balloon, you will feel no shock because the amount of current is so small.

For additional content background on this topic, go to the Glencoe Science Web site at science.glencoe.com.

IDENTIFYING Misconceptions

Find Out What Students Think

Students may think that . . .

- **Electricity travels from a battery to a light bulb and stops there.**

Electricity may cause misconceptions because it is not directly observed. Further, most students have little experience working directly with simple electrical circuits. It might seem to students that electrical devices are plugged into electrical outlets to get electricity just as a car is connected to a hose from a pump to get gasoline.

Demonstration

Hold up a flashlight and turn it on. Ask students to write down their predictions about what would happen if you left the flashlight on for a couple of days. Ask them to write down why they think their predictions would happen. Hold up one D battery, one flashlight bulb, and one wire with the insulation stripped off both ends. Ask students to draw one way they could make the bulb light using only these materials.

Promote Understanding

Activity

Give each pair of students one wire, one flashlight bulb, and one D battery and ask them to do the following:

- Connect the items as shown in your drawings and see if the bulb lights.
- Try other ways to get the bulb to light.
- Draw all the arrangements you attempt—both those that don't work and those that do work.

After 25 minutes some pairs probably will have determined how to complete the circuit to get the bulb to light. Possible ways to make the bulb light include touching the bulb to one side of the battery, while touching one end of the wire to the other side of the bulb, and touching the other end of the wire to the other side of the battery.

On one side of the board, have students draw ways that the materials were connected so that the bulbs did not light up. On the other side of the board, have students draw ways the materials were connected to produce a lit bulb.

Ask how the drawings on one side of the board are different from the drawings on the other side.

Based on the drawings, what is necessary to get a bulb to light? Establish that a complete circuit gives electrons a path through which to travel, while a power source, such as the battery, gives the electrons the impetus to move through the circuit.

Assess

After completing the chapter, see *Identifying Misconceptions* in the Study Guide.

Electricity

Chapter Vocabulary

ion
static charge
electric force
electric field
insulator
conductor
electric discharge
electric current
circuit
voltage
resistance
Ohm's law
series circuit
parallel circuit
electrical power

What do you think?

Science Journal The photo shows an electric spark jumping between the ends of two wires.

CHAPTER 15

Electricity

This spark generator uses voltages of millions of volts to produce these electric discharges that resemble lightning. Other electric discharges, like those that occur when you walk across a carpeted floor, are not as visible. In your home, electric currents flow through wires, and also power lights, televisions, and other appliances. In this chapter, you will learn about electric charges and the forces they exert on each other. You also will learn how electric charges moving in a circuit can do useful work.

What do you think?

Science Journal Look at the picture below with a classmate. Discuss what this might be. Here's a hint: *Think power—lots of power.* Write your best guess in your Science Journal.

438

Theme Connection

Systems and Interactions Electrical charges interact in observable ways with their environment. Electric circuits are systems of moving electrical charges. The movement of electrical charges in a circuit is controlled by interactions between parts of the circuit.

No computers? No CD players? No video games? Can you imagine life without electricity? You depend on it every day, and not just to make life more fun. Electricity heats and cools homes and provides light. It provides energy that can be used to do work. This energy comes from the forces that electric charges exert on each other. What is the nature of these electric forces?

Investigate electric forces

1. Inflate a rubber balloon.
2. Put some small bits of paper on your desktop and bring the balloon close to the bits of paper. Observe what happens.
3. Charge the balloon by holding it by the knot and rubbing the balloon on your hair or on a piece of wool.
4. Bring the balloon close to the bits of paper and observe what happens.
5. Charge two balloons using the procedure in step 3 and bring them close to each other.
6. Repeat step 3, then touch the balloon with your hand. Now what happens when you bring the balloon close to the bits of paper?

Observe

Record your observations of electric forces in your Science Journal.

Before You Read

Making a Vocabulary Study Fold **Make the following Foldable to help you better understand the terms *charge, current,* and *circuit.***

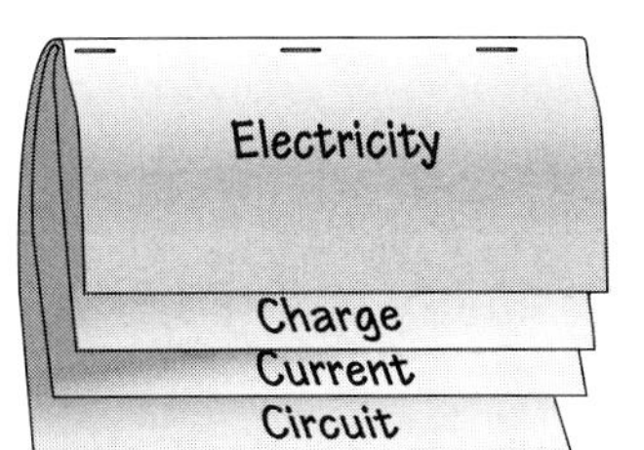

1. Stack two sheets of paper in front of you so the short side of both sheets is at the top.
2. Slide the top sheet up so that about 4 cm of the bottom sheet show.
3. Fold both sheets top to bottom to form four tabs and staple along the fold.
4. Label the tabs *Electricity, Charge, Current,* and *Circuit.*
5. Before you read the chapter, write your definition of charge, current, and circuit under the tabs. As you read the chapter, correct your definition and write more information about each.

439

Purpose Use the Explore Activity to introduce the concept of electrical charge. The moving paper in this activity is evidence of force and that work is being done. L2 ELL LS **Visual Spatial**

Preparation To save time, inflate balloons before class.

Materials 2 balloons, small bits of paper, wool cloth

Teaching Strategies After students charge the balloon using their hair, ask whether their hair acts differently or feels odd. Have students describe the connection between charging the balloon and the behavior of their hair.

Observe

In Step 2 the balloon has no effect on the paper. In Step 4 the balloon attracts the pieces of paper. In Step 5 the balloons repel each other. In Step 6 the balloon no longer affects the pieces of paper.

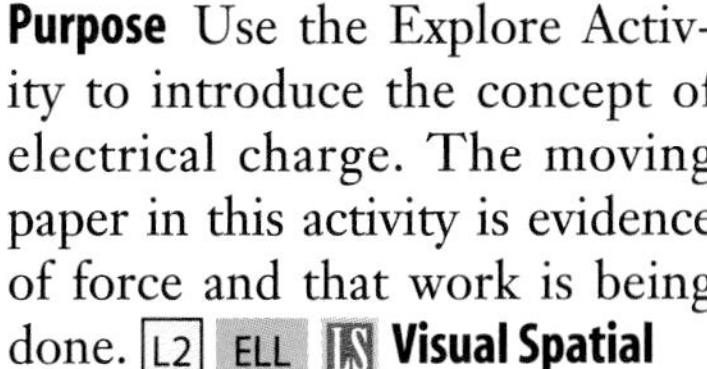

Performance Have students develop lists of questions about their observations. Questions should focus on the science concepts being explored; for example, why might the balloon and paper attract and why might they repel? Use **Performance Assessment in the Science Classroom,** p. 91.

Before You Read

FOLDABLES Reading & Study Skills

Dinah Zike Study Fold

Purpose To determine what students know about electricity before reading the chapter, and to provide a Foldable for recording and organizing notes on charges, currents, and circuits as students read

For additional help, see Foldables Worksheet, p. 17 in **Chapter Resources Booklet,** or go to the Glencoe Science Web site at **science.glencoe.com.** See After You Read in the Study Guide at the end of this chapter.

SECTION

Electric Charge

1 Motivate

Bellringer Transparency

Display the Section Focus Transparency for Section 1. Use the accompanying Transparency Activity Master. L2 ELL

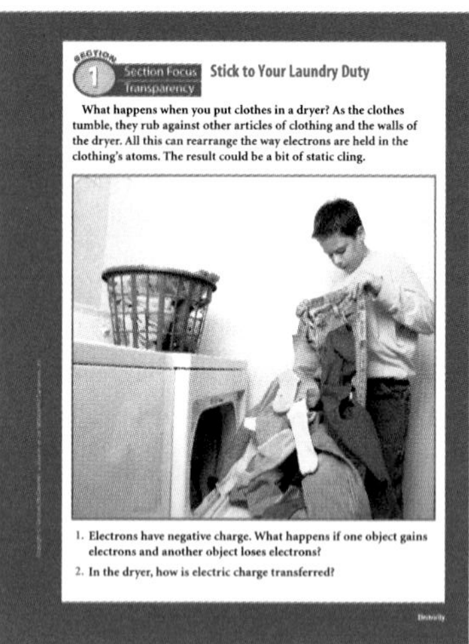

Section Focus Transparency 1 — Stick to Your Laundry Duty

What happens when you put clothes in a dryer? As the clothes tumble, they rub against other articles of clothing and the walls of the dryer. All this can rearrange the way electrons are held in the clothing's atoms. The result could be a bit of static cling.

1. Electrons have negative charge. What happens if one object gains electrons and another object loses electrons?
2. In the dryer, how is electric charge transferred?

Tie to Prior Knowledge

Ask students to describe experiences they have had with static electricity. They may mention that socks and sweaters cling together when first taken out of a dryer and make a snapping sound when pulled apart. They may also mention getting a shock when touching a doorknob after walking across a room. Tell students that this section explains how static electricity causes these things to happen.

Caption Answer

Figure 1 the nucleus

SECTION

Electric Charge

As You Read

***What* You'll Learn**

- **Describe** how objects can become electrically charged.
- **Explain** how electric charges affect other electric charges.
- **Distinguish** between insulators and conductors.
- **Describe** how electric discharges such as lightning occur.

Vocabulary

ion, static charge, electric force, electric field, insulator, conductor, electric discharge

***Why* It's Important**

Many devices and machines are powered by electricity. All electrical phenomena result from the behavior of electric charges.

Electricity

You can't see, smell, or taste electricity, so it might seem mysterious. However, electricity is not so hard to understand when you start by thinking small—very small. All solids, liquids, and gases are made of tiny particles called atoms. Atoms, as shown in **Figure 1,** are made of even smaller particles called protons, neutrons, and electrons. Protons and neutrons are held together tightly in the nucleus at the center of an atom, but electrons swarm around the nucleus in all directions. Protons and electrons possess electric charge, but neutrons have no electric charge.

Positive and Negative Charge Two types of electric charge exist—positive and negative. Protons carry a positive charge, and electrons carry a negative charge. The amount of negative charge on an electron is exactly equal to the amount of positive charge on a proton. Because atoms have equal numbers of protons and electrons, the amount of positive charge on all the protons in the nucleus of an atom is exactly balanced by the negative charge on all the electrons moving around the nucleus. Therefore, atoms are electrically neutral, which means they have no overall electric charge.

Some atoms can become negatively charged if they gain extra electrons. Other atoms can easily lose electrons thereby becoming positively charged. A positively or negatively charged atom is called an **ion** (I ahn).

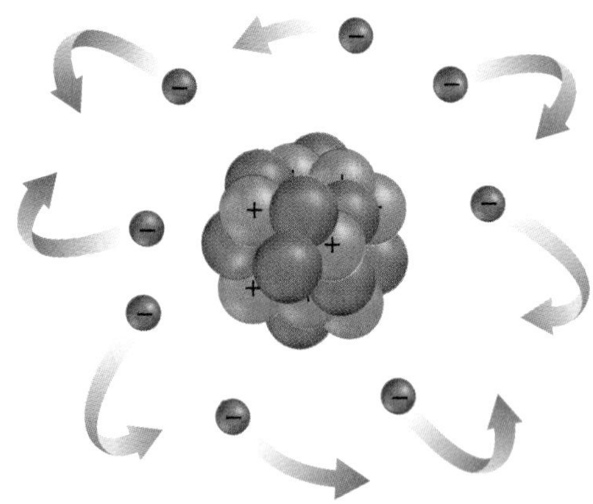

Figure 1
An atom is made of positively charged protons (orange), negatively charged electrons (red), and neutrons (blue) with no electric charge. *Where are the protons and neutrons located in an atom?*

Section Assessment Planner

PORTFOLIO
Assessment, p. 446

PERFORMANCE ASSESSMENT
Skill Builder Activities, p. 446
See page 466 for more options.

CONTENT ASSESSMENT
Section, p. 446
Challenge, p. 446
Chapter, pp. 466–467

Figure 2
Rubbing can move electrons from one object to another. Because rubber holds electrons more easily than hair does, electrons are pulled off the hair when the two make contact.
Which object has become positively charged and which has become negatively charged?

Electrons Move in Solids Electrons can move from atom to atom and from object to object. Rubbing is one way that electrons can be transferred. Anyone who has ever taken charged socks from a clothes dryer has experienced electrons that have been transferred by rubbing.

Suppose you rub a balloon on your hair as in the Explore Activity. The atoms on the balloon hold their electrons more tightly than the atoms in your hair hold theirs. As a result, electrons are transferred from the atoms in your hair to the atoms on the surface of the balloon, as shown in **Figure 2.** Because your hair loses electrons, it becomes positively charged. The balloon gains electrons and becomes negatively charged. Your hair and the balloon become attracted to one another and make your hair stand on end. This buildup of electric charge on an object is called a **static charge.** In solids, static charge is due to the movement of electrons. Protons are held tightly in the nucleus of an atom and cannot move easily from one object to another.

Reading Check *How does an object become electrically charged?*

Ions Move in Solutions Somtimes, a flow of charge can be caused by the movement of ions instead of the movement of electrons. Table salt—sodium chloride—is made up of sodium ions and chloride ions held in place in a solid. A charge cannot flow in solid salt. However, when salt is dissolved in water, the sodium and chloride ions break apart and spread out evenly in the water forming a solution, shown in **Figure 3.** Now the positive and negative ions are free to move. Solutions containing ions are an important factor in determining how different parts of your body communicate with each other. **Figure 4** diagrams how a nerve cell transmits charge. Charged signals moving throughout your body enable you to sense, move, and even think.

Figure 3
When table salt (NaCl) dissolves in water, the sodium ions and chloride ions break apart. These ions now are able to carry electric energy.

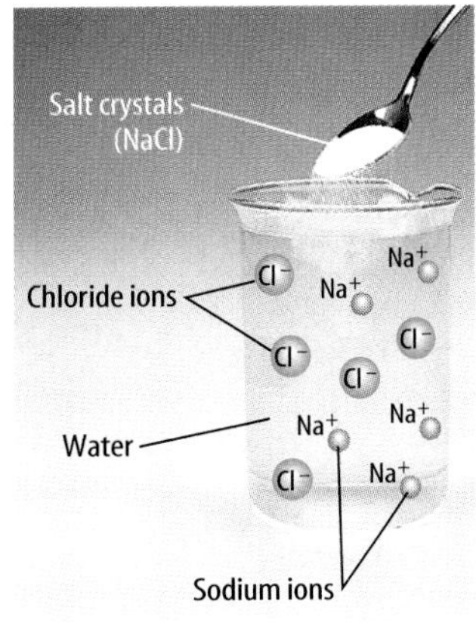

2 Teach

Electricity

Caption Answer

Figure 2 balloon, negative; hair, positive

Quick Demo

Rub a glass rod with a piece of silk. Quickly separate the rod from the silk. With the silk sitting on a wooden surface, bring the rod near it. **What effects do you see?** They should see the silk attracted to the rod. Next, rub two pieces of silk with a glass rod and bring them together. **What effects do you see?** They should see the two pieces repel each other. **Why do these effects occur?** When the silk was rubbed against the glass rod, one body lost electrons and one body gained electrons. The glass and silk attracted each other because they had different charges. The two pieces of silk repelled each other because they had the same charge. L2 LS **Visual-Spatial**

Extension

Have students research and report on how fabric softeners prevent excess electric charge on clothes. Fabric softeners coat laundry with chemicals that reduce wrinkling. The chemicals also help laundry retain moisture, which allows excess charge to dissipate. L3 LS **Linguistic**

Reading Check

Answer by gaining or losing electrons

Cultural Diversity

Electric Amber The word *electricity* comes from the Greek word for amber, *electron.* Ancient Greeks found that when amber was rubbed with a fur cloth, the amber attracted small pieces of straw.

Resource Manager

Chapter Resources Booklet
Transparency Activity, p. 44
Directed Reading for Content Mastery, pp. 19, 20
Note-taking Worksheets, pp. 33–35

Visualizing Nerve Impulses

Have students examine the pictures and read the captions. Then ask the following questions.

What must be occurring at the cell membrane in order for the concentration of the sodium ions to be controlled? The cell membrane must be capable of controlling its permeability.

Does the cell use energy to move the sodium ions to the outside of the membrane? Yes, this process (called active transport) requires energy because the process is creating a region of high concentration.

Once the impulse reaches the end of one nerve cell, how is the message continued on to the next nerve cell? A neurotransmitter is released that causes the next nerve cell to begin the process.

Activity

Have students write and perform a skit that illustrates the nerve impulse process. L2 **LS Kinesthetic**

Extension

Challenge students to research and find out how various diseases interrupt the process by which nerve cells transmit impulses. Have students present their finding to the class using visual aids. L3 **LS Linguistic**

Figure 4

The control and coordination of all your bodily functions involves signals traveling from one part of your body to another through nerve cells. Just as a solution containing ions can conduct an electric current, nerve cells use ions to carry signals from one nerve cell to another.

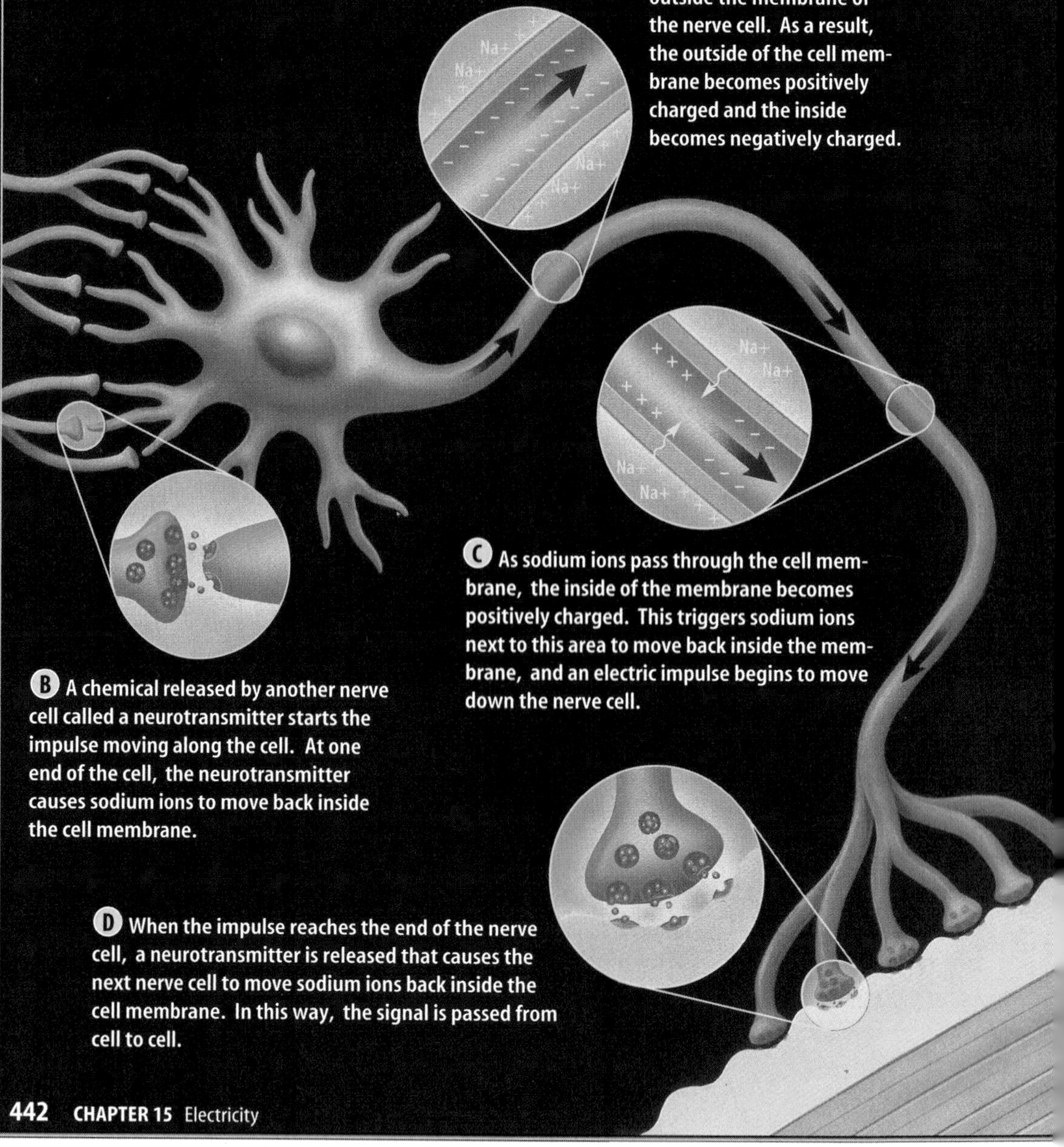

(A) When a nerve cell is at rest, it moves positively charged sodium ions (Na^+) outside the membrane of the nerve cell. As a result, the outside of the cell membrane becomes positively charged and the inside becomes negatively charged.

(B) A chemical released by another nerve cell called a neurotransmitter starts the impulse moving along the cell. At one end of the cell, the neurotransmitter causes sodium ions to move back inside the cell membrane.

(C) As sodium ions pass through the cell membrane, the inside of the membrane becomes positively charged. This triggers sodium ions next to this area to move back inside the membrane, and an electric impulse begins to move down the nerve cell.

(D) When the impulse reaches the end of the nerve cell, a neurotransmitter is released that causes the next nerve cell to move sodium ions back inside the cell membrane. In this way, the signal is passed from cell to cell.

Resource Manager

Chapter Resources Booklet

Enrichment, p. 30

Lab Activity, pp. 9–12

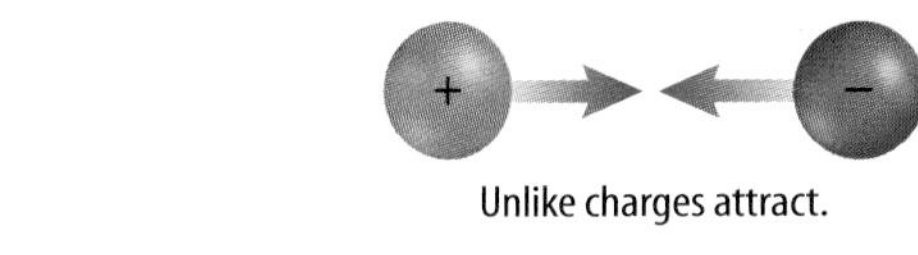
Unlike charges attract.

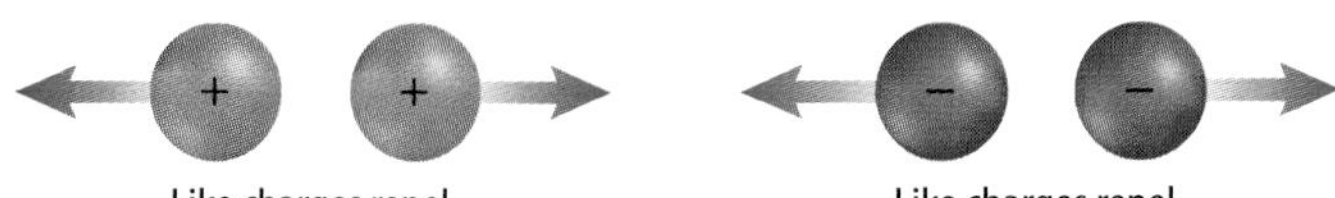
Like charges repel.
Like charges repel.

Figure 5
Two positive charges repel each other, as do two negative charges. A positive charge and a negative charge attract each other.

Electric Forces

In atoms, electrons swarm around the nucleus in all directions. What holds these electrons to the nucleus? The electrons respond to an attractive electric force exerted on them by the protons in the nucleus. All charged objects exert an **electric force** on each other. The electric force between two charges can be attractive or repulsive, as shown in **Figure 5.** Objects with the same type of charge repel one another and objects with opposite charges attract one another. This rule is often stated as "like charges repel, and unlike charges attract."

The electric force between two electric charges gets stronger as the distance between them decreases. A positive and a negative charge are attracted to each other more strongly if they are closer together. Two like charges are pushed away more strongly from each other the closer they are. The greater the distance between electric charges is, the weaker the electric force between them is.

Electric Fields You might have noticed that two charged balloons repel each other even though they are not touching, and that bits of paper and a charged balloon don't have to have contact for the balloon to attract the paper. These observations show that charged objects don't have to be touching to exert an electric force on each other. The electric force acts on charged objects even though they could be some distance apart. Consequently, you see the bits of paper fly up although they have not been touched.

Electric charges exert a force on each other at a distance through an **electric field** that exists around every electric charge. **Figure 6** shows the electric field around a positive and a negative charge. An electric field gets stronger as you get closer to a charge, just as the electric force between two charges becomes greater as the charges get closer together.

Figure 6
The lines with arrowheads represent the electric field around charges. The direction of each arrow is the direction a positive charge would move if it were placed in the field.

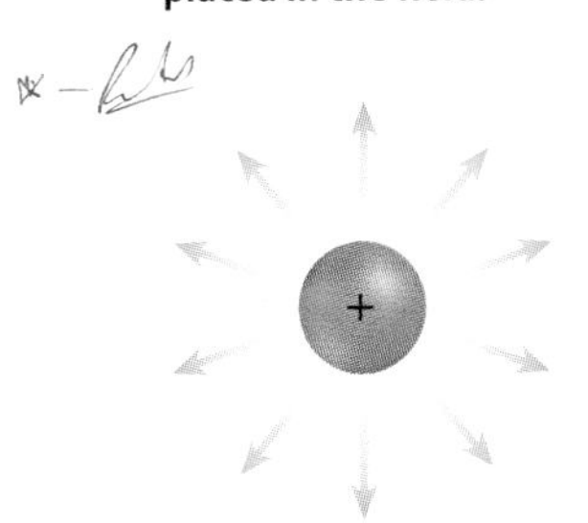

A The electric field arrows point away from a positive charge.

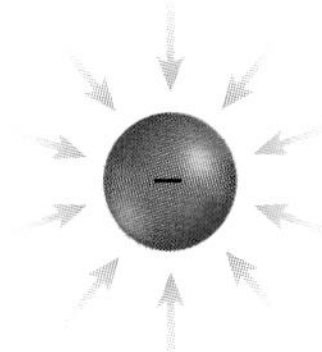

B The electric field arrows point toward a negative charge. *Why are these arrows in the opposite direction of the arrows around the positive charge?*

Electric Forces

Fun Fact

The process of charging things by rubbing is not completely understood. This branch of science is called triboelectricity.

IDENTIFYING Misconceptions

Students may think that static charge is caused by friction or that electrons are literally rubbed off one surface and onto another. Explain that static charge results from contact between two surfaces. Rubbing only increases the amount of contact area of the two bodies.

Quick Demo

To show how an electric charge can build up on a balloon, rub a balloon vigorously with a piece of polystyrene. In a dark room, quickly bring the charged balloon near a fluorescent light bulb. A small spark will jump, making the light bulb flash. This works best on a cold, dry day. L2 **Visual-Spatial**

Extension

Have students find out why the strong force is strong enough to hold protons and neutrons together but doesn't act on the electrons in an atom. The strong force acts only at extremely short distances—distances that are too short to affect the electrons moving around the nucleus of the atom. L3 **Linguistic**

Caption Answer

Figure 6B to show that the charges are opposite

Active Reading

Metacognition Journal In this strategy, each student analyzes his or her own thought processes. Have students divide the paper in half down the center. On the left, have them record what they have learned about electric charges. On the right, have them record the reason they learned it.

Insulators and Conductors

Visual Learning

Figure 7 Point out to students that the movement of electrons on conductors and insulators is similar to the way water behaves on porous and nonporous surfaces. When water falls on a nonporous surface, like the freshly waxed surface of a car, it can't be absorbed so it beads up. L2 LS **Visual-Spatial**

Use Science Words

Word Origins Have students look up the word *conductor* and explain where it comes from. The word *conductor* comes from the Latin word *conducere,* which means "to lead or bring together." Conductors bring together opposite electric charges. L2 LS **Linguistic**

Activity

Have groups of students brainstorm a list of objects and predict whether the objects are conductors or insulators. Then have each group use a battery, two wires, and a flashlight bulb to make a simple circuit tester and test the objects. Ask each group to make a table to summarize results. L3 ELL COOP LEARN LS **Kinesthetic**

Figure 7
Electric charges move more easily through conductors than through insulators.

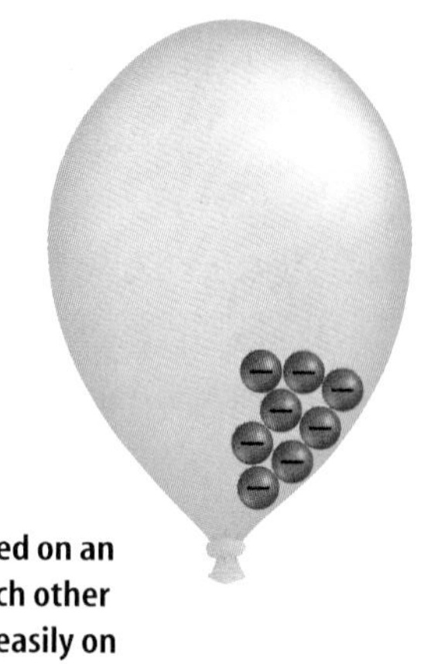

A Charges placed on an insulator repel each other but cannot move easily on the surface of the insulator. As a result, the charges remain in one place.

B Charges placed on a conductor repel each other but can move easily on the conductor's surface. Thus, they spread out as far apart as possible.

Insulators and Conductors

Rubbing a balloon on your hair transfers electrons from your hair to the balloon. However, only the part of the balloon that was rubbed on your hair becomes charged because electrons cannot move easily through rubber. As a result, the electrons that were rubbed onto the balloon stay in one place, as shown in **Figure 7A.** A material in which electrons cannot move easily from place to place is called an **insulator.** Examples of common materials that are insulators are plastic, wood, glass, and rubber.

Materials that are **conductors** allow electrons to move through them more easily. Look at **Figure 7B.** Electrons placed on the surface of a conductor spread out over the entire surface.

SCIENCE Online
Research Visit the Glencoe Science Web site at **science.glencoe.com** for news on recent breakthroughs in superconductor research. Communicate to your class what you learn.

Metals as Conductors The best conductors are metals such as copper, silver, and iron. Metals are good conductors because of the way that metal atoms are bonded in a solid. When metal atoms bond, some electrons are not held tightly to the nucleus of the atoms. Instead, the electrons can leave the atoms, creating metal ions. The loosely held electrons then can move freely among the many metal ions, allowing a current to flow. In an insulator, the electrons are held tightly to the nucleus of the atoms or ions and therefore cannot move around easily.

An electric wire is made from a conductor coated with an insulator such as plastic. Electrons move easily through the copper but do not move from the copper to the plastic insulation. This prevents electrons from escaping from the wire and causing an electric shock if someone touches the wire.

SCIENCE Online
Internet Addresses

Explore the Glencoe Science Web site at **science.glencoe.com** to find out more about topics in this section.

444 CHAPTER 15 Electricity

Induced Charge

Has this ever happened to you? You walk across a carpet and as you reach for a metal doorknob, you feel an electric shock. Maybe you even see a spark jump between your fingertip and the doorknob. To find out what happened, look at **Figure 8.**

As you walk, electrons are rubbed off the rug by your shoes. The electrons then spread over the surface of your skin. As you bring your hand close to the doorknob, the electric field around the excess electrons on your hand repel the electrons in the doorknob. Because the doorknob is a good conductor, its electrons move easily. The part of the doorknob closest to your hand then becomes positively charged. This separation of positive and negative charges due to an electric field is called an induced charge.

If the electric field in the space between your hand and the knob is strong enough, charge can be pulled across that space, as shown in **Figure 8C.** This rapid movement of excess charge from one place to another is an **electric discharge.** Lightning is also an electric discharge. In a storm cloud, air currents cause the bottom of the cloud to become negatively charged. This negative charge induces a positive charge in the ground below the cloud. Lightning occurs when electric charge moves between the cloud and the ground.

Lightning can occur in ways other than from a cloud to the ground. To find out more about lightning, see the **Lightning Field Guide** at the back of the book.

Figure 8
A spark that jumps between your fingers and a metal doorknob starts at your feet.

A As you walk across the floor, you rub electrons from the carpet onto the bottom of your shoes. These electrons then spread out over your skin, including your hands.

B As you bring your hand close to the metal doorknob, electrons on the doorknob move as far away from your hand as possible. The part of the doorknob closest to your hand is left with a positive charge.

C The attractive electric force between the electrons on your hand and the induced positive charge on the doorknob might be strong enough to pull electrons from your hand to the doorknob. You see this as a spark and feel a mild electric shock.

Induced Charge

Fun Fact

Until about 200 years ago, people thought electricity was an unseen fluid that flowed from one body to another. It was thought that a positively charged body had more of the electric fluid while a negatively charged body had less of the electric fluid.

Discussion

Electric forces between charges are enormous in comparison to gravitational forces. **Why then do we normally not sense electric forces between us and our surroundings, while we do sense gravitational interactions with Earth?** Most objects, including humans, have no net electric charge. Consequently, we do not interact electrically with most objects. L2
IS **Logical-Mathematical**

Grounding

Teacher FYI

If there is a very different voltage on the surface of an appliance than on a nearby object, you can be shocked if you touch them both at the same time. The voltage difference enables your body to be a path for excess charge on the surface of the appliance. Some appliances have a three-pronged plug to prevent this problem. The round prong is connected to a ground wire that directs charge on the outside of the appliance to the ground rather than through your body.

Science Journal

Keeping Away the Sparks When repairing computers, technicians take special care not to make sparks, which might cause severe damage to the computer's delicate wiring. Ask students to describe in their Science Journals ways technicians can avoid sparking when working on computers. Touching a grounded conductor before touching the computer. L2 IS **Logical-Mathematical**

Resource Manager

Chapter Resources Booklet
Reinforcement, p. 27

Science Inquiry Labs, pp. 44, 55

Grounding, continued

Caption Answer

Figure 9 a conductor

Answer with lightning rods

3 Assess

Reteach

Ask students to look up the word *static* and tell one reason this word is appropriate for the term *static electricity* and one reason the word is misleading. The word *static* means "not moving." It is true that static electricity is not in continual motion like current electricity. However, a static discharge is far from motionless; it is a very rapid, though noncontinuous, transfer of charge. L2 **IS Linguistic**

Challenge

Electrons and protons are electrically attracted to each other. However, all particles with mass are gravitationally attracted to one another. **Why do we ignore gravitational effects when we discuss the attraction of electrons and protons?** The masses of the particles are so small that the gravitational attraction is insignificant compared to the electrical attraction. L3 **IS Logical-Mathematical**

Assessment

Portfolio Have students draw pictures representing the charging of a balloon and the subsequent attraction of bits of paper. Encourage students to use symbols to represent positive and negative charge. Use **PASC**, p. 127. P

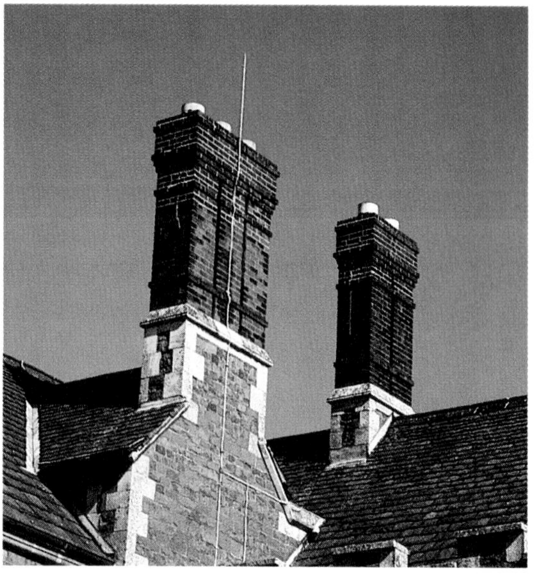

Figure 9
A lightning rod can protect a building from being damaged by a lightning strike. *Is a lightning rod an insulator or a conductor?*

Grounding

Lightning is an electric discharge that can cause damage and injury because a lightning bolt releases an extremely large amount of electric energy. Even electric discharges that release small amounts of energy can damage delicate circuitry in devices such as computers. One way to avoid the damage caused by electric discharges is to make the charges flow harmlessly into Earth's surface. Earth is a conductor, and because it is so large, it can absorb an enormous quantity of excess charge.

The process of providing a pathway to drain excess charge into Earth is called grounding. The pathway is usually a conductor such as a wire or a pipe. You might have noticed lightning rods at the top of buildings and towers, as shown in **Figure 9.** These rods are made of metal and are connected to metal cables that conduct electric charge into the ground if the rod is struck by lightning.

Reading Check *How can tall structures be protected against lightning strikes?*

Section  Assessment

1. What is the difference between an object that is negatively charged and one that is positively charged?
2. Two electrically charged objects repel each other. What can you say about the type of charge on each object?
3. Contrast insulators and conductors. List three materials that are good insulators and three that are good conductors.
4. Why does an electric discharge occur?
5. **Think Critically** Excess charge placed on the surface of a conductor tends to spread over the entire surface, but excess charge placed on an insulator tends to stay where it was placed originally. Explain.

Skill Builder Activities

6. **Recognizing Cause and Effect** Clothes that are dried on a clothesline outdoors don't stick to each other when they are taken out of the laundry basket. Clothes that are dried in a clothes drier do tend to stick to each other. What is the reason for this difference? **For more help, refer to the Science Skill Handbook.**
7. **Communicating** You are sitting in a car. You slide out of the car seat, and as you start to touch the metal car door, a spark jumps from your hand to the door. In your Science Journal, describe how the spark was formed. Use at least four vocabulary words in your explanation. **For more help, refer to the Science Skill Handbook.**

Answers to Section Assessment

1. Negatively charged objects have an excess of electrons while positively charged objects have a deficit of electrons.
2. The two objects have the same type of charge.
3. In conductors, electrons may move easily, and in insulators they do not. Accept all reasonable examples.
4. Because an electric field is strong enough to pull excess charge through air, which is normally an insulator.
5. Charge can move easily on conductors but not on insulators.
6. In a dryer, clothes continually rub against each other, transferring electrons, while on a clothesline they do not.
7. Your clothes rubbed electrons off the car seat. These then built up a static charge on your skin. When you brought your hand close to the car door, a conductor, the part of the door nearest to it became positively charged. The electric field was great enough to cause an electric discharge across the space.

SECTION 2

Electric Current

Flow of Charge

An electric discharge, such as a lightning bolt, can release a huge amount of energy in an instant. However, electric lights, refrigerators, TVs, and stereos need a steady source of electric energy that can be controlled. This source of electric energy comes from an **electric current,** which is the flow of charge through a conductor. In solids, the flowing charges are electrons. In liquids, the flowing charges are ions, which can be positively or negatively charged. Electric current is measured in units of amperes (A). A model for electric current is flowing water. Water flows downhill because a gravitational force acts on it. Similarly, electrons flow because an electric force acts on them.

A Model for a Simple Circuit How does a flow of water provide energy? If the water is separated from Earth by using a pump, the higher water now has gravitational potential energy, as shown in **Figure 10.** As the water falls and does work on the waterwheel, the water loses potential energy and the waterwheel gains kinetic energy. For the water to flow continuously, it must flow through a closed loop. Electric current will flow continuously only through a closed conducting loop called a **circuit.**

As You Read

***What* You'll Learn**

- **Relate** voltage to the electric energy carried by an electric current.
- **Describe** a battery and how it produces an electric current.
- **Explain** electrical resistance.

Vocabulary

electric current
circuit
voltage
resistance

***Why* It's Important**

The electric appliances you use rely on electric current.

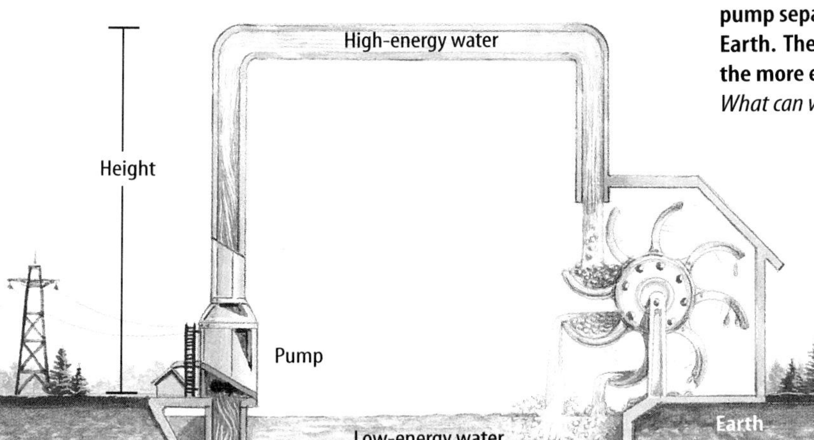

Figure 10
Water can acquire energy when a pump separates the water from Earth. The greater the height is, the more energy the water has.
What can water with energy do?

Section Assessment Planner

PORTFOLIO
Assessment, p. 451

PERFORMANCE ASSESSMENT
MiniLAB, p. 448
Skill Builder Activities, p. 451
See page 466 for more options.

CONTENT ASSESSMENT
Section, p. 451
Challenge, p. 451
Chapter, pp. 466–467

SECTION

Electric Current

1 Motivate

Bellringer Transparency

Display the Section Focus Transparency for Section 2. Use the accompanying Transparency Activity Master. L2 ELL

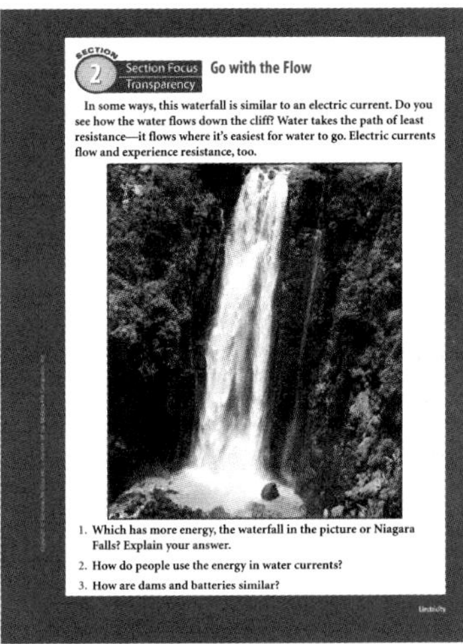

SECTION 2 Section Focus Transparency
Go with the Flow
In some ways, this waterfall is similar to an electric current. Do you see how the water flows down the cliff? Water takes the path of least resistance—it flows where it's easiest for water to go. Electric currents flow and experience resistance, too.
1. Which has more energy, the waterfall in the picture or Niagara Falls? Explain your answer.
2. How do people use the energy in water currents?
3. How are dams and batteries similar?

Tie to Prior Knowledge

Ask students what happens to devices like tape players when the batteries get old. They either run more slowly or stop working. Explain that this occurs because the batteries no longer produce adequate electric current.

Caption Answer

Figure 10 work

Resource Manager

Chapter Resources Booklet
Transparency Activity, p. 45
Directed Reading for Content Mastery, p. 21

2 Teach

Flow of Charge

Caption Answer

Figure 11 Some of the electric energy carried by the electrons is converted into radiant and thermal energy as the electrons pass through the light bulb.

Purpose Students observe static electricity with a comb. L2 ELL LS **Kinesthetic**

Materials plate, salt, pepper, rubber or plastic comb, wool clothing

Teaching Strategy Instruct students to rub the comb on the wool vigorously for several seconds and then comb through the particles immediately.

Analysis

1. The comb attracted the pepper flakes and some small crystals of salt.
2. Salt crystals are larger and heavier than pepper flakes, and the static electricity is only strong enough to lift the smaller crystals.

Performance Ask students to perform this activity for their family or friends as a "magic" trick. Have them explain how the trick works using static electricity. Use **PASC,** p. 97.

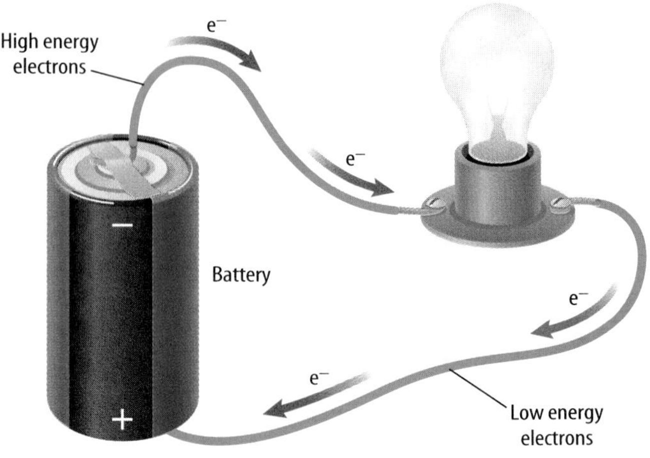

Figure 11
A battery causes electrons to move from the negative to the positive battery terminal. As the electrons move, they lose energy. *Why do electrons have less energy after passing through the lightbulb?*

How a Current Transfers Energy Just as the flow of water can do work in a waterwheel, current flow can do work in an electric device, such as a lightbulb. As current flows, it carries electrical energy through the wire. When the current passes through the wire in the lightbulb, the electrons in the bulb wire lose some of this energy, as shown in **Figure 11.** This energy is converted by the lightbulb to radiant and thermal energy.

Voltage—Electric Potential In a water circuit, water gains potential energy by being pumped from a lower level to a higher level. The pump provides this energy. In an electric circuit, a battery is a source of electric potential energy. In the water circuit, the distance the pump lifts the water is a measure of the available potential energy of the water. Likewise, the **voltage** of a battery is a measure of how much electric energy it can provide. Voltage is measured in volts (V). A typical flashlight battery is 1.5 V.

How a Current Flows You may think that when an electric current flows in a circuit, electrons are traveling completely around the circuit. Actually, individual electrons move slowly through a wire in an electric circuit. When the ends of the wire are connected to a battery, electrons in the wire begin to move toward the positive battery terminal. As an electron moves it collides with other electric charges in the wire, and is deflected in a different direction. After each collision the electron again starts moving toward the positive terminal. A single electron may undergo more than ten million million collisions each second. As a result, it may take three hours for an electron in the wire to travel one meter.

TRY AT HOME Mini LAB

Investigating the Electric Force

Procedure

1. Pour a layer of **salt** on a **plate.**
2. Sparingly sprinkle grains of **pepper** on top of the salt. Do not use too much pepper.
3. Rub a **rubber** or **plastic comb** on an article of **wool clothing.**
4. Slowly drag the comb through the salt and observe.

Analysis

1. How did the salt and pepper react to the comb?
2. Explain why the pepper reacted differently than the salt.

Cultural Diversity

Lewis Latimer Thomas Edison's first successful electric lamp had treated paper filaments that burned out quickly. In 1881, African American inventor Lewis Latimer patented an improved carbon-based filament that lasted much longer. Latimer also improved the lightbulb's socket. As part of Edison's team, Latimer helped supervise the installation of electric lights in New York, Philadelphia, Montreal, and London.

Resource Manager 

Chapter Resources Booklet
MiniLAB, p. 3
Lab Activity, pp. 13–15
Transparency Activity, pp. 47–48

Potential in a Battery A cutaway view of an alkaline battery is shown in **Figure 12.** A battery has two terminals—a negative terminal and a positive terminal. How does a battery produce electric potential energy? In batteries, the electric potential energy comes from chemical energy. At the negative terminal, a chemical reaction converts metal atoms into ions, releasing electrons. At the positive terminal, another reaction converts metal ions of a different metal into metal atoms by accepting the electrons.

These reactions create an electric potential difference between the two battery terminals. When the battery is connected to a circuit, this electric potential energy cause an electric current to flow from the negative terminal to the positive terminal. The energy carried by the circuit can then be used to light a flashlight or run a radio. The amount of electric potential energy—or voltage—that a battery has depends on the amount and type of chemicals used in the battery.

Battery Life Batteries don't supply power forever. Maybe you know someone whose car wouldn't start after the lights have been left on overnight. Why do batteries run down? Batteries contain only a limited amount of the chemicals that react to produce chemical energy. These reactions go on as the battery is used, and the chemicals are changed into other compounds. Once the original chemicals are used up, the chemical reactions stop, and the battery is dead.

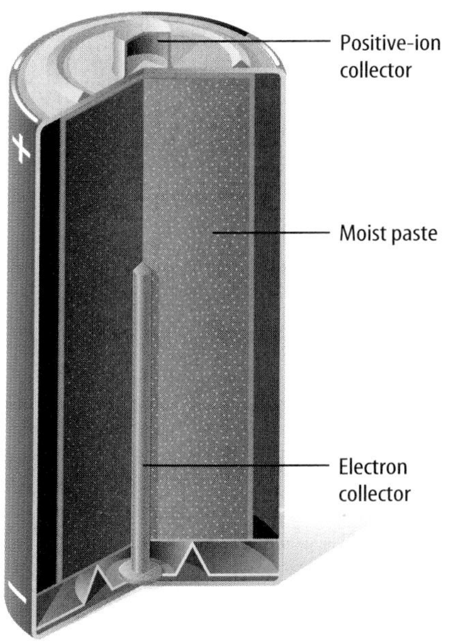

Figure 12
The chemical reactions in an alkaline battery create a difference in electric potential energy between the positive and negative terminals of the battery.

Many chemicals are used to make an alkaline battery. Zinc is a source of electrons and positive ions, manganese dioxide is used to collect the electrons at the positive terminal, and water is used to carry ions through the battery. Visit the Glencoe Science Web site at **science.glencoe.com** for information about the chemistry of batteries.

In an acidic dry cell, the ammonium chloride (NH_4Cl) is reduced: $2NH_4^+ + 2MnO_2 + 2e^- \longrightarrow Mn_2O_3 + 2NH_3 + H_2O$. A thin zinc cylinder serves as the anode and it undergoes oxidation: $Zn(s) \longrightarrow Zn^{+2} + 2e^-$. This dry cell produces about 1.5 volts. In the alkaline version, the ammonium chloride is replaced by KOH or NaOH and the half-cell reactions are: $Zn + 2OH^- \longrightarrow ZnO + H_2O + 2e^-$ and $2MnO_2 + 2e^- + H_2O \longrightarrow Mn_2O_3 + 2OH^-$. The alkaline dry cell lasts much longer as the zinc anode corrodes less rapidly under basic conditions than under acidic conditions.

IDENTIFYING Misconceptions

The net speed of charges in a wire carrying current is only about 1mm/s. Why does a light turn on immediately even though the lamp cord is long? The circuit that is completed when the switch is turned on sets up an electric field along the entire wire almost instantaneously. The charges already in the wire respond to the electric field, and the current starts throughout the wire all at once.

LAB DEMONSTRATION

Purpose to show how a battery works

Materials 10 pennies, 10 nickels, salt, water, paper towel, voltmeter

Alternate materials 10 pieces of aluminum foil, 10 dimes

Procedure Add as much salt to a cup of water as will dissolve. Soak a paper towel in the salt water. Make a stack by alternating pennies and nickels with pieces of the wet paper towel between them. Connect the voltmeter to each end of the stack and measure the voltage.

Expected Outcome Students should see the voltmeter jump slightly when the wires are connected.

What is happening in the stack of pennies and nickels? Chemical reactions are sending electrons to one end of the stack, making it negative and the other end positive. **How might this battery wear out?** The towel might dry out.

Resistance

Use an Analogy

Electrons encounter atoms and other electrons as they make their way through a wire in a way that is similar to the way you constantly bump against other people and objects as you move through a crowded hallway. You can't move as fast as you'd like because you must zigzag to avoid other people and objects. As you move, you lose some of your energy to the people you bump into.

Identifying Misconceptions

Students may think that electricity travels from a battery to a light bulb and stops there. See page 438F for teaching strategies that address this misconception.

Reading Check

Answer Yes; it can provide heat and light.

Caption Answer

Figure 13 to heat in the wire

Visual Learning

Figure 14 How does a narrow hose increase the resistance to water flow, and how does a thin wire increase the resistance to electron flow? The water in a narrow hose and the electrons in a thin wire don't have much space in which to travel.

Resistance

Electrons can move much more easily through conductors than through insulators, but even conductors interfere somewhat with the flow of electrons. The measure of how difficult it is for electrons to flow through a material is called **resistance.** The unit of resistance is the ohm (Ω). Insulators generally have much higher resistance than conductors.

As electrons flow through a circuit, they collide with the atoms and other electric charges in the materials that make up the circuit. Look at **Figure 13.** These collisions cause some of the electrons' electric energy to be converted into thermal energy—heat—and sometimes into light. The amount of electric energy that is converted into heat and light depends on the resistance of the materials in the circuit.

Wires and Filaments The amount of electric energy that is converted into thermal energy increases as the resistance of the wire increases. Copper, which is one of the best electric conductors, has low resistance. Copper is used in household wiring because little electric energy is lost as current flows through copper wires. This means that not much heat is produced. Because copper wires don't heat up much, the wires don't become hot enough to melt through their insulation, which makes fires less likely to occur. On the other hand, tungsten wire has a higher resistance. As current flows through tungsten wire, it becomes extremely hot—so hot, in fact, that it glows with a bright light. The high temperature makes tungsten a poor choice for household wiring, but the light it gives off makes it an excellent choice for the filaments of lightbulbs.

Reading Check *Is having resistance in electrical wires ever beneficial?*

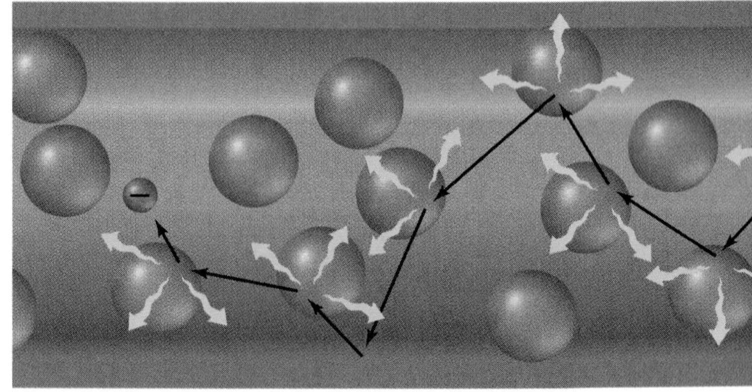

Figure 13
As electrons flow through a wire, they travel in a zigzag path as they collide with atoms and other electrons. These collisions cause the electrons to lose some electric energy. *Where does this electric energy go?*

Resource Manager 

Chapter Resources Booklet
Enrichment, p. 31
Reinforcement, p. 28

Teacher FYI

Some substances lose all resistance and become superconductors when they are cooled to temperatures approaching absolute zero (0 K). Scientists theorize that at these low temperatures electrons travel in pairs, which enables them to move through the crystal without having their motion disrupted by collisions with the lattice.

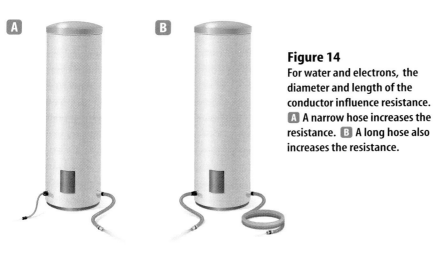

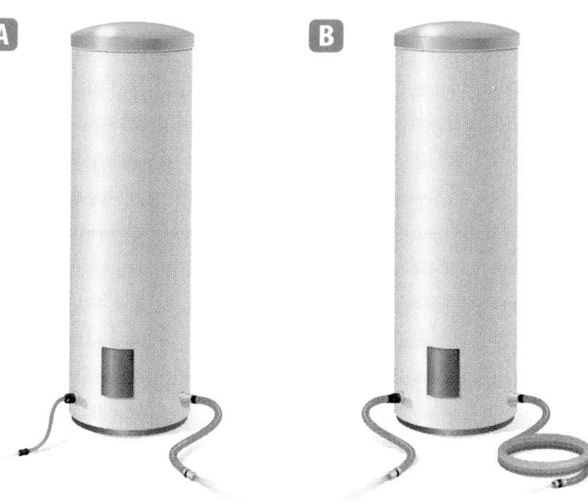

Figure 14
For water and electrons, the diameter and length of the conductor influence resistance. A A narrow hose increases the resistance. B A long hose also increases the resistance.

Slowing the Flow Think of water. What causes the flow of water through a hose to slow down? A narrow hose would slow the flow. Would a longer hose achive the same thing? **Figure 14** shows two examples of how the resistance of a water hose can be increased. Likewise, the length and diameter of a wire affects electron flow. A short, thick wire has less resistance than a long, thin wire, and it is a better conductor.

Section  Assessment

1. How does increasing the voltage in a circuit affect the energy of the electrons flowing in the circuit?
2. What causes positive and negative charges to be separated in a battery?
3. For the same length, which has more resistance—a garden hose or a fire hose? Which has more resistance—a thin wire or a thick wire?
4. Why is copper often used in household wiring?
5. **Think Critically** Some electrical devices require two batteries, usually placed end to end. How does the voltage of the combination compare with the voltage of a single battery? Try it.

Skill Builder Activities

6. **Drawing Conclusions** Observe the size of various batteries, such as a watch battery, a camera battery, a flashlight battery, and an automobile battery. Conclude whether the voltage produced by a battery is related to its physical size. **For more help, refer to the Science Skill Handbook.**
7. **Communicating** The terms *circuit, current,* and *resistance* are often used in everyday language. In your Science Journal, record several different ways of using the words *circuit, current,* and *resistance.* Compare and contrast the everyday use of the words with their scientific definitions. **For more help, refer to the Science Skill Handbook.**

3 Assess

Reteach

Ask students to relate current and voltage in a wire to the flow of water in a pipe. Water will flow through a pipe if the pressure at one end of the pipe is different from the pressure at the other end. Likewise, current flows through a wire if the voltage at one end of the wire is different from the voltage at the other end. L2 LS **Linguistic**

Challenge

Ask students to explain why rechargeable batteries recharge when a current passes through them. The current goes through the battery the opposite way and makes the chemical reaction run the opposite way. Once the battery is recharged, the original chemicals are again present. **Why does soaking a flashlight battery in vinegar sometimes give it a longer life?** The vinegar adds new chemical reactants to the battery. L3 LS **Logical-Mathematical**

Portfolio Have students make detailed posters of a particular type of battery. Labels should indicate the chemical reactions taking place and which way the charges will flow. Use **Performance Assessment in the Science Classroom,** p. 145. P

Answers to Section Assessment

1. It gives the electrons in the circuit more energy.
2. chemical reactions in the battery
3. the garden hose; a thin wire
4. It is a good conductor and does not heat up.
5. The combination has twice the voltage. The voltages of the batteries add together to produce the total voltage.
6. The voltage of a battery is not related to size. A car battery is 12 V. A D-cell battery is 1.5 V. A smaller camera battery is 6 V.
7. The word *circuit* refers to a path that is in the form of a closed loop. In electricity, a circuit is a closed loop path through which electrons flow. In everyday use, the word *current* refers to flow, as in currents of water in the ocean. In electricity, current describes the flow of electrons. When used in discussions of electricity, resistance means opposition to the flow of electrons. In everyday use, the word *resistance* also describes opposition.

SECTION

Electric Circuits

1 Motivate

Bellringer Transparency

Display the Section Focus Transparency for Section 3. Use the accompanying Transparency Activity Master. L2 ELL

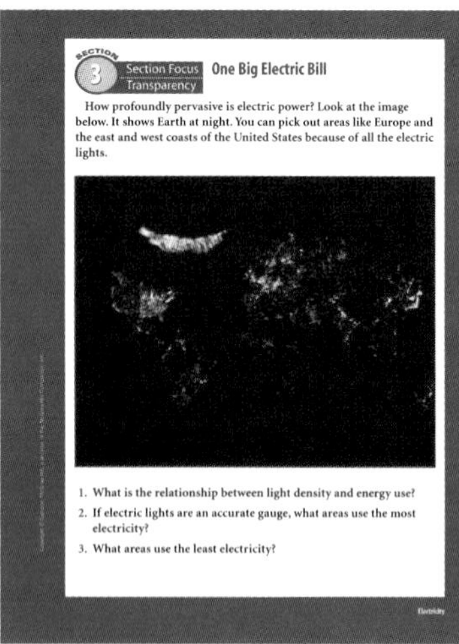

SECTION 3 Section Focus Transparency **One Big Electric Bill**

How profoundly pervasive is electric power? Look at the image below. It shows Earth at night. You can pick out areas like Europe and the east and west coasts of the United States because of all the electric lights.

1. What is the relationship between light density and energy use?
2. If electric lights are an accurate gauge, what areas use the most electricity?
3. What areas use the least electricity?

Electricity

Tie to Prior Knowledge

What happens to the water flowing from a hose that has been perforated with holes? Water flows out of all the holes, making the flow at the end of the hose weaker. Tell students that in this section they will learn how voltage and current can be modified as electric charge flows through a wire.

SECTION

Electric Circuits

As You Read

***What* You'll Learn**

- **Explain** how voltage, current, and resistance are related in an electric circuit.
- **Investigate** the difference between series and parallel circuits.
- **Determine** the electric power used in a circuit.
- **Describe** how to avoid dangerous electric shock.

Vocabulary

Ohm's law
series circuit
parallel circuit
electric power

***Why* It's Important**

Understanding how circuits work will help you better use electricity.

Controlling the Current

When you connect a conductor, such as a wire or a lightbulb, between the positive and negative terminals of a battery, an electric current flows through the circuit. The amount of current is determined by the voltage supplied by the battery and the resistance of the conductor. To help understand this relationship, imagine a bucket with a hose at the bottom, as shown in **Figure 15.** If the bucket is raised, water will flow out of the hose faster than before. Increasing the height will increase the current.

Voltage and Resistance Think back to the pump and waterwheel in **Figure 10.** Recall that the raised water has energy that is lost when the water falls. Increasing the height from which the water falls increases the energy of the water. Increasing the height of the water is similar to increasing the voltage of the electrons. Just as the water current increases when the height of the water increases, the electric current in a circuit increases as voltage increases.

If the diameter of the tube in **Figure 15** is decreased, resistance is greater and the flow of the water decreases. In the same way, as the resistance in an electric circuit increases, the current in the circuit decreases.

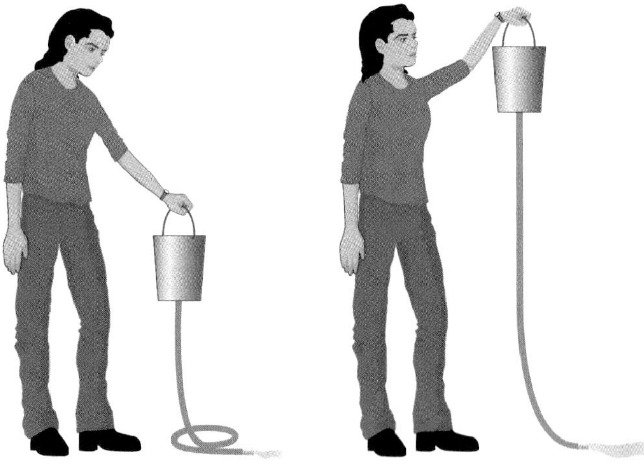

Figure 15
Raising the bucket higher increases the potential energy of the water in the bucket. This causes the water to flow out of the hose faster.

Section Assessment Planner

Portfolio
Visual Learning, p. 454

Performance Assessment
Math Skills Activity, p. 453
Try At Home MiniLAB, p. 454
Math Skills Activity, p. 456
Skill Builder Activities, p. 458
See page 467 for more options.

Content Assessment
Section, p. 458
Challenge, p. 458
Chapter, pp. 456–457

Ohm's Law A nineteenth-century German physicist, George Simon Ohm, carried out experiments that measured how changing the voltage and resistance in a circuit affected the current. The relationship he found between voltage, current and resistance is now known as **Ohm's law.** In equation form, Ohm's law is written as follows.

$$\text{current} = \frac{\text{voltage}}{\text{resistance}}$$

$$I\,(\text{A}) = \frac{V\,(\text{V})}{R\,(\Omega)}$$

According to Ohm's law, when the voltage in a circuit increases the current increases, just as water flows faster from a bucket that is raised higher. However, when the resistance is increased, the current in the circuit decreases.

Math Skills Activity

Calculating the Current Used by Lightbulbs

Example Problem

In homes, the standard electric outlet provides 120 V. What is the current through a lightbulb with a resistance of 240 Ω?

Solution

1. *This is what you know:* voltage: $V = 120$ V; resistance: $R = 240\ \Omega$
2. *This is what you need to find:* current: I
3. *This is the equation you need to use:* I = V/R
4. *Substitute the known values:* $I = 120\ \text{V}/240\ \Omega = 0.5$ A

Check your answer by multiplying it by the resistance of 240 Ω. Do you calculate the standard voltage of 120 V?

Practice Problems

1. What is the resistance of a lightbulb that requires a current of 0.2 A?
2. Which draws more current at the same voltage, a lightbulb with higher resistance or a lightbulb with lower resistance? Use a mathematical example to answer this question.

For more help, refer to the Math Skill Handbook.

2 Teach

Controlling the Current

Discussion

The text states that narrowing a tube will increase the resistance to the flow of water through the tube. This is similar to using a thinner wire to conduct charge. In what other ways could you increase resistance to the flow of water in a tube, and what would be similar ways to increase resistance to electric current in a conductor? Put material in the tube, which would be similar to using a material that wasn't as good an electrical conductor. Make knots in the tube, which would be similar to putting resistors in a circuit. L2 LS **Logical-Mathematical**

Make a Model

Have interested students make a mechanical model of an electric circuit. Students might rig a small motor to lift marbles to a height. The marbles would then roll down a ramp and return to the lift mechanism. Have students present their models to the class, describing how each segment represents one aspect of an electric circuit. L3 LS **Kinesthetic**

Math Skills Activity

National Math Standards

Correlation to Mathematics Objectives

1, 2, 6, 8, 9

Answers to Practice Problems

1. 600Ω
2. A lightbulb with a lower resistance draws more current. Accept all reasonable examples.

Curriculum Connection

History Ask students to find out more about George Simon Ohm. George Simon Ohm lived from 1787 to 1854. Ohm found that the resistance of a wire was independent of the current flowing through it. He theorized that electricity moved from particle to particle in a wire and formulated the law named for him. L2 LS **Linguistic**

Resource Manager

Chapter Resources Booklet

Transparency Activity, p. 46

Directed Reading for Content Mastery, pp. 21, 22

Series and Parallel Circuits

Purpose Students make a complete circuit. L2
LS **Logical-Mathematical**

Materials 5-inch piece of wire, D-cell battery, flashlight bulb

Teaching Strategies Have students diagram the ways that did and the ways that didn't work.

Analysis

In one possible circuit, the wire is attached to the negative terminal of the battery and to the side of the lightbulb. When the nub of the lightbulb touches the positive terminal of the battery, the bulb lights.

Assessment

Performance Have each student draw a cross section of a flashlight that shows the path of the current. After everyone has a design on paper, pass out flashlights for students to inspect and check the accuracy of their drawings. Use **Performance Assessment in the Science Classroom,** p. 127.

Reading Check

Answer Current has only one path through a series circuit.

Caption Answer

Figure 16 It stops.

Mini LAB

Identifying Simple Circuits

Procedure

1. The filament in a lightbulb is a piece of wire. For the bulb to light, an electric current must flow through the filament in a complete circuit. Examine the base of a **flashlight bulb** carefully. Where are the ends of the filament connected to the base?
2. Connect one piece of **wire,** a **battery,** and a flashlight bulb to make the bulb light. (There are four possible ways to do this.)

Analysis

Draw and label a diagram showing the path that is followed by the electrons in your circuit. Explain your diagram.

Series and Parallel Circuits

Circuits control the movement of electric current by providing a path for electrons to follow. For current to flow, the circuit must provide an unbroken path for current to follow. Have you ever been putting up holiday lights and had a string that would not light because a single bulb was missing or had burned out and you couldn't figure out which one it was? Maybe you've noticed that some strings of lights don't go out no matter how many bulbs burn out or are removed. These two strings of holiday lights are examples of the two kinds of basic circuits—series and parallel.

Wired in a Line A **series circuit** is a circuit that has only one path for the electric current to follow, as shown in **Figure 16.** If this path is broken, then the current no longer will flow and all the devices in the circuit stop working. If the entire string of lights went out when only one bulb burned out, then the lights in the string were wired as a series circuit. When the bulb burned out, the filament in the bulb broke and the current path through the entire string was broken.

Reading Check *How many different paths can electric current follow in a series circuit?*

In a series circuit, electrical devices are connected along the same current path. As a result, the current is the same through every device. However, each new device that is added to the circuit decreases the current throughout the circuit. This is because each device has electrical resistance, and in a series circuit, the total resistance to the flow of current increases as each additional device is added to the circuit. By Ohm's law, as the resistance increases, the current decreases.

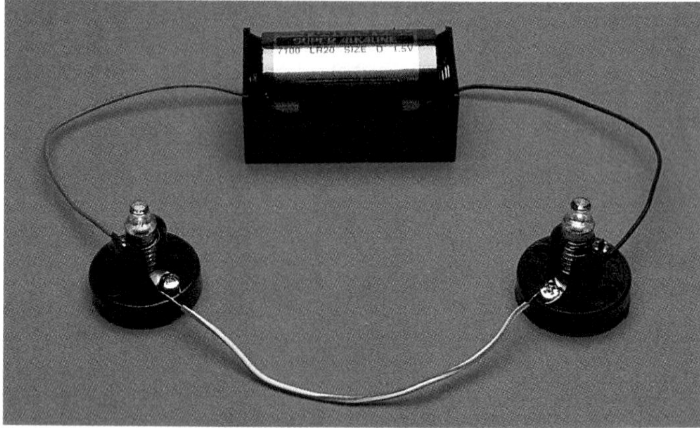

Figure 16
This circuit is an example of a series circuit. A series circuit has only one path for electric current to follow. *What happens to the current in this circuit if any of the connecting wires are removed?*

Visual Learning

Figures 16 and 17 Have students draw the two circuits with one device removed and show why current will still flow in the parallel circuit but not in the series circuit. L2 LS **Visual-Spatial**

Branched Wiring What if you wanted to watch TV and had to turn on all the lights, a hair dryer, and every other electrical appliance in the house to do so? That's what it would be like if all the electrical appliances in your house were connected in a series circuit.

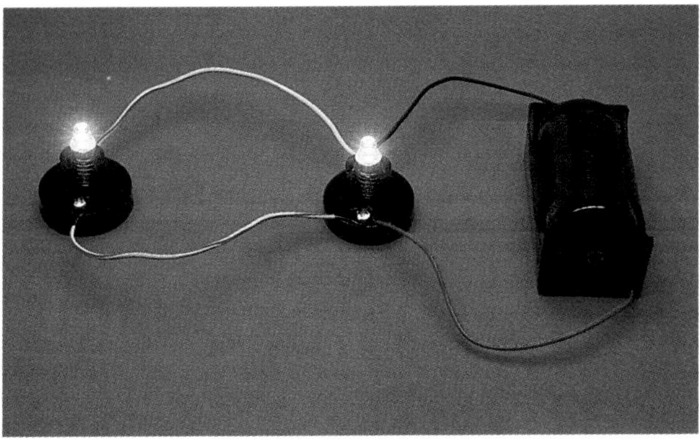

Instead, houses, schools, and other buildings are wired using parallel circuits. A **parallel circuit** is a circuit that has more than one path for the electric current to follow, as shown in **Figure 17.** The current leaving the battery or electric outlet branches so that electrons flow through each of the paths. If one path is broken, current continues to flow through the other paths. Adding or removing additional devices in one branch does not break the current path in the other branches, so the devices on those branches continue to work normally.

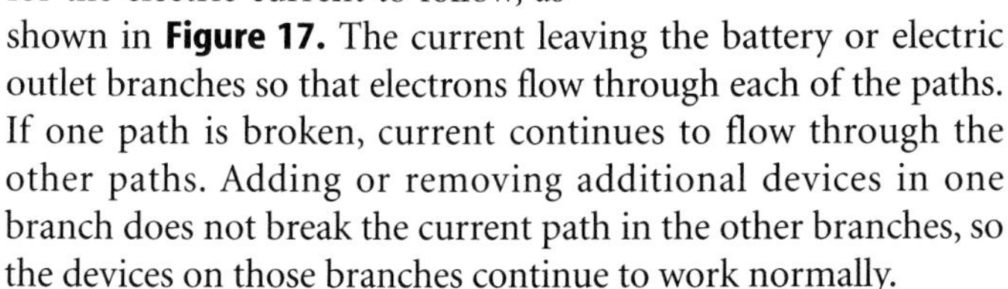

In a parallel circuit, the resistance in each branch can be different, depending on the devices in the branch. The lower the resistance is in a branch, the more current flows in the branch. So the current in each branch of a parallel circuit can be different.

Figure 17
This circuit is an example of a parallel circuit. A parallel circuit has more than one path for electric current to follow. *What happens to the current in the circuit if either of the wires connecting the two lightbulbs is removed?*

Protecting Electric Circuits

In a parallel circuit, the current that flows out of the battery or electric outlet increases as more devices are added to the circuit. As the current through the circuit increases, the wires heat up.

To keep the heat from building up and causing a fire, the circuits in houses and other buildings have fuses or circuit breakers like those shown in **Figure 18** that limit the amount of current in the wiring. When the current becomes larger than 15 A or 20 A, a piece of metal in the fuse melts or a switch in the circuit breaker opens, stopping the current. The cause of the overload can then be removed, and the circuit can be used again by replacing the fuse or resetting the circuit breaker.

Figure 18
You might have fuses in your home that prevent electric wires from overheating.

A In some buildings, each circuit is connected to a fuse. The fuses are usually located in a fuse box.

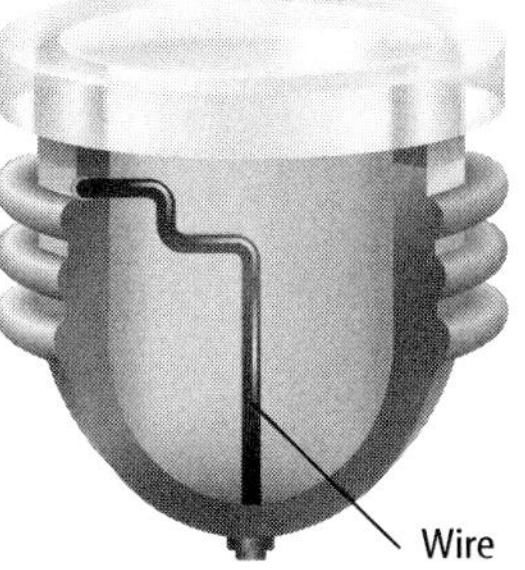

B A fuse contains a piece of wire that melts and breaks when the current flowing through the fuse becomes too large.

Caption Answer

Figure 17 It continues to flow through the bulb still connected to the battery.

Quick Demo

Connect one flashlight bulb to a battery and have students note the brightness. Then connect another bulb in series and have students identify what happens. The brightness of the two bulbs is less than the brightness of the single bulb. Next connect the bulbs in parallel and have students note the difference. Both should glow more brightly than the single bulb did.

IDENTIFYING Misconceptions

Emphasize to students that current is not used up when passing through an electric circuit. The electric charge moves from the battery, through the circuit, and back to the battery. To help students understand this, remind them that the word *circuit* means a closed path around an object.

Protecting Electric Circuits

Fun Fact

Today, many electrical devices have various types of circuit breakers of their own. The large plugs on many hairdryers and the buttons on the sides of power strips are circuit breakers that prevent these devices from drawing too much current or overheating.

Resource Manager

Chapter Resources Booklet
MiniLAB, p. 4
Enrichment, p. 32

Electric Power

Visual Learning

Table 1 Have students identify the appliances in most homes that use the most power. toaster, hairdryer **Why do these use the most power?** They produce heat. They have circuits that have low resistance and so draw a lot of current. L2 LS **Logical-Mathematical**

Make a Model

Explain to students that a circuit diagram is a model of an electric circuit. It shows the source of electric power, the arrangement of the wiring, and all of the devices that use electric power. Have students draw circuit diagrams of the wiring in one or two rooms in a house. Ask them to include in their diagrams at least six devices that use electricity. Students may use standard electrical symbols, or they may make up their own. Make sure they include a key to the symbols they use. L2 LS **Visual-Spatial**

Math Skills Activity

National Math Standards

Correlation to Mathematics Objectives

1, 2, 6, 8, 9

Answer to Practice Problem

0.2A

Table 1 Power Ratings of Common Appliances

Appliance	Power (W)
Computer	150
Color TV	140
Stereo	60
Refrigerator	350
Toaster	1,100
Microwave	800
Hair dryer	1,200

Electric Power

Electric energy is used in many ways to do useful work. Toasters and electric ovens convert electric energy to heat, stereos convert electric energy to sound, and a rotating fan blade converts electric energy to mechanical energy. The rate at which an appliance converts electric energy to another form of energy is the **electric power** used by the appliance.

Calculating Power The rate at which energy is used in the circuit is related to the amount of energy carried by the electrons, which increases as the voltage increases. The energy that is used also is related to the number of electrons flowing in the circuit. As a result, the power that is used in a circuit can be determined by multiplying the current by the voltage.

$$\text{Power} = \text{current} \times \text{voltage}$$
$$P\,(\text{W}) = I\,(\text{A}) \times V\,(\text{V})$$

Table 1 lists the power required by several common appliances. The unit of power is the watt, *W*.

Math Skills Activity

Calculating the Wattage of Lightbulbs

Example Problem

A 240-Ω lightbulb uses a current of 0.5 A. How much power does this lightbulb consume?

Solution

1. *This is what you know:* voltage: $V = 120$ V; current: $I = 0.5$ A
2. *This is what you need to find:* power: P
3. *This is the equation you need to use:* $P = I \times V$
4. *Substitute the known values:* $P = 0.5\text{ A} \times 120\text{ V} = 60\text{ W}$

Check your answer by dividing it by the current of 0.5 A. Do you calculate the standard voltage of 120 V?

Practice Problem

How much current does a 25-W bulb require?

For more help, refer to the Math Skill Handbook.

456 CHAPTER 15 Electricity

Science Journal

Power in the Home Have students collect the power information from some of the appliances in their homes. Have them calculate how much power each device uses in a month and write their findings in their Science Journals. L2 LS **Logical-Mathematical**

Resource Manager

Chapter Resources Booklet

Reinforcement, p. 29

Cost of Electrical Energy Power is the rate at which energy is used, or the amount of energy that is used per second. When you use a hair dryer, the amount of electric energy that is used depends on the power of the hair dryer and the amount of time you use it. If you used it for 5 min yesterday and 10 min today, you used twice as much energy today as yesterday.

Using electric energy costs money. Electric companies generate electric energy and sell it in units of kilowatt-hours to homes, schools, and businesses. One kilowatt-hour, kWh, is an amount of electric energy equal to using 1 kW of power continuously for 1 h. This would be the amount of energy needed to light ten 100-W lightbulbs for 1 h, or one 100-W lightbulb for 10 h.

Figure 19
Electric meters measure the amount of electric energy used in kilowatt-hours. *Find the electric meter that records the electric energy you use.*

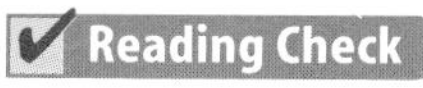
What does kWh stand for and what does it measure?

An electric company usually charges its customers for the number of kilowatt-hours they use every month. The number of kilowatt-hours used in a building such as a house or a school is measured by an electric meter, which usually is attached to the outside of the building, as shown in **Figure 19.**

Electrical Safety

Have you ever had a mild electric shock? You probably felt only a mild tingling sensation, but electricity can have much more dangerous effects. In 1993, electric shocks killed an estimated 550 people in the United States. **Table 2** lists a few safety tips to help prevent electrical accidents.

Data Update Visit the Glencoe Science Web site at **science.glencoe.com** to find the cost of electric energy in various parts of the world. Communicate to your class what you learn.

Table 2 Situations to Avoid
Never use appliances with frayed or damaged electric cords.
Unplug appliances before working on them, such as when prying toast out of a jammed toaster.
Avoid all water when using plugged-in appliances.
Never touch power lines with anything, including kite string and ladders.
Always respect warning signs and labels.

Caption Answer

Figure 19 Electric meters are usually on the outside of houses.

Answer kWh stands for kilowatt-hours. A kWh is the amount of electrical energy equal to using 1 kW of power continuously for an hour.

Electrical Safety

Teacher FYI

Current following a left-hand-to-either-foot path through the body poses the greatest threat of causing cardiac arrest. The damage done by electric shock depends on the amount of electric current and the length of time of the shock. For the average adult experiencing a 200 mA left-hand-to-either-foot current, the threshold for muscular contractions causing breathing difficulties is approximately 50 ms, while the threshold for ventricular fibrillation is about 400 ms.

Identifying Misconceptions

Students may think that a higher voltage is always more dangerous than a lower voltage. Remind them that a higher voltage can be less dangerous than a lower voltage if the lower voltage carries more current.

Curriculum Connection

Math Have students read the electric meters for their homes at the beginning of the week and at the end of the week. If they can find the price per kilowatt-hour, have them calculate the cost of the week's electric usage. L2 LS **Logical-Mathematical**

Internet Addresses

Explore the Glencoe Science Web site at **science.glencoe.com** to find out more about topics in this section.

Electrical Safety, continued

Have students investigate the first-aid procedures for treating electric shock. What first-aid procedures should you be aware of? Possible answer: CPR to restart the heart and treatment for shock L2

LS **Kinesthetic**

Reteach

Bring to class an energy-rating label from a new appliance. Have students use the energy specifications of the appliance to determine the energy it will use and its power. Have them estimate the cost to run the appliance for one year. L2

LS **Logical-Mathematical**

Challenge

With students, do an electrical safety check of the classroom. Identify electrical hazards, such as frayed cords and too many appliances running from a single outlet. Also check the placement of appliances and consider whether any might be in a dangerous spot. L2 LS **Visual-Spatial**

Process Provide students with basic circuit diagrams. Have them describe which devices are in series and which devices are in parallel. Have them predict the changes that occur when one device is turned off or removed. Use **Performance Assessment in the Science Classroom,** p. 89.

The scale below shows how the effect of electric current on the human body depends on the amount of current that flows into the body.

Current	Effect
0.0005 A	Tingle
0.001 A	Pain threshold
0.01 A	Inability to let go
0.025 A	
0.05 A	Difficulty breathing
0.10 A	
0.25 A	
0.50 A	Heart failure
1.00 A	

Electric Shock You experience an electric shock when an electric current enters your body. In some ways your body is like a piece of insulated wire. The solution inside your body is a good conductor of electricity. The electrical resistance of dry skin is much higher. Skin insulates the body like the plastic insulation around a copper wire. Your skin helps keep electric current from entering your body.

A current can enter your body when you accidentally become part of an electric circuit. Whether you receive a deadly shock depends on the amount of current that flows into your body. The current that flows through the wires connected to a 60 W lightbulb is 0.5 A. This amount of current entering your body could be deadly. Even a current as small as 0.001 A can be painful.

Lightning Safety On average, more people are killed every year by lightning in the United States than by hurricanes or tornadoes. Most lightning deaths and injuries occur outdoors. If you are outside and can see lightning or hear thunder, you should take shelter in a large, enclosed building if possible. A metal vehicle such as a car, bus, or van can provide protection if you avoid contact with metal surfaces.

You should avoid high places and open fields, and stay away from isolated high objects such as trees, flagpoles or light towers. Avoid picnic shelters, baseball dugouts, bleachers, metal fences, and bodies of water. If you are caught outdoors, get in the lightning-safety position—squat low to the ground on the balls of your feet with your hands on your knees.

Section  Assessment

1. As the resistance in a simple circuit increases, what happens to the current?
2. What are the differences between a series circuit and a parallel circuit?
3. You have the stereo on while you're working on the computer. Which appliance is using more power?
4. How is your body like a piece of insulated wire?
5. **Think Critically** What determines whether a 100-W lightbulb costs more to use than a 1,200-W hair dryer does?

Skill Builder Activities

6. **Making and Using Graphs** Using 1,000 W for 1 h costs around $0.20. Calculate the cost of using each of the appliances in **Table 1** for 24 h. Present your results in a table. **For more help, refer to the Science Skill Handbook.**
7. **Using Proportions** A typical household uses 1,000 kWh of electrical energy every month. If a power company supplies electrical energy to 10,000 households, how much electrical energy must it supply every year? **For more help, refer to the Math Skill Handbook.**

Answers to Section Assessment

1. It decreases.
2. Series circuits have only one path for current to follow. Parallel circuits have multiple paths.
3. the computer
4. Your dry skin is a much better insulator than the solutions inside your body.
5. The length of time that each is used determines the energy consumed and so the cost of using each.
6. Using the formula W/1000 × 0.2 × 24, to run 24 hours, the computer would cost $0.72, color TV would cost $0.67, stereo would cost $0.29, refrigerator would cost $1.68, toaster would cost $5.28, microwave would cost $3.84, hair dryer would cost $5.76, and the lightbulb would cost $0.36.
7. 1,000 kWh × 12 months = 12,000 kWh; 12,000 kWh × 10,000 households = 120,000,000 kWh

Activity

Current in a Parallel Circuit

In this activity, you will investigate how the current in a circuit changes when two or more lightbulbs are connected in parallel. Because the brightness of a lightbulb increases or decreases as more or less current flows through it, the brightness of the bulbs in the circuits can be used to determine which circuit has more current.

Materials

1.5-V lightbulbs (4)
1.5-V batteries (2)
10-cm-long pieces of insulated wire (8)
battery holders (2)
minibulb sockets (4)

What You'll Investigate

How does connecting devices in parallel affect the electric current in a circuit?

Goal

- **Observe** how the current in a parallel circuit changes as more devices are added.

Safety Precautions 

Procedure

1. Connect one lightbulb to the battery in a complete circuit. After you've made the bulb light, disconnect the bulb from the battery to keep the battery from running down. This circuit will be the brightness tester.

2. Make a parallel circuit by connecting two bulbs as shown in the diagram. Reconnect the bulb in the brightness tester and compare its brightness with the brightness of the two bulbs in the parallel circuit. Record your observations.
3. Add another bulb to the parallel circuit as shown in the figure. How does the brightness of the bulbs change?

4. Disconnect one bulb in the parallel circuit. What happens to the brightness of the remaining bulbs?

Conclude and Apply

1. Compared to the brightness tester, is the current in the parallel circuit more or less?
2. How does adding additional devices affect the current in a parallel circuit?
3. Are the electric circuits in your house wired in series or parallel? How do you know?

Communicating Your Data

Compare your conclusions with those of other students in your class. **For more help, refer to the Science Skill Handbook.**

Activity

BENCH TESTED

Purpose Students determine how adding and removing devices affects parallel circuits. L2 LS **Kinesthetic**

Process Skills observing, comparing and contrasting, classifying, forming operational definitions, experimenting

Time Required 30 minutes

Safety Precautions The wires can become hot, especially if the wires short-circuit the battery. Rechargeable batteries are particularly susceptible to becoming hot when short-circuited. Bulbs can break. Be sure students are aware of classroom safety procedures for taking care of broken glass.

Troubleshooting If repeated trials fail to light the bulb, make sure the batteries and bulbs are in proper working order.

Answers to Questions

1. The current is greater in the parallel circuit.
2. It causes the current to increase.
3. The electric circuits in a house are wired in parallel. When one device is turned off, the other devices do not stop working.

Assessment

Performance Have each student design and make a circuit. Have students place construction paper over their circuits and cut holes where the bulbs are. By only unscrewing and rescrewing lightbulbs, have other students try to determine the hidden wiring pattern. Use **PASC**, p. 97.

Communicating Your Data

Have students use a computer drawing program to draw the circuits they made in this activity. Encourage them to devise symbols for the different elements in the circuits (i.e., batteries and bulbs).

Resource Manager 

Chapter Resources Booklet
Activity Worksheet, pp. 5–6

Activity

BENCH TESTED

What You'll Investigate

Purpose

Students investigate how the height of water and width of a tube affect the flow of water and relate the results to current, voltage, and resistance in electric circuits. L2 ELL LS **Kinesthetic**

Process Skills

measuring, experimenting, making a model, making and using a table, recognizing cause and effect

Time Required

50 minutes

Procedure

Teaching Strategies

- Discuss with students how to measure the diameter of tubing.
- Students may need help calculating rate. Present a simple calculation of rate on the board. Rate = volume ÷ time

Tie to Prior Knowledge Before the experiment, have students discuss potential energy. **What does gravitational potential energy depend upon?** mass, gravity, and height **What variable is manipulated in the experiment?** height

Troubleshooting Demonstrate the proper way to connect tubing of different diameters to the funnels.

Expected Outcome

The flow rate is lower with the smaller diameter tubing and when the funnel is lower.

Activity

A Model for Voltage and Current

The flow of electrons in an electric circuit is something like the flow of water. By raising or lowering the height of a water tank, you can increase or decrease the potential energy of the water. In this activity, you will use a water system to investigate how the flow of water in a tube depends on the height of the water and the diameter of the tube.

What You'll Investigate

How is the flow of water through a tube affected by changing the height of a container of water and the diameter of the tube?

Materials

plastic funnel
rubber or plastic tubing of different diameters (1 m each)
meterstick
ring stand with ring
stopwatch
**clock displaying seconds*
hose clamp
**binder clip*
500-mL beakers (2)
**Alternate Materials*

Goal

- **Model** the flow of current in a simple circuit.

Safety

Flow Rate Data

Trial	Height (cm)	Diameter (cm)	Time (s)	Flow Rate (mL/s)
1	40	0.5	4	25
2	40	0.25	15	6.7
3	30	0.5	5	20
4	20	0.5	6	17

Inclusion Strategies

Behaviorally Disordered The day before students do the activity, provide them with a step-by-step description of the procedure. Explain that the objective of the activity is to observe how the rate of the flow of water changes as the diameter of the tubing changes. Give them time to read the description, and answer any questions they have. Tell them when the activity will occur and how long they will have to complete it.

Procedure

1. **Design** a data table in which to record your data. It should be similar to the table on the previous page.
2. Connect the tubing to the bottom of the funnel and place the funnel in the ring of the ring stand.
3. **Measure** the inside diameter of the rubber tubing. Record your data.
4. Place a 500-mL beaker at the bottom of the ring stand and lower the ring so the open end of the tubing is in the beaker.
5. Use the meterstick to measure the height from the top of the funnel to the bottom of the ring stand.
6. Working with a classmate, pour water into the funnel fast enough to keep the funnel full but not overflowing. Measure and record the time needed for 100 mL of water to flow into the beaker. Use the hose clamp to start and stop the flow of water.
7. Connect tubing with a different diameter to the funnel and repeat steps 2 through 6.
8. Reconnect the original piece of tubing and repeat steps 4 through 6 for several lower positions of the funnel, lowering the height by 10 cm each time.
9. **Calculate** the rate of flow for each trial by dividing 100 mL by the measured time.

Conclude and Apply

1. Make a graph that shows how the rate of flow depends on the funnel height. How does the rate of flow depend on the height of the funnel?
2. How does the rate of flow depend on the diameter of the tubing? Is this what you expected to happen? Explain.
3. Which of the variables that you changed in your trials corresponds to the voltage in a circuit? The resistance?
4. Based on your results, how would the current in a circuit depend on the voltage? How would the current depend on the resistance?

Communicating Your Data

Share your graph with other students in your class. Did other students draw the same conclusions as you? **For more help, refer to the Science Skill Handbook.**

Conclude and Apply

1. Student graphs should indicate that flow rate increases as height increases.
2. As the diameter of the tube decreases, the rate of flow of the water decreases.
3. The height of the funnel corresponds to voltage. The width of the tube corresponds to resistance.
4. As voltage increases, the current increases. As resistance increases, the current decreases.

Error Analysis

Ask students whether their answers make intuitive sense. Have them explain why they did or didn't expect their results. Have students work with their lab partners to brainstorm possible errors that might have occurred in the experiment, including using dry tubing versus wet tubing, a change in water temperature, and using different pouring techniques.

Assessment

Oral This activity uses an analogy between voltage and gravitational potential energy. Ask students to explain the real difference between these two quantities. Use **Performance Assessment in the Science Classroom,** p. 89.

Resource Manager

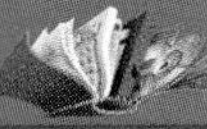

Chapter Resources Booklet
Activity Worksheet, pp. 7–8
Lab Management and Safety, p. 71

Communicating Your Data

Suggest that students use pencil and paper or computer drawing software to design other systems of tubing for water to flow through. Have them identify the areas of their designs that offer the greatest resistance to the flow of water.

Content Background

Fuel, oxygen, and heat must be present for a fire to continue burning. Therefore, modern firefighting tactics concentrate on removing one or more of these elements to suppress or contain forest fires.

Typically, the initial attack effort involves making a fuel break. To do this, hand crews and bulldozers remove unburned fuel from the path of a fire. The firefighters use specialized tools to form a fire line, in which all vegetation is removed down to the mineral soil. These tools include shovels, chain saws, and combination tools like the Pulaski. The Pulaski has a hatchet blade that is used for chopping and a hoe-type blade that is used for digging. Backfires are another, riskier technique used to remove unburned fuel. Backfires are fires that are purposely set between a fuel break and the front of a forest fire.

Helicopters and airplanes are also used to fight fires. Helicopters shuttle firefighting crews and supplies and also may be used to transport and drop water on a fire. Airplanes are used to transport smoke jumpers, specialized firefighters who parachute to the fire, and to drop water or fire retardant chemicals on the fire.

After a fire has been contained, the mop up activity begins. Mopping up involves putting out hot spots still burning within the fire perimeter.

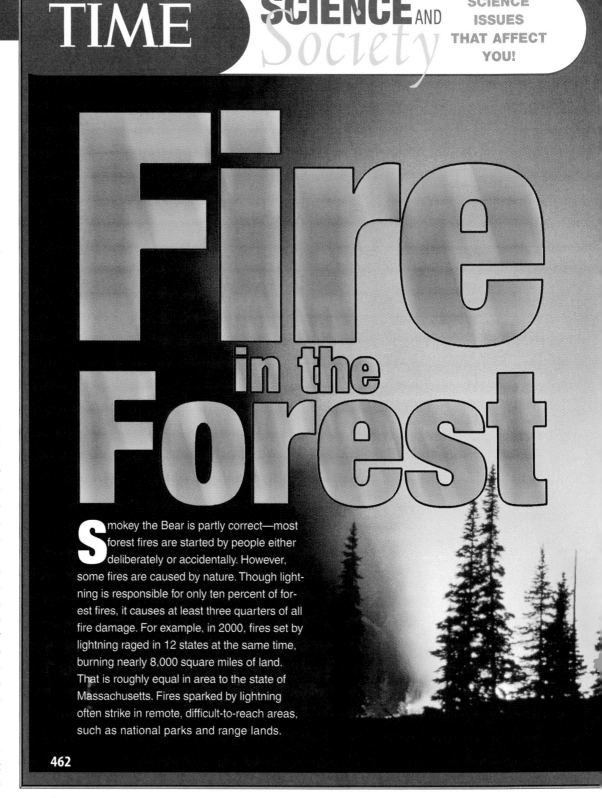

Fire in the Forest

Smokey the Bear is partly correct—most forest fires are started by people either deliberately or accidentally. However, some fires are caused by nature. Though lightning is responsible for only ten percent of forest fires, it causes at least three quarters of all fire damage. For example, in 2000, fires set by lightning raged in 12 states at the same time, burning nearly 8,000 square miles of land. That is roughly equal in area to the state of Massachusetts. Fires sparked by lightning often strike in remote, difficult-to-reach areas, such as national parks and range lands.

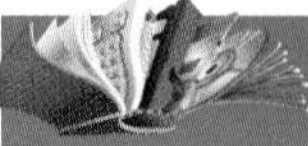

Resources for Teachers and Students

Fire: Friend or Foe, Dorothy Hinshaw Patent, Clarion Books, 1998.

Forests On Fire: The Fight to Save Our Trees, Gregory Vogt, An Impact Book, Franklin Watts, 1990.

Smoke Jumper, Keith Elliot Greenberg, Blackbirch Press, Inc., 1995.

Young Men and Fire, Norman Maclean, University of Chicago Press, 1992.

Burning undetected for days, these fires can spread out of control and are hard to extinguish. Sometimes, fire-fighters must jump into the heart of these blazing areas to put the fires out. In addition to threatening lives, the fires can destroy millions of dollars worth of homes and property. Air pollution caused by smoke from forest fires also can have harmful effects on people. When wood products and fossil fuels are burned, they release particulate matter into the atmosphere. This can damage the human respiratory system, especially for those with preexisting conditions, such as asthma.

People aren't the only victims of forest fires. The fires kill animals, as well. Those who survive the blaze often perish because their habitats have been destroyed. Monster blazes also cause damage to the environment. They spew carbon dioxide and other polluting gases into the atmosphere. These gases may contribute to the greenhouse effect that warms the planet. In addition, fires give off carbon monoxide, which causes ozone to form. In the lower atmosphere, ozone can damage vegetation, kill trees, and irritate lung tissue. Moreover, massive forest fires harm the logging industry, cause soil erosion in the ruined land, and are responsible for the loss of water reserves that normally collect in a healthy forest.

Plant life returns after a forest fire in Yellowstone National Park.

But fires caused by lightning also have some positive effects. In old, thick forests, trees often become diseased and insect-ridden. By removing these unhealthy trees, fires allow healthy trees greater access to water and nutrients. Fires also clean away a forest's dead trees, underbrush, and needles. This not only clears out space for new vegetation, it provides new food for them, as well. Dead organic matter returns its nutrients to the ground as it decays, but it can take a century for dead logs to rot completely.

Fires ignited by lightning might not be all bad

A fire completes the decay process almost instantly, allowing nutrients to be recycled a lot faster. The removal of these combustible materials prevents more widespread fires from occurring. It also lets new grasses and trees grow on the burned ground. The new types of vegetation attract new types of animals. This, in turn, creates a healthier and more diverse forest.

CONNECTIONS **Research Find out more about the job of putting out forest fires. What training is needed? What gear do firefighters wear? Why would people risk their lives to save a forest? Use the media center to learn more about forest firefighters and their careers. Report to the class.**

Online

For more information, visit science.glencoe.com

Discussion

Scientists have determined that some fires may be beneficial to forests. **What are some positive effects caused by forest fires?** Possible responses: Clearing away diseased trees gives healthy trees greater access to the remaining water and nutrients; removing dead trees and underbrush creates space for new vegetation; regular removal of fuels helps prevent large, uncontrollable fires; burned vegetation returns its nutrients to the soil quicker than rotting vegetation; heat is needed for some seeds to germinate. L2

LS **Logical-Mathematical**

Investigate the Issue

Oxygen, fuel, and heat must be present for a fire to burn. Ask students to speculate how fire-fighters remove oxygen, fuel, and heat from a fire. Explain that water is used to remove oxygen and to cool flames and that fire lines and backfires are used to remove fuels. Mention that chemicals may be added to water to form a foam that will adhere to materials and smother flames more effectively.

CONNECTIONS Large fires require a number of support personnel to perform a variety of tasks, including setting up and maintaining communications, supplying provisions and fuel, coordinating crews and equipment, monitoring the weather, and catering food. Ask each student to find information on a task provided by a member of a fire support team and prepare a report for the class.

Online

Internet Addresses

Explore the Glencoe Science Web site at **science.glencoe.com** to find out more about topics in this feature.

Chapter 15 Study Guide

Reviewing Main Ideas

Preview

Students can answer the questions in their Science Journals. Discuss the answers as you go through the chapter. **LS Linguistic**

Review

Students can write their answers, then compare them with those of other students. **LS Interpersonal**

Reteach

Students can look at the illustrations and describe details that support the main ideas of the chapter. **LS Visual-Spatial**

Answers to Chapter Review

Section 1

4. The electric charge is directed to the ground by a lightning rod.

Section 2

4. because the path has been broken

Section 3

4. The button stops the flow of current in the hairdryer if it becomes too great. The reset mechanism works by reconnecting the circuit inside the hairdryer.

Chapter 15 Study Guide

Reviewing Main Ideas

Section 1 Electric Charge

1. The two types of electric charge are positive and negative. Like charges repel and unlike charges attract.
2. An object becomes negatively charged if it gains electrons and positively charged if it loses electrons.
3. Electrically charged objects have an electric field surrounding them and exert electric forces on one another.
4. Electrons can move easily through conductors, but not so easily through insulators. *Why isn't the building shown below harmed when lightning strikes it?*

Section 2 Electric Current

1. Electric current is the flow of charge—either flowing electrons or flowing ions.
2. The energy carried by electrons in a circuit increases as the voltage in the circuit increases.
3. A battery provides a source of electric current by using chemical reactions to separate positive and negative charges.
4. As electrons flow in a circuit, some of their electrical energy is lost due to resistance in the circuit. *In a simple circuit, why do electrons stop flowing if the circuit is broken?*

Section 3 Electric Circuits

1. In an electric circuit, the voltage, current, and resistance are related by Ohm's law, expressed as $V = I \times R$.
2. The two basic kinds of electric circuits are parallel circuits and series circuits. A series circuit has only one path for the current to follow, but a parallel circuit has more than one path.
3. The rate at which electric devices use electrical energy is the electric power used by the device. Electric companies charge customers for using electrical energy in units of kilowatt-hours.
4. The amount of current flowing through the body determines how much damage occurs. The current from wall outlets can be dangerous. Hair dryers often come with a reset button. *What is the purpose of the button, and how might the reset mechanism work?*

FOLDABLES Reading & Study Skills — After You Read

Using the information on your Foldable, under the *Electricity* tab, explain the differences between the two types of charges and between the two types of circuits.

FOLDABLES Reading & Study Skills — After You Read

After students have read the chapter and completed the Foldable described in Before You Read, have them do the activity on the student page.

Visualizing Main Ideas

Correctly order the following concept map, which illustrates how electric current moves through a simple circuit.

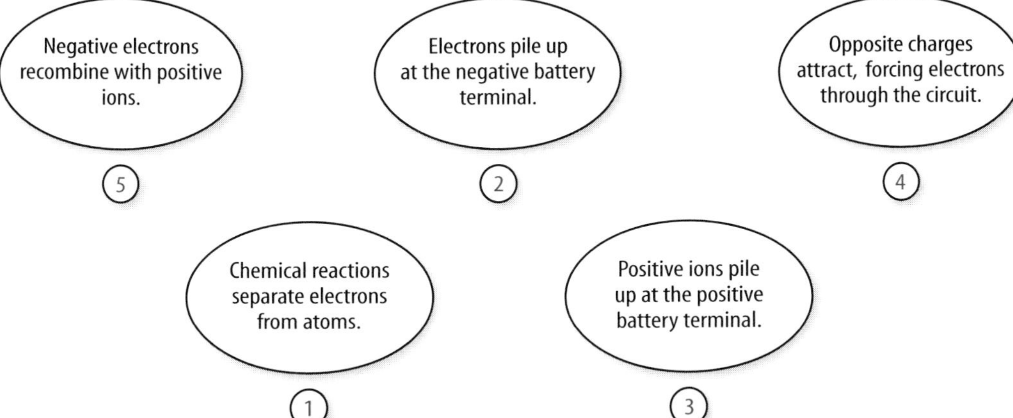
Negative electrons recombine with positive ions.
5
Electrons pile up at the negative battery terminal.
2
Opposite charges attract, forcing electrons through the circuit.
4
Chemical reactions separate electrons from atoms.
1
Positive ions pile up at the positive battery terminal.
3

Vocabulary Review

Vocabulary Words

a. circuit
b. conductor
c. electric current
d. electric discharge
e. electric field
f. electric force
g. electric power
h. insulator
i. ion
j. Ohm's law
k. parallel circuit
l. resistance
m. series circuit
n. static charge
o. voltage

THE PRINCETON REVIEW Study Tip

Whether or not you've taken a particular type of test or practiced for an exam many times, it's a good idea to start by reading the instructions provided at the beginning of each section. It only takes a moment.

Using Vocabulary

Answer the following questions using complete sentences.

1. What is the term for the flow of charge?
2. What is the relationship among voltage, current, and resistance in a circuit?
3. In which material do electrons move easily?
4. What is the name for the unbroken path that charge follows?
5. What is the term for a buildup of electric charge in one place?
6. What is an atom that has lost or gained electrons called?
7. Which circuits have more than one path for electrons to follow?
8. What is the rate at which electrical energy is converted to other forms of energy?

Chapter 15 Study Guide

Visualizing Main Ideas

See student page.

Vocabulary Review

Using Vocabulary

1. Electric current is the flow of charge.
2. Ohm's law states that voltage equals current times resistance.
3. Electrons move most easily through conductors.
4. The unbroken path through which a charge flows is a circuit.
5. A buildup of charge in one place is a static charge.
6. An atom that has gained or lost electrons is called an ion.
7. Parallel circuits have more than one path for electrons.
8. The rate at which electrical energy is converted into another form of energy is electrical power.

IDENTIFYING Misconceptions

Assess

Use the assessment as follow-up to page 438F after students have completed the chapter.

Materials 2 ammeters, circuit with battery and bulb, **Figure 1**

Procedure Show students **Figure 1**. Ask if the number of electrons passing through point A is the same as the number of electrons passing through point B. Place ammeters in the circuit at points A and B.

Expected Outcome The two points have the same current and therefore the same number of electrons passing through them.

Figure 1

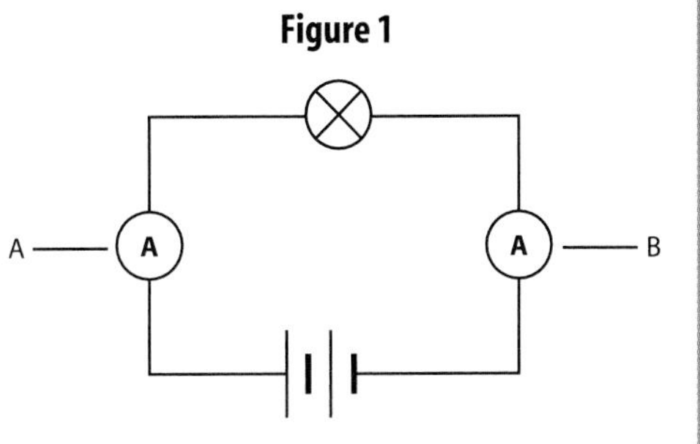
A
A
A
B

Chapter 15 Assessment

Checking Concepts

1. B
2. D
3. D
4. A
5. C
6. D
7. B
8. D
9. D
10. A

Thinking Critically

11. Electrons collide with the atoms and other electrons in the material. This causes the electrons to lose energy and slow down.
12. The charge on the balloon induces an opposite charge on the wall. The charges in the balloon and the charges in the wall attract each other.
13. No. Think of two tanks of water connected by a hose at the bottom. One tank also has a nozzle at the bottom from which water can flow out. If you were to open that nozzle, water could only flow as quickly as the water pressure in that tank was pushing it out. If the tanks had been placed in series, however (one on top of the other), the water pressure would have been greater and so would have pushed more water out.
14. Bring the two objects together. If they move toward each other, they are of opposite charge. If they move away from each other, they have the same charge.
15. Plastic is an insulator and so shields the electric current from the surroundings. It also insulates against the heat electric currents can generate when they pass through a metal.

Chapter 15 Assessment

Checking Concepts

Choose the word or phrase that best answers the question.

1. An object that is postively charged _____.
   A) has more neutrons than protons
   B) has more protons than electrons
   C) has more electrons than protons
   D) has more electrons than neutrons
2. What is the force between two electrons?
   A) unbalanced **C)** attractive
   B) neutral **D)** repulsive
3. How much power does the average hair dryer use?
   A) 20W **C)** 750W
   B) 75W **D)** 1,200W
4. What property of a wire increases when it is made thinner?
   A) resistance **C)** current
   B) voltage **D)** charge
5. What property does Earth have that causes grounding to drain static charges?
   A) It is a planet.
   B) It has a high resistance.
   C) It is a conductor.
   D) It is like a battery.
6. Why is a severe electric shock dangerous?
   A) It can stop the heart from beating.
   B) It can cause burns.
   C) It can interfere with breathing.
   D) All of the above are true.
7. Because an air conditioner uses more electric power than a lightbulb in a given amount of time, what also must be true?
   A) It must have a higher resistance.
   B) It must use more energy every second.
   C) It must have its own batteries.
   D) It must be wired in series.
8. What unit of electrical energy is sold by electric companies?
   A) ampere **C)** volt
   B) ohm **D)** kilowatt-hour
9. What surrounds electric charges that causes them to affect each other even though they are not touching?
   A) an induced charge **C)** a conductor
   B) a static discharge **D)** an electric field
10. As more devices are added to a series circuit, what happens to the current?
    A) decreases **C)** stays the same
    B) increases **D)** stops

Thinking Critically

11. Why do materials have electrical resistance?
12. Explain why a balloon that has a static charge will stick to a wall.
13. If you connect two batteries in parallel, will the lightbulb glow brighter than if just one battery is used? Explain, using water as an analogy.

14. If you have two charged objects, how can you tell whether the type of charge on them is the same or different?
15. Explain why the outside cases of electric appliances usually are made of plastic.

Developing Skills

16. **Classifying** Look at several objects around your home. Classify these objects as insulators or conductors.

Chapter Assessment Planner

Portfolio Encourage students to place in their portfolios one or two items of what they consider to be their best work. Examples include:

- Assessment, p. 446
- Assessment, p. 451
- Visual Learning, p. 454

Performance Additional performance assessments, Performance Task Assessment Lists, and rubrics for evaluating these activities can be found in Glencoe's **Performance Assessment in the Science Classroom.**

17. **Making and Using Graphs** The following data show the current and voltage in a circuit containing a portable CD player and in a circuit containing a portable radio.
   a. Make a graph with the horizontal axis as current and the vertical axis as voltage. Plot the data for both appliances.
   b. Which line is more horizontal—the plot of the radio data or the CD player data?
   c. Use Ohm's law to determine the electrical resistance of each device.
   d. For which device is the line more horizontal—the device with the higher or lower resistance?

Portable Radio

Voltage (V)	Current (A)
2.0	1.0
4.0	2.0
6.0	3.0

Portable CD Player

Voltage (V)	Current (A)
2.0	0.5
4.0	1.0
6.0	1.5

18. **Collecting Data** Determine the total cost of keeping all the lights turned on in your living room for 24 h if the cost of electricity is $0.08 per kilowatt-hour.

Performance Assessment

19. **Design a Board Game** Design a board game about a series or parallel circuit. The rules of the game could be based on opening or closing the circuit, adding fuses, and/or resetting a circuit breaker.

Technology

Go to the Glencoe Science Web site at **science.glencoe.com** or use the **Glencoe Science CD-ROM** for additional chapter assessment.

THE PRINCETON REVIEW Test Practice

A student is interested in setting up and comparing four different circuits. The table below lists her results.

Type of Electrical Circuit

Circuit	Number of Resistors	Circuit Type	Total Voltage
A	2	Series	6 V
B	3	Parallel	12 V
C	4	Series	4 V
D	5	Parallel	8 V

Study the chart above and answer the following questions.

1. The voltage across a resistor in a parallel circuit equals the battery voltage. In a series circuit, the voltage across a resistor is less than the battery voltage. In which circuit is the voltage across an individual resistor the greatest?
   A) Circuit A
   B) Circuit B
   C) Circuit C
   D) Circuit D
2. A toy truck requires at least 5 volts to run. According to the table, which circuit could NOT be used to run the truck?
   F) Circuit A
   G) Circuit B
   H) Circuit C
   J) Circuit D

Assessment Resources

Reproducible Masters

Chapter Resources Booklet
Chapter Review, pp. 37–88
Chapter Tests, pp. 39–42
Assessment Transparency Activity, p. 49

Glencoe Science Web site
Interactive Tutor
Chapter Quizzes

Glencoe Technology
Assessment Transparency
Interactive CD-ROM Chapter Quizzes
ExamView Pro Test Bank
Vocabulary PuzzleMaker Software
MindJogger Videoquiz DVD/VHS

Chapter 15 Assessment

THE PRINCETON REVIEW Test Practice

The Test-Taking Tip was written by The Princeton Review, the nation's leader in test preparation.

1. B
2. H

Developing Skills

16. Accept all reasonable answers.
17. a. Both graphs are straight lines. The line for the CD player has a steeper slope
   b. radio
   c. $R = V/I$; radio: 2 volts/1 amp = 2 ohms; CD player: 2 volts/0.5 amps = 4 ohms
   d. the device with the lower resistance
18. Answers will depend on the number and type of lights.

Performance Assessment

19. Check student's games. Use **PASC**, p. 117.

Section/Objectives	Standards		Activities/Features
	National	State/Local	
Chapter Opener	See p. 5T for a Key to Standards.		**Explore Activity:** Observe and measure force between magnets, p. 469 **Before You Read,** p. 469
Section 1 What is magnetism? 3 sessions 1.5 blocks 1. **Describe** the behavior of magnets. 2. **Relate** the behavior of magnets to magnetic fields. 3. **Explain** the source of all magnetic fields.	National Content Standards: UCP2, A1, B1, B2, E2		**Problem-Solving Activity:** Finding the Magnetic Declination, p. 473 **MiniLAB:** Observing Magnetic Fields, p. 474 **Science Online,** p. 475 **Activity:** Make a Compass, p. 476
Section 2 Electricity and Magnetism 4 sessions 2 blocks 1. **Describe** the relationship between electricity and magnetism. 2. **Explain** how electricity can produce motion. 3. **Explain** how motion can produce electricity.	National Content Standards: UCP2, A1, B1, B2, B3, D2, F5, G1		**MiniLAB:** Assembling an Electromagnet, p. 478 **Visualizing Voltmeters and Ammeters,** p. 479 **Science Online,** p. 483 **Activity:** How does an electric motor work?, pp. 488–489

Activity Materials	Reproducible Resources	Section Assessment	Technology
Explore Activity: 2 bar magnets, sheet of paper, metric ruler	**Chapter Resources Booklet** Foldables Worksheet, p. 13 Directed Reading Overview, p. 15 Note-taking Worksheets, pp. 27–28	GLENCOE'S ASSESSMENT ADVANTAGE	
MiniLAB: iron filings, plastic petri dish, tape, several magnets **Activity:** petri dish, water, sewing needle, magnet, tape, marker, paper, plastic spoon *Need materials?* Contact Science Kit at 1-800-828-7777 or www.sciencekit.com on the Internet.	**Chapter Resources Booklet** Transparency Activity, p. 38 MiniLAB, p. 3 Enrichment, p. 25 Reinforcement, p. 23 Directed Reading, p. 16 Lab Activity, pp. 9–10 Activity Worksheet, pp. 5–6 **Earth Science Critical Thinking/ Problem Solving,** p. 8	Portfolio Assessment, p. 474 Performance Problem Solving Activity, p. 473 MiniLAB, p. 474 Skill Builder Activities, p. 475 Content Section Assessment, p. 475	Section Focus Transparency Interactive CD-ROM/DVD Guided Reading Audio Program
MiniLAB: wire, 16-penny steel nail, D-cell battery, paper clips **Activity:** 22-gauge enameled wire (4 m), steel knitting needle, 4 nails, hammer, 2 ceramic magnets, 18-gauge insulated wire (60 cm), masking tape, fine sandpaper, 15-cm wooden board, 6-V battery, wire cutters, 2 wooden blocks	**Chapter Resources Booklet** Transparency Activity, p. 39 MiniLAB, p. 4 Enrichment, p. 26 Reinforcement, p. 24 Directed Reading, pp. 17, 18 Lab Activity, pp. 11–12 Transparency Activity, pp. 41–42 Activity Worksheet, pp. 7–8 **Lab Management and Safety,** p. 64 **Science Inquiry Labs,** pp. 9, 55 **Physical Science Critical Thinking/ Problem Solving,** p. 20	Portfolio Visual Learning, p. 478 Cultural Diversity, p. 481 Performance MiniLAB, p. 478 Skill Builder Activities, p. 485 Content Section Assessment, p. 485	Section Focus Transparency Teaching Transparency Interactive CD-ROM/DVD Guided Reading Audio Program

End of Chapter Assessment

GLENCOE'S ASSESSMENT ADVANTAGE

Blackline Masters	Technology	Professional Series
Chapter Resources Booklet Chapter Review, pp. 31–32 Chapter Tests, pp. 33–36 **Standardized Test Practice by The Princeton Review,** pp. 67–70	MindJogger Videoquiz CD-ROM Explorations and Quizzes Vocabulary Puzzle Makers ExamView Pro Test Bank Interactive Lesson Planner Interactive Teacher's Edition	Performance Assessment in the Science Classroom (PASC)

Transparencies

Section Focus

Section 1 Section Focus Transparency — Magnetic Appeal

The word levitation may evoke magicians rather than scientists, but scientists can levitate, too. This photo shows a magnet levitating over a superconductor. Magnetic levitation has applications ranging from advertising displays to high-speed trains.

1. What happens as you move a magnet closer to a refrigerator door?
2. How long can this magnetic field be sustained?

L2

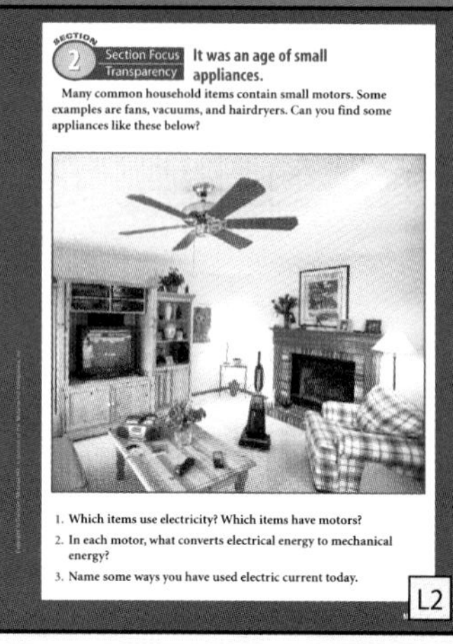
Section 2 Section Focus Transparency — It was an age of small appliances.

Many common household items contain small motors. Some examples are fans, vacuums, and hairdryers. Can you find some appliances like these below?

1. Which items use electricity? Which items have motors?
2. In each motor, what converts electrical energy to mechanical energy?
3. Name some ways you have used electric current today.

L2

This is a representation of key blackline masters available in the Teacher Classroom Resources. See Resource Manager boxes within the chapter for additional information.

Assessment

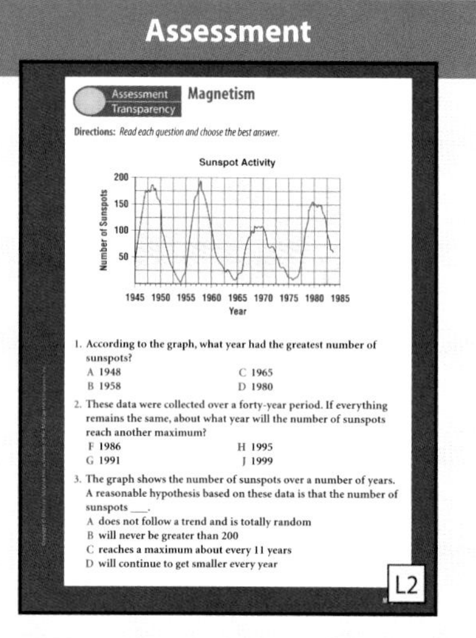
Assessment Transparency — Magnetism

Directions: *Read each question and choose the best answer.*

1. According to the graph, what year had the greatest number of sunspots?
   A 1948 C 1965
   B 1958 D 1980
2. These data were collected over a forty-year period. If everything remains the same, about what year will the number of sunspots reach another maximum?
   F 1986 H 1995
   G 1991 J 1999
3. The graph shows the number of sunspots over a number of years. A reasonable hypothesis based on these data is that the number of sunspots ___.
   A does not follow a trend and is totally random
   B will never be greater than 200
   C reaches a maximum about every 11 years
   D will continue to get smaller every year

L2

Teaching

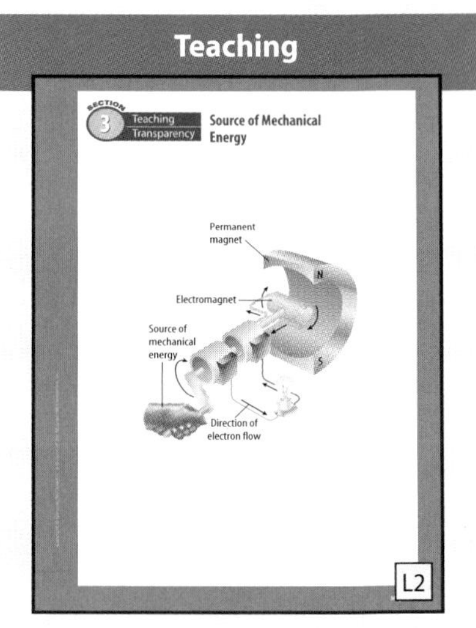
Section 3 Teaching Transparency — Source of Mechanical Energy

L2

Key to Teaching Strategies

The following designations will help you decide which activities are appropriate for your students.

- L1 Level 1 activities should be appropriate for students with learning difficulties.
- L2 Level 2 activities should be within the ability range of all students.
- L3 Level 3 activities are designed for above-average students.
- ELL ELL activities should be within the ability range of English Language Learners.
- COOP LEARN Cooperative Learning activities are designed for small group work.
- LS Multiple Learning Styles logos, as described on page 22T, are used throughout to indicate strategies that address different learning styles.
- P These strategies represent student products that can be placed into a best-work portfolio.

Hands-on Activities

Activity Worksheets

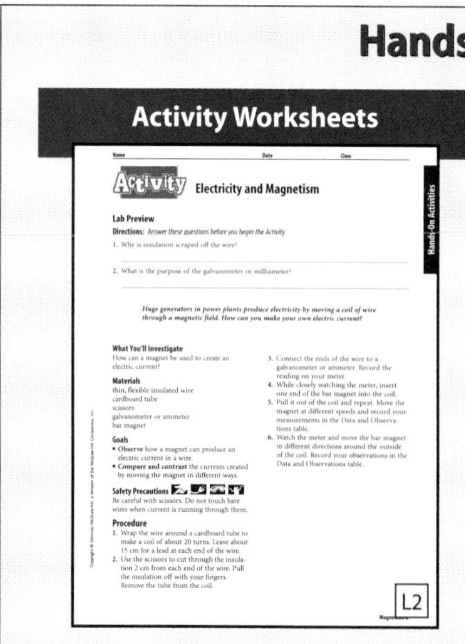
Name Date Class

Activity — Electricity and Magnetism

Hands-On Activities

Lab Preview

Directions: *Answer these questions before you begin the Activity.*

1. Why is insulation scraped off the wire?
2. What is the purpose of the galvanometer or milliameter?

Huge generators in power plants produce electricity by moving a coil of wire through a magnetic field. How can you make your own electric current?

What You'll Investigate
How can a magnet be used to create an electric current?

Materials
thin, flexible insulated wire
cardboard tube
scissors
galvanometer or ammeter
bar magnet

Goals
- **Observe** how a magnet can produce an electric current in a wire.
- **Compare and contrast** the currents created by moving the magnet in different ways.

Safety Precautions
Be careful with scissors. Do not touch bare wires when current is running through them.

Procedure
1. Wrap the wire around a cardboard tube to make a coil of about 20 turns. Leave about 15 cm for a lead at each end of the wire.
2. Use the scissors to cut through the insulation 2 cm from each end of the wire. Pull the insulation off with your fingers. Remove the tube from the coil.
3. Connect the ends of the wire to a galvanometer or ammeter. Record the reading on your meter.
4. While closely watching the meter, insert one end of the bar magnet into the coil.
5. Pull it out of the coil and repeat. Move the magnet at different speeds and record your measurements in the Data and Observations table.
6. Watch the meter and move the bar magnet in different directions around the outside of the coil. Record your observations in the Data and Observations table.

L2

Laboratory Activities

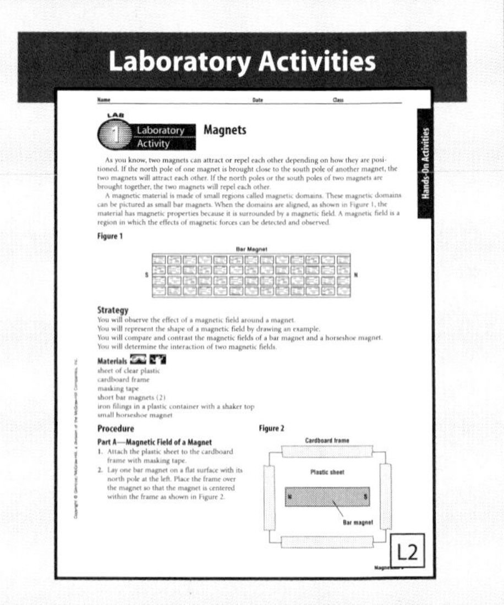
Name Date Class

Lab 1 Laboratory Activity — Magnets

Hands-On Activities

As you know, two magnets can attract or repel each other depending on how they are positioned. If the north pole of one magnet is brought close to the south pole of another magnet, the two magnets will attract each other. If the north poles or the south poles of two magnets are brought together, the two magnets will repel each other.

A magnetic material is made of small regions called magnetic domains. These magnetic domains can be pictured as small bar magnets. When the domains are aligned, as shown in Figure 1, the material has magnetic properties because it is surrounded by a magnetic field. A magnetic field is a region in which the effects of magnetic forces can be detected and observed.

Figure 1

Strategy
You will observe the effect of a magnetic field around a magnet.
You will represent the shape of a magnetic field by drawing an example.
You will compare and contrast the magnetic fields of a bar magnet and a horseshoe magnet.
You will determine the interaction of two magnetic fields.

Materials
sheet of clear plastic
cardboard frame
masking tape
short bar magnets (2)
iron filings in a plastic container with a shaker top
small horseshoe magnet

Procedure

Part A—Magnetic Field of a Magnet
1. Attach the plastic sheet to the cardboard frame with masking tape.
2. Lay one bar magnet on a flat surface with its north pole at the left. Place the frame over the magnet so that the magnet is centered within the frame as shown in Figure 2.

Figure 2

L2

Meeting Different Ability Levels

Content Outline

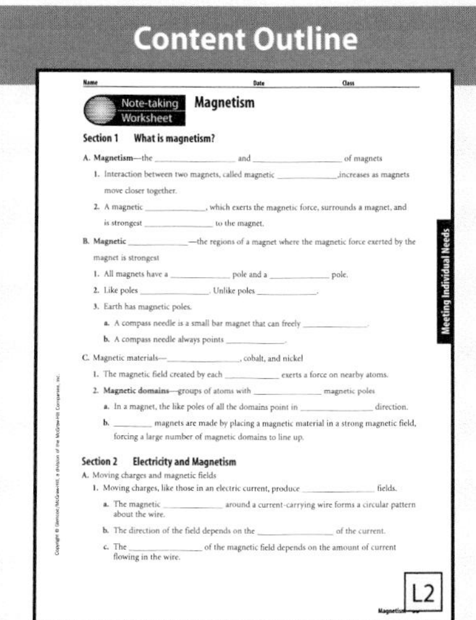

Note-taking Worksheet — Magnetism

Section 1 What is magnetism?

L2

Reinforcement

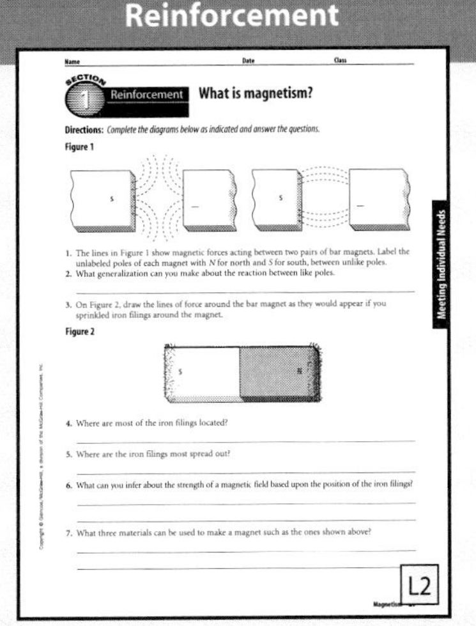

Section 1 Reinforcement — What is magnetism?

L2

Directed Reading

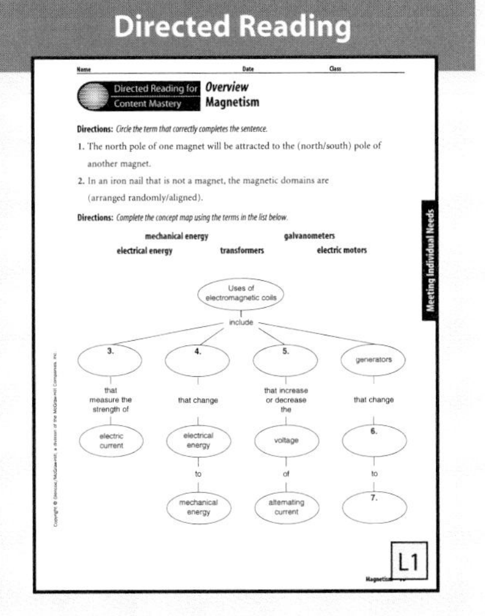

Directed Reading for Content Mastery — Overview — Magnetism

Directions: Circle the term that correctly completes the sentence.

1. The north pole of one magnet will be attracted to the (north/south) pole of another magnet.
2. In an iron nail that is not a magnet, the magnetic domains are (arranged randomly/aligned).

Directions: Complete the concept map using the terms in the list below.

L1

Enrichment

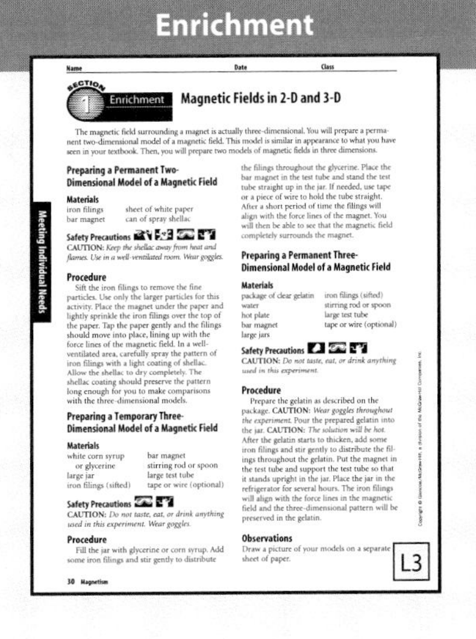

Section 1 Enrichment — Magnetic Fields in 2-D and 3-D

L3

Spanish Directed Reading

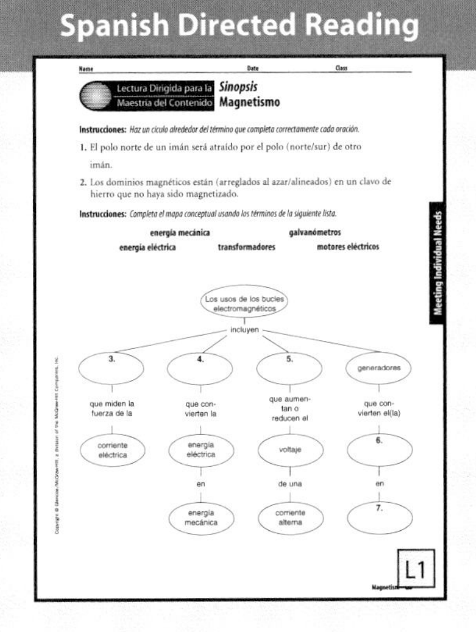

Lectura Dirigida para la Maestría del Contenido — Sinopsis — Magnetismo

L1

Assessment

Chapter Tests

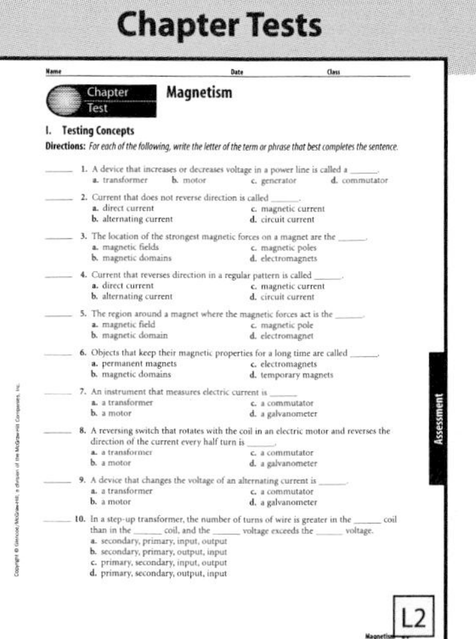

Chapter Test — Magnetism

I. Testing Concepts

L2

Test Practice Workbook

Standardized Test Practice Teacher Edition

Glencoe Science

Introduction to Physical Science

L2

Chapter Review

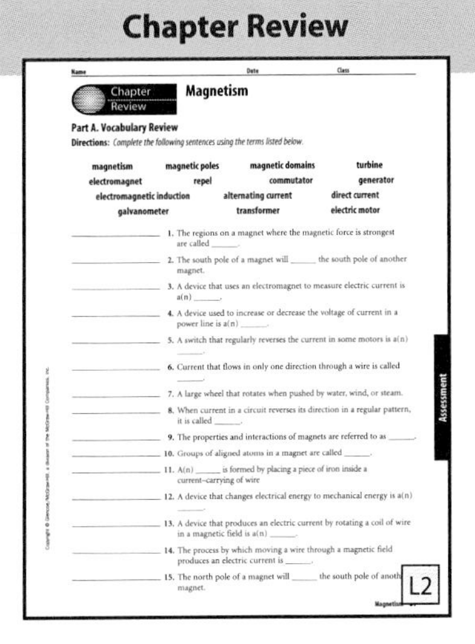

Chapter Review — Magnetism

Part A. Vocabulary Review

L2

Science Content Background

SECTION 1 What is magnetism?

Magnets

In naturally magnetic materials, an electron makes a tiny current loop as it moves around the nucleus of an atom, producing a magnetic field. The side of the loop with field lines passing out is the north pole. The side with field lines passing in is the south pole. This also explains why you cannot isolate a single magnetic pole by breaking a magnet into smaller and smaller pieces.

The lines that represent magnetic fields are called magnetic field lines. By convention, the lines are shown going from north poles to south poles. These lines can be used to describe any magnetic fields: the field around a magnet, the field between two or more magnets, the field around celestial objects such as Earth, or the field produced by a changing electric field.

Student Misconception

Students may think that Earth's geographic North Pole is a magnetic north pole and Earth's geographic South Pole is a magnetic south pole.

Refer to the facing page for teaching strategies to address this misconception. Refer to pages 473–475 for content related to this topic.

Earth's Magnetic Field

The naming of a magnet's poles can cause some confusion. By convention we call one pole of a magnet north and the other part south. The part of a freely turning magnet that faces geographic north is called the north pole of the magnet. Like poles repel and unlike poles attract. Thus, Earth's north pole is really a south magnetic pole because it attracts the north end of magnets. If you picture Earth's magnetic field as being produced by a large bar magnet, the magnet's south pole would be at Earth's north pole, attracting the north poles of compass needles. This is confusing for many people.

Another way of explaining this is to say that magnetic field lines go into south poles and come out of north poles. Compasses show the direction of the magnetic field lines. Thus if the north end of a compass points at something it must be a magnetic south pole.

SECTION 2 Electricity and Magnetism

Moving Charge Forms a Magnet

In 1820, Hans Christian Oersted discovered that an electric current could deflect a magnetic compass needle. Michael Faraday's experimental work and James Clerk Maxwell's mathematical development of Faraday's ideas established electricity and magnetism as two aspects of one force, electromagnetism. Electromagnetism is one of the four fundamental forces known. Gravity, the strong nuclear force, and the weak nuclear force are the other three. These fundamental forces all act at a distance through a field. They are fundamental because they explain other forces. Familiar contact forces, such as friction between a book and a table, the normal force of the table holding up the book, or your ability to push a book with your hand, are due to the electromagnetic force of the atoms in the books, your hand, and the tabletop.

For additional content background on this topic, go to the Glencoe Science Web site at science.glencoe.com.

Misconceptions

Find Out What Students Think

Students may think that . . .

- **Earth's north and south geographic poles are corresponding north and south magnetic poles.**

Most people assume that we call the north pole "north" because it is a magnetic north pole. This is logical reasoning. However, Earth's geographic north pole is actually its magnetic south pole because it attracts the north end of a magnet. The convention for naming north and south came before people had a strong understanding of magnets. The part of the magnet that pointed to the north was called north. Later, people realized that the north pointing part of a magnet is actually attracted to a south magnetic pole. Since the convention naming north and south on Earth was already established it has been kept, even though it causes confusion.

Demonstration

Give each group sheets of paper, a strip of masking tape, and a bar magnet that is labeled N (north) and S (south). Ask them to use the bar magnet as the center of Earth and to draw around the magnet to make a model of Earth. Direct students to label the equator, the northern hemisphere, and the southern hemisphere. Then have them decide whether the N or the S end of the magnet should be in the Northern Hemisphere.

Promote Understanding

Activity

- Give each group of students a compass.
- Review with students that the north end of the compass needle points to the northern part of our planet.
- Ask students to check their models using the compass to make sure the north end of the compass needle points toward the Northern Hemisphere of their models.
- If the compass needle points the wrong way, have students rearrange their models to make the compass needle point to the Northern Hemisphere.

Many students will have made models of Earth with the north pole of the magnet in the Northern Hemisphere. They will see that the north end of the compass needle points away from this rather than towards it. In their models, the south pole of the magnet should be in the Northern Hemisphere.

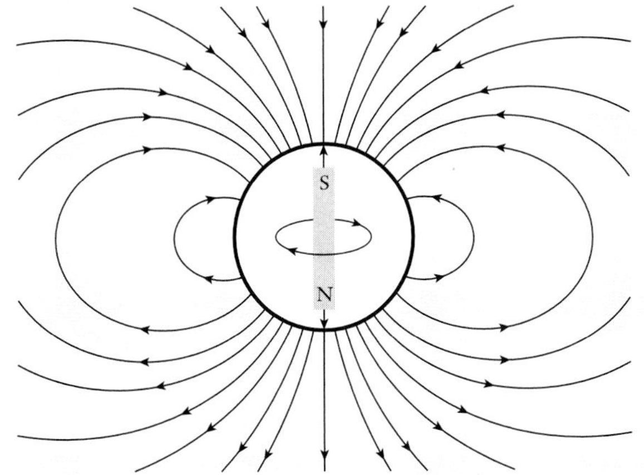

Assess

After completing the chapter, see *Identifying Misconceptions* in the Study Guide.

Magnetism

Chapter Vocabulary

magnetic field
magnetic domain
magnetosphere
electromagnet
motor
aurora
generator
alternating current
transformer

What do you think?

Science Journal The photo shows a neodymium magnet. This magnet is strong enough to attract through a hand. A second magnet is stuck to the back of the hand.

Magnetism

This maglev train is designed to travel at speeds over 500 km/h. However, you won't see any steam or exhaust coming out of its engine. In fact this train is not even touching the track. That's because it is suspended by magnetic forces and propelled by a traveling magnetic field. In this chapter, you will learn why magnets attract and repel certain materials. You will also learn how electricity and magnetism are connected, and how an electric current can create a magnetic field.

What do you think?

Science Journal Look at the picture below with a classmate. Discuss what is happening. Here's a hint: *No glue or tape is involved.* Write your answer or best guess in your Science Journal.

468

Theme Connection

Systems and Interactions Electric and magnetic fields form a system in which one of the fields produces the other.

Perhaps you've driven bumper cars with your friends, and remember the jolt you felt when you crashed into another car. Quite a force can be generated from that small car powered by an electric motor. How does the motor produce a force that gets the tires moving? The answer involves magnetism. The following activity will demonstrate how a magnetism is able to exert forces.

Observe and measure force between magnets 

1. Place two bar magnets on opposite ends of a sheet of paper.
2. Slowly slide one magnet toward the other until it moves. Measure the distance between the magnets.
3. Turn one magnet around 180°. Repeat the activity. Then turn the other magnet and repeat again.
4. Repeat the activity with one magnet perpendicular to the other, in a T shape.

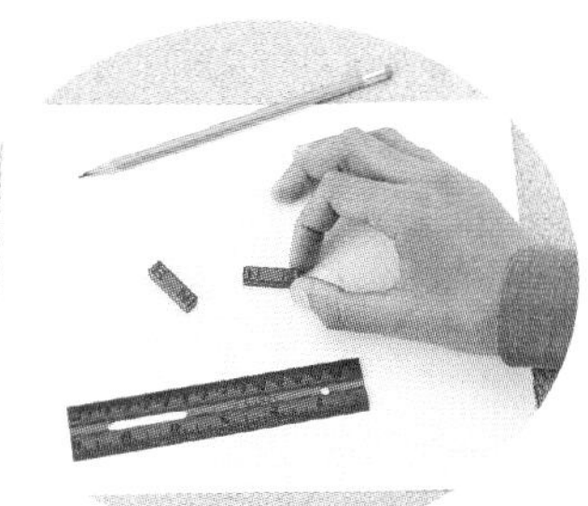

Observe

In your Science Journal, record your results. In each case, how close did the magnets have to be to affect each other? Did the magnets move together or apart? Could magnetism be used to make a large object, like a train, move? Explain.

Before You Read

Making a Compare and Contrast Study Fold **Make the following Foldable to help you see how magnetic forces and magnetic fields are similar and different.**

1. Place a sheet of paper in front of you so the long side is at the top. Fold the paper in half from the left side to the right side. Unfold.
2. Fold each side in to the fold line to divide the paper into fourths.
3. Label the flaps *Magnetic Force* and *Magnetic Field*.
4. As you read the chapter, write information about each on the back of flaps.

Magnetic Force

Magnetic Field

Before You Read

FOLDABLES Reading & Study Skills

Dinah Zike Study Fold

Purpose Students use this Foldable to differentiate between "magnetic force" and "magnetic field." They then use what they have learned to explain what they have in common.

For additional help, see Foldables Worksheet p. 13 in **Chapter Resources Booklet** or go to the Glencoe Science Web site at **science.glencoe.com.** See After You Read in the Study Guide at the end of this chapter.

Explore Activity

Purpose Use the Explore Activity to introduce students to the forces between two magnets. L2 ELL LS **Kinesthetic**

Materials paper, metric ruler, two bar magnets

Teaching Strategy Graph paper can be substituted for the paper and ruler. If it is, review with students how to use graph paper to measure distance.

Observe

The magnets move together when unlike poles face each other and move apart when like poles face each other. If the magnets were big enough, they could be used to move large things such as a train.

Process Have students sketch each arrangement of the magnets and draw arrows to indicate the direction of movement. Use **Performance Assessment in the Science Classroom,** p. 127.

SECTION

What is magnetism?

1 Motivate

Bellringer Transparency

Display the Section Focus Transparency for Section 1. Use the accompanying Transparency Activity Master. L2 ELL

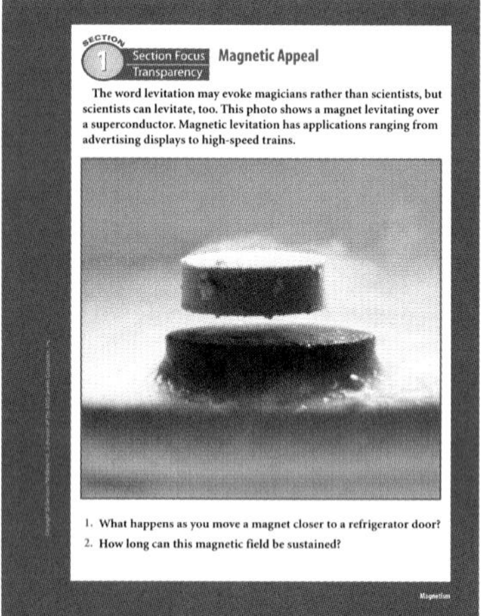
SECTION 1 Section Focus Transparency **Magnetic Appeal**

The word levitation may evoke magicians rather than scientists, but scientists can levitate, too. This photo shows a magnet levitating over a superconductor. Magnetic levitation has applications ranging from advertising displays to high-speed trains.

1. What happens as you move a magnet closer to a refrigerator door?
2. How long can this magnetic field be sustained?

Magnetism

Tie to Prior Knowledge

Ask students to think of examples of the effects of magnetism that they have experienced. List these on the chalkboard. Refrigerator magnets, cabinet locks, and audiotapes or videotapes are possibilities.

SECTION

What is magnetism?

As You Read

What You'll Learn

- **Describe** the behavior of magnets.
- **Relate** the behavior of magnets to magnetic fields.
- **Explain** the source of all magnetic fields.

Vocabulary

magnetic field
magnetic domain
magnetosphere

Why It's Important

Magnetism is one of the basic forces of nature.

Early Uses

Do you use magnets to attach papers to a metal surface such as a refrigerator? Have you ever wondered how magnets and metal attract? Thousands of years ago, people noticed that a certain mineral, called magnetite, attracted other pieces of magnetite and small bits of iron. They discovered that when they rubbed small pieces of iron with magnetite, the iron began to act like magnetite. When these pieces were free to turn, one end pointed north. These were the first compasses. The compass was an important development for navigation and exploration, especially at sea. Before compasses, sailors had to depend on the Sun or the stars to know in which direction they were going.

Magnets

A piece of magnetite is a magnet. Magnets attract objects made of iron or steel, such as nails and paper clips. Magnets also can attract or repel other magnets. Every magnet has two ends, or poles. One end is called the north pole and the other is the south pole. As shown in **Figure 1,** a north magnetic pole always repels other north poles and always attracts south poles. Likewise, a south pole always repels other south poles and attracts north poles.

Figure 1
Two north poles or two south poles repel each other. North and south magnetic poles are attracted to each other.

Two north poles repel

Two south poles repel

Opposite poles attract

Section Assessment Planner

PORTFOLIO
Assessment, p. 474

PERFORMANCE ASSESSMENT
Problem-Solving Activity, p. 473
MiniLAB, p. 474
Skill Builder Activities, p. 475
See page 492 for more options.

CONTENT ASSESSMENT
Section, p. 475
Challenge, p. 475
Chapter, pp. 492–493

The Magnetic Field You have to handle a pair of magnets for only a short time before you can feel that magnets attract or repel without touching each other. How can a magnet cause an object to move without touching it? Recall that a force is a push or a pull that can cause an object to move. Just as with gravity and electricity, a magnetic force can be exerted even when objects are not touching. And like these forces, the magnetic force becomes weaker as the magnets get farther apart. This magnetic force is exerted through a **magnetic field.** Magnetic fields surround all magnets. If you sprinkle iron filings near a magnet, the iron filings will outline the magnetic field around the magnet. Take a look at **Figure 2A.** The iron filings form a pattern of curved lines that start on one pole and end on the other. These curved lines are called magnetic field lines. Magnetic field lines show the direction of the magnetic force.

A Iron filings show the magnetic field lines around a bar magnet.

B Magnetic field lines start at the north pole of the magnet and end on the south pole.

Figure 2
A magnetic field surrounds a magnet. Where the magnetic field lines are close together, the field is strong. *Which part of the field is strongest?*

Reading Check *What is the evidence that a magnetic field exists?*

Magnetic field lines begin at a magnet's north pole and end on the south pole, as shown in **Figure 2B.** The field lines are close together where the field is strong and get farther apart as the field gets weaker. As you can see in the figures, the magnetic field is strongest close to the magnetic poles and grows weaker farther from the poles.

Field lines that curve toward each other show attraction. Field lines that curve away from each other show repulsion. **Figure 3** illustrates the magnetic field lines between a north and a south pole and the field lines between two north poles.

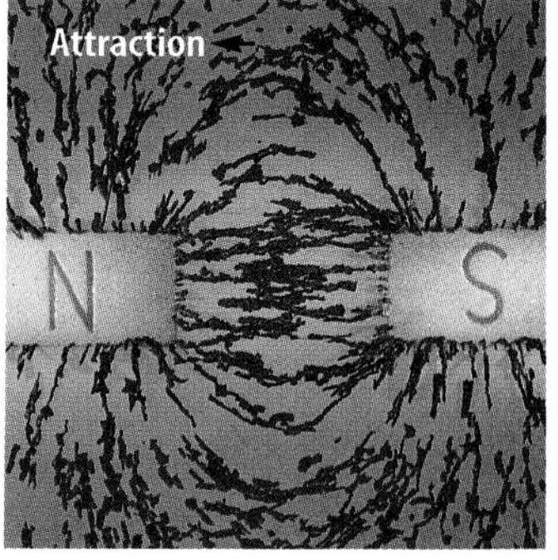

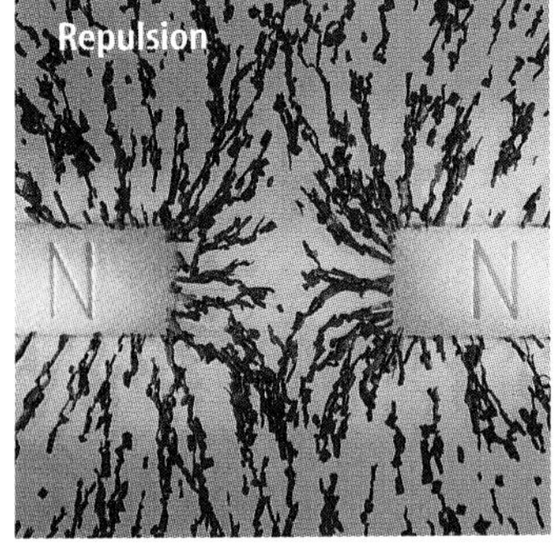
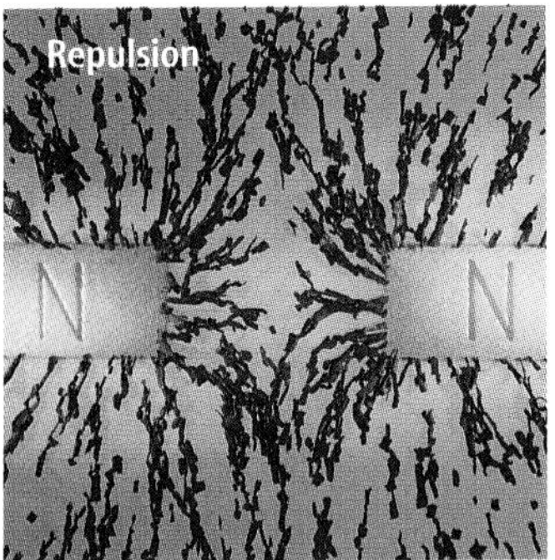

Figure 3
Magnetic field lines show attraction and repulsion. *What would the field between two south poles look like?*

2 Teach

Magnets

Extension

Have students use small metal objects such as BBs to quantify the strength of a magnetic field. Have them place the objects in a cup and count how many are picked up by a magnet held above the objects at heights of 1 cm, 2 cm, and so on. Ask students to use a spreadsheet program to organize their findings. L2 LS **Kinesthetic**

Caption Answer

Figure 2 near the poles

Reading Check

Answer Magnets exert a force on objects they don't touch.

Visual Learning

Figure 3 Iron filings in the presence of a magnetic field show where the field is strongest and where it is weakest. **What differences would you expect to see in the magnetic field for magnets of different shapes?** The field will always be strongest at the poles and weakest in the middle. The length of the field will vary with the length of the magnet. For a horseshoe magnet, the field will be strongest between the ends of the horseshoe. L2 LS **Visual-Spatial**

Caption Answer

Figure 3 The field lines would curve away from each other, as in the picture with two north poles.

Curriculum Connection

Math Explain to students that the force of a magnet falls off with the square of the distance between the magnet and the object on which it acts. This means that the force on an iron nail 2 cm from a strong magnet is one-fourth as strong as the force on the same nail 1 cm from the magnet. Have students make graphs showing magnetic force versus distance for a magnet that has a strength of 100 units at a distance of 1 cm.

Resource Manager

Chapter Resources Booklet

Transparency Activity, p. 13
Directed Reading for Content Mastery, pp. 15, 16
Note-taking Worksheets, pp. 27–28

Magnets, continued

Caption Answer

Figure 4 spinning and movement around an atom's nucleus

Use an Analogy

Magnetizing an object is analogous to giving an object a static charge. When you rub a balloon against a piece of wool, you cause the electrons to move in a way that induces a temporary static charge in the wool and in the balloon. When you rub a magnet against a steel nail, you cause the electrons to move in a way that induces a temporary magnetic field around the nail.

Students probably think that all magnets are made of iron. But not all magnets are made of iron or even of metal. Some manufactured magnets contain ceramics, for example. Any material can become a magnet if its atoms can be aligned properly.

Activity

Have students practice inducing magnetism in different objects by rubbing the objects in the same direction about 20 times with a magnet. Then ask students to determine the strength of any magnetic field induced. For example, they can test to see how many paper clips a magnetized paper clip will attract. L2 ELL Kinesthetic

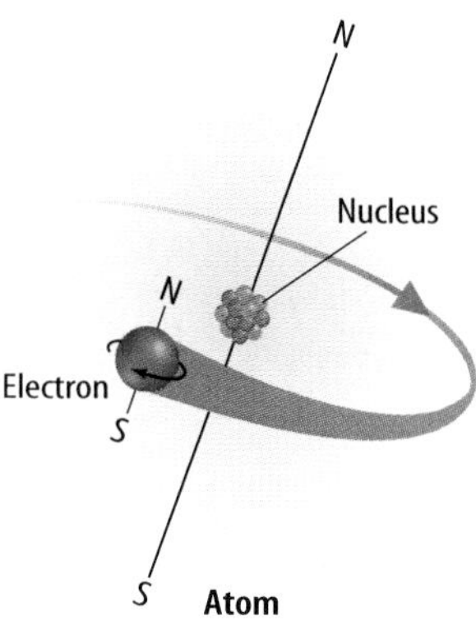

Figure 4
Movement of electrons produces magnetic fields. *What are the two types of motion shown in the illustration?*

Making Magnetic Fields So far you have learned that magnetism is a force and that this force is exerted through a magnetic field. How are magnetic fields made? A moving electric charge creates a magnetic field.

Inside every magnet are moving charges. All atoms contain negatively charged particles called electrons. Not only do these electrons swarm around the nucleus of an atom, they also spin, as shown in **Figure 4.** Because of its movement, each electron produces a magnetic field. The atoms that make up magnets have their electrons arranged so that each atom is like a small magnet. In a material such as iron, a large number of atoms will have their magnetic fields pointing the same direction. This group of atoms, with their fields pointing in the same direction, is called a **magnetic domain.**

A material that can become magnetized, such as iron or steel, contains many magnetic domains. When the material is not magnetized, these domains are oriented in different directions, as shown in **Figure 5A.** The magnetic fields created by the domains cancel, so the material does not act like a magnet.

A magnet contains a large number of magnetic domains that are lined up and pointing in the same direction. Suppose a strong magnet is held close to a material such as iron or steel. The magnet causes the magnetic field in each magnetic domain to line up with the magnet's field, as shown in **Figure 5B.** As you can see in **Figure 5C** this method magnetizes paper clips.

Figure 5
Some materials can become temporary magnets.

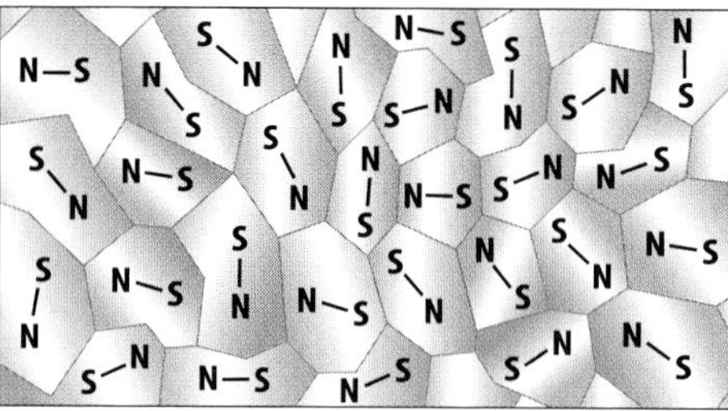

A Microscopic sections of iron and steel act as tiny magnets. Normally, these domains are oriented randomly and their magnetic fields cancel each other.

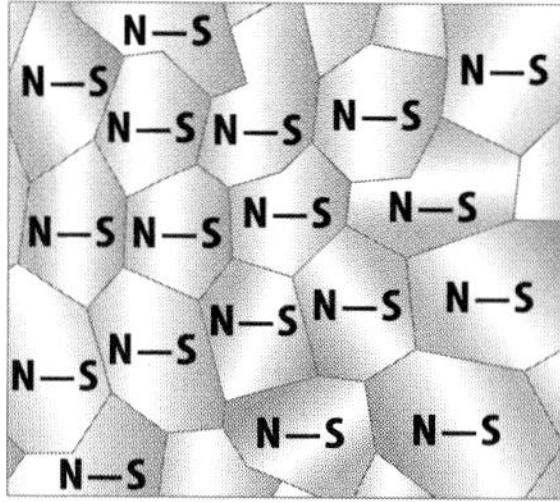

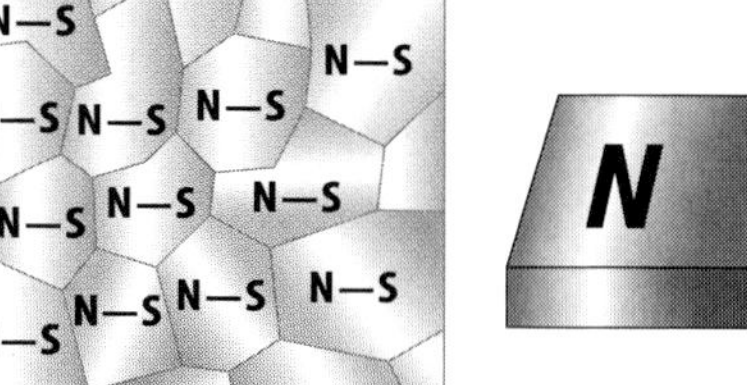

B When a strong magnet is brought near the material, the domains line up, and their magnetic fields add together.

C The bar magnet magnetizes the paper clips. The top of each paper clip is now a north pole, and the bottom is a south pole.

Teacher FYI

Records suggest that 2,000 years ago in Egypt, magnets were used to make statues appear as if they were floating in midair. The statues were carved of magnetite, and magnets with their poles carefully aligned in the floor, ceiling, and walls were able to overcome the effect of gravity on the statues.

Inclusion Strategies

Visually Impaired Pair visually impaired students with sighted students. Provide each pair with two magnets, one large and one small, and have them map the magnetic field of the large magnet by moving the small magnet around it. Have the sighted student use raised lines (of glue, for example) to make tactile models of the magnetic field. The visually impaired student can then feel the field lines with his or her hands.

472 CHAPTER 16 Magnetism

Earth's Magnetic Field

Magnetism isn't limited to bar magnets and iron. Earth has a magnetic field. This field extends into space and is called the **magnetosphere** (mag NEE tuh sfihr). The origin of Earth's magnetic field is deep within Earth in the outer core layer. One theory is that movement of molten iron in the outer core is responsible for generating a substantial magnetic field that can be detected at Earth's surface, as shown in **Figure 6.** The shape of Earth's magnetic field is similar to that of a huge bar magnet tilted about 11° from Earth's geographic north and south poles.

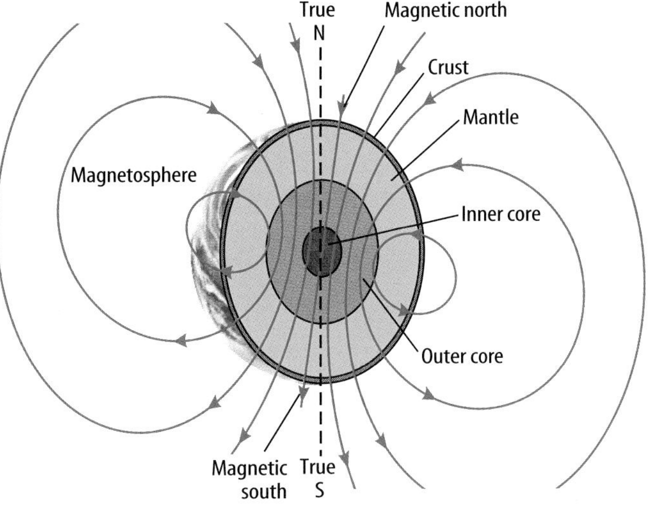

Figure 6
Earth has a magnetic field similar to the field of a bar magnet.

Problem-Solving Activity

Finding the Magnetic Declination

The north pole of a compass points toward the magnetic pole, rather than true north. Imagine drawing a line between your location and the north pole, and a line between your location and the magnetic pole. The angle between these two lines is called the magnetic declination. Sometimes knowing the magnetic declination can be important if you need to know the direction to true north, rather than to the magnetic pole. However, the magnetic declination changes depending on your position.

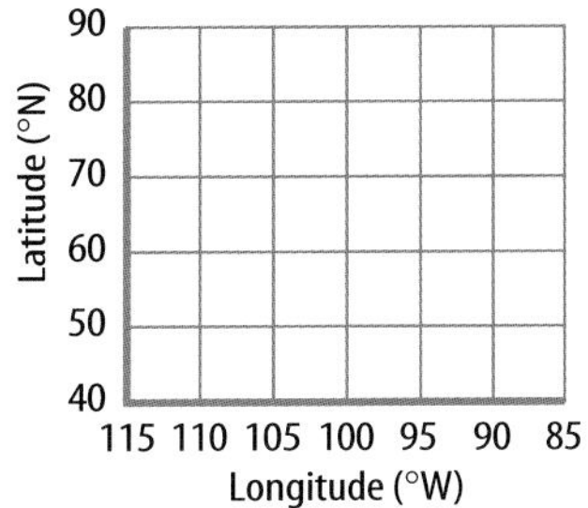

Identifying the Problem

Suppose your location is at 50° N and 110° W. You wish to head true north. The location of the north pole is at 90° N and 110° W, and the location of the magnetic pole is at about 80° N and 105° W. What is the magnetic declination angle at your location?

Solving the Problem

1. Label a graph like the one shown above.
2. On the graph, plot your location, the location of the magnetic pole, and the location of the north pole.
3. Draw a line from your location to the north pole, and a line from your location to the magnetic pole.
4. Using a protractor measure the angle between the two lines.

Earth's Magnetic Field

Quick Demo

Put a clear plate or petri dish over a piece of a natural magnet and use iron filings to show the shape of the magnetic field. Discuss why the shape of the field around the natural magnet is irregular. Ask students whether Earth's magnetic field is completely uniform. Possible answer: Probably not, because Earth is not perfectly round. L3

LS **Logical-Mathematical**

Discussion

How are gravity, electricity, and magnetism alike? How are they different? All have fields and act at a distance. Gravity always attracts, but electricity and magnetism can attract or repel. Gravity exists between all objects, while only certain objects are affected by electric and magnetic fields. L2

LS **Logical-Mathematical**

IDENTIFYING Misconceptions

Some students think that Earth's north and south geographic poles are corresponding north and south magnetic poles. See page 468F for teaching strategies that address this misconception.

✔ Active Reading

Quickwrite Have students write a list of ideas about magnetism and then share these ideas with the class. Next, have students write their ideas about magnetism freely in a paragraph without worrying about punctuation, spelling, and grammar. Have students then share their paragraphs.

Resource Manager

Chapter Resources Booklet
Enrichment, p. 25

Physical Science Critical Thinking/Problem Solving, p. 18

Problem-Solving Activity

National Math Standards

Correlation to Mathematics Objectives
2, 3, 6, 9, 10

Answer to Practice Problem

The Magnetic declination is about 20°.

Earth's Magnetic Field, continued

Caption Answer

Figure 7 farther north

Purpose Students observe magnetic fields. L2 LS **Kinesthetic**

Materials iron filings, plastic petri dish, tape, magnets

Safety Precaution Make sure to use iron filings only. DO NOT use iron powder, as it presents a serious risk of fire and explosion.

Teaching Strategies

- Suggest students seal the petri dish with tape or glue to keep the filings off the magnets.
- Field lines around magnets can be illustrated with an overhead projector, using a clear petri dish containing iron filings and magnets of different shapes and strengths.

Analysis

1. Filings are densest at the poles. They are less dense farther away from the poles.
2. The stronger the magnet, the denser the field.

Assessment

Performance Have students use iron filings to design an experiment to show that flexible magnetic strips are actually a series of magnets, each with a north and south pole. Use **Performance Assessment in the Science Classroom**, p. 95. P

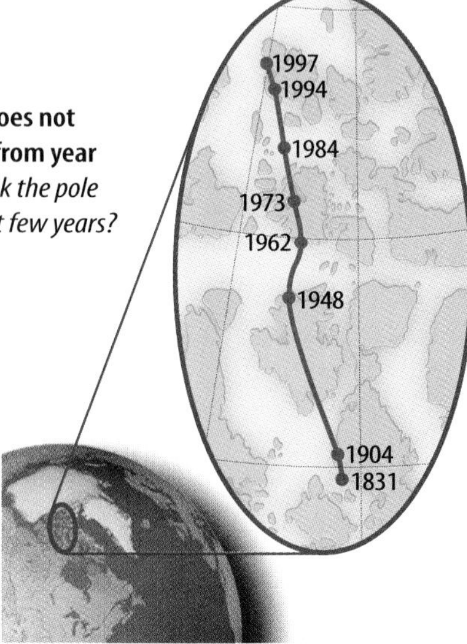

Figure 7
Earth's magnetic pole does not remain in one location from year to year. *How do you think the pole might move over the next few years?*

Mini LAB

Observing Magnetic Fields

Procedure

1. Place **iron filings** in a **plastic petri dish.** Cover the dish and **tape** it closed.
2. Collect **several magnets.** Place the magnets on the table and hold the dish over each one. Draw a diagram of what happens to the filings in each case.
3. Arrange two or more magnets under the dish. Observe the pattern of the filings.

Analysis

1. What happens to the filings close to the poles? Far from the poles?
2. Compare the fields of the individual magnets. How can you tell which magnet is strongest? Weakest?

Nature's Magnets Honeybees, rainbow trout, and homing pigeons have something in common with sailors and hikers. They take advantage of magnetism to find their way. Instead of using compasses, these animals and others have tiny pieces of magnetite in their brains. These pieces are so small that they may contain a single magnetic domain. Scientists have shown that several animals use these natural magnets to detect Earth's magnetic field. They use Earth's magnetic field, along with other clues like the position of the Sun or stars, to help them navigate.

Earth's Changing Magnetic Field If animals depend on Earth's magnetic field to help them find their way, what might happen if the magnetic field changes? Earth's magnetic poles do not stay in one place. The magnetic pole in the north today is in a different place than it was 20 years ago, as shown in **Figure 7.** In fact, Earth's magnetic field has reversed—a million years ago, a compass would not point to the north, but to the south. Since the time of the dinosaurs, Earth's magnetic field has reversed more than 100 times. Scientists have learned this by studying the magnetism of ancient rocks. When molten rock cools, the magnetic domains of iron in the rock line up with Earth's magnetic field. After the rock cools, the orientation of these domains is frozen into position. Consequently, these old rocks preserve the orientation of Earth's magnetic field as it was long ago.

Resource Manager

Chapter Resources Booklet
MiniLAB, p. 3
Lab Activity, pp. 9–10

Performance Assessment in the Science Classroom, p. 35

Visual Learning

Figure 7 The illustration shows that Earth's magnetic field is moving. **What does this suggest is going on inside Earth?** If the magnetic field arises from Earth's molten-iron core, it suggests that the core is shifting, too. L3 LS **Logical-Mathematical**

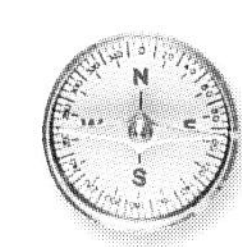
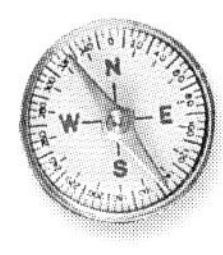

Figure 8
The compass needles align with the magnetic field lines around the magnet. *What happens to the compass needles when the bar magnet is removed?*

The Compass How can humans detect and measure Earth's magnetic field? The compass is a useful tool for finding and mapping magnetic fields. A compass has a needle that is free to turn. The needle itself is a small magnet with a north and a south magnetic pole. A magnet placed close to a compass causes the needle to rotate until it is aligned with the magnetic field line that passes through the compass, as shown in **Figure 8.**

Earth's magnetic field also causes a compass needle to rotate. The north pole of the compass needle points toward Earth's magnetic pole that is near the geographic north pole. Unlike poles attract, so this magnetic pole is actually a magnetic south pole. Earth's magnetic field is like that of a bar magnet with the magnet's south pole near Earth's north pole.

SCIENCE Online

Research A compass needle doesn't point directly toward the north. How much the needle is offset from the north varies from place to place. Visit the Glencoe Science Web site at **science.glencoe.com** to find out where the compass points in your location.

Section  Assessment

1. Why do atoms behave like magnets?
2. Explain why magnets attract metal but do not attract paper.
3. If you were in a deep cave, would a compass still point north? Explain.
4. Around a magnet, where is the field the strongest? Where is it the weakest?
5. **Think Critically** A horseshoe magnet is a bar magnet bent into the shape of the letter U. When would two horseshoe magnets attract each other? Repel? Have little effect?

Skill Builder Activities

6. **Comparing and Contrasting** Compare and contrast the three phenomena of *gravity, electricity,* and *magnetism*. Use the terms *force* and *field* in your comparison. **For more help, refer to the Science Skill Handbook.**
7. **Communicating** Imagine you are an early explorer. In your Science Journal, explain how a compass would change your work. Describe the difficulties of working without a compass. **For more help, refer to the Science Skill Handbook.**

Answers to Section Assessment

1. They contain moving electrons.
2. Some metals have magnetic domains in which atoms are oriented in the same direction. Paper does not.
3. Yes, the material around you would not block Earth's magnetic field.
4. The field is strongest near the magnet's poles and weakest far from the poles.
5. If like poles face each other, the magnets will repel each other. If opposite poles face each other, the magnets will attract each other. If the rounded parts of the magnets face each other, the magnets will have no effect on each other.
6. All act at a distance through fields whose force decreases with distance. In electricity and magnetism, like repels like, and opposites attract. Gravity has no charges or poles.
7. It would tell you the direction in which you were traveling, even if you could not see the Sun or stars.

Caption Answer

Figure 8 They align with Earth's magnetic field.

Internet Addresses

Explore the Glencoe Science Web site at **science.glencoe.com** to find out more about topics in this section.

3 Assess

Reteach

Use iron filings to display the magnetic fields surrounding a variety of magnets. Have students identify where the fields are strongest and weakest.
LS **Visual-Spatial**

Challenge

Have students research recent work involving the induction of magnetism in nonmetal objects. Why can almost any material be magnetized? If a strong enough magnetic field is applied, the magnetic poles in all the atoms align. L3 LS **Linguistic**

Performance Have students use a paper clip, a magnet, and materials such as paper or aluminum foil to determine whether materials can shield magnetic forces. Use **Performance Assessment in the Science Classroom,** p. 97.

Activity BENCH TESTED

Purpose Students discover how magnetism can be used to find direction on Earth. L2 ELL
LS **Kinesthetic**

Process Skills observing, inferring, comparing and contrasting, interpreting data

Time Required 45 minutes

Safety Precautions Caution students about responsible and careful handling of the needles. Collect and count needles before the end of class.

Teaching Strategies Needles can be difficult to handle; help students place them on the water.

Troubleshooting Caution students about disturbing the water and needle as little as possible when moving the dish.

Answers to Questions

1. The needle always aligns itself north-south.
2. The compass needle moved to align itself with the magnet's field.
3. The marked end of the needle pointed to the north pole of the bar magnet. The marked end of the needle is a north magnetic pole. Opposite poles attract and the marked end was attracted to the south pole of a magnet.

Assessment

Performance Have students find out what orienteering is. Have them learn how to find objects using only a compass and directions. Ask them to write about what they find. Use **PASC**, p. 159.

Activity

Make a Compass

A valuable tool for any nature enthusiast is a compass. More than 1,000 years ago, Chinese inventors found a way to magnetize pieces of iron. They used this method to manufacture compasses. You can use the same procedure to make a compass.

What You'll Investigate

How do you construct a compass?

Materials

petri dish	tape
**clear bowl*	marker
water	paper
sewing needle	plastic spoon
magnet	**Alternate material*

Goals

- **Observe** induced magnetism.
- **Build** a compass.

Safety

Procedure

1. Reproduce the circular protractor shown. Tape it under the bottom of your dish so it can be seen but not get wet. Add water until the dish is half full.
2. Mark one end of the needle with a marker. Magnetize a needle by placing it on the magnet aligned north and south for 1 min.
3. Float the needle carefully in the dish. Use a plastic spoon to lower the needle onto the water. Turn the dish so the marked part of the needle is above the 0° mark. This is your compass.
4. Bring the magnet near your compass. Observe how the needle reacts. Measure the angle the needle turns.

0° 30° 60° 90° 120° 150° 180° 210° 240° 270° 300° 330°

Conclude and Apply

1. **Explain** why the marked end of the needle always pointed the same way in step 3, even though you rotated the dish.
2. **Describe** the behavior of the compass when the magnet was brought close.
3. Does the marked end of your needle point to the north or south pole of the bar magnet? Infer whether the marked end of your needle is a north or a south pole. How do you know?

Communicating Your Data

Make a half-page insert that will go into a wilderness survival guide to describe the procedure for making a compass. Share your half-page insert with your classmates. **For more help, refer to the Science Skill Handbook.**

Communicating Your Data

Students can use a word processing program and a scanner to help them produce their directions for making a compass. Scanned photos could show how to magnetize a needle and how to mount it.

Resource Manager

Chapter Resources Booklet
Activity Worksheet, pp. 5–6

SECTION

Electricity and Magnetism

Moving Charge Creates a Magnet

In the first section, you learned that a moving electric charge makes a magnetic field. You also learned that electrons moving around the nucleus of an atom produce tiny magnetic fields, and in some materials these magnetic fields can group together into domains, making a magnet. In addition to their movement in atoms, electrons can be made to move in other ways. When an electric current is created, electrons flow in a wire. These moving electrons also produce a magnetic field. **Figure 9A** shows the magnetic field produced around a current-carrying wire.

Look at the magnetic field lines around the coils of wire in **Figure 9B.** The magnetic fields around each coil of wire add together to form a stronger magnetic field inside the coil. When the coils are wrapped around an iron core, the magnetic field of the coils magnetizes the iron. The iron then becomes a magnet, which adds to the strength of the magnetic field inside the coil. A current-carrying wire wrapped around an iron core is called an **electromagnet,** as shown in **Figure 9C.**

As You Read

What You'll Learn

- **Describe** the relationship between electricity and magnetism.
- **Explain** how electricity can produce motion.
- **Explain** how motion can produce electricity.

Vocabulary

electromagnet	generator
motor	alternating current
aurora	transformer

Why It's Important

The electric current that comes from your wall socket is available because of magnetism.

Figure 9
A current-carrying wire produces a magnetic field.

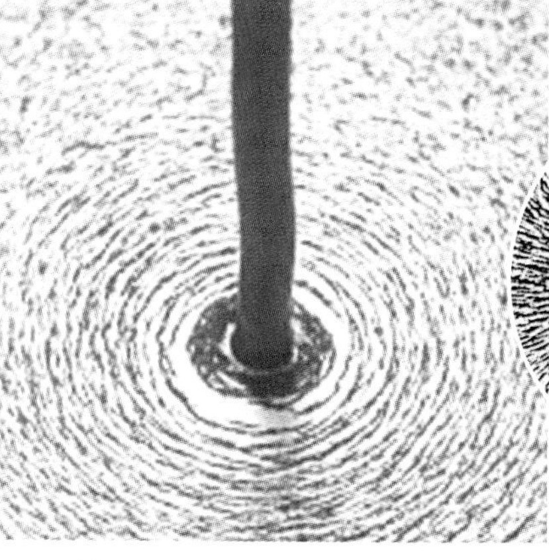

A Iron particles show the magnetic field lines around a current-carrying wire.

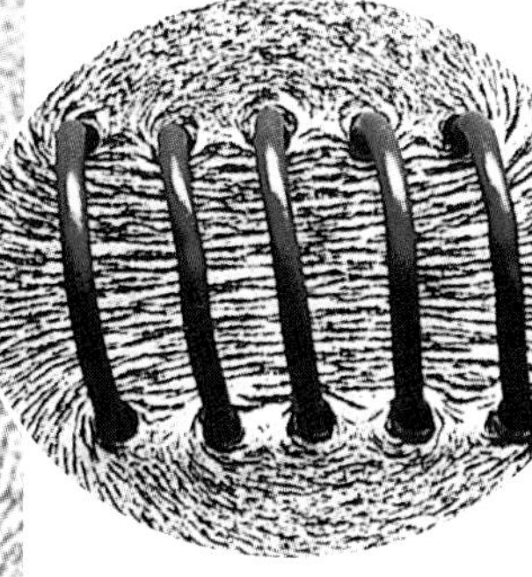

B When a wire is wrapped in a coil, the field inside the coil is made stronger.

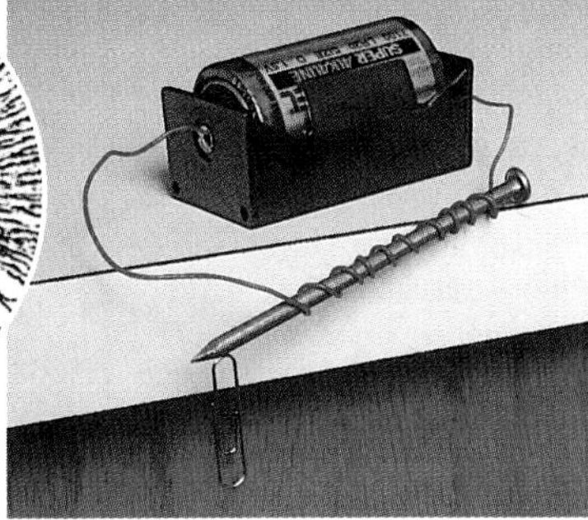

C An iron core inside the coils increases the magnetic field because the core becomes magnetized.

SECTION

Electricity and Magnetism

1 Motivate

Bellringer Transparency

Display the Section Focus Transparency for Section 2. Use the accompanying Transparency Activity Master. L2 ELL

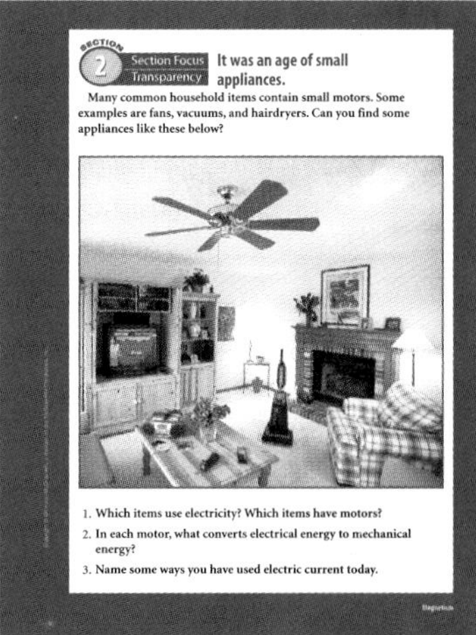

Section 2 Section Focus Transparency It was an age of small appliances.

Many common household items contain small motors. Some examples are fans, vacuums, and hairdryers. Can you find some appliances like these below?

1. Which items use electricity? Which items have motors?
2. In each motor, what converts electrical energy to mechanical energy?
3. Name some ways you have used electric current today.

Tie to Prior Knowledge

Ask students in what context, other than when discussing magnetism, they've heard that like repels like and opposites attract. electricity Explain that in this section they will learn more about how electricity and magnetism are related.

Section Assessment Planner

PORTFOLIO
Visual Learning, p. 478
Cultural Diversity, p. 481

PERFORMANCE ASSESSMENT
Try At Home MiniLAB, p. 478
Skill Builder Activities, p. 485
See page 492 for more options.

CONTENT ASSESSMENT
Section, p. 485
Challenge, p. 485
Chapter, pp. 492–493

2 Teach

Moving Charge Creates a Magnet

Caption Answer

Figure 10 The hammer striking the bell opens the circuit, which turns off the electromagnet.

TRY AT HOME
Mini
LAB

Purpose Students build an electromagnet. L2
Kinesthetic

Materials insulated wire, 16-penny steel nail, D-cell battery, paper clips

Teaching Strategy Provide sealed iron filings or compasses so students can investigate the fields produced by their electromagnets.

Safety Precautions Make sure students do not leave the electromagnets connected to the battery for long periods of time.

Troubleshooting Make sure students use insulated wire and do not short the batteries by wiring directly across the terminals.

Analysis

1. The more coils on the electromagnet, the more paper clips it picked up.
2. The five-coil electromagnet should pick up about half as many paper clips as the ten-coil electromagnet.

✔Assessment

Oral Have students summarize the relationship between the number of coils and the number of paper clips an electromagnet can pick up. The more coils, the greater the number of paper clips that can be picked up. Use **PASC,** p. 89.

Figure 10
An electric doorbell uses an electromagnet. Each time the electromagnet is turned on, the hammer strikes the bell. *How is the electromagnet turned off?*

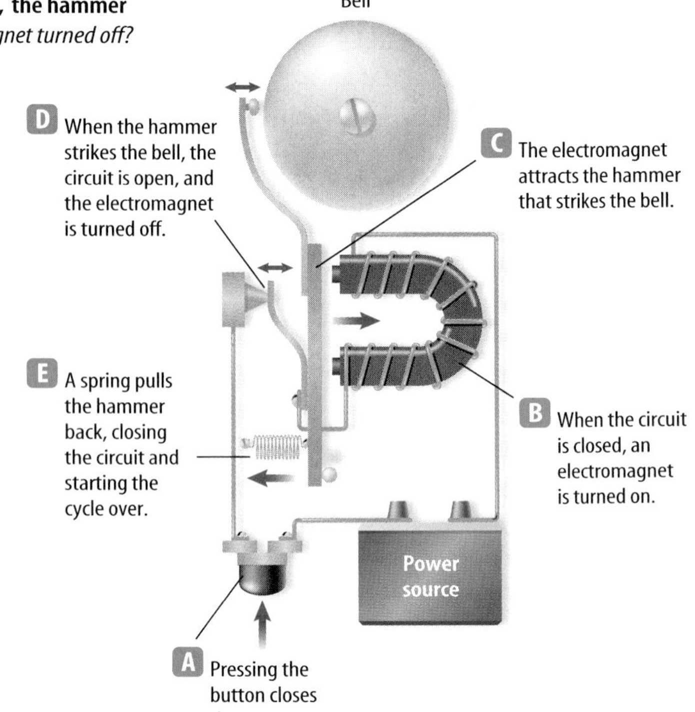

Bell
D When the hammer strikes the bell, the circuit is open, and the electromagnet is turned off.
C The electromagnet attracts the hammer that strikes the bell.
E A spring pulls the hammer back, closing the circuit and starting the cycle over.
B When the circuit is closed, an electromagnet is turned on.
Power source
A Pressing the button closes the circuit.

TRY AT HOME Mini LAB

Assembling an Electromagnet

Procedure

1. Wrap a **wire** around a **16-penny steel nail** ten times. Connect one end of the wire to a **D-cell battery,** as shown in **Figure 9C.** Leave the other end loose until you use the electromagnet. **WARNING:** *When current is flowing in the wire, it can become hot over time.*
2. Connect the wire. Observe how many **paper clips** you can pick up with the magnet.
3. Disconnect the wire and rewrap the nail with 20 coils. Connect the wire and observe how many paper clips you can pick up. Disconnect the wire again.

Analysis

1. How many paper clips did you pick up each time? Did more coils make the electromagnet stronger or weaker?
2. Graph the number of coils versus number of paper clips attracted. Predict how many paper clips would be picked up with five coils of wire. Check your prediction.

Using Electromagnets The magnetic field of an electromagnet is turned on or off when the electric current is turned on or off. By changing the current, the strength and direction of the magnetic field of an electromagnet can be changed. This has led to a number of practical uses for electromagnets. A doorbell, as shown in **Figure 10,** is a familiar use of an electromagnet. When you press the button by the door, you close a switch in a circuit that includes an electromagnet. The magnet attracts an iron bar attached to a hammer. The hammer strikes the bell. When the hammer strikes the bell, the hammer has moved far enough to open the circuit again. The electromagnet loses its magnetic field, and a spring pulls the iron bar and hammer back into place. This movement closes the circuit, and the cycle begins again. The hammer strikes the bell several times each second.

Some gauges, such as the gas gauge in a car, use a galvanometer to move the gauge pointer. **Figure 11** shows how a galvanometer makes a pointer move. Ammeters and voltmeters used to measure current and voltage in electric circuits also use galvanometers, as shown in **Figure 11.**

Inclusion Strategies

Physically Challenged An electromagnet can be made with larger equipment that will make the manipulation easier. A tall metal cylinder can be used in place of the nail and a spray-painted metal spring toy can be used in place of the wire. Kinesthetic

Visual Learning

Figure 10 Have students use the illustration and text description to make a flowchart that traces the sequence of events that results in a doorbell ringing. Possible answer: Pushing the button closes the circuit, which activates the electromagnet and causes an iron bar to move a hammer that strikes a bell. The bell rings, and the hammer movement opens the circuit again, shutting off the current. L2 Visual-Spatial P

VISUALIZING VOLTMETERS AND AMMETERS

Figure 11

The gas gauge in a car uses a device called a galvanometer to make the needle of the gauge move. Galvanometers are also used in other measuring devices. A voltmeter uses a galvanometer to measure the voltage in a electric circuit. An ammeter uses a galvanometer to measure electric current. Multimeters, like those on the right, can be used as an ammeter or voltmeter by turning a switch.

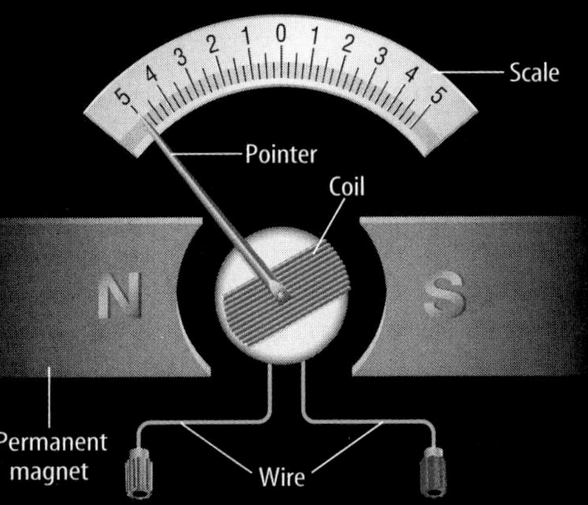

A galvanometer has a pointer attached to a coil that can rotate between the poles of a permanent magnet. When a current flows through the coil, it becomes an electromagnet. Attraction and repulsion between the magnetic poles of the electromagnet and the poles of the permanent magnet makes the coil rotate. The amount of rotation depends on the amount of current in the coil.

To measure the current in a circuit an ammeter is used. An ammeter contains a galvanometer and has low resistance. To measure current, an ammeter is connected in series in the circuit, so all the current in the circuit flows through it. The greater the current in the circuit, the more the needle moves.

To measure the voltage in a circuit a voltmeter is used. A voltmeter also contains a galvanometer and has high resistance. To measure voltage, a voltmeter is connected in parallel in the circuit, so almost no current flows through it. The higher the voltage in the circuit, the more the needle moves.

NATIONAL GEOGRAPHIC

Visualizing Voltmeters and Ammeters

Have students examine the pictures and read the captions. Then ask the following questions.

Why is it important that the resistance of an ammeter be small compared to the other resistance in a circuit? If it weren't, the meter would change the amount of current flowing in the circuit that it is measuring.

Why must a direct current meter be hooked up so that the portion of the circuit going to the positive of the battery is connected to the positive side of the meter? Connecting it improperly could ruin the meter.

Activity

Have students diagram how they would connect an ammeter to find the current flowing when a motor is connected to a battery. Then have them diagram how they would connect a voltmeter to find the voltage in a circuit with a motor connected to a battery. **Visual-Spatial**

Extension

Have interested students research the differences between a microammeter, a milliammeter, and an ammeter. Have them prepare posters with labeled diagrams that explain the differences in the meters.

Resource Manager 

Chapter Resources Booklet
Transparency Activity, p. 39
MiniLAB, p. 4

Home and Community Involvement, p. 49

Magnets Push Currents

Quick Demo

Show students how electricity and magnetism are related by setting up a DC circuit and showing how the needle of a compass is deflected in opposite directions when the compass is held over and under the wire. If possible, set this up on an overhead projector so students can see it better. Most compasses are transparent. Ask students to describe a way to move the wire that will keep the compass spinning. L3 LS **Logical-Mathematical**

Visual Learning

Figure 13B The illustration shows that the current loop spins because of the force exerted on it by the magnetic field. Help students see that to keep the loop spinning, some mechanism must be in place that changes the direction of the current each half-turn. This is done by two split rings connected to the ends of the loop. These establish connections with the battery terminals. When the loop spins, the rings also spin and come in contact with the opposite terminals. This changes the direction of the current and keeps the motor operating. L2 LS **Visual-Spatial**

Fun Fact

The relationship between electricity and magnetism was discovered by Hans Oersted in 1820, when he saw that an electric current in a wire could deflect a compass needle. In 1825 an English electrical engineer named William Sturgeon perfected the first practical electromagnet.

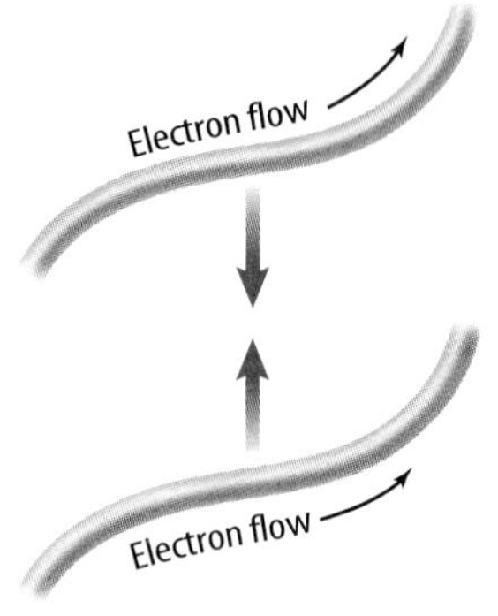

Magnets Push Currents

Look around for electric appliances that produce motion, such as a fan. How does the electric energy entering the fan transform into the kinetic energy of the moving fan blades? Recall that current-carrying wires produce a magnetic field. This magnetic field behaves the same way as the magnetic field that a magnet produces. Two current-carrying wires can attract each other as if they were two magnets, as shown in **Figure 12.**

Figure 12
Two wires carrying current in the same direction attract each other, just as unlike magnetic poles do.

Electric Motor Just as two magnets exert a force on each other, a magnet and a current-carrying wire exert forces on each other. The magnetic field around a current-carrying wire will cause it to be pushed or pulled by a magnet, depending on the direction the current is flowing in the wire. This behavior can be used to convert the electric energy carried by the current into kinetic energy of the moving wire, as shown in **Figure 13A.** Any device that converts electric energy into kinetic energy is a **motor.** To keep a motor running, the current-carrying wire is formed into a loop so the magnetic field can force the wire to spin continually, as shown in **Figure 13B.**

Figure 13
An electric motor uses the interaction between electricity and magnetism to transform electric energy into kinetic energy.

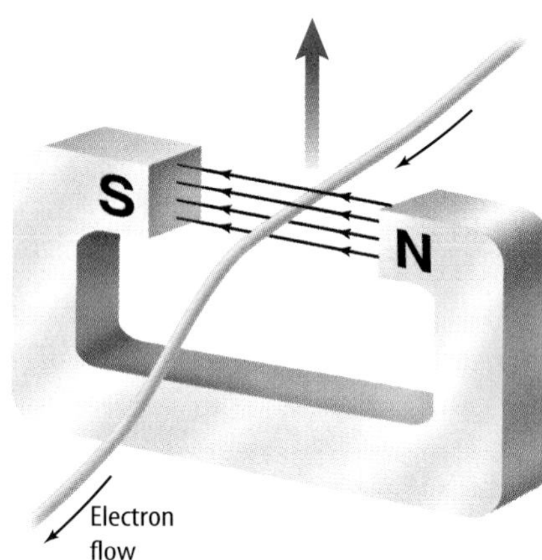

A **A magnetic field like the one shown will push a current-carrying wire upward.**

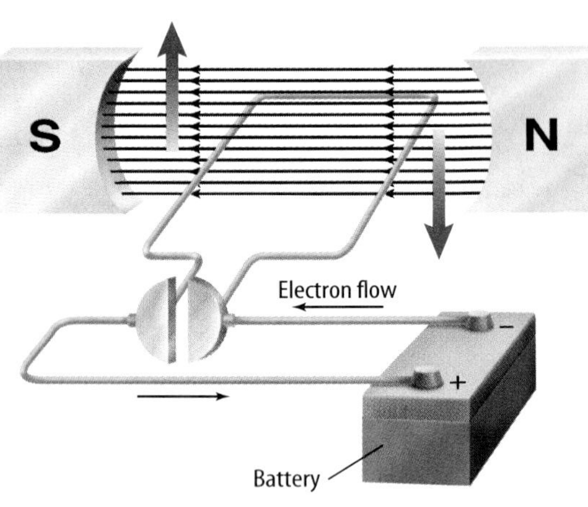

B **The magnetic field exerts a force on the wire loop, causing it to spin as long as current flows in the loop.**

Teacher FYI

Electromagnetic interactions are important in the operation of television sets. Magnets control the beam of electrons that forms the television picture. Many laboratory balances also work by balancing a weight with an electromagnetic force.

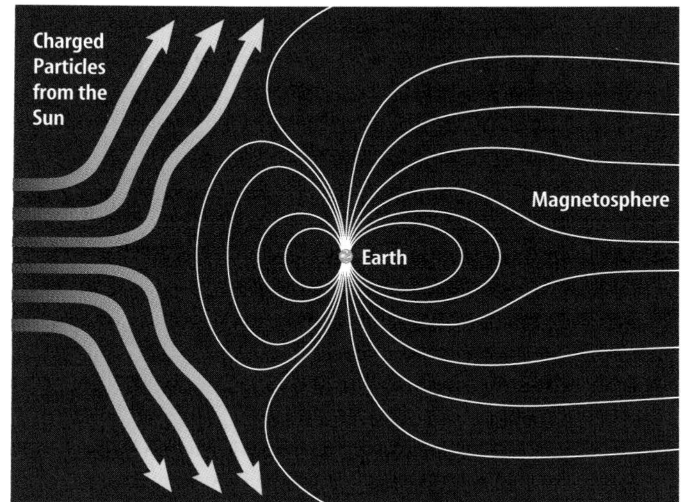

Figure 14
Earth's magnetosphere deflects most of the charged particles streaming from the Sun. A few, however, are trapped and spiral down toward the poles of Earth. *Why is the magnetosphere stretched away from the Sun?*

Pushing on Currents in Space Every minute the Sun is emitting charged particles that stream through the solar system like an enormous electric current. Just like a current-carrying wire is pushed or pulled by a magnetic field, Earth's magnetic field pushes and pulls on the electric current generated by the Sun. This causes most of the charged particles in this current to be deflected so they never strike Earth, as shown in **Figure 14.** As a result, living things on Earth are protected from damage that might be caused by these charged particles. At the same time, the solar current pushes on Earth's magnetosphere so it is stretched away from the Sun.

The Aurora Most of the charged particles from the Sun are deflected by Earth's magnetosphere. However, some charged particles spiral along Earth's magnetic field lines. These field lines come together at the magnetic poles, so these particles eventually enter Earth's atmosphere high above Earth's poles. There they collide with atoms in the atmosphere. These collisions transfer energy to the atoms, which then immediately reemit the energy in the form of light. The light emitted forms a display known as the **aurora** (uh ROR uh), as shown in **Figure 15.** When the aurora can be seen in northern latitudes, it is sometimes called the northern lights.

Figure 15
An aurora is a natural light show that occurs in the southern and northern skies.

Caption Answer

Figure 14 The charged particles from the Sun push it out as they move past Earth.

Teacher FYI

The solar particles that give rise to the auroras can affect the operation of electrical devices on Earth. If a sufficient number of these particles gets trapped in Earth's atmosphere, they can interfere with radio communications. They even can damage satellites by causing electrical discharges that overload the delicate circuitry inside.

Extension

The color of the aurora depends on the atoms that are struck (nitrogen or oxygen) and the height at which the charged particles strike them. The colors for oxygen and nitrogen vary as follows:

green—oxygen up to 150 miles

red—oxygen more than 150 miles up

blue—nitrogen up to 60 miles

purple/violet—nitrogen more than 60 miles up

Have students obtain color photos of the auroras and use the information above to identify the atoms producing the colors and the heights at which they were struck. L2

LS **Logical-Mathematical**

Cultural Diversity

Light Folklore Some Inuit believed that Earth was enclosed in a dark dome and that the aurora were lights from a higher source that came in through holes in the dome. Europeans of the Middle Ages believed the lights were deceased soldiers doing battle in the sky. Have students report on other folklore about the northern and southern lights or write their own creative stories about them. L2 LS **Linguistic** P

Resource Manager

Chapter Resources Booklet
Directed Reading, pp. 17, 18

Mathematics Skill Activities, p. 1

A Magnet Pushes on Moving Charge

Use Science Words

Word Meaning Tell students that scientists often use the word *induce* to describe what happens between electricity and magnets. Have students use a dictionary to find the meaning of the word *induce*. *Induce* means "to bring about by some influence." Ask students to relate this meaning to what happens in a generator. Possible answer: In a generator, a magnetic field is used to bring about an electric current.

L2 LS **Linguistic**

Fun Fact

The frequency of alternating current in Europe is 50 cycles per second.

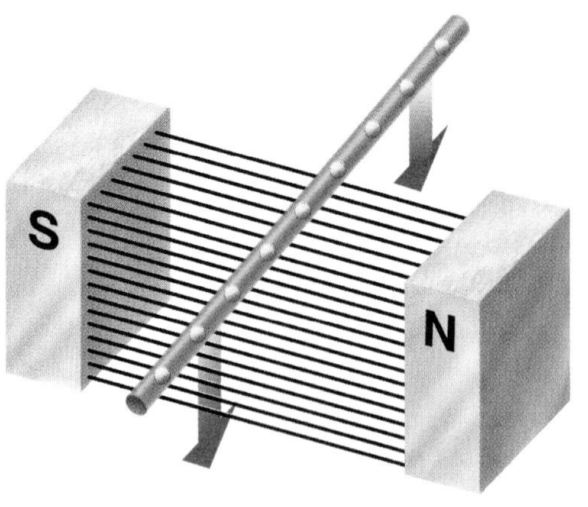

A If a wire is pulled through a magnetic field, the electrons in the wire also move downward.

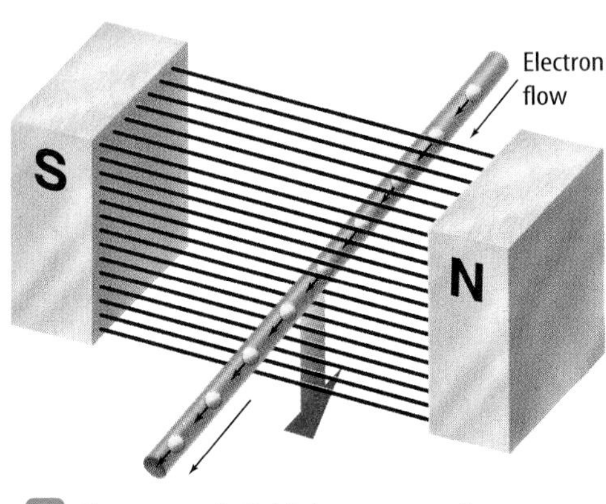

B The magnetic field then exerts a force on the moving electrons, causing them to move along the wire.

Figure 16
When a wire is made to move through a magnetic field, an electric current can be produced in the wire.

A Magnet Pushes on Moving Charge

In an electric motor, a magnetic field turns electricity into motion. A device called a **generator** uses a magnetic field to turn motion into electricity. Electric motors and electric generators both involve conversions between electric energy and kinetic energy. In a motor, electric energy is changed into kinetic energy. In a generator, kinetic energy is changed into electric energy. **Figure 16** shows how a current can be produced in a wire that moves in a magnetic field. As the wire moves, the electrons in the wire also move in the same direction, as shown in **Figure 16A.** The magnetic field exerts a force on the moving electrons that pushes them along the wire, as shown in **Figure 16B,** creating an electric current.

Figure 17
In a generator, a power source spins a loop in a magnetic field. Every half turn, the current will reverse direction. This type of generator supplies alternating current to the lightbulb.

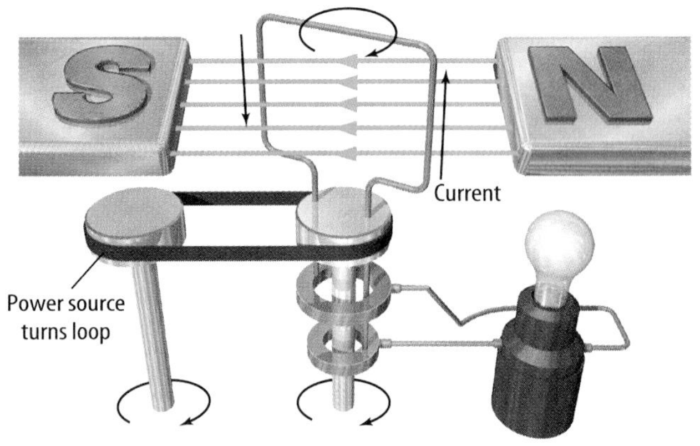

Generating Electricity To produce electric current, the wire is fashioned into a loop, as in in **Figure 17.** A power source provides the kinetic energy to spin the wire loop. With each half turn, the current in the loop changes direction. This causes the current to alternate from positive to negative. Such a current is called an **alternating current** (AC). In the United States, electric currents change from positive to negative to positive 60 times each second.

LAB DEMONSTRATION

Purpose to build an electric generator

Materials four small bar magnets; 70 m #30 wire; holiday lightbulb; small cardboard box; 11 long nails, tape

Procedure Poke holes in the long sides of the box. Insert the nail so that it spans the box opening and spins freely. Tape the magnets to the nail, 2 on each side. Wrap wire around the sides of the box. Use tape to keep the wire away from the nail holes. Attach each wire end to one wire of the bulb. Hand spin the nail vigorously.

Expected Outcome The bulb glows dimly. To increase brightness, clamp the nail into the chuck of a hand drill. (brace and bit)

Why does the bulb light only dimly? Not much current is produced. **Why is the bulb brighter when the nail is turned faster?** The faster the magnetic field moves, the more current is generated.

Types of Current A battery produces direct current instead of alternating current. In a direct current (DC) electrons flow in one direction. In an alternating current, electrons change their direction of movement many times each second. Some generators are built to produce direct current instead of alternating current.

Reading Check *What type of currents can be produced by a generator?*

Power Plants Electric generators are used to produce electric energy all over the world. Small generators can produce energy for one household, and large generators in electric power plants can provide electric energy for thousands of homes. Different energy sources such as gas, coal, and water are used to provide the kinetic energy to rotate coils of wire in a magnetic field. Coal-burning power plants, like the one pictured in **Figure 18,** are the most common. More than half of the electric energy generated by power plants in the United States comes from burning coal.

Voltage The electric energy produced at a power plant is carried to your home in wires. Recall that voltage is a measure of how much energy that electric charges in a current are carrying. The electric transmission lines from electric power plants transmit electric energy at a high voltage of about 700,000 V. Transmitting electric energy at low voltage is less efficient because more electric energy is converted into heat in the wires. However, high voltage is not safe for use in homes and businesses. A device is needed to reduce the voltage.

SCIENCE Online

Research Visit the Glencoe Science Web site at **science.glencoe.com** for more information about the different types of power plants used in your region of the country. Communicate to your class what you learn.

Figure 18
Coal-burning power plants supply much of the electric energy for the world.

483

Reading Check

Answer direct current and alternating current

SCIENCE Online
Internet Addresses

Explore the Glencoe Science Web site at **science.glencoe.com** to find out more about topics in this section.

Quick Demo

To illustrate the difference between alternating and direct current, make a circuit with an AC power source, a lightbulb, and an ammeter. Have students note how the needle fluctuates between positive and negative values. Next, connect the ammeter to a DC power source, and have students note the constant positive value. L2
LS **Visual-Spatial**

Science Journal

Providing Power Have students research in more detail how power gets from the power plant to their homes. Ask them to outline the steps in their Science Journals, paying particular attention to those steps that in some way involve magnets. L2 LS **Linguistic**

Resource Manager 

Chapter Resources Booklet
Enrichment, p. 26
Lab Activity, pp. 11–12
Science Inquiry Labs, pp. 9, 55

Changing Voltage

Activity

Collect several discarded transformers from used or broken appliances and break open their outer, plastic casings. Organize the class into groups and give each a transformer and its casing. Describe the power-converting specifications of each transformer. If possible, tell students what device each transformer was used to operate. Have students identify the input coil, output coil, and iron core. Have them try to determine from the windings to what voltage the transformer converts the 120 V from an outlet and whether their findings match the rating stated on the case. L3

LS **Logical-Mathematical**

IDENTIFYING Misconceptions

Make sure students understand that transformers work only with alternating current and not with direct current. This is because the constant electrical field of direct current induces a constant magnetic field that cannot induce an electrical field in the secondary winding.

Reading Check

Answer It can increase or decrease voltage.

Caption Answer

Figure 20 180V

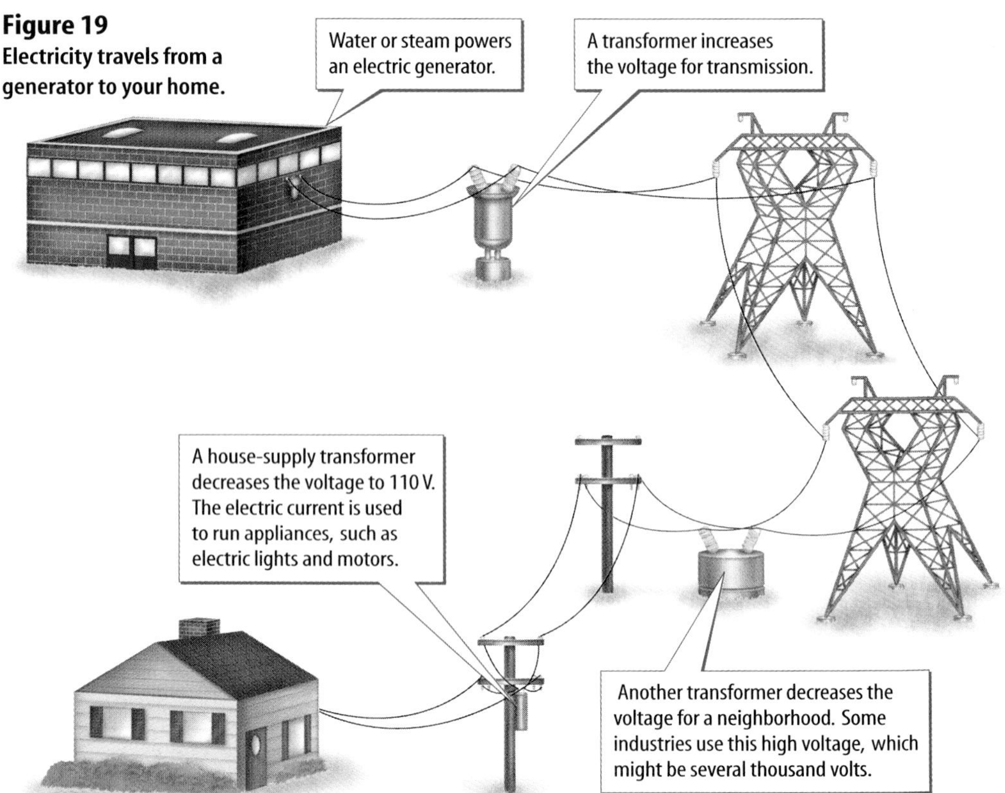

Water or steam powers an electric generator.
A transformer increases the voltage for transmission.
A house-supply transformer decreases the voltage to 110 V. The electric current is used to run appliances, such as electric lights and motors.
Another transformer decreases the voltage for a neighborhood. Some industries use this high voltage, which might be several thousand volts.

Figure 19
Electricity travels from a generator to your home.

Figure 20
A transformer can increase or decrease voltage. The ratio of input coils to output coils equals the ratio of input voltage to output voltage. *If the input voltage here is 60 V, what is the output voltage?*

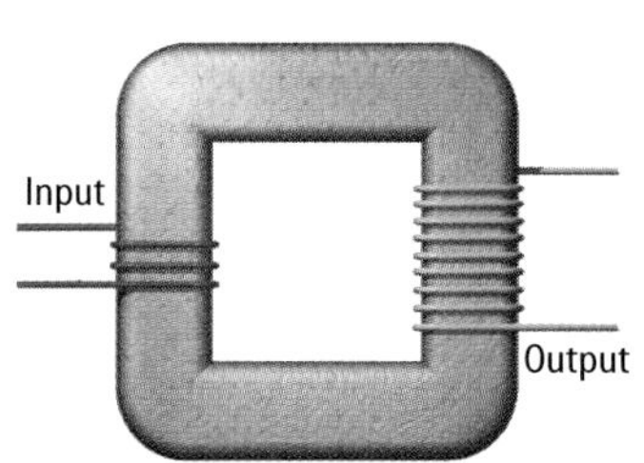

Changing Voltage

A **transformer** is a device that changes the voltage of an alternating current with little loss of energy. Transformers are used to increase the voltage before transmitting an electric current through the power lines. Other transformers are used to decrease the voltage to the level needed for home or industrial use. Such a power system is shown in **Figure 19.** Transformers also play a role in power adaptors. For battery-operated devices, a power adaptor must change the 120 V from the wall outlet to a voltage that matches the device's batteries.

Reading Check *What does a transformer do?*

A transformer has two coils of wire wrapped around an iron core, as shown in **Figure 20.** One coil is connected to an alternating current source. The current creates a magnetic field in the iron core, just like in an electromagnet. Because the current is alternating, the magnetic field also alternates, switching direction when the current does. This alternating magnetic field in the core then causes an alternating current in the other wire coil.

Science Journal

AC versus DC When Thomas Edison first installed his electric lamps, he powered them with direct current. Have students find out and write in their Science Journals why alternating current became the preferred electrical current. Alternating current could travel farther and be stepped up and stepped down using transformers.

L2 LS **Linguistic**

Resource Manager

Chapter Resources Booklet

Reinforcement, p. 24

Transparency Activity, pp. 41–42

The Transformer Ratio Whether a transformer increases or decreases the input voltage depends on the number of coils on each side of the transformer. The ratio of the number of coils on the input side to the number of coils on the output side is the same as the ratio of the input voltage to the output voltage. For the transformer in **Figure 20** the ratio of the number of coils on the input side to the number of coils on the output side is three to nine, or one to three. If the input voltage is 60 V, the output voltage will be 180 V.

In a transformer the voltage is greater on the side with more coils. If the number of coils on the input side is greater than the number of coils on the output side, the voltage is decreased. If the number of coils on the input side is less than the number on the output side, the voltage is increased.

Superconductors

Electric current can flow easily through materials, such as metals, that are electrical conductors. However, even in conductors, there is some resistance to this flow and heat is produced as electrons collide with atoms in the material.

Unlike an electrical conductor, a material known as a superconductor has no resistance to the flow of electrons. Superconductors are formed when certain materials are cooled to low temperatures. For example, aluminum becomes a superconductor at about −272°C. When an electric current flows through a superconductor, no heat is produced and no electric energy is converted into heat.

Superconductors and Magnets Superconductors also have other unusual properties. For example, a magnet is repelled by a superconductor. As the magnet gets close to the superconductor, the superconductor creates a magnetic field that is opposite to the field of the magnet. The field created by the superconductor can cause the magnet to float above it, as shown in **Figure 21.**

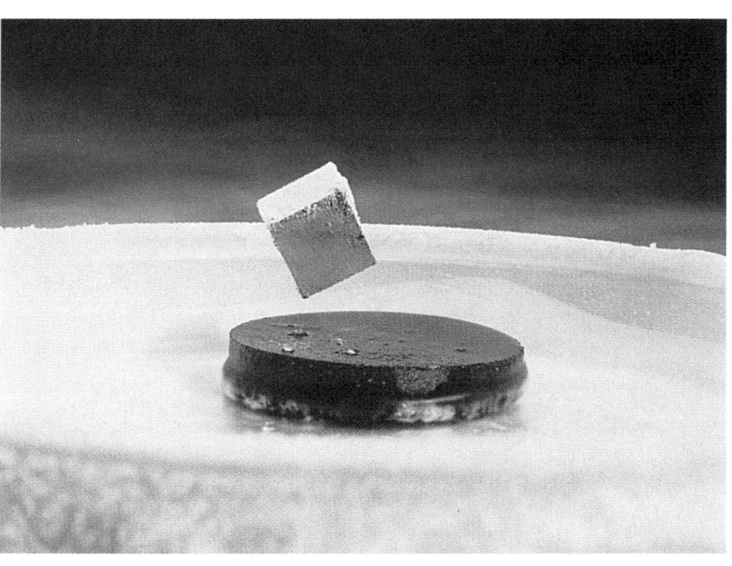

Figure 21
A small magnet floats above a superconductor. The magnet causes the superconductor to produce a magnetic field that repels the magnet.

Make a Model

Have students roll cardboard into a tube and wind different colors of string around it to make a model of a transformer. Give them several different voltage conversions to model, such as 60 V to 120 V, 120 V to 3 V, and 120 V to 220 V. L2

LS **Kinesthetic**

Activity

Draw simple transformers similar to the one that appears on page 484 on the board. Write the following information beside each transformer and have the students determine whether the transformer is increasing or decreasing the voltage and determine the new voltage:

- Transformer #1:
  Input: 5 turns, 50 volts
  Output: 15 turns, ? volts
  Increasing the voltage, 150 volts
- Transformer #2:
  Input: 50 turns, 300 volts
  Output: 5 turns, ? volts
  Decreasing the voltage, 30 volts
- Transformer #3:
  Input: 150 turns, 600 volts
  Output: 30 turns, ? volts
  Decreasing the voltage, 120 volts

Superconductors

Use Science Words

Word Usage Have students use the word *superconductor* in a sentence describing characteristics of these materials.

Cultural Diversity

Japan's Maglev Train Japanese engineers have built a maglev train that can travel 517 km/h (321 mph). This train is levitated above the track by magnets, hence the name maglev. Levitation of the train is achieved by the magnetic repulsion of helium-cooled, superconducting magnets on the vehicle and electromagnets of the same polarity in the guideway track. Have students research how these trains work in detail. Students should prepare a poster explaining the procedure. Germany has built maglev trains using different technology. For comparison, part of the class can research Germany's version of the maglev train and report their results.

Superconductors, continued

Extension

Have students research how superconductors are used in an application. Urge students to find uses that are not in the textbook, if possible. Have them prepare an oral report of their findings to present to the class. A visual aid detailing how the superconductor is used in their selected application would be helpful.

Magnetic Resonance Imaging

Discussion

Compare and contrast magnetic resonance imaging and X-ray imaging. Both types of imaging give images inside the human body without surgery. MRI gives detailed images of soft tissue. X rays give images of bones. X-ray radiation can damage tissue, but apparently there is no damage from the radio waves and magnetic fields that are used in an MRI.

What are the benefits of MRI imaging compared to exploratory surgery? Possible answer: There are no risks from infection, excessive bleeding, and anesthesia when using a MRI.

Figure 22
The particle accelerator at Fermi National Accelerator Laboratory near Batavia, Illinois, accelerates atomic particles to nearly the speed of light. The particles travel in a beam only a few millimeters in diameter. Magnets made of superconductors keep the beam moving in a circular path about 2 km in diameter.

Using Superconductors Large electric currents can flow through electromagnets made from superconducting wire and can produce extremely strong magnetic fields. The particle accelerator shown in **Figure 22** uses more than 1,000 superconducting electromagnets to help accelerate subatomic particles to nearly the speed of light.

Other uses for superconductors are being developed. Transmission lines made from a superconductor could transmit electric power over long distances without having any electric energy converted to heat. It also may be possible to construct extremely fast computers using microchips made from superconductor materials.

Figure 23
A patient is being placed inside an MRI machine. The strong magnetic field inside the machine enables images of tissues inside the patient's body to be made.

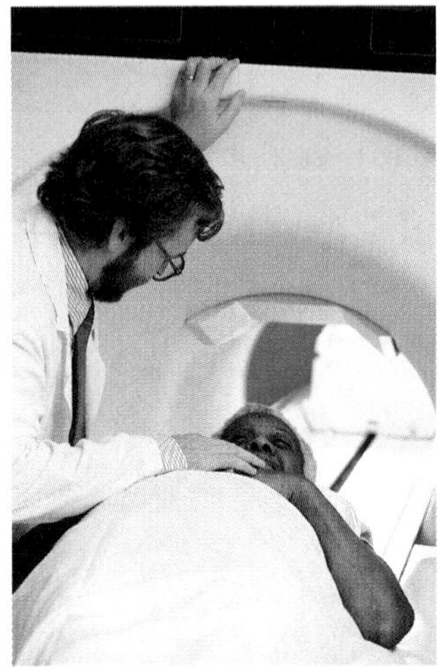

Magnetic Resonance Imaging

A method called magnetic resonance imaging, or MRI, uses magnetic fields to create images of the inside of a human body. MRI images can show if tissue is damaged or diseased, and can detect the presence of tumors.

Unlike X-ray imaging, which uses X-ray radiation that can damage tissue, MRI uses a strong magnetic field and radio waves. The patient is placed inside a machine like the one shown in **Figure 23.** Inside the machine an electromagnet made from superconductor materials produces a magnetic field more than 20,000 times stronger than Earth's magnetic field.

Curriculum Connection

Chemistry Atoms are composed of protons, neutrons, and electrons. Protons and neutrons are classified as hadrons. Quarks are thought to be elementary particles that form hadrons. Scientists theorized that there were six quarks. Scientists discovered the first five quarks, but the sixth quark eluded them for some time. Finally, confirmation of the existence of the sixth or *top* quark was made at the Fermi National Accelerator Laboratory in March of 1995. Challenge students to research more about quarks and report to their class what they have learned.

Producing MRI Images About 63 percent of all the atoms in your body are hydrogen atoms. The nucleus of a hydrogen atom is a proton, which behaves like a tiny magnet. The strong magnetic field inside the MRI tube causes these protons to line up along the direction of the field. Radio waves are then applied to the part of the body being examined. The protons absorb some of the energy in the radio waves, and change the direction of their alignment.

When the radio waves are turned off, the protons emit the energy they absorbed and realign themselves with the magnetic field. The amount of energy emitted depends on the type of tissue in the body. This energy emitted is detected and a computer uses this information to form an image, like the one shown in **Figure 24.**

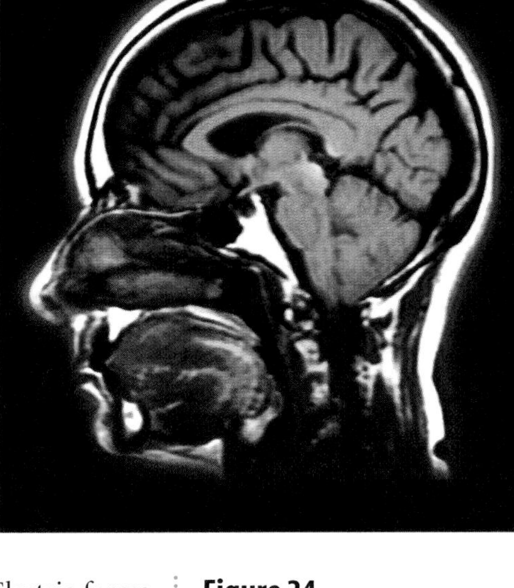

Figure 24
This MRI image shows a side view of the brain. An MRI scan can produce images from several angles, as well as cross-sections.

Connecting Electricity and Magnetism Electric forces and magnetic forces are similar in some ways. Both forces can repel or attract. Like electric charges repel each other, and like magnetic poles repel each other. Positive and negative electric charges attract, and north and south magnetic poles attract.

Electric charges and magnets are connected in another important way. Moving electric charges produce magnetic fields, and magnetic fields exert forces on moving electric charges. It is this connection enables electric motors and generators to operate.

Section  Assessment

1. What is an electromagnet? How can you make one in the classroom?
2. How does a transformer work?
3. How does a magnetic field affect a current-carrying wire?
4. How does a generator turn motion into electrical energy?
5. **Think Critically** How is an electric motor similar to an aurora? Use the terms current, field, and kenetic energy in your answer.

Skill Builder Activities

6. **Researching Information** Research how electricity is generated in your state. Make a poster showing the fuels that are used. **For more help, refer to the Science Skill Handbook.**
7. **Calculating Ratios** A transformer has ten turns of wire on the input side and 50 turns of wire on the output side. If the input voltage is 120 V, what will the output voltage be? **For more help, refer to the Math Skill Handbook.**

3 Assess

Reteach

Ask students to predict how various electromagnets with different numbers of windings compare. Then give students sample transformer ratios and ask them whether each will increase or decrease voltage. [L2]
LS **Logical-Mathematical**

Challenge

Stereo speakers rely on interactions between magnets and electricity to produce sound. Have students find out how the magnets in stereo speakers work. A stereo speaker has a permanent magnet and an electromagnet. The electromagnet can move and is attached to a cone of paper. The varying electrical signal carrying the information about the sound flows through the electromagnet, causing a varying magnetic field around it. This magnetic field interacts with the constant magnetic field of the permanent magnet, causing the electromagnet, and the paper cone to which it is attached, to move. This motion of the paper cone creates the sounds heard from the speaker. [L3]
LS **Logical-Mathematical**

Performance Have students take an inventory of their homes and list all the items that make use of an electric motor. Have them summarize their findings in a spreadsheet or table. Use **Performance Assessment in the Science Classroom,** p. 109.

Answers to Section Assessment

1. A device that uses electricity to generate magnetism; wind wire around an iron nail and attach the wire to a battery.
2. An alternating current in the input coil induces a magnetic field in the core. This induces an alternating current in the output coil.
3. It exerts a force on the wire.
4. A power source spins a wire loop surrounded by a magnet. The movement of the wire relative to the magnetic field induces current in the wire.
5. In an electric motor, the forces exerted by a magnetic field make a current-carrying loop rotate, changing electrical energy to kinetic energy. In an aurora, Earth's magnetic field exerts a force on charged particles emitted by the Sun, makeing them spiral along Earth's magnetic field lines, changing kinetic energy to radiant energy.
6. Check students' posters.
7. (50 turns ÷ 10 turns) × 120 V = 600 V

Activity

BENCH TESTED

What You'll Investigate

Purpose

Students build an electric motor.

L2 ELL LS **Kinesthetic**

Process Skills

observing and inferring, recognizing cause and effect, interpreting scientific illustrations, formulating models

Time Required

1 class period

Materials

You can obtain wood blocks from your school's wood shop or from a lumber yard's scraps.

Safety Precautions

Caution students to hold only the insulated part of each wire when wires are attached to the battery.

Procedure

Teaching Strategy

Show students how to use sandpaper to strip the insulation off the wire without cutting the wire itself. Make certain all batteries are charged.

Tie to Prior Knowledge

Ask students whether they have ever seen a tiny, electric motor in a toy or model. Did they notice that there were magnets in it?

Troubleshooting

Be sure students attach the wire securely to the battery terminals and to the knitting needles.

Activity

How does an electric motor work?

Electric motors are used in many appliances. For example, a computer contains a cooling fan and motors to spin the hard drive. A CD player contains electric motors to spin the CD. Some cars contain electric motors that move windows up and down, change the position of the seats, and blow warm or cold air into the car's interior. All these electric motors consist of an electromagnet and a permanent magnet. In this activity you will build a simple electric motor that will work for you.

What You'll Investigate

How can you change electric energy into motion?

Goals

- **Design** a small electric motor.
- **Observe** how the motor works.

Safety Precautions

Hold only the insulated part of each wire when they are attached to the battery. Use care when hammering the nails. After cutting the wire, the ends will be sharp.

Materials

22-gauge enameled wire (4 m)
steel knitting needle
**steel rod*
nails (4)
hammer
ceramic magnets (2)
18-gauge insulated wire (60 cm)
masking tape
fine sandpaper
approximately 15-cm wooden board
wooden blocks (2)
6-V battery
**1.5-V batteries connected in a series* (4)
wire cutters
**scissors*
**Alternate materials*

488

Inclusion Strategies

Physically Challenged Pair physically challenged students with others who work well in the lab. Have the physically challenged student read the instructions aloud as the other student builds the model. Have both students evaluate the setup to make sure the needle is as close to the magnets as possible.

Active Reading

Synthesis Journal In this strategy, students reflect on a project, a paper, or a performance in light of their own experiences and plan for personal application. Have each student divide a piece of paper into three sections. Have them record "What I did," "What I learned," and "How I can use it." Have students write a Synthesis Journal entry for this activity.

Procedure

1. Use sandpaper to strip the enamel from about 4 cm of each end of the 22-gauge wire.
2. Leaving the stripped ends free, make this wire into a tight coil of at least 30 turns. A D-cell battery or a film canister will help in forming the coil. Tape the coil to hold it in place.
3. Insert the knitting needle through the coil. Center the coils on the needle. Pull the wire's two ends to one end of the needle.
4. Near the ends of the wire, wrap masking tape around the needle to act as insulation. Then tape one bare wire to each side of the needle at the spot where the masking tape is.
5. Tape a ceramic magnet to each block so that a north pole extends from one and a south pole from the other.
6. Make the motor. Tap the nails into the wood block as shown in the figure. Try to cross the nails at the same height as the magnets so the coil will be suspended between them.

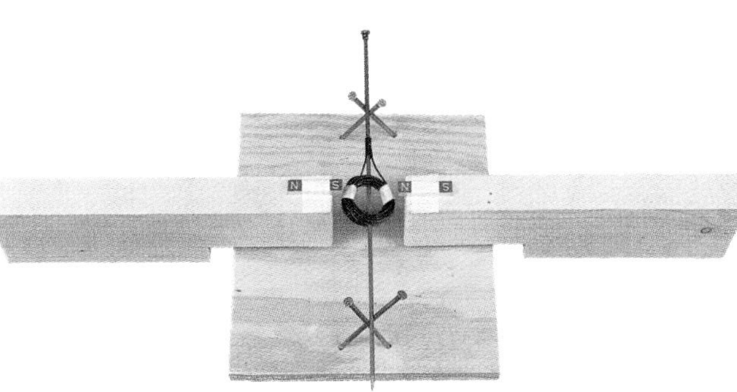

7. Place the needle on the nails. Use bits of wood or folded paper to adjust the positions of the magnets until the coil is directly between the magnets. The magnets should be as close to the coil as possible without touching it.
8. Cut two 30-cm lengths of 18-gauge wire. Use sandpaper to strip the ends of both wires. Attach one wire to each terminal of the battery. Holding only the insulated part of each wire, place one wire against each of the bare wires taped to the needle to close the circuit. Observe what happens.

Conclude and Apply

1. **Describe** what happens when you close the circuit by connecting the wires. Were the results expected?
2. **Describe** what happens when you open the circuit.
3. **Predict** what would happen if you used twice as many coils of wire.

Communicating Your Data

Compare your conclusions with other students in your class. **For more help, refer to the Science Skill Handbook.**

Expected Outcome

The wire coil will spin when the current is turned on and stop when the current stops.

Conclude and Apply

1. The coil starts to spin.
2. The coil stops spinning.
3. A larger magnetic field would be induced by the coil, so the coil would spin faster.

Error Analysis

What happens if the magnets are far from the coil? What happens if the coil is not between the magnets but slightly above or below?

Assessment

Performance Have students design machines that could use this motor. They should consider how much force this motor can apply. Possibilities include using the motor as a fan, to spin an artistic design, or to lift a small object. Use **Performance Assessment in the Science Classroom,** p. 117.

Resource Manager

Chapter Resources Booklet
Activity Worksheet, pp. 7–8
Lab Management and Safety, p. 64

Communicating Your Data

Have students make diagrams of their motors including explanations of how the parts worked, what worked well, and what didn't work.

Chapter 16 Study Guide

Reviewing Main Ideas

Preview

Students can answer the questions in their Science Journals. Discuss the answers as you go through the chapter. LS **Linguistic**

Review

Students can write their answers, then compare them with those of other students. LS **Interpersonal**

Reteach

Students can look at the illustrations and describe details that support the main ideas of the chapter. LS **Visual-Spatial**

Answers to Chapter Review

Section 1

2. Magnets stick only to those objects whose atoms have magnetic fields in alignment. Atoms in some metals have their magnetic fields in alignment.
4. charged particles from the Sun hitting Earth's magnetosphere

Section 2

1. Electricity has induced a magnetic field in the electromagnet.
4. the input coil

Chapter 16 Study Guide

Reviewing Main Ideas

Section 1 What is magnetism?

1. All magnets have two poles—north and south. Like poles repel each other and unlike poles attract.
2. Electrons act like tiny magnets. Groups of atoms can align to form magnetic domains. If domains align, then a magnet is formed. *Why do magnets stick to some objects, such as refrigerators, but not others?*

3. A magnetic force acts through a magnetic field. Magnetic fields extend through space and point from a north to a south pole.
4. Earth has a magnetic field that can be detected using a compass. *What might be the cause for these green and red lights above Earth in the photo taken from the space shuttle in orbit?*

Section 2 Electricity and Magnetism

1. Electric current creates a magnetic field. Electromagnets are made from a coil of wire wrapped around an iron core. *What is the mechanism that allows this crane to lift the scrap iron?*

2. A magnetic field exerts a force on a moving charge or a current-carrying wire.
3. Motors transform electric energy into kinetic energy. Generators transform kinetic energy into electric energy.
4. Transformers are used to increase and decrease voltage in AC circuits. *In this step-down transformer, which has more turns, the input coil or the output coil?*

FOLDABLES Reading & Study Skills

After You Read

Using the information on your Foldable, compare and contrast the terms *magnetic force* and *magnetic field.* Write your observations under the flaps in your Foldable.

FOLDABLES Reading & Study Skills

After You Read

After students have read the chapter and completed the Foldable described in Before You Read, have them do the activity on the student page.

Dinah Zike

Chapter 16 Study Guide

Visualizing Main Ideas

Complete the following concept map.

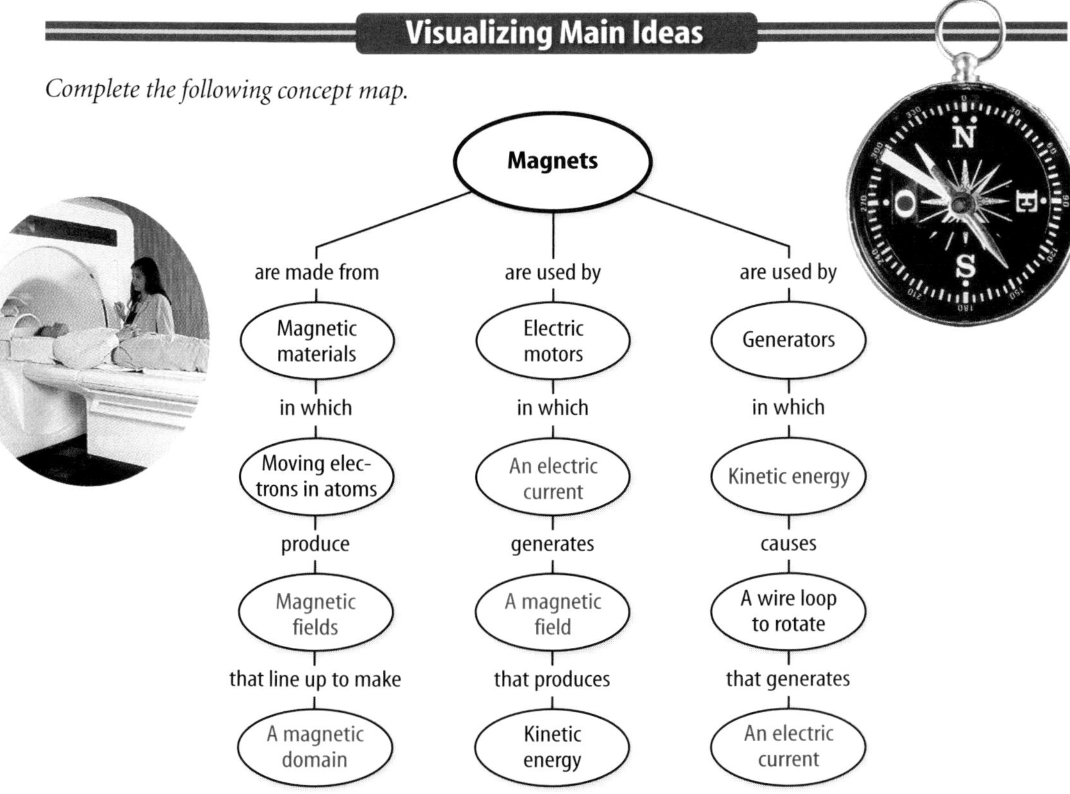

Vocabulary Review

Vocabulary Words

a. alternating current
b. aurora
c. electromagnet
d. generator
e. magnetic domain
f. magnetic field
g. magnetosphere
h. motor
i. transformer

Study Tip

Look for examples in your home of what you are studying in science class. For instance, where can you find electric motors in your home?

Using Vocabulary

Explain the relationship that exists between each set of vocabulary words below.

1. generator, transformer
2. magnetic force, magnetic field
3. alternating current, direct current
4. current, electromagnet
5. motor, generator
6. electron, magnetism
7. magnetosphere, aurora
8. magnet, magnetic domain

IDENTIFYING Misconceptions

Assess

Use the assessment as follow-up to page 468F after students have completed the chapter.

Materials bar magnets on which the N and S label have been covered with masking tape, compasses

Procedure Use the compasses to determine which end of each magnet is the north pole and which end is the south pole. Write the labels N and S on the tape, exchange magnets with another student, and determine if the other magnet is labeled correctly. Tell the other student what you think and return the magnet. Take off the tape to see which end is actually N and which is S.

Expected Outcome The north end of a compass needle points at a magnet's south pole.

See student page.

Vocabulary Review

Using Vocabulary

1. A generator produces an electric current; a transformer can change the voltage of that current.
2. A magnetic field is the space in which a magnetic force acts.
3. Alternating current changes direction while direct current does not.
4. Electric current induces magnetism in an electromagnet.
5. A motor changes electrical energy to kinetic energy, while a generator reverses the process to change kinetic energy to electrical energy.
6. Moving electrons cause magnetism.
7. Charged particles from the Sun are deflected to the poles by Earth's magnetosphere. There they cause energy changes in gas particles that are seen as the aurora.
8. Magnetic domains are the collection of atoms with aligned magnetic poles that are present in magnets.

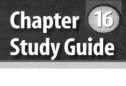

Checking Concepts

1. A
2. D
3. C
4. B
5. B
6. B
7. A
8. B
9. D
10. A

Thinking Critically

11. Gravity and friction hold them in place.
12. Use another magnet that is already marked to see which end is attracted and which is repelled by a given pole.
13. A south pole; because the nail's field is aligned with the bar magnet's field, the head is a north pole and the point is a south pole.
14. Stronger; each coil adds its magnetic field to the field of the other coils. If the current increases, the magnet gets stronger.
15. Moving electrons; you can show this by holding a compass near a wire carrying direct current. The current will deflect the needle of the compass.

Chapter 16 Assessment

Checking Concepts

Choose the word or phrase that best answers the question.

1. What can iron filings be used to show?
   A) magnetic field
   B) electric field
   C) gravitational field
   D) none of these

2. Why does the needle of a compass point to magnetic north?
   A) Earth's north pole is strongest.
   B) Earth's north pole is closest.
   C) Only the north pole attracts compasses.
   D) The compass aligns itself with Earth's magnetic field.

3. What will the north poles of two bar magnets do when brought together?
   A) attract
   B) create an electric current
   C) repel
   D) not interact

4. How many poles do all magnets have?
   A) one
   B) two
   C) three
   D) one or two

5. When a current-carrying wire is wrapped around an iron core, what can it create?
   A) an aurora
   B) a magnet
   C) a generator
   D) a motor

6. What does a transformer between utility wires and your house do?
   A) increases voltage
   B) decreases voltage
   C) leaves voltage the same
   D) changes DC to AC

7. Which types of energy does an electric motor convert between?
   A) electrical to kinetic
   B) electrical to thermal
   C) potential to kinetic
   D) kinetic to electrical

8. What prevents most charged particles from the Sun from hitting Earth?
   A) the aurora
   B) Earth's magnetic field
   C) high-altitude electric fields
   D) Earth's atmosphere

9. Which of these objects do magnetic fields NOT interact with?
   A) magnets
   B) steel
   C) current
   D) paper

10. Which types of energy does an electric generator convert between?
    A) electrical and kinetic
    B) electrical and thermal
    C) potential and kinetic
    D) potential and thermal

Thinking Critically

11. Why don't ordinary bar magnets line themselves up with Earth's magnetic field when you set them on a table?

12. If you were given a magnet with unmarked poles, how could you determine which pole was which?

13. A nail is magnetized by holding the south pole of a magnet against the head of the nail. Is the point of the nail a north or a south pole? Sketch your explanation.

14. If you add more coils to an electromagnet, does the magnet get stronger or weaker? Why? What happens if the current increases?

15. What are the sources of magnetic fields? How can you demonstrate this?

Chapter Assessment Planner

Portfolio Encourage students to place in their portfolios one or two items of what they consider to be their best work. Examples include:
- Assessment, p. 474
- Visual Learning, p. 478
- Cultural Diversity, p. 481

Performance Additional performance assessments, Performance Task Assessment Lists, and rubrics for evaluating these activities can be found in Glencoe's **Performance Assessment in the Science Classroom.**

Chapter 16 Assessment

Developing Skills

16. **Identifying and Manipulating Variables and Controls** How could you test and compare the strength of two different magnets?
17. **Forming Operational Definitions** Give an operational definition of an electromagnet.
18. **Concept Mapping** Explain how a doorbell uses an electromagnet by placing the following phrases in the cycle concept map: *circuit open, circuit closed, electromagnet turned on, electromagnet turned off, hammer attracted to magnet and strikes bell,* and *hammer pulled back by a spring.*

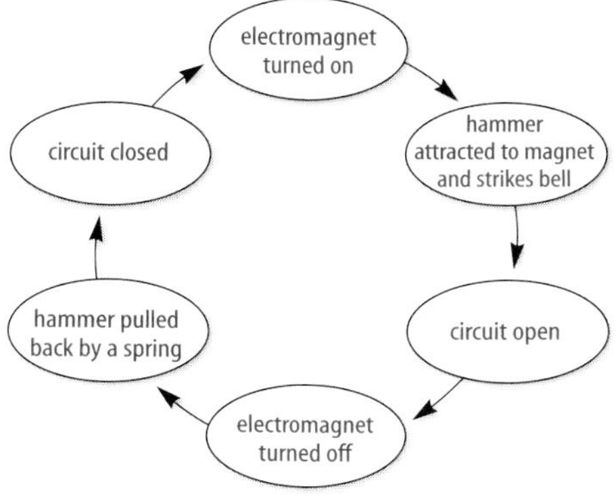

Performance Assessment

19. **Multimedia Presentation** Prepare a multimedia presentation to inform your classmates on the future uses of magnets and magnetism.

TECHNOLOGY

Go to the Glencoe Science Web site at **science.glencoe.com** or use the **Glencoe Science CD-ROM** for additional chapter assessment.

THE PRINCETON REVIEW Test Practice

Magnetism affects all aspects of modern life. The table below lists some examples of processes involving magnetic fields.

Processes Involving Magnetic Fields

Example	Process	Result
Motor	Converts electrical energy into kinetic	Used in elecric fans
Generator	Converts mechanical energy into electrical	Produce light
Charged particles from Sun	Accidentally trapped in Earth's magnetosphere	Aurora
Transformer	Change voltage through power lines	Deliver power to homes

Study the table and answer the following questions.

1. According to this information, which process most likely occurs naturally?
   A) conversion of electrical energy into kinetic
   B) conversion of mechanical energy into electric energy
   C) trapped charged particles in Earth's magnetosphere
   D) voltage changes through power lines
2. Dams use the gravitational potential energy of water to turn turbines, which then produce electricity. According to this information, which process would dams belong to?
   F) motor
   G) generator
   H) charged particles
   J) transformer

Assessment Resources

 **Reproducible Masters**

Chapter Resources Booklet
Chapter Review, pp. 31–32
Chapter Tests, pp. 33–36
Assessment Transparency Activity, p. 43

Glencoe Science Web site
Interactive Tutor
Chapter Quizzes

Glencoe Technology
Assessment Transparency
Interactive CD-ROM Chapter Quizzes
ExamView Pro Test Bank
Vocabulary PuzzleMaker Software
MindJogger Videoquiz DVD/VHS

Chapter 16 Assessment

Test Practice

The Test-Taking Tip was written by The Princeton Review, the nation's leader in test preparation.

1. C
2. G

Developing Skills

16. Record how many uniform objects each could move or pick up.
17. An electromagnet is a device in which a magnetic field is generated by passing current through coils of wire.
18. See student page.

Performance Assessment

19. Ask students to note the sources of their information. Use **PASC,** p. 149.

Reading Comprehension

QUESTION 1: B

Students need to reread the passage in order to identify the best summary.

- **Choice A** No; this is not supported by information in the passage.
- **Choice B** Yes; this is a summary of the information in the passage.
- **Choice C** No; this is not supported by information in the passage.
- **Choice D** No; this is a detail from the passage.

QUESTION 2: F

Students must determine the meaning of the underlined word *conventional* using context clues.

All questions written and validated by The Princeton Review.

Reading Comprehension

Read the passage. Then read each question that follows the passage. Decide which is the best answer to each question.

Magnetic Levitation Train

One of the first things people learn about magnets is that like magnetic poles repel each other. This is the basic principle behind the Magnetic Levitation Train, or Maglev.

Maglev is a high-speed train. It uses high-strength magnets to lift and propel the train to incredible speeds as it hovers only a few centimeters above the track. A full-size Maglev in Japan achieved a speed of over 500 km/h! Its electromagnetic motor can be precisely controlled to provide smooth acceleration and braking between stops. The magnetic field prevents the vehicle from drifting away from the center of the guideway.

Because there is no friction between wheels and rails, Maglevs eliminate the principal limitation of <u>conventional</u> trains, which is the high cost of maintaining the tracks to avoid excessive vibration and wear that can cause dangerous derailments. Critics point out that Maglevs require enormous amounts of energy. However, studies have shown that Maglevs use 30 percent less energy than other high-speed trains traveling at the same speed. Others worry about the dangers from magnetic fields; however, measurements show that humans are exposed to magnetic fields no stronger than those from toasters or hair dryers.

This year in Japan a series of Maglevs will be tested on a 27-mile demonstration line. In Germany, a 180-mile Maglev line between Berlin and Hamburg will go into service in 2005. Perhaps someday Maglevs will carry commuters to and from work and school in the United States.

Test-Taking Tip After you read the passage, write a one-sentence summary of the main idea for each paragraph.

This is a Maglev train test in Japan.

1. Which of the following statements best summarizes this passage?
   - **A)** Maglev transportation is currently in use in Germany and Japan.
   - **B)** Maglev is a high-speed transport system of the future.
   - **C)** Maglevs use more energy than conventional high-speed trains.
   - **D)** Maglevs can reach high speeds because there is no friction.

2. In this passage, the word <u>conventional</u> means _____.
   - **F)** customary
   - **G)** innovative
   - **H)** political
   - **J)** unusual

Reasoning and Skills

Read each question and choose the best answer.

1. Voltage increases when the output coil in a transformer has more turns of wire than the input coil. Which of the following increases voltage the most?

A) 

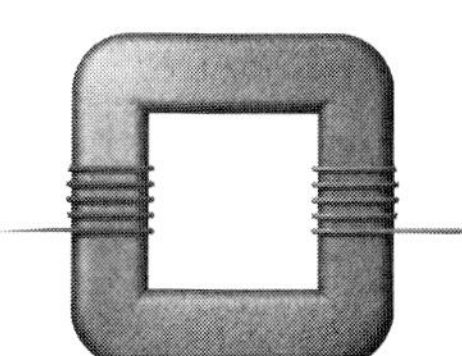

B)

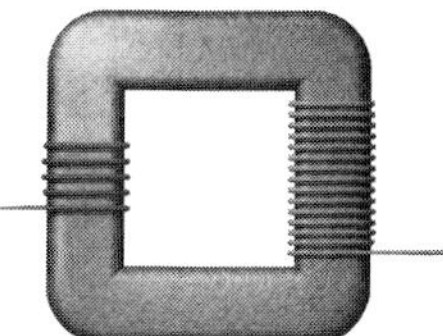

C)

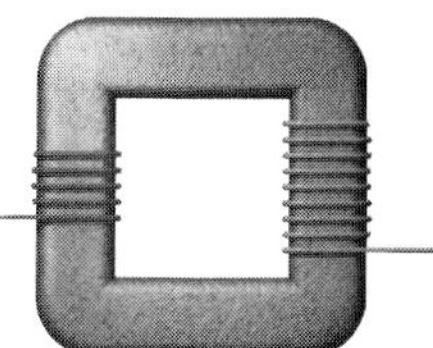

D)

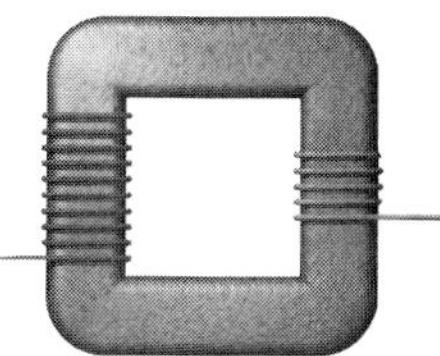

Test-Taking Tip Use the information provided in the question to closely consider each answer choice.

2. Which of the following materials would make a good conductor?
   - **F)** plastic
   - **G)** wood
   - **H)** glass
   - **J)** copper

Test-Taking Tip Remember that electrons move easily through conductors.

3. Shahid wanted to pick up pieces of metal with a magnet. Which of the following statements describes a situation in which the magnet would NOT pick up the pieces of metal?
   - **A)** The metal pieces were too close to the magnet.
   - **B)** The magnet was brand new.
   - **C)** The metal pieces were made out of aluminum foil.
   - **D)** The metal pieces and the magnet have the same magnetic poles.

Test-Taking Tip Review what you have learned about magnetic materials.

Consider this question carefully before writing your answer on a separate sheet of paper.

4. Recall what you know about the production of electric current. Explain the similarities and differences between direct current (DC) and alternating current (AC).

Test-Taking Tip Use the clues *direct* and *alternating* to guide your answer.

Standardized Test Practice

Reasoning and Skills

QUESTION 1: B

Students must understand voltage and transformers and look carefully at the diagram to determine the correct answer choice. Choice B has the greatest ratio of output turns of wire to input turns of wire.

QUESTION 2: J

Students must understand that metals are better conductors than nonmetals.

QUESTION 3: C

Students must know that magnets can only pick up objects that are made of iron, cobalt, or nickel.

QUESTION 4: Answers will vary.

Students should mention that alternating current (AC) changes direction many times each second.

Student Resources

CONTENTS

Field Guides 498

Skill Handbooks 518

Reference Handbook 543

About the Field Guide

- This field guide contains information that enables the user to identify homogeneous and heterogeneous mixtures, acids, chemical changes, and physical changes.
- This field guide applies nationally. Parts of the field guide apply in many other countries as well.
- Encourage students to use the field guide while preparing or consuming foods at home or elsewhere.

Tie to Prior Knowledge

All students are familiar with foods and, to a varying extent, with food preparation. But they may not have associated their experiences and observations with the kinds of mixtures and changes studied in science classes. Have students analyze foods they have eaten at restaurants and other locations outside their homes.

Field Activity

Have students work in small groups to discuss the types of mixtures and changes they have observed, particularly those that differ from the ones used as examples in the field guide. Responses may include homogeneous and heterogeneous mixtures, acids, and various types of chemical and physical changes.

Kitchen Chemistry

It's early morning in the kitchen, and, whether you know it or not, chemistry is occurring all around you. Breakfast—with its wake-up sights and smells—is almost ready. Butter, syrup, freshly squeezed orange juice, hot tea, and yogurt with strawberries wait on the counter. Eggs and pancakes sizzle on the griddle. Slices of bread are toasting. Some foods are liquids. Others are solids. Most are mixtures. Some of these are undergoing changes while you watch. Using this field guide, you can identify the different types of mixtures you drink and eat, and the chemical and physical changes that occur as foods are prepared.

How are mixtures classified?

Mixtures contain two or more substances that have not combined to form a new substance. The proportions of the substances that make up a mixture can vary. Mixtures are classified as homogeneous or heterogeneous.

You cannot see the separate substances in a homogeneous mixture no matter how closely you look. Cranberry juice is a homogenous mixture. You can easily identify the separate substances that are in a heterogeneous mixture. Breakfast cereals are heterogeneous mixtures.

Homogeneous Mixtures

Homogeneous mixtures can be solids, liquids, or gases. Stainless steel, for example, is a solid mixture of iron, carbon, and chromium. You might have cookware, containers, and utensils made of stainless steel. Also found in abundance in your kitchen is a familiar mixture of gases, primarily nitrogen, oxygen, and argon. This mixture is the air you breathe. Much of the chemistry in your kitchen occurs in solutions. Solutions are homogeneous mixtures, therefore you cannot see their different parts. Tea and syrup are solutions of solids that are dissolved in liquids.

Tea and syrup

Stainless steel is a homogeneous mixture.

Field Activity

Use this field guide to help identify the mixtures and changes in your kitchen. Observe the preparation of a few meals. In your Science Journal, record the meal being prepared and a description of the types of mixtures, chemical changes, and physical changes you observe.

Resources for Teachers and Students

The Epicurean Laboratory, by Tina Seelig, W.H. Freeman and Company, 1990.

Simple Kitchen Experiments: Learning Science with Everyday Foods, by Muriel Mandell, Sterling Publishing Company, Inc., 1994.

Science Projects about Kitchen Chemistry, by Robert Gardner, Enslow Publishers Inc., 1999.

Kitchen Chemistry and Front Porch Physics, by Marie A. Hoyt, Educational Services Press, 1983.

Kitchen Chemistry: Fun and Fascinating Science Experiments to Do at Home, by Lori Andres, Scholastic, Inc., 1995.

Kitchen Chemistry: Science Experiments to Do at Home, by Robert Gardner, Silver Burdett Press, 1989.

Field Guide

Heterogeneous Mixtures

You can see the different parts of a heterogeneous mixture. Familiar heterogeneous mixtures tend to be solids or solids and liquids. For example, the strawberries are visible in the bowl of yogurt and so are the blueberries in the muffin.

If you have left butter or cooking oil heating too long in a frying pan, you know that the smoke that rises from the pan is visible in the air. This mistake created a heterogeneous mixture.

Blueberry muffins and yogurt with strawberries are heterogeneous mixtures.

How are changes classified?

A change to a substance can be classified as chemical or physical. During a chemical change, one or more new substances are formed. When a physical change occurs, the identity of the substance remains the same.

Chemical Changes in the Kitchen

You can recognize a chemical change if one or more of the following occurs: the substance changes color, the substance produces a new odor, the substance absorbs or releases heat or light; or the substance releases a gas.

rilled hamburgers and vegetables re examples of chemical changes.

Browning

Browning is a chemical change that occurs when sugars and proteins in foods form new flavors and smells. It produces the barbecue flavors of foods that are cooked on a grill and the caramelized flavor of a roasted marshmallow.

A marshmallow is browning on a skewer.

Quick Demo

Show students how water reacts with baking soda and baking powder. Wearing goggles and an apron, use a dropper to add water to small samples of each solid in a dish. Explain that because baking soda contains only sodium hydrogen carbonate, it does not fizz when mixed with water. However, baking powder contains this chemical along with an acidic substance that is water soluble. After water dissolves the acidic substance, it reacts with the sodium hydrogen carbonate to produce carbon dioxide.

LS Visual-Spatial

Field Guides

Teacher FYI

Smoke, although it looks like a gas, is actually a mixture of solid particulates in gaseous air. It is these particulates that are so dangerous to people caught in fires. The particulates clog the breathing passages, causing death by asphyxiation.

Discussion

What is the solvent and primary solute in the homogeneous mixture maple syrup? Water is the solvent and sugar is the primary solute. **What is the additional solute present in a carbonated beverage?** carbon dioxide

Teacher FYI

Mixtures can be separated into two groups: homogeneous, which means the same throughout, and heterogeneous, which means different throughout. Heterogeneous mixtures usually can be separated by physical means such as filtration or distillation. Examples of heterogeneous mixtures are sand and water, sand and iron filings, and the contents of a jar of pickles. Homogeneous mixtures have the same composition throughout and usually cannot be separated easily. Examples of homogeneous mixtures are glass, unsaturated salt or sugar solutions, and ordinary white vinegar.

Visual Learning

Pancake Batter Why do bubbles form in fresh pancake batter and in the pancakes as they cook? Students may think that pancakes rise during cooking because the cooking process produces gases within the cake. Explain that a chemical reaction produces the gas, which expands as it is heated during cooking.

Fun Fact

Egg whites coagulate at about 60°C. Egg yolks, which contain fat and somewhat more protein than egg whites, coagulate at about 68°C. These differences allow you to cook a sunny-side-up egg by coagulating most of the egg white but little of the yolk.

Extension

Have students investigate what solutes are present in hard water and soft water and how the solutes affect soap added to the water. Hard water contains significant concentrations of calcium and magnesium ions, which react with soap to form the precipitate soap scum. Soft water contains small concentrations of these ions but also may contain a significant concentration of sodium ions. Sodium ions do not react with soap to form insoluble soap scum.

L2 LS **Logical-Mathematical**

Protein Denaturation

A protein in its natural state is a long chain of chemical units. After it has formed, this chain folds into a specific shape determined by attractions, or weak bonds, between chemical units in that protein. Denaturation involves breaking the weak bonds in a protein and changing its shape.

The proteins in a raw egg are folded into balls, sheets, and coils. Heating the egg breaks some of the weak bonds that hold the proteins in these tight shapes. As cooking continues, the proteins unravel and begin forming weak bonds with other proteins. This causes the egg to solidify.

Eggs that are cooked sunny side up are an example of protein denaturation.

Bubbling pancake batter shows gas production.

Gas Production

The new substances that are produced during a chemical change are sometimes gases. Gas production occurs in the preparation of some foods.

The bubbles you see in pancake batter as it cooks are caused by a chemical change in the batter. Baking powder is a mixture of baking soda, $NaHCO_3$ (sodium bicarbonate), and an acidic substance. When water is added to baking powder, the acidic solution that forms reacts with baking soda to make carbon dioxide gas. As a pancake cooks, the bubbles of carbon dioxide rise through the batter, leaving spaces that fluff out the pancake making it light in texture.

Inclusion Strategies

Learning Disabled Have students label three pages in their Science Journals. The first page should be labeled "Mixtures," the second "Chemical Changes," and the third "Physical Changes." Have them divide the page labeled "Mixtures" in half lengthwise, and label one side "Homogeneous Mixtures" and the other "Heterogeneous Mixtures." On each page have students write all of the information they know about each topic. Then have them use their textbooks to check the information they have recorded, add additional information, and list examples. Encourage students to list examples that are not in their textbooks. Check students' work for accuracy. Encourage students to refer to these Journal pages to review what each term means. L1 LS **Linguistic**

Field Guide

Physical Changes in the Kitchen

You can recognize a physical change when the substance changes shape, size, or state. For example, water can become ice, or a chocolate bar can melt.

Melting

Melting is the physical change in which a solid becomes a liquid. The pat of butter is changing from a solid to a liquid. Melting occurs because heat from the warm toast weakens the attractions between the molecules of butter. The cheese in a grilled-cheese sandwich is another good example.

Melting butter is an example of a solid becoming a liquid.

Freezing

Freezing is the physical change in which a liquid becomes a solid. Chemical substances have a freezing point—the temperature at which this change occurs. Most of the water in a liquid ice-cream mixture freezes into small ice crystals, and air bubbles give the solid mixture its smooth, creamy texture. Water frozen in the form of ice cubes is used to chill beverages. Freezing also is used to preserve a wide variety of foods.

Making ice cream demonstrates how a liquid becomes a solid.

Boiling

Boiling is the physical change in which a liquid becomes a gas. Popcorn kernels contain 11 percent to 14 percent water. When it is heated, that water changes to steam. Because steam takes up many times the volume of liquid water, it creates enough pressure to burst the kernels. Some cereals, vegetables, and other foods can be cooked in boiling water or in the steam that is produced when water boils.

Popcorn is produced by boiling.

Visual Learning

Butter, Ice Cream, and Popcorn Have students describe the energy changes that accompany the physical changes shown on this page. As heat energy is transferred from the hot toast to the cold butter, the butter melts. As ice cream freezes, it gives off heat energy to the mixture of ice and salt that surrounds it. The water in the popcorn kernels absorbs heat energy, boils, and causes the kernel to explode.

Field Guides

Discussion

- **Is an assembled taco a homogeneous or heterogeneous mixture?** heterogeneous mixture
- **Identify which of the following are chemical changes and which are physical changes: shredding cabbage, toasting bread, souring milk, thawing orange juice, and peeling carrots.** physical: shredding cabbage, thawing orange juice, peeling carrots; chemical: toasting bread, souring milk

Science Journal

Taco Changes Have students list in their Science Journals all of the chemical and physical changes that occur when tacos are prepared for dinner. Possible answers: Cooking the hamburger meat—chemical change; shredding the cheese and lettuce—physical change; chopping the tomatoes and onion—physical change

SCIENCE Online

Internet Addresses

Explore the Glencoe Science Web site at **science.glencoe.com** to find out more about topics in this field guide.

About the Field Guide

- This field guide contains information that enables the user to identify how the laws of motion apply to amusement park rides and to classify the rides according to their movements.
- In using a field guide, students will apply steps of a scientific method as they observe, investigate, and draw conclusions.
- This field guide provides general information about several types of amusement park rides. Information about specific rides often can be obtained locally.
- Encourage students to use this field guide to analyze rides they see at an amusement park or playground.

Tie to Prior Knowledge

Have students name their favorite amusement park rides. Record their responses. **How did you feel when you were on the rides?** Students may describe feeling "weightless" or feeling a strong tendency to move in various directions.

Field Activity

After students have completed this activity, have several volunteers show their drawings to the class and explain the movement of the ride. Allow class time for an open discussion of the forces involved.

Amusement Park Rides

If you like smooth, gentle rides, don't expect to get one at an amusement park. Amusement park rides are designed to provide thrills—plummeting down hills at 160 km/h, whizzing around curves so fast you think you'll fall out of your seat, zooming upside down, plunging over waterfalls, dropping so fast and far that you feel weightless. It's all part of the fun.

May the Force Be with You

What you might not realize as you're screaming with delight is that amusement park rides are lessons in physics. You can apply Newton's laws of motion to everything from the water slide and the bumper cars to the roller coaster. Amusement park ride designers know how to use the laws of motion to jolt, bump, and jostle you enough to make you scream while still keeping you safe from harm. They don't just plan how the laws of motion cause these rides to move, they also plan how you will move when you are on the rides. These designers also use Newton's law of motion when they design and build the rides to make the structures safe and lasting. Look at the forces at work on some popular amusement park rides.

Free-Fall

Free-fall ride

Slowly you rise up, up, up. Gravity is pulling you downward, but your seat exerts an upward force on you. Then, in an instant, you're plummeting toward the ground at speeds of more than 100 km/h. When you fall, your seat falls at the same rate and no longer exerts a force on you. Because you don't feel your seat pushing upward, you have the feeling of being weightless—at least for a few seconds.

Field Activity

The next time you're at an amusement park, watch the rides. When you return home, make drawings of the rides using arrows to show how they move. Group the rides according to their movements. Compare your drawings and observations to the information in this field guide.

Resources for Teachers and Students

Amusement Park Physics, by Nathan A. Unterman, J. Weston Walch Publishers, 1999.

Roller Coaster: Wooden and Steel Coasters, Twisters and Corkscrews, by David Bennett, Book Sales, Inc., 1998.

Roller Coaster Science, by Jim Wiese, John Wiley & Sons, 1994.

"Amusement Park Physics," by Carole Escobar, *The Physics Teacher*, Volume 28, No. 7, pp. 446–453, October 1990.

"The Amateur Scientist," by Jearl Walker, *Scientific American*, Volume 249, No. 4, pp. 162–169, October 1983.

Roller Coaster: Design

The biggest coasters—some as tall as a 40-story building—are made of steel. Steel roller coasters are stronger and sway less than wooden roller coasters. This allows for more looping, more hills, and faster speeds.

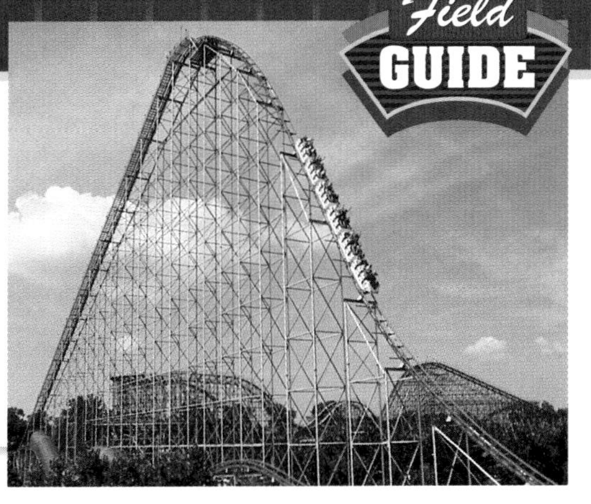

Roller coaster

Roller Coaster: The Coaster's Motion

Roller coasters are gravity-powered trains. The coaster's motor-driven chain lifts its cars to the top of the first hill. Then, gravity keeps it going.

The first hill is the highest point on the track. As the coaster rolls down the first hill, it converts potential energy to kinetic energy that sends it up the next hill. With each hill it climbs, it loses a little energy due to friction. That is why each hill is generally lower than the one before it.

Roller Coaster: Your Ride

Inertia is at work when you sweep around curves on a roller coaster. Inertia is the tendency for a body that's moving in a certain direction to keep moving in the same direction. For example, when the coaster swings right, inertia tries to keep you going in a straight line at a constant speed. As a result, you are pushed to the left side of your car.

Inertia tends to keep bodies moving in a straight line.

Discussion

How is your weight affected during freefall? Your weight is unchanged because the force of gravity is unchanged. You feel "weightless" because your downward acceleration is about the same as the acceleration resulting from gravity.

Activity

On the board, draw a sketch of a typical roller coaster track. Ask students to describe the forces and movement of a car at the top of a hill, along a straight part of the track, and at various places on a loop. At the top of a hill, the car moves slowly, and gravity accelerates it rapidly down the hill. On straight parts of the track, the car moves at its highest rate of speed. As it climbs a loop, gravity slows the car down, but it bends tightly around the top of the loop. Although the car slows down near the top, the passengers feel a strong deceleration. The car speeds up again coming down the other side of the loop. L2 LS **Visual-Spatial**

Fun Fact

The first true roller coaster constructed in the United States was the *Gravity Pleasure Switchback Railway.* It was built in 1884 at Coney Island in Brooklyn, New York.

Teacher FYI

Most vertical loops in roller coasters are elliptical rather than circular. This shape, called a clothoid loop, has a greater height than width. This shape causes the cars to travel faster at the top of the loop so that they don't fall away from the track. It also prevents the cars from traveling out of the loop too fast.

Curriculum Connection

Geography Have students work with a partner to research a popular roller coaster in the United States. Pairs should collaborate on making a poster that shows the location of the roller coaster on an outline map of the United States. Posters should also include a drawing of the coaster and statistics such as how high it is and its maximum speed. L2 LS **Interpersonal**

Visual Learning

Bumper Cars: Your Ride Explain to students that the electricity used to power bumper cars flows from a wire grid above the cars down the metal poles attached to the back of each car. **Why do you think this method of powering the cars is used?** Possible answers: It allows the cars freedom of movement around the floor; using electricity avoids the use of batteries that would constantly have to be recharged; having the electricity flow from the ceiling is safer for people who must walk across the enclosed floor.

Activity

Explain to students that a bumper car's momentum is the product of its mass (including the mass of the passenger) and its velocity. Allow students to use momentum carts to demonstrate that the speed and direction of cars after a collision is determined by conservation of momentum. Suggest that they vary the mass in the carts as well as the speed at which the carts approach one another. L2 LS **Kinesthetic**

Use Science Words

Word Usage Ask students to write definitions for the word *inertia*, first as it is used in science and then as it is used in everyday life. For each definition, have students write a sentence using the word. In science, inertia refers to the tendency of an object to remain at rest or to remain in motion at a constant speed unless acted upon by a force. In everyday life, inertia refers to the tendency to avoid changes in condition.

Field Guide

Bumper Cars: The Car's Motion

You control your bumper car's acceleration with the accelerator. When the car you're in bumps head-on into another car, your car comes to an abrupt stop. The big rubber bumper around the bottom of the car diffuses the force of the collision, but it also prolongs the impact.

Bumper Cars: Your Ride

When you first accelerate in a bumper car, you feel as though you are being pushed back in your seat. This sensation and the jolt you feel when you hit another car are due to inertia. On impact, your car stops, but your inertia makes you continue to move forward. It's the same jolt you feel in a car when someone slams on the brakes.

In a bumper-car collision, inertia keeps each rider moving forward.

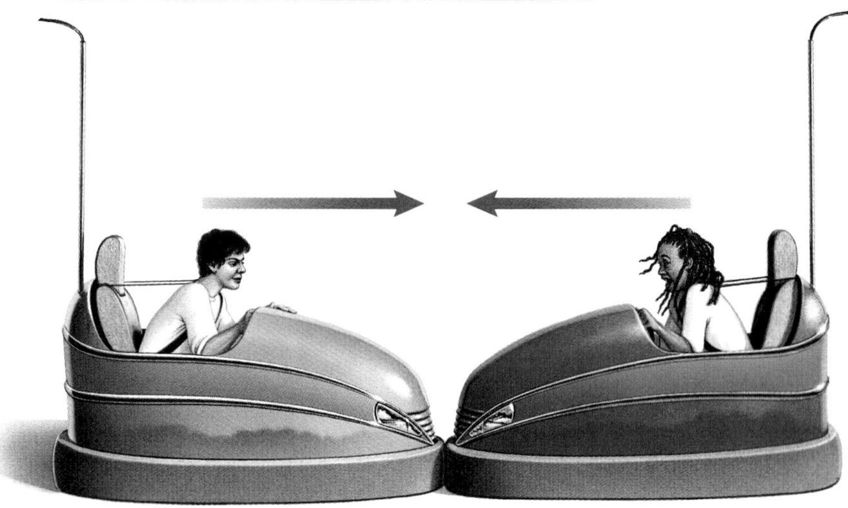

504 STUDENT RESOURCES

Science Journal

Experiences at Amusement Parks Have students write short stories about a time when they visited an amusement park. If they have never visited an amusement park, their stories can be fictional. Encourage students to describe the different rides they went on and the motion they experienced during the ride. LS **Linguistic**

Internet Addresses

Explore the Glencoe Science Web site at **science.glencoe.com** to find out more about topics in this field guide.

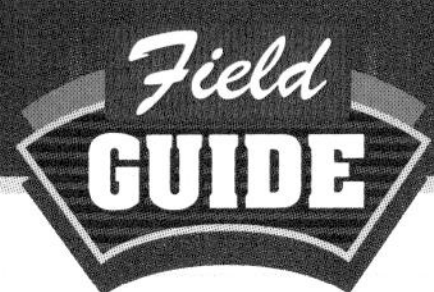

Field Guide

Swing Ride: Design

Some of the more powerful swing rides make about eight revolutions around the central pole each minute. These swing rides are capable of moving their riders at speeds of close to 50 km/h.

Swing Ride: Forces

As the swings rotate, your inertia wants to fling you outward, but the chain that connects your seat to the ride's central pole prevents you from being flung into space. You can see the changes in force as the swing ride changes speeds. As the ride speeds up and the forces exerted on the chain increase, your swing rises, moves outward, and travels almost parallel to the ground. As the ride slows, these forces on the chains decrease, returning the swings slowly to their original position.

The arrows show the forces at work in a swing ride.

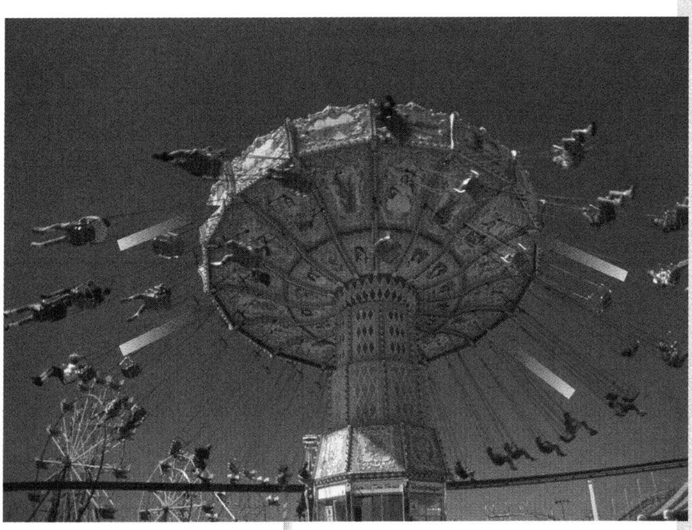

Field Guides

Quick Demo

Demonstrate how the swing ride works by attaching a string to a one-hole rubber stopper and swinging it in a circle beside you. Show students that the stopper swings higher and with a larger radius if you increase its speed. When the speed is decreased, the stopper again swings lower and with a smaller radius. Help students understand that the vertical component of the string's tension balances the gravitational force. LS **Visual-Spatial**

Extension

Ask students to make a drawing that explains why swings can never go higher than a horizontal plane. Drawings should include arrows that show the gravitational force and the tension in the chain. Above the horizontal plane, the net force would be downward and the swing would become unstable.

Make a Model

Have students work in small groups to make a small model of a new amusement park ride. Each group should give a presentation demonstrating how the ride works. All members of the group should be prepared to answer questions from the class about the forces involved in the ride's movement. L2 COOP LEARN LS **Interpersonal**

Teacher FYI

Some amusement park rides, including roller coasters and swing rides, have a circular motion that makes you feel as if you are being forced outward from the circle. You have this feeling not as the result of an outward force, but because your tendency to move in a line tangential to the circle is opposed by the centripetal acceleration pointing inward.

Inclusion Strategies

Learning Disabled When students are making the amusement park ride models, have them draw clear designs on paper before they begin construction. Encourage them to draw arrows showing the direction of the normal force and the gravitational force. Some students may need help understanding the forces involved in the movement. L1 LS **Visual-Spatial**

About the Field Guide

- This field guide contains descriptions that enable the user to identify and classify musical instruments.
- In using a field guide, students will apply steps of a scientific method as they observe, investigate, infer, and draw conclusions.
- This field guide describes some musical instruments commonly used in the United States. Information about musical instruments used in other countries and cultures can be found in musical dictionaries and encyclopedias.
- Encourage students to use the field guide outside the classroom.

Tie to Prior Knowledge

Ask students to name their favorite musical instruments. Have them describe how the instruments sound. For example, they might say a saxophone has a mellow sound or a piccolo has a shrill sound. Encourage students to compare the sounds made by various instruments.

Field Activity

If students have had little experience with musical instruments, show them pictures of assorted instruments before having them do the Field Activity. Encourage students to bring in any band or orchestra instruments they play and demonstrate them for the class.

Some people have defined music as "patterns of tones." A tone is a sound with a specific pitch. In music, a tone might also be called a note. Pitch describes how high or low the tone is. Like all sounds, musical tones are produced when an object vibrates. Higher pitches are produced by more vibrations per second, and therefore have a higher frequency.

Most musical instruments use resonance to amplify sounds. To amplify a sound means to increase its volume. Resonance occurs when one object causes another object to vibrate at the same frequency—or pitch.

How Resonance Works

A vibrating object produces sound waves. These waves can affect other objects and cause them to vibrate. As more matter vibrates, a louder sound is produced. For example, resonance is at work in a guitar. When a guitar's strings are plucked or strummed, the strings vibrate. The strings' vibrations make the thin soundboard—in this case, the front of the guitar—vibrate. The soundboard's vibrations make the air inside the guitar's hollow body vibrate. The vibrating air amplifies the sounds that were first produced by the strings.

Musical Instrument

Mandolin

Stringed Instruments

Tones are produced in stringed instruments by making stretched strings vibrate. Each string is tuned to a different pitch. When playing stringed instruments such as the harp, each string produces only one pitch. The player creates different pitches by plucking different strings.

When playing stringed instruments such as the guitar and violin, the player can change the pitch of each string by pressing down on one end and making it shorter. Stringed instruments may be strummed, plucked, or played with a bow.

Harp

Field Activity

Watch an orchestra or band perform in a live concert or on television. In your Science Journal, name all of the different instruments you recognize. Then use this field guide to identify the category in which each instrument is classified.

Resources for Teachers and Students

The New Grove Dictionary of Musical Instruments, Vol. 1, 2, 3, ed. Stanley Sadie, Macmillan Press, 1984.

Music (Eyewitness Books), by Neil Ardley, Alfred A. Knopf, Inc., 1989.

The Physics of Musical Instruments, by Neville H. Fletcher and Thomas D. Rossing, Springer-Verlag Telos, 1998.

Musical Instruments, Traditions Around the World, by Louise Tythacott, Thomson Learning, 1995.

Rattles, Bells, and Chiming Bars, by Karen Foster, Merlion Publishing, 1992.

Wind Instruments—Woodwinds

Woodwind instruments include the clarinet, the saxophone, and the recorder. These instruments are played by blowing into a mouthpiece or across a hole. Some woodwinds, such as clarinets, have a thin flexible reed in the mouthpiece that vibrates. The reed causes the air in the tube to vibrate. As the air vibrates inside the woodwind's hollow tube, tones are produced. Musicians change this instrument's pitch by covering holes with their fingers or by pressing keys that cover holes. Covering a hole lengthens or shortens the column of air inside the tube.

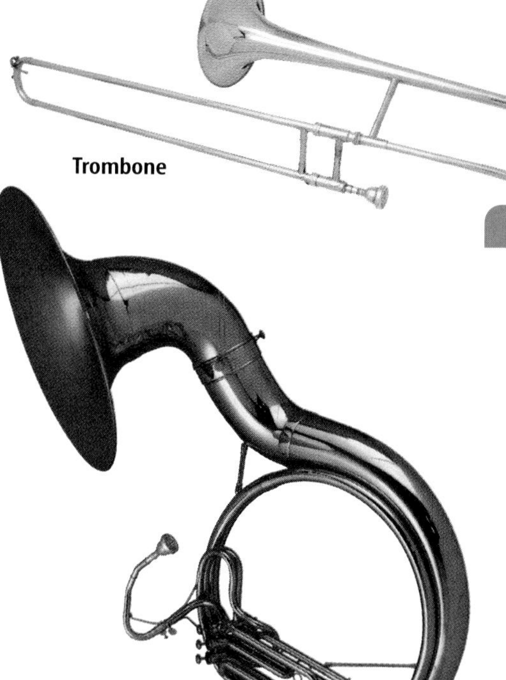

Wind Instruments—Brass

Brass instruments include the trumpet, the trombone, and the tuba. Their mouthpieces are larger than woodwinds' mouthpieces. Brass instruments are played by pressing the lips against a mouthpiece and blowing so the lips vibrate. Musicians change brass instruments' pitches by tensing or relaxing their lips. With most brass instruments, the pitch also can be changed by pressing valves, which changes the length of the vibrating column of air inside the instrument.

Quick Demo

Blow across the top of a soda bottle partially filled with water to demonstrate how the height of a resonating column affects sound. First, have a small amount of water in the bottle when you blow across it. Continue adding small amounts of water and blowing across the bottle so students can hear the change in pitch. **Why does the pitch become higher as more water is added to the bottle?** As the column of air becomes shorter, only short wavelengths can resonate in the bottle. The shorter wavelengths correspond to higher pitches.

Visual Learning

Wind Instruments Students might notice from the pictures on this page that most wind instruments have a bell at the end of an air column. **What is the purpose of this bell?** The bell amplifies the sound by increasing the amplitude of the waves before they leave the instrument. LS **Visual-Spatial**

Discussion

Does closing all the holes in the clarinet or saxophone produce a higher or lower pitch? Closing the holes produces a lower pitch because it lengthens the air column.

Curriculum Connection

Health Vocal cords produce sounds in much the same way as wind instruments do. These elastic folds of mucous membrane vibrate to form sounds as air blows over them; resonance increases the volume. **Why do men usually have lower voices than women?** Men's vocal cords are usually longer and thicker so the air passage is wider. LS **Logical-Mathematical**

Science Journal

Making Music Ask students to choose two different instruments. Have them write paragraphs in their Science Journals comparing and contrasting how each makes music. For example, students might compare a flute and a trumpet. LS **Linguistic**

FIELD GUIDE 507

Science Words

Word Origin The word *idiophone* comes from the Greek words *idios*, meaning "pertaining to one's self," and *phonema*, meaning "sound." Ask students to explain how these word origins apply to the idiophone. An idiophone produces sound by vibrating itself. Have students find another word that uses the root word "idio" and give its meaning. Possible answer: *idiosyncrasy*, meaning "something peculiar about a person"

Discussion

How would the sound produced by a xylophone differ if you held your hand against the wooden bars as you hit them with the mallet? The vibrations would be dampened, so the sound would be a dull thud.

Activity

Ask students to bring in any musical instruments that they play. Have volunteers demonstrate how their instruments sound and how they are played. Ask all volunteers to play the same simple tune, such as "Hot Cross Buns," so that the class can compare the differences in sound. For each of the instruments, have the class discuss how sound is produced. For stringed and wind instruments, students can discuss how changing the finger position or some other technique is used to alter the pitch. LS **Auditory-Musical**

Field Guide

Percussion Instruments—Idiophones

Idiophones vibrate to produce tones. Musicians play them by hitting, shaking, scraping, or plucking them. Idiophones such as cymbals, bells, gongs, music boxes, and xylophone keys play only one pitch. Triangles, clappers, rattles, and cymbals have indefinite pitches—their pitches depend on how they are played and how they are constructed.

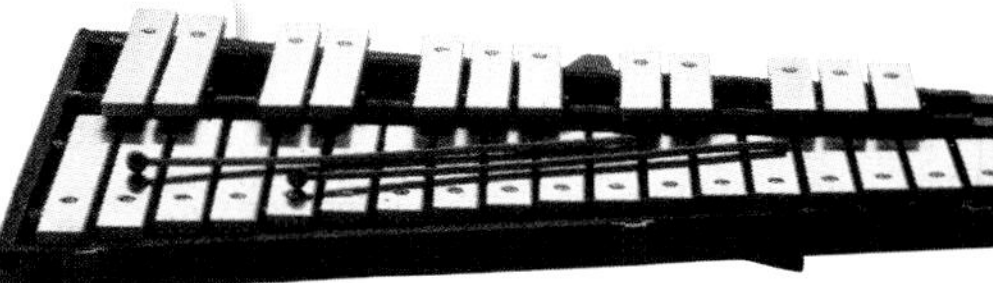

Xylophone

Percussion Instruments—Membranophones

Membranophones produce sound when their membranes—the stretched tops of drums or the tiny membranes within kazoos—vibrate. Drums are usually struck with hands, with beaters such as drumsticks, or with knotted cords to produce tones.

Bongo

Electric Instruments

Electric instruments such as the electric guitar and electric violin are played like regular instruments. However, rather than using resonance to amplify their sound, their vibrations are converted to electrical signals that are amplified electronically. The amplified electric signal is then converted to sound by a loudspeaker.

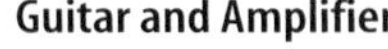

Guitar and Amplifier

Teacher FYI

When a mallet strikes a xylophone bar, the bar vibrates with its middle first up and then down, while the ends are down and then up (opposite to the position of the middle of the bar). The xylophone must be constructed so that the bars are supported about a quarter of the way from the ends at the bar's vibrational nodes.

Inclusion Strategies

Learning Disabled To help students visualize how vibrations create the sound of a drum, place a handful of rice on the top of a drumhead. Direct students to observe how the rice vibrates as you hit the drumhead with a stick. Explain that just as the vibrating drumhead causes the rice to vibrate, it also causes air to vibrate, creating sound waves. L1 LS **Visual-Spatial and Auditory-Musical**

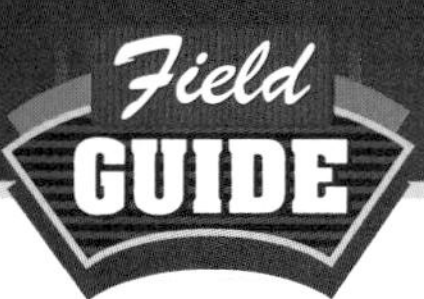

Keyboard Instruments—Piano

Each piano key is attached to a small hammer. When the player presses a key, the hammer hits a string and makes it vibrate. The strings are different lengths and each string produces a different pitch. The piano's body amplifies the tones.

Piano

Pipe Organ

Keyboards—Pipe Organ

Pressing a pipe organ's key opens a pipe to let air vibrate inside it. The pipes are different lengths, and each produces a different pitch.

Synthesizer

Electronic Instruments

Unlike all other types of musical instruments, electronic instruments do not rely on vibrations to produce sounds. Instead, these instruments produce electrical signals that a computer then converts to sounds. Even though a synthesizer has a keyboard, it is classified as an electronic instrument because it produces sounds electronically. Today, it is the most widely used electronic instrument.

Make a Model

Ask students to work in small groups to make models of musical instruments. For example, they could blow across soda bottles filled with different amounts of water to model a pipe organ. They might make a model of a xylophone by constructing a base with wooden slabs on it. Allow groups to be creative in designing their models. When they present their models to the class, each member of the group should be able to explain how sound is produced in the instrument. L2 COOP LEARN LS **Kinesthetic**

Visual Learning

Keyboard Instruments—Piano Have students notice the shape of the grand piano. Explain that the wider area contains long strings for playing lower-pitched sounds and the narrower area contains shorter strings for playing higher-pitched sounds. Point out that the top of grand pianos are propped open to increase the volume of the sound. LS **Visual-Spatial**

Fun Fact

The largest musical instrument in the world is located in the Luray Caverns in Virginia. Electronic mallets are wired to strike stalactites throughout the cavern, creating organ music that resonates throughout the cavern.

Curriculum Connection

History One of the earliest forms of the piano was invented by Bartolomeo Cristofori in 1709. Since that time the piano has gone through numerous revisions, including the fortepiano, the square piano, the pianoforte, and the upright. Have students prepare reports about how the piano developed into its present-day form. L2 LS **Logical-Mathematical**

Internet Addresses

Explore the Glencoe Science Web site at **science.glencoe.com** to find out more about topics in this field guide.

About the Field Guide

- This field guide contains representative descriptions and photos of different types of lightning. These illustrations enable the user to identify different types of lightning.
- In using a field guide, students will apply steps of a scientific method as they observe, investigate, and draw conclusions.
- Encourage students to use this field guide outside the classroom.

Tie to Prior Knowledge

Have students discuss any past observations they have made of lightning. **Under what circumstances did the lightning occur? Was it accompanied by thunder? At what times of day and during which seasons did the lightning occur? Did any damage occur as a result of the lightning?**

Field Activity

Have students use a stopwatch to determine the length of time between the lightning bolt and the sound of thunder. Explain that the sound of thunder travels 1.6 km every 5 seconds. Then have students compute the distance of the source of the lightning from their location.

Lightning

When storm clouds form, the particles in clouds collide with one another, removing electrons from some and adding them to others. Positive charges accumulate at the top of the cloud, leaving the negative ones at the bottom. These negative charges repel electrons in the ground below. As a result, the ground beneath the cloud becomes positively charged. The negative charges in the cloud are attracted toward the positively charged ground. They move downward in a zigzag path called a stepped leader. As the leader approaches the ground, a streamer of positive charges rises to meet it. When they meet, a return stroke—an electric spark called lightning—blasts up to the cloud.

The cycle of leader and return strokes can repeat many times in less than a second to comprise a single flash of lightning that you see.

Common Types of Lightning

The most common type of lightning strikes from one part of a cloud to another part of the same cloud. This type of lightning can occur ten times more often than lightning from a cloud to the ground. Other forms include strikes from one cloud to a different cloud, and from a cloud to the surrounding air.

Cloud-to-Ground Lightning

This type of lightning is characterized by a single streak of light connecting the cloud and the ground or a streak with one or more forks in it. Occasionally, a tall object on Earth will initiate the leader strike, causing what is known as cloud-to-ground lightning.

Cloud-to-ground lightning

Field Activity

During a thunderstorm, observe lightning from a safe location in your home or school. Using this field guide, identify and record in your Science Journal the types of lightning you saw. Also, note the date and time of the thunderstorm in your Science Journal.

Resources for Teachers and Students

Lightning: Sheets, Streaks, Beads, and Balls, by Suzanne Harper, Franklin Watts, 1997.

Raging Planet: Lighting, Videotape, Discovery Communications, 1997.

Lightning, by Seymour Simon, Morrow Junior Books, 1997.

How the Weather Works, by Michael Allaby, Dorling Kindersley Limited, 1995.

Cloud-to-Cloud Lightning

Cloud-to-cloud lightning is the most common type of lightning. It can occur between clouds (intercloud lightning) or within a cloud (intracloud lightning). The lightning is often hidden by the clouds, such that the clouds themselves seem to be glowing flashes of light.

Cloud-to-Air Lightning

When a lightning stroke ends in midair above a cloud or forks off the main stroke of cloud-to-ground lightning, it causes what is known as cloud-to-air lightning. This type of lightning is usually not as powerful or as bright as cloud-to-ground lightning.

Cloud-to-air lightning

Internet Addresses

Explore the Glencoe Science Web site at **science.glencoe.com** to find out more about topics in this field guide.

Content Background

Lightning can heat the air around it up to 30,000°C. Temperatures this high force air molecules to separate instantaneously. The sound wave caused by the explosion of air molecules is thunder.

Aside from being associated with thunderstorms, lightning can also occur among the ash clouds from a volcanic eruption. The static electricity that builds up among particles released by the volcano can cause cloud-to-cloud lightning as well as cloud-to-ground lightning.

Despite the detrimental effects lightning strikes can have on people or property, forest fires caused by lightning strikes are part of the natural process of forest regeneration. A form of nitrogen usable by plants is released from the atmosphere as lightning heats the air it travels through. In its new form this nitrogen reaches plants as rainwater is absorbed from the soil.

Use Science Words

Word Meaning Have students find the meaning of the word *fulgurite.* **How does this word relate to the subject of lightning?** Possible answer: Fulgurites are little tubes of glassy rock that have been fused from all other sorts of rocks by lightning strikes. Fulgurites are especially frequent in exposed crags on mountain tops. Fulgurite comes from the Latin root *fulgur* which means "lightning."

Visual Learning

All Lightning Photographs Have students examine pictures of lightning in other books. Challenge them to use this field guide to determine the type of lightning shown in each photo. Have the students explain their reasons for their classifications. LS **Visual-Spatial**

Discussion

Have the class discuss lightning safety. **What should a person do (or not do) when lightning occurs?** Expand the discussion to include different settings such as at home, outside, at a pool, or on a boat when the lightning occurs. Possible answers: At home: Do not touch electrical appliances or stand near open windows, doors, or fireplaces. Outside: Do not take cover under a tree. In an open area such as a field or a beach, crouch down into a ball and balance on the balls of your feet. Near water: Exit the area as quickly as possible.

Extension

Have students formally research lightning safety. Suggest that they present their findings on a poster entitled "Lightning Safety Tips." Challenge students to relate the tips to the science of lightning. For example, crouching in a ball and balancing on the balls of the feet reduces contact with the ground, which can carry an electrical charge. This position also can help protect internal organs if a person is struck by lightning. L3 LS **Logical-Mathematical**

Field Guide

Some forms of lightning differ in appearance from the forked flashes commonly considered to be lightning. However, the discharge in the cloud occurs for the same reason—to neutralize the accumulation of charge.

Sheet lightning

Sheet Lightning

Sheet lightning appears to fill a large section of the sky. Its appearance is caused by light reflecting off the water droplets in the clouds. The actual strokes of lightning are far away or hidden by the clouds. When the lightning is so far away that no thunder is heard, it is often called heat lightning and usually can be seen during summer nights.

Ribbon Lightning

Ribbon lightning is a thicker flash than ordinary cloud-to-ground lightning. In this case, wind blows the channel that is created by the return stroke sideways. Because each return stroke follows this channel, each is moved slightly to the side of the last stroke, making each return stroke of the flash visible, and thus a wider, ribbonlike band of light is produced.

Ribbon lightning

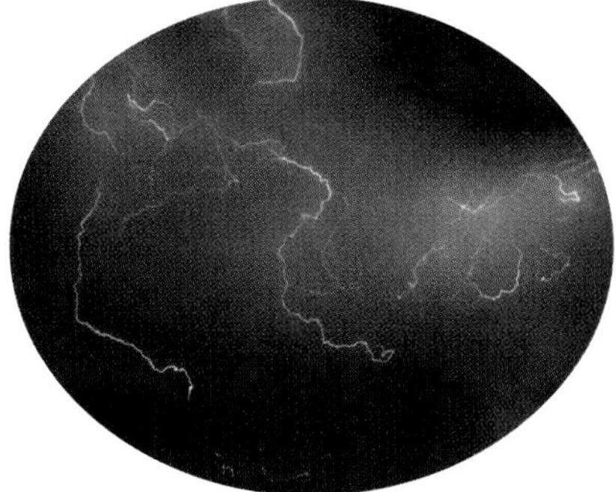

Bead lightning

Chain Lightning

Chain lightning, also called bead lightning, is distinguished by a dotted line of light as it fades. The cause is still uncertain, but it might be due to the observer's position relative to lightning or to parts of the flash being hidden by clouds or rain.

Cultural Diversity

Lightening Tales Have students research how ancient civilizations such as the Greeks, the Romans, the Chinese, or Native Americans explained the occurrence of lighting. Students can record what they discover in their Science Journals. LS **Linguistic**

Some forms of lightning are rare or poorly understood and have different appearances than the previously described forms.

Sprites

Sprites are red or blue flashes of light that are sometimes cone shaped and occur high above a thundercloud, 60 to 100 km above Earth. The flashes are associated with thunderstorms that cover a vast area. Sprites are estimated to occur in about 1 percent of all lightning strokes.

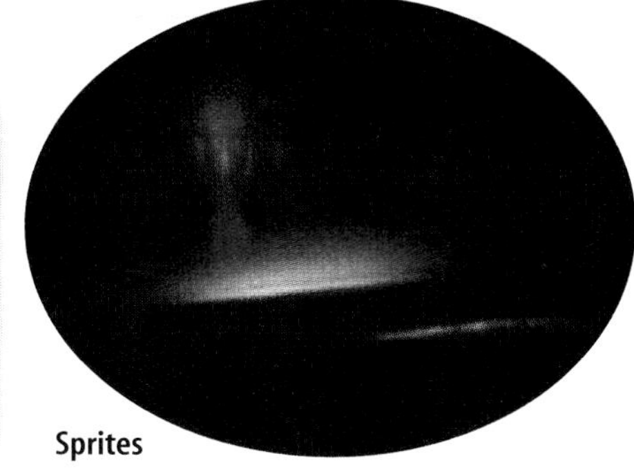

Sprites

Ball Lightning

There have been numerous eyewitness accounts of the existence of ball lightning, which appears as a sphere of red, yellow, orange or white light, usually between 1 cm to 1 m in size. Ball lightning seems to occur during thunderstorms, and appears within a few meters of the ground. The ball may move horizontally at a speed of a few meters per second, or may float in the air. Ball lightning usually lasts for several seconds and may vanish either quietly or explosively. Unlike other forms of lightning which can be seen by many observers at large distances, the small size of ball lightning and its random occurrence make it difficult to study. As a result, the causes of ball lightning still are not known, and even its existence is disputed.

St. Elmo's Fire

St. Elmo's Fire is a bluish-green glowing light that sometimes appears during thunderstorms around tall, pointed objects like the masts of ships and lightning rods. It also occurs around the wings and propellers of airplanes flying through thunderstorms. A sizzling or crackling noise often accompanies the glow. St. Elmo's Fire is caused by the strong electric field between the bottom of a thundercloud and the ground. This electric field is strongest around pointed objects. If this field is strong enough, it can pull electrons from atoms in the air. The glow is produced when these electrons collide with other atoms and molecules in the air.

Activity

Have students compile a class booklet of lightning "fun facts" by answering questions such as: Which areas of the world receive the most lighting in a year? Which areas receive the least? How much lightning occurs in our local area over the course of a year? Encourage students to dispel common myths about lightning, such as lightning never strikes twice in the same place. Students can present their results in a show-and-tell format using any visual aids they make or that are available. L2 LS **Linguistic**

Fun Fact

The first visual documentation of sprites occurred in 1989. This rare form of lighting has since been captured on film thousands of times.

Teacher FYI

Some lightning, including sprites, jets, and elves, erupts from the tops of thunderclouds up into the stratosphere. A jet is a bright burst of light that discharges at a high rate of speed—up to 6,000 km/hr. Elves, first described in 1995, are wide, spherical bursts of light. These flashes are so short lived—lasting less than a millisecond—that their color remains undefined.

Curriculum Connection

History Benjamin Franklin invented the lightning rod. Lightning rods are still used today to protect buildings and high structures such as the space shuttle launching platform from the effects of lightning strikes. A lighting rod is mounted on the top of a structure and is grounded some distance away from the structure. When lighting strikes, it is attracted to the rod, which then safely distributes the charge of electricity away from the structure itself. Have students research other lightning-related discoveries made by Benjamin Franklin. L2 LS **Linguistic**

About the Field Guide

- This field guide contains descriptions and photos representative of the environment of space and how daily activities are affected in this unique environment.
- In using a field guide, students will apply steps of a scientific method as they observe, investigate, and draw conclusions.
- This field guide applies nationally; local and regional field guides are usually available for more specific local use.
- Encourage students to use this field guide outside the classroom.

Tie to Prior Knowledge

Have students list the basic requirements for human survival. These should include the need for food, water, and a suitable environment with the proper temperature, pressure, and air that contains oxygen. Have students think about the details behind accomplishing daily tasks such as preparing food and maintaining hygiene. Responses should include the need for electricity, refrigeration, clean running water, and products such as soap and toothpaste.

Field Activity

Have students write their own science fiction description of how daily tasks would be performed in space. Students can draw the inner workings of a spacecraft or a space station to further illustrate ideas.

Living in Space

Early astronauts were crammed into tiny space capsules where they could barely move in their seats. Food was a tasteless paste squeezed from a tube or a hard, bite-sized cube. Today, space shuttle astronauts have a two-level cabin with sleeping bunks, a galley for preparing food, and exercise equipment. Living in space isn't what it used to be.

Living in Orbit

Although conditions on a spacecraft are better now than in the past, the problems astronauts face are the same. They still go about their daily life, but space has no air, food, or water. This makes it hard to prepare meals and wash dishes afterward. It complicates how you drink beverages out of a glass. Due to these challenges, space shuttle crews must carry everything they need with them to survive in space.

By far the biggest challenges for astronauts come from the effects of weightlessness. Imagine eating a meal as part of it floats away, or sleeping in a bed that drifts into walls. NASA scientists have found ways to overcome such problems. This field guide offers a look at some of them.

Life Support System

People need oxygen to breathe. The shuttle carries canisters of super-cold liquid oxygen and pressurized nitrogen to create an atmosphere in the crew compartment that is similar to Earth's—79 percent nitrogen and 21 percent oxygen. The shuttle also circulates air through canisters of lithium hydroxide and activated charcoal, removing carbon dioxide and odors from it. Crew members must change one of the two canisters every 12 h.

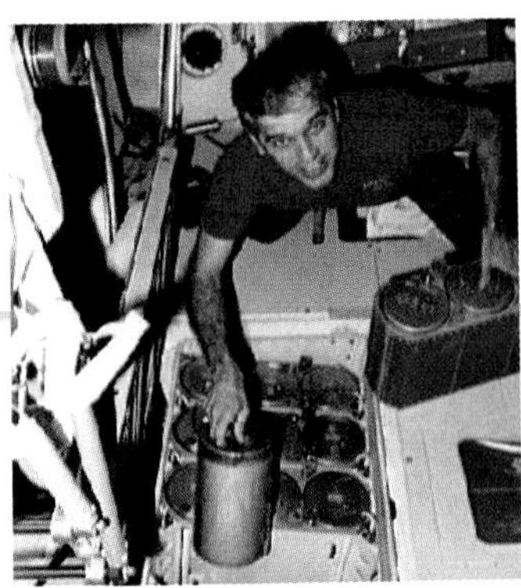

Field Activity

Read a science-fiction description of people living and working in space. In your Science Journal, describe how people performed daily tasks such as eating, sleeping, and getting around. Go to the Glencoe Science Web site at **science.glencoe.com** and click on the NASA link to find out more about living and working in space. Compare what you wrote with what you learn in this field guide.

Resources for Teachers and Students

Living in Space: A Handbook for Work and Exploration Stations Beyond the Earth's Atmosphere, by G. Harry Stine, M. Evans and Company, Inc., 1997.

Introduction to Space: The Science of Spaceflight, by Thomas Damon, Krieger Publishing Company, 1995.

Living in Space: From Science Fiction to the International Space Station, by Giovanni Caprara, Firefly Books LTD., 2000.

Field GUIDE

Electricity

Fuel cells generate electricity by chemically combining hydrogen and oxygen. As a by-product, they produce 3 kg of water each hour—some of which is used to prepare food.

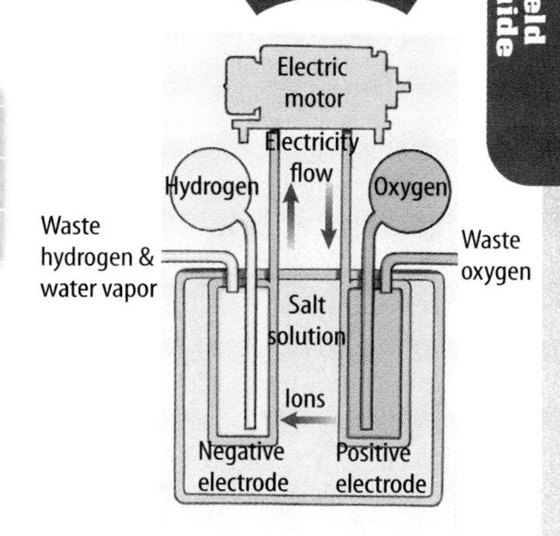

The Shuttle Café

BREAKFAST
DRIED APRICOTS · BREAKFAST ROLL
GRANOLA W/BLUEBERRIES · VANILLA
INSTANT BREAKFAST · GRAPEFRUIT DRINK

LUNCH
GROUND BEEF · PICKLE SAUCE · NOODLES AND CHICKEN · STEWED TOMATOES · PEARS · ALMONDS
STRAWBERRY DRINK

DINNER
TUNA · MACARONI AND CHEESE · PEAS W/BUTTER SAUCE · PEACH AMBROSIA · LEMONADE
CHOCOLATE PUDDING

CONDIMENTS
PEPPER · SALT · BARBECUE SAUCE · CATSUP · HOT PEPPER SAUCE
MAYONNAISE
MUSTARD

A Typical Menu

Astronauts eat three meals per day, chosen for them from a list of 70 foods and 20 beverages. They eat foods such as sausage, eggs, bread, fruits, vegetables, rice, and even turkey with gravy.

Food Preservation

Foods are not refrigerated. Some foods are freeze-dried, so water is added before they are eaten. Some foods are heated to kill bacteria and sealed in airtight foil packets. Irradiated food, such as bread and some meat, has been exposed to radiation to kill bacteria.

This astronaut is injecting water into dried food.

Food Preparation

Astronauts prepare and eat their food in the galley. A different person serves each meal, which takes about 20 min to prepare. The astronaut injects water into dried or powdered foods that need it, and puts hot dishes into the oven to warm them. Some foods can be eaten right out of the pouches.

Quick Demo

Obtain some freeze-dried food and prepare it in front of the class. Have students taste the finished product and compare the taste to that of freshly cooked food. Students can write about the experience in their Science Journals.

Content Background

Although a dog and chimpanzees preceded humans in space flight, on April 12, 1961 the first human orbited the earth. It was Russian cosmonaut Yuri Gagarin. Alan Shepard was the first American astronaut in space on May 5, 1961. He was followed by John Glenn who orbited Earth in February of 1962. Between 1962 and 1969 missions to space continued and on July 20, 1969 Neil Armstrong walked on the Moon. Today, the International Space Station orbits Earth from an altitude of 400km. The station is the result of a joint effort between the United States, Canada, Japan, Brazil, and the European Space Agency. It contains state of the art laboratories that will allow for on-going studies in many different areas of science. Some research will focus on the long-term effects of low gravity on the human body, while other research will be concerned with the effects of space on metals and other materials. Long term changes in Earth's environment will also be able to be monitored from orbit.

Science Journal

Astronauts Have students research information about an astronaut of their choice, including the missions they participated in, and what happened during those missions. Students can record their findings in their Science Journal.

SCIENCE Online

Internet Addresses

Explore the Glencoe Science Web site at **science.glencoe.com** to find out more about topics in this field guide.

Discussion

- **What is gravity?** Gravity is the attraction between all matter.
- **What is weight?** Weight is the measure of the force of gravity on an object.
- **What effect does gravity have on weight?** As the force of gravity increases, the weight of an object increases. As the force of gravity decreases, the weight of an object decreases.
- **How does having no gravity in space affect the completion of daily tasks?** Answers will vary but should include the idea that, in space, everything is weightless and, unless bolted or strapped down, will float.

Activity

In groups of 4 or 5, have students write and act out a skit that involves astronauts communicating with control centers on Earth or even doing television interviews. Communications can deal with daily tasks on the ship or the report of a problem.

Using Science Words

Word Origin Have students find the origins of the words astronaut and cosmonaut. Astronaut comes from the Latin *astr* or *astro*, meaning "star" and the Greek *nautes*, meaning "sailor." Cosmonaut is derived from the Russian word *kosmonavt*, which comes from the Greek *kosmo* and Russian *navt*. A cosmonaut is an astronaut in the Russian space program.

Field Guide

Working Out

To help prevent bone and muscle deterioration due to space's weightless environment, astronauts exercise for 15 min each day on 7-day to 14-day missions. They work out for 30 min daily on 30-day missions. They can use a treadmill, a rowing machine, or an exercise bike. Even with this exercise, astronauts can lose more than one percent of their bone density for each month they are in space.

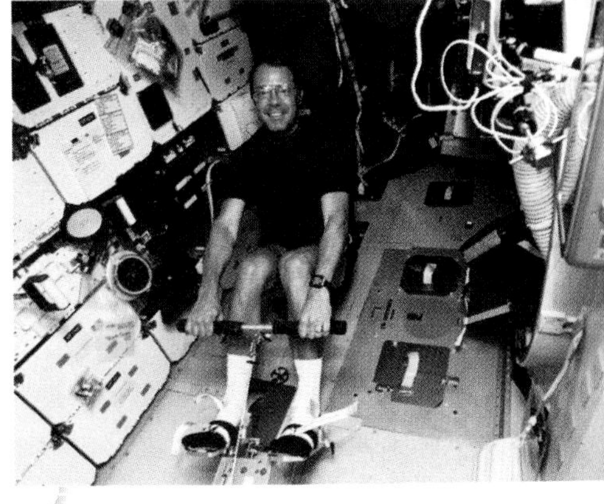

Using a rowing machine

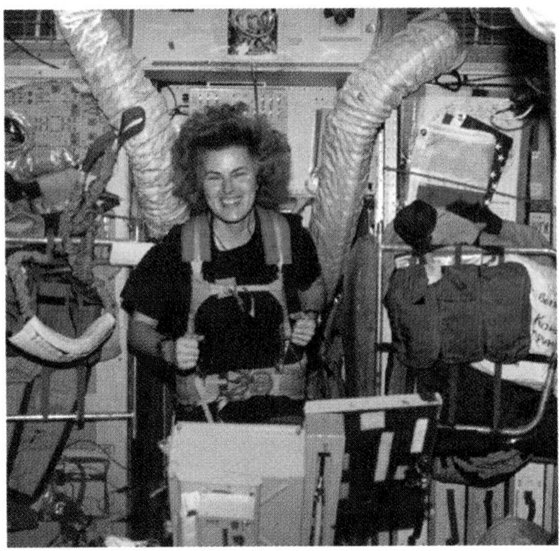

Using a treadmill

Exercise Equipment

The base of the treadmill hooks into the floor or walls. An astronaut can stand on the treadmill with rubber bungee cords attached to a belt and shoulder harness. The cord is tightened to increase resistance.

Getting Some Sleep

The condition of weightlessness enables astronauts to sleep in unusual places. Each astronaut's sleep station contains a bed made up of a padded board with a fireproof sleeping bag attached. Two astronauts sleep on bunks facing up. One sleeps on the underside of the lower bunk, facing the floor. The fourth sleeps vertically against the wall.

Sleeping compartments

Curriculum Connection

Health Have students research the importance of maintaining bone density. **What is osteoporosis?** A condition that results from a loss of bone density, or porous bones. Bones become brittle and break easily in this condition.

This is their hand-washing station.

This astronaut uses a wet cloth to keep clean.

Cleaning Up

After 8 h of sleep, astronauts have 45 min for morning hygiene. There aren't any showers or baths in space. To keep clean, astronauts just wipe themselves (and their hair) off with a wet cloth. They also can wash their hands at the hand-washing station. Water is air-blasted at their hands and then immediately sucked up.

Waste Management

Astronauts have a special toilet they use in space. It utilizes air instead of water to remove bodily wastes. The waste is then held in a tank until the spacecraft returns to Earth.

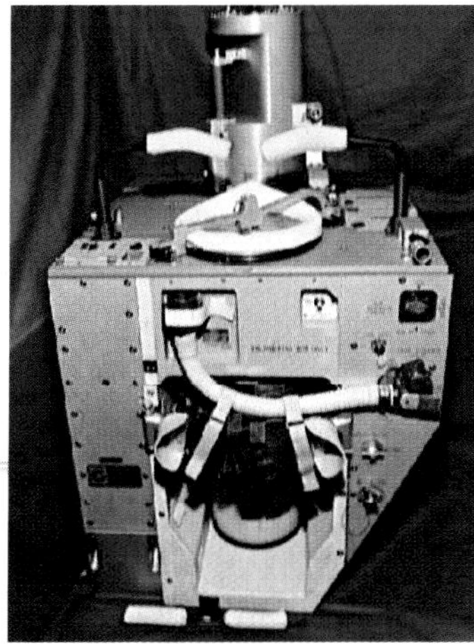

Here is a space shuttle toilet.

Visual Learning

Using the photos and information in the field guide, have students make a schedule of a "typical" day in space. The schedule should include time for meals, sleep, exercise, hygiene, and daily maintenance of the space craft, such as cleaning after meals and replacing airfilters. L2
LS **Logical-Mathematical**

Extension

Have students research current events in space travel, such as ongoing missions and planet exploration. Students can present their results in a show and tell format, using newspaper, magazine, or Internet articles or they may choose to make a poster based on the results of their research.

Fun Fact

The weightlessness of objects that results from zero gravity causes disruptions even on the smallest level. During previous missions in space, male astronauts dry shaved using an electric razor. The shaved whiskers floated around the cabin causing problems by getting caught in equipment, as well as in the astronauts' eyes and lungs.

Organizing Information

As you study science, you will make many observations and conduct investigations and experiments. You will also research information that is available from many sources. These activities will involve organizing and recording data. The quality of the data you collect and the way you organize it will determine how well others can understand and use it. In **Figure 1,** the student is obtaining and recording information using a thermometer.

Putting your observations in writing is an important way of communicating to others the information you have found and the results of your investigations and experiments.

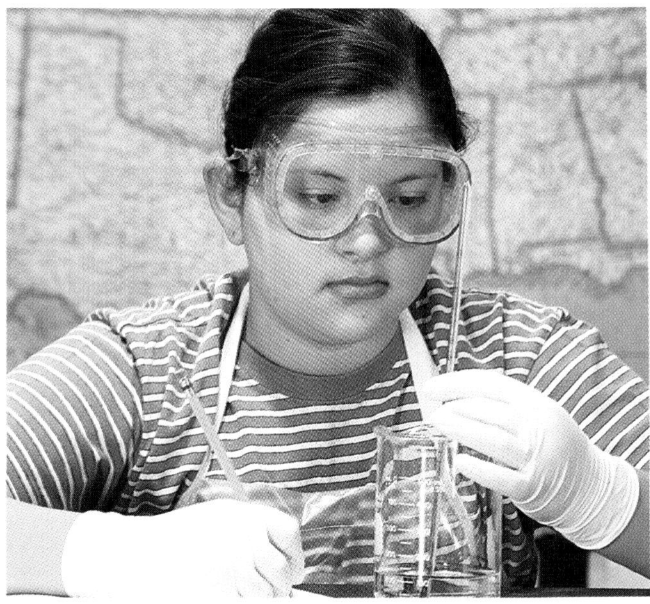

Figure 1
Making an observation is one way to gather information directly.

Researching Information

Scientists work to build on and add to human knowledge of the world. Before moving in a new direction, it is important to gather the information that already is known about a subject. You will look for such information in various reference sources. Follow these steps to research information on a scientific subject:

Step 1 Determine exactly what you need to know about the subject. For instance, you might want to find out about one of the elements in the periodic table.

Step 2 Make a list of questions, such as: Who discovered the element? When was it discovered? What makes the element useful or interesting?

Step 3 Use multiple sources such as textbooks, encyclopedias, government documents, professional journals, science magazines, and the Internet.

Step 4 List where you found the sources. Make sure the sources you use are reliable and the most current available.

Evaluating Print and Nonprint Sources

Not all sources of information are reliable. Evaluate the sources you use for information, and use only those you know to be dependable. For example, suppose you want to find ways to make your home more energy efficient. You might find two Web sites on how to save energy in your home. One Web site contains "Energy-Saving Tips" written by a company that sells a new type of weatherproofing material you put around your door frames. The other is a Web page on "Conserving Energy in Your Home" written by the U.S. Department of Energy. You would choose the second Web site as the more reliable source of information.

In science, information can change rapidly. Always consult the most current sources. A 1985 source about saving energy would not reflect the most recent research and findings.

Interpreting Scientific Illustrations

As you research a science topic, you will see drawings, diagrams, and photographs. Illustrations help you understand what you read. Some illustrations are included to help you understand an idea that you can't see easily by yourself. For instance, you can't see the tiny particles in an atom, but you can look at a diagram of an atom as labeled in **Figure 2** that helps you understand something about it. Visualizing a drawing helps many people remember details more easily. Illustrations also provide examples that clarify difficult concepts or give additional information about the topic you are studying.

Most illustrations have a label or caption. A label or caption identifies the illustration or provides additional information to better explain it. Can you find the caption or labels in **Figure 2?**

Figure 2
This drawing shows an atom of carbon with its six protons, six neutrons, and six electrons.

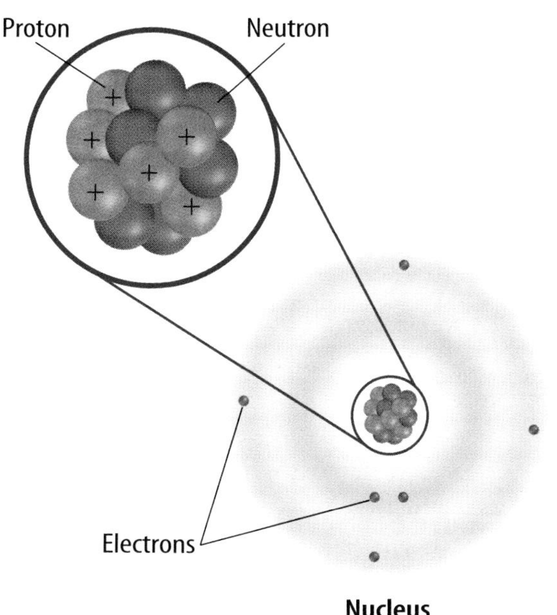

Concept Mapping

If you were taking a car trip, you might take some sort of road map. By using a map, you begin to learn where you are in relation to other places on the map.

A concept map is similar to a road map, but a concept map shows relationships among ideas (or concepts) rather than places. It is a diagram that visually shows how concepts are related. Because a concept map shows relationships among ideas, it can make the meanings of ideas and terms clear and help you understand what you are studying.

Overall, concept maps are useful for breaking large concepts down into smaller parts, making learning easier.

Venn Diagram

Although it is not a concept map, a Venn diagram illustrates how two subjects compare and contrast. In other words, you can see the characteristics that the subjects have in common and those that they do not.

The Venn diagram in **Figure 3** shows the relationship between two different substances made from the element carbon. However, due to the way their atoms are arranged, one substance is the gemstone diamond, and the other is the graphite found in pencils.

Figure 3
A Venn diagram shows how objects or concepts are alike and how they are different.

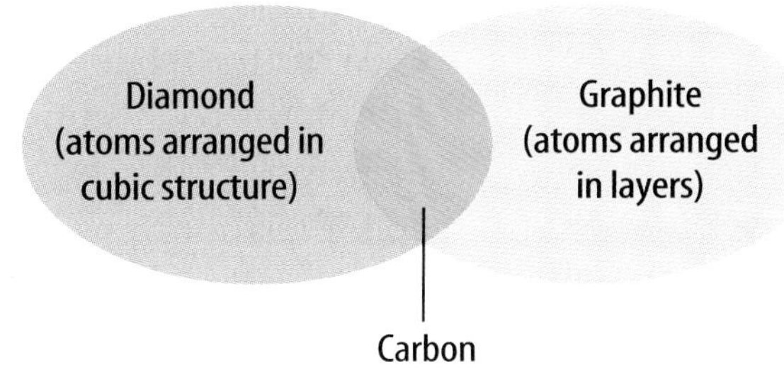

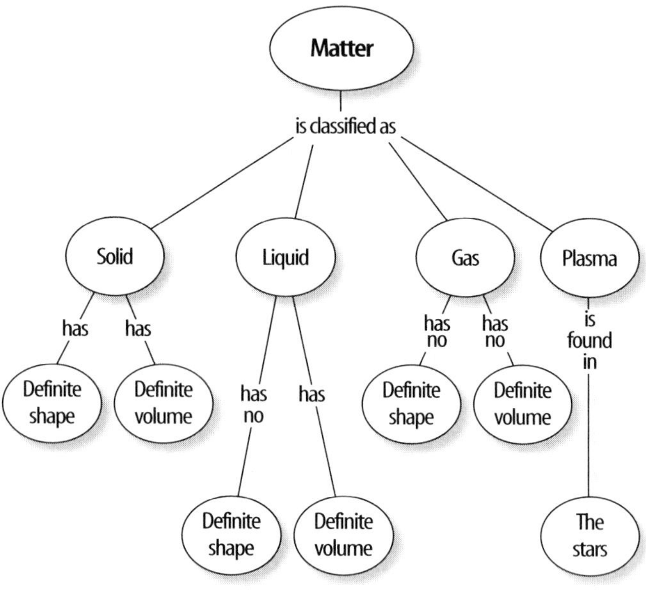

Figure 4
A network tree shows how concepts or objects are related.

Network Tree Look at the concept map in **Figure 4,** that describes the different types of matter. This is called a network tree concept map. Notice how some words are in ovals while others are written across connecting lines. The words inside the ovals are science terms or concepts. The words written on the connecting lines describe the relationships between the concepts.

When constructing a network tree, write the topic on a note card or piece of paper. Write the major concepts related to that topic on separate note cards or pieces of paper. Then arrange them in order from general to specific. Branch the related concepts from the major concept and describe the relationships on the connecting lines. Continue branching to more specific concepts. Write the relationships between the concepts on the connecting lines until all concepts are mapped. Then examine the concept map for relationships that cross branches, and add them to the concept map.

Events Chain An events chain is another type of concept map. It models the order of items or their sequence. In science, an events chain can be used to describe a sequence of events, the steps in a procedure, or the stages of a process.

When making an events chain, first find the one event that starts the chain. This event is called the *initiating event.* Then, find the next event in the chain and continue until you reach an outcome. Suppose you are asked to describe why and how a sound might make an echo. You might draw an events chain such as the one in **Figure 5.** Notice that connecting words are not necessary in an events chain.

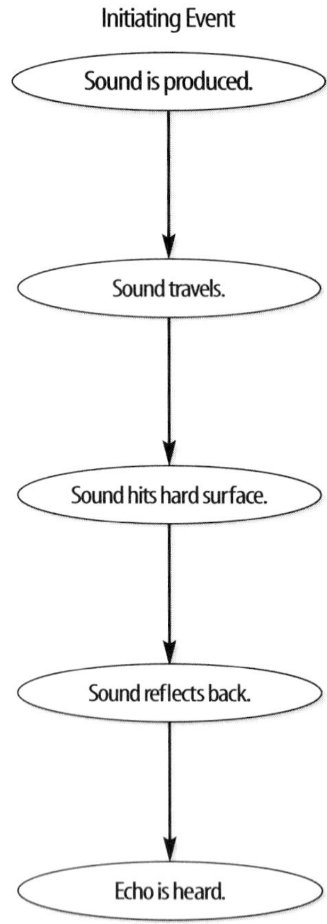

Figure 5
Events chains show the order of steps in a process or event.

Cycle Map A cycle concept map is a specific type of events chain map. In a cycle concept map, the series of events does not produce a final outcome. Instead, the last event in the chain relates back to the beginning event.

You first decide what event will be used as the beginning event. Once that is decided, you list events in order that occur after it. Words are written between events that describe what happens from one event to the next. The last event in a cycle concept map relates back to the beginning event. The number of events in a cycle concept varies, but is usually three or more. Look at the cycle map, as shown in **Figure 6.**

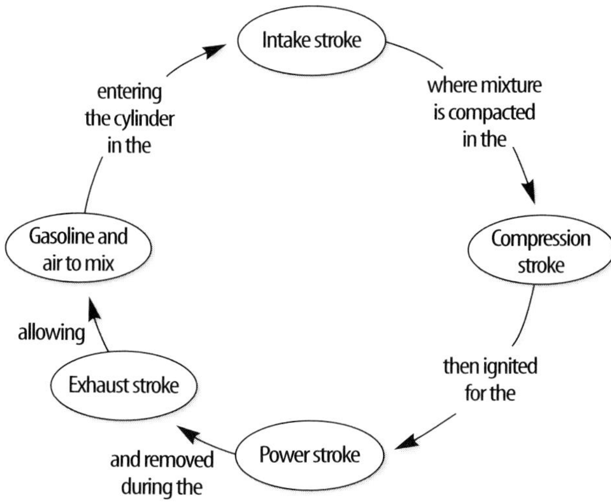

Figure 6
A cycle map shows events that occur in a cycle.

Spider Map A type of concept map that you can use for brainstorming is the spider map. When you have a central idea, you might find you have a jumble of ideas that relate to it but are not necessarily clearly related to each other. The spider map on sound in **Figure 7** shows that if you write these ideas outside the main concept, then you can begin to separate and group unrelated terms so they become more useful.

Figure 7
A spider map allows you to list ideas that relate to a central topic but not necessarily to one another.

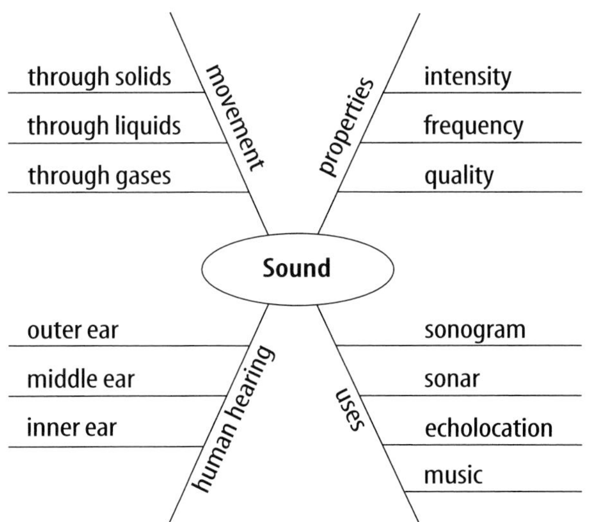

Writing a Paper

You will write papers often when researching science topics or reporting the results of investigations or experiments. Scientists frequently write papers to share their data and conclusions with other scientists and the public. When writing a paper, use these steps.

Step 1 Assemble your data by using graphs, tables, or a concept map. Create an outline.

Step 2 Start with an introduction that contains a clear statement of purpose and what you intend to discuss or prove.

Step 3 Organize the body into paragraphs. Each paragraph should start with a topic sentence, and the remaining sentences in that paragraph should support your point.

Step 4 Position data to help support your points.

Step 5 Summarize the main points and finish with a conclusion statement.

Step 6 Use tables, graphs, charts, and illustrations whenever possible.

Investigating and Experimenting

You might say the work of a scientist is to solve problems. When you decide to find out why your neighbor's hydrangeas produce blue flowers while yours are pink, you are problem solving, too. You might also observe that your neighbor's azaleas are healthier than yours are and decide to see whether differences in the soil explain the differences in these plants.

Scientists use orderly approaches to solve problems. The methods scientists use include identifying a question, making observations, forming a hypothesis, testing a hypothesis, analyzing results, and drawing conclusions.

Scientific investigations involve careful observation under controlled conditions. Such observation of an object or a process can suggest new and interesting questions about it. These questions sometimes lead to the formation of a hypothesis. Scientific investigations are designed to test a hypothesis.

Identifying a Question

The first step in a scientific investigation or experiment is to identify a question to be answered or a problem to be solved. You might be interested in knowing how beams of laser light like the ones in **Figure 8** look the way they do.

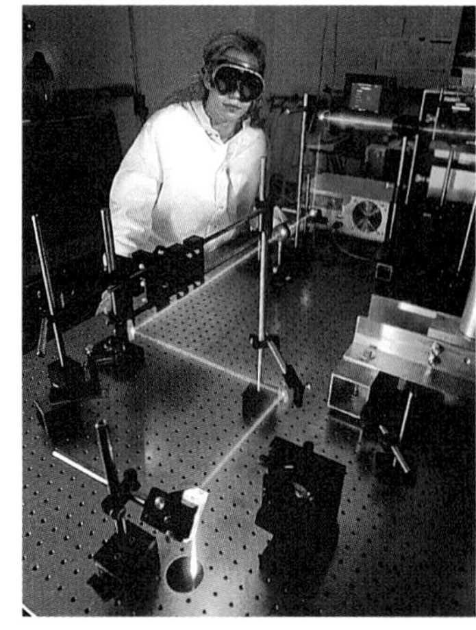

Figure 8
When you see lasers being used for scientific research, you might ask yourself, "Are these lasers different from those that are used for surgery?"

Forming Hypotheses

Hypotheses are based on observations that have been made. A hypothesis is a possible explanation based on previous knowledge and observations.

Perhaps a scientist has observed that certain substances dissolve faster in warm water than in cold. Based on these observations, the scientist can make a statement that he or she can test. The statement is a hypothesis. The hypothesis could be: *A substance dissolves in warm water faster.* A hypothesis has to be something you can test by using an investigation. A testable hypothesis is a valid hypothesis.

Predicting

When you apply a hypothesis, or general explanation, to a specific situation, you predict something about that situation. First, you must identify which hypothesis fits the situation you are considering. People use predictions to make everyday decisions. Based on previous observations and experiences, you might form a prediction that if substances dissolve in warm water faster, then heating the water will shorten mixing time for powdered fruit drinks. Someone could use this prediction to save time in preparing a fruit punch for a party.

Testing a Hypothesis

To test a hypothesis, you need a procedure. A procedure is the plan you follow in your experiment. A procedure tells you what materials to use, as well as how and in what order to use them. When you follow a procedure, data are generated that support or do not support the original hypothesis statement.

For example, premium gasoline costs more than regular gasoline. Does premium gasoline increase the efficiency or fuel mileage of your family car? You decide to test the hypothesis: "If premium gasoline is more efficient, then it should increase the fuel mileage of my family's car." Then you write the procedure shown in **Figure 9** for your experiment and generate the data presented in the table below.

Figure 9
A procedure tells you what to do step by step.

Procedure

1. Use regular gasoline for two weeks.
2. Record the number of kilometers between fill-ups and the amount of gasoline used.
3. Switch to premium gasoline for two weeks.
4. Record the number of kilometers between fill-ups and the amount of gasoline used.

Gasoline Data

Type of Gasoline	Kilometers Traveled	Liters Used	Liters per Kilometer
Regular	762	45.34	0.059
Premium	661	42.30	0.064

These data show that premium gasoline is less efficient than regular gasoline in one particular car. It took more gasoline to travel 1 km (0.064) using premium gasoline than it did to travel 1 km using regular gasoline (0.059). This conclusion does not support the hypothesis.

Are all investigations alike? Keep in mind as you perform investigations in science that a hypothesis can be tested in many ways. Not every investigation makes use of all the ways that are described on these pages, and not all hypotheses are tested by investigations. Scientists encounter many variations in the methods that are used when they perform experiments. The skills in this handbook are here for you to use and practice.

Identifying and Manipulating Variables and Controls

In any experiment, it is important to keep everything the same except for the item you are testing. The one factor you change is called the independent variable. The factor that changes as a result of the independent variable is called the dependent variable. Always make sure you have only one independent variable. If you allow more than one, you will not know what causes the changes you observe in the dependent variable. Many experiments also have controls—individual instances or experimental subjects for which the independent variable is not changed. You can then compare the test results to the control results.

For example, in the fuel-mileage experiment, you made everything the same except the type of gasoline that was used. The driver, the type of automobile, and the type of driving were the same throughout. In this way, you could be sure that any mileage differences were caused by the type of fuel—the independent variable. The fuel mileage was the dependent variable.

If you could repeat the experiment using several automobiles of the same type on a standard driving track with the same driver, you could make one automobile a control by using regular gasoline over the four-week period.

Collecting Data

Whether you are carrying out an investigation or a short observational experiment, you will collect data, or information. Scientists collect data accurately as numbers and descriptions and organize it in specific ways.

Observing Scientists observe items and events, then record what they see. When they use only words to describe an observation, it is called qualitative data. For example, a scientist might describe the color, texture, or odor of a substance produced in a chemical reaction. Scientists' observations also can describe how much there is of something. These observations use numbers, as well as words, in the description and are called quantitative data. For example, if a sample of the element gold is described as being "shiny and very dense," the data are clearly qualitative. Quantitative data on this sample of gold might include "a mass of 30 g and a density of 19.3 g/cm^3." Quantitative data often are organized into tables. Then, from information in the table, a graph can be drawn. Graphs can reveal relationships that exist in experimental data.

When you make observations in science, you should examine the entire object or situation first, then look carefully for details. If you're looking at an element sample, for instance, check the general color and pattern of the sample before using a hand lens to examine its surface for any smaller details or characteristics. Remember to record accurately everything you see.

Scientists try to make careful and accurate observations. When possible, they use instruments such as microscopes, metric rulers, graduated cylinders, thermometers, and balances. Measurements provide numerical data that can be repeated and checked.

Sampling When working with large numbers of objects or a large population, scientists usually cannot observe or study every one of them. Instead, they use a sample or a portion of the total number. To *sample* is to take a small, representative portion of the objects or organisms of a population for research. By making careful observations or manipulating variables within a portion of a group, information is discovered and conclusions are drawn that might apply to the whole population.

Estimating Scientific work also involves estimating. To estimate is to make a judgment about the size or the number of something without measuring or counting every object or member of a population. Scientists first measure or count the amount or number in a small sample. A geologist, for example, might remove a 10-g sample from a large rock that is rich in copper ore, as in **Figure 10.** Then a chemist would determine the percentage of copper by mass and multiply that percentage by the total mass of the rock to estimate the total mass of copper in the large rock.

Figure 10
Determining the percentage of copper by mass that is present in a small piece of a large rock, which is rich in copper ore, can help estimate the total mass of copper ore that is present in the rock.

Measuring in SI

The metric system of measurement was developed in 1795. A modern form of the metric system, called the International System, or SI, was adopted in 1960. SI provides standard measurements that all scientists around the world can understand.

The metric system is convenient because unit sizes vary by multiples of 10. When changing from smaller units to larger units, divide by a multiple of 10. When changing from larger units to smaller, multiply by a multiple of 10. To convert millimeters to centimeters, divide the millimeters by 10. To convert 30 mm to centimeters, divide 30 by 10 (30 mm equal 3 cm).

Prefixes are used to name units. Look at the table below for some common metric prefixes and their meanings. Do you see how the prefix *kilo-* attached to the unit *gram* is *kilogram*, or 1,000 g?

Metric Prefixes

Prefix	Symbol	Meaning	
kilo-	k	1,000	thousand
hecto-	h	100	hundred
deka-	da	10	ten
deci-	d	0.1	tenth
centi-	c	0.01	hundredth
milli-	m	0.001	thousandth

Now look at the metric ruler shown in **Figure 11.** The centimeter lines are the long, numbered lines, and the shorter lines are millimeter lines.

When using a metric ruler, line up the 0-cm mark with the end of the object being measured, and read the number of the unit where the object ends, in this instance it would be 4.5 cm.

Figure 11
This metric ruler has centimeter and millimeter divisions.

Liquid Volume In some science activities, you will measure liquids. The unit that is used to measure liquids is the liter. A liter has the volume of 1,000 cm^3. The prefix *milli-* means "thousandth (0.001)." A milliliter is one thousandth of 1 L, and 1 L has the volume of 1,000 mL. One milliliter of liquid completely fills a cube measuring 1 cm on each side. Therefore, 1 mL equals 1 cm^3.

You will use beakers and graduated cylinders to measure liquid volume. A graduated cylinder, as illustrated in **Figure 12,** is marked from bottom to top in milliliters. This one contains 79 mL of a liquid.

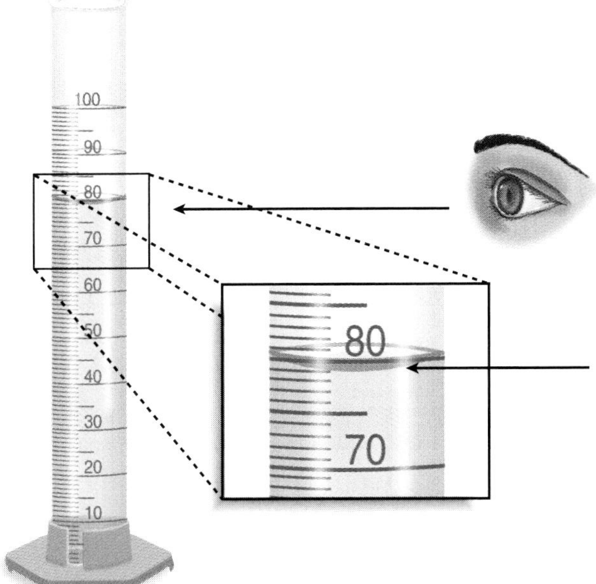

Figure 12
Graduated cylinders measure liquid volume.

Mass Scientists measure mass in grams. You might use a beam balance similar to the one shown in **Figure 13.** The balance has a pan on one side and a set of beams on the other side. Each beam has a rider that slides on the beam.

Before you find the mass of an object, slide all the riders back to the zero point. Check the pointer on the right to make sure it swings an equal distance above and below the zero point. If the swing is unequal, find and turn the adjusting screw until you have an equal swing.

Place an object on the pan. Slide the largest rider along its beam until the pointer drops below zero. Then move it back one notch. Repeat the process on each beam until the pointer swings an equal distance above and below the zero point. Sum the masses on each beam to find the mass of the object. Move all riders back to zero when finished.

Figure 13
A triple beam balance is used to determine the mass of an object.

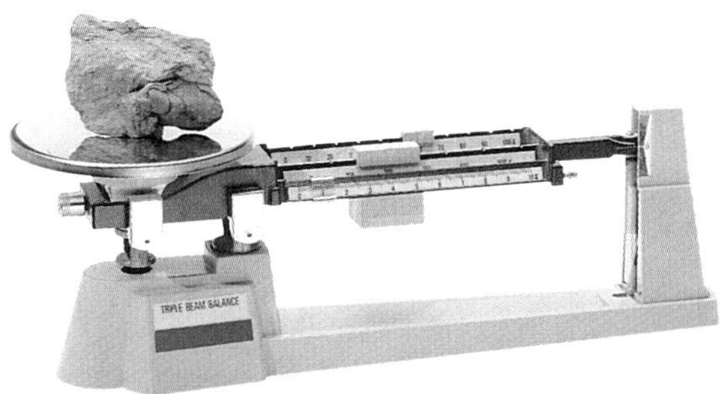

You should never place a hot object on the pan or pour chemicals directly onto the pan. Instead, find the mass of a clean container. Remove the container from the pan, then place the chemicals in the container. Find the mass of the container with the chemicals in it. To find the mass of the chemicals, subtract the mass of the empty container from the mass of the filled container.

Making and Using Tables

Browse through your textbook and you will see tables in the text and in the activities. In a table, data, or information, are arranged so that they are easier to understand. Activity tables help organize the data you collect during an activity so results can be interpreted.

Making Tables To make a table, list the items to be compared in the first column and the characteristics to be compared in the first row. The title should clearly indicate the content of the table, and the column or row heads should tell the reader what information is found in there. The table below lists materials collected for recycling on three weekly pick-up days. The inclusion of kilograms in parentheses also identifies for the reader that the figures are mass units.

Recyclable Materials Collected During Week

Day of Week	Paper (kg)	Aluminum (kg)	Glass (kg)
Monday	5.0	4.0	12.0
Wednesday	4.0	1.0	10.0
Friday	2.5	2.0	10.0

Using Tables How much paper, in kilograms, is being recycled on Wednesday? Locate the column labeled "Paper (kg)" and the row "Wednesday." The information in the box where the column and row intersect is the answer. Did you answer "4.0"? How much aluminum, in kilograms, is being recycled on Friday? If you answered "2.0," you understand how to read the table. How much glass is collected for recycling each week? Locate the column labeled "Glass (kg)" and add the figures for all three rows. If you answered "32.0," then you know how to locate and use the data provided in the table.

Recording Data

To be useful, the data you collect must be recorded carefully. Accuracy is key. A well-thought-out experiment includes a way to record procedures, observations, and results accurately. Data tables are one way to organize and record results. Set up the tables you will need ahead of time so you can record the data right away.

Record information properly and neatly. Never put unidentified data on scraps of paper. Instead, data should be written in a notebook like the one in **Figure 14.** Write in pencil so information isn't lost if your data gets wet. At each point in the experiment, record your data and label it. That way, your information will be accurate and you will not have to determine what the figures mean when you look at your notes later.

Figure 14
Record data neatly and clearly so it is easy to understand.

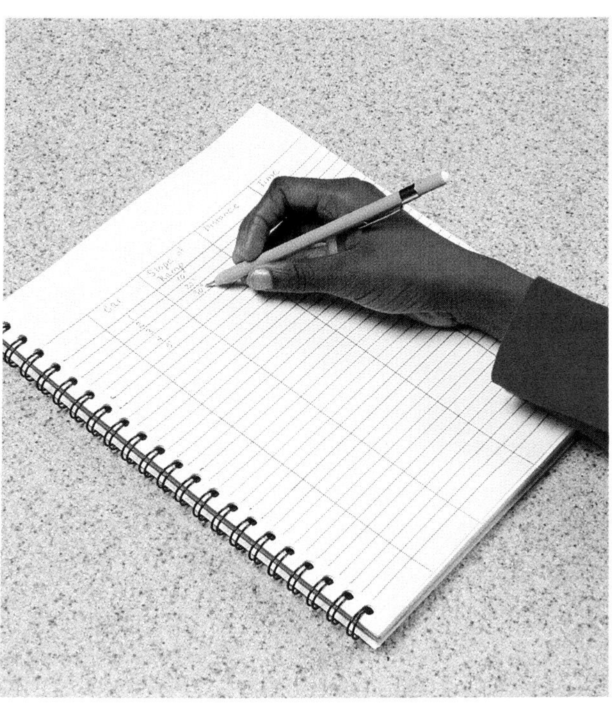

Recording Observations

It is important to record observations accurately and completely. That is why you always should record observations in your notes immediately as you make them. It is easy to miss details or make mistakes when recording results from memory. Do not include your personal thoughts when you record your data. Record only what you observe to eliminate bias. For example, when you record the time required for five students to climb the same set of stairs, you would note which student took the longest time. However, you would not refer to that student's time as "the worst time of all the students in the group."

Making Models

You can organize the observations and other data you collect and record in many ways. Making models is one way to help you better understand the parts of a structure you have been observing or the way a process for which you have been taking various measurements works.

Models often show things that are too large or too small for normal viewing. For example, you normally won't see the inside of an atom. However, you can understand the structure of the atom better by making a three-dimensional model of an atom. The relative sizes, the positions, and the movements of protons, neutrons, and electrons can be explained in words. An atomic model made of a plastic-ball nucleus and pipe-cleaner electron shells can help you visualize how the parts of the atom relate to each other.

Other models can be devised on a computer. Some models, such as those that illustrate the chemical combinations of different elements, are mathematical and are represented by equations.

Making and Using Graphs

After scientists organize data in tables, they might display the data in a graph that shows the relationship of one variable to another. A graph makes interpretation and analysis of data easier. Three types of graphs are the line graph, the bar graph, and the circle graph.

Line Graphs A line graph like in **Figure 15** is used to show the relationship between two variables. The variables being compared go on two axes of the graph. For data from an experiment, the independent variable always goes on the horizontal axis, called the *x*-axis. The dependent variable always goes on the vertical axis, called the *y*-axis. After drawing your axes, label each with a scale. Next, plot the data points.

A data point is the intersection of the recorded value of the dependent variable for each tested value of the independent variable. After all the points are plotted, connect them.

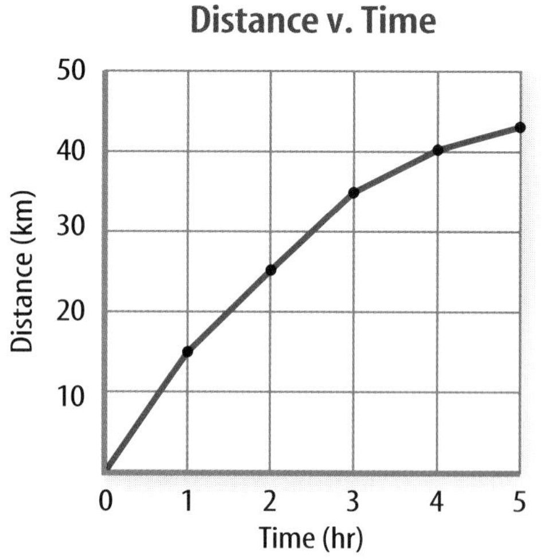

Distance v. Time

Distance (km): 10, 20, 30, 40, 50

Time (hr): 0, 1, 2, 3, 4, 5

Figure 15
This line graph shows the relationship between distance and time during a bicycle ride lasting several hours.

Bar Graphs Bar graphs compare data that do not change continuously. Vertical bars show the relationships among data.

To make a bar graph, set up the *y*-axis as you did for the line graph. Draw vertical bars of equal size from the *x*-axis up to the point on the *y*-axis that represents value of *x*.

Figure 16
The amount of aluminum collected for recycling during one week can be shown as a bar graph or circle graph.

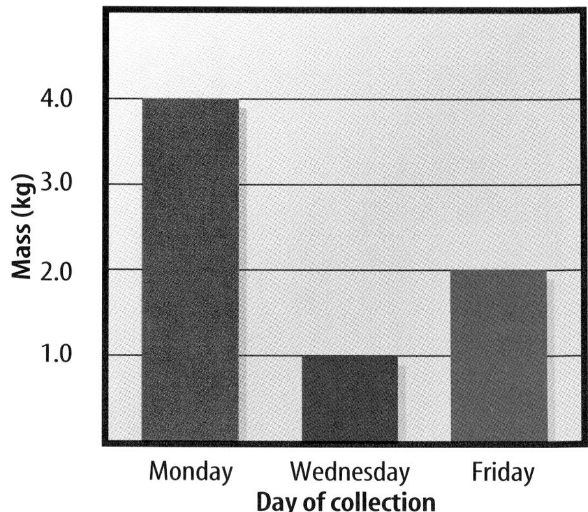

Circle Graphs A circle graph uses a circle divided into sections to display data as parts (fractions or percentages) of a whole. The size of each section corresponds to the fraction or percentage of the data that the section represents. So, the entire circle represents 100 percent, one-half represents 50 percent, one-fifth represents 20 percent, and so on.

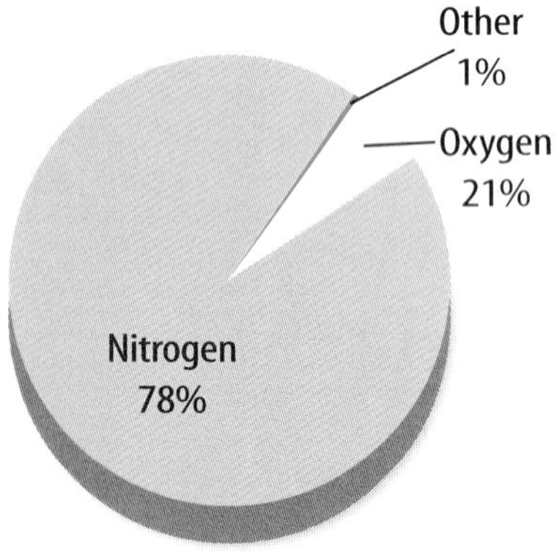

Other 1%

Oxygen 21%

Nitrogen 78%

Analyzing Results

To determine the meaning of your observations and investigation results, you will need to look for patterns in the data. You can organize your information in several of the ways that are discussed in this handbook. Then you must think critically to determine what the data mean. Scientists use several approaches when they analyze the data they have collected and recorded. Each approach is useful for identifying specific patterns in the data.

Forming Operational Definitions

An operational definition defines an object by showing how it functions, works, or behaves. Such definitions are written in terms of how an object works or how it can be used; that is, they describe its job or purpose.

For example, a ruler can be defined as a tool that measures the length of an object (how it can be used). A ruler also can be defined as something that contains a series of marks that can be used as a standard when measuring (how it works).

Classifying

Classifying is the process of sorting objects or events into groups based on common features. When classifying, first observe the objects or events to be classified. Then select one feature that is shared by some members in the group but not by all. Place those members that share that feature into a subgroup. You can classify members into smaller and smaller subgroups based on characteristics.

How might you classify a group of chemicals? You might first classify them by state of matter, putting solids, liquids, and gases into separate groups. Within each group, you could then look for another common feature by which to further classify members of the group, such as color or how reactive they are.

Remember that when you classify, you are grouping objects or events for a purpose. For example, classifying chemicals can be the first step in organizing them for storage. Both at home and at school, poisonous or highly reactive chemicals should all be stored in a safe location where they are not easily accessible to small children or animals. Solids, liquids, and gases each have specific storage requirements that may include waterproof, airtight, or pressurized containers. Are the dangerous chemicals in your home stored in the right place? Keep your purpose in mind as you select the features to form groups and subgroups.

Figure 17
Color is one of many characteristics that are used to classify chemicals.

Comparing and Contrasting

Observations can be analyzed by noting the similarities and differences between two or more objects or events that you observe. When you look at objects or events to see how they are similar, you are comparing them. Contrasting is looking for differences in objects or events. The table below compares and contrasts the characteristics of two elements.

Elemental Characteristics		
Element	Aluminum	Gold
Color	silver	gold
Classification	metal	metal
Density (g/cm^3)	2.7	19.3
Melting Point (°C)	660	1064

Recognizing Cause and Effect

Have you ever heard a loud pop right before the power went out and then suggested that an electric transformer probably blew out? If so, you have observed an effect and inferred a cause. The event is the effect, and the reason for the event is the cause.

When scientists are unsure of the cause of a certain event, they design controlled experiments to determine what caused it.

Interpreting Data

The word *interpret* means "to explain the meaning of something." Look at the problem originally being explored in an experiment and figure out what the data show. Identify the control group and the test group so you can see whether or not changes in the independent variable have had an effect. Look for differences in the dependent variable between the control and test groups.

These differences you observe can be qualitative or quantitative. You would be able to describe a qualitative difference using only words, whereas you would measure a quantitative difference and describe it using numbers. If there are differences, the independent variable that is being tested could have had an effect. If no differences are found between the control and test groups, the variable that is being tested apparently had no effect.

For example, suppose that three beakers each contain 100 mL of water. The beakers are placed on hot plates, and two of the hot plates are turned on, but the third is left off for a period of 5 min. Suppose you are then asked to describe any differences in the water in the three beakers. A qualitative difference might be the appearance of bubbles rising to the top in the water that is being heated but no rising bubbles in the unheated water. A quantitative difference might be a difference in the amount of water that is present in the beakers.

Inferring Scientists often make inferences based on their observations. An inference is an attempt to explain, or interpret, observations or to indicate what caused what you observed. An inference is a type of conclusion.

When making an inference, be certain to use accurate data and accurately described observations. Analyze all of the data that you've collected. Then, based on everything you know, explain or interpret what you've observed.

Drawing Conclusions

When scientists have analyzed the data they collected, they proceed to draw conclusions about what the data mean. These conclusions are sometimes stated using words similar to those found in the hypothesis formed earlier in the process.

Conclusions To analyze your data, you must review all of the observations and measurements that you made and recorded. Recheck all data for accuracy. After your data are rechecked and organized, you are almost ready to draw a conclusion such as "salt water boils at a higher temperature than freshwater."

Before you can draw a conclusion, however, you must determine whether the data allow you to come to a conclusion that supports a hypothesis. Sometimes that will be the case, other times it will not.

If your data do not support a hypothesis, it does not mean that the hypothesis is wrong. It means only that the results of the investigation did not support the hypothesis. Maybe the experiment needs to be redesigned, but very likely, some of the initial observations on which the hypothesis was based were incomplete or biased. Perhaps more observation or research is needed to refine the hypothesis.

Avoiding Bias Sometimes drawing a conclusion involves making judgments. When you make a judgment, you form an opinion about what your data mean. It is important to be honest and to avoid reaching a conclusion if there were no supporting evidence for it or if it were based on a small sample. It also is important not to allow any expectations of results to bias your judgments. If possible, it is a good idea to collect additional data. Scientists do this all the time.

For example, the *Hubble Space Telescope* was sent into space in April, 1990, to provide scientists with clearer views of the universe. The *Hubble* is the size of a school bus and has a 2.4-m-diameter mirror. The *Hubble* helped scientists answer questions about the planet Pluto.

For many years, scientists had only been able to hypothesize about the surface of the planet Pluto. The *Hubble* has now provided pictures of Pluto's surface that show a rough texture with light and dark regions on it. This might be the best information about Pluto scientists will have until they are able to send a space probe to it.

Evaluating Others' Data and Conclusions

Sometimes scientists have to use data that they did not collect themselves, or they have to rely on observations and conclusions drawn by other researchers. In cases such as these, the data must be evaluated carefully.

How were the data obtained? How was the investigation done? Was it carried out properly? Has it been duplicated by other researchers? Were they able to follow the exact procedure? Did they come up with the same results? Look at the conclusion, as well. Would you reach the same conclusion from these results? Only when you have confidence in the data of others can you believe it is true and feel comfortable using it.

Communicating

The communication of ideas is an important part of the work of scientists. A discovery that is not reported will not advance the scientific community's understanding or knowledge. Communication among scientists also is important as a way of improving their investigations.

Scientists communicate in many ways, from writing articles in journals and magazines that explain their investigations and experiments, to announcing important discoveries on television and radio, to sharing ideas with colleagues on the Internet or presenting them as lectures.

Computer Skills

People who study science rely on computers to record and store data and to analyze results from investigations. Whether you work in a laboratory or just need to write a lab report with tables, good computer skills are a necessity.

Using a Word Processor

Suppose your teacher has assigned a written report. After you've completed your research and decided how you want to write the information, you need to put all that information on paper. The easiest way to do this is with a word processing application on a computer.

A computer application that allows you to type your information, change it as many times as you need to, and then print it out so that it looks neat and clean is called a word processing application. You also can use this type of application to create tables and columns, add bullets or cartoon art to your page, include page numbers, and check your spelling.

Helpful Hints

- If you aren't sure how to do something using your word processing program, look in the help menu. You will find a list of topics there to click on for help. After you locate the help topic you need, just follow the step-by-step instructions you see on your screen.
- Just because you've spell checked your report doesn't mean that the spelling is perfect. The spell check feature can't catch misspelled words that look like other words. If you've accidentally typed *cold* instead of *gold*, the spell checker won't know the difference. Always reread your report to make sure you didn't miss any mistakes.

Figure 18
You can use computer programs to make graphs and tables.

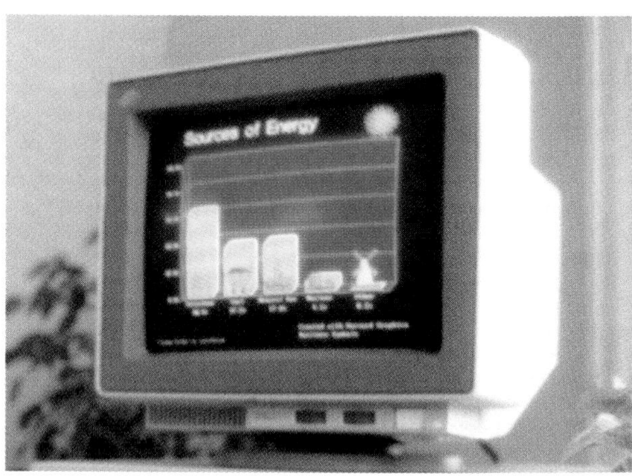

Using a Database

Imagine you're in the middle of a research project, busily gathering facts and information. You soon realize that it's becoming more difficult to organize and keep track of all the information. The tool to use to solve information overload is a database. Just as a file cabinet organizes paper records, a database organizes computer records. However, a database is more powerful than a simple file cabinet because at the click of a mouse, the contents can be reshuffled and reorganized. At computer-quick speeds, databases can sort information by any characteristics and filter data into multiple categories.

Helpful Hints

- Before setting up a database, take some time to learn the features of your database software by practicing with established database software.
- Periodically save your database as you enter data. That way, if something happens such as your computer malfunctions or the power goes off, you won't lose all of your work.

Doing a Database Search

When searching for information in a database, use the following search strategies to get the best results. These are the same search methods used for searching internet databases.

- Place the word *and* between two words in your search if you want the database to look for any entries that have both the words. For example, "gold *and* silver" would give you information that mentions both gold and silver.
- Place the word *or* between two words if you want the database to show entries that have at least one of the words. For example "gold *or* silver" would show you information that mentions either gold or silver.
- Place the word *not* between two words if you want the database to look for entries that have the first word but do not have the second word. For example, "gold *not* jewelry" would show you information that mentions gold but does not mention jewelry.

In summary, databases can be used to store large amounts of information about a particular subject. Databases allow biologists, Earth scientists, and physical scientists to search for information quickly and accurately.

Using an Electronic Spreadsheet

Your science fair experiment has produced lots of numbers. How do you keep track of all the data, and how can you easily work out all the calculations needed? You can use a computer program called a spreadsheet to record data that involve numbers. A spreadsheet is an electronic mathematical worksheet.

Type your data in rows and columns, just as they would look in a data table on a sheet of paper. A spreadsheet uses simple math to do data calculations. For example, you could add, subtract, divide, or multiply any of the values in the spreadsheet by another number. You also could set up a series of math steps you want to apply to the data. If you want to add 12 to all the numbers and then multiply all the numbers by 10, the computer does all the calculations for you in the spreadsheet. Below is an example of a spreadsheet that records test car data.

Helpful Hints

- Before you set up the spreadsheet, identify how you want to organize the data. Include any formulas you will need to use.
- Make sure you have entered the correct data into the correct rows and columns.
- You also can display your results in a graph. Pick the style of graph that best represents the data with which you are working.

Figure 19
A spreadsheet allows you to display large amounts of data and do calculations automatically.

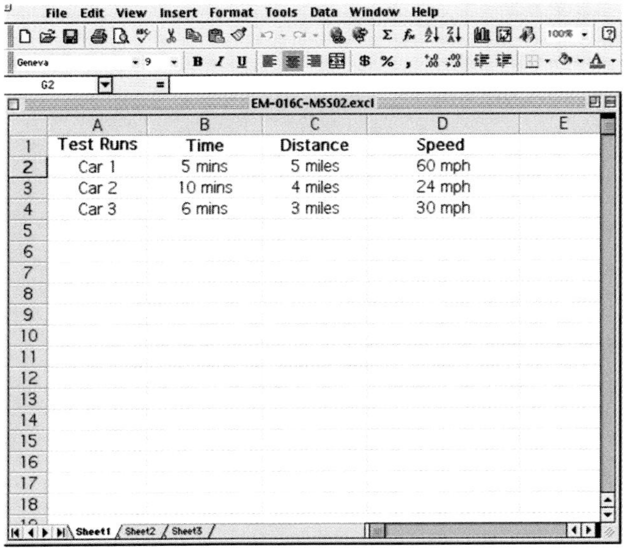

File Edit View Insert Format Tools Data Window Help

EM-016C-MSS02.excl

	A	B	C	D	E
1	Test Runs	Time	Distance	Speed	
2	Car 1	5 mins	5 miles	60 mph	
3	Car 2	10 mins	4 miles	24 mph	
4	Car 3	6 mins	3 miles	30 mph	

Sheet1 / Sheet2 / Sheet3

Using a Computerized Card Catalog

When you have a report or paper to research, you probably go to the library. To find the information you need in the library, you might have to use a computerized card catalog. This type of card catalog allows you to search for information by subject, by title, or by author. The computer then will display all the holdings the library has on the subject, title, or author requested.

A library's holdings can include books, magazines, databases, videos, and audio materials. When you have chosen something from this list, the computer will show whether an item is available and where in the library to find it.

Helpful Hints

- Remember that you can use the computer to search by subject, author, or title. If you know a book's author but not the title, you can search for all the books the library has by that author.
- When searching by subject, it's often most helpful to narrow your search by using specific search terms, such as *and, or,* and *not.* If you don't find enough sources this way, you can broaden your search.
- Pay attention to the type of materials found in your search. If you need a book, you can eliminate any videos or other resources that come up in your search.
- Knowing how your library is arranged can save you a lot of time. If you need help, the librarian will show you where certain types of materials are kept and how to find specific holdings.

Using Graphics Software

Are you having trouble finding that exact piece of art you're looking for? Do you have a picture in your mind of what you want but can't seem to find the right graphic to represent your ideas? To solve these problems, you can use graphics software. Graphics software allows you to create and change images and diagrams in almost unlimited ways. Typical uses for graphics software include arranging clip art, changing scanned images, and constructing pictures from scratch. Most graphics software applications work in similar ways. They use the same basic tools and functions. Once you master one graphics application, you can use other graphics applications.

Figure 20
Graphics software can use your data to draw bar graphs.

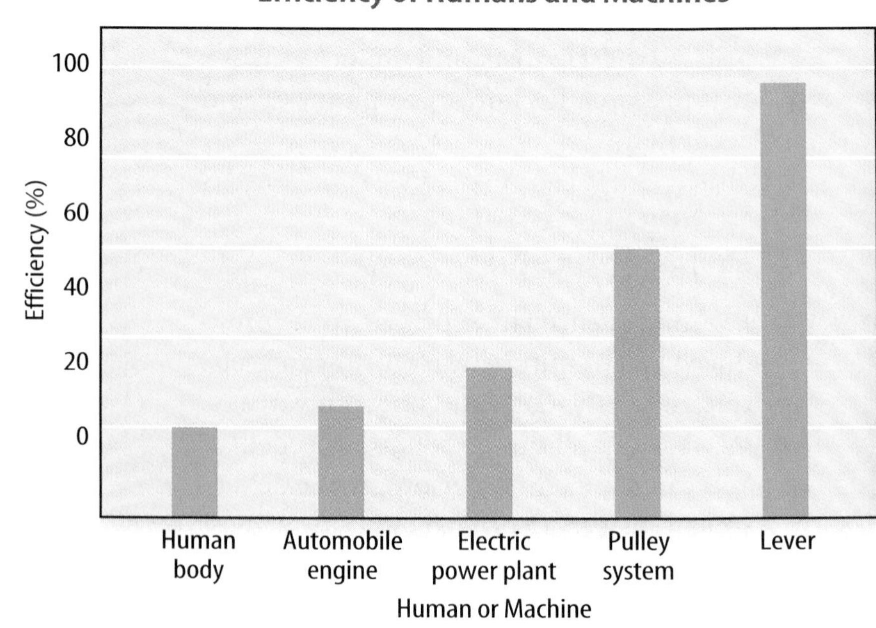

Figure 21
Graphics software can use your data to draw circle graphs.

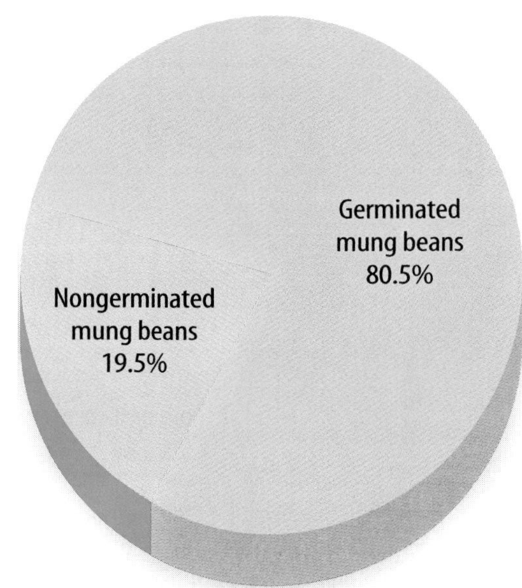

Helpful Hints

- As with any method of drawing, the more you practice using the graphics software, the better your results will be.
- Start by using the software to manipulate existing drawings. Once you master this, making your own illustrations will be easier.
- Clip art is available on CD-ROMs and the Internet. With these resources, finding a piece of clip art to suit your purposes is simple.
- As you work on a drawing, save it often.

Developing Multimedia Presentations

It's your turn—you have to present your science report to the entire class. How do you do it? You can use many different sources of information to get the class excited about your presentation. Posters, videos, photographs, sound, computers, and the Internet can help show your ideas.

First, determine what important points you want to make in your presentation. Then, write an outline of what materials and types of media would best illustrate those points. Maybe you could start with an outline on an overhead projector, then show a video, followed by something from the Internet or a slide show accompanied by music or recorded voices. You might choose to use a presentation builder computer application that can combine all these elements into one presentation. Make sure the presentation is well constructed to make the most impact on the audience.

Figure 22
Multimedia presentations use many types of print and electronic materials.

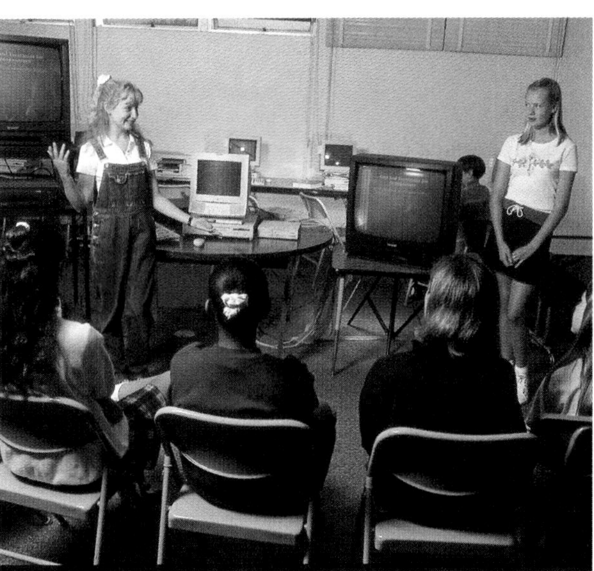

Helpful Hints

- Carefully consider what media will best communicate the point you are trying to make.
- Make sure you know how to use any equipment you will be using in your presentation.
- Practice the presentation several times.
- If possible, set up all of the equipment ahead of time. Make sure everything is working correctly.

Use this Math Skill Handbook to help solve problems you are given in this text. You might find it useful to review topics in this Math Skill Handbook first.

Converting Units

In science, quantities such as length, mass, and time sometimes are measured using different units. Suppose you want to know how many miles are in 12.7 km?

Conversion factors are used to change from one unit of measure to another. A conversion factor is a ratio that is equal to one. For example, there are 1,000 mL in 1 L, so 1,000 mL equals 1 L, or:

$$1{,}000 \text{ mL} = 1 \text{ L}$$

If both sides are divided by 1 L, this equation becomes:

$$\frac{1{,}000 \text{ mL}}{1 \text{ L}} = 1$$

The **ratio** on the left side of this equation is equal to one and is a conversion factor. You can make another conversion factor by dividing both sides of the top equation by 1,000 mL:

$$1 = \frac{1 \text{ L}}{1{,}000 \text{ mL}}$$

To **convert units,** you multiply by the appropriate conversion factor. For example, how many milliliters are in 1.255 L? To convert 1.255 L to milliliters, multiply 1.255 L by a conversion factor.

Use the **conversion factor** with new units (mL) in the numerator and the old units (L) in the denominator.

$$1.255 \cancel{\text{L}} \times \frac{1{,}000 \text{ mL}}{1 \cancel{\text{L}}} = 1{,}255 \text{ mL}$$

The unit L divides in this equation, just as if it were a number.

Example 1 There are 2.54 cm in 1 inch. If a meterstick has a length of 100 cm, how long is the meterstick in inches?

Step 1 Decide which conversion factor to use. You know the length of the meterstick in centimeters, so centimeters are the old units. You want to find the length in inches, so inch is the new unit.

Step 2 Form the conversion factor. Start with the relationship between the old and new units.

$$2.54 \text{ cm} = 1 \text{ inch}$$

Step 3 Form the conversion factor with the old unit (centimeter) on the bottom by dividing both sides by 2.54 cm.

$$1 = \frac{2.54 \text{ cm}}{2.54 \text{ cm}} = \frac{1 \text{ inch}}{2.54 \text{ cm}}$$

Step 4 Multiply the old measurement by the conversion factor.

$$100 \cancel{\text{cm}} \times \frac{1 \text{ inch}}{2.54 \cancel{\text{cm}}} = 39.37 \text{ inches}$$

The meter stick is 39.37 inches long.

Example 2 There are 365 days in one year. If a person is 14 years old, what is his or her age in days? (Ignore leap years)

Step 1 Decide which conversion factor to use. You want to convert years to days.

Step 2 Form the conversion factor. Start with the relation between the old and new units.

$$1 \text{ year} = 365 \text{ days}$$

Step 3 Form the conversion factor with the old unit (year) on the bottom by dividing both sides by 1 year.

$$1 = \frac{1 \text{ year}}{1 \text{ year}} = \frac{365 \text{ days}}{1 \text{ year}}$$

Step 4 Multiply the old measurement by the conversion factor:

$$14 \cancel{\text{years}} \times \frac{365 \text{ days}}{1 \cancel{\text{year}}} = 5{,}110 \text{ days}$$

The person's age is 5,110 days.

Practice Problem A book has a mass of 2.31 kg. If there are 1,000 g in 1 kg, what is the mass of the book in grams? 2310 g

Using Fractions

A **fraction** is a number that compares a part to the whole. For example, in the fraction $\frac{2}{3}$, the 2 represents the part and the 3 represents the whole. In the fraction $\frac{2}{3}$, the top number, 2, is called the numerator. The bottom number, 3, is called the denominator.

Sometimes fractions are not written in their simplest form. To determine a fraction's **simplest form,** you must find the greatest common factor (GCF) of the numerator and denominator. The greatest common factor is the largest factor that is common to the numerator and denominator.

For example, because the number 3 divides into 12 and 30 evenly, it is a common factor of 12 and 30. However, because the number 6 is the largest number that evenly divides into 12 and 30, it is the **greatest common factor.**

After you find the greatest common factor, you can write a fraction in its simplest form. Divide both the numerator and the denominator by the greatest common factor. The number that results is the fraction in its **simplest form.**

Example Twelve of the 20 chemicals used in the science lab are in powder form. What fraction of the chemicals used in the lab are in powder form?

Step 1 Write the fraction.

$$\frac{\text{part}}{\text{whole}} = \frac{12}{20}$$

Step 2 To find the GCF of the numerator and denominator, list all of the factors of each number.

Factors of 12: 1, 2, 3, 4, 6, 12 (the numbers that divide evenly into 12)

Factors of 20: 1, 2, 4, 5, 10, 20 (the numbers that divide evenly into 20)

Step 3 List the common factors.

1, 2, 4.

Step 4 Choose the greatest factor in the list of common factors.

The GCF of 12 and 20 is 4.

Step 5 Divide the numerator and denominator by the GCF.

$$\frac{12 \div 4}{20 \div 4} = \frac{3}{5}$$

In the lab, $\frac{3}{5}$ of the chemicals are in powder form.

Practice Problem There are 90 rides at an amusement park. Of those rides, 66 have a height restriction. What fraction of the rides has a height restriction? Write the fraction in simplest form. $\frac{11}{15}$

Skill Handbooks

Calculating Ratios

A **ratio** is a comparison of two numbers by division.

Ratios can be written 3 to 5 or 3:5. Ratios also can be written as fractions, such as $\frac{3}{5}$. Ratios, like fractions, can be written in simplest form. Recall that a fraction is in **simplest form** when the greatest common factor (GCF) of the numerator and denominator is 1.

Example A chemical solution contains 40 g of salt and 64 g of baking soda. What is the ratio of salt to baking soda as a fraction in simplest form?

Step 1 Write the ratio as a fraction. $\frac{\text{salt}}{\text{baking soda}} = \frac{40}{64}$

Step 2 Express the fraction in simplest form. The GCF of 40 and 64 is 8.

$$\frac{40}{64} = \frac{40 \div 8}{64 \div 8} = \frac{5}{8}$$

The ratio of salt to baking soda in the solution is $\frac{5}{8}$.

Practice Problem Two metal rods measure 100 cm and 144 cm in length. What is the ratio of their lengths in simplest fraction form? $\frac{5}{6}$

Using Decimals

A **decimal** is a fraction with a denominator of 10, 100, 1,000, or another power of 10. For example, 0.854 is the same as the fraction $\frac{854}{1{,}000}$.

In a decimal, the decimal point separates the ones place and the tenths place. For example, 0.27 means twenty-seven hundredths, or $\frac{27}{100}$, where 27 is the **number of units** out of 100 units. Any fraction can be written as a decimal using division.

Example Write $\frac{5}{8}$ as a decimal.

Step 1 Write a division problem with the numerator, 5, as the dividend and the denominator, 8, as the divisor. Write 5 as 5.000.

Step 2 Solve the problem.

```
   0.625
8)5.000
  48
   20
   16
    40
    40
     0
```

Therefore, $\frac{5}{8} = 0.625$.

Practice Problem Write $\frac{19}{25}$ as a decimal. 0.76

Using Percentages

The word *percent* means "out of one hundred." A **percent** is a ratio that compares a number to 100. Suppose you read that 77 percent of Earth's surface is covered by water. That is the same as reading that the fraction of Earth's surface covered by water is $\frac{77}{100}$. To express a fraction as a percent, first find an equivalent decimal for the fraction. Then, multiply the decimal by 100 and add the percent symbol. For example, $\frac{1}{2} = 1 \div 2 = 0.5$. Then $0.5 = 0.50 = 50\%$.

Example Express $\frac{13}{20}$ as a percent.

Step 1 Find the equivalent decimal for the fraction.

$$\begin{array}{r} 0.65 \\ 20\overline{)13.00} \\ \underline{12\,0} \\ 100 \\ \underline{100} \\ 0 \end{array}$$

Step 2 Rewrite the fraction $\frac{13}{20}$ as 0.65.

Step 3 Multiply 0.65 by 100 and add the % sign.

$0.65 \cdot 100 = 65 = 65\%$

So, $\frac{13}{20} = 65\%$.

Practice Problem In one year, 73 of 365 days were rainy in one city. What percent of the days in that city were rainy? 20%

Using Precision and Significant Digits

When you make a **measurement,** the value you record depends on the precision of the measuring instrument. When adding or subtracting numbers with different precision, the answer is rounded to the smallest number of decimal places of any number in the sum or difference. When multiplying or dividing, the answer is rounded to the smallest number of significant figures of any number being multiplied or divided. When counting the number of **significant figures,** all digits are counted except zeros at the end of a number with no decimal such as 2,500, and zeros at the beginning of a decimal such as 0.03020.

Example The lengths 5.28 and 5.2 are measured in meters. Find the sum of these lengths and report the sum using the least precise measurement.

Step 1 Find the sum.

5.28 m	2 digits after the decimal
+ 5.2 m	1 digit after the decimal
10.48 m	

Step 2 Round to one digit after the decimal because the least number of digits after the decimal of the numbers being added is 1.

The sum is 10.5 m.

Practice Problem Multiply the numbers in the example using the rule for multiplying and dividing. Report the answer with the correct number of significant figures. 27.5 m^2

Skill Handbooks

Solving One-Step Equations

An **equation** is a statement that two things are equal. For example, $A = B$ is an equation that states that A is equal to B.

Sometimes one side of the equation will contain a **variable** whose value is not known. In the equation $3x = 12$, the variable is x.

The equation is solved when the variable is replaced with a value that makes both sides of the equation equal to each other. For example, the solution of the equation $3x = 12$ is $x = 4$. If the x is replaced with 4, then the equation becomes $3 \cdot 4 = 12$, or $12 = 12$.

To solve an equation such as $8x = 40$, divide both sides of the equation by the number that multiplies the variable.

$$8x = 40$$
$$\frac{8x}{8} = \frac{40}{8}$$
$$x = 5$$

You can check your answer by replacing the variable with your solution and seeing if both sides of the equation are the same.

$$8x = 8 \cdot 5 = 40$$

The left and right sides of the equation are the same, so $x = 5$ is the solution.

Sometimes an equation is written in this way: $a = bc$. This also is called a **formula.** The letters can be replaced by numbers, but the numbers must still make both sides of the equation the same.

Example 1 Solve the equation $10x = 35$.

Step 1 Find the solution by dividing each side of the equation by 10.

$$10x = 35 \qquad \frac{10x}{10} = \frac{35}{10} \qquad x = 3.5$$

Step 2 Check the solution.

$$10x = 35 \qquad 10 \times 3.5 = 35 \qquad 35 = 35$$

Both sides of the equation are equal, so $x = 3.5$ is the solution to the equation.

Example 2 In the formula $a = bc$, find the value of c if $a = 20$ and $b = 2$.

Step 1 Rearrange the formula so the unknown value is by itself on one side of the equation by dividing both sides by b.

$$a = bc$$
$$\frac{a}{b} = \frac{bc}{b}$$
$$\frac{a}{b} = c$$

Step 2 Replace the variables a and b with the values that are given.

$$\frac{a}{b} = c$$
$$\frac{20}{2} = c$$
$$10 = c$$

Step 3 Check the solution.

$$a = bc$$
$$20 = 2 \times 10$$
$$20 = 20$$

Both sides of the equation are equal, so $c = 10$ is the solution when $a = 20$ and $b = 2$.

Practice Problem In the formula $h = gd$, find the value of d if $g = 12.3$ and $h = 17.4$. $d = 1.4$

Using Proportions

A **proportion** is an equation that shows that two ratios are equivalent. The ratios $\frac{2}{4}$ and $\frac{5}{10}$ are equivalent, so they can be written as $\frac{2}{4} = \frac{5}{10}$. This equation is an example of a proportion.

When two ratios form a proportion, the **cross products** are equal. To find the cross products in the proportion $\frac{2}{4} = \frac{5}{10}$, multiply the 2 and the 10, and the 4 and the 5. Therefore $\mathbf{2 \cdot 10 = 4 \cdot 5}$**, or** $\mathbf{20 = 20}$**.**

Because you know that both proportions are equal, you can use cross products to find a missing term in a proportion. This is known as **solving the proportion.** Solving a proportion is similar to solving an equation.

Example The heights of a tree and a pole are proportional to the lengths of their shadows. The tree casts a shadow of 24 m at the same time that a 6-m pole casts a shadow of 4 m. What is the height of the tree?

Step 1 Write a proportion.

$$\frac{\text{height of tree}}{\text{height of pole}} = \frac{\text{length of tree's shadow}}{\text{length of pole's shadow}}$$

Step 2 Substitute the known values into the proportion. Let *h* represent the unknown value, the height of the tree.

$$\frac{h}{6} = \frac{24}{4}$$

Step 3 Find the cross products.

$$h \cdot 4 = 6 \cdot 24$$

Step 4 Simplify the equation.

$$4h = 144$$

Step 5 Divide each side by 4.

$$\frac{4h}{4} = \frac{144}{4}$$

$$h = 36$$

The height of the tree is 36 m.

Practice Problem The ratios of the weights of two objects on the Moon and on Earth are in proportion. A rock weighing 3 N on the Moon weighs 18 N on Earth. How much would a rock that weighs 5 N on the Moon weigh on Earth? 30 N

Using Statistics

Statistics is the branch of mathematics that deals with collecting, analyzing, and presenting data. In statistics, there are three common ways to summarize the data with a single number—the mean, the median, and the mode.

The **mean** of a set of data is the arithmetic average. It is found by adding the numbers in the data set and dividing by the number of items in the set.

The **median** is the middle number in a set of data when the data are arranged in numerical order. If there were an even number of data points, the median would be the mean of the two middle numbers.

The **mode** of a set of data is the number or item that appears most often.

Another number that often is used to describe a set of data is the range. The **range** is the difference between the largest number and the smallest number in a set of data.

A **frequency table** shows how many times each piece of data occurs, usually in a survey. The frequency table below shows the results of a student survey on favorite color.

Color	Tally	Frequency
red	||||	4
blue	~~||||~~	5
black	||	2
green	|||	3
purple	~~||||~~ ||	7
yellow	~~||||~~ |	6

Based on the frequency table data, which color is the favorite?

Example The speeds (in m/s) for a race car during five different time trials are 39, 37, 44, 36, and 44.

To find the mean:

Step 1 Find the sum of the numbers.

$$39 + 37 + 44 + 36 + 44 = 200$$

Step 2 Divide the sum by the number of items, which is 5.

$$200 \div 5 = 40$$

The mean measure is 40 m/s.

To find the median:

Step 1 Arrange the measures from least to greatest.

$$36,\ 37,\ \underline{39},\ 44,\ 44$$

Step 2 Determine the middle measure.

The median measure is 39 m/s.

To find the mode:

Step 1 Group the numbers that are the same together.

44, 44, 36, 37, 39

Step 2 Determine the number that occurs most in the set.

$\underline{44, 44}$, 36, 37, 39

The mode measure is 44 m/s.

To find the range:

Step 1 Arrange the measures from largest to smallest.

44, 44, 39, 37, 36

Step 2 Determine the largest and smallest measures in the set.

$\underline{44}$, 44, 39, 37, $\underline{36}$

Step 3 Find the difference between the largest and smallest measures.

$$44 - 36 = 8$$

The range is 8 m/s.

Practice Problem Find the mean, median, mode, and range for the data set 8, 4, 12, 8, 11, 14, 16.

mean, 10; median, 11; mode, 8; range, 12

Safety in the Science Classroom

1. Always obtain your teacher's permission to begin an investigation.
2. Study the procedure. If you have questions, ask your teacher. Be sure you understand any safety symbols shown on the page.
3. Use the safety equipment provided for you. Goggles and a safety apron should be worn during most investigations.
4. Always slant test tubes away from yourself and others when heating them or adding substances to them.
5. Never eat or drink in the lab, and never use lab glassware as food or drink containers. Never inhale chemicals. Do not taste any substances or draw any material into a tube with your mouth.
6. Report any spill, accident, or injury, no matter how small, immediately to your teacher, then follow his or her instructions.
7. Know the location and proper use of the fire extinguisher, safety shower, fire blanket, first aid kit, and fire alarm.
8. Keep all materials away from open flames. Tie back long hair and tie down loose clothing.
9. If your clothing should catch fire, smother it with the fire blanket, or get under a safety shower. NEVER RUN.
10. If a fire should occur, turn off the gas then leave the room according to established procedures.

Follow these procedures as you clean up your work area

1. Turn off the water and gas. Disconnect electrical devices.
2. Clean all pieces of equipment and return all materials to their proper places.
3. Dispose of chemicals and other materials as directed by your teacher. Place broken glass and solid substances in the proper containers. Make sure never to discard materials in the sink.
4. Clean your work area. Wash your hands thoroughly after working in the laboratory.

First Aid

Injury	Safe Response ALWAYS NOTIFY YOUR TEACHER IMMEDIATELY
Burns	Apply cold water.
Cuts and Bruises	Stop any bleeding by applying direct pressure. Cover cuts with a clean dressing. Apply ice packs or cold compresses to bruises.
Fainting	Leave the person lying down. Loosen any tight clothing and keep crowds away.
Foreign Matter in Eye	Flush with plenty of water. Use eyewash bottle or fountain.
Poisoning	Note the suspected poisoning agent.
Any Spills on Skin	Flush with large amounts of water or use safety shower.

PERIODIC TABLE OF THE ELEMENTS

Columns of elements are called groups. Elements in the same group have similar chemical properties.

Element — Hydrogen
Atomic number — 1
Symbol — H
Atomic mass — 1.008
State of matter

Each element has a block in the periodic table. Within a block, you can find important information about the element.

Period	1	2	3	4	5	6	7	8	9
1	Hydrogen 1 H 1.008								
2	Lithium 3 Li 6.941	Beryllium 4 Be 9.012							
3	Sodium 11 Na 22.990	Magnesium 12 Mg 24.305							
4	Potassium 19 K 39.098	Calcium 20 Ca 40.078	Scandium 21 Sc 44.956	Titanium 22 Ti 47.88	Vanadium 23 V 50.942	Chromium 24 Cr 51.996	Manganese 25 Mn 54.938	Iron 26 Fe 55.847	Cobalt 27 Co 58.933
5	Rubidium 37 Rb 85.468	Strontium 38 Sr 87.62	Yttrium 39 Y 88.906	Zirconium 40 Zr 91.224	Niobium 41 Nb 92.906	Molybdenum 42 Mo 95.94	Technetium 43 Tc 97.907	Ruthenium 44 Ru 101.07	Rhodium 45 Rh 102.906
6	Cesium 55 Cs 132.905	Barium 56 Ba 137.327	Lanthanum 57 La 138.906	Hafnium 72 Hf 178.49	Tantalum 73 Ta 180.948	Tungsten 74 W 183.84	Rhenium 75 Re 186.207	Osmium 76 Os 190.2	Iridium 77 Ir 192.22
7	Francium 87 Fr 223.020	Radium 88 Ra 226.025	Actinium 89 Ac 227.028	Rutherfordium 104 Rf (261)	Dubnium 105 Db (262)	Seaborgium 106 Sg (263)	Bohrium 107 Bh (262)	Hassium 108 Hs (265)	Meitnerium 109 Mt (266)

Rows of elements are called periods. Atomic number increases across a period.

The arrow shows where these elements would fit into the periodic table. They are moved to the bottom of the page to save space.

Series					
Lanthanide series	Cerium 58 Ce 140.115	Praseodymium 59 Pr 140.908	Neodymium 60 Nd 144.24	Promethium 61 Pm 144.913	Samarium 62 Sm 150.36
Actinide series	Thorium 90 Th 232.038	Protactinium 91 Pa 231.036	Uranium 92 U 238.029	Neptunium 93 Np 237.048	Plutonium 94 Pu 244.064

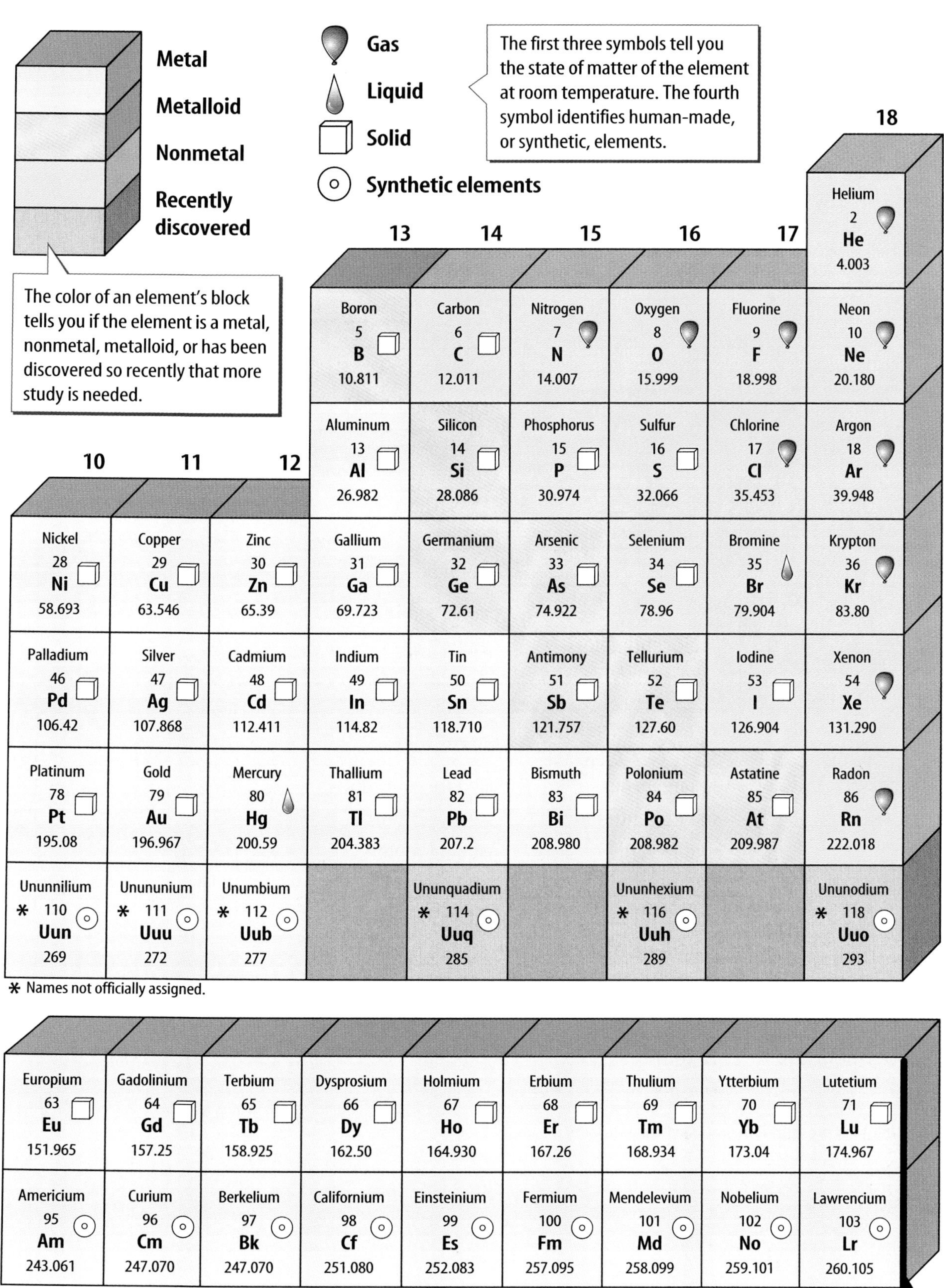

Metal
Metalloid
Nonmetal
Recently discovered
The color of an element's block tells you if the element is a metal, nonmetal, metalloid, or has been discovered so recently that more study is needed.
Gas
Liquid
Solid
Synthetic elements
The first three symbols tell you the state of matter of the element at room temperature. The fourth symbol identifies human-made, or synthetic, elements.
18
13
14
15
16
17
Helium 2 He 4.003
Boron 5 B 10.811
Carbon 6 C 12.011
Nitrogen 7 N 14.007
Oxygen 8 O 15.999
Fluorine 9 F 18.998
Neon 10 Ne 20.180
10
11
12
Aluminum 13 Al 26.982
Silicon 14 Si 28.086
Phosphorus 15 P 30.974
Sulfur 16 S 32.066
Chlorine 17 Cl 35.453
Argon 18 Ar 39.948
Nickel 28 Ni 58.693
Copper 29 Cu 63.546
Zinc 30 Zn 65.39
Gallium 31 Ga 69.723
Germanium 32 Ge 72.61
Arsenic 33 As 74.922
Selenium 34 Se 78.96
Bromine 35 Br 79.904
Krypton 36 Kr 83.80
Palladium 46 Pd 106.42
Silver 47 Ag 107.868
Cadmium 48 Cd 112.411
Indium 49 In 114.82
Tin 50 Sn 118.710
Antimony 51 Sb 121.757
Tellurium 52 Te 127.60
Iodine 53 I 126.904
Xenon 54 Xe 131.290
Platinum 78 Pt 195.08
Gold 79 Au 196.967
Mercury 80 Hg 200.59
Thallium 81 Tl 204.383
Lead 82 Pb 207.2
Bismuth 83 Bi 208.980
Polonium 84 Po 208.982
Astatine 85 At 209.987
Radon 86 Rn 222.018
Ununnilium * 110 Uun 269
Unununium * 111 Uuu 272
Unumbium * 112 Uub 277
Ununquadium * 114 Uuq 285
Ununhexium * 116 Uuh 289
Ununodium * 118 Uuo 293
* Names not officially assigned.
Europium 63 Eu 151.965
Gadolinium 64 Gd 157.25
Terbium 65 Tb 158.925
Dysprosium 66 Dy 162.50
Holmium 67 Ho 164.930
Erbium 68 Er 167.26
Thulium 69 Tm 168.934
Ytterbium 70 Yb 173.04
Lutetium 71 Lu 174.967
Americium 95 Am 243.061
Curium 96 Cm 247.070
Berkelium 97 Bk 247.070
Californium 98 Cf 251.080
Einsteinium 99 Es 252.083
Fermium 100 Fm 257.095
Mendelevium 101 Md 258.099
Nobelium 102 No 259.101
Lawrencium 103 Lr 260.105

Reference Handbook

Reference Handbook C

SI—Metric/English, English/Metric Conversions

	When you want to convert:	To:	Multiply by:
Length	inches	centimeters	2.54
	centimeters	inches	0.39
	yards	meters	0.91
	meters	yards	1.09
	miles	kilometers	1.61
	kilometers	miles	0.62
Mass and Weight*	ounces	grams	28.35
	grams	ounces	0.04
	pounds	kilograms	0.45
	kilograms	pounds	2.2
	tons (short)	tonnes (metric tons)	0.91
	tonnes (metric tons)	tons (short)	1.10
	pounds	newtons	4.45
	newtons	pounds	0.22
Volume	cubic inches	cubic centimeters	16.39
	cubic centimeters	cubic inches	0.06
	liters	quarts	1.06
	quarts	liters	0.95
	gallons	liters	3.78
Area	square inches	square centimeters	6.45
	square centimeters	square inches	0.16
	square yards	square meters	0.83
	square meters	square yards	1.19
	square miles	square kilometers	2.59
	square kilometers	square miles	0.39
	hectares	acres	2.47
	acres	hectares	0.40
Temperature	To convert °Celsius to °Fahrenheit		°C × 9/5 + 32
	To convert °Fahrenheit to °Celsius		5/9 (°F − 32)

*Weight is measured in standard Earth gravity.

Reference Handbook

English Glossary

This glossary defines each key term that appears in bold type in the text. It also shows the chapter, section, and page number where you can find the words used.

A

acceleration: rate of change of velocity; can cause an object to speed up, slow down, or turn, and can be calculated by dividing the change in speed by the given time. (Chap. 6, Sec. 2, p. 172)

accuracy: compares a measurement to the true value. (Chap. 2, Sec. 1, p. 45)

alternating current (AC): electric current that changes its direction many times each second. (Chap. 16, Sec. 2, p. 482)

alternative resources: any renewable and inexhaustible sources of energy to generate electricity, including solar energy, wind, and geothermal energy. (Chap. 8, Sec. 3, p. 246)

amplitude: distance a wave rises above or falls below its normal level, which is related to the energy that the wave carries; in a transverse wave, is one half the distance between a crest and a trough. (Chap. 11, Sec. 2, p. 321)

Archimedes' (ar kuh MEE deez) **principle:** states that the buoyant force on an object is equal to the weight of the fluid displaced by the object. (Chap. 4, Sec. 3, p. 123)

atom: a very small particle that makes up most kinds of matter and consists of smaller parts called protons, neutrons, and electrons. (Chap. 3, Sec. 1, p. 75)

atomic mass: average mass of an atom of an element; its unit of measure is the atomic mass unit (u), which is 1/12 the mass of a carbon-12 atom. (Chap. 3, Sec. 2, p. 86)

atomic number: number of protons in the nucleus of each atom of a given element; is the top number in the periodic table. (Chap. 3, Sec. 2, p. 85)

aurora: southern and northern lights that appear when charged particles trapped in the magnetosphere collide with Earth's atmosphere above the poles. (Chap. 16, Sec. 2, p. 481)

B

balanced forces: two or more equal forces whose effects cancel each other out and do not change the motion of an object. (Chap. 7, Sec. 1, p. 195)

bar graph: a type of graph that uses bars of varying sizes to show relationships between variables. (Chap. 2, Sec. 3, p. 58)

buoyant force: upward force exerted on an object immersed in a fluid. (Chap. 4, Sec. 3, p. 122)

C

carrier wave: particular transmission frequency assigned to a radio station. (Chap. 13, Sec. 3, p. 390)

chemical change: any change of a material into a new material with different properties. (Chap. 5, Sec. 3, p. 147)

chemical energy: energy that is stored in chemicals. (Chap. 8, Sec. 1, p. 231)

chemical property: characteristic of something that permits its change to something new. (Chap. 5, Sec. 2, p. 141)

circle graph: a type of graph that shows the parts of a whole; sometimes called a pie graph, each piece of which represents a percentage of the total. (Chap. 2, Sec. 3, p. 58)

circuit: closed conducting loop through which electric current can flow. (Chap. 15, Sec. 2, p. 447)

compound: a substance produced when elements combine and whose properties are different from each of the elements in it. (Chap. 3, Sec. 3, p. 89)

compound machine: device made up of a combination of two or more simple machines. (Chap. 9, Sec. 3, p. 269)

compressional wave: a type of mechanical wave in which matter in the medium moves forward and backward in the same direction the wave travels. (Chap. 11, Sec. 1, p. 319)

concave lens: lens that is thicker at its edges than in the middle and causes light rays traveling parallel to the optical axis to diverge. (Chap. 14, Sec. 3, p. 419)

condensation: change of matter from a gas to a liquid state. (Chap. 4, Sec. 2, p. 115) (Chap. 10, Sec. 3, p. 301)

conduction: transfer of heat by direct contact; occurs when particles of one substance collide with particles of another substance, transferring kinetic energy. (Chap. 10, Sec. 2, p. 291)

conductor: material, such as copper or silver, through which electrons can move easily or any material that transfers heat easily. (Chap. 10, Sec. 2, p. 293) (Chap. 15, Sec. 1, p. 444)

constant: variable that is not changed in an experiment. (Chap. 1, Sec. 2, p. 18)

controlled experiment: involves observing the effect of one thing while keeping all other things constant. (Chap. 1, Sec. 2, p. 18)

convection: transfer of thermal energy by the movement of heated molecules from one place to another in a gas or liquid. (Chap. 10, Sec. 2, p. 292)

convex lens: converging lens that is thicker in the middle than at its edges. (Chap. 14, Sec. 3, p. 418)

critical thinking: involves using knowledge and thinking skills to evaluate evidence and explanations. (Chap. 1, Sec. 4, p. 27)

D

density: physical property of matter that can be found by dividing the matter's mass by its volume. (Chap. 4, Sec. 3, p. 123) (Chap. 5, Sec. 1, p. 136)

diffraction: bending of waves around a barrier. (Chap. 11, Sec. 3, p. 330)

direct current (DC): electric current that flows only in one direction. (Chap. 16, Sec. 2, p. 15)

Doppler effect: change in the frequency or pitch of a sound that occurs when the sound source and the listener are in motion relative to each other. (Chap. 12, Sec. 1, p. 350)

E

eardrum: membrane stretching across the ear canal that vibrates when sound waves reach the middle ear. (Chap. 12, Sec. 2, p. 362)

Earth science: study of Earth systems and systems in space, including weather and climate systems and the study of nonliving things such as rocks, oceans, and planets. (Chap. 1, Sec. 1, p. 10)

echo: a reflected sound wave. (Chap. 12, Sec. 1, p. 349)

efficiency: ability of a machine to convert input work to output work. (Chap. 9, Sec. 2, p. 267)

electrical energy: energy carried by electric current that comes out of batteries and wall sockets, is generated at large power plants, and is readily transformed into other types of energy. (Chap. 8, Sec. 1, p. 232)

electric current: flow of charge—either flowing electrons or flowing ions—through a conductor. (Chap. 15, Sec. 2, p. 447)

electric discharge: rapid movement of excess charge from one place to another. (Chap. 15, Sec. 1, p. 445)

electric field: field through which electric charges exert a force on each other. (Chap. 15, Sec. 1, p. 443)

electric force: attractive or repulsive force exerted by all charged objects on each other. (Chap. 15, Sec. 1, p. 443)

electric power: rate at which an electric appliance converts electrical energy into another form of energy; usage is measured by electric meters in kilowatt-hours. (Chap. 15, Sec. 3, p. 456)

electromagnet: magnet created by wrapping a current-carrying wire around an iron core. (Chap. 16, Sec. 2, p. 477)

electromagnetic spectrum: range of electromagnetic waves, including radio waves, visible light, and X rays, with different frequencies and wavelengths. (Chap. 13, Sec. 2, p. 379)

electromagnetic waves: transverse waves that can travel through matter or space, are produced by the motion of electrically charged particles, and include X rays, ultraviolet waves, and visible light. (Chap. 11, Sec. 1, p. 320) (Chap. 13, Sec. 1, p. 374)

electron: invisible, negatively charged particle located in a cloudlike formation that surrounds the nucleus of an atom. (Chap. 3, Sec. 1, p. 78)

element: natural or synthetic material that cannot be broken down into simpler materials by ordinary means; has unique properties and is generally classified as a metal, metalloid, or nonmetal. (Chap. 3, Sec. 2, p. 82)

energy: the ability to cause change. (Chap. 8, Sec. 1, p. 228)

engine: device that converts thermal energy into mechanical energy. (Chap. 10, Sec. 4, p. 303)

estimation: method of making an educated guess at a measurement. (Chap. 2, Sec. 1, p. 43)

F

focal length: distance along the optical axis from the center of a concave mirror to the focal point. (Chap. 14, Sec. 2, p. 412)

focal point: single point on the optical axis of a concave mirror where reflected light rays pass through. (Chap. 14, Sec. 2, p. 412)

force: a push or a pull. (Chap. 7, Sec. 1, p. 194)

freezing: change of matter from a liquid state to a solid state. (Chap. 4, Sec. 2, p. 113)

frequency: number of wavelengths that pass a given point in one second, measured in hertz (Hz). (Chap. 11, Sec. 2, p. 323)

friction: rubbing force that acts against the motion between two touching surfaces and always slows an object down. (Chap. 7, Sec. 1, p. 196)

fundamental frequency: lowest natural frequency that is produced by a vibrating string or vibrating column of air. (Chap. 12, Sec. 2, p. 357)

G

gamma ray: highest-frequency, most penetrating electromagnetic wave. (Chap. 13, Sec. 2, p. 384)

gas: matter that does not have a definite shape or volume; has particles that move at high speeds in all directions. (Chap. 4, Sec. 1, p. 108)

generator: device that uses a magnetic field to turn kinetic energy into electrical energy and can produce direct current and alternating current. (Chap. 8, Sec. 2, p. 238) (Chap. 16, Sec. 2, p. 482)

Global Positioning System (GPS): uses satellites, ground-based stations, and portable units with receivers to locate objects on Earth. (Chap. 13, Sec. 3, p. 393)

graph: used to collect, organize, and summarize data in a visual way, making it easy to use and understand. (Chap. 2, Sec. 3, p. 57)

H

heat: movement of thermal energy from a substance at a higher temperature to a substance at a lower temperature. (Chap. 4, Sec. 2, p. 110) (Chap. 10, Sec. 2, p. 290)

heat of fusion: the energy that is necessary for a solid to change to a liquid at the melting point. (Chap. 10, Sec. 3, p. 299)

heat of vaporization: the amount of heat needed to change 1kg of a liquid to a gas. (Chap. 10, Sec. 3, p. 300)

hypothesis: reasonable guess that can be tested and is based on what is known and what is observed. (Chap. 1, Sec. 2, p. 14)

I

inclined plane: simple machine with a flat, sloped surface, or ramp, that makes it easier to lift a heavy load by using less force over a greater distance. (Chap. 9, Sec. 3, p. 269)

inertia: tendency of an object to resist a change in its motion. (Chap. 6, Sec. 3, p. 177)

infer: to draw a conclusion based on observation. (Chap. 1, Sec. 2, p. 16)

infrared wave: electromagnetic wave that is sensed as heat and is emitted by almost every object. (Chap. 13, Sec. 2, p. 381)

input force: force exerted on a machine; also called effort force. (Chap. 9, Sec. 2, p. 264)

instantaneous speed: the speed of an object at one instant of time. (Chap. 6, Sec. 1, p. 169)

insulator: material, such as wood or glass, through which electrons cannot move easily. (Chap. 15, Sec. 1, p. 444)

interference: ability of two or more waves to combine and form a new wave when they overlap. (Chap. 11, Sec. 3, p. 332)

internal combustion engine: engine in which fuel is burned in a combustion chamber inside the engine. (Chap. 10, Sec. 4, p. 304)

ion: a positively or negatively charged atom. (Chap. 15, Sec. 1, p. 440)

isotopes (I suh tohps): two or more atoms of the same element that have different numbers of neutrons in their nuclei. (Chap. 3, Sec. 2, p. 85)

K

kelvin (K): SI unit for temperature. (Chap. 2, Sec. 2, p. 54)

kilogram (kg): SI unit for mass. (Chap. 2, Sec. 2, p. 53)

kinetic energy: energy an object has due to its motion. (Chap. 8, Sec. 1, p. 229)

L

law of conservation of energy: states that energy can change its form but it is never created or destroyed. (Chap. 8, Sec. 2, p. 234)

law of conservation of matter: states that matter is not created or destroyed but only changes its form. (Chap. 3, Sec. 1, p. 76)

law of conservation of momentum: states that the total momentum of objects that collide with each other doesn't change. (Chap. 6, Sec. 3, p. 179)

law of reflection: states that the angle of incidence is equal to the angle of reflection. (Chap. 14, Sec. 2, p. 409)

lens: transparent object that has at least one curved surface that causes light to bend. (Chap. 14, Sec. 3, p. 417)

lever: simple machine consisting of a rigid rod or plank that pivots or rotates about a fulcrum. (Chap. 9, Sec. 3, p. 272)

life science: study of living systems and how they interact. (Chap. 1, Sec. 1, p. 9)

light ray: narrow beam of light traveling in a straight line. (Chap. 14, Sec. 1, p. 404)

line graph: a type of graph used to show the relationship between two variables that are numbers on an *x*-axis and a *y*-axis. (Chap. 2, Sec. 3, p. 57)

liquid: matter with a definite volume but no definite shape that can flow from one place to another. (Chap. 4, Sec. 1, p. 106)

loudness: the human perception of how much energy a sound wave carries. (Chap. 12, Sec. 1, p. 346)

M

magnetic domain: group of atoms whose fields point in the same direction. (Chap. 16, Sec. 1, p. 472)

magnetic field: area surrounding a magnet through which magnetic force is exerted and that extends between a magnet's north and south poles. (Chap. 16, Sec. 1, p. 471)

magnetosphere: magnetic field surrounding Earth that deflects most of the charged particles flowing from the Sun. (Chap. 16, Sec. 1, p. 473)

mass: amount of matter in an object. (Chap. 2, Sec. 2, p. 53)(Chap. 6, Sec. 3, p. 177)

mass number: sum of the number of protons and neutrons in the nucleus of an atom. (Chap. 3, Sec. 2, p. 85)

matter: anything that takes up space and has mass. (Chap. 3, Sec. 1, p. 74) (Chap. 4, Sec. 1, p. 104)

measurement: way to describe objects and events with numbers—for example, length, volume, mass, weight, and temperature. (Chap. 2, Sec. 1, p. 42)

mechanical advantage: number of times the input force is multiplied by a machine; can be calculated by dividing the output force by the input force. (Chap. 9, Sec. 2, p. 265)

mechanical wave: a type of wave that can travel only through matter. (Chap. 11, Sec. 1, p. 317)

medium: material through which a wave can travel. (Chap. 14, Sec. 1, p. 405)

melting: change of matter from a solid state to a liquid state. (Chap. 4, Sec. 2, p. 111)

metal: element that is malleable, ductile, a good conductor of electricity, and generally has a shiny or metallic luster. (Chap. 3, Sec. 2, p. 86)

metalloid: element that has characteristics of both metals and nonmetals and is a solid at room temperature. (Chap. 3, Sec. 2, p. 87)

meter (m): SI unit for length. (Chap. 2, Sec. 2, p. 51)

mixture: a combination of compounds and elements that has not formed a new substance and whose proportions can be changed without changing the mixture's identity. (Chap. 3, Sec. 3, p. 91)

model: any representation of an object or an event that is used as a tool for understanding the natural world; can communicate observations and ideas, test predictions, and save time, money, and lives. (Chap. 1, Sec. 3, p. 21)

momentum: a measure of how difficult it is to stop a moving object; a product of mass and velocity. (Chap. 6, Sec. 3, p. 178)

motor: device that transforms electrical energy into kinetic energy. (Chap. 16, Sec. 2, p. 480)

N

natural frequency: frequency at which a musical instrument or other object vibrates when it is struck or disturbed; relative to its size, shape, and the material it is made from. (Chap. 12, Sec. 2, p. 355)

net force: combination of all forces acting on an object. (Chap. 7, Sec. 1, p. 195)

neutron: an uncharged particle located in the nucleus of an atom. (Chap. 3, Sec. 1, p. 80)

Newton's first law of motion: states that objects at rest will remain at rest or move with a constant velocity unless a force is applied. (Chap. 7, Sec. 1, p. 196)

Newton's second law of motion: states that an object acted upon by a net force will accelerate in the direction of the force. (Chap. 7, Sec. 2, p. 200)

Newton's third law of motion: states that forces always act in equal but opposite pairs. (Chap. 7, Sec. 3, p. 207)

nonmetals: elements that are usually gases or brittle solids and poor conductors of electricity and heat; are the basis of the chemicals of life. (Chap. 3, Sec. 2, p. 87)

nonrenewable resources: any energy sources that eventually will run out, such as coal and oil. (Chap. 8, Sec. 3, p. 242)

nuclear energy: energy stored in atomic nuclei that can be transformed into other forms of energy by complex power plants. (Chap. 8, Sec. 1, p. 232)

nucleus (NEW klee us): positively charged, central part of an atom. (Chap. 3, Sec. 1, p. 79)

O

Ohm's law: relationship among voltage, current, and resistance in a circuit. (Chap. 15, Sec. 3, p. 453)

output force: force exerted by a machine to overcome some resistance; also called resistance force. (Chap. 9, Sec. 2, p. 264)

overtones: multiples of the fundamental frequency. (Chap. 12, Sec. 2, p. 357)

P

parallel circuit: circuit that has more than one path for electric current to follow. (Chap. 15, Sec. 3, p. 455)

Pascal's principle: states that when a force is applied to a confined fluid, an increase in pressure is transmitted equally to all parts of the fluid. (Chap. 4, Sec. 3, p. 124)

photovoltaic: device that transforms radiant energy directly into electrical energy. (Chap. 8, Sec. 3, p. 247)

physical change: any change in the size, shape, form, or state of matter in which the matter's identity remains the same. (Chap. 5, Sec. 3, p. 145)

physical property: any characteristic of matter—such as color, shape, and taste—that can be detected by the senses without changing the identity of the matter. (Chap. 5, Sec. 1, p. 136)

physical science: study of matter, which is anything that takes up space and has mass, and the study of energy, which is the ability to cause change. (Chap. 1, Sec. 1, p. 10)

pitch: how high or low a sound is. (Chap. 12, Sec. 1, p. 348)

potential energy: energy stored in an object due to its position. (Chap. 8, Sec. 1, p. 230)

power: rate at which work is done. (Chap. 9, Sec. 1, p. 261)

precision: describes how closely measurements agree with each other and how carefully measurements were made. (Chap. 2, Sec. 1, p. 44)

pressure: force exerted on a surface divided by the total area over which the force is exerted. (Chap. 4, Sec. 3, p. 118)

proton: positively charged particle located in the nucleus of an atom; counted to identify the atomic number. (Chap. 3, Sec. 1, p. 79)

pulley: simple machine made from a grooved wheel with a rope or chain wrapped around the groove. (Chap. 9, Sec. 3, p. 274)

R

radiant energy: energy carried by an electromagnetic wave. (Chap. 8, Sec. 1, p. 231) (Chap. 13, Sec. 1, p. 378)

radiation: transfer of thermal energy by electromagnetic waves. (Chap. 10, Sec. 2, p. 291)

radio waves: lowest-frequency electromagnetic waves that carry the least amount of energy and are used in most forms of telecommunications technology—such as TVs, telephones, and radios. (Chap. 13, Sec. 2, p. 380)

rate: a ratio of two different kinds of measurements. (Chap. 2, Sec. 2, p. 54)

reactivity: describes how easily something reacts with something else. (Chap. 5, Sec. 2, p. 142)

reflecting telescope: uses a concave mirror to gather light from distant objects. (Chap. 14, Sec. 4, p. 423)

reflection: occurs when a wave strikes an object or surface and bounces off. (Chap. 11, Sec. 3, p. 328) (Chap. 14, Sec. 1, p. 405)

refracting telescope: uses two convex lenses to gather light and form an image of a distant object. (Chap. 14, Sec. 4, p. 422)

refraction: bending of a wave as it moves from one medium into another medium. (Chap. 11, Sec. 3, p. 329) (Chap. 14, Sec. 3, p. 417)

renewable resources: any energy sources that are replenished continually. (Chap. 8, Sec. 3, p. 245)

resistance: a measure of how difficult it is for electrons to flow through a material; unit is the ohm (Ω). (Chap. 15, Sec. 2, p. 450)

resonance: sound amplification that occurs when an object is vibrated at its natural frequency by absorbing energy from a sound wave or other object vibrating at this frequency. (Chap. 12, Sec. 2, p. 356)

reverberation: repeated echoes of sounds. (Chap. 12, Sec. 2, p. 361)

S

salts: compounds made of a metal and a nonmetal that are formed along with water when acids and bases react with each other. (Chap. 5, Sec. 2, p. 144)

science: way of learning more about the natural world that provides possible explanations to questions and involves using a collection of skills. (Chap. 1, Sec. 1, p. 6)

scientific law: a rule that describes a pattern in nature but does not try to explain why something happens. (Chap. 1, Sec. 1, p. 7)

scientific theory: a possible explanation for repeatedly observed patterns in nature. (Chap. 1, Sec. 1, p. 7)

screw: simple machine made from an inclined plane wrapped around a cylinder. (Chap. 9, Sec. 3, p. 271)

series circuit: circuit that has only one path for electric current to follow. (Chap. 15, Sec. 3, p. 454)

SI: International System of Units, related by multiples of ten, that allows quantities to be measured in the exact same way throughout the world. (Chap. 2, Sec. 2, p. 50)

simple machine: device that has only one movement; an inclined plane, lever, wheel and axle, and pulley. (Chap. 9, Sec. 3, p. 269)

solid: matter with a definite shape and volume; has tightly packed particles that move mainly by vibrating. (Chap. 4, Sec. 1, p. 105)

specific heat: amount of energy necessary to raise the temperature of 1 kg of a substance by 1°C. (Chap. 10, Sec. 2, p. 294)

speed: rate of change of position, which can be calculated by dividing the distance traveled by the time it takes to travel that distance. (Chap. 6, Sec. 1, p. 168)

state of matter: physical property that describes a substance as a solid, liquid, or gas. (Chap. 5, Sec. 1, p. 138)

static charge: buildup of electric charge on an object. (Chap. 15, Sec. 1, p. 441)

substance: matter that has the same composition and properties throughout. (Chap. 3, Sec. 3, p. 89)

system: collection of structures, cycles, and processes that relate to and interact with each other. (Chap. 1, Sec. 1, p. 8)

T

table: presents information in rows and columns, making it easier to read and understand. (Chap. 2, Sec. 3, p. 57)

technology: use of science to help people in some way. (Chap. 1, Sec. 1, p. 11)

temperature: measure of average value of the kinetic energy of the particles in a substance; can be measured using Fahrenheit, Celsius, and Kelvin scales. (Chap. 4, Sec. 2, p. 110) (Chap 10, Sec. 1, p. 286)

terminal velocity: constant speed of an object reached when the force of gravity is balanced by air resistance. (Chap. 7, Sec. 2, p. 205)

thermal energy: total value of the kinetic and potential energy of a group of molecules. (Chap. 8, Sec. 1, p. 230)(Chap. 10, Sec. 1, p. 289)

thermal pollution: an increase in the temperature of a body of water caused by adding warmer water. (Chap. 10, Sec. 2, p. 294)

transformer: device used to increase or decrease the voltage of an alternating current with little loss of energy. (Chap. 16, Sec. 2, p. 484)

transverse wave: a type of mechanical wave in which the wave energy causes matter in the medium to move up and down or back and forth at right angles to the direction the wave travels. (Chap. 11, Sec. 1, p. 318)

turbine: set of steam-powered fan blades that spins a generator at a power plant. (Chap. 8, Sec. 2, p. 238)

U

ultraviolet radiation: electromagnetic waves with higher frequencies and shorter wavelengths than visible light. (Chap. 13, Sec. 2, p. 383)

unbalanced forces: two or more unequal forces acting on an object, causing the object to accelerate. (Chap. 7, Sec. 1, p. 195)

V

vaporization: change of matter from a liquid state to a gas. (Chap. 4, Sec. 2, p. 114) (Chap. 10, Sec. 3, p. 300)

variable: factor that can be changed in an experiment. (Chap. 1, Sec. 2, p. 18)

velocity: speed and direction of a moving object. (Chap. 6, Sec. 1, p. 171)

visible light: electromagnetic waves with wavelengths between 0.4 and 0.7 millionths of a meter that can be seen with your eyes. (Chap. 13, Sec. 2, p. 380)

voltage: a measure of how much electrical energy each electron of a battery has; measured in volts (V). (Chap. 15, Sec. 2, p. 448)

W

wave: rhythmic disturbance that carries energy but not matter. (Chap. 11, Sec. 1, p. 316)

wavelength: in transverse waves, the distance between the tops of two adjacent crests or the bottoms of two adjacent troughs; in compressional waves, the distance from the centers of adjacent rarefactions. (Chap. 11, Sec. 2, p. 322)

wedge: simple machine consisting of an inclined plane that moves; can have one or two sloping sides. (Chap. 9, Sec. 3, p. 270)

weight: the gravitational force between you and Earth. (Chap. 7, Sec. 2, p. 201)

wheel and axle: simple machine made from two different-sized, circular objects that are attached and rotate together. (Chap. 9, Sec. 3, p. 272)

work: is done when a force exerted on an object causes that object to move some distance; is equal to force times distance. (Chap. 9, Sec. 1, p. 258)

X

X ray: high-energy electromagnetic wave that is highly penetrating and can be used for medical diagnosis. (Chap. 13, Sec. 2, p. 384)

Este glosario define cada término clave que aparece en negrillas en el texto. También muestra el capítulo, la sección y el número de página en donde se usa dicho término.

A

acceleration / aceleración: tasa de cambio en la velocidad; gracias a ella, un objeto puede acelerar, decelerar o girar; se puede calcular dividiendo el cambio en rapidez entre el tiempo dado. (Cap. 6, Sec. 2, pág. 172)

accuracy / exactitud: compara una medida con el verdadero valor. (Cap. 2, Sec. 1, pág. 45)

alternating current (AC) / corriente alterna (CA): corriente eléctrica que cambia de dirección muchas veces cada segundo. (Cap. 16, Sec. 2, pág. 482)

alternative resources / recursos alternos: toda fuente de energía, tanto renovable como inagotable, que se utiliza para generar electricidad; incluye la energía solar, la energía eólica y la energía geotérmica. (Cap. 8, Sec. 3, pág. 246)

amplitude / amplitud: distancia a la cual una onda sube o baja de su nivel normal, la cual se relaciona con la energía que transporta la onda; en una onda transversal, es la mitad de la distancia entre una cresta y un seno. (Cap. 11, Sec. 2, pág. 321)

Archimedes' principle / principio de Arquímides: establece que la fuerza de flotación de un cuerpo equivale al peso del líquido que ese cuerpo desplaza. (Cap. 4, Sec. 3, pág. 123)

atom / átomo: partícula diminuta que forma la mayoría de la materia y que está a su vez formada por partículas más pequeñas llamadas protones, neutrones y electrones. (Cap. 3, Sec. 1, pág. 75)

atomic mass / masa atómica: masa promedio del átomo de un elemento; su unidad de medida es la unidad de masa atómica (u), que equivale a 1/12 de la masa de un átomo de carbono 12. (Cap. 3, Sec. 2, pág. 86)

atomic number / número atómico: número de protones en el núcleo de cada átomo de un elemento determinado; es el número en la parte superior de cada casilla en la tabla periódica. (Cap. 3, Sec. 2, pág. 85)

aurora / aurora: luces boreales y australes que parecen cambiar cuando las partículas atrapadas en la magnetosfera chocan con la atmósfera de la Tierra por encima de los polos. (Cap. 16, Sec. 2, pág. 481)

B

balanced forces / fuerzas equilibradas: dos o más fuerzas iguales cuyos efectos se anulan entre sí y no cambian el movimiento de un objeto. (Cap. 7, Sec. 1, pág. 195)

bar graph / gráfica de barras: tipo de gráfica que usa barras de distintos tamaños para mostrar relaciones entre variables. (Cap. 2, Sec. 3, pág. 58)

buoyant force / fuerza de flotabilidad: fuerza ascendente que se ejerce sobre un cuerpo sumergido en un líquido. (Cap. 4, Sec. 3, pág. 122)

C

carrier wave / onda portadora: frecuencia de transmisión particular asignada a una estación radial. (Cap. 13, Sec. 3, pág. 390)

chemical change /cambio químico: cualquier cambio de un material a otro material nuevo con distintas propiedades. (Cap. 5, Sec. 3, pág. 147)

chemical energy / energía química: energía almacenada en sustancias químicas. (Cap. 8, Sec. 1, pág. 231)

chemical property / propiedad química: Característica de algo en la naturaleza que le permite convertirse en algo nuevo. (Cap. 5, Sec. 2, pág. 141)

circle graph / gráfica circular: tipo de gráfica que muestra partes de un todo; cada parte de la gráfica es un sector que representa un porcentaje del total. (Cap. 2, Sec. 3, pág. 58)

circuit / circuito: bucle conductor cerrado por donde puede fluir la corriente eléctrica. (Cap. 15, Sec. 2, pág. 447)

compound / compuesto: sustancia formada por la combinación de elementos y cuyas propiedades son diferentes a las de los elementos que la forman. (Cap. 3, Sec. 3, pág. 89)

compound machine / máquina compuesta: dispositivo hecho de una combinación de máquinas simples. (Cap. 9, Sec. 3, pág. 269)

compressional wave / onda de compresión: tipo de onda mecánica en la cual la materia del medio oscila en la misma dirección en que viaja la onda. (Cap. 11, Sec. 1, pág. 319)

concave lens / lente cóncavo: lente que es más gruesa en los bordes que en el medio y que desvía los rayos luminosos que viajan paralelos al eje óptico. (Cap. 14, Sec. 3, pág. 419)

condensation / condensación: cambio de la materia del estado gaseoso al líquido. (Cap. 4, Sec. 2, pág. 115; Cap. 10, Sec. 3, pág. 301)

conduction / conducción: transferencia de energía por contacto directo; ocurre cuando las partículas de una sustancia chocan contra las partículas de otra sustancia y transfieren energía cinética. (Cap. 10, Sec. 2, pág. 291)

conductor / conductor: material, como el cobre o la plata, a través del cual los electrones se pueden desplazar fácilmente o cualquier material que transfiere energía fácilmente. (Cap. 10, Sec. 2, pág. 293; Cap. 15, Sec. 1, pág. 444)

constant / constante: variable que no se cambia en un experimento. (Cap. 1, Sec. 2, pág. 18)

controlled experiment / experimento controlado: implica la observación del efecto que produce una cosa mientras se mantienen constantes las demás cosas. (Cap. 1, Sec. 2, pág. 18)

convection / convección: transferencia de energía térmica de un lugar a otro en un gas o un líquido debido al movimiento de moléculas calentadas. (Cap. 10, Sec. 2, pág. 292)

convex lens / lente convexo: lente convergente que es más gruesa en el medio que en los bordes. (Cap. 14, Sec. 3, pág. 418)

critical thinking / pensamiento crítico: implica el uso del conocimiento y las destrezas del pensamiento para evaluar pruebas y explicaciones. (Cap. 1, Sec. 4, pág. 27)

D

density / densidad: propiedad física de la materia que se puede calcular dividiendo la masa de la materia entre su volumen. (Cap. 4, Sec. 3, pág. 123; Cap. 5, Sec. 1, pág. 136)

diffraction / difracción: desviación de las ondas alrededor de un obstáculo. (Cap. 11, Sec. 3, pág. 330)

direct current (DC) / corriente directa (CD): corriente eléctrica que fluye en una sola dirección. (Cap. 16, Sec. 2, pág. 15)

Doppler effect / efecto Doppler: cambio en la frecuencia o el tono de un sonido, el cual ocurre cuando la fuente sonora y el oyente están en movimiento relativo uno del otro. (Cap. 12, Sec. 1, pág. 350)

E

eardrum / tímpano: membrana que se extiende a través del canal auditivo y la cual vibra cuando las ondas sonoras llegan al oído medio. (Cap. 12, Sec. 2, pág. 362)

Earth science / ciencias terrestres: estudio de los sistemas terrestres y los espaciales, entre ellos, los sistemas del tiempo y del clima, y el estudio de las cosas sin vida como las rocas, los océanos y los planetas. (Cap. 1, Sec. 1, pág. 10)

echo / eco: onda sonora reflejada. (Cap. 12, Sec. 1, pág. 349)

efficiency / eficiencia: capacidad de una máquina de convertir el trabajo de entrada en trabajo de salida. (Cap. 9, Sec. 2, pág. 267)

electrical energy / energía eléctrica: energía transportada por la corriente eléctrica que sale de las pilas y de los enchufes de pared, se genera en centrales eléctricas grandes y se transforma fácilmente en otros tipos de energía. (Cap. 8, Sec. 1, pág. 232)

electric current / corriente eléctrica: flujo de corriente, ya sea un flujo de electrones o de iones, a través de un conductor. (Cap. 15, Sec. 2, pág. 447)

electric discharge / descarga eléctrica: movimiento rápido del exceso de carga de un lugar a otro. (Cap. 15, Sec. 1, pág. 445)

electric field / campo eléctrico: campo a través del cual las cargas eléctricas ejercen una fuerza mutua. (Cap. 15, Sec. 1, pág. 443)

electric force / fuerza eléctrica: fuerza de atracción o de repulsión que ejercen todos los objetos con carga. (Cap. 15, Sec. 1, pág. 443)

electric power / potencia eléctrica: tasa a la cual un artefacto eléctrico convierte la energía eléctrica en otra forma de energía; su uso se mide en kilovatios-hora con contadores de electricidad. (Cap. 15, Sec. 3, pág. 456)

electromagnet / electroimán: imán que se crea al enrollar un alambre que conduce corriente alrededor de un núcleo de hierro. (Cap. 16, Sec. 2, pág. 477)

electromagnetic spectrum / espectro electromagnético: rango de ondas electromagnéticas, que incluyen las ondas radiales, la luz visible y los rayos X, las cuales poseen distintas frecuencias y longitudes de onda. (Cap. 13, Sec. 2, pág. 379)

electromagnetic waves / ondas electromagnéticas: ondas transversales que pueden viajar a través de la materia o el espacio, se producen debido al movimiento de partículas cargadas eléctricamente e incluyen los rayos X, las ondas ultravioletas y la luz visible. (Cap. 11, Sec. 1, pág. 320; Cap. 13, Sec. 1, pág. 374)

electron / electrón: partícula invisible y de carga negativa localizada en una región en forma de nube que rodea el núcleo de un átomo. (Cap. 3, Sec. 1, pág. 78)

element / elemento: material natural o sintético que no puede romperse en materiales más simples mediante métodos ordinarios; tiene propiedades especiales y generalmente se clasifica como metal, metaloide o no metal. (Cap. 3, Sec. 2, pág. 82)

energy / energía: la capacidad de causar cambios. (Cap. 8, Sec. 1, pág. 228)

engine /motor: dispositivo que convierte la energía térmica en energía mecánica. (Cap. 10, Sec. 4, pág. 303)

estimation / estimación: método de hacer una conjetura razonada de una medida. (Cap. 2, Sec. 1, pág. 43)

F

focal length / longitud focal: distancia a lo largo del eje óptico desde el centro de un espejo cóncavo al punto focal. (Cap. 14, Sec. 2, pág. 412)

focal point / punto focal: punto único en el eje óptico de un espejo cóncavo a través del cual pasan los rayos luminosos reflejados. (Cap. 14, Sec. 2, pág. 412)

force / fuerza: un empuje o un jalón. (Cap. 7, Sec. 1, pág. 194)

freezing / congelación: cambio de la materia del estado líquido al sólido. (Cap. 4, Sec. 2, pág. 113)

frequency / frecuencia: número de longitudes de onda que pasan por un punto dado en un segundo; se miden en hertz (Hz). (Cap. 11, Sec. 2, pág. 323)

friction / fricción: fuerza frotadora que actúa contra el movimiento entre dos superficies en contacto y que siempre aminora la velocidad de un objeto. (Cap. 7, Sec. 1, pág. 196)

fundamental frequency / frecuencia fundamental: frecuencia natural más baja que produce una cuerda o una columna de aire que vibra. (Cap. 12, Sec. 2, pág. 357)

G

gamma ray / rayo gama: la onda electromagnética más penetrante y de alta frecuencia. (Cap. 13, Sec. 2, pág. 384)

gas / gas: materia que no posee una forma o un volumen definido; posee partículas que se mueven a gran velocidad en todas direcciones. (Cap. 4, Sec. 1, pág. 108)

generator / generador: dispositivo que utiliza un campo magnético para convertir la energía cinética en energía eléctrica y el cual puede producir corriente directa y corriente alterna. (Cap. 8, Sec. 2, pág. 238; Cap. 16, Sec. 2, pág. 482)

Global Positioning System (GPS) / Sistema de Posición Global (SPG): usa satélites, estaciones terrestres y equipo portátil con receptores para ubicar objetos sobre la Tierra. (Cap. 13, Sec. 3, pág. 393)

graph / gráfica: se usa para recopilar, organizar y resumir datos de una manera visual, facilitando de esta manera su uso y comprensión. (Cap. 2, Sec. 3, pág. 57)

H

heat / calor: movimiento de la energía térmica de una sustancia con mayor temperatura a una sustancia con menor temperatura. (Cap. 4, Sec. 2, pág. 110; Cap. 10, Sec. 2, pág. 290)

heat of fusion / calor de fusión: cantidad de calor necesario para la transición de un material en su punto de fusión entre el estado sólido y el líquido. (Cap. 10, Sec. 3, pág. 299)

heat of vaporization / calor de vaporización: cantidad de energía necesaria para convertir un kg de un líquido en un gas. (Cap. 10, Sec. 3, pág. 300)

hypothesis / hipótesis: conjetura razonable que se puede poner a prueba y que se basa en lo que se sabe y lo observable. (Cap. 1, Sec. 2, pág. 14)

I

inclined plane / plano inclinado: máquina simple con una superficie plana e inclinada, o rampa, que facilitar levantar cargas pesadas requiriendo menos fuerza a lo largo de una distancia mayor. (Cap. 9, Sec. 3, pág. 269)

inertia / inercia: tendencia que muestra un objeto de resistir cambios en su movimiento. (Cap. 6, Sec. 3, pág. 177)

infer / inferir: sacar una conclusión basándose en una observación. (Cap. 1, Sec. 2, pág. 16)

infrared wave / onda infrarroja: onda electromagnética que se siente como calor y la cual emiten casi todos los objetos. (Cap. 13, Sec. 2, pág. 381)

input force / fuerza de entrada: fuerza que se ejerce sobre una máquina, también se conoce como fuerza de esfuerzo. (Cap. 9, Sec. 2, pág. 264)

instantaneous speed / rapidez instantánea: rapidez de un cuerpo en un momento dado de tiempo. (Cap. 6, Sec. 1, pág. 169)

insulator / aislador: material a través del cual no pueden fluir los electrones fácilmente; por ejemplo, la madera o el vidrio. (Cap. 15, Sec. 1, pág. 444)

interference / interferencia: capacidad de dos o más ondas de combinarse y formar una nueva onda cuando se traslapan. (Cap. 11, Sec. 3, pág. 332)

internal combustion engine / motor de combustión interna: motor en que el combustible se quema en una cámara de combustión dentro del motor. (Cap. 10, Sec. 4, pág. 304)

ion / ion: átomo con carga positiva o negativa. (Cap. 15, Sec. 1, pág. 440)

isotopes / isótopos: dos o más átomos del mismo elemento que tienen números diferentes de neutrones en su núcleo. (Cap. 3, Sec. 2, pág. 85)

K

kelvin (K) / kelvin (K): unidad de temperatura del SI. (Cap. 2, Sec. 2, pág. 54)

kilogram (kg) / kilogramo (kg): unidad de masa del SI. (Cap. 2, Sec. 2, pág. 53)

kinetic energy / energía cinética: energía que tiene un cuerpo debido a su movimiento. (Cap. 8, Sec. 1, pág. 229)

L

law of conservation of energy / ley de conservación de la energía: establece que la energía puede transformarse pero nunca se crea ni se destruye. (Cap. 8, Sec. 2, pág. 234)

law of conservation of matter / ley de la conservación de la materia: enuncia que la materia no se puede crear ni destruir, sino que sólo cambia de forma. (Cap. 3, Sec. 1, pág. 76)

law of conservation of momentum / ley de conservación del momento: establece que el momento total de los cuerpos que chocan entre sí no cambia. (Cap. 6, Sec. 3, pág. 179)

law of reflection / ley de la reflexión: establece que el ángulo de incidencia es igual al ángulo de reflexión. (Cap. 14, Sec. 2, pág. 409)

lens / lente: objeto transparente que tiene por lo menos una superficie que hace que la luz se doble. (Cap. 14, Sec. 3, pág. 417)

lever / palanca: maquina simple que consta de una barra o tablón que gira alrededor de un fulcro. (Cap. 9, Sec. 3, pág. 272)

life science / ciencias biológicas: estudio de los sistemas vivos y sus interacciones. (Cap. 1, Sec. 1, pág. 9)

light ray / rayo luminoso: rayo angosto de luz que viaja en línea recta. (Cap. 14, Sec. 1, pág. 404)

line graph / gráfica lineal: tipo de gráfica que se utiliza para mostrar la relación entre dos variables, en forma de números, en un eje *x* y un eje *y*. (Cap. 2, Sec. 3, pág. 57)

liquid / líquido: materia que posee un volumen definido pero no una forma definida y que puede fluir de un lugar a otro. (Cap. 4, Sec. 1, pág. 106)

loudness / volumen: el grado de fortaleza de un sonido; se mide según la amplitud (grado de compresión) de una onda sonora y se puede describir según la escala de decibeles. (Cap. 12, Sec. 1, pág. 346)

M

magnetic domain / dominio magnético: grupo de átomos cuyos campos magnéticos apuntan en la misma dirección. (Cap. 16, Sec. 1, pág. 472)

magnetic field / campo magnético: área que rodea un imán a través de la cual se ejerce la fuerza magnética y que se extiende entre el polo norte del imán y el polo sur. (Cap. 16, Sec. 1, pág. 471)

magnetosphere / magnetosfera: campo magnético que rodea la Tierra y el cual desvía la mayor parte de las partículas cargadas provenientes del Sol. (Cap. 16, Sec. 1, pág. 473)

mass / masa: cantidad de materia que posee un cuerpo. (Cap. 2, Sec. 2, pág. 53; Cap. 6, Sec. 3, pág. 177)

mass number / número de masa: suma del número de protones y neutrones en el núcleo de un átomo. (Cap. 3, Sec. 2, pág. 85)

matter / materia: todo lo que ocupa espacio y posee masa. (Cap. 3, Sec. 1, pág. 74; Cap. 4, Sec. 1, pág. 104)

measurement / medida: manera de describir objetos y eventos con números; por ejemplo: longitud, volumen, masa, peso y temperatura. (Cap. 2, Sec. 1, pág. 42)

mechanical advantage / ventaja mecánica: número de veces que una máquina multiplica una fuerza de entrada; se puede calcular dividiendo la fuerza de salida entre la fuerza de entrada. (Cap. 9, Sec. 2, pág. 265)

mechanical wave / onda mecánica: tipo de onda que sólo puede viajar a través de la materia. (Cap. 11, Sec. 1, pág. 317)

medium / medio: material a través del cual puede viajar una onda. (Cap. 14, Sec. 1, pág. 405)

melting / fusión: cambio de la materia del estado sólido al líquido. (Cap. 4, Sec. 2, pág. 111)

metal / metal: elemento maleable, dúctil, buen conductor de electricidad y que generalmente tiene lustre metálico o brillante. (Cap. 3, Sec. 2, pág. 86)

metalloid / metaloide: elemento que tiene tanto características de metales como de no metales y que es sólido a temperatura ambiente. (Cap. 3, Sec. 2, pág. 87)

meter (m) / metro (m): unidad de longitud del SI. (Cap. 2, Sec. 2, pág. 51)

mixture / mezcla: una combinación de compuestos y elementos que no ha formado una nueva sustancia y cuyas proporciones pueden variarse al cambiar la identidad de la mezcla. (Cap. 3, Sec. 3, pág. 91)

model / modelo: cualquier representación

de un objeto o un fenómeno que se utiliza como instrumento para comprender el mundo natural; puede comunicar observaciones e ideas. probar predicciones y ahorrar tiempo, dinero y vidas. (Cap. 1, Sec. 3, pág. 21)

momentum / momento: medida del grado de dificultad que existe para detener un cuerpo en movimiento; el producto de la masa por la velocidad. (Cap. 6, Sec. 3, pág. 178)

motor / motor: dispositivo que puede transformar la energía eléctrica en energía cinética. (Cap. 16, Sec. 2, pág. 480)

N

natural frequency / frecuencia natural: frecuencia a la cual vibra un instrumento musical u otro objeto cuando se puntea o se perturba, con relación a su tamaño, forma y el material del cual está hecho. (Cap. 12, Sec. 2, pág. 355)

net force / fuerza neta: combinación de todas las fuerzas que actúan sobre un objeto. (Cap. 7, Sec. 1, pág. 195)

neutron / neutrón: partícula sin carga ubicada en el núcleo de un átomo. (Cap. 3, Sec. 1, pág. 80)

Newton's first law of motion / primera ley del movimiento de Newton: establece que los objetos en reposo permanecerán en reposo o se moverán a una velocidad constante, a menos que se les aplique una fuerza. (Cap. 7, Sec. 1, pág. 196)

Newton's second law of motion / segun--da ley del movimiento de Newton: establece que un objeto, al cual se le ha aplicado una fuerza neta, acelerará en la dirección de tal fuerza. (Cap. 7, Sec. 2, pág. 200)

Newton's third law of motion / tercera ley del movimiento de Newton: establece que las fuerzas siempre actúan en pares iguales pero opuestos. (Cap. 7, Sec. 3, pág. 207)

nonmetals / no metales: elementos que por lo general son gases o sólidos quebradizos y malos conductores de electricidad y calor; son las bases de las sustancias químicas de la vida. (Cap. 3, Sec. 2, pág. 87)

nonrenewable resources / recursos no renovables: toda fuente de energía que se agota a la larga, como por ejemplo, el carbón y el petróleo. (Cap. 8, Sec. 3, pág. 242)

nuclear energy / energía nuclear: energía almacenada en los núcleos atómicos que se puede transformar en otras formas de energía en centrales eléctricas muy complejas. (Cap. 8, Sec. 1, pág. 232)

nucleus / núcleo: parte central de un átomo; tiene carga positiva. (Cap. 3, Sec. 1, pág. 79)

O

Ohm's law / ley de Ohm: relación entre el voltaje, la corriente y la resistencia en un circuito. (Cap. 15, Sec. 3, pág. 453)

output force / fuerza de salida: fuerza ejercida por una máquina para sobreponer alguna resistencia; conocida también como fuerza de resistencia. (Cap. 9, Sec. 2, pág. 264)

overtones / sobretonos: múltiplos de la frecuencia fundamental. (Cap. 12, Sec. 2, pág. 357)

P

parallel circuit / circuito paralelo: circuito que tiene más de una trayectoria para el flujo de la corriente eléctrica. (Cap. 15, Sec. 3, pág. 455)

Pascal's principle / principio de Pascal: establece que cuando se le aplica una fuerza a un líquido confinado, un aumento en la presión se transmite de manera uniforme a todas las partes del líquido. (Cap. 4, Sec. 3, pág. 124)

photovoltaic / célula fotovoltaica: dispositivo que transforma la energía radiante directamente en energía eléctrica. (Cap. 8, Sec. 3, pág. 247)

physical change / cambio físico: cualquier cambio en tamaño, aspecto o estado de la materia en que la identidad de una muestra de materia permanece igual. (Cap. 5, Sec. 3, pág. 145)

physical property / propiedad física: cualquier característica de la materia, como color, forma y sabor, que pueden detectar los sentidos sin cambiar la identidad de la materia. (Cap. 5, Sec. 1, pág. 136)

physical science / ciencias físicas: estudio de la materia, que es todo lo que ocupa espacio y posee masa, y el estudio de la energía, la cual es la capacidad de producir cambios. (Cap. 1, Sec. 1, pág. 10)

pitch / tono: el grado de agudeza o gravedad de un sonido. (Cap. 12, Sec. 1, pág. 348)

potential energy / energía potencial: energía almacenada en un cuerpo debido a su posición. (Cap. 8, Sec. 1, pág. 230)

power / potencia: tasa a la cual se realiza trabajo. (Cap. 9, Sec. 1, pág. 261)

precision / precisión: describe el grado de aproximación de las medidas entre sí y el grado de exactitud con que se tomaron tales medidas. (Cap. 2, Sec. 1, pág. 44)

pressure / presión: fuerza ejercida sobre una superficie dividida entre el área total sobre la cual se ejerce la fuerza. (Cap. 4, Sec. 3, pág. 118)

proton / protón: partícula con carga positiva ubicada en el núcleo de un átomo y la cual se cuenta para identificar el número atómico. (Cap. 3, Sec. 1, pág. 79)

pulley / polea: máquina simple compuesta de una rueda acanalada con una cuerda o cadena enrollada alrededor de la parte acanalada. (Cap. 9, Sec. 3, pág. 274)

R

radiant energy / energía radiante: energía que transportan las ondas electromagnéticas. (Cap. 8, Sec. 1, pág. 231; Cap. 13, Sec. 1, pág. 378)

radiation / radiación: transferencia de energía térmica por las ondas magnéticas. (Cap. 10, Sec. 2, pág. 291)

radio waves / ondas radiales: ondas electromagnéticas de la más baja frecuencia que transportan la menor cantidad de energía y las cuales se utilizan en casi todas las formas de telecomunicaciones, por ejemplo, los televisores, los telfonos y los radios. (Cap. 13, Sec. 2, pág. 380)

rate / tasa: razón de dos clases distintas de medidas. (Cap. 2, Sec. 2, pág. 54)

reactivity / reactividad: describe el grado de facilidad de una sustancia. (Cap. 5, Sec. 2, pág. 142)

reflecting telescope / telescopio reflector: usa un espejo cóncavo para recoger la luz de objetos distantes. (Cap. 14, Sec. 4, pág. 423)

reflection / reflexión: ocurre cuando una onda choca contra un cuerpo o una superficie y rebota. (Cap. 11, Sec. 3, pág. 328; Cap. 14, Sec. 1, pág. 405)

refracting telescope / telescopio refractor: usa dos lentes convexas para recoger la luz y formar una imagen de un objeto distante. (Cap. 14, Sec. 4, pág. 422)

refraction / refracción: desviación de una onda a medida que se mueve de un medio a otro. (Cap. 11, Sec. 3, pág. 329; Cap. 14, Sec. 3, pág. 417)

renewable resources / recursos renovables: toda fuente de energía que se regenera continuamente. (Cap. 8, Sec. 3, pág. 245)

resistance / resistencia: una medida del grado de dificultad con que los electrones pueden fluir a través de un material; la unidad de medida es el omnio (Ω). (Cap. 15, Sec. 2, pág. 450)

resonance / resonancia: amplificación sonora que ocurre cuando un objeto vibra a su frecuencia natural al absorber energía de una onda sonora u otro objeto que vibra a esa misma frecuencia. (Cap. 12, Sec. 2, pág. 356)

reverberation / reverberación: ecos de sonidos repetidos. (Cap. 12, Sec. 2, pág. 361)

S

salts / sales: compuestos hechos de metales y no metales que se forman junto con el agua cuando los ácidos y las bases reaccionan entre sí. (Cap. 5, Sec. 2, pág. 144)

science / ciencia: manera de aprender más acerca de la naturaleza que ofrece posibles explicaciones a preguntas e implica el uso de un número de destrezas. (Cap. 1, Sec. 1, pág. 6)

scientific law / ley científica: una regla que describe un patrón en la naturaleza pero que no intenta explicar por qué suceden las cosas. (Cap. 1, Sec. 1, pág. 7)

scientific theory / teoría científica: una posible explicación para los patrones que se observan repetidamente en la naturaleza. (Cap. 1, Sec. 1, pág. 7)

screw / tornillo: máquina simple hecha de un plano inclinado enrollado alrededor de un silingro. (Cap. 9, Sec. 3, pág. 271)

series circuit / circuito en serie: circuito con una sola trayectoria a través de la cual puede fluir la corriente eléctrica. (Cap. 15, Sec. 3, pág. 454)

SI / SI: Sistema internacional de unidades, relacionado por múltiplos de diez, que permite que las cantidades se midan de la misma manera exacta en todo el mundo. (Cap. 2, Sec. 2, pág. 50)

simple machine / máquina simple: dispositivo que sólo tiene un movimiento; plano inclinado, rueda y eje y polea. (Cap. 9, Sec. 3, pág. 269)

solid / sólido: materia con forma y volumen definidos; tiene partículas muy apretadas que se mueven principalmente por vibración. (Cap. 4, Sec. 1, pág. 105)

specific heat / calor específico: cantidad de energía necesaria para elevar 1°C la temperatura de un kg de una sustancia. (Cap. 10, Sec. 2, pág. 294)

speed / rapidez: tasa de cambio de posición, la cual se puede calcular dividiendo la distancia viajada entre el tiempo que se toma viajar tal distancia. (Cap. 6, Sec. 1, pág. 168)

state of matter / estado de la materia: propiedad física que describe una sustancia como un sólido, un líquido o un gas. (Cap. 5, Sec. 1, pág. 138)

static charge / carga estática: acumulación de cargas eléctricas en un objeto. (Cap. 15, Sec. 1, pág. 441)

substance / sustancia: materia que tiene la misma composición y propiedades a lo largo de toda su extensión. (Cap. 3, Sec. 3, pág. 89)

system / sistema: conjunto de estructuras, ciclos y procesos que se relacionan e interactúan entre sí. (Cap. 1, Sec. 1, pág. 8)

T

table / tabla: despliega información en hileras y columnas facilitando la lectura y comprensión de los datos. (Cap. 2, Sec. 3, pág. 57)

technology / tecnología: uso de la ciencia para ayudar a las personas de alguna manera. (Cap. 1, Sec. 1, pág. 11)

temperature / temperatura: medida de la energía cinética promedio de las partículas de una sustancia; puede medirse usando las escalas Fahrenheit, Celsius o Kelvin. (Cap. 4, Sec. 2, pág. 110; Cap. 10, Sec. 1, pág. 286)

terminal velocity / velocidad terminal: rapidez constante de un objeto que se alcanza cuando la fuerza de gravedad es equilibrada por la resistencia del aire. (Cap. 7, Sec. 2, pág. 205)

thermal energy / energía térmica: valor total de la energía cinética y la potencial de un grupo de moléculas. (Cap. 8, Sec. 1, pág. 230; Cap. 10, Sec. 1, pág. 289)

thermal pollution / contaminación térmica: aumento en la temperatura de una masa de agua, el cual ocurre cuando se añade agua más caliente en la masa de agua. (Cap. 10, Sec. 2, pág. 294)

transformer / transformador: dispositivo que se usa para aumentar o rebajar el voltaje de una corriente alterna y el cual produce poca pérdida de energía. (Cap. 16, Sec. 2, pág. 484)

transverse wave / onda transversal: tipo de onda mecánica en la cual la energía de la onda hace que la materia del medio suba o baje u oscile formando ángulos rectos con la dirección en que viaja la onda. (Cap. 11, Sec. 1, pág. 318)

turbine / turbina: conjunto de álabes accionados a vapor que hace girar un generador en una central eléctrica. (Cap. 8, Sec. 2, pág. 238)

U

ultraviolet radiation / radiación ultravioleta: ondas electromagnéticas con frecuencias más altas y longitudes de onda más cortas que la luz visible. (Cap. 13, Sec. 2, pág. 383)

unbalanced forces / fuerzas desequilibradas: dos o más fuerzas desiguales que actúan sobre un objeto, haciendo que éste acelere. (Cap. 7, Sec. 1, pág. 195)

vaporization / vaporización: cambio de la materia del estado líquido al gaseoso. (Cap. 4, Sec. 2, pág. 114; Cap. 10, Sec. 3, pág. 300)

variable / variable: factor que se puede cambiar en un experimento. (Cap. 1, Sec. 2, pág. 18)

velocity / velocidad: rapidez y dirección de un cuerpo en movimiento. (Cap. 6, Sec. 1, pág. 171)

visible light / luz visible: ondas electromagnéticas con longitudes de onda entre 0.4 y 0.7 millonésimas de metro y las cuales se pueden ver a simple vista. (Cap. 13, Sec. 2, pág. 382)

voltage / voltaje: una medida de la cantidad de energía eléctrica que tiene cada electrón en una batería; se mide en voltios (V). (Cap. 15, Sec. 2, pág. 448)

W

wave / onda: perturbación rítmica que transporta energía pero no materia. (Cap. 11, Sec. 1, pág. 316)

wavelength / longitud de onda: en las ondas transversales, es la distancia entre la parte superior de dos crestas adyacentes o la parte inferior de dos senos adyacentes; en las ondas de compresión, es la distancia desde los centros de rarefacciones adyacentes. (Cap. 11, Sec. 2, pág. 322)

wedge / cuña: máquina simple que consta de un plano inclinado que se mueve; puede tener un o dos lados inclinados. (Cap. 9, Sec. 3, pág. 270)

weight / peso: fuerza gravitatoria entre cualquier cuerpo y la Tierra. (Cap. 7, Sec. 2, pág. 201)

wheel and axle / rueda y eje: máquina simple compuesta de dos objetos circulares de distinto tamaño que están unidos y que giran juntos. (Cap. 9, Sec. 3, pág. 272)

work / trabajo: se hace trabajo cuando una fuerza ejercida sobre un objeto hace que el objeto se mueve cierta distancia; es igual a fuerza por distancia. (Cap. 9, Sec. 1, pág. 258)

X

X ray / rayo X: onda electromagnética de alta frecuencia que es muy penetrante y la cual se usa en el diagnóstico médico. (Cap. 13, Sec. 2, pág. 384)

Index

The index for *Introduction to Physical Science* will help you locate major topics in the book quickly and easily. Each entry in the index is followed by the number of the pages on which the entry is discussed. A page number given in boldfaced type indicates the page on which that entry is defined. A page number given in italic type indicates a page on which the entry is used in an illustration or photograph. The abbreviation *act.* indicates a page on which the entry is used in an activity.

A

B

C

Index

D

Index

Index

Index

N

O

Index

Index

W

Art Credits

Glencoe would like to acknowledge the artists and agencies who participated in illustrating this program: Absolute Science Illustration; Andrew Evansen; Argosy; Articulate Graphics; Craig Attebery represented by Frank & Jeff Lavaty; CHK America; Gagliano Graphics; Pedro Julio Gonzalez represented by Melissa Turk & The Artist Network; Robert Hynes represented by Mendola Ltd.; Morgan Cain & Associates; JTH Illustration; Laurie O'Keefe; Matthew Pippin represented by Beranbaum Artist's Representative; Precision Graphics; Publisher's Art; Rolin Graphics, Inc.; Wendy Smith represented by Melissa Turk & The Artist Network; Kevin Torline represented by Berendsen and Associates, Inc.; WILDlife ART; Phil Wilson represented by Cliff Knecht Artist Representative; Zoo Botanica.

Photo Credits

Abbreviation key: AA=Animals Animals; AH=Aaron Haupt; AMP=Amanita Pictures; BC=Bruce Coleman, Inc.; CB=CORBIS; DM=Doug Martin; DRK=DRK Photo; ES=Earth Scenes; FP=Fundamental Photographs; GH=Grant Heilman Photography; IC=Icon Images; KS=KS Studios; LA=Liaison Agency; MB=Mark Burnett; MM=Matt Meadows; PE=PhotoEdit; PD=PhotoDisc; PQ=PictureQuest; PR=Photo Researchers; SB=Stock Boston; TSA=Tom Stack & Associates; TSM=The Stock Market; VU=Visuals Unlimited.

Cover Paul Ruben

vii Tom Prettyman/PE; **ix** NASA; **x** Siegfried Layda/Stone; **xi** Doug Cheeseman/Peter Arnold, Inc.; **xii** VCG/FPG; **xiii** Lester Lefkowitz/TSM; **xiv** Roger Ressmeyer/CB; **xv** file photo; **xvi** Ken Frick; **xvii** D. Boone/CB; **xviii** Ernst Haas/Stone; xix MB; **1** Bob Daemmrich; **2** PD; **2-3** Wolfgang Kaehler; **3** PD; **4** National Marine Mammal Lab; **4-5 14** Richard Hutchings; **15** MM; **16** IC; **17** Richard Hutchings/PE/PQ; **18** Rudi VonBriel; **19** Bob Daemmrich; **20** Glasheen Graphics/Index Stock; **21** (t)David Young-Wolff/PE, (c)John Bavosi/Science Photo Library/PR, (bl)A. Ramey/PE, (br)Donald C. Johnson/TSM; **22** CB/PQ; **23** Todd Gipstein/CB; **24** (tl)Betty Pat Gatliff, (tr)Richard Nowitz/Words & Pictures/PQ, (c)Betty Pat Gatliff, (bl)Michael O'Brian/Mud Island, Inc., (br)Betty Pat Gatliff; **25** (tl)CB, (tr)Tom Wurl/SB/PQ, (b)Jim Sugar Photography/CB; **26** (l)Stock Montage, (r)North Wind Picture Archives; **27** Digital Art/CB; **28** SuperStock; **29** (t)Lester V. Bergman/CB, (b)Bob Handelman/Stone; **31** John Evans; **32** (t)AH, (b)MM; **34** Benainous-Deville/LA; **35** (t)UPI/Bettmann/CB, (b)Reuters/CB; **36** Robert Glusic/PD; **38** Tim Courlas; **39** Charles D. Winters/PR; **40** First Image; **40-41** Brent Jones/SB; **41** MM; **42** Paul Almasy/CB; **43** AFP/CB; **44** David Young-Wolff/PE; **45** (tl)Lowell D. Franga, (tr)The Purcell Team/CB, (b)Len Delessio/Index Stock; **46** Photos by Richard T. Nowitz, imaging by Janet Dell Russell Johnson; **47** MM; **49** First Image; **51** Tom Prettyman/PE; **53** (t)Michael Dalton/FP, (cl)David Young-Wolff/PE, (cr)Dennis Potokar/PR, (b)MM; **55** Michael Newman/PE; **57** John Cancalosi/SB; **60 61** Richard Hutchings; **62** (t)Fletcher & Baylis/PR, (b)Owen Franken/CB; **63** CMCD/PD; **64** Fred Bavendam/Stone; **65** First Image; **69** MM; **70** CB/PQ; **70-71** Stephen Frisch/SB/PQ; **72** AMP; **72-73** Jack Affleck/Index Stock; **73** Morrison Photography; **74** (l)Gary C. Will/VU, (c)MB/SB, (r)CB; **76** MB; **77** (l)MB, (r)NASA; **78** Van Bucher/PR; **82** Fermi National Accelerator Laboratory/Science Photo Library/PR; **83** Tom Stewart/TSM; **84** (t cl cr)Bettmann/CB, (b)New York Public Library, General Research Division, Astor, Lenox, and Tilden Foundations; **86** Emmanuel Scorcelletti/LA; **88** DM; **89** NASA; **90** MB; **91** Klaus Guldbrandsen/Science Photo Library/PR; **92** (tl)Mark Thayer, (tr)CB, (bl)Kenneth Mengay/LA, (bc)Arthur Hill/VU, (br)RMIP/Richard Hayes; **92-93** KS; **94** IC; **95** Michael Newman/PE; **96** (tl)Stone, (tr)John Eastcott & Yva Momatiuk/DRK, (c)Robert Essel/TSM, (bl)Ame Hodalic/CB, (br)Norman Owen Tomalin/BC; **98** (tl)Skip Comer, (tr)DM, (b)AMP; **102** Jim Cummins/FPG; **102-103** Roger Ressmeyer/CB; **103** First Image; **104** Layne Kennedy/CB; **105** (t)Telegraph Colour Library/FPG, (b)Paul Silverman/FP; **106** Bill Aron/PE; **107** (l)John Serrao/PR, (r)H. Richard Johnston/FPG; **108** Tom Tracy/Photo Network/PQ; **109** Annie Griffiths Belt/CB; **110** AMP; **111** (t)David Weintraub/SB, (b)James L. Amos/Peter Arnold, Inc.; **112** Dave King/DK Images; **113** Joseph Sohm/ChromoSohm/CB; **114** Michael Dalton/FP; **115** Swarthout & Associates/TSM; **116** Tony Freeman/PE; **118** David Young-Wolff/PE; **119** (tl tr)Joshua Ets-Hokin/PD, (b)Richard Hutchings; **120** Robbie Jack/CB; **121** Dominic Oldershaw; **122** A. Ramey/SB; **123** First Image; **124** (l)Tony Freeman/PE, (r)Stephen Simpson/FPG; **126** (l)Lester Lefkowitz/TSM, (r)Bob Daemmrich; **127** Bob Daemmrich; **128 129** Daniel Belknap; **130** (t bl)KS, (br)Jeff Smith/Fotosmith; **131** (l)Andrew Ward/Life File/PD, (r)NASA/TRACE; **134** Bruce Dale/National Geographic; **134-135** Frank Lane Picture Agency/CB; **135** MM; **136** Steven R. Krous/SB/PQ;

137 Ryan McVay/PD; **138** David W. Hamilton/Image Bank; **139** (t)Morrison Photography, (b)Jose Azel/Aurora/PQ; **140** Morrison Photography; **141** (l)AH, (r)Arthur S. Aubry/PD; **142** (t c)Morrison Photography, (b)Bob Daemmrich/SB; **143** Morrison Photography; **144** AH; **145** AFP/CB; **146** (tl)Morrison Photography, (tr)Art Montes de Oca/FPG, (bl)Anthony Ise/PD, (br)Novastock/Index Stock; **147** (l)John Maher/SB/PQ, (c)MM, (r)AP Photo/Jim McKnight; **148** Morrison Photography; **149** (l)Brenda Tharp/PR, (r)Charles Benes/FPG; **150** Gerry Ellis/ENP Images; **151 152 153** Morrison Photography; **154** (l)Will & Deni McIntyre/PR, (r)Robert Nickelsberg/Time Magazine; **154-155** Morton Beebe, SF/CB; **156** (t)AH, (c)AMP, (b)MM; **157** (l)file photo, (r)courtesy Diamond International; **159** (tr)Michael Nelson/FPG, (others)Morrison Photography; **162-163** John Terence Turner/FPG; **163** (t)Artville, (b)Charles L. Perrin; **164** Jeremy Woodhouse/PD; **164-165** Peter Griffith/Masterfile; **165** MB; **166** Telegraph Colour Library/FPG; **167** Geoff Butler; **170** Richard Hutchings; **173** Runk/Schoenberger from Grant Heilman; **175** Mark Doolittle/Outside Images/PQ; **176** Rick Graves/Stone; **177** (l)TSM, (r)Will Hart/PE; **179** (t)Richard Megna/FP, (bl)Jodi Jacobson/Peter Arnold, Inc., (br)Jules Frazier/PD; **180** MB; **181** Slim Films; **182** Robert Brenner/PE; **183** Laura Sifferlin; **184** (t)Richard Olivier/CB, (b)IC; **185** IC; **187** Alexis Duclos/LA; **188** Tom & DeeAnn McCarthy/TSM; **189** (t)Rudi Von Briel/PE, (bl)AFP/CB, (br)PD; **192** Russell D. Curtis/PR; **192-193** Fujifotos/The Image Works; **193** Richard Hutchings; **194** (l)Globus Brothers Studios, NYC, (r)SB; **195** Bob Daemmrich; **196** (t)Beth Wald/Adventure Photo, (b)David Madison; **197** Rhoda Sidney/SB/PQ; **199** (l)Myrleen Cate/PE, (r)David Young-Wolff/PE; **200** Bob Daemmrich; **202** (t)Stone, (b)Myrleen Cate/PE; **204** David Madison; **206** (t)Tom Sanders/Adventure Photo, (b)Richard Fuller/David Madison Sports Images; **207** Mary M. Steinbacher/PE; **208** (t)Betty Sederquist/VU, (b)Jim Cummins/FPG; **209** (tl)Denis Boulanger/Allsport, (tr)Donald Miralle/Allsport, (b)Tony Freeman/PE/PQ; **210** (t)David Madison, (b)NASA; **212** NASA; **213** Richard Hutchings; **214 215** First Image; **216** Didier Charre/Image Bank; **217** Tom Wright/CB; **218** (t)William R. Sallaz/Duomo, (c)Bob Daemmrich, (b)First Image; **219** (t)Philip Bailey/TSM, (c)Romilly Lockyer/Image Bank, (b)Tony Freeman/PE; **222** Tony Freeman/PE; **224-225** Douglas Peebles/CB; **225** Henry Ford Museum & Greenfield Village; **226** Charles Krebs/Stone; **226-227** Roger Ressmeyer/CB; **227** Bob Daemmrich; **228** (l)file photo, (c)file photo, (r)MB; **229** (t)Bob Daemmrich, (c)Al Tielemans/Duomo, (b)Bob Daemmrich; **230** KS; **231** (tl tr) Bob Daemmrich, (b)Andrew McClenaghan/Science Photo Library/PR; **232** MB/PR; **233** Lori Adamski Peek/Stone; **234** Richard Hutchings; **235** Ron Kimball/Ron Kimball Photography; **236** (tl)Judy Lutz, (tc tr bl)Stephen R. Wagner, (br)Lennart Nilsson; **238 240** KS; **246** (t)Dr. Jeremy Burgess/Science Photo Library/PR, (b)John Keating/PR; **247** Geothermal Education Office; **248** Carsand-Mosher; **249** Billy Hustace/Stone; **250** SuperStock; **251** Roger Ressmeyer/ CB; **252** (t)James Blank/FPG, (c)Robert Torres/Stone, (bl br)SuperStock; **253** (l)Lowell Georgia/CB, (r)Mark Richards/PE; **254** Reuters NewMedia Inc./CB; **256** (t)Sandia National Laboratories, (b)Tony Page/Stone; **256-257** Dan Habib/Impact Visuals/PQ; **257** MB; **258** Mary Kate Denny; **259** (t)Tony Freeman/PE, (b)Richard Hutchings; **266** (l)Frank Siteman/SB, (r)David Young-Woolf/PE; **269** Duomo; **270** Robert Brenner/PE; **271** (t)Tom McHugh/PR, (b)AMP; **272** AMP; **273** (t)Dorling Kindersley, (bl br)Bob Daemmrich; **274** (l)Siegfried Layda/Stone, (r)Wernher Krutein/LA; **276** Tony Freeman/PE; **277** AH; **278** (l)Ed Kashi/CB, (r)Secci-Lecaque/Roussel-USCLAF/CNRI-Science Photo Library/PR; **279** (t)Keri Pickett, (b)James Balog/Contact; **280** (tl)Gabe Palmer/TSM, (tr)Ken Frick, (b)StudiOhio; **281** (l)Inc. Janeart/The Image Bank, (r)Ryan McVay/PD; **284** Archive Photos; **284-285** Dave Jacobs/Stone; **285** AH; **286** John Evans; **287** (t)Nancy P. Alexander/VU, (b)Morton & White; **289** Tom Stack; **290** DM; **291** MM; **292** Jeremy Hoare/PD; **293** Donnie Kamin/PE; **294** SuperStock; **295** Colin Raw/Stone; **296** AH; **298** (l)Barbara Stitzer/PE, (c)Doug Menuez/PD, (r)Addison Geary/SB; **299** Slim Films; **300** C. Squared Studios/PD; **302 303** Morton & White; **304-305** Chip Simons/FPG; **305** Joseph Sohm/CB; **306** (l)James Holmes/Science Photo Library/PR, (r)Jenny Hager/The Image Works; **307** SuperStock; **312-313** Matthew Borkoski/SB/PQ; **313** L. Fritz/H. Armstrong Roberts; **314** Jerome Wexler/PR; **314-315** Douglas Peebles/CB; **315** Spencer Grant/PE; **316** (l)file photo, (r)David Young-Wolff/PE; **317** David Young-Wolff/PE; **318** Mark Thayer; **321** Steven Starr/SB; **327** Ken Frick; **328** MB; **329** Ernst Haas/Stone; **330** Peter Beattie/LA; **332** (t)D. Boone/CB, (b)Stephen R. Wagner; **333** Seth Resnick/SB; **334** (t)Reuters NewMedia, Inc./CB, (b)Timothy Fuller; **336** (t)John Evans, (b)SuperStock; **337** Roger Ressmeyer/CB; **338** Mark Thayer; **342** Paul Silverman/FP; **342-343** Roger Ressmeyer/CB; **343** Timothy Fuller; **347** (t)Joe Towers/TSM, (c)Bob Daemmrich/SB/PQ, (b)Jean-Paul Thomas/Jacana Scientific Control/PR; **349** Stephen Dalton/PR; **350** NOAA; **351** Slim Films; **352** Spencer Grant/PE; **354** Timothy Fuller; **356** Mark Thayer;

358 Dilip Mehta/Contact Press Images/PQ; **359** (tl)CB, (tr)Paul Seheult/Eye Ubiquitous/CB, (b)IC; **360** William Whitehurst/TSM; **361** SuperStock; **362** (t)Geostock/PD, (b)SuperStock; **363** Fred E. Hossler/VU; **364** (t)Ryan McVay/PD, (b)Oliver Benn/Stone; **366** Douglas Whyte/TSM; **367** (t)Steve Labadessa/Time Inc., (c)courtesy 3M, (b)Bernard Roussel/The Image Bank; **368** (t)Edmond Van Hoorick/PD, (c)Will McIntyre/PR, (b)Kim Steele/PD; **369** (tl)The Photo Works/PR, (tr)PD, (cl)Artville, (cr)PD, (b)Gary Braasch/Stone; **370** (t)PhotoSpin/Artville/PQ, (b)C. Squared Studios/PD; **372** Stephanie Maze/CB; **372-373** Roger Ressmeyer/CB; **373** IC; **374** (l)Bob Abraham/TSM, (r)Jeff Greenberg/VU; **375** (l)David Young-Wolff/PE, (r)NRSC, Ltd./Science Photo Library/PR; **376** (t)Grantpix/PR, (b)Richard Megna/FP; **378** Luke Dodd/Science Photo Library/PR; **380** (t)MM, (b)Jean Miele/TSM; **382** (t)Gregory G. Dimijian/PR, (b)Charlie Westerman/Liaison; **383** AH; **385** (l)MM, (r)Bob Daemmrich/The Image Works; **386** Yohkoh Data Archive Centre; **386** (t)Max Planck Institute for Radio Astronomy/Science Photo Library/PR, (b)ESA/Science Photo Library/PR; **387** (l)NASA/Science Photo Library/PR, (c)Harvard-Smithsonian Center for Astrophysics, (r)ESA; **388** Timothy Fuller; **391** MM; **393** Ken M. Johns/PR; **394** Michael Thomas/Stock South/PQ; **395** Dominic Oldershaw; **396** (t)Culver Pictures, (b)Hulton Getty Library/LA; **397** Aurthur Tilley/FPG; **398** (t)G. Brad Lewis/LA, (c)George B. Diebold/TSM, (b)Yoav Levy/Phototake/PQ; **399** (l)Macduff Everton/CB, (r)NASA/Mark Marten/PR; **400** Michael Thomas/Stock South/PQ; **402** Novastock/PE; **402-403** Cary Wolinsky/SB/PQ; **403** MM; **404** Dick Thomas/VU; **405** John Evans; **406** (t)Bob Woodward/TSM, (cl)Ping Amranand/Pictor, (cr)SuperStock, (b)Runk/Schoenberger from Grant Heilman; **407** (l)Mark Thayer, (r)Dr. Dennis Kunkel/PhotoTake NYC; **410** David Toase/PD; **412** (l)Bill Aron/PE, (r)Paul Silverman/FP; **413** (l)Digital Stock, (r)Joseph Pamieri/Pictor; **415** Geoff Butler; **417** Richard Megna/FP; **420** David M. Dennis; **421** David Young-Wolff/PE; **422 423** Roger Ressmeyer/CB; **425** Charles O'Rear/CB; **426** (t)MM, (b)Geoff Butler; **427** Geoff Butler; **428-429** Ed Welche's Antiques/Winslow, ME; **429** (t)courtesy Cheryl Landry, (b)The Stapleton Collection/Bridgeman Art Library; **430** (t)file photo, (c)MB, (b)Jeremy Horner/Stone; **432** Carol Christensen/Stock South/PQ; **436** Layne Kennedy/CB; **436-437** Richard Pasley/SB/PQ; **437** MB; **438** AH; **438-439** Peter Menzel/SB/PQ; **439** Geoff Butler; **441** (t)Richard Hutchings, (b)KS; **442** Stephen R. Wagner; **446** J. Tinning/PR; **454** DM; **455** (t)DM, (b)Geoff Butler; **457** Bonnie Freer/PR; **459** MM; **460 461** Richard Hutchings; **462-463** Tom & Pat Leeson/PR; **463** William Munoz/PR; **464** (t)DM, (c)AP Photo/Matt York, (b)IC; **466** DM; **468** John Evans; **468-469** Argus Fotoarchiv/Peter Arnold, Inc.; **469** MM; **471** Richard Megna/FP; **472** AMP; **474** PD; **475** John Evans; **477** (l)Kodansha, (c)Manfred Kage/Peter Arnold, Inc., (r)DM; **481** Bjorn Backe Papilio/CB; **483** Norbert Schafer/TSM; **485** AT&T Bell Labs/Science Photo Library/PR; **486** (tl)Science Photo Library/PR, (tr)Fermilab/Science Photo Library/PR, (b)SuperStock; **487** PD; **488** (t)file photo, (b)AH; **489** AH; **490** (tl)IC, (tr)Digital Vision/PQ, (bl)Stock-Trek/PD, (br)Spencer Grant/PE; **491** (l)SIU/Peter Arnold, Inc., (r)Latent Image; **492** file photo; **496-497** PD; **498** (t)KS, (b)Bill Aron/PR; **499** (t)IC, (bl br)KS; **500** (t)Don Tremain/PD, (b)AH; **501** KS; **502** file photo; **503** (t)Dan Feicht, (b)VU; **504** Jose Carrillo/PE; **505** (t)AH, (b)Michael J. Howell/Rainbow/PQ; **506** (t)CB, (b)Artville; **507** (tl tr c)PD, (b)Artville; **508** (t c)Artville, (b)StudiOhio; **509** (t)PD, (c)Wolfgang Kaehler/CB, (b)CB; **510** CB; **511** (t)Bill Vaine/CB, (b)John Dudak/PhotoTake NYC/PQ; **512** (t)NOAA Photo Library/Central Library, OAR/ERL/National Severe Storms Laboratory (NSSL), (c)Richard Hamilton Smith/CB, (b)Jeffry W. Myers/CB; **513** AP Photo/Geophysical Institute, University of Alaska Fairbanks via RE/MAX; **514** NASA; **515** (l)NASA, (r)Roger Ressmeyer/CB; **516** (t)NASA/Roger Ressmeyer/CB, (c b)NASA; **517** NASA; **518** Timothy Fuller; **522** Roger Ball/TSM; **524** (l)Geoff Butler, (r)Coco McCoy/Rainbow/PQ; **525** Dominic Oldershaw; **526** StudiOhio; **527** First Image; **529** MM; **532** Paul Barton/TSM; **535** Davis Barber/PE.

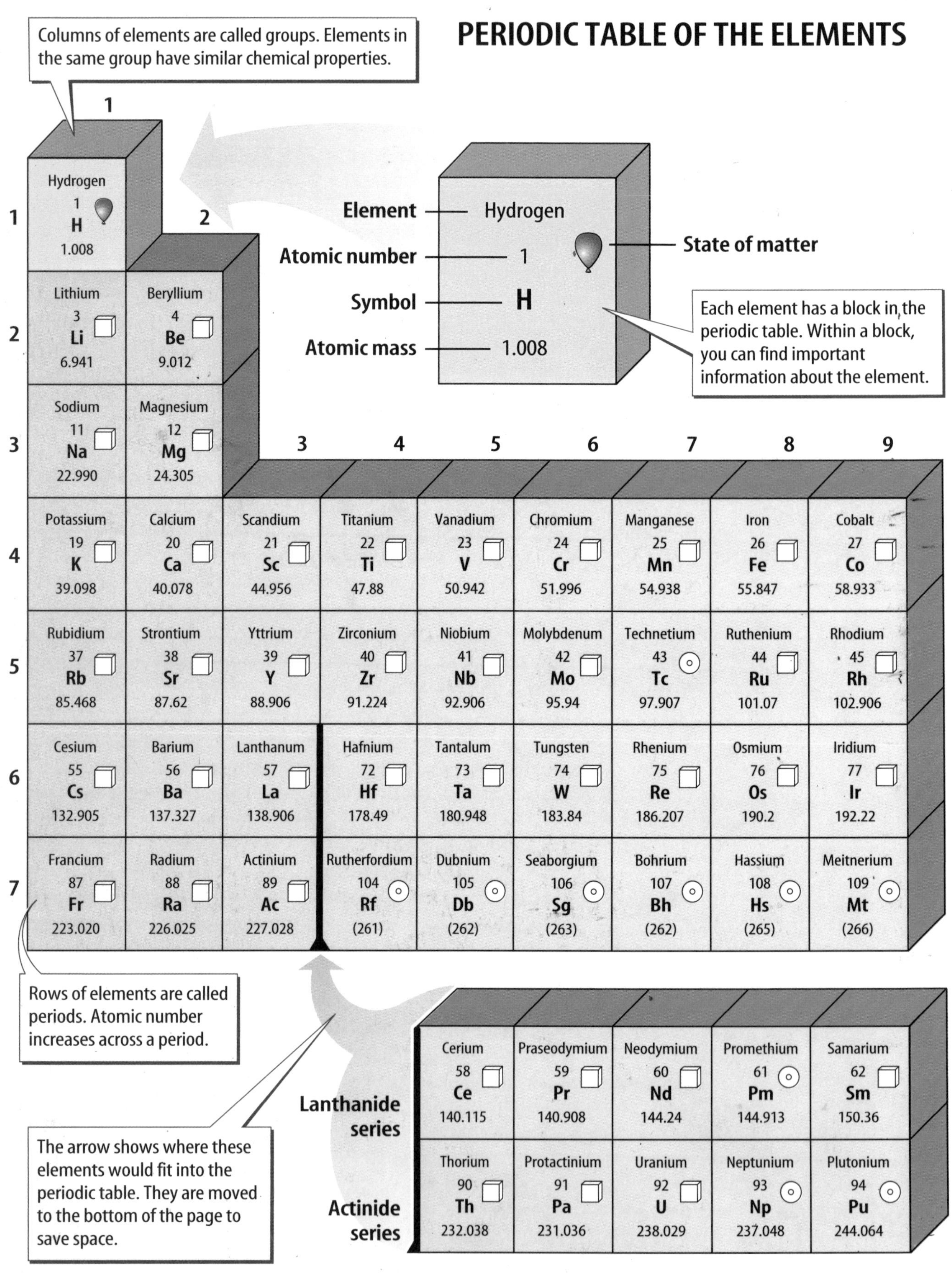

PERIODIC TABLE OF THE ELEMENTS

Columns of elements are called groups. Elements in the same group have similar chemical properties.

Element — Hydrogen
Atomic number — 1
Symbol — H
Atomic mass — 1.008
State of matter

Each element has a block in the periodic table. Within a block, you can find important information about the element.

Period	1	2	3	4	5	6	7	8	9
1	Hydrogen 1 H 1.008								
2	Lithium 3 Li 6.941	Beryllium 4 Be 9.012							
3	Sodium 11 Na 22.990	Magnesium 12 Mg 24.305							
4	Potassium 19 K 39.098	Calcium 20 Ca 40.078	Scandium 21 Sc 44.956	Titanium 22 Ti 47.88	Vanadium 23 V 50.942	Chromium 24 Cr 51.996	Manganese 25 Mn 54.938	Iron 26 Fe 55.847	Cobalt 27 Co 58.933
5	Rubidium 37 Rb 85.468	Strontium 38 Sr 87.62	Yttrium 39 Y 88.906	Zirconium 40 Zr 91.224	Niobium 41 Nb 92.906	Molybdenum 42 Mo 95.94	Technetium 43 Tc 97.907	Ruthenium 44 Ru 101.07	Rhodium 45 Rh 102.906
6	Cesium 55 Cs 132.905	Barium 56 Ba 137.327	Lanthanum 57 La 138.906	Hafnium 72 Hf 178.49	Tantalum 73 Ta 180.948	Tungsten 74 W 183.84	Rhenium 75 Re 186.207	Osmium 76 Os 190.2	Iridium 77 Ir 192.22
7	Francium 87 Fr 223.020	Radium 88 Ra 226.025	Actinium 89 Ac 227.028	Rutherfordium 104 Rf (261)	Dubnium 105 Db (262)	Seaborgium 106 Sg (263)	Bohrium 107 Bh (262)	Hassium 108 Hs (265)	Meitnerium 109 Mt (266)

Rows of elements are called periods. Atomic number increases across a period.

The arrow shows where these elements would fit into the periodic table. They are moved to the bottom of the page to save space.

Lanthanide series	Cerium 58 Ce 140.115	Praseodymium 59 Pr 140.908	Neodymium 60 Nd 144.24	Promethium 61 Pm 144.913	Samarium 62 Sm 150.36
Actinide series	Thorium 90 Th 232.038	Protactinium 91 Pa 231.036	Uranium 92 U 238.029	Neptunium 93 Np 237.048	Plutonium 94 Pu 244.064